THERAPYED'S
National Occupational Therapist Certification Exam Review & Study Guide

10th EDITION

RITA P. FLEMING-CASTALDY, PHD, OTL, FAOTA

Professor Emeritus

University of Scranton

Scranton, PA

TherapyEd
Chicago, Illinois
United States of America

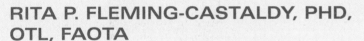

The authors and contributors have made a faithful attempt to include relevant summaries of current occupational therapy practice and other information related to the NBCOT® certification exam for the occupational therapist, registered (OTR®) available at the time of publication. It is recognized that recommended practices, drug therapies, equipment, devices, technology, governmental regulations, administrative procedures, and other protocols and factors may change or be open to other interpretations. Occupational therapy practitioners have an ethical responsibility to stay current with advances in the field that may occur through research, theory development, federal legislation and regulations, and/or revised guidelines for evidence-based practice.

The publisher disclaims any liability or loss incurred as a result of direct or indirect use of this book. Use of this book does not guarantee successful passage of the NBCOT® certification exam.

Copies of this book and software may be obtained from:
TherapyEd
3023 N. Clark St. Suite 119
Chicago, IL 60657
Toll-free: 888-369-0743
Outside US: (847) 328-5361
Email: info@therapyed.com
www.TherapyEd.com

How Can TherapyEd Help *YOU PASS* the NBCOT® Exam and Other FAQs about the NBCOT® Exam and Effective Exam Preparation

 ## TherapyEd's Experience and Expertise

Since 1997, TherapyEd has been the leader in preparing graduates of occupational therapist education programs for their NBCOT® certification exam. All members of our team have extensive experience in helping aspiring occupational therapists pass this high stakes exam to become licensed occupational therapists and occupational therapists, registered (OTR®s).

As occupational therapy (OT) practitioners, educators, and academic program directors with 30 to 45+ years of experience, TherapyEd's text authors, course instructors, and tutors have worked with thousands of students each year to develop the content knowledge and text-taking skills needed to pass the NBCOT® OTR® exam. The following series of questions are ones that we are frequently asked by those preparing for their certification exam. We hope that our answers and the additional information provided in this text's chapters will enable you confidently and effectively prepare for your NBCOT® certification exam.

 ## Why do I have to take and pass the NBCOT® exam?

A passing score on the NBCOT® certification exam for the OTR® is required to:

- earn the professional credential of registered occupational therapist (OTR®).
- be eligible for licensure as an occupational therapist in any state in the United States, the District of Columbia, Puerto Rico, and Guam.

– You *cannot* legally practice as an occupational therapist in the United States and its territories without a license.

Chapter 1 in this *Review and Study Guide* provides more information about professional licensure and certification.

▶ There are a *LOT* of certification exam preparation products available, why should I use TherapyEd's text to prepare for my NBCOT® exam?

The amount of certification exam preparation resources available can be overwhelming. The quality of these products can vary greatly. It can be hard to know if a product is providing accurate and complete information or not. The cost of buying multiple products can be substantial. Knowing which resource(s) will most effectively support your certification exam success can be difficult.

Since the first edition of TherapyEd's *National Occupational Therapist Review and Study Guide (RSG)*

was published in 2000, it has been the #1 best-selling text for NBCOT® certification exam preparation with complete practice exams. TherapyEd's *RSG* has been consistently well received because it provides NBCOT® OTR® exam candidates with a reliable, efficient, and economical way to effectively prepare for their certification exam. Box A describes these qualities.

BOX A ▶ **Characteristics of TherapyEd's *Review and Study Guide***

TherapyEd's *Review and Study Guide* is:

- **Reliable:** The content experts who authored the chapters and exams in this text have ensured that they have:
  - provided accurate, current, and relevant information.
  - fully covered the content that is included in the *latest* NBCOT® OTR® exam content outline.
  - composed practice exam items that mirror the NBCOT® OTR® exam content and format.

- **Efficient:** TherapyEd's *RSG* is widely recognized as the most comprehensive and up-to-date resource that provides all the content information that must be mastered to pass the certification exam in one single text. TherapyEd's *RSG* is purposefully designed to:
  - synthesize all the content knowledge that may be tested on the NBCOT® OTR® exam.
  - simplify exam preparation by presenting information in an easy-to-follow outline format.
  - highlight essential information in over 890 Tables, Boxes, Figures, and Review Questions.
  - describe strategies for selecting correct answers to OTR® certification exam items including the traditional three or four option multiple choice items and the six-option multi-select Scenario Set items.
  - provide opportunities to practice the use of test-taking strategies via three complete online practice exams.
  - supply detailed rationales for exam item answers, including critical reasoning rationales.

- **Economical:** Purchasing multiple exam preparation products is expensive. Only using practice exams and a review of their answers can lead to unidentified content gaps that can hinder exam success. Failing the NBCOT® exam is costly. The *RSG* is the *only single* certification exam preparation product that includes:
  - current and accurate info about the NBCOT®'s exam's content, format, and procedures.
  - comprehensive content according to the NBCOT® OTR® exam content outline.
  - content-specific chapter review questions to help you "jump start" the thought processes you will need to apply your studying of text content to the answering of exam items.
  - effective test-taking and time management strategies to help you successfully answer all 180 NBCOT® exam items within the allotted time.
  - three complete online practice exams with comprehensive score reports and extensive rationales to help you determine your exam readiness.

What are some of the unique features of TherapyEd's *RSG*?

TherapyEd's *RSG* provides a comprehensive overview of the depth and breadth of current OT practice as tested on the NBCOT® certification exam in an easy-to-read outline format. It is organized into sections that cover the foundations of OT practice, the clinical conditions that clients who receive OT services may have, and the evaluation and intervention approaches that are commonly used in OT practice and identified in the NBCOT® OTR® exam content outline.

This content organization and the text's outline format can help you develop a targeted exam preparation plan that focuses on key points, rather than extraneous information. Additional unique features of TherapyEd's *RSG* include:

- **EXAM HINT** boxes that describe the relationship of key chapter content to the most current NBCOT® OTR® certification exam content outline. This outline identifies the domains, tasks, and knowledge that the NBCOT® considers essential for competent and safe entry-level OTR® practice. It is the primary source for what is tested on the NBCOT® certification exam (NBCOT®, 2022). The **EXAM HINT** boxes also provide exam preparation strategies and test-taking

hints to support effective studying and increase exam efficacy.
- CAUTION boxes that identify precautions, contraindications, risk factors, and actions that do not reflect best practice. Because ignoring these can result in potential harm, they must be taken into account when determining correct answers to NBCOT® exam items.
- RED FLAG boxes that describe unsafe actions, contraindications, and serious risk factors that are known to cause harm and situations which require an immediate response to ensure a person's safety and well-being. Because ensuring client safety is a primary ethical responsibility of OT practitioners, these important safety considerations must be considered to select correct answers to NBCOT® exam items.
- **CONTENT-SPECIFIC REVIEW QUESTIONS** about chapter content that must be mastered for certification exam success. These questions are designed to help you assess your knowledge of key content in Chapters 3-16. In-depth answers to the chapter-specific questions are provided in Appendix 2 of this text.

There is so much to study, how can I use TherapyEd's *RSG* to prepare for the NBCOT® exam without being overwhelmed?

Read Chapter 2 *before* you begin studying Chapters 3-16. This chapter outlines major concepts, principles, and actions for developing and maintaining a positive psychological outlook about exam preparation and test-taking. Chapter 2 also describes principles of effective exam preparation, provides clear guidelines for structuring and implementing an individualized *and manageable* exam preparation plan, and explains how you can apply your clinical and critical reasoning skills to the NBCOT® exam.

By using the information provided in Chapter 2, you can construct a personalized exam preparation plan that builds on your strengths and targets your unique needs. The time and effort you take to identify content you need to review versus content you must study will be well spent. Knowing that you do not need to study *all* text content can make the exam preparation process less daunting. The dual review/ study nature of effective exam preparation is why TherapyEd's text was purposefully called a *review and*

study guide, not just a study guide. When studying the content of Chapters 3-16, you can use the EXAM HINT, CAUTION, and RED FLAG boxes and the Tables, Boxes, Figures, and Review Questions to prioritize what is most important to study.

Throughout your exam preparation, it is important to remember that to be eligible for the NBCOT® exam, you must provide proof that you have graduated from an accredited graduate program for the occupational therapist. To attain this status, you had to complete rigorous graduate coursework and challenging fieldworks. When your academic and clinical educators recorded a passing grade for you, they asserted that you possessed the knowledge and skills needed for entry-level practice as an occupational therapist. If, and when, you become overwhelmed with your exam preparation, remind yourself of this reality. Chapter 2 provides information about additional resources that can be used to help you prepare for your certification exam in a calm, focused, and effective manner.

Are TherapyEd's online practice exams similar to the NBCOT® certification exam?

Yes, the three online practice exams that accompany this text were intentionally authored to mirror the format and content of the NBCOT® certification exam for the OTR®. Just like the NBCOT® exam, TherapyEd's online practice exams contain 180 items that test the four OTR® exam domains via traditional single-response three or four option multiple-choice items and six-option multiselect Scenario Set items.

The test-taking program used for TherapyEd's online exam is also consistent with NBCOT®'s exam administration program (e.g., you can change your answers, you must select three answer options for the six-option multiselect Scenario Set items). Chapter 1 provides comprehensive information about the OTR® exam content, item types, and administration.

 ## When should I take the online practice exams that accompany this text?

It is best to take your first online practice exam *after* you have implemented your personal exam preparation plan and acquired the knowledge that you need to determine correct answers to exam items. Completing a practice exam *before* you have attained mastery of essential content will only reinforce that you have key gaps in your foundational knowledge. This can diminish your confidence, lower your self-esteem, and make the prospect of studying more overwhelming. In contrast, taking your first practice exam *after* you have studied can help you more successfully identify correct answers to exam items. This can increase your confidence.

You can use the extensive feedback you receive after you complete a TherapyEd online practice exam to determine the efficacy of your exam preparation plan and revise it before taking another practice exam. The *Guidelines for Effective Use of the Online Practice Exams* that are provided at the end of this text and Chapter 2 provide additional information about how to most effectively integrate the TherapyEd's three online practice exams into your exam preparation plan.

 ## What information will I receive after I complete a TherapyEd online practice exam?

Immediately after you complete an online practice exam, TherapyEd's learning portal will display an individualized score report about your exam performance. This personal score report will identify the:

- exam items you answered correctly and incorrectly.
- the percentage of items you answered correctly according to the:
  - four NBCOT® OTR® exam domains,
  - five critical reasoning skills, and
  - nine content knowledge categories that align with TherapyEd's *RSG* chapters.
- amount of time you took to complete the exam.

When you receive this detailed score report, you will be able to click on each exam item to be immediately linked to a detailed explanation about its answer rationale. These rationales explain the content knowledge that supports the item's correct answer, the reasons why wrong answers were incorrect, and the critical reasoning skill needed to determine the item's correct answer.

Each online exam score report and all online exam answer rationales will remain available to you for the full duration of your 12-month access to TherapyEd's learning portal.

How should I use TherapyEd's online practice exam score reports to help ensure my exam success?

The comprehensive information provided in TherapyEd's online exam score reports and in the exam item answer rationales can help you determine your preparedness for the NBCOT® certification exam. The *Guidelines for Effective Use of the Online Practice Exams* that are provided at the end of this text and Chapter 2 provide suggestions and strategies about how to most effectively do this.

In Chapter 2, *Box 2-1 NBCOT® Exam Domain Score Report Content and Utility* and *Box 2-2 Content Category Score Report Content and Utility* describe how your performance in these areas can be used to revise your exam preparation plan to address identified gaps.

Box 2-3 Critical Reasoning Score Report Content and Utility explains how the information provided about your performance in the five types of critical reasoning can be used to improve your critical reasoning skills. Table 2-5 outlines the *RSG* chapters you should study if your performance in a content category is less than satisfactory.

Proactively using this information after you receive each practice exam score report can help you develop the knowledge and skills you need to pass the NBCOT® certification exam for the OTR®.

Does TherapyEd have additional resources that I can use to help me pass the NBCOT® exam?

Yes, TherapyEd offers intensive and highly interactive two-day online and in-person exam preparation courses, a mobile test prep app, individual and small group tutoring, free weekly online office hours that include content reviews, a weekly exam item of the week, and open access to recorded online office hour sessions and exam

preparation webinars. Chapter 2 and the inside covers of this text provide information about these additional exam preparation resources. To register for a course, purchase the app, sign into an online office hour session, and/or schedule a tutoring session, visit OT Exam Prep - Occupational Therapy Exam Prep (therapyed.com).

References

National Board for Certification in Occupational Therapy (NBCOT®). (2022). 2022 Occupational Therapist Registered (OTR®) Examination Content Outline (nbcot.org)

▶ Table of Contents

▶ Contributors[1]

Cynthia H. August, Ph.D., OT/L
Assistant Professor
Occupational Therapy Department
Mount Mary University
Milwaukee, Wisconsin

Stephanie Beisbier, PP-OTD, OTR/L
Associate Professor, Professional Entry Program
Director
Occupational Therapy Department
Mount Mary University
Milwaukee, Wisconsin

Ann Burkhardt, OTD, OTR/L, FAOTA
Associate Clinical Professor
Binghamton University
Post-professional OTD Program
Binghamton NY

Donna M. Costa, DHS, OTR/L, FAOTA
Associate Professor in Residence/Part-time Instructor
Occupational Therapy Program
School of Integrated Health Sciences
University of Nevada, Las Vegas, NV

Christina Gavalas-Valdivia, MS, OTR/L
Occupational Therapist
Transitions of Long Island, Northwell Health
Manhasset, New York
Administrative Assistant, OT Leaders & Legacies Society

Daniel Geller, EdD, MPH, OTR/L
Assistant Professor of Rehabilitation and Regenerative
Medicine (Occupational Therapy) at CUMC
Department of Rehabilitation and Regenerative
Medicine
Vagelos College of Physicians and Surgeons
Columbia University Medical Center
New York, New York

Glen Gillen, EdD, OTR, FAOTA
Professor of Rehabilitation and Regenerative Medicine
(Occupational Therapy) at CUMC
Department of Rehabilitation and Regenerative
Medicine
Vagelos College of Physicians and Surgeons
Columbia University Medical Center
New York, New York

Karen Gualtieri, MS, OTR/L
Private Practitioner
Northeast Pennsylvania

Kari Inda, PhD, OTR/L, CEAS
Professor and Chairperson
Occupational Therapy Department
Mount Mary University
Milwaukee, Wisconsin

---

[1] Contributors to prior editions of this text, who provided foundational information for this tenth edition, include Marge E. Moffett Boyd, Josephine Dolera, Jan Garbarinii, Linda Kahn-D'Angelo, Colleen McCaul De Riitis, Mackenzie Thompson, Janice Romeo, Susan Robertson, Todd C. Sander, Susan B. O'Sullivan, Julie Ann Starr, Thomas Sutlive, and Toni Thompson.

William L. Lambert, MS, OTR/L
Faculty Specialist, Retired
Department of Occupational Therapy
The University of Scranton
Scranton, Pennsylvania

Regina M. Lehman, MS, OT/L
Professor and Program Director
Occupational Therapy Assistant Program
LaGuardia Community College
Long Island City, New York

Helene Lohman, OTD, OTR/L, FAOTA
Professor
Occupational Therapy Department
Creighton, University
Omaha, Nebraska

Colleen Maher, OTD, OTR/L, CHT
Assistant Professor of Rehabilitation and Regenerative
    Medicine (Occupational Therapy) at CUMC
Department of Rehabilitation and Regenerative
    Medicine
Vagelos College of Physicians and Surgeons
Columbia University Medical Center
New York, New York

Geraldine Healy Marini, OTD, MSH, OT,
    ASDCS
Assistant Professor of Occupational Therapy
Department of Occupational Therapy
College of Allied Health
Saint Joseph's University
Philadelphia, PA

Rochelle J. Mendonca, PhD, OTR/L
Assistant Professor of Rehabilitation and Regenerative
    Medicine (Occupational Therapy) at CUMC
Department of Rehabilitation and Regenerative
    Medicine
Vagelos College of Physicians and Surgeons
Columbia University Medical Center
New York, New York

Marlene Joy Morgan, EdD, OTR/L
Associate Professor
Department of Occupational Therapy
The University of Scranton
Scranton, Pennsylvania

Patricia Wisniewski, EdD, OTR/L, CPRP
Faculty Specialist
Department of Occupational Therapy
The University of Scranton
Scranton, Pennsylvania

Acknowledgments

Organizing the depth and breadth of occupational therapy education and practice into a comprehensive review book and study guide for a national certification exam can be a daunting task. It can easily become overwhelming if it were not for the capable assistance of others. Over the course of the past three years, I have had the good fortune to receive essential research and production support from Nicholas Chiara, Emily Clark, Clare DiGiovanni, Jenny Kim, Alicia O'Toole, Erin A. Quinn, and Kathryn Zaverdas. The services these University of Scranton alumni and students provided in a timely and highly competent manner were vital to the completion of this tenth edition.

Past editions of this text benefited from the outstanding assistance of Kristin Leccese, Jenna Osborn, and John Patro (former UoS graduate assistants); Christina Gavalas, Victoria Crociata, Katherine Regimbal, Samantha Zarro, and Stephanie Freije (former UoS work-study employees); Sue Ward (former secretary for TherapyEd), Kathleen Smyth (former personal administrative assistant), and Raymond Siegelman, President Emeritus of TherapyEd.

Final, and most important, acknowledgements are due to Christine Becker, Production Manager for Progressive Publishing Services and Christina Gavalas-Valdivia, TherapyEd per diem administrative assistant. Their collaborative nature, attention to detail, and commitment to excellence greatly contributed to the high quality of this final product.

1

Certification of the Occupational Therapist, Registered (OTR®)

RITA P. FLEMING-CASTALDY

Chapter Outline

Chapter 1

► Credentialing Agencies

National Board for Certification in Occupational Therapy (NBCOT®)

1. The NBCOT® is currently the only national independent credentialing agency for occupational therapy (OT) practitioners, including occupational therapists and occupational therapy assistants (OTAs).
2. The NBCOT® develops and implements all policies related to OT professional certification, including the national certification examinations and the NBCOT® certification renewal program.
   a. NBCOT® holds the copyright to the designations certified occupational therapy assistant (COTA®) and occupational therapist, registered (OTR®).
      (1) Individuals not certified by NBCOT® cannot use these credentials.
   b. NBCOT® certification is *not equivalent to state licensure*, which is regulated by state regulatory boards.
   c. NBCOT® certification is initially granted for three years. Certification must be renewed every three years according to the procedures of the NBCOT® Certification Renewal Program.
3. NBCOT®'s official website (www.nbcot.org) contains all current information about the NBCOT® certification process.
   a. As an independent organization, NBCOT® can change their certification requirements and procedures *at any time;* therefore, this website should be consulted on a regular basis by exam candidates.

State Regulatory Boards (SRBs)

1. SRBs are public bodies created by legislation to define and regulate the qualifications a professional must have to practice within their state.
2. All states in the United States (U.S.), require occupational therapists and OTAs to be licensed by their SRB to practice occupational therapy.
   a. Requirements for licensure can vary from state to state; therefore, each state regulation should be carefully reviewed to ensure understanding of its requirements and provisions.
   b. Currently, all states, the District of Columbia, Puerto Rico, and Guam require a passing grade on the NBCOT® certification exam for occupational therapists as a qualifying criterion for initial state licensure.
   c. Some states grant temporary practice licenses to individuals eligible to become licensed in the state.
3. SRBs should be contacted directly to obtain their regulations and an application.
   a. To obtain state-specific information, refer to NBCOT Occupational Therapy Regulatory Body Contact List by State (NBCOT®, 2023a).

> **RED FLAG:** It is against the law to practice OT without meeting state requirements for certification, registration, or licensure.

4. Currently, most states do not have reciprocal agreements, so OT practitioners must apply to and meet the requirements of every state in which they intend to practice.
5. In 2020, the American Occupational Therapy Association (AOTA) and the NBCOT®, with the assistance of the Council of State Governments (CSG), initiated the Occupational Therapy Licensure Compact (OT Compact) effort.
   a. This initiative sought to obtain formal agreements or contracts between state governments to enable interstate practice for licensed OT practitioners. Occupational Therapy Licensure Compact | AOTA.
   b. Occupational therapists and OTAs who are licensed to practice in a Compact member state, and are deemed to be in good standing, will be able to practice in other Compact member states via a "compact privilege".
      (1) A compact privilege is considered the equivalent to the Compact state's professional license.
   c. Compact privileges to practice occupational therapy in member states have been projected to be implemented in mid-2024.
      (1) Refer to https://otcompact.org for up-to-date information about the status of this initiative.

Certification Examination Content

Background Information

1. Practice analysis.
   a. The NBCOT® conducts a practice analysis every five years to determine "the core tasks that comprise entry-level practice and the knowledge required to perform those tasks." (NBCOT®, 2022a, p. 3).
      (1) The most recent analysis included an internal and external review of the existing exam content outline, and a national validation survey of entry-level OTR®s.
         (a) The NBCOT® considers entry-level practitioners to be those who have been certified for 36 months or less.
   b. The results of the practice analysis is used to construct the content of the exam, create exam specifications, and guide the writing of exam items.
   c. As of January 1, 2024, the content of the OTR® certification exam is derived from the outcomes of a practice analysis study completed in 2022 (NBCOT®, 2022a).
      (1) This Review and Study Guide presents the most current information available at the time of its publication about the NBCOT® exam's content, format, administration, and scoring.
2. Item development.
   a. Exam items are developed by subject matter consultants (SMCs) who represent a diversity of practice settings, geographic regions, and demographics (e.g., ethnicity, gender) (NBCOT®, 2023b).
   b. Items are designed to differentiate the presence of inadequate from adequate entry-level practice knowledge and skills.
   c. All exam items are critically reviewed by a SMC committee to ensure they measure the knowledge and skills needed for entry-level OT practice according to the exam specifications developed from the practice analysis.
   d. All items approved by the SMC committee are field-tested prior to their use as scored items on the exam.

> **EXAM HINT:** The rigor of NBCOT®'s item development and review processes results in a valid and fair exam with each item meeting established standards for validity and fairness. Thus, statements on social media and in promotional materials from companies that sell exam preparation products that question the integrity of the NBCOT exam (i.e., it is 'tricky') should be ignored.

   e. All exam items are also reviewed to ensure that the language, context, terminology, descriptions, and content are unbiased, inoffensive, and appropriate to all population groups.

Content Specifics

1. The NBCOT®'s OTR® exam tests four domains of OT practice, with each domain comprising a set percentage of the exam. These domains and percentages are presented in Table 1-1.
2. Specific task and knowledge statements for each domain are provided in the 2022 NBCOT (OTR®) examination content outline (NBCOT®, 2022b), which is available on the NBCOT®'s website.

Table 1-1

NBCOT® Exam Domains for the OTR®	
DOMAIN DESCRIPTIONS	**EXAM %**
"Domain 1 Evaluation and Assessment: Acquire information regarding factors that influence occupational performance on an ongoing basis throughout the occu-pational therapy process" (NBCOT®, 2022b, p. 3)	23%
"Domain 2 Analysis, Interpretation, and Planning: Formulate conclusions regarding client needs and priorities to develop and monitor an intervention plan throughout the occupational therapy process" (NBCOT®, 2022b, p. 5)	23%
"Domain 3 Select and Manage Interventions: Select and implement interventions to promote healing and enhance engagement in occupation-based activities" (NBCOT®, 2022b, p. 7).	38%
"Domain 4 Competency and Practice Management: Manage professional activities of self and relevant others as guided by evidence, regulatory compliance, and standards of practice to promote quality care" (NBCOT®, 2022b, p. 12).	16%

Reference: National Board for Certification in Occupational Therapy (NBCOT®). (2022b). 2022 Occupational Therapist Registered (OTR®) Examination Content Outline (nbcot.org).

Chapter 1

EXAM HINT: Throughout this text, green EXAM HINT boxes place chapter content into the context of the NBCOT®'s OTR® exam content outline that identifies the domains, tasks, and knowledge that are essential for competent and safe OT practice.

3. Exam content reflects language typically used in practice and is not solely based on any one practice framework model.
   a. Certain aspects of a given practice framework (e.g., the AOTA's) may be integrated into the exam's content if they represent exam specifications as determined by the NBCOT® practice analysis.
4. A large item bank is maintained so that each exam will be composed of a unique combination of items drawn from this bank.
   a. Different versions of the exam are offered simultaneously.

b. Items are selected according to the weightings of exam domains and content areas to ensure each exam contains consistent percentages of each domain and content area.

EXAM HINT: As noted in Table 1-1, 84% of the certification exam for the OTR® is focused on direct services to clients. However, because entry-level occupational therapists have many professional responsibilities beyond direct service provision (e.g., supervision, risk management, research, and program development, implementation, management, and evaluation), you may be presented with an exam item that will require the application of your knowledge about Domain 4 tasks. Chapter 4 in this text provides comprehensive information about these responsibilities and tasks. This Chapter's subsequent section on test-taking strategies describes specific strategies for successfully answering exam items.

Certification Examination Format

Overview

1. The NBCOT® exam for the occupational therapist is composed of 180 multiple-choice (MC) items.
   a. These include traditional three- and four-option single-response MC items and six-option multi-select scenario sets.
      (1) There is no separate section for the scenario sets.
         (a) The scenario sets are distributed throughout the exam in between the traditional three- and four-option single-response MC items.
      (2) There is no predetermined exam percentage for the traditional three- and four-option single-response MC item or the six-option multi-select scenario set items.
         (a) The totality of the traditional MC items and the scenario sets on the certification exam for the occupational therapist meet the domain-level percentages outlined in the 2022 NBCOT® exam content outline for the OTR®. Refer to Table 1-1.
2. Each administered exam contains items that the NBCOT® is field testing for future exams.
   a. The field-test items are not considered operational and they are not scored.
   b. The field-test items are intermixed with the items that are scored.
   c. Field-test items that perform well statistically will become part of the operational pre-equated item bank used for future exams.

3. Items that are scored items have been pre-equated by NBCOT® and deemed operational (NBCOT®, 2023b).

EXAM HINT: There are no identifying characteristics to distinguish unscored field-test items from the scored operational items; therefore, you must answer each item as if it counts.

Traditional Multiple-choice (MC) Item Format

1. Traditionally formatted multiple-choice (MC) items are composed of an item stem that contains basic information (e.g., a diagnosis and practice setting) followed by a question or statement that addresses a specific aspect of OT practice (e.g., the best assessment to use).
   a. There are three or four answer options with only one correct response for each item.

EXAM HINT: No answers are provided in a combination format (e.g., "b and d," "all," or "none of the above").

   b. Three and four option MC items are nonsequential.
      (1) Each item contains a 'stand-alone' question that does not relate to the ones preceding or following it.

Scenario Set Format

1. Scenario sets have four related six-option multi-select items.
   a. Each multi-select item includes a question stem and six answer options.
      (1) Three of the six answer options will be correct and three will be incorrect.

(2) You are required to select the *three* best responses from the six choices.

> **EXAM HINT:** No answers in the six-option mult-iselect scenario set items are provided in a combination format (e.g., "a and c," "all," or "none of the above").

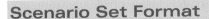

Certification Examination Application Procedures

Eligibility Requirements for the NBCOT®'s Certification Examination

1. General requirements.
   a. Information submitted on the application must be accurate and truthful.
   b. Candidates submitting misleading or inaccurate information will be prohibited from taking the certification exam.
   c. Information related to felonies must be provided by all candidates.
   d. The NBCOT® conducts background checks on all exam applicants.
      (1) There is no additional cost for the background check.

> **CAUTION:** If, after taking the exam, it is determined that a candidate was ineligible to take the exam (or that eligibility was questionable), the NBCOT® will either hold or void the exam. If a candidate was certified and later found to be ineligible for the exam, certification will be revoked.

   e. The NBCOT®'s Disciplinary Action Committee reviews cases of questionable eligibility for the exam to determine if any disciplinary action is warranted and if the candidate will or will not be permitted to take the exam at a future date.
2. Specific requirements.
   a. The NBCOT® clearly delineates exam eligibility requirements for graduates of entry-level post-baccalaureate OT programs within the U.S. that are accredited by the Accreditation Council for Occupational Therapy Education (ACOTE) of the AOTA and graduates of post-baccalaureate international OT education programs.
      (1) Eligibility requirements and application procedures for candidates who are graduates of an NBCOT® recognized entry-level post-baccalaureate degree are described in detail in the NBCOT® Certification Exam Handbook.

      (2) Eligibility requirements and application procedures for candidates who are not graduates of an NBCOT® recognized entry-level post-baccalaureate degree are described in detail in the Occupational Therapist Eligibility Determination (OTED®) Handbook.
   b. Candidates not seeking NBCOT® certification may take the exam to meet state regulatory requirements.
      (1) The NBCOT® should be contacted directly to obtain information about licensure only application procedures.
      (2) Applications for state credentialing must be submitted to the SRB, not the NBCOT®.
3. Examination eligibility limit.
   a. The NBCOT® has no set limit on the number of times a candidate is eligible to take the certification exam.
      (1) The NBCOT® Certification Examination Handbook is the primary source for information about retaking the exam.
   b. All exam candidates who do not pass the NBCOT® exam should consult the SRB of the state in which they seek to obtain a license to determine the state's standards regarding limits on the number of times and/or the length of time post-graduation the exam can be taken to obtain licensure.

Examination Application Process

1. The NBCOT® Certification Exam Handbook provides detailed instructions for completion of the application (NBCOT®, 2023c).
   a. There is a separate link on the NBCOT® website for internationally educated exam candidates. There are two main differences between the application process for internationally educated exam candidates and U.S. educated ones.
      (1) Internationally educated exam candidates must complete an Occupational Therapist Eligibility Determination (OTED®) form.
      (2) Internationally educated exam candidates who are not U.S. citizens must submit a Visa Credential Verification Certificate (VCVC).

b. The Certification Exam Handbook and application forms are available at https://www.nbcot.org/-/media/PDFs/Cert_Exam_Handbook.pdf.

2. Application directions and procedures must be adhered to strictly.

   a. Applicants are required to complete a character review section that asks questions about their past history.

      (1) The NBCOT® completes a background check as part of their character review of an applicant.

> **CAUTION:** If an applicant's answers to the character questions do not honestly reflect their background, this will violate the NBCOT®'s Code of Conduct. Thus, applicants are *strongly* encouraged to answer all questions honestly. If you must answer yes to a character question(s), follow the directions in the NBCOT® Certification Examination Handbook for submitting the additional documentation that is required for your application. It is important to know that yes answers to the character questions do not automatically result in the denial of an application. Likewise, the subsequent review of your documentation will not automatically result in a denial. The NBCOT® reviews each case individually to determine an applicant's exam eligibility.

   b. Applications that are incomplete, inaccurate, and/or do not follow instructions will be rejected and returned to the applicant.

   c. Review and proof your application carefully before submitting it.

      (1) If you make any changes or corrections, other than updating contact/address information after your initial application submission, the NBCOT® will charge a fee to process these.

3. Only one application is required. Do not complete an online and a paper post-mailed application.

4. When completing the application, be sure to use your first and last names as they appear on the two forms of identification that you will bring to the testing center.

   a. The names you provide on your application will be those that will be printed on the letter that will authorize you to take the NBCOT® exam, so they must match the forms of identification that you will present at the exam administration site; middle names do not count.

      (1) If your name changes after your application has been submitted to the NBCOT® and/or your ATT letter has been generated, you must follow NBCOT® guidelines for processing a name change.

5. After submitting your application and payment, you must have your college or university verify your eligibility by sending your official, final transcript or Degree Verification Form (DVF) directly to the NBCOT®.

   a. Do not ask your school to submit your transcript or DVF before you have completed your application.

6. NBCOT® must approve the application.

   a. Upon payment, *the application is valid for 90 days.*

7. Within three business days of the NBCOT® approving a completed application, you will receive an Authorization to Test (ATT) letter via an email from the NBCOT®. The ATT letter will also be available in your MyNBCOT account.

   a. The ATT letter gives you permission to schedule an exam administration date with Pearson VCU to take the NBCOT® certification exam for the OTR®.

   b. The ATT letter will include information about how to schedule your exam.

   c. The ATT letter is active for 90 days.

      (1) If needed, you can request an ATT letter for an additional 90 days.

         (a) Reasons ATT letters are reissued and the actions you need to take to request a reissue of an active ATT are provided in the NBCOT® Certification Exam Handbook.

         (b) This request must occur while your exam application is still valid.

   d. Carefully review your name as it appears on the ATT letter to be sure that it matches exactly with the identification that you will present on the exam day (middle names or initials do not matter).

      (1) To correct any errors on the ATT letter, follow NBCOT® published guidelines.

   e. The ATT letter is required for entry into the test-taking area.

 # Testing Accommodations

Testing Accommodations Eligibility

1. Candidates with disabilities can receive testing accommodations (TAs) that can support their success on the NBCOT® exam.

2. The NBCOT® uses the definition of disability set forth in the Americans with Disabilities Act (ADA) to determine eligibility for TAs.

   a. Candidates must have a documented disability, which can include a mental or physical impairment (e.g., learning, cognitive, or psychological disability;

hearing, visual, speech, or orthopedic impairment) that substantially limits a major life activity.

3. Candidates who have medical or health conditions (e.g., diabetes) that may require them to have a snack or water and/or take medicine or restroom breaks should contact the NBCOT® for information about how to obtain TAs based on medical necessity.

   a. If a pregnancy results in a medical complication, TAs may be considered due to medical necessity; however, these are not automatically granted since pregnancy is not defined as a disability in the ADA.

4. Candidates with temporary conditions that do not meet the ADA definition of disability (e.g., fractures) but who may need TAs (e.g., wheelchair access) should contact NBCOT® for information about how to obtain special testing arrangements.

   a. If a temporary disability warrants TAs after you have an ATT letter and a scheduled exam, you will need to have a new ATT letter re-issued by the NBCOT® and may have to reschedule your exam.

5. English as a second language is not considered a disability; therefore, the use of a dictionary and/or extra time to complete the exam due to language difficulty are not permitted for individuals for whom English is not their primary language.

6. Test anxiety and technophobia are not defined as disabilities in the ADA; consequently, TAs will not be considered for these conditions.

Applying for Testing Accommodations

> **EXAM HINT:** The decision to request, or not request, TAs for the NBCOT® exam is a personal decision that is often influenced by an exam candidate's personal experience with TAs during their education; however, it is important to recognize that this experience may *NOT* generalize to the challenging and comprehensive NBCOT® exam. The content, format, and test-taking experience of the NBCOT® exam differs from the objective exams that are typically used to test mastery of course material. Refer to Table 1-2.
>
> We strongly urge all eligible exam candidates to apply for *any and all* accommodations for which they are eligible.

1. Exam candidates seeking TAs should download the Testing Accommodations Handbook from the NBCOT® website. Refer to NBCOT Testing Accommodations Handbook for OTR and COTA (NBCOT®, 2023d).

> **CAUTION:** All the steps outlined for requesting TAs in this handbook should be strictly followed (NBCOT®, 2023d). The NBCOT® will not issue an ATT letter until after TA decisions have been made.

2. The application for TAs must be filled out accurately with all documentation completed according to the instructions.

   a. TA documentation must be submitted (uploaded) at the same time an online application for the certification exam is submitted.

   b. Incomplete applications or applications with insufficient documentation will not be considered by the NBCOT®, and TAs will not be made for a candidate.

   c. Documentation completed by a qualified professional must establish a *current* need for TAs.

      (1) The submission of a detailed, comprehensive, written report completed and dated *within seven years* of the exam application is required.

      (2) The receipt of accommodations during an OT education program does not guarantee that accommodations will be provided for the NBCOT® exam.

      (3) If there is no prior accommodation history in educational and/or testing experiences, the submitted documentation needs to explain why no accommodations were needed in the past and justify why accommodations are needed for the NBCOT® exam.

      (4) All required documentation must be received by the NBCOT® before the review of a TA application can begin.

> **EXAM HINT:** Candidates who have multiple disabilities that warrant distinct TAs must submit separate documentation for each disability to support each accommodation that is being requested.

3. TA recommendations made by professionals are considered and reviewed by the NBCOT® but are not automatically granted.

   a. Denials of requests for TAs can be appealed according to procedures provided in the Testing Accommodations Handbook.

4. All information about a candidate's disability and request for TAs is confidential.

   a. The NBCOT® and its testing agency only communicate with the candidate; the candidate's authorized, verified representative; and/or a professional knowledgeable about the candidate's disability with the candidate's permission.

Chapter 1

Table 1-2

NBCOT® Exam Activity Demands and Environmental Contexts as Compared to Course Exams		
FACTORS TO CONSIDER	**COURSE EXAMS**	**NBCOT EXAM**
Activity Demands	• Typically assess specific, well-defined course content. • Limited cognitive shifts are required in a topic-focused exam. • Exam items are typically presented in a familiar single response MC format. • MC items typically test the recall of knowledge. • Comprehensive exams are typically based on prior quizzes and tests for which feedback has been received.	• Assesses the depth and breadth of entry-level OTR® practice. • Numerous cognitive shifts are required; each MC item will have a unique focus. • Includes four-section six-option multi-select scenario sets that are in a novel and often unfamiliar format. • Exam items on the OTR® certification exam go beyond purely testing knowledge by requiring the application and analysis of the provided information.
Environmental Contexts	• Exams are taken in a familiar environment either at home/in dorm room or in a classroom that test-takers are able to enter freely once available. • There is the possibility for test-takers to self-select a classroom seat, often in their preferred location. • Test-takers are surrounded by familiar persons who are all taking the same exam that begins and ends at specific pre-determined points in time for all test-takers; test-takers who end their exam early, typically do so within a limited time range.	• The exam may be taken in an unfamiliar setting; test-takers may need to complete a security check-in prior to entering the exam room. • The likelihood of a test-taker being able to self-select a computer station at a testing center is low. • In a test-center, test-takers are surrounded by strangers taking diverse tests with different administration timeframes; thus, there are people beginning and ending their exams throughout the duration of the NBCOT® exam.

b. No information about the candidate's application or request for TA is released by the NBCOT® or its testing agency without the written authorization of the candidate.

5. All TAs must be approved by the NBCOT® prior to the issuance of an ATT letter.

a. No requests for TAs will be approved at the test site.

b. After taking the exam, a candidate cannot retroactively declare a disability.

(1) If a candidate with a disability fails the exam because they did not apply for TAs, they can submit all needed documentation to obtain TAs when they reapply to take the exam.

6. There are no additional fees required to apply for or receive TAs.

Types of Accommodations

1. The NBCOT® adheres to ADA's guidelines for accommodations.

2. Pearson VUE's test accommodations may include extra testing time. a separate testing room, and breaks.

a. Pearson VUE test centers allow test-takers to use specific comfort aids; these items do not require pre-approval.

(1) Refer to Box 1-1.

(a) On your exam day, Pearson VUE test center staff will visually inspect these items prior to allowing them into the testing area.

b. For more information about Pearson VUE's test accommodations refer to https://home.pearsonvue .com/Test-takers/Accommodations.aspx

---

BOX 1-1 ▷ Comfort Aid Items, No Pre-approval Required

• Medicine and medical devices
  – Medical alert bracelet
  – Earplugs (foam, no strings or wires)
  – Bandages, braces, casts, arm/shoulder slings, walking boot casts, surgical face masks, and cervical collars
  – Eyeglasses (without the case), eye patches, and eye drops
  – Handheld magnifying glass (nonelectric and without a case)
  – Glucose monitor and tablets (tablets must be unwrapped)
  – EpiPen or inhaler
  – Ice pack, heating pad
  – Cough drops and pills, must be unwrapped
• Medical devices attached to the body
  – Cochlear implants/hearing aids
  – Heart rate monitor
  – Oxygen tank
  – Insulin pump
  – Spinal cord stimulator
  – TENS units
  – Catheter, urine drainage bag, and colostomy bag
• Communication aids
  – Hearing aid/cochlear implant
• Ergonomic positioning supplies
  – Stool for elevating a leg
  – Pillow/lumbar support
• Mobility devices
  – Cane, crutches, wheelchair, motorized scooters/chairs, walker
• Service animals

Examination Administration and Scheduling

Examination Administration

1. As of January 2 2024, Pearson VUE is the only test-taking company authorized by the NBCOT® exam to administer the OTR® certification exam.
2. Information about scheduling an exam with Pearson VUE is available at https://home.pearsonvue.com/

Examination Scheduling

1. Exam scheduling should be completed by following the instructions provided in the ATT. Letter.
2. Exams are offered on a continuous, on demand basis and can be scheduled by a candidate throughout the year.

> **EXAM HINT:** It is wise to try to schedule your exam for the time of day that you are at your best. Do not schedule a morning exam if you are still bleary eyed at 11 a.m. or an afternoon exam if you fade after lunch. Respect your natural rhythms. Your NBCOT® exam administration is *not* the time to ignore your internal clock.

3. Candidates who experience a personal or medical emergency that will prevent them from taking a scheduled exam must notify the NBCOT® and request a rescheduled exam in writing.
   a. Supporting documentation and payment of a fee must accompany this notification and request.
4. If you are late for your exam or need to cancel or reschedule it, you must follow the procedures and pay the fees that are outlined in the Certification Exam Handbook (NBCOT®, 2023c).

 # The Examination Day

Pre-Preparation Plans

1. Be prepared physically.
   a. Get a good night's sleep.
   b. Eat a well-balanced, high-protein meal to sustain you.
   c. Avoid too much caffeine.
   d. Wear clothing that can be comfortable in a warm or cold room and adjusted if the room temperature changes (e.g., a long-sleeved cotton knit shirt that you can roll the sleeves up and down).
   e. Be aware of the testing center's procedures for approved clothing (e.g., head coverings worn for religious purposes; donning/doffing clothing during the exam).

> **CAUTION:** Do not wear clothing that can raise unnecessary security concerns (e.g., avoid 'hoodies,' jackets with pockets, and 'cargo' shorts or pants with deep pockets).

> **CAUTION:** It is wise to check with the staff at your test site about their current clothing and jewelry requirements and enforcement procedures; these can change at any time due to new security concerns.

2. Be prepared emotionally.

> **EXAM HINT:** Remind yourself of past achievements (e.g., completing a rigorous graduate program in OT) and adopt the attitude that passing the NBCOT® exam is one more accomplishment to be added to this list.

   a. Plan to arrive earlier than required to eliminate the anxiety of being late and being refused admittance.

> **CAUTION:** If you have never traveled to the test site, do a trial run before your exam date on the same day of the week that you are planning to take the exam. Exam day is not the time to discover that mass transportation or traffic patterns are different from those with which you are familiar.

Test Center Procedures

1. Follow the guidelines provided by the NBCOT® and Pearson VUE regarding your expected time of arrival.
   a. Plan to arrive early to allow sufficient time to *calmly* check in.

> **RED FLAG:** No one is admitted without an ATT letter.

   b. survey, and other administrative requirements.
2. You will be required to present two forms of identification at the test center.

a. Be certain to follow the guidelines for acceptable personal forms of identification that are provided by the NBCOT®.

> **RED FLAG:** No one is admitted without required identification.

3. Upon check-in, if you applied for and obtained TAs, confirm that these TAs are available for you.
4. If you need to use any of the comfort items outlined in Box 1-1, be sure you are compliant with the published policies about their use. Refer to https://home.pearsonvue.com/Test-takers/Accommodations.aspx.

> **EXAM HINT:** Be judicious about your food and drink consumption prior to the exam and during the exam to decrease the need for bathroom breaks.

5. The personnel can provide an orientation to the exam.
    a. They are available prior to the exam's start to answer questions and clarify the exam procedures.
6. For more information about test center procedures, refer to https://home.pearsonvue.com/Test-takers/Resources.aspx.
7. Test centers do not dedicate times just for NBCOT® test-takers. Many individuals taking a variety of exams may be coming, going, or receiving orientation during your exam.
    a. Some individuals find the use of earplugs or noise reducing headphones helpful in decreasing these auditory distractions.

(1) These are considered a comfort aid in Pearson VUE Centers and must be provided by the test center.
(2) If you anticipate using earplugs or headphones during your exam administration, you should use these when you complete the online practice exams that accompany this text.
    (a) These practice sessions can help you determine if the use of earplugs or headphones enhances or hinders your ability to concentrate.
8. There are no scheduled breaks during the exam unless pre-arranged as a TA for a disability or medical necessity.
    a. You are allowed to take a breaks during the exam; however, the exam clock keeps running.
    b. The test center personnel can inform you about the procedures for taking a break.
9. You are not allowed to talk or read aloud during the exam unless you have received the accommodation of a private testing room.
10. If you take a break and are observed using a banned electronic device (e.g., a cell phone, iPad, smart watch), your exam will be terminated.
    a. The test center staff will notify the NBCOT® of your infraction.
    b. Your eligibility to take a future NBCOT® exam will be determined by the NBCOT® after a review of your case.

Examination Procedures and Test-Taking Strategies

Examination Set-up

1. A tutorial on how to use the computer and complete the exam items is available prior to commencement of the exam.
    a. Candidates who have not taken an exam preparation course and/or completed practice exams and who are not familiar with the exam format are strongly advised to take the tutorial.
    b. The completion of this tutorial does not count toward the four-hour administration time, so you can use this time to get physically comfortable (e.g., move the computer screen to decrease glare, adjust the chair, take a bathroom break).
    c. You are not allowed to take notes during the tutorial or at any time before you start your exam.

> **EXAM HINT:** Notes can be taken *after* the exam clock has started counting down.

2. All exam candidates can choose to use a color scheme feature when taking their exam.

a. This feature allows you to select from a predetermined list of background and font colors to customize the exam's visual presentation.

Time and Time Keeping

1. There are four hours allowed to complete the exam.
2. Additional time is not provided for any reason other than as a pre-approved TA for a disability.

> **EXAM HINT:** It is recommended that you spend an *average* of about 45 seconds to complete each three-option single-choice exam item, one minute to complete each four-option single-choice exam item, and one minute 30 seconds to complete *each* of the four six-option multi-select items in a scenario set. This pace will enable you to accrue a bank of approximately 20–30 minutes that you can use to review and answer more challenging exam items. This extra time can also be used to take a break during the exam.

3. A running clock on the computer will indicate the total exam time remaining, and a counter will indicate the number of exam items left to answer so you can readily see if you are progressing at the needed pace.
   a. Periodically check the clock and/or counter to be sure that you are on track with your timing.
      (1) Avoid spending too much time checking this clock and counter.
   b. If you are behind schedule, your pace is too slow and you will need to speed up to complete the exam.
      (1) Do not belabor difficult questions; you do not have to get every item correct to pass the exam. Move on to other exam items.
   c. If you are ahead of schedule, take a brief breather and congratulate yourself; then maintain this pace, for you can use this additional time later during the exam to take a short break.
4. Some test-takers report feeling listless as the exam progresses, and they have found a brief break re-energized them and enabled them to resume the exam at a revitalized pace.
   a. While there are no scheduled breaks during the exam unless pre-arranged as a TA, breaks are allowed during the exam. Taking one to go to the restroom or have a drink and/or snack can be time well spent if it enables you to return to the exam with renewed energy.

Test-Taking Strategies

1. Decrease your anxiety level before you begin by taking the tutorial and asking any and all questions.
2. Do not panic. OT programs are challenging, but you passed your coursework and fieldwork to get to this point, so you must have done something right! Remember this and give yourself credit.
   a. If you find yourself becoming stressed and anxious during your exam, remind yourself of this reality.
3. Pace yourself using the timing advice provided in the prior section.
4. Select the best answer(s).
   a. Think logically and eliminate obviously wrong answers.
   b. Jot down notes on the dry erase board or paper that will be provided to you upon request.
      (1) Often visualizing the remaining options of a familiar list (e.g., Allen's Cognitive Levels) will jog one's memory and make it easier to arrive at a correct answer.

   c. Narrow your choices to the best possible answers and use your knowledge of the clinical condition and OT standards of practice to clinically reason and determine the best answer.
   d. Do not read extra information into the exam item; just consider what is stated in the item.
      (1) Decide what the exam item is basically about by looking for key words (e.g., initial intervention, discharge).
   e. Avoid thinking "but" and "what if." Often your first selections are accurate, so decrease second guessing.
   f. Do not think about people you know with this condition or practice you've seen in the clinic; think of and apply basic OT principles (i.e., what the book says, not what you saw during fieldwork).
   g. It may help to read the answer choices before you read the exam item and its question. Then you will be able to focus your reading on the issues that are directly related to the answer choices.
      (1) It may also help to try to answer the question without first reading the answer choices. However, be certain to read *all* answer choices before making your final choice.
   h. The answer should be grammatically consistent with the exam item's question.
      (1) After you have selected your answer, read the question, then your answer. Does it flow? If not, review other options.
         (a) Save this hint for ones you're not sure of (who said APA would not come in handy?!).
      (2) If English is your second language, you must remember to "think" in English when reading exam items and answering questions.
         (a) Noting past versus present tense in an item is particularly important.

> **EXAM HINT:** Use the test-taking strategies outlined in Table 1-3 when taking practice exams to develop the skills you need to effectively and correctly answer NBCOT® exam items.

Completion of the Examination

1. Answers can be recorded by using keystrokes or the mouse.
2. To answer the exam items, use the strategies provided in Table 1-3.

Chapter 1

Table 1-3

Strategies for Answering NBCOT® Exam Items

- Read the exam item carefully before selecting a response to the question posed.
  - Avoid reading into an exam item. Read the question asked and nothing but the question.
  - Identify the theme of the exam item. Ask yourself, "What is the question *REALLY* asking?"
- Employ relevant clinical experience.
  - Remember trends and consistent cases in your experience.
  - Do not call on unusual cases or atypical presentations.
- Identify the stage of the OT process (e.g., screening, evaluation, initial intervention, discharge) and the practice setting (e.g., acute care, school, skilled nursing facility).
  - Correct answers will be consistent with established standards of practice for the stage of the OT process and the practice setting; incorrect answers will not.
- Read the exam item for key words that set a priority (e.g., pain, disorientation, initial intervention, discharge).
- Use your knowledge of medical terminology to decipher unknown terms by applying the meanings of known prefixes, suffixes, and root words. Refer to Appendix 1.
- More than one answer option may seem correct. Choose the one that is *MOST* correct.
  - For the three- or four-option single-response exam items, you must choose the option that is *most* correct.
  - For the six-option multi-select Scenario Set exam items, you must choose the *three* correct options.
- Eliminate unsafe options (e.g., choices that include contraindicated actions); these must be incorrect.
  - The Red Flag and Caution boxes provided in Chapters 3-16 highlight actions that are unsafe, contraindicated, and/or place a person at risk. The application of knowledge about this content can help you determine correct answers.
- Consider eliminating options that state "always," "never," "all," or "only" as there are few absolutes in OT practice.
- Select positive, active options (e.g., train, teach, adapt, grade). These are typically more often correct than passive, negative options.
- Select responses that most closely reflect the fundamental tenets of OT (e.g., therapeutic use of self, ethical actions, the use of meaningful occupations and purposeful activities, client-centered, person-directed practice).
  - Correct answers will be consistent with these core tenets; incorrect answers will not.
- Identify choices that are very similar or equally plausible.
  - If two choices basically say the same thing or use synonyms in their answers both cannot be right; therefore, both can be eliminated.
- Carefully consider choices that are opposites of one another. If you cannot eliminate both opposites right away, one may be the correct answer.
- Use your clinical judgment to support the best answer.
  - Apply clinical reasoning skills to determine the relevance of item information (i.e., diagnosis, stage of the OT process, setting, intervention methods, and theoretical principles).
  - Table 2-2 in Chapter 2 describes the major types of clinical reasoning and questions that should be considered for each reasoning type prior to selecting answers for exam items.
- Choose answers that reflect entry-level OT practice.
  - Remember the NBCOT® exam is not a specialty certification exam.
- Before hitting next, check your answer to see if it is:
  - theoretically consistent with the exam scenario (e.g., the use of a biomechanical approach for a person with a musculoskeletal condition).
  - diagnostically consistent with the exam scenario (e.g., the recommended interventions for persons with different TBI levels according to the Rancho Los Amigos Scale).
  - developmentally consistent with the exam scenario (e.g., the selection of play activities that match a child's cognitive level according to Piaget).
- Before changing an answer make sure that you have a good reason to eliminate your original choice and a good reason to make your new choice. Refer to the Exam Hint on this page that outlines good reasons for changing an answer.
  - Do not let second-guessing talk you out of the correct answer.

a. You can use the available highlight and strike out features to help with your decision-making.
3. If you are uncertain of an answer to an exam item, mark the item by using the mark/unmark button.
   a. You can return to a marked exam item to review and change the answer (if desired) at any time *BEFORE* you end your exam.
4. Do not skip any exam item.
   a. Although not all of the exam items are scored, there is no way to know which items are operational or not; therefore, you must answer all items to the best of your ability.
5. Only change the answer to an exam item if you have a good reason to reject your first choice.

> **EXAM HINT:** Solid reasons for changing an answer include the following:
> - You missed an important key word like "pain," "disorientation," "initial," or "best."
> - Your original answer was not consistent with the stage of the OT process (e.g., screening, evaluation, intervention, discharge).
> - You obtained a solid hint from a subsequent exam item (e.g., spinal cord injury [SCI] levels).
>
> Before you change your answer to an exam item, you should feel as if a brilliant light bulb has been turned on in your brain to illuminate the correct answer. If you do not experience a 'light bulb' moment, *do not* change your answer.

6. If you remain unsure of an answer to an exam item, make a logical guess. Because there is no penalty for an incorrect answer, it is worth guessing; you may guess correctly and add to your exam score.

7. Do not communicate with anyone other than the test center personnel while completing the exam.
   a. An innocent passing remark to another person can be mistaken for an attempt to cheat.

8. Keep your eyes on your own computer screen and do not look at other screens if you take a break.
   a. A fleeting glance at another computer screen can be interpreted as an attempt to cheat.

9. Actively manage your stress throughout the exam.
   a. Do not panic if you are stumped by some exam item questions.
   b. Focus on what you know, because it is likely you know a lot.
   c. We often tend to remember our 'failures' and not our 'successes.' Be kind to yourself.

10. Congratulate yourself for what you know and make educated guesses on what you don't know. You do not need to answer 100%, 90%, or even 80% of the exam items correctly in order to pass the NBCOT® exam.

> **EXAM HINT:** If you are running out of time on the exam and have not answered all exam items pick a letter (i.e., A, B, or C) and mark *all* remaining answers in the three- and four-option single-response MC items using that one letter choice. For the scenario set items, select three letters and mark your answers to each six-option multi-select item with these letters.
> - Laws of probability will result in some of these item answers being correct.
> - After clicking on your chosen letter for all remaining items, use the time you have left to calmly and thoughtfully revisit your answers to determine if your selected answer was correct or not.
> - If you determine that your answer was incorrect, use all of the strategies identified in this Chapter to determine the best answer and change your response.
> - If you determine that your answer was correct, say a silent "YES!" to yourself and continue your review of these items until your exam administration time runs out.

> **EXAM HINT:** There is no penalty on the OTR® certification exam for incorrect answers, so do not leave any answer blank.

After the Examination

Administrative or Technical Problem Reporting

1. If you experience an administrative or technical issue during your exam, *immediately* after you complete your exam and *before leaving the center*, follow NBCOT® guidelines for submitting an administrative or technical complaint.
   a. Only complaints regarding an administrative or technical problem with the exam are accepted (e.g., the computer screen freezes).
   b. Test centers are in the business of providing optimal environments for test-taking, so administrative and technical problems are rare.
   c. Time spent to remedy a technical malfunction *will not* count against your exam administration time.
   d. If a technical problem cannot be resolved within 30 minutes, you have the right to reschedule the exam for another day within your eligible time period (NBCOT®, 2023c).

> **CAUTION:** Be certain to adhere to all of the complaint guidelines in the NBCOT® Certification Examination Handbook. There are no exceptions.

   (1) Complaints are investigated by the NBCOT® and the testing agency, and written responses are sent to the candidate.
   (2) The reporting of your exam score will be held until your complaint has been investigated and resolved.

Waiting for Examination Results

1. Accept that the exam is done and move on to other enjoyable activities.
2. Focus on your successes. Congratulate yourself on items you answered confidently.
3. Avoid focusing on exam difficulties. For example, the exam was not solely about the two obscure diagnoses

that you could not recall. Remember, there were many other items about content that you knew well that were scored as correct.
4. Surround yourself with your 'fan club,' people who assure you of your competencies.

> CAUTION: Avoid and ignore individuals who continually question the exam's fairness and perseverate about their ability to pass. The NBCOT® exam may be challenging, but it *is* constructed and scored fairly.

5. Ignore rumors about the exam's pass rate.
   a. No one has access to exam pass rates.
      (1) The NBCOT® only publicly reports annual pass rates; they do not report pass rates for each exam administration.
   b. OT educational programs do not receive exam pass rates for their graduates until after the graduates have received their personal score reports.
6. OT educational programs do not receive any reports that identify the names of graduates who do not pass the exam.

► Examination Scoring, Reporting, and Score Implications

Overview

1. Item analysis.
   a. All exams use items that the NBCOT® has analyzed as performing well on previous exams.
   b. All scored items are pre-equated and determined to have sound statistical attributes.
2. Equating.
   a. The passing score for each exam is statistically adjusted to compensate for differences in the difficulty level of each exam.
   b. This equating is completed to help ensure that candidates with equivalent abilities will be equally likely to pass the exam.
   c. From the NBCOT®'s and their testing agency's points of view, all exam candidates have a fair and equal chance to pass the exam, regardless of the administration date.
3. Scoring processes.
   a. Only pre-equated operational items are scored; the field-test items are not scored.
   b. Credit is awarded for the selection of a correct response.
      (1) There are no penalties for incorrect or blank answers.
   c. Statistical procedures convert candidates' raw scores into 'scaled scores,' which are then comparable for all exams based upon the equating process.
   d. The exam results are reported on a scale from 300 to 600 points.
   e. A scaled score of at least 450 is needed to pass the exam.
   f. This passing score of 450 remains the same for all exam administration dates. There are no adjustments made after the score is determined by the equating process.

Score Reporting

1. Several steps are followed by the testing agency to produce accurate score reports in as timely a manner as possible.
   a. Early score results are not given.
2. Exams are scored several times a month.
   a. The exam scoring schedule is posted on the NBCOT®'s website at www.nbcot.org.
   b. The NBCOT® notifies candidates via email when their exam results have been posted online.
   c. Exam candidates can access their score online by logging into their MyNBCOT® account.
      (1) Candidates who submitted a transcript with their application can typically access their score on the next business day after their exam was scored.
         (a) Candidates must use their user name and password to access this score information.
      (2) Candidates who submitted a DVF with their application cannot obtain their score until an official final transcript is received by the NBCOT®.
3. Candidates who pass the exam receive an initial certificate package within four to six weeks of their exam score date.
   a. This package includes a letter of congratulations and an official NBCOT® certificate and wallet card verifying their OTR® certification status.
   b. If you do not receive an initial certificate package within six weeks, you should contact the NBCOT® within two months of your exam score date to be reissued a certification certificate at no cost.
      (1) Certificate requests submitted after eight weeks of a score date will incur a fee.

Chapter 1

4. Candidates who fail the exam receive a feedback report that includes their total score, information on their performance in each exam domain, an explanation for interpreting their overall score and domain-level performance, and answers to questions that are frequently asked about the feedback report and retaking the exam.
5. Score reports are only provided to exam candidates or their legally verified representative.
6. The NBCOT® sends a candidate's score report to the SRB(s) and others that the candidate requested receive a score report on their application.
   a. Additional score reports can be sent to additional regulatory agencies or other parties upon the written authorization of the exam candidate.
7. Aggregate score reports are provided to the Program Directors of OT Education Programs for candidates who are graduates of their programs.

Scoring Implications

1. If your score report indicates that you passed, congratulate yourself and begin your lifelong pursuit of a rewarding career in OT.
2. If your score report indicates that you did not pass, do not denigrate yourself; rather, make a plan to retake the exam and succeed. Refer to the following section.
3. The implications of not passing the NBCOT® exam vary from state to state. You must follow your SRB's procedures for notification of exam failure.
4. If you are currently employed as an occupational therapist or you have specific plans to begin employment, you must notify your employer immediately.
5. Depending on the state, you may be able to continue employment under an extension of a temporary license or have your position reconfigured to be a rehabilitation aide/associate, with a corresponding decrease in responsibility and salary.

Retaking the Examination

1. A new and complete application must be submitted to retake the NBCOT® exam.
2. The NBCOT® requires a waiting period after a failed exam administration date before you can take the exam again. Use this time to do the following.
   a. Obtain support to handle your legitimate disappointment.
   b. Review exam results to identify and analyze overall areas of strength and weakness; do not agonize over exact percentages in your score report.
   c. Reflect on your exam experience to identify behaviors that may have hindered success. Common mistakes include the following.
      (1) Taking too much time to answer difficult questions.

(2) Becoming anxious or upset over a question that seemed to have no good answer, two good answers for a single-response item, or more than three good answers for a six-option multi-select item.
(3) Using a test-taking personality that is not effective for exam success.
   (a) Table 2-6 in Chapter 2 outlines typical test-taker personalities, their corresponding characteristics, and effective behavior management strategies that can be used to support NBCOT® exam success.
(4) Becoming distracted by other test-takers.
(5) Arriving in a rushed, harried manner.
(6) Not seeking and obtaining TAs when qualified to receive these as a candidate with a disability.
3. Be realistic about the obstacles you can change and those you cannot. For example, if you were stressed due to a traffic jam, you can leave earlier or stay overnight in a nearby hotel. On the other hand, you cannot change the fact that the exam is on a computer even though you dislike this format.

> **EXAM HINT:** If your exam performance was negatively impacted by your response to difficult exam items, remember you do *NOT* have to correctly answer every item to pass your exam. For your next exam, avoid repeating what did not work well on your prior exam (e.g., taking too much time to answer an item, becoming overanxious when an item's content was unfamiliar, getting frustrated when all answers seemed correct, or none did). Instead, when presented with an exam item that confuses, frustrates, or overwhelms you, plan to select your favorite letter as your answer to a single-response exam item or your favorite three letters as your responses to a six option multi-select scenario set item and then hit NEXT!

4. Increase your comfort level with taking a computerized exam by taking the online practice exams that accompany this text.
5. If you had received TAs for your previous exam, you need to notify the NBCOT® that you are requesting these accommodations again for your next exam.
6. If you are eligible for TAs but did not previously request them, follow the NBCOT®'s guidelines and adhere to the deadline dates to attain needed TAs.
   a. Since the NBCOT® exam requires four hours of computer work to complete, carefully and realistically assess your cognitive, physical, and psychosocial abilities for this task.
7. Develop a plan of action to ensure success.
   a. Review this text's Chapter 2 on effective exam preparation, critically evaluate what you did to prepare for your first exam, and design and implement a new exam preparation plan to address identified gaps and build on your strengths.

Chapter 1

b. Take (or re-take) an exam preparatory course.

(1) TherapyEd offers free re-takes of its two-day exam preparation course. Your first-hand exam experience can help you more effectively identify your test-taking strengths and weaknesses, and make the strategies taught in the course for selecting the best answer and managing stress and time more relevant.

> **CAUTION:** Do not rush to re-take the exam, for this may not allow you sufficient time to adequately prepare for the exam. It is better to delay the exam than rush your preparation and risk being underprepared.

8. Adopt the perspective that your first experience with the exam can be viewed positively, in that you can re-take the exam with a clear idea of what the experience is like.

a. You are aware of your strong and weak points; therefore, your chances of passing the re-take are greater.

9. Recognize that there are many skilled and competent OT practitioners who did not pass the certification exam on their first (or even their second) attempt.

a. You can join their ranks by honestly self-assessing your exam preparedness and taking concrete steps to remediate your difficulties and build upon your strengths.

b. Being able to practice OT is well worth the effort.

 ## References

Fleming-Castaldy, R.P. (2020). FAQs on effective NBCOT® certification exam preparation. OT Practice, 25(11), 11–14.

Killen, E. (2017). Preparing to take the NBCOT® exam. OT Practice, 22(11), 24–25.

National Board for Certification in Occupational Therapy (NBCOT®). (2022a). 2022 Practice Analysis of the Occupational Therapist Registered (OTR) Executive Summary (nbcot.org).

National Board for Certification in Occupational Therapy (NBCOT®). (2022b). Occupational Therapist Registered (OTR®) examination content outline. https://www.nbcot.org/-/media/PDFs/2022_OTR_Content_Outline.pdf.

National Board for Certification in Occupational Therapy. (NBCOT®). (2023a). NBCOT Occupational Therapy Regulatory Body Contact List by State. https://www.nbcot.org/-/media/PDFs/State_Contact_List.pdf

National Board for Certification in Occupational Therapy (NBCOT®). (2023b). Foundations of the Certification Examinations. https://www.nbcot.org/exam-info/foundations.

National Board for Certification in Occupational Therapy (NBCOT®). (2023c). NBCOT® certification examination handbook. https://www.nbcot.org/-/media/PDFs/Cert_Exam_Handbook.pdf

National Board for Certification in Occupational Therapy (NBCOT®). (2023d). Testing accommodations handbook. https://www.nbcot.org/exam/accommodations.

Occupational Therapy Licensure Compact. https://otcompact.org/

Sides, M., & Korcheck, N. (Eds.). (1998). Successful test-taking: Learning strategies for nurses. Lippincott.

Wilmarth, C. (2022, December). Occupational therapy licensure compact. OT Practice, 4–5, 7.

2

Effective Examination Preparation: Principles and Strategies

RITA P. FLEMING-CASTALDY and KARI INDA

Effective Examination Preparation

Overview and General Guidelines

1. The NBCOT® exam tests general knowledge and fundamentals of occupational therapy (OT) in an integrated manner.
2. There are four main levels of objective exam questions.
   a. Table 2-1 describes each question level, its relevance to the NBCOT® exam, and strategies on how to effectively use TherapyEd's *National Occupational Therapist Certification Exam Review and Study Guide* (hereafter simply called the *Review and Study Guide*) to prepare for your certification exam.

> **EXAM HINT:** The effective application of clinical and critical reasoning skills is needed to correctly answer NBCOT® exam items. Table 2-2 describes the major types of clinical reasoning, questions that should be considered for each reasoning type prior to selecting answers for exam items, and their role in determining correct answers on the NBCOT® exam for the occupational therapist, registered (OTR®). Using the information provided in Table 2-2 and the critical reasoning information subsequently provided in this Chapter can facilitate certification exam success.

3. This Chapter provides comprehensive information about effective exam preparation principles and strategies, including an extensive discussion about the relationship between critical reasoning and NBCOT® exam performance.

Psychological Outlook

1. When preparing for a professional certification exam, your psychological outlook is a critical aspect of effective exam preparation.
   a. Table 2-3 outlines the major concepts, principles, and actions that contribute to a positive psychological perspective about test-taking.
   b. Taking the actions described in Table 2-3 can help you replace fears, doubts, and negative attitudes with a positive "I can" outlook.

> **EXAM HINT:** To be eligible for the NBCOT® exam, you had to complete rigorous graduate coursework and challenging fieldworks. Therefore, if you are questioning your ability to pass the certification exam, remember that your academic and clinical educators have asserted that you possess the knowledge and skills needed for entry-level OT practice by passing you.

Table 2-1

Levels of Exam Questions

QUESTION LEVEL AND DESCRIPTION	RELEVANCE TO NBCOT® EXAM	NBCOT® EXAM PREPARATION STRATEGY[1]
1. Knowledge Recall of basic information, often tested by matching column type questions. For example, DSM diagnoses medical terminology, spinal cord levels, types of wheelchair.	A solid knowledge foundation of all information related to entry-level OT practice is required to answer certification exam items. It is highly likely that *no* items on the NBCOT® exam are solely at this level.	A strong commitment to studying is needed to remember all the information acquired during your OT education. Fortunately, this *Review and Study Guide* provides extensive information in an outline format to ease your review. Mastery of this knowledge is required to be able to readily recall it to answer the 180 exam items on the NBCOT® OTR® certification exam.
2. Comprehension Understanding information to determine significance, consequences, or implications. For example, the impact of a tenodesis grasp on function.	The NBCOT® exam is not a matching column type of test; therefore, you cannot just recall information to be able to succeed on this exam. You must fully understand the content area to be able to understand the nuances of an exam item. A few items on the NBCOT® exam may be at this level; most will require you to apply your comprehension of foundational content.	When studying this *Review and Study Guide* to review basic content and acquire your foundational knowledge, ask yourself how and why this fundamental information is important. Studying with a peer or a study group can provide you with additional insights about the relevance, significance, consequences, and implications of the information. Reviewing the EXAM HINT, CAUTION, and RED FLAG boxes in this text can also be helpful for increasing your comprehension of core content. Do not enter the exam without strong comprehension of all major areas of OT practice.

(Continued)

Table 2-1

Levels of Exam Questions (*Continued*)

QUESTION LEVEL AND DESCRIPTION	RELEVANCE TO NBCOT® EXAM	NBCOT® EXAM PREPARATION STRATEGY[1]
3. Application Use of information and application of rules, procedures, or theories to new situations. For example, the classroom modifications that an OT practitioner would make for a child with autism.	The NBCOT® exam requires you to use your knowledge and comprehension as described above, along with the competencies you developed during your clinical fieldworks, in a manner that best fits the specific practice situation in an exam item. Many NBCOT® exam items are likely at this level for a main goal of the exam is to assess your ability to respond competently to different situations.	Once you have acquired a solid knowledge base and good comprehension skills in all domains of OT as put forth in this *Review and Study Guide*, you should take the online practice exams that accompany this *Review and Study Guide*. These exams require you to apply your knowledge in a manner similar to the NBCOT® exam. Upon completion of these exams, you receive an analysis of your performance so that you can determine how well you are applying your knowledge.
4. Analysis Recognition of interrelationships between principles and interpretation or the evaluation of the information presented. For example, choosing the most appropriate focus for discharge planning for a parent with a stroke requires the integration of knowledge about the diagnosis, parenting tasks, and activity analysis.	The NBCOT® exam assumes that you have mastered and comprehend entry-level knowledge and that you can competently apply this to diverse situations. Therefore, it will ask you to analyze and respond to situations that have more than one dimension and do not only have a by-the-book answer. Many NBCOT® exam items are likely at this level for the main objective of the exam is to determine your ability to be competent in complex practice situations.	Use the analyses of this *Review and Study Guide*'s practice exams to reflect on your reasoning errors. Critically review the extensive rationales for the correct and incorrect answers that are provided with the score reports you will receive for each completed online practice exam. Reflecting with a peer or study group can be helpful in determining your gaps in analysis of exam items. Review this Chapter's section on critical reasoning skills and reflect on the questions provided in Table 2-7 to ascertain the actions you need to take to adequately prepare for the complexities of the NBCOT® exam.

[1]TherapyEd's exam preparation course emphasizes the development of the skills needed to correctly answer exam items at the application and analysis level. Refer to this Chapter's subsequent section on key exam preparation resources.

Table 2-2

Clinical Reasoning Applied to NBCOT® Exam Items

TYPE OF REASONING[1]	QUESTIONS TO CONSIDER	RELATIONSHIP TO EXAM SUCCESS[2]
Procedural Reasoning Requires the systematic gathering and interpreting of data to identify problems, set goals, plan intervention, and implement treatment strategies. It is the "doing" of practice.	What does the exam item tell/ask you about: diagnosis? symptoms? prognosis? assessment methods? treatment protocols? theories/practice frameworks to support procedures?	Correct answers on the NBCOT® exam will be consistent with the published evaluation standards and intervention protocols for a given clinical condition and congruent with established theories and relevant practice frameworks.
Interactive Reasoning Focuses on the client as a person and involves the therapeutic relationship between the practitioner, the individual, caregivers, and significant others.	What does the exam item tell/ask you about: rapport building? family/caregiver involvement? therapeutic use of self? teaching/learning styles? successful collaboration?	Correct answers on the NBCOT® exam will have the OT practitioner engaging with the person, family, caregivers, and others in an empathetic, caring, respectful, collaborative, and empowering manner.
Pragmatic Reasoning Considers the context(s) of service delivery including the person's situation and the practice environment to identify the realistic possibilities for a person in a given setting.	What does the exam item tell/ask you about: person's client factors? practice setting characteristics? reimbursement issues? legal parameters? referral options?	Correct answers on the NBCOT® exam will be realistic given the person's assets and limitations, their environmental supports and barriers, the practice setting's inherent opportunities and constraints, federal laws, and reimbursement policies.
Conditional Reasoning Represents an integration of procedural, interactive, and pragmatic reasoning in the context of the client's narrative.[1] Focuses on past, current, and possible future social contexts.	What does the exam item tell/ask you about: the individual's unique roles, values, goals? impact of illness on this person's function? how the condition's course will influence the person's future? where the person will be able to live after discharge?	Correct answers on the NBCOT® exam will take into account all case information that is provided in the exam item. NBCOT® exam items do not include extraneous details so carefully reflect on the relevance of the information provided in each exam item to determine the best answer.

(Continued)

Table 2-2

Clinical Reasoning Applied to NBCOT® Exam Items (*Continued*)

TYPE OF REASONING[1]	QUESTIONS TO CONSIDER	RELATIONSHIP TO EXAM SUCCESS[2]
Ethical Reasoning Ensures that all actions an OT practitioner takes are consistent with the profession's Code of Ethics. Helps the OT practitioner effectively address situations that present ethical dilemmas and distress. Informs ethical actions for a situation.	What does the exam item tell/ask you about: the need for more information to resolve an ethical dilemma? obtaining informed consent about the potential benefits, limitations, and risks of an intervention or research project? respecting a client's right to refuse treatment or participation? unjust situations (e.g., service delivery constraints and participation barriers) that require remediation?	Correct answers on the NBCOT® exam will always be ethical. Chapter 4 has extensive information about OT's Code of Ethics, the application of ethical principles to OT practice, ethical dilemmas and ethical distress, and ethical decision-making.

References:

Boyt Schell, B., & Schell, J.W. (2008). Clinical and professional reasoning in occupational therapy. Wolters Kluwer/Lippincott and Wilkins.

Fleming-Castaldy, R. (2010, November 8). The NBCOT® examination: Strategies for success. OT Practice, 7–10.

[1]The application of narrative reasoning is not likely required during the NBCOT® exam since this type of reasoning deals with the individual's occupational story and uses critical imagination to help the person reach an imagined future. This important process is not readily measured by objective exam questions.

[2]TherapyEd's exam preparation course emphasizes the application of clinical reasoning skills to exam items via numerous experiential activities. Refer to this Chapter's subsequent section on key exam preparation resources.

Table 2-3

Psychology of Successful Test-Taking

CONCEPT	PRINCIPLE	ACTIONS
Control	Only you can determine your future.	• Take charge; determine exactly what is needed to succeed. • Set goals to meet these needs. • Develop and implement concrete plans to succeed.
Self-awareness	Knowing one's innate capabilities enables one to build on strengths and effectively deal with limitations.	• Critically analyze test-taking errors and content knowledge gaps. • Be honest about your test-taking and content knowledge, strengths and limitations. • Avoid self-defeatist behaviors.
Self-confidence	Your past accomplishments provide a solid foundation for future success.	• Review exam content prior to completing practice exams. • Use a diversity of learning methods to achieve mastery. • Recognize and celebrate your successes and achievements.
Self-fulfilling prophecy	Your self-expectancy will influence the outcomes of your efforts.	• Expect success. • Use positive self-talk throughout exam preparation. • Continue to think positively during the exam administration.
Self-esteem	You are a person capable of excellence.	• Remember your personal and academic achievements. • OT academic course work and fieldwork are demanding; give yourself well-earned credit for your success.
Motivation	Your desire to succeed and a fear of failure can be channeled for success.	• Understand that the early stages of studying will have uncertain results. • Remind yourself of what initially motivated you to enter OT school. • Harness fear and establish a do-able study plan.
Courage	Taking responsibility for one's failures is key to success.	• Honestly critique precipitators/reasons for an exam failure. • Do not make excuses. • Do not strive for perfection.
Perseverance	You can only succeed if you persevere.	• Re-establish goals. • Seek support for goal attainment. • Utilize multiple resources to stay on track.
Freedom	You can freely choose your attitude.	• View test-taking as an opportunity. • Keep your "eye on the prize." • Exam success equates to achievement of your goal to become an OT practitioner.

Reference: Sides, M. (1998). Forming the psychology of test-taking success. In M. Sides & N. Korcheck (Eds.), Successful test-taking: Learning strategies for nurses (pp. 49–61). Lippincott.

c. Because developing a positive attitude can be difficult to do alone, surround yourself with your "fan club," people who know that you will be a terrific occupational therapist.

d. Practice techniques to reduce anxiety during the exam while preparing for it.

(1) Visual imagery, muscle relaxation, controlled diaphragmatic breathing, cognitive-behavioral strategies, mindfulness, meditation, positive self-talk, and/or exercise can be just as beneficial for you as the individuals with whom you will be working.

2. Keep your "eye on the prize."

a. Write down two reasons why you want to be an occupational therapist.

(1) Keep these statements where you will read them every day so that they help you to stay motivated.

b. Write down two reasons why you *WILL* pass the exam. For instance, "I passed the hardest class in the curriculum with the most difficult teacher ever." "I will pass the certification exam because I have developed a clear study plan and will implement it."

3. If you have previously failed the exam, honestly critique what did not work for you in preparing for and taking your prior exam (e.g., did you not practice taking a complete exam during an uninterrupted four-hour period; did you ignore studying professional competence and practice management because you found your management class boring; did you not obtain testing accommodations even though you were eligible?).

a. Develop and implement remediation strategies to effectively deal with these difficulties.

b. Maintain a positive attitude; but be careful and do not accept false reassurance from others.

c. Review the following sections on structuring a review of professional education and exam preparation resources.

Structuring an Individualized Exam Preparation Plan

General Exam Preparation Guidelines

1. Establish your knowledge and skill level.

a. The NBCOT® exam tests general knowledge and fundamentals of OT in an integrated manner. Refer to Chapter 3 for a review of the foundations of OT practice.

b. Critique your knowledge of the four domains that are covered in the NBCOT® exam to identify your areas of strength and weakness to create a personal study plan (NBCOT®, 2022). Refer to Chapter 1.

c. Review your academic history to help clarify strengths and weaknesses. Honestly appraise which course topics you mastered and the ones with which you struggled.

2. Be realistic about your inherent capabilities (e.g., being a poor memorizer) and your external constraints (e.g., being a single parent who must rely on childcare) when planning the amount of study time needed to ensure success.

3. Critically assess the study habits and routines you used in OT school to identify those that worked most effectively for you and increased your confidence (e.g., studying with a peer or small group) and those that were less effective and/or stressful (e.g., cramming).

> CAUTION: Studying in cram sessions can increase anxiety, result in knowledge gaps, and contribute to burnout.

4. Establish a study schedule and routine and adhere to it strictly.

a. Study one major content area per study session.

b. Limit interruptions.

(1) Turn your cell phone *OFF* so that you are not distracted by text messages, phone calls, emails, tweets, etc. (if needed, place your cell phone in a difficult place to access it; e.g., your car's glove compartment).

(2) *DO NOT* study by a computer or tablet; an attractive ad for a favorite product and/or a social media post from a person you follow will be far more interesting than Medicare guidelines or wheelchair measurements.

(3) If you are a parent and/or caregiver, arrange for child, adult, and/or respite care.

> RED FLAG: If an unexpected event results in a loss of planned study time, schedule time to make up for this loss as soon as possible. Not doing so can result in a significant gap in content knowledge that can hinder exam success.

5. Use the NBCOT® OTR® exam content outline to prioritize the amount of time you devote to studying specific areas. Table 2-4 lists the four Domains that comprise the NBCOT® exam for the occupational therapist in descending order from the Domain that comprises the highest percentage of the OTR® exam to the Domain that comprises the lowest.

Table 2-4

NBCOT® OTR® Exam Domains and Percentages

DOMAIN	EXAM %
"Domain 3 Select and Manage Interventions: Select and implement interventions to promote healing and enhance engagement in occupation-based activities" (NBCOT®, 2022, p. 7).	38%
"Domain 1 Evaluation and Assessment: Acquire information regarding factors that influence occupational performance on an ongoing basis throughout the occupational therapy process" (NBCOT®, 2022, p. 3).	23%
"Domain 2 Analysis, Interpretation, and Planning: Formulate conclusions regarding client needs and priorities to develop and monitor an intervention plan throughout the occupational therapy process" (NBCOT®, 2022, p. 5).	23%
"Domain 4 Competency and Practice Management: Manage professional activities of self and relevant others as guided by evidence, regulatory compliance, and standards of practice to promote quality care" (NBCOT®, 2022, p. 12).	16%

Reference: National Board for Certification in Occupational Therapy (NBCOT®). (2022). 2022 Occupational Therapist Registered (OTR®) Examination Content Outline (nbcot.org).

6. Allow yourself sufficient time to study over a period of time and set aside enough time to master your weakest areas and to review all areas in general.
   a. Your aim is to enter the exam with solid knowledge in all critical content areas.
7. Take a certification exam preparation course.
   a. The inside covers of this *Review and Study Guide* and a subsequent section in this Chapter provide information about key exam preparation resources including TherapyEd's highly regarded two-day preparation course for the NBCOT® OTR® exam.

> **EXAM HINT:** The FAQs and their answers about the NBCOT® OTR® exam and effective exam preparation that are provided at the beginning of this *Review and Study Guide* and the following section about specific guidelines for the strategic use of this text can help you develop and implement an individualized exam preparation plan to enable your certification exam success.

Guidelines for Using the *Review and Study Guide* for Exam Preparation

1. TherapyEd's *Review and Study Guide* covers all practice domains, tasks, and knowledge statements established by the NBCOT®'s most current OTR® exam content outline (NBCOT®, 2022).
   a. This *Review and Study Guide* synthesizes the content that may be tested on the NBCOT® OTR® exam in an organized outline format that facilitates efficient and effective certification exam preparation.
2. Before you start studying specific content, review Chapters 3-16 and rate your knowledge of key content according to a scale of know very well, know adequately, know very little, know nothing.
   a. Based on this critical self-assessment, make a personal "OT Knowledge Continuum" for yourself, listing topics from strongest to weakest.
3. Develop and implement an individualized exam preparation plan.
   a. Content areas that are rated as "know nothing" or "know very little" will become your "Must Study" list.
   b. Content areas that are rated as "know very well" or "know adequately" will become your "Review" list.
4. Organize your "Must Study" list and "Review" list into a logical schedule that facilitates connections between content.
   a. For example, if your knowledge of activity analysis, gradation, and modification, is weak, study this content in Chapter 3 before you study the intervention approaches that are used to enable occupational engagement and performance that are described in Chapter 15. Many of these interventions use activity analysis, gradation, and modification. Therefore, knowing the foundational principles that are used to inform these interventions can help you master this content in a more efficient and integrated manner.

> **EXAM HINT:** The NBCOT® exam often includes items with specific diagnoses that test knowledge about the approaches that are typically used with these conditions. Studying this *Review and Study Guide's* chapters about these diagnoses along with their related evaluation and intervention chapters will provide an integrative learning experience. For example, you should pair Chapter 6: Musculoskeletal System Disorders with Chapter 11: Biomechanical Approaches: Evaluation and Intervention; Chapter 7: Neurological System Disorders with Chapter 12: Neurological Approaches: Evaluation and Intervention; and Chapter 10: Psychiatric and Cognitive Disorders with Chapter 14: Psychosocial Approaches: Evaluation and Intervention. The content in Chapter 13: Cognitive-Perceptual Approaches: Evaluation and Intervention is applicable to several of the clinical conditions that are described in Chapters 7 and 10.

5. Allocate your study time according to your "OT Knowledge Continuum," "Must Study" list, and "Review" list beginning with your weakest area first.
   a. After you master a weak content area, reward yourself by reviewing a content area of strength.
   b. Continue studying to progress along your knowledge continuum, alternating between your "Must Study" list and "Review" list. This will help prevent exam preparation fatigue and burnout.

EXAM HINT: Throughout Chapters 3–16, green EXAM HINT boxes identify how chapter content relates to the domains, tasks, and knowledge statements that are delineated in the most recent NBCOT® OTR® exam content outline (NBCOT®, 2022). Use these hints to prioritize the content that must be mastered to help ensure exam success.

6. Plan to spend more time studying chapter content that addresses Domain 3 Select and Manage Interventions, especially if these areas are on the low end of your "OT Knowledge Continuum" and on your "Must Study" list.
   a. As noted in Table 2-4, this Domain comprises the greatest percent of the exam content; therefore, the time and effort you devote to mastering chapter content related to interventions will be well spent.

EXAM HINT: Chapters 3-16 in this text include a set of questions about chapter content that must be mastered for certification exam success. These open-ended questions are provided to help you "jump start" the thought processes you will need to apply your studying of content to the answering of exam items. After you finish studying a chapter, you should answer these content-specific review questions to assess your understanding of its content. Answers to these review questions are provided in Appendix 2. Comparing your answers to the ones provided in Appendix 2 can help you assess your content knowledge strengths and gaps. These insights can help you revise your exam preparation plan to ensure you master core content *before* you take your first online practice exam.

RED FLAG: *DO NOT* take the online practice exams that accompany this *Review and Study Guide* until after you have implemented your exam preparation plan and gained mastery of your "Must Study" list. Completing a practice exam *before* you have attained mastery of essential content will only reinforce that you have key gaps in your foundational knowledge. This can diminish confidence, lower self-esteem, and make the prospect of studying more overwhelming.

7. *After* the full implementation of your exam preparation plan, review the *Guidelines for Effective Use of the Online Practice Exams* that are provided at the end of this text.
8. After you review these recommendations, take the first online practice exam that accompanies this *Review and Study Guide* using the test-taking strategies provided in Chapter 1.
   a. Completing an online exam *after* you have studied all essential content will provide you with the opportunity to apply your acquired knowledge.
      (1) This can increase confidence, boost self-esteem, and enable your subsequent studying to be more targeted on areas that you had initially

not focused on in depth or had not sufficiently mastered.
      (2) Because TherapyEd's online practice exams are summative exams designed to mirror the NBCOT® exam administration experience, each online practice exam can only be taken once.

EXAM HINT: Be certain to complete your online practice exams in their entirety during a continuous four-hour period to increase comfort with the cognitive, visual, and ergonomic demands of the actual testing situation and help habituate effective test-taking skills.

CAUTION: During your exam simulation, be sure to include a 10–15 minute break since it is highly likely that you will need to take a restroom break during your exam administration. This amount of break time may be needed if the test center requires you to check out from the exam administration area to go to the restroom and check in to return to the exam administration area. This process may require you to wait while other test-takers are checking in and/or out.

9. Reflect on the analysis of your exam performance that will be provided immediately after you complete each TherapyEd online practice exam via an individualized score report.
   a. Your personal score report will identify the exam items you answered correctly and incorrectly.
   b. Review the rationales that are provided for the incorrect *and* correct answers for each exam item.
      (1) These rationales provide clear and detailed explanations about the content knowledge and critical reasoning skills that were required to determine correct answers.

EXAM HINT: It is essential to review the rationales for the exam items you answered incorrectly to ensure that you acquire the foundational knowledge and skills that are needed to determine correct answers. It is also important to review the rationales for the exam items you answered correctly to make sure that your selected answer was based on your knowledge and skills, not a lucky guess. A review of the rationales for your correct answers can help you assess your existing content knowledge, critical reasoning, test-taking, and time management skills and the efficacy of your exam preparation plan.

   c. The score report's analysis of your performance will provide information about your exam domain, content knowledge, and critical reasoning strengths and gaps.
      (1) Box 2-1 describes how information about your performance in the four NBCOT® OTR® exam domains can be used to revise your exam preparation plan.

(2) Box 2-2 describe how the information provided about your performance in nine content categories can be used to develop a revised and targeted study plan.

(a) Table 2-5 outlines the *Review and Study Guide* chapter(s) you should study if your performance in a content category is less than satisfactory.

(3) Box 2-3 describes how the information provided about your performance in five types of critical reasoning can be used to improve your critical reasoning skills.

EXAM HINT: To support your ability to effectively use TherapyEd's online practice exams during your preparation for the NBCOT® exam, our practice exam score reports and rationales remain available on TherapyEd's portal for the duration of your access (i.e., 12 months).

The Guidelines for Effective Use of Online Practice Exams included at the end of this text provides further information about the content of the score reports and their utility.

d. The amount of time you took to complete the online practice exam is also reported.

10. Implement your revised exam preparation plan by using the guidelines provided in Boxes 2-1 to 2-3 and studying the chapters listed in Table 2-5.

EXAM HINT: Because many people have a specific test-taking personality, it is important to identify your style to be sure that it is effective. Completing the three online practice exams that accompany this text will help you identify your test-taking personality so that you can use strategies to effectively counter the pitfalls that may occur with ineffective test-taker styles. Table 2-6 outlines typical test-taker personalities, their corresponding characteristics, and effective behavior management strategies that can be used to support NBCOT® exam success.

11. Complete the second online practice exam that accompanies this *Review and Study Guide* by using the test-taking strategies provided in Chapter 1, the clinical reasoning questions outlined in Table 2-2, the test-taker personality management strategies described in Table 2-6, and the critical reasoning strategies subsequently provided in this Chapter to effectively address the errors you made on your first practice exam.

a. Reflect on the analysis of your second online practice exam performance that will be provided after you complete the exam.

b. Update your exam preparation plan to address remaining concerns by using the guidelines provided in Boxes 2-1 to 2-3 and studying the chapters listed in Table 2-5.

BOX 2-1 ▷ NBCOT® Exam Domain Score Report Content and Utility

• A test-taker's performance on TherapyEd's online practice exams will be analyzed according to the four NBCOT® OTR® exam domains. These include:
  – Domain 1 Evaluation and Assessment
  – Domain 2 Analysis, Interpretation, and Planning
  – Domain 3 Select and Manage Interventions
  – Domain 4 Competency and Practice Management

• For domain scores that are less than satisfactory, test-takers should:
  – carefully review the EXAM HINTS in Chapters 3-16 that describe how chapter content is directly related to the NBCOT® OTR® exam domains and their corresponding task and knowledge statements.
  – prioritize their studying to concentrate on the content that is known to be tested on the NBCOT® exam.
  – learn more about the content of the NBCOT® exam for the occupational therapist by reviewing the complete content outline at www.nbcot.org.

BOX 2-2 ▷ Content Category Score Report Content and Utility

• A test-taker's performance on TherapyEd's online practice exams will be analyzed according to nine content knowledge categories. These include:
  – C1 Human Development Across the Lifespan
  – C2 Foundations of Occupational Therapy Practice
  – C3 Musculoskeletal System Disorders and Biomechanical Approaches
  – C4 Neurological System Disorders and Neurological Approaches
  – C5 Cardiopulmonary, Gastrointestinal, Renal-genitourinary, Immunological, Endocrine, and Integumentary System Disorders and Evaluation and Intervention Approaches
  – C6 Psychiatric Disorders and Psychosocial Approaches
  – C7 Cognitive-Perceptual Disorders and Approaches
  – C8 Evaluation and Intervention for Occupational Engagement and Performance and Environmental Mastery
  – C9 Competency and Professional Management

• For content category scores that are less than satisfactory, test-takers should:
  – review the practice exam item rationales in the categories of concern to increase awareness of the specific content that must be mastered.
  – identify their content knowledge gaps and strengths.
  – revise their exam preparation plan to target content areas that were not previously studied or sufficiently mastered.
  – implement the revised plan by studying the content in the chapters that align with the score report content categories. Refer to Table 2-5.

Table 2-5

Online Practice Exam Score Report Content Categories and Corresponding Text Chapters

SCORE REPORT CONTENT CATEGORIES	CORRESPONDING TEXT CHAPTERS
C1 Human Development Across the Lifespan	Chapter 5: Human Development Across the Lifespan
C2 Foundations of Occupational Therapy Practice	Chapter 3: Foundations of Occupational Therapy Practice
C3 Musculoskeletal System Disorders and Biomechanical Approaches	Chapter 6: Musculoskeletal System Disorders Chapter 11: Biomechanical Approaches: Evaluation and Intervention
C4 Neurological System Disorders and Neurological Approaches	Chapter 7: Neurological System Disorders Chapter 12: Neurological Approaches: Evaluation and Intervention
C5 Cardiopulmonary, Gastrointestinal, Renal-genitourinary, Immunological, Endocrine, and Integumentary System Disorders and Evaluation and Intervention Approaches	Chapter 8: Cardiovascular and Pulmonary System Disorders Chapter 9: Gastrointestinal, Renal-Genitourinary, Endocrine, Immuno-logical, and Integumentary System Disorders
Psychiatric Disorders and Psychosocial Approaches	Chapter 10: Psychiatric and Cognitive Disorders Chapter 14: Psychosocial Approaches: Evaluation and Intervention
Cognitive-perceptual Disorders and Approaches	Chapter 13: Cognitive-Perceptual Approaches: Evaluation and Intervention
Evaluation and Intervention for Occupational Engagement and Performance and Environmental Mastery	Chapter 15: Occupational Engagement and Performance: Evaluation and Intervention Chapter 16: Mastery of the Environment: Evaluation and Intervention
Competency and Practice Management	Chapter 4: Competency and Practice Management

12. Repeat this process for the third online practice exam that accompanies this *Review and Study Guide*.

> **EXAM HINT:** Completing each of the online practice exams that accompany this *Review and Study Guide* in a timed manner can increase your comfort with the format and pace of the NBCOT® exam. This ease can contribute to a less stressful experience when you are taking your actual exam. When you take each online exam, practice using the test-taking strategies provided in Chapter 1 and the test-taking personality behavior management strategies provided in Table 2-6 to facilitate the habituation of these effective techniques. This habit training will help you be well prepared to use these strategies during your NBCOT® exam.

13. Do not memorize practice exam items.

> **CAUTION:** Similar items may be on the NBCOT® exam and answer choices may even be the same. However, a change of only one word (e.g., "initially," "discharge") can significantly alter the focus of an exam item, and as a result, change the correct answer.

Additional Exam Preparation Resources

1. Effective preparation for the NBCOT® OTR® exam requires the recognition that there are two components to exam success. They are adequate content knowledge *and* solid objective exam test-taking skills.

> **BOX 2-3 ◐ Critical Reasoning Score Report Content and Utility**
>
> • A test-taker's performance on TherapyEd's online practice exams will be analyzed according to five types of critical reasoning. These include:
>   – Inductive Reasoning
>   – Deductive Reasoning
>   – Analytical Reasoning
>   – Inferential Reasoning
>   – Evaluative Reasoning
> • For critical reasoning scores that are less than satisfactory, test-takers should:
>   – review this Chapter's comprehensive information about the relevance and application of critical reasoning to the NBCOT® exam.
>   – reflect on the questions provided in Table 2-7 to determine the nature of their critical reasoning difficulties.
>   – implement the strategies identified in Table 2-7 to strengthen their critical reasoning skills.

2. This *Review and Study Guide* has been designed to be a *primary* content knowledge resource for studying for the NBCOT® certification exam for the OTR®.
   a. Our chapter authors have used the major OT textbooks identified by NBCOT® as providing the foundation for exam items as their chapter references.
   b. If you are particularly weak in a certain area, additional OT textbooks, course notes and handouts

Chapter 2

Table 2-6

Personalities of Test-Takers

PERSONALITY TYPE	CHARACTERISTICS	STRATEGIES
The Rusher	• Impatient. • Jumps to conclusions. • Skips key words. • Inadequate consideration of exam items.	• Take practice exams in a timed manner to establish a non-desperate pace and help realize that the time allotted for the exam is sufficient. • Use positive self-talk and relaxation techniques during exam. • Employ the strategies provided in Table 1-3 in Chapter 1 to slow your pace and not make the errors that are endemic to rushing.
The Turtle	• Overly slow and methodical. • Over attention to extraneous detail. • Reads and rereads exam item's details. • Misses theme of exam items.	• Take practice exams in a timed manner to establish a pace of completing approximately 45 exam items in an hour. • Study in bullet format. • Use the strategies provided in Table 1-3 in Chapter 1 to identify each item's focus and select the best answer, and then move on to the next item.
Philosopher	• Is a thoughtful, talented, intelligent, and disciplined student. • Excels in essay questions. • Over-analyzes and reads into exam items. • Wants to know everything and answer everything about the topic. • Over-applies clinical knowledge.	• Study in bullet, not paragraph form. • Focus only on the exam item. • Look for simple, straightforward answers. • Remind yourself that your "job" on the exam is to select the best answer for the question posed, not to address all possible aspects of an item's scenario. • Apply the strategies provided in Table 1-3 in Chapter 1 to stay focused on answering each item as it is presented.
Lawyer	• Is a thoughtful, talented, intelligent and disciplined student. • Picks out some bit of information and builds a case on that. • Reads into an exam item to make a case for a preferred answer instead of determining what the question is asking.	• Focus on what the exam item is asking and only what the exam item is asking. • Remind yourself that your "job" is to pass the NBCOT® exam, not prove a point. • Remember you can train to be an NBCOT® exam item writer and write "better" exam items after you pass the exam.

Second-Guesser	• Often a philosopher who reads into an item.
	• Frequently looks at the exam item from every angle.
	• Keeps changing answers, increasing anxiety, thinking less clearly and then changing answers more rapidly.
		• Apply the "light bulb" strategy described in Chapter 1.
		  – Identify a good reason to reject your first answer (i.e., missing a key word).
		  – Identify a good reason to select a new answer (i.e., obtaining a solid hint from a subsequent exam item).
		• If you do not experience a "light bulb" moment, do not change your answer.

Squisher/Procrastinator	• Puts things off. • Does not reschedule missed study time. • Mastery of exam content is not attained and major knowledge gaps remain.	• Focus on developing a step-by-step study plan. • Dig in and get started. • Adopt a "no excuses" attitude. • Join a study group or work with a study partner to stay on track.

Reference: Korchek, N. (1998). Personalities of test-takers. In M. Sides & N. Korcheck (Eds.), Successful test-taking: Learning strategies for nurses (pp. 77–89). Lippincott.

can be helpful to supplement your studying from this *Review and Study Guide*.

3. Knowledge of exam content does not ensure success on the NBCOT® exam.

a. Competent students with good histories of academic success and successful fieldwork experiences have reported failing the NBCOT® exam because they have poor objective exam test-taking skills.

(1) Entrenched test-taking personalities as described in Table 2-6 must be effectively managed for exam success.

4. Exam preparatory courses can develop your ability to apply clinical reasoning and critical thinking skills to correctly answer OTR® certification exam items.

5. TherapyEd offers an intensive two-day course that focuses on the self-assessment of test-taking abilities and exam content knowledge through the answering and discussion of practice exam items and their answer rationales.

a. Courses are offered in-person throughout the United States and online in different time zones.

(1) Over 150 OT academic programs host a TherapyEd course each year for their graduates with the *vast majority of courses open to all exam candidates.*

b. The effective management of test-taking personalities and the development of an efficient exam preparation plan are emphasized.

c. Extensive participant feedback has indicated that TherapyEd's certification exam preparation course when used in combination with this *Review and Study Guide* is highly effective for achieving NBCOT® certification exam success.

d. If you purchased this *Review and Study Guide* from TherapyEd, your purchase price can be credited to the course registration fee.

e. Refer to www.TherapyEd.com for further information and participant reviews.

6. Additional exam preparation resources that TherapyEd provides to exam candidates include the following.

a. Free weekly online office hours conducted by TherapyEd course instructors who review specific content that is identified as required knowledge on the NBCOT® OTR® exam content outline, and answer participants' questions about their exam preparation, test-taking strategies, the exam format and content, and any other concerns they may have.

(1) For more information refer to OT Office Hours (therapyed.com).

b. A weekly exam item of the week with a rationale that is posted on TherapyEd's social media channels and discussed during its corresponding online office hour session.

c. Open access to recorded online office hour content review sessions and webinars about exam preparation on TherapyEd's You Tube channel.

d. A mobile test prep app that allows you to take as many or as few exam items as you desire throughout your exam preparation. The app items can be filtered according to the NBCOT® OTR® exam domains, nine content categories, and five critical reasoning strategies.

(1) Using the app items to test your knowledge in areas that you identify as requiring more preparation before you take the complete online practice exams that accompany this *Review and Study Guide* can increase the efficacy of your exam preparation plan.

(2) For more information refer to OT Exam Mobile App - TherapyEd.

e. Individual and small group tutoring sessions that are personalized to address each exam candidate's specific needs and support their strengths.

(1) For more information refer to OT Exam Tutoring (therapyed.com).

7. Fellow exam candidates are valuable resources for obtaining information about the efficacy of exam preparation resources.

Critical Reasoning and NBCOT® Exam Performance

Overview of Critical Reasoning

1. Critical reasoning is a decision-making process which utilizes a person's knowledge, skills, experience, and logic to draw conclusions about everyday situations.

a. Critical reasoning skills are the foundation for how we reason through the situations we encounter in daily life.

b. They are the base from which people draw conclusions about their world and what they determine to be true.

c. When used judiciously, critical reasoning is undertaken with purpose, clarity, accuracy, and thoroughness.

Relationship to the NBCOT® Exam

1. Critical reasoning is vitally important for NBCOT® exam success.

a. The NBCOT® exam does not merely test the ability to recall facts that are readily found in books.

> **EXAM HINT:** Knowledge of facts is a vital foundation for NBCOT® exam success, but accurately answering the OTR® exam items requires more than the simple recall of knowledge. As outlined in Table 2-1, the NBCOT® exam integrates higher levels of objective questions (i.e., application and analysis) to measure the knowledge, skills, and behaviors needed for competent entry-level OT practice.

Chapter 2

b. Most NBCOT® OTR® certification exam items focus on contextualized practice situations which test your ability to correctly reason and make prudent decisions about challenging clinical circumstances and/or complex practice situations.

c. Factual information (e.g., a person's symptoms, diagnosis) must be applied to practice scenarios in which you will need to draw conclusions (e.g., most appropriate intervention, expected outcome).

2. Due to its daily use and intuitive nature, the relationship between critical reasoning and professional exam success is often not acknowledged. Therefore, the conscious and proactive use of critical reasoning skills is an important part of your NBCOT® exam preparation.

a. The three online practice exams that accompany this *Review and Study Guide* provide multiple opportunities for you to demonstrate how well you can reason out challenging practice situations as you answer their 540 exam items.

(1) Each exam item will require you to draw upon your knowledge, skills, and experiences to arrive at a correct conclusion.

(a) This accurate determination is made through critical reasoning.

3. The development of critical reasoning skills is fostered during OT academic coursework and fieldwork, so at this point you will have developed a solid repertoire of critical reasoning skills.

a. Your achievement of this level of critical reasoning skills has enabled you to succeed in your pursuit of an OT graduate degree.

b. These capabilities will serve you well in your preparation for the NBCOT® OTR® exam.

(1) Increasing your awareness about how these critical reasoning skills are reflected in NBCOT®'s OTR® certification exam items will further enhance your exam success.

4. The following sections will make explicit important facets of critical reasoning skills and help you prepare to successfully complete the NBCOT® exam.

Five Subskills of Critical Reasoning

1. There are five subskills of critical reasoning which provide the foundation for good critical reasoning.

a. They are described by Facione and Facione (1990a, 1990b, 2006) and are based on a consensus of many critical thinking experts about the skills used in reasoning out challenging circumstances.

b. They include inductive, deductive, analytical, inferential, and evaluative reasoning.

2. These subskills and their relevance to the NBCOT® exam are described in the following sections.

Inductive Reasoning

1. The process of reasoning in which the assumptions of an argument are believed to endorse the conclusion, but do not guarantee it.

2. Starts with reasoning in specific situations and then moves to more generalized situations.

3. An important skill clinically because it helps us to look at all our possible options in a circumstance and determine which seems most reasonable.

4. Used in diagnostic thinking to form assumptions about what to expect from a diagnosis as it evolves and changes over time.

5. May start with observations in a specific situation and then lead to drawing conclusions about larger circumstances.

a. This generalization process can lead to flawed reasoning.

(1) For example, upon observing a person post–cerebral vascular accident (CVA) with dysarthria, an OT practitioner concludes that all individuals post-CVA have dysarthria, which is untrue.

(a) This false conclusion is reflective of a faulty reasoning process which applied an observation from a specific situation to a larger, more global assumption.

CAUTION: Inductive reasoning must be used cautiously when answering NBCOT® exam items because situation-specific knowledge is not an adequate foundation for making universal assumptions. Recognizing the limitations of inductive reasoning is an important part of successful exam performance; additional critical reasoning skills are required to adequately analyze exam items.

EXAM HINT: Be sure not to make hasty generalizations about an exam item practice scenario. Generalizations are needed in life and even during the NBCOT® OTR® exam, but you must be prudent in making such generalizations and not jump to conclusions when answering exam items.

6. To help you identify exam items that require the formation of assumptions, the rationales for this *Review and Study Guide's* three online practice exams will have a picture of binoculars next to inductive reasoning exam items.

Deductive Reasoning

1. The process of reasoning in which conclusions are drawn based on facts, laws, rules, or accepted principles.

2. The reverse thinking process of inductive reasoning.

3. Starts with information about larger circumstances, broader principles, and general theories and applies this knowledge to specific situations.
   a. For example, an OT practitioner applies the OT ethical principle of veracity to conclude that a fellow practitioner who falsely documents a treatment procedure to fraudulently bill Medicare is behaving in an unethical manner.
4. Provides important guidelines for OT practice by putting forth protocols (e.g., diagnostic-specific intervention guidelines), procedures (e.g., correlation data analysis), rules (e.g., AOTA code of ethics), and laws (e.g., IDEA, ADA) that can be applied to a specific practice scenario without necessitating independent judgment for the situation.

> **CAUTION:** Deductive reasoning must be used cautiously when answering NBCOT® exam items because erroneous assumptions about the premises of a theory can be made and then mistakenly applied to a specific circumstance. For example, an OT practitioner who staunchly adheres to the belief that all persons with disabilities want to be independent in all activities of daily living would be wrong to apply this viewpoint to a person from a cultural background that views family-provided assistance as a sign of loving care. This practitioner would be deducing from a flawed premise which would lead to a faulty conclusion.

> **EXAM HINT:** Recognizing the limitations of deductive reasoning is an important part of successful exam performance; the soundness and trustworthiness of the applied procedures, theories, principles, and concepts must be thoughtfully critiqued before they are applied to a specific situation.

5. To help you identify NBCOT® exam items that require their correct answers to be based on facts, laws, rules, or accepted principles, the rationales for this *Review and Study Guide's* three online practice exams will have a picture of a microscope next to deductive reasoning exam items.

Analytical Reasoning or Analysis

1. The process of interpreting the meaning of information, determining relationships within the information presented, and then making assumptions or judgments about that information.
   a. Helps to examine ideas and concepts and the relationships between them.
2. Information presented in the form of graphs, charts, tables, and pictures encourage analytical reasoning skills because one must interpret the information that is depicted and determine what it precisely means.

a. Information can also be presented in a narrative manner that requires one to make a "mental chart" of the information presented.
3. Used in OT practice to interpret evaluation results (e.g., the Executive Function Performance Test), categorize information (e.g., define a symptom based on a behavioral description, or determine a diagnosis based on a cluster of reported symptoms).
   a. Important in OT practice, because it helps the OT practitioner determine the potential impact of a clinical condition on occupational performance.
4. Analysis is required to correctly answer many NBCOT® certification exam items.
   a. Analytical reasoning is used when some descriptors are included in an exam item stem (e.g., member characteristics of a mature-level group), but some key descriptors needed to answer the item's question are not provided (e.g., the leader's role in a mature group); thus the test-taker must make assumptions about what the best answer would be (e.g., type of activity used in the group) based on the partial information provided.

> **EXAM HINT:** Analysis exam items are often frustrating because limited information upon which an answer must be selected is provided; however, they accurately reflect the practice reality that OT practitioners rarely have complete information about a person or group.

5. To help you identify exam items that require the examination of ideas and concepts and the relationships between them, the rationales for this *Review and Study Guide's* three online practice exams will have a picture of a beaker next to analytical reasoning exam items.

Inferential Reasoning or Inference

1. The process of drawing conclusions or making logical judgments based on facts, concepts, and evidence rather than direct observations.
2. Used in practice situations when an OT practitioner infers the symptoms to expect based on a diagnosis (e.g., a person with a left CVA will exhibit right hemiplegia and aphasia) or the likely progression of a disease or disorder (e.g., amyotrophic lateral sclerosis [ALS] will steadily progress until death while the course of multiple sclerosis [MS] is characterized by exacerbations and remissions).
   a. Inferences about the nature of a disease, all of its possible symptoms, and its sequelae are not guaranteed to be 100% accurate; therefore, skilled inference must be based on the OT practitioner's knowledge and experience.

3. Inferential reasoning is also utilized in practice situations when OT practitioners have to decide on the best course of action.
   a. Inferences about clinical courses of action are not guaranteed to be 100% accurate. For example, when treating an individual with a rotator cuff tear, a practitioner cannot be 100% certain that the chosen intervention will result in the successful therapeutic outcome of improved occupational performance. Therefore, skilled inference must be based on the practitioner's knowledge and experience.
4. Inferential reasoning is regularly used by OT practitioners in their decision-making process and this reality is precisely why the skill is important for successful NBCOT® exam performance.
5. Inference is required to correctly answer many NBCOT® exam item questions.
   a. Questions that ask the test-taker to determine what is best, most important, or most likely to occur often require inferential reasoning.

> **CAUTION:** Inferential reasoning must be used cautiously when answering NBCOT® exam items because inadequate consideration of the information presented in an exam item or the use of faulty or hasty logic to determine what may occur in certain situations can lead to the selection of an incorrect answer. For example, an OT practitioner determines that it is most appropriate for a person with T12 paraplegia to focus on the upper trapezius and levator scapulae muscles in preparation for functional mobility with crutches, rather than the triceps and lower trapezius muscles. This decision is erroneous because it does not consider the nature of the task at hand (i.e., ambulation with crutches).

> **EXAM HINT:** Exam items of this nature can be difficult because they ask the test-taker to determine what is believed to be true even though there is no 100% assurance that the selected answer is correct; however, they accurately reflect the realistic uncertainties of OT practice.

6. Since quick decisions can lead to suboptimal intervention, the NBCOT® exam requires judicious use of inferential reasoning.
7. To help you identify exam items that require you to draw conclusions or make logical judgments based on facts, concepts, and evidence rather than direct observations, the rationales for this *Review and Study Guide's* three online practice exams will have a picture of a light bulb next to inferential reasoning exam items.

Evaluative Reasoning or Evaluation

1. The process by which the merits of an argument are weighed for their validity and the inherent value of the argument itself is critiqued.
   a. The determination that an argument "holds any water" or not.
   b. If there is value found in the argument itself, the assignment of a value to it.
2. People make judgments about the merits and value of the information they receive all the time and are often unconscious of the thought process that is involved.
3. In OT practice, evaluative reasoning must be conscious.
   a. A good evaluative thinker listens with a skeptical ear to determine the trustworthiness of information before assigning a value to it.
   b. Accepting information at face value can be a reasoning pitfall since there can be additional information needed to complete an accurate assessment of a situation.
4. Evaluative reasoning helps guide thinking about a correct course of action.
5. Evaluation is often used in OT practice when difficult decisions must be made in areas that have no clear-cut answers.
   a. Practice situations can be ambiguous and require the OT practitioner to evaluate the situation, weigh the information presented, and determine a correct course of action, given their knowledge and experience.
   b. These dilemmas pose a challenge to practitioners since the correct course of action must be determined.
   c. For example, during an intervention session, an OT practitioner observes bruises on an older adult resident in a skilled nursing facility and must determine if the correct course of action is immediately notifying the charge nurse, the physician, adult protective services, and/or the family; or asking the resident to explain the source of the bruises; or documenting the observation and continuing with the session as planned.
6. Pitfalls in evaluative reasoning lie in assigning great value to information that has little value to the situation, not assigning enough value to highly valuable information, and finally not utilizing principles and guidelines that are put into place to help guide one's thinking (e.g., AOTA Code of Ethics, treatment protocols).
   a. For example, an OT practitioner working in home care with a patient who becomes short of breath must determine if they should immediately call 911, notify the physician, or continue with the treatment session.

(1) It would help the OT practitioner to know if the shortness of breath is an expected symptom given the patient's diagnosis, medical history, and past response to treatment. This information would guide the practitioner's thinking about a correct course of action.

(2) Evaluative reasoning is important in this clinical situation because the practitioner could overreact to the situation and call 911 for expected shortness of breath that often accompanies chronic obstructive pulmonary disease or under-react and fail to call 911 when a person is also complaining of co-occurring severe unremitting substernal pain which can be indicative of a myocardial infarction.

> **EXAM HINT:** Evaluative reasoning is often required during the NBCOT® exam to correctly answer exam items about ethical dilemmas.

7. To help you identify exam items that pose challenging practice situations and ethical dilemmas, the rationales for this *Review and Study Guide's* three online practice exams will have a picture of a cogwheel next to evaluative reasoning exam items.

Developing Critical Reasoning Skills for NBCOT® Exam Success

1. Since critical reasoning is not learned during a quick lesson or improved upon by simply reading the above basic descriptions of it, it is essential to practice with items that test reasoning skills and provide feedback on your performance.
   a. The good news is that this *Review and Study Guide* provides hundreds of opportunities to develop your reasoning skills.
      (1) Each exam item in the three online practice exams that accompany this *Review and Study Guide* provide comprehensive rationales for the correct and incorrect answer choices.
         (a) The rationale for each exam item also includes an explanation of its corresponding critical reasoning subskill and the foundational knowledge and/or skills required to select the correct answer.
2. When reviewing the analysis of your exam performance on this *Review and Study Guide's* three online practice exams, pay particular attention to the five types of critical reasoning that are listed with each exam item.
   a. The five symbols assigned to designate the different types of critical reasoning are:

 = Inductive Reasoning.

 = Deductive Reasoning.

 = Analytical Reasoning.

 = Inferential Reasoning.

 = Evaluative Reasoning.

3. Carefully review this feedback to identify any performance patterns that emerge.
   a. Is your exam performance weaker in a certain area of reasoning?
      (1) Since critical reasoning skills are based on knowledge and day to day experiences, it is not uncommon to be stronger in certain areas of reasoning than others.
4. If you have a weakness in a certain area(s) of reasoning, do not despair.
   a. Being aware of your gaps in reasoning is the first essential step in the development of a corrective plan of action.
5. As you review the rationales provided for the exam items that accompany this *Review and Study Guide*, refer back to your incorrect responses and see if there is a pattern to the types of items you are answering incorrectly related to a sub-skill of critical reasoning.
   a. Do you notice that you have difficulty with certain types of questions?
6. Once you have identified a weakness in critical reasoning, take some time to reflect on why this is so.
   a. Ask yourself the questions identified in Table 2-7 and determine if they are reflective of your exam performance.
      (1) Questions answered affirmatively can help you identify critical reasoning skills that can be improved.
      (2) Implement the corresponding suggested exam preparation strategies to develop needed critical reasoning skills.

> **EXAM HINT:** The honest appraisal of your performance patterns and the thoughtful application of relevant exam preparation strategies will help you build your knowledge of, and acquire experience with, the effective application of critical reasoning skills.

7. This preparation will help you successfully meet the challenges of the NBCOT® exam.

Chapter 2

Table 2-7

Critical Reasoning Self-Assessment Questions

OBSERVED EXAM DIFFICULTY	REASONING CHALLENGE	NBCOT® EXAM PREPARATION STRATEGY
Do you: – have difficulty with taking specific information and applying it to larger populations? – select incorrect answers because you cannot generalize your knowledge?	Inductive	When studying a specific content area, think about how the discrete information that you are reviewing can be applied to a diversity of situations. Use a reflective "what if" stance to think how this information may be generalized to a broader context. This can be a fun and effective study group activity.
Do you: – prefer to follow your instincts rather than the guidelines that a protocol may provide? – select incorrect answers because you are unfamiliar with established practice standards or major theoretical approaches?	Deductive	Be sure when you study that you master all major facts, laws, rules, and accepted principles that guide OT practice. Carefully review all of the frames of reference, practice models, and intervention protocols and procedures provided in Chapters 11–16 and the AOTA Code of Ethics and legislation information provided in Chapter 4.
Do you: – tend to misinterpret information provided, make poor judgments, and apply inadequately conceived assumptions about it? – select incorrect answers because you misjudged the effects of a clinical condition on occupational performance?	Analytical	Be sure to obtain a solid knowledge of all major clinical conditions, their symptoms, diagnostic testing and criteria, anticipated sequelae, and expected outcomes. This information is extensively reviewed in Chapters 6–10 to help you make accurate judgments and correct assumptions about the potential impact of a clinical condition on occupational performance.
Do you: – have difficulty with thinking about how clinical conditions and practice situations may evolve over time? – assume information is valid when in fact it is not true? – select incorrect answers because you have difficulty deciding the best course of action in a practice scenario?	Inferential	When studying the clinical conditions in the chapters identified above, be sure to think about how the presentation of these conditions may sometimes vary from textbook descriptions. Use the knowledge and experience you acquired during your clinical fieldworks to assess the trustworthiness of your assumptions. Study the frames of reference and practice models presented in Chapters 11–14 to develop a solid foundation on how to decide the best course of action based on facts, concepts, and evidence.
Do you: – feel anxious when you have exam items that are ambiguous and you cannot find answers to them in a textbook? – rely on protocols and guidelines more than gut instinct? – select incorrect answers because you become overwhelmed by questions that present ethical dilemmas?	Evaluative	When reviewing specific content, think about the practice ambiguities and ethical dilemmas you observed during your fieldworks related to these areas. Be sure to study the guidelines for ethical decision making that are provided in Chapter 4 to help you evaluate NBCOT® question scenarios, weigh the information presented, and determine a correct course action.

This table was adapted with permission from Dr. Kari Inda's research on critical reasoning and the OT certification exam.

Critical Reasoning Challenges

1. Understanding the critical reasoning process and how it can help you effectively dissect NBCOT® exam items to determine correct answers can be challenging.
2. To develop your critical reasoning capacity, the questions provided in Box 2-4 can be used as a guide to break down exam items.
   a. Practice using the reasoning framework provided in Box 2-4 when you take the online practice exams that accompany this text.
      (1) The more you use this reasoning framework when answering practice exam items, the stronger your ability to carry over these reasoning skills will be; success will follow!

   b. Given the time constraints of the NBCOT® exam, it will not be practical to use the 14-point checklist provided in Box 2-4 for each item on the certification exam you will take.
      (1) To help develop your ability to discern relevant questions, Box 2-5 presents two critical reasoning challenges. Use the exam question checklist provided in Box 2-4 to solve each challenge.
         (a) Not all points will be relevant and a mental "not applicable" ("NA") can be applied. The answers and explanations to the exam questions are organized in this way.
         (b) The answers to each challenge are provided in the appendices at the end of this Chapter.

BOX 2-4 ▷ NBCOT® Exam Question Checklist

- What NBCOT® OTR® exam domain does this question represent?
  - Domain 1: Evaluation and Assessment
  - Domain 2: Analysis, Interpretation, and Planning
  - Domain 3: Select and Manage Interventions
  - Domain 4: Competency and Practice Management
- What is the diagnosis, condition, or presenting problem of the client?
- What age is the client (if relevant)?
- What deficit(s) or problem(s) does the client have?
- How does the deficit or problem affect the client's function?
- What is the setting for services (e.g., inpatient, outpatient, early intervention, school)?
- What KEY WORDS indicate importance or priority (e.g., best, first, next, initial, most effective)?
- What information is needed to answer the question (e.g., stage of condition/disease, evaluation tool, intervention technique, knowledge of statistics, type of equipment or modality)?
- Is any information in the question stem irrelevant or included only as a distracter?
- What is your rationale for why each choice is correct or why it should be eliminated?
- What type of critical reasoning subtype is needed to answer this question?
  - Inductive
  - Deductive
  - Analytical
  - Inferential
  - Evaluative

BOX 2-5 ▷ Critical Reasoning Challenge Examples

1. An occupational therapy practitioner in an outpatient orthopedic clinic receives orders for orthosis fabrication for an adult client with a boutonniere deformity of the fourth finger. The client states that the deformity interferes with daily tasks, especially fine motor. Which is the best orthotic option to manage the deformity of the digit?
   A. An orthosis that positions the proximal interphalangeal joint in slight flexion.
   B. An orthosis that maintains extension of the proximal interphalangeal joint.
   C. A gutter orthosis that accommodates the position of the finger joints.
2. A school-based occupational therapist and OTA work with a student with Duchenne muscular dystrophy. The student has difficulty using a standard mouse to access the computer. Which adaptation should the therapist and OTA recommend for improving the student's ability to independently use a computer?
   A. Use of a trackball.
   B. Use of voice recognition software.
   C. Use of a touch screen.

practice to change the way you think about the world and everyday situations.

a. Once you begin to use these strategies, they become part of your everyday life and you may not even notice that you are asking the deeper questions that help you to get to the truth.

   (1) You become more comfortable with ambiguity and uncertainty, and you do not shy away from a challenge that will take some time to overcome.

       (a) These are the habits that propel people toward success.

3. Why does critical thinking and reasoning matter for the certification exam? It is, in part, what helps you succeed on high-stakes examinations.

a. Critical thinking and reasoning provide you with the stamina to stay focused, to minimize frustration, and to have clarity of mind as you analyze each exam item and answer each question on the certification exam.

   (1) It requires you to go deeper than you may be comfortable doing right now.

4. If you find yourself struggling with certain items on TherapyEd's online practice exams or specific study content in this *Review & Study Guide*, take the time to go deeper.

a. Think about the subject of the exam item or chapter content at a level deeper than what you may be accustomed to doing right now.

Enhancing Critical Thinking Skills

1. What makes a person an excellent critical thinker? There are various attributes that are associated with sound critical thinking and reasoning ability.

a. It is not just the skills one has acquired with time and practice, but also the habits of mind that provide a solid foundation for deeper thinking and reasoning about everyday life.

b. Critical thinking includes a natural curiosity about what we see and hear, a systematic way of thinking about life, approaches for seeking truth and solving problems, and the reduction of bias that can interfere with our ability to see the truth and determine a correct course of action.

2. Critical thinking and reasoning abilities are not learned in a few quick lessons. It takes time and

(1) It is understandable to want to answer a question and go immediately to the location of the correct answer. We want instant gratification. We want to know if we are on track with our studies.

(2) Avoid the press to immediately know. Instead, when you encounter a challenging exam item or difficult content area, follow the steps outlined in Box 2-6.

5. Deeper level thinking is analogous to the layers of rock that form with weather, time, and erosion, also known as strata. Refer to Figure 2-1.

a. With rock strata, there are typically horizontal layers of soil, sand, pebbles, shells, and other material that settle with the passage of time. Some layers are more superficial and easily seen while others can be very deep and take effort to dig down toward.

(1) This is how the development of critical thinking and reasoning occurs.

6. Wherever you are, or wherever you think you are, in your comfort with critical thinking, your goal is to dig deeper into territories where you are less comfortable.

a. Take opportunities to explore the "it depends" scenarios; ask the "how might this change if . . ." questions.

b. Select content to explore what you have identified through your studies that you are less comfortable with and find most difficult.

(1) Taking the time to explore, ask challenging questions, and dig deeper into a topic will help solidify your knowledge of this content in a more effective and efficient way than reading, filling out web-based note cards, or memorizing facts.

Figure 2-1 **Stratified Rock Near La Paz, Baja California Sur, Mexico.** Wonderlane. Uploaded from http://flickr.com/photos/71401718@N00/3542465243.

BOX 2-6 ▷ How Do I Think More Deeply?

• The first step in thinking more deeply is to stop and ask yourself, "What do I know about this subject? What do I remember?"

 – Write everything you can remember (e.g., symptoms, stages) without seeking the answers.

 – Recognize that it is okay if you do not remember a lot.

 – Be comfortable with what you do and do not know.

• Next, consider the typical and commonly used approaches relevant to the exam item or content. For example, when analyzing an exam item about working with a person with Parkinson's disease (PD), consider the following.

 – What are the typical assessment and intervention approaches for PD and how might the practice setting change how you approach your evaluation and intervention with this person?

 – Where is the person in their stage of PD and their adjustment to living with PD? How does this status change your approach to care?

• Then, go a level deeper. Consider issues and specific situations that may alter the course of therapy (e.g., other disciplines that may be providing services, family members'/caregivers' concerns, the discharge plan, the environment the client hopes to transition toward).

 – Ask yourself, "How might I approach therapy for this client with PD?" After considering the variables that could possibly affect the course of their therapy, you should immediately say, "Well, it depends." These "it depends" situations, can be affected by:

  • the practice setting (e.g., acute rehabilitation, home care, skilled nursing facility).

  • the stage of the person's disease process. If the person is in an early stage, they are likely to be ambulatory and you can work on ADL and functional mobility to reduce fall risk. If they are in the late stage of the PD, they are likely non-ambulatory and may be confined to a bed and you would focus on client and caregiver education (e.g., wound prevention).

  • the individual's personal and environment contexts.

• Taking additional time to think, play out different scenarios and situations in your mind, and test your ability to develop multiple approaches to solving problems can help you learn to think more deeply. These deep-thinking skills can increase your comfort with analyzing practice situations without having all the answers readily in front of you. This can contribute to certification exam success.

7. Reflect on your academic experience and what you can learn from this. Have you ever had a situation in school where you thought you did well on an exam, only to find out that your grade was lower than expected? You may have asked yourself, "What happened? I knew this! At least I thought I did."

a. Often a student receives a lower grade than expected on an exam because they just memorized the facts of the material and they failed to understand the concepts, the complexities, and how the facts change according to the circumstances at hand.

(1) Box 2-7 provides an example as to how a common academic exam preparation approach can jeopardize NBCOT® exam success.

8. When an exam demands thinking beyond facts, memorization alone is not enough.

a. As you prepare for the NBCOT® exam, keep in mind that the quantity of your studying is not important; it is the quality. One of the most common statements uttered by students who fail high-stakes exams is, "I don't know why I failed. I read the book cover to cover three times."

b. A statement about the quantity of study, rather than the quality, is a sign of insufficient studying.

9. Your exam preparation should not be about how many topics you can cram into a study session. It should be about the insights you have gained from the material you studied.

a. The illustration in Figure 2-2 can help you apply the analogy of the strata to your studying for the NBCOT® certification exam. Box 2-8 outlines a stratified approach to studying using spina bifida as an example.

(1) Find a challenging topic and start at the top of Figure 2-2 by studying basic foundational information and asking the first set of questions in Box 2-8.

(2) After they have been answered, go to the next layer of depth and answer those questions. Keep going until you have reached the deepest layer and have pondered all the questions about your chosen topic.

(3) After that has been accomplished, use this *Review and Study Guide* to verify how you did. Look up the topic. What did you remember? What information did you not recall? Did you

---

BOX 2-7 ⊳ How Do I Learn From Past Test-taking Experiences?

If you have had the experience of not doing as well on a course exam as you anticipated, you may feel anxious about your ability to pass the NBCOT® exam. To help you assess the efficacy of your past academic test-taking experiences, consider the following about how a student may prepare for a comprehensive exam about neurological system disorders and the implications of their approach.

- If the student memorizes the symptoms of a left cerebral vascular accident (CVA) and right CVA perfectly, will that serve them well on an exam comprised mainly of questions about CVA?

  – YES, if the exam is *only* about remembering the differences between left and right CVA, which is most often not the case on a comprehensive exam.

  – NO, if the exam also asks questions about other types of CVA (e.g., those that occur in different vessels or regions of the cortex, or are caused by different physiological mechanisms [i.e., a thrombosis or embolism]), which is likely the case on a comprehensive exam.

- What if the exam includes questions about how to plan and implement intervention for someone who incurred a left CVA?

  – The student could hope to extrapolate what might be relevant and effective given their memorization of left CVA symptoms. That expectation will very likely fall short. Facts can guide the determination of correct answers, but only to the extent that the facts are accurate *and* complete.

- By relying on memorization alone, the student will not be adequately prepared for their exam and a lower grade will be earned.

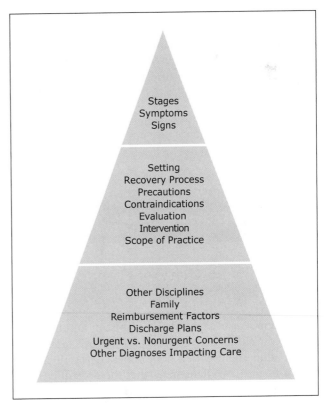

Figure 2-2 **Critical Reasoning Strata Applied to the Study Process.**

BOX 2-8 ▷ A Stratified Approach to Studying

The application of the rock strata to the studying of this *Review and Study Guide's* content can help you think more deeply about what you need to know to be adequately prepared for the NBCOT® exam. Using the below stratified approach can help you acquire the knowledge you need for certification exam success.

- For example, if you refer to the spina bifida section in Chapter 7: Neurological System Disorders and immediately think to yourself, "I don't remember a lot about this," organize your studying according to the following steps.

- First, close the book and start at the surface and ask yourself the following questions.
  - What do I remember about this diagnosis?
  - What are the typical symptoms?
  - Where might the damage be present?
  - How does this condition typically present?

- Next, go deeper and ask the following questions.
  - If I worked in an inpatient setting, what would be the typical evaluation and intervention approaches for spina bifida? What if I worked in an outpatient setting?
  - What if the person with spina bifida is an infant, adolescent, or adult?
  - What if the type of spina bifida was meningocele versus myelomeningocele?
  - What are the precautions and contraindications I should be aware of when working with this condition?

- Then, after you have recalled as much as you can about these topics, go to a deeper level where you reach the uncertainties. Ask yourself the "it depends" questions such as those outlined in Box 2-6 and the following.
  - If other professionals and/or family members/caregivers are involved in care, how might I work with them to ensure a successful outcome for the client?
  - Would bowel and bladder dysfunction be a consideration for this client, and if so, how would I address that?

confuse any topics for a closely related diagnosis or situation?

(4) Based on this process and assessment of your knowledge, you can accomplish deeper levels of thinking and reasoning and expand your current level of knowledge about the content.

Additional Resources for Developing Critical Reasoning Skills

1. This *Review and Study Guide* was intentionally designed to provide a comprehensive overview of the depth and breadth of OT practice, strategies for effective exam preparation and successful test-taking, and multiple opportunities to apply these skills via the accompanying three online practice exams.
   a. It is beyond the scope and focus of this book to provide more detailed information about critical reasoning.
      (1) Burger and Starbird (2012) provide a helpful guide with practical strategies for implementing critical thinking at deeper levels.
      (2) Insight Assessment Inc. offers periodic free mini-tests with rationales for correct and incorrect answers and resources that discuss the various reasoning types at www.insightassessment.com.
2. Since 2000, NBCOT® exam candidates have followed the guidelines provided and used the resources described in this Chapter's section on structuring an individualized exam preparation plan to pass their certification exam. Your proactive use of these can help ensure you achieve the same.

Appendix 2A

Answers to Critical Reasoning Challenge #1

Exam Item: An occupational therapist in an outpatient orthopedic clinic receives orders for orthosis fabrication for an adult client with a boutonniere deformity of the fourth finger. The client states that the deformity interferes with daily tasks, especially fine motor. Which is the best orthotic option to manage the deformity of the digit?

    A. An orthosis that positions the proximal interphalangeal joint in slight flexion.

    B. An orthosis that maintains extension of the proximal interphalangeal joint.

    C. A gutter orthosis that accommodates the position of the finger joints.

Questions and Answers

1. What domain and category does this question represent?
   Domain: 3: Select and Manage Interventions.
2. What is the diagnosis, condition, or presenting problem of the client?
   Boutonniere deformity.

3. What age is the client (if relevant)?
Adult (age not specified).
4. What deficit(s) or problem(s) does the client have?
Deformity affects the 4th finger.
5. How does the deficit or problem affect the client's function?
Deformity interferes with daily tasks, especially fine motor.
6. What is the setting for services?
Outpatient orthopedic clinic.
7. What KEY WORD(S) indicate importance or priority?
Best.
8. What information is needed to answer the question?
Knowledge of joints impacted by boutonniere deformity and in what manner, knowledge of orthotic options that effectively manage boutonniere deformities.
9. Is any information in the question stem irrelevant or included only as a distracter?
Yes, the setting of outpatient orthopedic clinic is not relevant to determining the correct answer.

10. What is your rationale for why Choice A is correct or why it should be eliminated?
Choice A should be ELIMINATED. This is an approach for a person with a swan neck deformity, not a boutonniere deformity.
11. What is your rationale for why Choice B is correct or why it should be eliminated?
Choice B is CORRECT. An orthosis that positions the proximal interphalangeal joint in extension realigns the lateral bands for preventing preventing deformity.
12. What is your rationale for why Choice C is correct or why it should be eliminated?
Choice C should be ELIMINATED. A gutter orthosis is used for finger fractures, dislocations, or ligament injuries, not a boutonniere deformity.
13. What type of critical reasoning subtype is needed to answer this question?
Inductive.

Appendix 2B

Answers to Critical Reasoning Challenge #2

Exam Item: A school-based occupational therapist occupational therapist and OTA work with a student with Duchenne muscular dystrophy. The student has difficulty using a standard mouse to access the computer. Which adaptation should the therapist recommend for improving ability to independently use a computer?

A. Use of a trackball.
B. Use of voice recognition software.
C. Use of a touch screen.

Questions and Answers

1. What domain and category does this question represent?
Domain 3: Select and Manage Interventions.
2. What is the diagnosis, condition, or presenting problem of the client?
Duchenne muscular dystrophy.
3. What age is the client (if relevant)?
Child (age not specified).
4. What deficit(s) or problem(s) does the client have?
Difficulty using a standard mouse.

5. How does the deficit or problem affect the client's function?
Difficulty accessing the computer due to current mouse.
6. What is the setting for services?
School setting.
7. What KEY WORD(S) indicate importance or priority?
Recommend, adaptation.
8. What information is needed to answer the question?
Knowledge of Duchenne muscular dystrophy, knowledge of computer adaptations to match the abilities of a child with this diagnosis.
9. Is any information in the question stem irrelevant or included only as a distracter?
No.
10. What is your rationale for why Choice A is correct or why it should be eliminated?
Choice A is CORRECT. A trackball is effective for a child with low muscle tone and weakness associated with Duchenne muscular dystrophy.
11. What is your rationale for why Choice B is correct or why it should be eliminated?
Choice B should be ELIMINATED. There in nothing in the item stem that indicates a need for voice recognition. Voice recognition software may be an adaptation that is needed in the future.

12. What is your rationale for why Choice C is correct or why it should be eliminated?

Choice C should be ELIMINATED. A touch screen requires the use of hand and upper extremity movement against gravity. This leads to fatigue.

13. What type of critical reasoning subtype is needed to answer this question?

Inferential.

 ## References

Boyt Schell, B., & Schell, J.W. (2008). Clinical and professional reasoning in occupational therapy. Wolters Kluwer/Lippincott and Wilkins.

Burger, E. B., & Starbird, M. (2012). The 5 elements of effective thinking. Princeton University Press.

Facione, P. (1990a). Critical thinking: A statement of expert consensus for purposes of educational assessment and instruction. Research findings and recommendations. American Psychological Association.

Facione, P. (1990b). Critical thinking: A statement of expert consensus for purposes of educational assessment and instruction ("Executive summary: The Delphi report"). California Academic Press.

Facione, P. (2006). Critical thinking: What it is and why it counts. California Academic Press.

Facione, N. C., & Facione, P. A. (2006). The health sciences reasoning test HSRT: Test manual 2006 edition. California Academic Press.

Fleming-Castaldy, R. (2010, November 8). The NBCOT® examination: Strategies for success. OT Practice, 7–10.

Fleming-Castaldy, R. (2023). Occupational therapy course manual (8th ed.). TherapyEd.

Fleming-Castaldy, R.P. (2020). FAQs on effective NBCOT® certification exam preparation. OT Practice, 25(11), 11–14.

National Board for Certification in Occupational Therapy (NBCOT®). (2022). 2022 Occupational Therapist Registered (OTR®) examination content outline. https://www.nbcot.org/-/media/PDFs/2022_OTR_Content_Outline.pdf

Sides, M., & Korcheck, N. (Eds.). (1998). Successful test-taking: Learning strategies for nurses. Lippincott.

Chapter 2

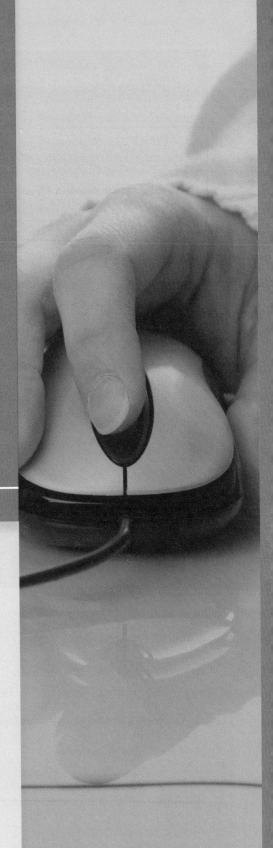

3

Foundations of Occupational Therapy Practice

RITA P. FLEMING-CASTALDY

Chapter 3

The Occupational Therapy Process

> **EXAM HINT:** The National Board for Certification in Occupational Therapy (NBCOT®) exam for the the OTR® places a heavy emphasis on the occupational therapy (OT) process with 84% of the exam focused on direct services (i.e., evaluation and assessment, analysis and interpretation for intervention planning, and intervention management); the remaining 16% is focused on professional competencies and practice management (e.g., ethical decision-making, professional behaviors, research, quality improvement, and professional development) (NBCOT®, 2022, p. 2).

Overview

1. The occupational therapy (OT) process is composed of three main aspects of service delivery: evaluation, intervention, and outcomes (American Occupational Therapy Association [AOTA], 2020).
2. The clients who receive OT services include individual persons (including caregivers), groups (a collection of people who share certain characteristics, goals, purposes, occupational challenges, activities, and/or interests); or populations ("an aggregate of people with common attributes such as contexts, characteristics, or concerns, including health risks" [AOTA, 2020, p. 81]).
   a. In practice, the individual recipients of OT services are typically called patients in traditional institutional medical model settings (e.g., inpatient hospitals), clients in community-based medical model settings (e.g., outpatient clinics), consumers in person-directed programs (e.g., day treatment programs), members in recovery model programs (e.g., clubhouses), students in educational settings, and residents in skilled nursing facilities and residential settings (e.g., group homes, halfway houses).
3. The OT process is client-centered, person-directed, interactive, and dynamic.
4. Table 3-1 provides a summary of the OT process as put forth in the AOTA Practice Framework, 4th edition (OTPF-4) for persons, groups, and populations.
5. All aspects of the OT process must be documented according to established standards and guidelines. Refer to Chapter 4.

Referral and Screening

Referral

1. The basic request for OT services. This may also be termed an order or a consultation.
2. Sources include the individual, family or caregivers, physicians, social workers, physical therapists, nurse practitioners, allied health professionals, teachers, administrators, payers, employers, and private, state, and local public agencies.
3. The content and form of a referral/order varies among program types and practice areas and can range from the highly specific (e.g., a resting hand orthosis) to the very general (e.g., evaluate for developmental delay).
4. While anyone can refer themselves or others to OT services, the ability of the OT practitioner to act upon the referral is determined by state licensure laws and/or third-party payers (AOTA, 2021).

> **EXAM HINT:** While the legal standards for OT referrals can vary from state to state, the NBCOT® is a national certification exam so it will only ask questions about national standards (e.g., Medicare guidelines, AOTA standards for practice).

Screening

1. The acquisition of information to determine the need for evaluation and to obtain a preliminary understanding of the client's goals, needs, priorities, strengths, limitations, assets, and resources.
2. Screening procedures are usually brief and easy to administer since they must be applied to many individuals (i.e., all persons who receive an OT referral need to be screened to determine the appropriateness of the referral).

Table 3-1

Occupational Therapy Process for Persons, Groups, and Populations

The occupational therapy process applies to work with persons, groups, and populations. The process for groups and populations mirrors that for persons. The process for populations includes public health approaches, and the process for groups may include both person and population methods to address occupational performance (Scaffa & Reitz, 2014).

PROCESS COMPONENT	PROCESS STEP		
	PERSON	GROUP	POPULATION
Evaluation	*Consultation and screening:* • Review client history • Consult with interprofessional team • Administer standardized screening tools	*Consultation and screening, environmental scan:* • Identify collective need on the basis of available data • For each individual in the group, – Review history – Administer standardized screening tools – Consult with interprofessional team	*Environmental scan, trend analysis, preplanning:* • Collect data to inform design of intervention program by identifying information needs • Identify health trends in targeted population and potential positive and negative impacts on occupational performance
	Occupational profile: • Interview client and caregiver	*Occupational profile or community profile:* • Interview persons who make up the group • Engage with persons in the group to determine their interests, needs, and priorities	*Needs assessment, community profile:* • Engage with persons within the population to determine their interests and needs and opportunities for collaboration • Identify priorities through – Surveys – Interviews – Group discussions or forums
	Analysis of occupational performance: • Assess occupational performance • Conduct occupational and activity analysis • Assess contexts • Assess performance skills and patterns • Assess client factors	*Analysis of occupational performance:* • Conduct occupational and activity analysis • Assess group context • Assess the following for individual group members: – Occupational performance – Performance skills and patterns – Client factors • Analyze impact of individual performance on the group	*Needs assessment, review of secondary data:* • Evaluate existing quantitative data, which may include – Public health records – Prevalence of disease or disability – Demographic data – Economic data
	Synthesis of evaluation process: • Review and consolidate information to select occupational outcomes and determine impact of performance patterns and client factors on occupation	*Synthesis of evaluation process:* • Review and consolidate information to select collective occupational outcomes • Review and consolidate information regarding each member's performance and its impact on the group and the group's occupational performance as a whole	*Data analysis and interpretation:* • Review and consolidate information to support need for the program and identify any missing data
Intervention	*Development of the intervention plan:* • Identify client goals • Identify intervention outcomes • Select outcome measures • Select methods for service delivery, including theoretical framework	*Development of the intervention plan or program:* • Identify collective group goals • Identify intervention outcomes for the group • Select outcome measures • Select methods for service delivery, including theoretical framework	*Program planning:* • Identify short-term program objectives • Identify long-term program goals • Select outcome measures to be used in program evaluation • Select strategies for service delivery, including theoretical framework
	Intervention implementation: • Carry out occupational therapy intervention to address specific occupations, contexts, and performance patterns and skills affecting performance	*Intervention or program implementation:* • Carry out occupational therapy intervention or program to address the group's specific occupations, contexts, and performance patterns and skills affecting group performance	*Program implementation:* • Carry out program or advocacy action to address identified occupational needs

(Continued)

Table 3-1

Occupational Therapy Process for Persons, Groups, and Populations (*Continued*)

PROCESS COMPONENT	PROCESS STEP		
	PERSON	GROUP	POPULATION
	Intervention review: • Reevaluate and review client's response to intervention • Review progress toward goals and outcomes • Modify plan as needed	*Intervention review or program evaluation:* • Reevaluate and review individual members' and the group's response to intervention • Review progress toward goals and outcomes • Modify plan as needed • Evaluate efficiency of program • Evaluate achievement of determined objectives	*Program evaluation:* • Gather information on program implementation • Measure the impact of the program • Evaluate efficiency of program • Evaluate achievement of determined objectives
Outcomes	*Outcomes:* • Use measures to assess progress toward outcomes • Identify change in occupational participation	*Outcomes:* • Use measures to assess progress toward outcomes • Identify change in occupational performance of individual members and the group as a whole	*Outcomes:* • Use measures to assess progress toward long-term program goals • Identify change in occupational performance of targeted population
	Transition: • Facilitate client's move from one life role or experience to another, such as – Moving to a new level of care – Transitioning between providers – Moving into a new setting or program	*Transition:* • Facilitate group members' move from one life role or experience to another, such as – Moving to a new level of care – Transitioning between providers – Moving into a new setting or program	*Sustainability plan:* • Develop action plan to maintain program • Identify sources of funding • Build community capacity and support relationships to continue program
	Discontinuation: • Discontinue care after short- and long-term goals have been achieved or client chooses to no longer participate • Implement discharge plan to support performance after discontinuation of services	*Discontinuation:* • Discontinue care after the group's short- and long-term goals have been achieved • Implement discharge plan to support performance after discontinuation of services	*Dissemination plan:* • Share results with participants, stakeholders, and community members • Implement sustainability plan

American Occupational Therapy Association. (2020). Occupational therapy practice framework: Domain and process (4th ed. pp. 55–56). Reprinted with permission.

3. Screening tools measure broad performance abilities and include chart/medical record reviews, checklists, structured observations of performance in a basic activity of daily living, and/or brief interviews with the individual, family members, and/or caregivers.

4. The outcome of the screening will determine the client's occupations, contexts, performance patterns, performance skills, and/or client factors that require further evaluation.

EXAM HINT: If an exam item identifies screening as the current stage of the OT process, any answer choice that includes goal-setting, intervention planning, and/or implementing/managing intervention(s) would be incorrect because goals cannot be established or treatment implemented and/or managed until after an evaluation is completed.

5. For groups, the screening process includes screening, consultation, and an environmental scan. Refer to Table 3-1.

6. For populations, the screening process includes pre-planning, an environmental scan, and trend analysis. Refer to Table 3-1.

Role of the OTA/COTA® in Referral and Screening

1. According to established practice standards, if an occupational therapy assistant (OTA) or a certified occupational therapy assistant (COTA®) receive a referral, the OTA/COTA® must give the referral to the supervising occupational therapist who is responsible for responding to the referral.

2. The OTA/COTA® contributes to the screening process in collaboration with the supervising occupational therapist.
   a. The OTA/COTA® can administer screening tools with supervision from the occupational therapist and report their findings to the therapist.
      (1) The level of supervision required will depend upon the OTA's/COTA®'s experience, the establishment of their service competency, state laws, and other regulatory and payer requirements.
3. Data collected during screening is analyzed by the occupational therapist to determine the areas of performance, performance components, and/or performance contexts that require further evaluation.
4. All screening activities completed by an OTA/COTA® must comply with federal and state laws and other regulatory and payer requirements (AOTA, 2021).

Evaluation

Overview

1. "The comprehensive process of obtaining and interpreting data necessary for necessary to understand the person, system, or situation . . . . Evaluation requires synthesis of all data obtained, analytic interpretation of that data, reflective clinical reasoning, and consideration of occupational performance and contextual factors" (AOTA, 2021, p. 2).
2. The evaluation process includes obtaining the client's occupational profile and an analysis of their occupational performance.
   a. Refer to Table 3-1.
3. Assessments selected for evaluation should follow a "top-down" approach to consider the client's occupations first, rather than a "bottom-up" approach, which focuses on client factors and performance skills.
   a. In certain practice settings (e.g., acute care with a one-to-three-day length of stay) and in certain clinical situations (e.g., there are major concerns for a client's safety) the determination of underlying problems may need to take precedence over the determination of an occupational profile (Gutman, Mortera, Hinojosa, & Kramer, 2007).
4. Standardized and/or nonstandardized assessments are selected and used to obtain detailed information about the client's capabilities and limitations for occupational performance and participation.
   a. Chapters 5-16 provide information about evaluation approaches and assessments that are typically used in OT practice.
5. The results of screening are used to determine which assessment instrument or tool will attain information essential for setting goals and planning intervention.
6. Considerations in determining the assessments that will be most effective to use with a specific client include the following.
   a. The client's baseline functional level (i.e., client factors, performance skills, and performance patterns)

and their major concerns and pressing needs as determined through the screening process.
   b. The environmental context in which the assessment will be conducted.
      (1) The length of stay of the setting influences the comprehensiveness of evaluation.
      (2) The primary focus of the setting (e.g., prevocational versus self-management).
      (3) Legislative guidelines and restrictions (e.g., according to the Individuals with Disabilities Education Improvement Act (IDEA) of 2004, the education of disabled students aged 3-21 must include special education and related services that prepare them for independent living, further education, and/or employment).
      (4) The facility's resources of space, equipment, and supplies (e.g., the administration of the Executive Function Performance Test (EFPT) requires the equipment and ingredients needed to cook hot oatmeal on a stovetop; whereas the administration of the Canadian Occupational Performance Measure (COPM) only requires the COPM rating scale form and a pen.
   c. The environmental context of the client's current and expected environment.
      (1) Sociocultural aspects including roles, values, norms, and supports (e.g., in some cultures, home management is only considered a valued role for females, so there is no need to do a home management evaluation for a male of this cultural background).
      (2) Physical environment characteristics (e.g., it would be essential to measure the functional mobility endurance of a person who lives in a third-floor walk-up apartment).
   d. The temporal contexts of the client and their condition and/or disability.
      (1) The client's chronological and developmental age.
      (2) The anticipated duration of their condition and/or disability (e.g., short-term, long-term, permanent).

(3) If the client's current condition and/or disability is a recent occurrence or an exacerbation of a long-standing, chronic condition and/or disability.

(4) The client's stage of illness (e.g., acute stage versus terminal stage).

e. The evaluation tool's compatibility with the frame of reference/model of practice selected to guide intervention planning.

7. Assessments are administered according to recommended guidelines, administration protocols, and/or standardized procedures.

> **RED FLAG:** Standard precautions must be observed during *all* evaluation procedures, and transmission-based precautions must also be implemented as needed to prevent infection. Refer to Appendix 3A and Appendix 3B.

8. If the OT practitioner and the client do not share a common language, an interpreter must be used to ensure the validity of the information obtained and that no cultural or religious norms are violated that may compromise the therapeutic process.

9. Assessment results are scored or rated according to published guidelines and/or standardized procedures.

> **CAUTION:** The interpretation of information based on a client's self-report or the results of a highly structured assessment may not reflect actual performance in their natural contexts.

10. The occupational therapist interprets the assessment results in relation to commonly used and recognized terminology (e.g., the OTPF-4) and/or a specific frame of reference/model of practice.

11. The information gathered from assessment(s) is integrated with referral, screening, and diagnostic information to identify strengths and limitations in occupational performance and participation relevant to the client's occupations, roles, and environmental contexts.

a. In schools, assessment reports that are used to determine IDEA eligibility and formulate Individualized Education Plans (IEPs) must include relevant functional and developmental information about the student, not only information related to their academic capabilities.

12. The therapist collaborates with the individual, family, caregivers, and other team members to obtain a broader picture of the client's situation and to put the OT assessment results into a larger context.

13. The ethical concerns of all parties that have an interest in the process and outcomes of an OT evaluation are considered. Table 3-2 describes the ethical responsibilities of OT practitioners in the selection and use of OT assessments.

14. Identified problems are prioritized in collaboration with the client to develop an intervention or program plan. Chapter 4 provides information about program planning.

15. The evaluation findings are documented and communicated to relevant parties (i.e., the client, team members, and third-party payers).

16. Referrals to other professionals or specialists within the OT profession for further evaluation are completed as needed.

17. If a client is a group or population, evaluation would be a core component of the needs assessment that must be completed to inform the development of a program. Refer to Table 3-1.

a. Box 4-16 in Chapter 4 outlines the steps for the completion of a needs assessment.

> **EXAM HINT:** The NBCOT® OTR® exam content outline identifies knowledge of the "administration, purpose, indications, advantages, and limitations of standardized and nonstandardized screening and assessment tools . . . . (including) criterion-referenced tests (and) norm-referenced tests" (NBCOT®, 2022, p. 4) as essential for competent practice. The application of knowledge about the previously stated general evaluation guidelines and the following specific information about assessment psychometrics and the various evaluation methods and tools used in OT practice can help you determine the correct answer for NBCOT® Domain 1 Evaluation and Assessment exam items.

Psychometric Properties of Assessments

1. Standardization.
   a. A standardized evaluation is one that is uniform and well established.
   b. It is always the same in content, administration, and scoring.
   c. Characteristics of a standardized instrument.
      (1) A description of its purpose.
      (2) An administration and scoring protocol.
      (3) Established norms and validity.
2. The administration protocol.
   a. Provides instructions on what to do, ensuring all administrations of the assessment are consistent.
   b. Identifies materials needed for the assessment.
   c. Provides exact wording of directions to give to the individual.

> **EXAM HINT:** When you study the standardized assessments that are described in this text, be sure to pay close attention to the information that is provided about their administration and scoring protocols. Correct answers to an exam item about the use of a standardized assessment tool by an OT practitioner will include adherence to their standardized procedures.

Table 3-2

Ethical Considerations for the Selection and Use of Occupational Therapy Assessments

OCCUPATIONAL THERAPIST COMPETENCIES

The occupational therapist must ensure they have the knowledge, skills, and attitudes to competently:

- determine assessment foci based on the needs and goals of the person being assessed
- select, administer, and interpret assessment results using established evaluation guidelines
- complete standardized assessments according to published protocols
- supervise other OT personnel in their collection of assessment data
- ensure all delegated assessment tasks are completed in a competent manner
- document the assessment in a manner that accurately describes its procedures and outcomes

OCCUPATIONAL THERAPY ASSISTANT COMPETENCIES

The OT assistant must ensure they have the knowledge, skills, and attitudes to competently:

- complete the assessment data collection that they are responsible to perform
- determine that their training and supervision is adequate to carry out assigned assessment procedures
- report the assessment data in an accurate manner
- contribute to the evaluation process

CLIENT/CONSUMER AND/OR THEIR CAREGIVER/GUARDIAN VESTED INTERESTS

The OT practitioner must ensure that the person being assessed and/or their caregiver/guardian:

- have provided input about their needs and goals to inform the assessment process
- have been fully informed about the purposes and administrative procedures of an assessment
- understand how the assessment results will be used to inform intervention
- have been provided the opportunity to decide if the assessment should be administered
- know how the assessment will be billed

EMPLOYER AND INTER-DISCIPLINARY TEAM MEMBERS VESTED INTERESTS

The OT practitioner must ensure that:

- the assessment is consistent with the mission of the setting and helps attain desired outcomes
- the assessment's findings, interpretation, and recommendations are effectively communicated to team members and meaningfully contribute to an inter-disciplinary intervention plan

PAYER VESTED INTERESTS

The OT practitioner must ensure that:

- the assessment is a necessary and billable service that is accurately documented for reimbursement
- if there is no third-party reimbursement, the person being assessed knows this and has given consent before the completion of an assessment
- payment is requested only for the services provided

PROFESSIONAL STANDARDS

The OT practitioner must ensure that:

- selected assessments are evidence-based (to the extent possible) and within OT's recognized scope of practice
- specific training and/or specialized credentials required to use an assessment have been completed by the assessment's administrator
- permission to use copyrighted assessments has been obtained, fees to use an assessment have been paid, and assessment use complies with the laws regulating their use
- the assessment does not hinder the fair and equitable distribution of OT services to all persons in a setting needing OT services

Adapted by Rita Fleming-Castaldy from Hansen, R.A. (1990). Lesson 10: Ethical considerations. In C.B. Royeen (Ed.), AOTA self-study series: Assessing functions (p. 9). American Occupational Therapy Association.

Chapter 3

3. The scoring protocol.
   a. Provides ratings and criteria for determining ratings.
   b. Provides norms for the range of ratings for a specific population.
   c. Types of normative data.
      (1) Age.
      (2) Gender.
      (3) Diagnostic groupings.
   d. Norms are used for a comparative analysis of an individual's score.
      (1) A client's characteristics must match the characteristics of the population used to establish the norms (e.g., you cannot compare a 25-year-old's score with norms based on a 10-year-old or a 65-year-old).

> RED FLAG: If a client's characteristics are different from the normed population of an evaluation tool, any interpretation of the assessment results based on these norms would be inaccurate. Therefore, this normed assessment would be an incorrect answer choice for a MC item and a NO response for a CST item.

4. Validity measures the assessment's accuracy to determine if the tool measures what it was intended to measure.
   a. Table 3-3 outlines the different validity types.

BOX 3-1 ▷ Reliability Types and Reporting

- Interrater reliability or interobserver reliability establishes that different raters using the same assessment tool will achieve the same results.
- Test-retest reliability establishes that the same results will be obtained when the evaluation is administrated twice by the same administrator.
- Reliability is scored and reported as either a correlation or a percentage to identify the degree to which the two items agree/relate.

---

5. Reliability establishes the consistency and stability of the evaluation.
   a. If reliable, the evaluation measurements/scores are the same from time to time, place to place, and evaluation to evaluation.
   b. Box 3-1 describes the different types of reliability and how reliability is scored and reported.

Assessment Tools

1. Observation involves visual assessment of a client, their behavior, and environmental contexts. An overview of the skills needed for accurate observations is provided in the following section.

Table 3-3

Types of Validity[1]

Face Validity: establishes how well an assessment appears "on the face of it" to meet its stated purpose.
Example: an activity configuration looks like it measures time use.

Content Validity: establishes that the content included in an assessment is representative of the content that could be measured.
Example: the content of a role checklist provides an inclusive and representative listing of roles.

Construct Validity: establishes that an assessment is consistent with the principles of a specific theory and is related to the theoretical constructs the evaluation is intended to measure.
Example: the Allen Cognitive Level Test aligns well with the Cognitive Disabilities model.

Criterion Validity: compares one assessment to another one with already established validity. Types include:
   Concurrent validity compares the results of two instruments given at about the same time.
   Example: does a self-report of everyday functioning that is completed by an older adult living with a mild cognitive disorder identify similar strengths and limitations as those identified by a performance-based measure of their everyday functioning?
   Example: do the Functional Independence Measure for Children (WeeFIM(™)) and the Pediatric Evaluation of Disabilities Inventory (PEDI) measure similar constructs in children with developmental disabilities and acquired brain injuries?
   Predictive validity compares the degree to which an instrument can predict performance on a future criterion.
   Example: do scores on balance confidence and fear of falling avoidance assessments predict future falls in older adults?
   Example: does the Assessment of Motor and Process Skills (AMPS) predict the ability of patients to manage safely after discharge home from hospital?
Criterion validity is reported as a correlation.
The higher the correlation, the better is the criterion validity.

Ecological Validity establishes that an assessment can measure, obtain, and record information that is relevant to a person's typical daily living contexts.
Example: do the measures used to contribute to the development of a person's occupational profile provide adequate contextual information about their occupations, performance skills, performance patterns, and client factors?

[1] Marlene Joy Morgan, EdD, OTR/L contributed to this table.

2. Interviews involve the OT practitioner asking the client specific questions. An overview of interviewing techniques is provided in a subsequent section.
3. Self-report requires the client to disclose personal information in an organized manner; e.g., through the completion of a questionnaire.
4. Checklists require the use of a predetermined listing of criteria against which a client's knowledge, skills, and/or performance are assessed to determine their abilities and/or limitations related to each criterion.
5. Rating scales require the client or the OT practitioner to provide a numeric (e.g., 1 to 5) or descriptive (e.g., most important to not important at all) rating about specific items according to the established scale.
6. Goal Attainment Scaling (GAS) uses interviews and rating scales during initial sessions to facilitate clients' participation in the goal-setting process by identifying intervention outcomes that are personally relevant to them.
   a. GAS is used during post-treatment sessions to assess client progress toward desired goals.
7. Performance tests involve structured guidelines and/or standardized procedures for engaging the client in performing an activity and for scoring their activity performance.
8. Norm-referenced assessments produce scores that compare the client's performance to a set population's performance.
9. Criterion-referenced assessments provide scores that compare the client's performance to a pre-established criterion.
10. Specific tools for assessing occupations, contexts, performance skills, performance patterns, and client factors are described in Chapters 5-16.

Observation Skills

1. Observation of a client during actual occupational performance is critical.
   a. Observation must be done in different contexts and in structured and unstructured situations.

CAUTION: Observations must always have a clear therapeutic purpose and respect a client's privacy.

2. Observation of environmental contexts is also important to assess physical, social, cultural, and attitudinal supports and/or barriers to participation and occupational performance.
3. Use of a structured tool to note observations can increase reliability.
4. Observations must be ongoing to assess the nuances of performance and subtle changes in function.

CAUTION: Occupational therapy practitioners must be aware of their own sociocultural backgrounds, as this is the lens through which they observe, and these perspectives can influence the interpretation of observations (e.g., the appropriateness of the client's nonverbal behavior). Therefore, OT practitioners must validate their interpretation of all observations with the client and/or caregiver(s).

Interviewing Guidelines

1. Establish the purpose of the interview.
   a. Questions that are asked and the information sought should be consistent with the interview's stated purpose.
      (1) Box 3-2 outlines key questions that are used to obtain a client's occupational profile.
   b. The interviewee should feel each question is relevant and significant.
   c. Irrelevant, spurious, and/or extraneous questions should not be asked.
2. Establish rapport with the interviewee.
   a. Establish an atmosphere of respect by being on time, asking pertinent questions, and actively listening.

BOX 3-2 ▷ Questions for Obtaining an Occupational Profile

- What are the client's reasons for seeking services?
  - What are their priorities and desired OT outcomes related to their health and wellness, well-being and quality of life, occupational performance, and engagement in desired roles?
- What does the client value? What is important to them?
- What are the client's current concerns about their engagement in desired occupations and performance of daily life activities?
- What are the client's skills, client factors, and performance patterns that enable successful participation and performance?
- What are the client's environmental and personal contexts that support engagement in desired occupations and performance of daily life activities?
- What are the client's limitations, client factors, and performance patterns that impede successful participation and performance?
- What are the client's environmental and personal contexts that hinder engagement in desired occupations and performance of daily life activities?
- What is the client's occupational history?
  - What are their lived experiences with occupations?
  - How have the client's patterns of engagement in occupations changed over time?

b. Set an atmosphere of trust by maintaining confidentiality.

c. The initial interview is often the beginning of a long-term therapeutic relationship.

3. Lead and direct the interview to achieve its stated purpose.
   a. Ask questions in an organized, formalized manner that is client centered.
      (1) Interviews are not casual conversations.
      (2) A haphazard approach will not obtain information needed to achieve the purpose of the interview.
   b. Numerous assessment tools are available to structure and guide interviews (e.g., the COPM, the Occupational Performance History Interview-II [OPHI]-II). Refer to Chapter 14.

4. Observe interviewee's nonverbal communications during the interview.
   a. What is not said during an interview can be as important as what is said.
      (1) Gaps in information presented.
      (2) Affect and mood.
      (3) Physical mannerisms.
      (4) Speech patterns and inflections.
   b. Interpret the congruence or incongruence of nonverbal behaviors with actual verbalizations.

5. Listen before talking to counteract preconceived views and prevent premature recommendations.

6. Question and requestion, as needed, to obtain essential information.
   a. Follow up questions should be specific.
   b. Open-ended, leading questions facilitate discussion.
   c. Questions that can be answered by yes or no should be avoided.

7. Comment in a limited manner and only when comments are directly related to the stated purpose of the interview.
   a. Reassuring comments are used to facilitate interviewee's participation.
   b. Specific suggestions or advice should only be given if intervention is part of interview's purpose.

8. Answer personal questions directed to interviewer by interviewee in a direct and honest manner.
   a. Purposes of personal questions asked by interviewee.
      (1) To show a general polite interest in interviewer.
      (2) To move the therapeutic relationship to a closer level.
      (3) To indirectly introduce a personal concern of their own.
   b. After providing a brief, truthful answer, the interviewer should redirect the interviewee to the purpose of interview and to themselves.

9. Interpret verbalizations and nonverbal communications to formulate hypotheses about the interviewee's situation.

> **CAUTION:** Confidentiality must be maintained at all times.

10. Develop a plan based on the information obtained from the interview and the hypotheses formulated about the client's situation.
    a. The plan can include the need for further evaluation to obtain more information.
    b. The use of an interview to formulate a plan can prevent interviewing just for the sake of interviewing.
    c. Plans for intervention should be developed collaboratively with the individual using a client-centered and person-directed approach.

> **EXAM HINT:** The NBCOT® OTR® exam content outline identifies knowledge of the "administration, purpose, indications, advantages, and limitations of…nonstandardized screening and assessment tools…(including)…client and caregiver interviews (and) observation" (NBCOT®, 2022, p. 4) and "interpretation of qualitative findings (including the) occupational profile . . . (and) results from interviews or observations" (NBCOT®, 2022, p. 5) as essential for competent practice. The application of knowledge about the observation and interview guidelines described above and in the preceding sections and the questions to inform an occupational profile that are provided in Box 3-2 can help you determine the correct answer for NBCOT® Domain 1 exam items about evaluation and assessment.

Developmental Considerations for Evaluation

> **EXAM HINT:** The NBCOT® OTR® exam content outline identifies the task of identifying "the influence of development . . . on a client's occupational performance" (NBCOT®, 2022, p. 3) as essential for competent practice. The application of knowledge about the following developmental considerations can help you determine the correct answer for NBCOT® Domain 1 exam items about evaluation and assessment.

1. A "top-down" approach should be used to first obtain information about the child's occupational profile, rather than a "bottom-up" approach which focuses on client factors and performance skills.
   a. The desired outcome of evaluation is the identification of the child's occupational performance needs, wants, strengths, and challenges and the establishment of the child's and their parents'/caregivers' intervention priorities.

2. Select assessments that are consistent with the child's developmental level and related to the reason(s) the child was referred to OT.

a. Refer to Chapter 5 for information about the components of a developmental evaluation and specific developmental assessments.

b. Refer to Chapters 6–12 for information about the assessment of client factors and performance skills that are impacted by specific pediatric clinical conditions.

c. Refer to Chapter 15 for information about the assessment of activities of daily living, play, education, prevocational, and social participation skills.

d. Refer to Chapter 16 for information about the assessment of functional mobility, positioning and seating, and technology needs.

3. Actively engage the child's parents/caregivers by interviewing them and completing in-home observations.

a. Acquire knowledge about the child's environmental contexts that support or inhibit engagement in desired occupations.

b. Identify the family's supports and community resources.

c. Determine and respect the family's cultural values and family-centered priorities.

4. Actively engage the child's teachers by interviewing them and completing classroom observations.

The Role of the OTA/COTA® in Evaluation

1. The OTA/COTA® can contribute to the evaluation process in collaboration with the supervising occupational therapist.

a. The level of supervision an OTA/COTA® will require depends upon their experience, established service competence, state laws, and other regulatory and payer requirements.

2. The OTA/COTA® can collect evaluation data and administer assessments of occupations, client factors, performance skills, patterns, and contexts and report assessment results to the supervising occupational therapist.

3. The supervising occupational therapist is responsible for determining which assessment(s) will attain information essential for setting goals and planning intervention and the interpretation of the information reported by the OTA/COTA®.

a. The OTA/COTA® can contribute to these processes.

4. All evaluation activities completed by a OTA/COTA® must comply with federal and state laws and other regulatory and payer requirements (AOTA, 2021).

> **EXAM HINT:** The NBCOT® identifies a client as a person, group, or population. Therefore, you should be prepared to answer questions about the evaluation and intervention process for different client types. Table 3-1 describes how these are applied to individuals, groups, and populations. Correct answers to NBCOT® exam items about direct services to individuals, groups, or populations will adhere to the guidelines provided in this table for evaluation and intervention.

Intervention

Overview

1. The intervention process is informed by knowledge about a client that was obtained during the evaluation process, the theoretical principles of established models of practice and frames of reference, and published research about evidence-based practices.

2. The intervention process includes planning, implementing, reviewing, and revising interventions as needed to attain client goals.

3. Intervention consists of skilled services provided by OT "practitioners in collaboration with clients to facilitate engagement in occupation related to health,

well-being, and achievement of established goals consistent with the various service delivery models" (AOTA, 2020, p. 24).

Intervention Approaches and Foci

1. Prevention: interventions designed to promote wellness, prevent disabilities and illnesses, and maintain health.

a. Primary prevention: the reduction of the incidence or occurrence of a disease or disorder within a population that is currently well or considered to be potentially at risk (e.g., parenting skills classes for teen parents to prevent child neglect or abuse).

(1) In the AOTA OTPF-4, primary prevention is termed "create/promote" and "health promotion" (AOTA, 2020).

(a) Interventions focus on providing enrichment experiences to enhance clients' occupational performance in their natural contexts.

b. Secondary prevention: the early detection of problems in a population at risk to reduce the duration of a disorder/disease and/or minimize its effects through early detection/diagnosis, early appropriate referral, and early and effective intervention (e.g., the screening of infants born prematurely for developmental delays and the immediate implementation of intervention for identified delays).

c. Tertiary prevention: the elimination or reduction of the impact of dysfunction on an individual (e.g., the provision of rehabilitation services to maximize community participation).

d. In the AOTA OTPF-4, the term "disability prevention" is used to designate interventions that address the needs of persons with or without disabilities who are considered at risk for problems with their occupational performance (AOTA, 2020).

(1) Interventions focus on preventing the occurrence or minimizing the effects of barriers to occupational performance.

2. Meeting health needs: interventions designed to satisfy inherent, universal human needs. These needs and intervention examples are described in Table 3-4.

a. In the AOTA OTPF-4, meeting health needs is not specifically identified as a specific intervention approach; however, this focus is consistent with the AOTA OTPF-4's statement that OT services are provided to promote the wellness and health of persons with and without disabilities (AOTA, 2020).

3. The change process: interventions designed to achieve behavioral changes and functional outcomes (e.g., restoring a person's upper extremity function after rotator cuff surgery; developing the ability of person with a C7 spinal cord injury to independently complete desired activities using a tenodesis orthosis and a tenodesis grasp).

a. This intervention focus is the most common in OT practice and the one that is most often reimbursable.

b. In medical model settings, this is often the only form of intervention discussed or documented.

c. Many practice guidelines for intervention planning and intervention implementation relate directly to this process.

d. In the AOTA OTPF-4, the terms "establish/restore/remediation/restoration" are used to describe interventions that change a person in some manner.

(1) Interventions to achieve change focus on establishing a skill or ability that a client had never developed and/or restoring a skill or ability that the client had lost due to impairment (AOTA, 2020).

4. Management: interventions designed to reduce or minimize disruptive or undesirable behavior that interferes with therapeutic activities or procedures needed to attain intervention goals. For example, in response to a person becoming very anxious prior to their first use of a wheelchair in a supermarket, the OT practitioner modifies the planned community mobility activity to not include a shopping activity. In addition to decreasing the activity demands, the OT practitioner provides additional support to decrease the person's anxiety; thereby, enabling the person to work on the development of essential community mobility skills.

a. In the AOTA OTPF-4, the terms "modify/compensation/adaptation" are used to distinguish

Table 3-4

Health Needs and Practice Examples

DESCRIPTION OF NEED	PRACTICE EXAMPLE
Psychophysical: the need for adequate shelter, food, material goods, sensory stimulation, physical activity, and rest.	A homeless person needs to overcome formidable obstacles to access restroom facilities and shelter for rest and sleep and to obtain food, clothing, and other material goods (e.g., toiletries).
Temporal balance and regularity: the need for a satisfying balance between work/productive activities, leisure/play, and rest.	A person who incurs a C-4 spinal cord injury who cannot return to their full-time job as a carpenter will have a significant unanticipated increase of their leisure time and require intervention to regain temporal balance.
Pleasure: the need to do things just for fun.	A home program designed for a child with a significant physical disability should include interventions that support spontaneous play.
Self-actualization: the need to engage in activities just for one's self and for personal satisfaction.	A non-verbal person learns to use an augmentative communication device to compose poetry and/or music for the joy of free expression.

interventions that alter the context or demands of an activity to reduce distracting features.

(1) Compensation and adaptation techniques are also used to alter the context or demands of an activity to support the person's ability to engage in areas of occupation (e.g., the provision of cues) (AOTA, 2020).

5. Maintenance: interventions designed to support and preserve a client's health, well-being, and quality of life by maintaining their current performance capabilities so that they can continue to meet their occupational needs (e.g., a reminiscence group to maintain the cognitive and social skills of individuals with early to mid-stage neurocognitive disorders).

a. While no improvement in function is anticipated due to the chronicity of a disorder or the progression of a disease, the use of maintenance interventions can prevent a decline in function, as much and for as long as possible.

b. Maintenance programs include familial, environmental, and social supports and consistent and regularly scheduled follow-ups.

c. While maintenance has historically not been reimbursed by third-party payers, it has always been a major type of OT intervention because OT practitioners often work with people who have chronic and progressive disorders.

d. In 2013, the Centers for Medicare and Medicaid Services (CMS) recognized that services to prevent or slow deterioration and maintain a person at their highest possible functional level are skilled and covered if these services are reasonable and necessary. Refer to Chapter 4.

e. In the AOTA OTPF-4, the term "maintain" is used to designate these interventions (AOTA, 2020).

Intervention Planning

1. The formulation of the plan for intervention based upon an analysis of evaluation results according to relevant frame(s) of reference/models of practice and evidence-based practice.

2. Collaboration with the individual, family members, significant others, and/or caregivers is essential to establish a relevant, meaningful plan that will be followed.

> CAUTION: If the OT practitioner does not share a common language with the individual, family, significant others, and/or caregivers, an interpreter must be used to ensure that their perspectives are obtained to inform and guide the development of an intervention plan.

3. Prioritization of concerns to be addressed in intervention.

a. Concrete and specific concerns are more likely to be effectively resolved than abstract global ones.

b. The values, interests, and needs of the individual, family, significant others, and caregivers.

c. The individual's current and expected roles and environmental contexts.

d. The treatment setting's characteristics, resources, and limitations (e.g., length of stay).

e. The likelihood that the person's concerns can be addressed by the interventions provided in the given setting.

(1) Services must be available within the setting to effectively address the concern; otherwise, a referral is indicated.

4. Formats of written intervention plans can vary from setting to setting.

5. Intervention plan content.

a. Long-term goals (LTGs): the change in activity limitations and participation restriction that will occur, prior to the termination of intervention, in order to achieve the desired functional occupational performance outcome.

b. Short-term goals (STGs) or objectives: the component subskills which are to be achieved over shorter time frames, leading to the attainment of the long-term goals.

(1) STGs must be directly related to the LTGs.

(2) Due to the reality of very brief lengths of stay (LOS) in some settings, only STGs may be accomplished prior to the termination of intervention.

(3) Referrals to other settings with longer LOS or home care services may be required for intervention to attain LTGs.

c. Intervention methods.

(1) The meaningful occupations and purposeful activities and their associated tasks, techniques, procedures, and modalities that are used to achieve goals.

(2) Methods of intervention must be clearly related to, and theoretically consistent with, the established goals.

(3) Home programs and/or family caregiver education and training may be included.

(4) Adaptive equipment, assistive technology, orthotics, prosthetics, mobility aids, and/or environmental modifications to meet the client's needs are specified.

d. Duration, frequency, and number and type of intervention sessions planned to attain goals are specified (e.g., 10 community mobility groups, meeting for one hour, three times per week).

e. Recommendations for additional OT services and/or referrals to other professionals are provided, if needed.

f. The design of all intervention plans must actively use clinical and professional reasoning to ensure that each plan's primary focus is on the client's engagement in occupation and participation in their chosen contexts. Refer to this Chapter's section on clinical and professional reasoning.

g. The existing evidence to support potential interventions must be reviewed and used to guide the intervention plan.

> **EXAM HINT:** In the NBCOT® OTR® exam content outline, "Domain 2 Analysis, Interpretation, and Planning: Formulate conclusions regarding client needs and priorities to develop and monitor an intervention plan throughout the occupational therapy process" (NBCOT®, 2022, p. 2) comprises 23% of the exam. Thus, knowledge of the previously mentioned intervention planning guidelines can help you determine correct answers for Domain 2 NBCOT® exam items.

Intervention Implementation

1. Fundamental OT principles are used to guide OT interventions. Refer to Table 3-5 Principles of Occupations.
2. Clinical and professional reasoning is used to ensure that the implementation of intervention is relevant to the individual and the uniqueness of their situation. Refer to this Chapter's section on clinical and professional reasoning.
3. Individual or group interventions may be used. Refer to Table 3-6 for a comparison of indications for individual versus group interventions.

> **EXAM HINT:** The NBCOT® OTR® exam content outline identifies knowledge of the "factors for determining and managing context and activities to meet individual and group intervention goals and objectives" (NBCOT®, 2022, p. 7) as essential for competent practice. Knowing the information provided in Table 3-6 can help you determine the correct answer for NBCOT® exam items about determining when to use individual versus group interventions.

Table 3-5

Principles of Occupations That Support Their Value and Use in Intervention

PRINCIPLE	EXPLANATION	EXAMPLE
Occupations and activities act as a therapeutic change agent to *remediate* or *restore*.	People have the potential to improve performance skills, patterns (habits, routines, and rituals), and body functions.	A homemaker who has impairments and problems in motor skills resulting from a stroke benefits more from working in the actual occupation of preparing meals in conjunction with exercises to increase her ROM, muscle strength, and coordination as opposed to solely using exercise equipment and objects stimulating the motor actions of the activity (Gasser-Wieland & Rice, 2002).
The use of new occupations as interventions provides the means for *establishing* performance skills and for developing habits.	The features of the context and environment may have changed and thus may demand the use of new performance skills and habits for the client to perform successfully.	Women with developmental delays and psychiatric conditions had a reduced rate of inappropriate behaviors and increased rate of socially appropriate behaviors in a new community living arrangement when given positive reinforcement in perusing everyday occupations (Holm, Santangelo, Fromuth, Brown, & Walter, 2000).
Valued occupations are *inherently motivating*.	Chosen occupations often are a reflection of what people value and enjoy and thus are more likely to be satisfying.	Older adults were motivated to resume engagement in occupations because of opportunities to reestablish relationships with others during engagement in valued occupations (Chan & Spencer, 2004).
Occupations promote the identification of *values and interests*.	Values influence occupational choice. When active in occupations, one experiences pleasure and satisfaction, thus generating interests (Kielhofner, 2002).	Older adults living within their communities related the three most important activities required for them to remain in their communities as using the telephone, using transportation, and reading; health professionals' list consisted of using the telephone, managing medications, and preparing snacks (Fricke & Unsworth, 2001).
Occupations create opportunities to *practice* performance skills and to *reinforce* performance.	The client must have the opportunity to develop patterns that include the remediated skill in routine daily tasks (Holm, Rogers, & Stone, 2003, p. 477).	Elementary students with learning disabilities and handwriting problems who practiced keyboarding in a training program improved written communication skills for performance at school (Handley-More, Deitz, Billingsley, & Coggins, 2003).
Active engagement in occupations produces *feedback*.	Corrective feedback regarding performance helps the client modify behavior.	A computer system was modified for a person with a head injury to provide an auditory prompt to mark the commencement of each planned activity. "I was just sitting there on the sofa doing something like reading a newspaper, and had completely forgotten the swimming bath, the computer started to bleep; oh, what had I forgotten now?" (Erikson, Karlsson, Soderstrom, & Tham, 2004, p. 267).

Table 3-5

Principles of Occupations That Support Their Value and Use in Intervention (*Continued*)

PRINCIPLE	EXPLANATION	EXAMPLE
Engagement in occupations facilitates *mastery* or *competence* in performing daily activities.	Successes motivate further change and continued use and practice of newly learned performance skills during engagement in occupations.	People with severe mental illness developed skills and competence in work and social activities while participating in a supported work setting (Gahnstrom-Strandqvist, Liukko, & Tham, 2003).
Selected occupations promote *participation* with individuals or groups.	Interventions designed to eliminate physical and social barriers increase opportunities for social interaction, leading to increased interaction and sense of control in context and environment.	Children with impaired performance skills used an adapted powered-mobility riding toy, which increased opportunities for participation with other children and adults during the occupation of play (Deitz, Swinth, & White, 2002).
Through engagement in occupations, people learn to *assume responsibility for their own health and wellness.*	Interventions that focus on improving a client's ability to self-direct change in lifestyle choices can lead to a sense of control.	People with chronic disorders who participated in community-based group services developed responsibility for their own health by empowerment of the group members (Taylor, Braveman, & Hammel, 2004).
Occupations exert a positive influence on *health* and *well-being* (Law, 2002b).	Regardless of the presence of impairments, a person may remain active and engaged in healthy occupations.	People with fibromyalgia who successfully used activity modification strategies to complete daily activities reported positive quality of life and health (Lindberg & Schkade, 2001).
Occupations provide the means for people to *adapt* to changing needs and conditions.	A person's capacity for performance is affected by the status of body structures and functions. Permanent loss of capacity necessitates modification of the context and environment and of activity demands.	Patients who had hip fractures demonstrated more efficiency and greater satisfaction in recovering performance skills in daily occupations when modified activity procedures were emphasized (Jackson & Schkade, 2001).
Occupations contribute to the creation and maintenance of *identity* (AOTA, 2002; Christiansen, 1999).	Discovering identity is related to what a person does and to those people with whom they come in contact during daily occupations and activities.	People with injuries to the hand resumed occupations that facilitated resumption of their identity (Chan & Spencer, 2004).
Successful performance in occupation can positively affect *psychological* functioning.	A person's evaluation of performance in occupations and activities influences perceptions about himself or herself.	People recovering from a stroke demonstrated positive views and acceptance of the need for a wheelchair, described opportunities for continuity of previous life activities, maintenance of mobility, and decreased burden on the caregiver (Barker, Reid, & Cott, 2004).
Occupations have unique *meaning* and *purpose* for each person, which influences the quality of performance (AOTA, 2002).	The meaning of occupations refers to the subjective experience one has when engaging in activities.	People recovering from a stroke stood longer when performing personally meaningful tasks (Dolecheck & Schkade, 1999).
Engagement in occupations gives a sense of *satisfaction* and *fulfillment* (AOTA, 2002).	Performance of valued occupations provides for achievement of personal goals in a variety of roles.	Satisfaction through occupations was found when older adults maintained daily routines and engaged in fulfilling occupations (Bontje, Kinebanian, Josephsson, & Tamura, 2004). Goldberg, Brintell, and Golberg (2002) found a correlation between engagement in meaningful activities and life satisfaction.
Occupations influence how people spend time and *make decisions* (AOTA, 2002).	People occupy time through engagement in activity.	In a study of time use, older people spent most of their time completing activities that were meaningful for them and not necessarily the activities that were necessary for them to remain in the community (Fricke & Unsworth, 2001).

From: Moyers, P.A., & Dale, L. (2007). The guide to occupational therapy practice (2nd ed., pp. 45–46). Copyright 2007 by the American Occupational Therapy Association. Reprinted with permission.

Chapter 3

Chapter 3

Table 3-6

Individual vs. Group Intervention	
Individual	Learning capacity of the person
	Amount of attention and skill required from the occupational therapy practitioner owing to body structure and function impairments
	Need for privacy
	Need for greater control over the context and environment
	Difficulty or complexity of occupation and activity demands, performance skills and performance patterns
	Inappropriate or dangerous behavior of the person
Group	Developing interpersonal skills
	Engaging in socialization
	Receiving feedback from people experiencing similar conditions
	Being motivated by peer role models
	Learning from other people
	Placing one's own condition into perspective
	Developing group normative behavior for successful performance in shared occupations (e.g., work, study, and leisure groups)

From: Moyers, P.A., & Dale, L. (2007). The guide to occupational therapy practice (2nd ed., p. 47). Copyright 2007 by the American Occupational Therapy Association. Reprinted with permission.

4. Standard precautions are observed in all practice settings with all persons. Refer to Appendix 3A.
5. Transmission-based precautions are used for persons with known or suspected infections of highly transmissible or epidemiologically important pathogens; includes airborne precautions, droplet precautions, and contact precautions. Refer to Appendix 3B.

> **RED FLAG:** Standard precautions must be observed during *all* intervention procedures, and transmission-based precautions must also be implemented as needed to prevent infection.

> **EXAM HINT:** The NBCOT® OTR® exam content outline identifies knowledge of the "infection control procedures and universal precautions for reducing transmission of contaminants (including) . . . PPE, isolation precautions, (and) cleaning equipment" (NBCOT®, 2022, p. 13) as essential for competent practice. Knowing the standard and transmission-based precautions that are outlined in Appendix 3A and Appendix 3B can help you determine the correct answer for NBCOT® Domain 4 exam items which focus on the incorporation of "risk management techniques at an individual and practice-setting level to protect clients, self, staff, and others from injury or harm" during interventions (NBCOT®, 2022, p. 13).

Types of Intervention

1. Occupational therapy interventions that are used therapeutically to enable individuals, groups, and populations to engage in valued occupations, participate in desired roles, and foster health and wellness include the following.
   a. Occupations and activities.
      (1) Prior to using occupations and activities therapeutically, the OT practitioner should complete an analysis of their activity demands and synthesize the activity analysis with the results of the client's assessment to determine if an occupation or activity can be used to obtain intervention goals.
      (2) Refer to subsequent sections on occupations and purposeful activities and activity analysis and synthesis.
   b. Interventions to support occupations.
      (1) "Methods and tasks that prepare the client for occupational performance, used as part of a treatment session in preparation for or concurrently with occupations and activities or provided to a client as a home-based engagement to support daily occupational performance" (AOTA, 2020, p. 78).
      (2) These include physical agent modalities (PAMs), mechanical modalities, orthotics, prosthetics, assistive technology (AT), mobility aids, environmental modifications, and self-regulation.
         (a) Chapter 11 provides comprehensive information about PAMs and mechanical modalities that are commonly used in practice.
         (b) Chapters 6, 9, 11, and 12 provide information about the use of orthotics for specific disorders and conditions (e.g., hand injuries, burns, Bell's palsy, and neuromotor dysfunction). Chapters 11 and 12 provide clear information about the purposes, design standards, and mechanical principles of orthotics and client education and training in the use of orthotics.
         (c) Chapter 6 provides comprehensive information about prosthetics.
         (d) Chapter 16 provides extensive information about AT, mobility aids, and environmental modifications and adaptations.
         (e) Chapters 12 and 14 provide comprehensive information about models of practice and approaches that can be used to attain self-regulation intervention goals.
   c. Education and training.
      (1) Refer to subsequent section on education and training.

d. Advocacy and self-advocacy.
  (1) "Efforts directed toward promoting occupational justice and empowering clients to seek and obtain resources to support health, well-being, and occupational participation" (AOTA, 2020, p. 61).
  (2) Refer to subsequent section on education and training.
  (3) Chapters 4 and 15 provide information about the role of the OT practitioner as an advocate.
  (4) Chapters 14 and 15 provide information about models of practice and approaches that can be used to develop a client's self-advocacy skills.
e. Group intervention.
  (1) Refer to subsequent section on group dynamics and therapeutic groups.
  (2) Chapter 14 provides information comprehensive information about therapeutic groups that are commonly used in practice.
f. Virtual interventions.
  (1) The "use of simulated, real-time, and near-time technologies for service delivery absent of physical contact, such as telehealth or mHealth" (AOTA, 2020, p.62).
  (2) Chapter 4 provides information about the telehealth service delivery model.
  (3) Chapter 16 provides information about the virtual environment.

EXAM HINT: In the NBCOT® OTR® exam content outline, "Domain 3 Select and implement interventions to promote healing and enhance engagement in occupation-based activities" (NBCOT®, 2022, p. 7) comprises 38% of the exam. The application of knowledge about the types of intervention described in this section can help you effectively determine the best possible answer to Domain 3 exam items that address intervention management.

Developmental Considerations in Intervention

EXAM HINT: The NBCOT® OTR® exam content outline identifies knowledge of the "clinical decision-making for assessing and adapting the intervention plan and prioritizing goals based on client response to intervention . . . (including) . . . developmental needs" (NBCOT®, 2022, p. 7) as essential for competent practice. The application of knowledge about the following developmental considerations in intervention can help you determine the correct answer for NBCOT® Domain 2 exam items about analysis and interpretation of client information.

1. Consider and respect the family's cultural background.
2. Make sure all activities, toys, and other intervention media are appropriate to the child's developmental level.
3. Use play activities as the primary occupation intervention.
4. Provide interventions to facilitate sensorimotor, cognitive, and psychosocial development.
  a. Chapters 6–10 provide information about diagnostic-specific interventions for pediatric and developmental clinical conditions.
  b. Chapters 11, 12, 13, and 14, respectively, provide information about biomechanical, neurophysiological, cognitive, and psychosocial frames of reference/models of practice and their interventions.
5. Fabricate or requisition orthotics, adaptive equipment, assistive technology, and mobility and positioning equipment for occupational performance and social participation in the community, home and/or school. Refer to Chapters 11, 12, 15, and 16.
6. Provide family education and training to promote and develop health literacy and support positive intervention outcomes.
  a. Educate the child and their parents/caregivers about the purposes of intervention approaches, techniques, and strategies that enable participation and train them in their safe and effective use (e.g., sensory modulation, cognitive-behavioral therapy, assistive technology, mobility and positioning equipment).
  b. Provide advocacy training to help the child and their parents/caregivers successfully obtain needed services and access community resources.
  c. Refer to subsequent section on education and training.
7. Address the physical, social, and attitudinal environmental factors that hinder the child's development and participation in occupations and support those that facilitate their development and participation.
8. Provide consultation or direct treatment to facilitate school performance and achieve educational goals. Refer to Chapter 4.

The Role of the OTA/COTA in Intervention

1. The OTA/COTA® contributes to the intervention plan in collaboration with the client and the supervising occupational therapist.

2. The OTA/COTA® can implement intervention to contribute to the attainment of a client's intervention goals.
   a. Supervision by an occupational therapist is required.
      (1) The level of supervision required will be determined by the OTA's/COTA®'s experience established service competence, state laws, and other regulatory and payer requirements.
      b. Service competence must be established.
3. All intervention activities completed by an OTA/COTA® must comply with federal and state laws and other regulatory and payer requirements (AOTA, 2021).

 ## Clinical and Professional Reasoning

> **EXAM HINT:** In the NBCOT® OTR® exam content outline, the task of monitoring and modifying "the intervention plan, approach, context, and goals on an ongoing basis using clinical reasoning" (NBCOT®, 2022, p. 6) is identified as essential for competent practice. Applying your knowledge about the following information on clinical and professional reasoning can help you determine the correct answer for NBCOT® Domain 2 exam items on intervention planning and management.

Overview

1. Definition: the complex mental processes OT practitioners use when thinking about, planning, directing, implementing, and critically reflecting on the services they provide when working with individuals, groups, and populations.
   a. Because the word 'clinical' denotes a medical model approach that is not inclusive of the practice models that are used in community, school, and home-based settings, the term 'professional' reasoning has been adopted to recognize the reasoning OT practitioners use in these settings.
      (1) The term professional reasoning is also inclusive of the thought processes managers, supervisors, and educators use to guide their practice.
2. Value for OT practitioners in practice.
   a. Improves clinical and professional decision-making by giving OT practitioners tools they can use to consciously reflect on their decisions.
   b. Improves OT practitioners' ability to explain their rationales behind their decisions to clients, family members/caregivers, team members, administrators, students, and medical finance agencies (e.g., insurers), and policy makers (e.g., legislators).
   c. Improves job satisfaction by making OT practitioners more aware of the complexity of their work and the value of their practice.

Types of Clinical and Professional Reasoning

1. Table 3-7 describes five types of clinical and professional reasoning (i.e., procedural [including diagnostic and scientific], interactive, pragmatic, ethical, and conditional reasoning) and how they are used in OT practice.

> **EXAM HINT:** Table 3-7 does not include narrative reasoning because this type of reasoning involves the OT practitioner gathering and constructing a person's occupational story that is focused on the identification and attainment of an imagined future. This story is enacted during OT intervention with the person and their family members/caregivers via a highly interactive and personalized collaborative process that is difficult to replicate in an objective exam item. As a result, it is unlikely that this form of reasoning will be tested on the NBCOT® exam.

Table 3-7

Clinical and Professional Reasoning and Practice Examples

REASONING TYPE AND DESCRIPTION	PRACTICE EXAMPLES
Procedural Reasoning: the technical "doing" of practice. This reasoning: • involves objectively assessing an individual's status and systematically developing and implementing an intervention plan according to established protocols. • uses the principles of frames of reference and models of practice to inform evaluation and intervention. • includes diagnostic reasoning which involves using knowledge of the etiology, symptoms, functional impact, and prognosis of a disease or condition. • includes scientific reasoning which involves applying logic and scientific methods. • is the type that is most often documented for reimbursement purposes.	The use of standardized assessments (e.g., the Miller Function and Participation Scales [M-FUN]) to determine a child's status. The application of knowledge about what is "typical" for a disease or condition to inform evaluation and intervention. The use of evidence-based intervention protocols (e.g., constraint-induced movement therapy [CIMT]) to attain goals. The design of research projects to test a hypothesis.
Interactive Reasoning: the relationship aspects of practice. This reasoning: • deals with how a disability or disease affects the person; focuses on each person as an individual. • involves the therapeutic relationship between the OT practitioner, the individual, and caregivers. • facilitates effective treatment by focusing on the personal meaning of illness and disability which can influence how a person engages in treatment (i.e., how intrinsic and extrinsic motivational factors affect an individual's performance). • is congruent with the profession's philosophy and heritage of caring.	The obtainment of the client's unique perspective by completing an occupational profile. The formation and maintenance of a therapeutic relationship that is empathetic and encouraging (i.e., therapeutic use of self, rapport building). Working with clients in a collaborative manner that recognizes and respects their personal values and learning style to problem solve, set goals, and plan intervention. Modifying intervention in response to a client's input and empowering them to self-determine their desired outcome(s).
Pragmatic Reasoning: the 'real world' aspects of practice. This reasoning: • considers the practical issues affecting practice (e.g., setting type, a client's financial and social resources, reimbursement requirements, legal mandates, practitioner competencies). • focuses on the evaluation and intervention possibilities within a given setting. • reframes understanding of the influence of personal and practical constraints on OT practice. • is most effective when OT practitioners are able to negotiate pragmatic contextual issues in favor of quality care.	The use of assessments that can be completed and the establishment of intervention goals that can be attained within the length of stay of a practice setting. Considering the impact of payment constraints on intervention and problem-solving to determine viable alternatives (e.g., a three-in-one commode instead of a raised toilet seat and grab bars for a Medicare recipient). Ensuring OT service delivery is compliant with laws (e.g., HIPPA, ADA, IDEA) and within the OT practitioner's level of competence.
Ethical Reasoning: the moral aspects of practice. This reasoning: • ensures that all actions an OT practitioner takes are consistent with the profession's Code of Ethics, • helps the OT practitioner effectively address situations that present ethical dilemmas and distress. • informs ethical actions for a situation. Chapter 4's sections on AOTA's Code of Ethics, ethics in practice, and ethical decision-making provides foundational information for ethical reasoning.	Fully informing a client about the potential benefits, limitations, and risks of an intervention. Respecting a client's right to refuse treatment. Advocating that service delivery constraints be removed (e.g., obtaining an extension of a length of stay). Obtaining informed consent from participants in a research study.
Conditional Reasoning: combines all reasoning types to be able to flexibly respond to changing circumstances and proactively plan for the future. This reasoning: • integrates interactive, procedural, pragmatic, and ethical reasoning in the context of the person's narrative. • involves an ongoing revision of treatment. • focuses on current and possible future social contexts. • requires multidimensional thinking.	Envisioning multiple futures for a client and being proactive in helping them attain the one that best meets their needs. Identifying the intervention strategies that may bring about a change in a client's condition (procedural reasoning), helping the client believe in the potential of the intervention to have the desired outcome (interactive reasoning), determining that the intervention is do-able in the practice setting (pragmatic reasoning), and ensuring that the implementation of the intervention is does no harm and maintains the client's autonomy (ethical reasoning).

Chapter 3

Therapeutic Use of Self

EXAM HINT: In the NBCOT® OTR® exam content outline, the task of collaborating "with the client, the client's relevant others, occupational therapy colleagues, and other professionals using a client-centered approach and therapeutic use of self to manage occupational therapy services" (NBCOT®, 2022, p. 5) and knowledge of "client-centered approaches and considerations for coordinating occupational therapy services (including) therapeutic use of self" (NBCOT®, 2022, p. 6) are identified as essential for competent practice. Applying your knowledge about the following information on the therapeutic use of self can help you determine the correct answer for NBCOT® Domain 2 exam items on intervention planning and management.

Overview

1. Definition: the practitioner's conscious, planned interaction with the individual, family members, significant others, and/or caregivers.
   a. The conscious, planned use of one's personality, unique characteristics, perceptions, and insights during the therapeutic process.
2. Purposes of therapeutic use of self.
   a. Provide reassurance and/or information.
   b. Give advice.
   c. Alleviate anxiety and/or fear.
   d. Obtain needed information.
   e. Improve and maintain function.
   f. Promote growth and development.
   g. Increase coping skills.

Characteristics of Therapeutic Use of Self

1. Essential characteristics of therapeutic use of self.
   a. Perception of the individuality and uniqueness of each person.
   b. Respect for the dignity and rights of each individual regardless of their past, present, and/or anticipated future situations.
   c. Empathy to enter and share the experiences of an individual while maintaining one's own sense of self.

d. Compassion to be kind and alleviate pain and suffering.
   e. Humility to recognize one's own limitations.
   f. Unconditional positive regard to be nonjudgmental and accept, respect, and show concern and liking for each individual as a human being, regardless of presenting behaviors.
   g. Honesty to be truthful and straightforward.
   h. A relaxed manner to leave other concerns aside and schedule sufficient time to be with the client so that external issues do not impede on the relationship.
   i. Flexibility to modify behavior to meet the needs of each client and deal with circumstances as they arise or change.
   j. Self-awareness to accurately know one's assets and limitations and to be able to make changes as needed to interact more effectively in therapeutic relationships.
   k. Humor to appropriately recognize and/or use what is amusing and comical.
2. Supervision and support should be routinely used to develop the above characteristics and be able to use oneself therapeutically in a diversity of situations.
   a. Supervision and support can increase the OT practitioner's effectiveness in applying therapeutic principles in their daily practice.
   b. Supervision and support can help the OT practitioner address the challenges to their therapeutic use of self and the development and maintenance of a therapeutic relationship that are noted in following section.

Challenges to a Therapeutic Relationship

1. Common issues and responses that can affect the formation and/or sustainability of a therapeutic relationship may include the following.
   a. Negative attitudes, fear, or hostility toward individuals who are different and/or toward the unknown.
   b. Resistance to establishing a rapport due to past rejections and/or fear of future rejection.
   c. Communication difficulties.
      (1) Incongruence between verbal and nonverbal communications (when spoken words do not

match a person's facial expression, tone of voice, gestures, or postures) resulting in confusion.

(2) Language difficulties.

    (a) Psychiatric symptoms such as blocking, circumstantiality, flight of ideas, confabulation, grandiosity, articulated delusions, loosening of association, and/or poverty of content can hinder effective communication.

    (b) Cultural, class, educational, and/or regional differences can result in misunderstandings or lack of comprehension between individuals.

    (c) Misinterpretations can occur due to differences in primary language.

d. Dependency that is excessive and hinders the individual's growth toward interdependence and/or independence.

e. Transference and countertransference.

    (1) Transference is an unconscious response to an individual that is similar to the way one has responded to a significant person (e.g., the OT practitioner is responded to as a parent).

    (2) Countertransference is an unconscious response to transference in which the individual responds in a manner that is expected and desired by the person who has transference toward them (e.g., the OT practitioner assumes a parental role toward a client).

f. Difficulty in expressing feelings due to personal reticence or cultural background.

g. Over involvement that results in a loss of objectivity or a fear of involvement that leads to detachment.

h. Difficulty with developing an individual therapeutic style that is a comfortable "fit" so that being an OT practitioner becomes a natural part of one's self.

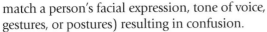

Occupation and Purposeful Activities

Occupations

1. Definition: occupations are the "everyday personalized activities that people do as individuals, in families, and with communities to occupy time and bring meaning and purpose to life" (AOTA, 2020, p. 79).

    a. They are goal-directed pursuits which typically extend over time.

    b. They have purpose, value, and meaning to the performer.

    c. They are the ordinary and familiar things that people do every day.

    d. They involve engaging in multiple activities and result in diverse outcomes.

2. Basic concepts of occupation.

    a. Every individual has multiple occupations that are meaningful (e.g., self-care, home management, work and leisure) and needed to function in roles (e.g., parent, worker, student, hobbyist).

    b. Humans are innately occupational beings and are driven by an inherent need for mastery, self-actualization, self-identity, competence, and social acceptance.

    c. Occupations have social, cultural, physical, and temporal contextual dimensions because they involve activities within specific settings and extend over time.

    d. Occupations have symbolic and spiritual dimensions, as individuals infuse individualized meanings into occupations.

    e. Occupations are interdependent (e.g., one must work to pay for leisure; one must have leisure to sustain and renew oneself for work).

    f. Health is attained when the dynamic balance between occupational performance, sleep, and rest is appropriate and meets the needs of the individual.

    g. Occupation can be viewed and used as a "means" or a method to change an individual's performance (e.g., playing a board game to increase motor skills).

    h. Occupation can also be viewed and used as an "end" or desired outcome (e.g., playing a board game to improve the ability to engage in developmentally appropriate social play).

    i. Engagement in occupation to support the client's participation in environment(s) of choice is the overriding desired outcome of OT.

3. Types of occupations.
  a. Activities of daily living (ADL): activities that involve care of self; often called personal activities of daily living (PADL) or basic activities of daily living (BADL) (e.g., toileting, showering, grooming, dressing, eating, sexual activity).
  b. Instrumental activities of daily living (IADL): activities that support living in one's home and community.
    (1) They often involve environmental interactions, are more complex than ADL, and can be optional (e.g., financial management, shopping, home establishment and management, care of pets and animals, child rearing. driving).
  c. Health management: activities to develop, manage, and maintain routines that improve or maintain health and wellness to support participation in other occupations (e.g., physical activity, medication management, communicating with health care providers).
  d. Work: "labor or exertion related to the development, production, delivery, or management of objects or services; benefits may be financial or nonfinancial (e.g., social connectedness, contributions to society, structure and routine to daily life)" (AOTA. 2020, p. 84).
  e. Education: activities that involve learning and participating in the role of a student in a formal or informal educational environment.
  f. Leisure: all non-obligatory, intrinsically motivated activities that are engaged in for pleasure, relaxation, diversion, amusement, and/or self-fulfillment during a person's discretionary time (i.e., time in which one is not working, completing ADL or IADL, or sleeping).
  g. Play: intrinsically motivated, internally controlled, and freely chosen activities that are engaged in for fun (e.g., pretend and fantasy play, games).
  h. Social participation: activities that support social interdependence and involve socially interacting with community members, family, peers, friends, and intimate partners.
  i. Rest and sleep: quiet and relaxing activities and daily routines that enable participation in sufficient restorative rest and sleep that are needed to support health and occupational engagement.
4. Chapter 15 provides comprehensive information about OT evaluation and intervention to enable occupational engagement and performance.

5. Chapter 16 provides extensive information about AT, mobility aids, and environmental modifications and adaptations that enable participation in occupations.

Purposeful Activities

1. Definition: doing processes that are directed toward a desired and intended outcome and require energy and thought to engage in and complete.
  a. The goal-directed tasks and/or behaviors that make up occupations.
2. Characteristics of purposeful activities.
  a. Universally, people participate in purposeful activities, although there are personal and sociocultural differences in the manner in which activities are performed (e.g., dressing).
  b. Fundamental to the development and acquisition of performance skills is active participation in purposeful activities (e.g., the development of eye-hand coordination through play).
  c. Fundamental to performance in areas of occupation is engagement in purposeful activities (e.g., work involves the completion of multiple tasks).
  d. Purposeful activities are composed of identifiable parts that can be analyzed.
  e. Purposeful activities are holistic.
  f. Purposeful activities can be manipulated and adapted to be appropriate to, and/or therapeutic for, the individual.
  g. Purposeful activities can be graded along many dimensions to meet the needs of an individual.
  h. Determination of the individual's differential responses to purposeful activities can provide information for the selection of appropriate activities for use in evaluation and intervention.
  i. Verbal and nonverbal communication is facilitated through engagement in purposeful activities.
  j. Organization and ability to focus are enhanced because purposeful activities provide concrete structure.
  k. Doing is emphasized.
  l. Involvement in, and with, the nonhuman environment is enhanced.
  m. Purposeful activities can vary on a continuum from conscious to not conscious/unconscious.
  n. Purposeful activities vary on a continuum from real to symbolic.
  o. Purposeful activities vary on a continuum from simulated in a clinical setting to real in the individual's natural environment.

Activity Analysis and Synthesis

EXAM HINT: The NBCOT® OTR® exam content outline identifies the task of performing "an activity analysis to determine the influence of task demands, current conditions, performance skills, and context on occupation" (NBCOT®, 2022, p. 4) and knowledge of "task requirements, steps to task completion, and task demands across contexts or settings" (NBCOT®, 2022, p. 5) as essential for competent and safe practice. The application of knowledge about the following activity analysis principles, purposes, and methods can help you determine the correct answer for NBCOT® Domain 1 exam items about evaluation and assessment.

Activity Analysis

1. Activity analysis is used to understand the activity demands that are typically required to perform a specific activity and the personal, social and cultural relevance and importance of the activity to the person.
   a. Activity demands are the "aspects of an activity needed to carry it out, including relevance and importance to the client, objects used and their properties, space demands, social demands, sequencing and timing, required actions and performance skills, and required underlying body functions and body structures" (AOTA, 2020, p.74).
2. Activity analysis contributes to the OT practitioner's professional and clinical reasoning by providing the foundational knowledge that is needed to select, adapt, and grade an activity.
3. Table 3-8 describes the purposes and methods of activity analysis.
4. Activity analysis principles and steps
   a. The exact activity to be analyzed must be specified (i.e., not just "dressing" but "donning a sweatshirt").
   b. The procedures, materials, and tools needed to complete the specific activity must be identified.
   c. The activity should be analyzed as it is typically performed under ordinary circumstances.
   d. During the analysis of an activity, all client factors, performance skills and patterns, and activity performance components and contexts should be considered.
   e. A frame of reference/model of practice should be selected and used to determine which aspects of the activity are important to emphasize in the analysis.

Table 3-8

Purposes and Methods of Activity Analysis and Synthesis

PURPOSE	ANALYSIS	SYNTHESIS
To teach an activity.	Analyze the nature and sequence of the subtasks within the activity.	Determine the best way to present the activity as a learning experience.
To determine if a person can perform an activity.	Analyze the activity demands for the typical performance of the activity.	Evaluate the client's functional capabilities and compare these to the activity demands of the activity.
To adapt an activity.	Analyze what parts of the activity can be changed.	Identify the adaptive strategies and/or equipment that can be used to enable effective performance of the activity if a client does not have all of the abilities needed to complete the activity without adaptations.
To grade an activity.	Determine what activity demands can be changed in the activity along a continuum of performance. Identify the client's assets and strengths that support activity performance, and their skill limitations and/or client factors requiring intervention to enable performance.	Upgrade or downgrade the complexity and difficulty level of the activity by systematically manipulating the properties of the environment and activity to meet the client's needs and provide them with the "just right" challenge to attain goals.

Activity Synthesis

1. The process of designing an activity for OT evaluation or intervention.
2. Combines information obtained from the activity analysis with assessment information about the client to ensure that a suitable match is made between the activity requirements and the client's needs and abilities.
3. Effective activity synthesis often requires the adaptation and/or gradation of the selected activity.
4. Table 3-8 describes the purposes and methods of activity synthesis.

> **EXAM HINT:** The NBCOT® OTR® exam content outline identifies knowledge of the "methods for grading an activity, task, or technique based on level of development, client status, response to intervention, and client needs" (NBCOT®, 2022, pp. 8–9) as essential for competent and safe practice. The application of knowledge about the principles and methods for grading an activity that are outlined in Table 3-8 can help you determine the correct answer for NBCOT® Domain 3 exam items about the implementation of occupation-based interventions.

Education and Training

Overview

1. Education is an intervention used by OT practitioners to provide clients and/or their family members/caregivers with the knowledge and information they need to develop and maintain helpful and effective behaviors, habits, and routines that enable health, well-being, engagement in desired occupations and participation in valued roles.
   a. Education interventions can be provided via direct services during an intervention session or by providing the client and/or their family members/caregivers with educational resources they can use on their own time. Refer to subsequent section on educational methods.
2. Training is an intervention used by OT practitioners to help clients and/or their family members/caregivers acquire the concrete skills they need to meet their specific occupational performance, health, well-being, and participation goals
   a. Training interventions can be provided is a real-life context (e.g., shopping in a supermarket) or in a simulated, applied situation (e.g., "shopping" in a rehabilitation center's pantry).
3. The purposes of education and training are closely related, and their interventions are often provided concurrently.
   a. They can be differentiated by their goals and desired outcomes (AOTA, 2020).
      (1) Education interventions seek to increase a client's and/or their family members'/caregivers' understanding (e.g., developing health literacy to prevent complications such as decubiti).
      (2) Training interventions aim to enhance a client's and/or their family members/caregivers' performance (e.g., the use of low- and high-tech assistive technology to complete tasks).

The Teaching-Learning Process

1. The process by which OT practitioners design experiences to help clients acquire the knowledge and skills they need to live a healthy and satisfying life.
2. Principles of learning.
   a. Learning is influenced by the individual's values, interests, age, gender identity, sociocultural factors, and current assets and limitations.
   b. Attention to the learning experience and perception of the situation influence learning.
   c. The learner's sources of motivation must be identified and used for engagement in learning experiences; learners engage in occupations, tasks, and activities that are meaningful to them.
   d. Learning goals made by the individual are more likely to be met than goals determined by others.
   e. Learning is enhanced when the individual understands the reason for and purpose of the learning activity.
   f. Learning is increased when it recognizes the learner's current functional level, and is initiated

within their capabilities (i.e., not too high or too low).

g. Learning is enhanced when activities and experiences proceed at a rate that is comfortable for the learner.

h. Learners who actively participate in the learning process learn more because experiential learning is more effective than didactic learning.

i. Reinforcement and feedback on the learner's behavior and/or task performance are important parts of the learning experience and can be used to support desired behaviors and extinguish undesirable behaviors.

j. Learning can be enhanced through trial and error, shaping, and imitation of models.

k. Frequent repetition and practice in different situations facilitate learning and encourages generalization.

l. Planned movement from simplified wholes to more complex wholes facilitates integration of what is to be learned.

m. Inventive solutions to problems (as well as more useful or typical solutions) should be encouraged.

n. The environment of the learning experience can strongly influence the success of that experience.

o. Individual differences in the way anxiety affects the learner must be considered.

p. Conflicts and frustrations, inevitably present in the learning situation, must be recognized and provisions made for their resolution or accommodation.

q. Self-awareness and self-monitoring skills should be developed and used by the learner.

r. Continuity between the planned therapeutic learning experiences and the real-life situations for which the learner needs to be prepared facilitates the effective transfer of learning and the generalization of knowledge and skills.

Teaching Methods

a. Definition: ways to present information and/or a task to a client on a one-to-one basis or in a group in a manner that facilitates learning.

b. The teaching method used should be compatible with the client's learning style, cognitive level, and the characteristics of the task that is being taught.

c. Table 3-9 describes major teaching methods that OT practitioners can use to help clients obtain their goals.

Health Literacy

> **EXAM HINT:** The NBCOT® OTR® exam content outline identifies knowledge of the "strategies for addressing health literacy with a client and relevant others (including) caregiver training, teaching-learning models, methods for making health information accessible, (and) informed decision-making" (NBCOT®, 2022, p. 6) as essential for competent and safe practice. The application of knowledge about the learning principles and teaching methods described in the previous sections and Table 3-9 and the following information can help you determine the correct answer for NBCOT® Domain 2 exam items about health literacy.

1. Health literacy includes the "ability of individuals to gather, interpret, and use information to make suitable health-related decisions . . . (and the) . . . professional communication skills, and the context or environment in which the information is being disseminated" (AOTA, 2017, p. 1).

> **CAUTION:** To effectively promote health-literacy, the teaching-learning approaches that OT practitioners use with clients and the educational materials they provide to them must be easy to understand, respect clients' culture, match their capabilities (e.g., communication, cognitive, and literacy skills), and be presented in accessible formats.

> **EXAM HINT:** Correct answers to NBCOT® exam items will adhere to the above standards.

2. Occupational therapy practitioners can develop people's health literacy and enable their participation in health-related activities by using an organized, systematic approach to formally present information about the following.

a. The nature of the client's illness, disease, or condition including its etiology, signs and symptoms, functional implications, prognosis, and intervention options to ensure informed decision-making.

b. Laws that support the civil rights and full participation of persons with disabilities (e.g., Americans with Disabilities Act [ADA], Technology Related Assistance for Individuals with Disabilities Act; Individuals with Disabilities Education Improvement Act). Refer to Chapter 4.

Table 3-9

Chapter 3

Teaching Methods and Practice Examples

METHOD	DESCRIPTION	PRACTICE EXAMPLE
Demonstration and Performance	The OT practitioner performs the task and the person imitates the OT practitioner's performance.	An OT practitioner working with a person with hemiplegia demonstrates the use of adaptive equipment and one-handed techniques for meal preparation and the individual imitates the practitioner's task performance.
Exploration and Discovery	A diversity of activities is made available, and the person is encouraged to choose any activity and try it without specific instructions or directions.	In an expressive arts group for survivors of domestic violence, an OT practitioner provides members a diversity of media to explore and discover their different qualities and then select a preferred medium to create individual personally meaningful works of art.
Explanation and Discussion	A verbal explanation of the task and a discussion of its components to either plan an activity or to review what occurred during the activity are provided by the OT practitioner.	In a vocational group, an OT practitioner reviews the steps for applying for a job, prior to clients submitting job applications, and the outcomes of the job interview is reviewed after the interview is completed.
Role Play	The OT practitioner and/or client(s) assume roles and act out scenarios to practice behavior(s) prior to doing the behavior(s) in a real situation.	In a high school self-advocacy transition group, an OT practitioner role plays a college admissions counselor, and the students role play college applicants inquiring about accommodations for their disabilities.
Simulation	The individual acts out an activity performance using simulated tasks and/or objects.	An OT practitioner working in a driver rehabilitation program has their clients use a driving simulator to develop their skills prior to driving a car on a roadway.
Problem-solving	The process of teaching a person to analyze a situation, define the problem, outline potential solutions, select the solution that appears to be most viable, implement it, evaluate its outcome to determine if the problem is resolved, and retry a new solution, if needed.	An OT practitioner working with a person living in a supportive apartment helps them develop strategies (e.g., the use of a weekly chore list) for engaging a roommate who does not complete any home management tasks in the completion of these on a regular and fair basis.
Audiovisual Aids	The use of slides, videos, and/or audio cassettes to teach material with or without the presence of an OT practitioner	An OT practitioner provides guided meditation tapes to clients with anxiety disorders to use when needed to manage their anxiety.
Repetition and Practice	The repetitious engagement in a task to increase efficacy, accuracy, and/or speed.	An OT practitioner working with a postal delivery person who incurred a back injury has the client practice lifting heavy packages using good ergonomics and then repeat these actions until they become habituated.
Behavioral Management	The implementation of a structured program to support the development of behaviors that have been identified as adaptive (e.g., age-appropriate social skills) and/or to extinguish those that have been identified as maladaptive (e.g., hitting people).	A preschooler with a proprioceptive sensory processing disorder uses too much force while playing. The OT practitioner develops a play program with the child's teacher that includes using diversion strategies when the child's behavior may be perceived by others as aggressive and the provision of play activities that provide heavy resistance and pressure (e.g., modeling clay) and proprioceptive input (e.g., yoga).
Client, Family, Caregiver Education	An organized, systematic approach to formally present information to increase knowledge about the nature of an illness or disease, including its etiology, signs and symptoms, functional implications, prognosis, and interventions. The maintenance of roles and occupational performance is emphasized. Methods for the prevention of secondary problems (e.g., decubiti, social isolation) are provided. Community resources and supportive services are explored with appropriate referrals made.	An OT practitioner presents an educational seminar to members of a multiple sclerosis (MS) support group. They provide information about the functional implications of MS symptoms and potential complications (e.g., fatigue, double vision, decreased strength, decubiti) on participation in occupations and desired roles. Strategies for preventing and managing symptoms and complications (e.g., the use of energy conservation techniques, an eye patch, a rolling cart, and pressure relief strategies) and resources to enable participation (e.g., non-profit organizations that modify homes) are provided.

c. Self-advocacy techniques, community resources, and supportive services that enable self-determination, health, well-being, and occupational participation (e.g., Centers for Independent Living [CILs]).

d. Strategies for attaining and maintaining health and wellness (e.g., engaging in physical activity, maintaining good nutrition, managing medication and personal care devices).

e. Methods to prevent complications and secondary problems (e.g., decubiti, social isolation).

f. Interventions to develop health literacy for specific conditions are provided in subsequent chapters.

Group Dynamics and Therapeutic Groups

EXAM HINT: The NBCOT® OTR® exam content outline identifies knowledge of the "considerations for facilitating individual and group participation in shared activities (including) group processes, group dynamics, (and) group type and function" (NBCOT®, 2022, p. 9) as essential for competent and safe practice. Knowing the following information about group process and therapeutic groups can help you determine the correct answer for NBCOT® exam items about group interventions.

Group Dynamics

1. Group dynamics are the forces which influence the nature of small groups, the interrelationships of their members, the events that typically occur in small groups, and, ultimately, the outcome(s) of these groups.

   a. Group dynamics can be examined and understood according to a group's structure (e.g., development, norms), content (e.g., goals, curative factors) and processes (e.g., member roles, communication, decision-making, cohesiveness, leadership styles).

2. Group development: the stages groups typically go through from their initial beginnings to their termination.

   a. Box 3-3 describes these stages of group development.

3. Group norms: the standards of behavior and attitudes that are considered appropriate and acceptable to the group.

   a. Behavior that falls outside of the group's range of acceptable behavior is considered deviant and is often negatively sanctioned.

b. Norms can be explicit and clearly verbalized (e.g., confidentiality is maintained by all group members, aggression is not tolerated).

BOX 3-3 ▷ Stages of Group Development

- **Origin phase:** involves the leader composing the group protocol and planning for the group (e.g., the size of the group, member characteristics, location of meetings).

- **Orientation phase:** involves members learning what the group is about, making a preliminary commitment to the group, and developing initial connections with other members.

- **Intermediate phase:** involves members developing interpersonal bonds, group norms, and specialized member roles through involvement in goal-directed activities and clarification of group's purpose.

- **Conflict phase:** involves members challenging the group's structure, purposes, and/or processes, and is characterized by dissension and disagreements among members.

  - Successful resolution of this phase results in modifications to the group that are acceptable to members, enabling the group to proceed to the next phase of development.

  > **CAUTION:** Unsuccessful resolution of this phase results in dissolution of the group or the continuation of a conflicted group that cannot attain group goals.

- **Cohesion phase:** involves members regrouping after the conflict with a clearer sense of purpose and a reaffirmation of group norms and values, leading to group stability.

- **Maturation phase:** involves members using their energies and skills to be productive and to achieve group's goals.

- **Termination phase:** involves dissolution of the group due to members' goal attainment, accomplishment of desired task(s), lack of member engagement, inability to resolve conflict, and/or administrative constraints (e.g., only four sessions allotted for a discharge planning group).

c. Norms can be nonexplicit and not verbalized (e.g., discussion topics that are taboo).

d. Norms can vary in different groups and can change as a group develops and/or membership changes.

e. Therapeutic norms.

(1) Encourage self-reflection, self-disclosure, and interaction among members.

(2) Reinforce the value and importance of the group by being on time and well-prepared.

(3) Establish an atmosphere of support and safety.

(4) Maintain confidentiality and respect.

(5) Regard group members as effective agents of change by not placing the group leader in the expert role.

> **EXAM HINT:** Knowledge of the above therapeutic group norms can help you determine the best answer for NBCOT® exam items about effective group interventions. Correct answers to exam items about therapeutic groups will include adherence to these norms; incorrect answers will violate these norms.

4. Curative factors of groups: the therapeutic factors that contribute to the efficacy of therapeutic groups, the value that group members ascribe to their group participation, and the attributes of groups that enable group participation to be a key agent of change.

a. Box 3-4 describes the 11 curative factors described by Yalom that can be present in all group interventions.

b. The conscious understanding and facilitation of these curative factors enhances the therapeutic value of a group.

> **EXAM HINT:** Knowledge of the curative factors of groups described in Box 3-4 can help you determine the best answer for NBCOT® exam items about effective group interventions. Correct answers to exam items about group interventions will maximize these curative factors; incorrect answers will ignore these factors.

5. Group goals: the desired outcomes of the group that are shared by a sufficient number of the group's members.

a. The group's effort is mostly aimed at attaining these goals.

b. Group goals provide focus for the group and guidelines for group activities and interactions.

c. Group goals are not a compilation of individual member goals. Members may have diverse goals, but attainment of the group goal will facilitate personal goal achievement.

> **BOX 3-4 ▷ Curative Factors of Groups**
>
> • **Altruism**: the giving of oneself to help others.
>
> • **Catharsis**: the relieving of emotions by expressing one's feelings.
>
> • **Universality**: recognizing shared feelings and that one's problems are not unique.
>
> • **Existential factors**: accepting the fact that the responsibility for change comes from within oneself.
>
> • **Self-understanding/insight**: involves discovering and accepting the unknown parts of oneself.
>
> • **Family re-enactment**: leads to understanding what it was like growing up in one's family through the group experience.
>
> • **Guidance**: accepting advice from other group members.
>
> • **Identification**: involves benefiting from the imitation of other group members' positive behaviors.
>
> • **Instillation of hope**: experiencing optimism through observing the improvement of other group members.
>
> • **Interpersonal learning**: occurs when receiving feedback from group members regarding one's behavior (input) or by learning successful ways of relating to group members (output).

d. Benefits of member participation in group goal setting.

(1) A match between members' goals and group's goal(s).

(2) Increased understanding of the requirements for achievement of the goal(s).

(3) Increased appreciation of each member's contribution to achieving group's desired outcomes.

6. Group membership roles: describe the patterns of behavior that are expected and typical within groups.

a. Instrumental roles are functional and assumed by members to help the group select, plan, and complete the group's task (e.g., initiator, organizer).

b. Expressive roles are functional and are assumed by members to support and maintain the overall group and to meet members' needs (e.g., encourager, compromiser).

> **CAUTION:** Individual roles are dysfunctional and contrary to functional group roles; they serve an individual purpose and interfere with successful group functioning (e.g., aggressor, blocker).

c. Box 3-5 outlines behavioral indicators for determining if a person can benefit from being a member of a therapeutic group.

BOX 3-5 ▷ Indicators for Group Membership

- **The Individual Is Able To:**
  - engage willingly in the group.
  - attend to the group guidelines/procedures.
  - actively participate in the group process.
  - benefit from group leadership input.
  - benefit from group membership/peer input.
  - respond appropriately throughout the group process.
  - incorporate feedback.
  - complete activities toward goal attainment.
  - attain greater benefit from the group intervention than from 1:1 intervention.

Reference: Adapted from United States Government Printing Office. Code of Federal Regulations, Title 42, Volume 3. Retrieved from http://www.cms.gov. December 21, 2003.

---

7. Group communication: the process of giving, receiving, and interpreting information through verbal and nonverbal expression.
   a. Effective group communication is a prerequisite to, and a requirement for, all group functioning.
   b. Effective communication occurs in a group when a member sends a message and the message is interpreted by the other group members in the manner that the sender intended.
   c. Sending and receiving messages often takes place simultaneously due to the dynamic process of verbal and nonverbal communication.
   d. Communication can take many forms, including monologue, criticism, orders, questions and answers, and open give-and-take.
   e. Group communication that is adaptive may include clarifying goals and the sharing of ideas, experiences, and feelings.

   CAUTION: Maladaptive group communications can include seeking to control the group by monopolizing the channels of communication and/or avoiding specific issues or members.

8. Group cohesiveness: the degree to which members are committed to a group and the extent of members' liking for the group (i.e., the sense of "we-ness").
   a. Factors that contribute to cohesiveness.
      (1) Extensive interaction between members.
      (2) Similarity or complementariness in member characteristics.
      (3) Perception of relevance of the group to one's individual needs.
      (4) Members' expectation of goal attainment and successful group outcomes.
      (5) Member cooperation and effective leadership. Refer to following section on leadership.

9. Group decision-making: the process of agreeing on a resolution to a problem. The solution may be obtained through different processes.
   a. Unanimous decision in which all group members agree.
   b. Consensus in which members agree to the majority's decision but retain the right to reconsider their decision.
   c. Majority rule in which the majority's decision is accepted with no re-evaluation of the decision by members.
   d. Compromise in which a combination of different points of view results in a decision that is different from each distinct point of view.

10. Group leadership.
    a. The leadership style that is a most effective for a group leader to use and the responsibilities they assume in a group will depend on the group type.
       (1) Box 3-6 outlines the major responsibilities of group leaders.
    b. The major styles of group leadership are directive, facilitative, and advisory. Refer to Table 3-10.
    c. Additional information about the role of the leader in specific types of activity groups and the five levels of developmental groups is provided in subsequent sections.

11. Co-leadership occurs when there is sharing of group leadership between two or more practitioners.
    a. Advantages.
       (1) Each leader can assume different leadership roles, tasks, and styles.
       (2) Both leaders can provide and obtain mutual support.

BOX 3-6 ▷ Criteria for Group Leadership

- **The Leader:**
  - provides active leadership.
  - instructs members as a group.
  - monitors and documents members' participation and response to intervention.
  - provides individualized guidance and feedback.
  - document each member's progress toward the goals defined in their intervention plan in objective, measurable, functional terms.

Reference: Adapted from United States Government Printing Office. Code of Federal Regulations, Title 42, Volume 3. Retrieved from http://www.cms.gov. December 21, 2003.

Table 3-10

Leadership Styles

Directive Leadership: takes place when the OT practitioner is responsible for the planning and structuring of much of what takes place in the group.
- This style is needed when the members' cognitive, social, and verbal skills and group engagement are limited (e.g., parallel or project/associative level groups).
- The directive leader's goal is for the members to accomplish the group's task(s).

Directive leaders:
- select the activities to be used in the group.
- fulfills most group maintenance roles.
- provide clear verbal and demonstrated instruction and feedback to complete tasks.

Facilitative Leadership: occurs when the OT practitioner shares responsibility for the group and for group process with the members.
- This style is advised when members' skill levels and engagement are moderate (e.g., egocentric-cooperative/basic cooperative or cooperative/supportive cooperative groups).
- The facilitative leader's goal is for members to acquire skills through experiential learning.

Facilitative leaders:
- collaborate with group members to select the activities to be used in a group.
- co-instruct with members throughout the group to foster activity engagement.
- facilitate members' fulfilment of group maintenance roles and their provision of feedback to each other.

Advisory Leadership: takes place when the OT practitioner functions as a resource to the group members who set the agenda and self-determine the group's structure and functioning.
- This style is assumed when members' skills and engagement are high (e.g., cooperative/supportive cooperative and mature groups).
- The advisory leader's goal is to have members understand and self-direct the process.

Advisory leaders:
- empower members to select and complete the group's activity.
- provides advice to members, if needed.
- encourage group members to independently assume group maintenance roles.
- recognize that feedback occurs as a natural part of the group's self-directed process.

---

(3) Observations and objectivity can increase.
(4) Co-leaders can share knowledge and skills.
(5) Co-leaders can model effective behaviors.

> **CAUTION:** Challenges to co-leadership may arise. These can include:
> - splitting by group member(s) of one leader against the other.
> - excessive competition among co-leaders.
> - unequal responsibilities resulting in an unbalanced workload among co-leaders.
>
> These challenges must be dealt with in a proactive manner to ensure effective co-leadership.

Types of Therapeutic Activity Groups

1. Major types of activity groups include evaluation, thematic, topical, task-oriented, instrumental, and developmental groups.
   a. Table 3-11 describes the purposes, assumptions of, and member criteria for each activity group type.
   b. Table 3-12 describes the role of the group leader and suitable activities for each activity group type.
2. Developmental groups are a continuum of groups consisting of parallel, project/associative, egocentric-cooperative/basic cooperative, cooperative/supportive cooperative, and mature groups.
   a. Table 3-13 describes the purposes and foci for the five levels of developmental groups.
   b. Table 3-14 describes the role of the leader and the activities that are used in the five levels of developmental groups.
3. Chapter 14 provides additional information about therapeutic groups.

> **EXAM HINT:** Because developmental groups are on a continuum, different levels of groups will be more common in different practice settings than others. For example, inpatient units will typically have more groups at the parallel and/or project/associative group level due to clients' acute symptoms and their short lengths of stay, while community-based settings with stable populations and extended (or unlimited) lengths of stay will typically have more groups at the cooperative/supportive cooperative and/or mature level. The application of knowledge about the purposes of each group level, their leadership roles, and suitable activities can help you determine the best answer for NBCOT® exam items about group interventions across the continuum of care.

Table 3-11

Activity Group Purposes, Assumptions, and Member Criteria

GROUP TYPE	PURPOSE	ASSUMPTION	MEMBER CRITERIA
Evaluation	To enable the client and the OT practitioner to assess the individual's skills, assets, and limitations regarding group interaction.	To accurately evaluate a person's functional abilities, one must observe them in a setting where these skills can be demonstrated.	All persons who will be involved in groups or who lack group interaction skills.
Thematic	To assist members in acquiring the knowledge, skills, and/or attitudes needed to perform a specific activity.	Improvement in the ability to engage in activities outside of a group can result from the teaching of these activities within a group. Learning is facilitated by experiencing and practicing needed and desired behaviors. Reinforcement of acquired skills and knowledge can help a person retain skills to effectively perform a desired activity in a satisfying manner.	Determined by the specific focus and goals of the group. Members' needs, concerns, and goals must match the focus and goals of the group.
Topical	To discuss specific activities that members are engaged in outside of the group to enable them to engage in the activities in a more effective, need-satisfying manner. Concurrent topical groups are concerned with activities already engaged in outside of group (e.g., a parenting skills group for parents of children with disabilities). Anticipatory topical groups are concerned with activities that are expected to be done in the future (e.g., a parenting skills group for parents with disabilities who are expecting a child).	Improvements in the ability to engage in specific activities outside of a group can result from a focused discussion of these activities. Discussion of members' experiences with and concerns about a particular activity can increase awareness about strengths and limitations that can impact activity performance. Brainstorming about potential solutions and social interaction strategies to enable satisfying and effective performance of an activity can be used to inform members' participation in a desired activity. Reinforcement of viable solutions and strategies can facilitate skill acquisition.	Individuals who share similar current or anticipatory problems in functioning. Members must have sufficient verbal and cognitive skills to engage in the group's discussion. Group interaction skills need to be at an egocentric-cooperative/basic cooperative skill level or higher.
Task-oriented	To increase members' awareness of their needs, values, ideas, feelings, and behaviors as they engage in a group task. To improve intra- and interpsychic functioning by focusing on problems which emerge in the process of choosing, planning, and implementing a group activity.	Activities elicit feelings, thoughts, and behaviors. Activities are the means by which members can explore and experience these thoughts, feelings, and actions. Through activities members can increase their self-awareness and practice new behaviors.	Individuals whose primary dysfunction is in the cognitive and socioemotional areas due to psychological or physical trauma. Group interaction skills need to be at an egocentric-cooperative/basic cooperative skill level or higher.
Instrumental	To help persons with limitations that cannot be remediated use their intact capabilities to engage in meaningful activities for as long as possible. To meet members' health needs. Refer to Table 3-4.	Individuals are functioning at their highest possible level and cannot change or progress due to the nature of their disease or condition (e.g., a neurocognitive disorder). A supportive, structured environment which provides meaningful activities can prevent regression, maintain function, and meet health needs.	Individuals who cannot independently meet their mental health needs and/or need assistance to maintain function due to cognitive, psychological, perceptual-motor, and/or social deficits.
Developmental	To teach and develop members' group interaction skills. Table 3-13 outlines the purposes and foci of parallel, project/associative, egocentric-cooperative/basic cooperative, cooperative/supportive cooperative, and mature groups.	Increasing awareness of and providing opportunities to engage in effective group behaviors can help a person acquire the interaction skills that are needed for participation in familial, social, work, school, play/leisure, and community groups. Ineffective behaviors result from deviations, lags, or insufficiencies in development. These developmental gaps can be treated by participating in groups that are similar to the ones in which the skills would have been developed. Subskills fundamental to mature group function must be acquired in a sequential manner.	Individuals with decreased group interaction skills.

Table 3-12

Activity Group Leadership Roles and Suitable Activities

GROUP TYPE	ROLE OF THE GROUP LEADER	SUITABLE ACTIVITIES
Evaluation	• Selects and orients clients to group's purpose. • Selects activities that require collaboration and interaction and provides needed supplies. • Does not participate or intervene in group (except to maintain safety, if needed), but observes and reports members' interaction and functional skill level to the treatment team. • Asks for clients' input. • Validates assessment and establishes treatment goals with each individual client.	• Tasks that can be completed in one session and require interaction to complete.
Thematic	• Selects, structures, and grades suitable activities to teach needed skills. • Interventions vary according to group's level, needs, and goals. • May range on a continuum from a highly structured, supportive director to a resource advisor. • Reinforces skill development. • Attention is not paid to intra- and interpersonal conflicts unless they interfere with or are directly related to the activity.	• Simulated, clearly defined, structured activities which enable members to practice and learn needed skills, attitudes, and knowledge within the group. • Activities selected are directly related to the skills needed to perform the activity outside of the group (e.g., a meal preparation group to learn how to prepare meals for one's self).
Topical	• Facilitates group discussion while maintaining focus on the circumscribed activity. • Helps members problem-solve, give feedback and support, and reinforce skill acquisition. • Shares leadership with members; act as a role model.	• A verbal discussion on a circumscribed activity that members are engaged in (concurrent) or will be engaged in (anticipatory) outside of the group (e.g., parenting, home maintenance, community participation, work, leisure). • Discussion may include members' current or anticipated concerns, fears, and problems; potential solutions; and coping mechanisms. • Role-play and "homework" may be utilized.
Task-Oriented	• Initially, very active, defines group goals and structure. • Assists with activity selection, offers guidelines and suggestions. • Facilitates discussion among members. • Gives feedback and support. • Assists members in exploring relationship between thoughts, feelings, and actions. • Encourages members to experiment with new behavior patterns. • As the group develops, the leader is less active and helps members give more feedback and input to each other; however, the therapist remains the leader and ensures that the task is a means to the end, not the end itself.	• Activities that are chosen by members and will create an end product or demonstrable service for the group itself or for persons outside the group. • Activities are selected, planned, and carried out by members with the understanding that the task is a means to study, understand, and practice behavior.
Instrumental	• Provides unconditional positive regard, support, and structure to create a comfortable, safe environment for patients. • Selects and designs activities that will meet member's health needs and maintain their highest possible level of function. • Assists members with activity as needed. • Makes no attempt to change the members.	• Members can successfully complete activities with structure and assistance of the leader as needed. • Nonthreatening and non-demanding activities that are interesting, enjoyable, and attractive to members are selected. • Activities meet the mental health needs of people by enabling them to experience pleasure, have fun, and socialize with others (e.g., a reminiscence group in an assistive living setting). • Activities maintain members' function by providing sensory, cognitive, perceptual-motor, and social input.
Developmental	• Assesses each client's group interaction developmental level (typically via an evaluation group) and places them in the group that is most appropriate for their level. • Table 3-14 outlines the leader's role in parallel, project/associative, egocentric-cooperative/basic cooperative, cooperative/supportive cooperative, and mature groups.	• Activities are selected to match the developmental level of group members and attain the goals that are appropriate for the specific developmental group. • Table 3-14 describes the activities that are used in parallel, project/associative, egocentric-cooperative/basic cooperative, cooperative/supportive cooperative, and mature groups.

Table 3-13

Purposes and Foci of Developmental Groups

GROUP TYPE	GROUP PURPOSES AND FOCI
Parallel	• To enable members to perform individual tasks in the presence of others. • To minimally interact verbally and nonverbally with others even though the task does not require interaction for successful completion. • To develop a basic level of awareness, trust, and comfort with others in group.
Project/Associative	• To develop the ability to perform a shared, short-term activity with another member in a comfortable, cooperative manner. • To develop interactions beyond those that the activity requires. • To enable members to give and seek assistance.
Egocentric-cooperative/ basic cooperative	• To enable members to select and implement a long-range activity which requires group interaction to complete. • To help members develop an understanding of group goals and group interaction norms. • To enable members to identify and meet the needs of themselves and others (e.g., safety, esteem).
Cooperative/supportive cooperative	• To enable members to engage in a group activity which facilitates the free expression of ideas and feelings. • To develop members' sense of trust, love and belonging, and cohesion. • To enable members to identify and meet socio-emotional needs.
Mature	• To enable members to assume all functional socio-emotional and task roles within a group. • To empower members to reinforce behaviors which result in need satisfaction and task completion.

Table 3-14

Developmental Group Leadership Roles and Activities

GROUP TYPE	ROLE OF THE GROUP LEADER	ACTIVITIES
Parallel	• Provide unconditional positive regard to develop trust. • Actively fill all leadership functions and meet all members' needs. • Reinforce all behaviors that are relevant to the group's purpose, no matter how small. • Provide structure. • Facilitate interaction.	• Members perform activities independently of others but in the presence of others. • Interactions are not required to successfully complete the activity. • Activities should be similar or utilize common tools or materials to facilitate interaction and sharing. • Activities should be relevant to a person's abilities, age, gender identity, and interests so that members will engage in the activity and potentially interact with others during the completion of them.
Project/Associative	• Select and structure activities that can be shared by two or more members. • Fulfill all of members' needs while encouraging members to give and seek assistance and interact beyond activity requirements. • Reinforce cooperation, mild competition, trial- and-error learning, sharing, and interactions.	• The activity is short term and requires the participation of two or more people. • The activity is shareable and requires interaction with another member and/or other members to successfully complete. • Group interaction, not project completion, is emphasized.
Egocentric-Cooperative/Basic Cooperative	• Less of an active, direct leader. • Facilitate and allow members to fulfill functional leadership roles to function independently. • Provide guidelines and assistance as needed. • Reinforce members' meeting needs of self and others. • Serve as a role model	• Activity allows 5–10 people to work together. • The activity is selected and implemented by members. • The activity is longer term, requiring more than two meetings to complete.
Cooperative/ Supportive Cooperative	• Act as a nonauthoritarian advisor and facilitator, not as a direct leader. • Leader and members are mutually responsible for giving feedback, identifying and meeting needs, and reinforcing behavior.	• Activities facilitate and allow for free expression of ideas and feelings. • Activity is secondary to need fulfillment and may not produce an end product.
Mature	• Acts as a peer, an equal, a group member. • Members assume all roles with the leader filling in only if and when needed to maintain group. • All members satisfy needs and reinforce behavior while maintaining a balance between need satisfaction and task completion.	• Activity requires a number of people to work together. • It requires an end product or has an inherent time limit for completion. • During a group session, the activity may be stopped for members to explore what is going on within the group.

Intervention Review and Discharge Planning

> **EXAM HINT:** The NBCOT® OTR® exam content outline identifies the task of monitoring and modifying "the intervention plan, approach, context, and goals on an ongoing basis using clinical reasoning" (NBCOT®, 2022, p. 6) and knowledge of the "processes for managing interprofessional intervention plans . . . (including) . . . discharge plans" (NBCOT®, 2022, p. 6) as essential for competent practice. The application of the following information about intervention review and discharge planning can help you determine correct answers to NBCOT® Domain 2 exam items.

Intervention Review

1. The process of determining whether the client's occupational performance, engagement, and participation have improved, declined, or remained the same after intervention.
   a. The re-evaluation and review of a client's response to intervention is an integral part of all OT interventions.
2. Effective interventions resulting in the client's progress require intervention plan modifications and an upgrading of goals, if there is a reasonable expectation that the client can benefit from the type of services that are provided within a given setting.
3. If the client is not progressing according to the established intervention plan, the development of new intervention goals, the use of different intervention methods to attain goals, referral(s) to other professionals or to another level of care, and/or discharge from intervention may be indicated.
4. If the client is progressing but the setting can no longer provide the services the client needs, discharge and referral(s) to other professionals or to another level of care is indicated.

Discharge Planning

1. Reasons for discharge.
   a. The client's goals have been met.
   b. The client no longer requires skilled services because maximum benefit has been achieved and/or the services to maintain them at their highest level of function are not considered skilled.

   (1) If a client is a Medicare beneficiary and they require skilled services to slow or prevent deterioration and maintain their maximum level of function, they do *not* have to be discharged from services (*nor should they be*), even if no improvement is expected (Jimmo v. Sebelius Settlement Agreement [cms.gov]).
      (a) This Medicare benefit may not be provided by state Medicaid programs or private insurance plans.
   c. The client chooses to no longer participate in therapy.
   d. An exacerbation of an illness or a medical crisis requires discharge to a higher level of care.
   e. The client's allotted length of stay (LOS) in the setting has expired and an extension of their LOS is not possible.
2. General principles of discharge planning.
   a. The outcomes of OT services are measured and reviewed to determine the client's progress toward goal attainment and their ability to engage in desired occupations and participate in valued roles.
      (1) This analysis of outcome measures and documented progress is used to determine if OT services should be continued or if the client should be discharged or transitioned to another service provider or level of care.
      (2) The discharge plan should be designed to support occupational performance, engagement, and participation after the discontinuation of services or the transition to another provider, type of service, or level of care.
   b. Discharge planning begins with the initial evaluation and is an inherent part of the intervention plan.
      (1) All interventions should be planned with consideration of the expected, planned discharge environment.
   c. Collaboration with the individual, family, significant others, caregivers, other professionals on the team, employers, and payers is required for an effective and realistic discharge plan.
   d. A well-planned discharge facilitates occupational performance, community participation, and the maintenance of function.
   e. Follow-up referrals for further OT intervention, other supportive services, and/or community resources should be included in the discharge plan (e.g., consumer-directed personal assistance services, Alcoholics Anonymous, adult day care).

Chapter 3

The Role of the OTA/COTA® in Intervention Review and Discharge Planning

1. The OTA/COTA® contributes to intervention review and discharge planning in collaboration with the supervising occupational therapist.
   a. The level of supervision required will be determined by the OTA/COTA®'s experience, established service competence, state laws, and other regulatory and payer requirements.
2. The OTA/COTA® shares all observations regarding an individual's response to intervention and any other information that may affect intervention and intervention plans.

3. The OTA/COTA® can administer assessments of occupations, client factors, performance skills, patterns, and contexts and reporting the results to the supervising occupational therapist to inform their intervention review and discharge planning.
   a. The OTA/COTA® cannot independently interpret assessment or re-evaluation results, modify the intervention plan, or determine discharge plans; however, they can contribute to these processes.
4. All re-evaluation/intervention review and discharge planning activities that are completed by an OTA/COTA® must comply with federal and state laws and other regulatory and payer requirements (AOTA, 2021).

Transition and Discontinuation

> **EXAM HINT:** The NBCOT® identifies a client as a person, group, or population. Therefore, you should be prepared to answer questions about the discharge planning process described above and the transition and discontinuation process described below for different client types. Table 3-1 describes how these are applied to individuals, groups, and populations. Correct answers to NBCOT® exam items about direct services to individuals, groups, or populations will adhere to the guidelines provided in this table for discharge planning, transition, and discontinuation.

Transition

1. The process by which a client moves from a provider and/or practice setting to a new provider and/or practice setting because another service and/or a new level of care is needed to attain their goals.
   a. For example, a transfer to a long-term care setting (e.g., a skilled nursing or assistive living facility) or an intermediate care facility (e.g., a halfway house); a referral to a work hardening or transitional employment program.
2. The occupational therapist is responsible for evaluating the client's status, documenting changes in their performance that warrant a transition to a new provider and/or setting, and determining which setting and/or provider can best provide the needed level of care.
   a. To ensure a safe and effective transition, the therapist must know the providers, practice settings, and resources that are available in the client's community.

3. Refer to Chapter 4 for more information about the major settings that are available within the continuum of care in the United States and the role of different professional and para-professional service providers.

Discontinuation

1. Services are discontinued when skilled services are no longer needed, the client's goals have been attained, their allotted LOS has expired and an extension is not possible, or the client decides to no longer participate in therapy.
2. If a client is being discharged to a private home, a predischarge home evaluation must be completed to ensure they will be safe and to identify needed home adaptations or supports (e.g., bathroom modifications, a home health aide).
   (a) If an on-site evaluation is not possible, alternative assessment methods must be used to obtain needed information (e.g., having a family member/caregiver complete a home safety checklist and photograph and/or video record the home environment).
   (b) Refer to Chapter 16 for comprehensive information about the evaluation of the home environment.
3. Prior to discharge, the client and/or their family members/caregivers should receive education and training about procedures that can maintain and/or improve the client's functional status and quality of life and ensure their safety.
   a. Refer to prior sections on the principles of discharge planning and education and training interventions.

The Role of the OTA/COTA® in Transition and Discontinuation

1. The OTA/COTA® can contribute to the transition and discontinuation plans by providing information and documentation to the occupational therapist related to the client's current status, their progress toward goals, and recommendations for follow-up care and resources.

2. The occupational therapist is responsible for the interpretation of this information and the development and implementation of transition and discontinuation plan.

    a. The OTA/COTA® can contribute to these processes.

3. All transition and discontinuation activities completed by an OTA/COTA® must comply with federal and state laws and other regulatory and payer requirements (AOTA, 2021).

▶ Appendix 3A

Standard Precautions

OVERVIEW

Standard precautions are used for all patient care in any health care setting. They're based on a risk assessment, assuming that any person or body substance is potentially infected or colonized with an organism that could be transmitted in the health care setting. Standard precautions make use of common sense practices and personal protective equipment (PPE) that protects healthcare providers from infection and prevents the spread of infection from patient to patient.

Apply the following infection control practices during the delivery of health care.

HAND HYGIENE

1. During the delivery of health care, avoid unnecessary touching of surfaces in close proximity to the patient to prevent both contamination of clean hand from environmental surfaces and transmission of pathogens from contaminated hands to surfaces.

2. When hands are visibly dirty, contaminated with proteinaceous material, or visibly soiled with blood or body fluids, wash hands with either a nonantimicrobial soap and water or an antimicrobial soap and water.

3. If hands are not visibly soiled, or after removing visible material with nonantimicrobial soap and water, decontaminate hands in the clinical situations described in a–f as follows. The preferred method of hand decontamination is with an alcohol-based hand rub. Alternatively, hands may be washed with an antimicrobial soap and water. Frequent use of an alcohol-based hand rub immediately following hand washing with nonantimicrobial soap may increase the frequency of dermatitis. Perform hand hygiene:

    a. Before having direct contact with patients.

    b. After contact with blood, body fluids or excretions, mucous membranes, nonintact skin, or wound dressings.

    c. After contact with a patient's intact skin (e.g., when taking a pulse or blood pressure or lifting a patient).

    d. If hands will be moving from a contaminated body site to a clean body site during patient care.

    e. After contact with inanimate objects (including medical equipment) in the immediate vicinity of the patient.

    f. After removing gloves.

4. Wash hands with nonantimicrobial soap and water or with antimicrobial soap and water if contact with spores (e.g., *Clostridium difficile* or *Bacillus anthracis*) is likely to have occurred. The physical action of washing and rinsing hands under such circumstances is recommended because alcohols, chlorhexidine, iodophors, and other antiseptic agents have poor activity against spores.

5. Do not wear artificial fingernails or extenders if duties include direct contact with patients at high risk for infection and associated adverse outcomes (e.g., those in intensive care units [ICUs] or operating rooms).

    a. Develop an organizational policy on the wearing of nonnatural nails by health-care personnel who have direct contact with patients outside of the groups as previously specified.

6. There may be specific PPE recommendations for specific diseases, such as Ebola. Clinical health care workers can find specific recommendations for a particular disease, if available, on the CDC's website.

Standard Precautions (*Continued*)

PERSONAL PROTECTIVE EQUIPMENT (PPE)

1. Observe the following principles of use:

   a. Wear PPE, as described in 2–4 as follows, when the nature of the anticipated patient interaction indicates that contact with blood or body fluids may occur.

   b. Prevent contamination of clothing and skin during the process of removing PPE.

   c. Before leaving the patient's room or cubicle, remove and discard PPE.

2. Gloves.

   a. Wear gloves when it can be reasonably anticipated that contact with blood or other potentially infectious materials, mucous membranes, nonintact skin, or potentially contaminated intact skin (e.g., of a patient incontinent of stool or urine) could occur.

   b. Wear gloves with fit and durability appropriate to the task.

      (1) Wear disposable medical examination gloves for providing direct patient care.

      (2) Wear disposable medical examination gloves or reusable utility gloves for cleaning the environment or medical equipment.

   c. Remove gloves after contact with a patient and/or the surrounding environment (including medical equipment) using proper technique to prevent hand contamination.

      (1) Do not wear the same pair of gloves for the care of more than one patient. Do not wash gloves for the purpose of reuse since this practice has been associated with transmission of pathogens.

   d. Change gloves during patient care if the hands will move from a contaminated body site (e.g., perineal area) to a clean body site (e.g., face).

3. Gowns.

   a. Wear a gown that is appropriate to the task to protect skin and prevent soiling or contamination of clothing during procedures and patient-care activities when contact with blood, body fluids, secretions, or excretions is anticipated.

      (1) Wear a gown for direct patient contact if the patient has uncontained secretions or excretions.

      (2) Remove gown and perform hand hygiene before leaving the patient's environment.

   b. Do not reuse gowns, even for repeated contacts with the same patient.

   c. Routine donning of gowns upon entrance into a high-risk unit (e.g., ICU, neonatal intensive care unit [NICU], hematopoietic stem cell transplantation [HSCT] unit) is not indicated.

4. Mouth, nose, eye protection.

   a. Use PPE to protect the mucous membranes of the eyes, nose, and mouth during procedures and patient-care activities that are likely to generate splashes or sprays of blood, body fluids, secretions, and excretions. Select masks, goggles, face shields, and combinations of each according to the need anticipated by the task performed.

5. During aerosol-generating procedures (e.g., bronchoscopy, suctioning of the respiratory tract [if not using in-line suction catheters], endotracheal intubation) in patients who are not suspected of being infected with an agent for which respiratory protection is otherwise recommended (e.g., M. tuberculosis, SARS, or hemorrhagic fever viruses), wear one of the following: a face shield that fully covers the front and sides of the face, a mask with attached shield, or a mask and goggles (in addition to gloves and gown).

6. There may be specific PPE recommendations for specific diseases, such as Ebola. Clinical health care workers can find specific recommendations for a particular disease, if available, on the CDC's website.

RESPIRATORY HYGIENE/COUGH ETIQUETTE

1. Educate health-care personnel on the importance of source control measures to contain respiratory secretions to prevent droplet and fomite transmission of respiratory pathogens, especially during seasonal outbreaks of viral respiratory tract infections (e.g., influenza, respiratory syncytial virus [RSV], adenovirus, parainfluenza virus) in communities.

2. Implement the following measures to contain respiratory secretions in patients and accompanying individuals who have signs and symptoms of a respiratory infection, beginning at the point of initial encounter in a health-care setting (e.g., triage, reception and waiting areas in emergency departments, outpatient clinics, and physician offices).

   a. Post signs at entrances and in strategic places (e.g., elevators, cafeterias) within ambulatory and inpatient settings with instructions to patients and other persons with symptoms of a respiratory infection to cover their mouths/noses when coughing or sneezing, use and dispose of tissues, and perform hand hygiene after hands have been in contact with respiratory secretions.

   b. Provide tissues and no-touch receptacles (e.g., foot pedal–operated lid or open, plastic-lined waste basket) for disposal of tissues.

   c. Provide resources and instructions for performing hand hygiene in or near waiting areas in ambulatory and inpatient settings; provide conveniently located dispensers of alcohol-based hand rubs and, where sinks are available, supplies for hand washing.

   d. During periods of increased prevalence of respiratory infections in the community (e.g., as indicated by increased school absenteeism, increased number of patients seeking care for a respiratory infection), offer masks to coughing patients and other symptomatic persons (e.g., persons who accompany ill patients) upon entry into the facility or medical office and encourage them to maintain special separation, ideally a distance of at least 3 feet, from others in common waiting areas.

      (1) Some facilities may find it logistically easier to institute this recommendation year-round as a standard of practice.

Chapter 3

Standard Precautions (*Continued*)

PATIENT PLACEMENT

1. Include the potential for transmission of infectious agents in patient placement decisions.

   a. Place patients who pose a risk for transmission to others (e.g., uncontained secretions, excretions or wound drainage, infants with suspected viral respiratory or gastrointestinal infections) in a single-patient room when available.

2. Determine patient placement based on the following principles:

   a. Route(s) of transmission of the known or suspected infectious agent.

   b. Risk factors for transmission in the infected patient.

   c. Risk factors for adverse outcomes resulting from a hospital-acquired infection (HAI) in other patients in the area or room being considered for patient placement.

   d. Availability of single-patient rooms.

   e. Patient options for room sharing (e.g., cohorting patients with the same infection).

PATIENT-CARE EQUIPMENT AND INSTRUMENTS/DEVICES

1. Establish policies and procedures for containing, transporting, and handling patient-care equipment and instruments/devices that may be contaminated with blood or body fluids.

2. Remove organic material from critical and semicritical instrument/devices, using recommended cleaning agents before high-level disinfection and sterilization to enable effective disinfection and sterilization processes.

3. Wear PPE (e.g., gloves, gown), according to the level of anticipated contamination, when handling patient-care equipment and instruments/devices that are visibly soiled or may have been in contact with blood or body fluids.

CARE OF THE ENVIRONMENT

1. Establish policies and procedures for routine and targeted cleaning of environmental surfaces as indicated by the level of patient contact and degree of soiling.

2. Clean and disinfect surfaces that are likely to be contaminated with pathogens, including those that are in close proximity to the patient (e.g., bed rails, over bed tables) and frequently touched surfaces in the patient-care environment (e.g., door knobs, surfaces in and surrounding toilets in patients' rooms) on a more frequent schedule compared to that for other surfaces (e.g., horizontal surfaces in waiting rooms).

3. Use Environmental Protection Agency (EPA)–registered disinfectants that have microbiocidal (i.e., killing) activity against the pathogens most likely to contaminate the patient-care environment. Use in accordance with manufacturer's instructions.

   a. Review the efficacy of in-use disinfectants when evidence of continuing transmission of an infectious agent (e.g., rotavirus, C. difficile, norovirus) may indicate resistance to the in-use product and change to a more effective disinfectant as indicated.

4. In facilities that provide health care to pediatric patients or have waiting areas with child play toys (e.g., obstetric/gynecology offices and clinics), establish policies and procedures for cleaning and disinfecting toys at regular intervals.

   a. Use the following principles in developing this policy and procedures:

      (1) Select play toys that can be easily cleaned and disinfected.

      (2) Do not permit use of stuffed furry toys if they will be shared.

      (3) Clean and disinfect large stationary toys (e.g., climbing equipment) at least weekly and whenever visibly soiled.

      (4) If toys are likely to be mouthed, rinse with water after disinfection; alternatively wash in a dishwasher.

      (5) When a toy requires cleaning and disinfection, do so immediately or store in a designated labeled container separate from toys that are clean and ready for use.

5. Include multiuse electronic equipment in policies and procedures for preventing contamination and for cleaning and disinfection, especially those items that are used by patients, those used during delivery of patient care, and mobile devices that are moved in and out of patient rooms frequently (e.g., daily).

   a. No recommendations are provided for use of removable protective covers or washable keyboards. This is an unresolved issue.

TEXTILES AND LAUNDRY

1. Handle used textiles and fabrics with minimum agitation to avoid contamination of air, surfaces, and persons.

2. If laundry chutes are used, ensure that they are properly designed, maintained, and used in a manner to minimize dispersion of aerosols from contaminated laundry.

SAFE INJECTION PRACTICES

These are not included here since OT practitioners do not give injections. Refer to the CDC website.

Standard Precautions (*Continued*)
WORKER SAFETY
Adhere to federal and state requirements for protection of health-care personnel from exposure to bloodborne pathogens.
Reference: Centers for Disease Control and Prevention. (2023, July 11). Infection control: Isolation precautions. https://www.cdc.gov/infectioncontrol/guidelines/isolation/index.html

 # Appendix 3B

Transmission-based Precautions
CONTACT PRECAUTIONS

In addition to Standard Precautions, use Contact Precautions, or the equivalent, for specified patients with known or suspected infections that are at an increased risk for contact transmission (i.e., direct patient contact such as hand or skin-to-skin, contact with items in the patient's environment).

1. Patient placement.

   a. A single or private room is recommended to serve as an isolation space.

   b. If a single-patient room is in short supply, patients with conditions that facilitate transmission (i.e., uncontained drainage) may be prioritized for a single-patient room, patients infected/colonized with the same pathogen may be placed together in the same room (cohort patients), or decisions may need to be made on a case-by-case basis by considering options that balance infection risks to other patients while minimizing the potential adverse psychological impact on the infected or colonized patient.

   c. If it becomes necessary to place patients who require Contact Precautions in a room with a patient who does not have the same infection, avoid placing with patients who have increased risk of adverse outcomes (e.g., immunocompromised), ensure that patients are physically separated (i.e., >3 feet apart, curtain drawn), and change protective attire and perform hand hygiene between contact with patients.

2. Use of PPE.

   a. Gloves: wear gloves whenever touching the patient's intact skin or surfaces and articles in close proximity to the patient (e.g., medical equipment, bed rails). Don gloves upon entry into the room and doff just before leaving the room.

   b. Gown: wear a gown whenever anticipating that clothing will have direct contact with the patient or potentially contaminated environmental surfaces or equipment in close proximity to the patient. Don gown upon entry into the room. Remove gown and observe hand hygiene before leaving the patient-care environment. After gown removal, ensure that clothing and skin do not contact potentially contaminated environmental surfaces that could result in possible transfer of microorganism to other patients or environmental surfaces.

3. Patient transport.

   a. Limit transport and movement of patients outside of the room to medically-necessary purposes.

   b. If transport or movement is necessary, ensure that infected or colonized areas of the patient's body are contained and covered. Remove and dispose of contaminated PPE and perform hand hygiene prior to transporting patients; don clean PPE to handle the patient at the transport destination.

4. Patient-care equipment and instruments/devices.

   a. Use disposable noncritical patient-care equipment (e.g., blood pressure cuffs) or implement patient-dedicated use of such equipment. If common use of equipment for multiple patients is unavoidable, clean and disinfect such equipment before use on another patient.

   b. Limit the amount of non-disposable patient-care equipment brought into the room or homes of patients on Contact Precautions. Whenever possible, leave patient-care equipment in the patient's room until discharged or precautions are discontinued.

   c. Environmental measures: ensure that rooms of patients on Contact Precautions are prioritized for frequent cleaning and disinfection (e.g., at least daily) with a focus on frequently-touched surfaces (e.g., bed rails, overbed table, bedside commode, lavatory surfaces in patient bathrooms, doorknobs) and equipment in the immediate vicinity of the patient.

(*Continued*)

Transmission-based Precautions (*Continued*)

DROPLET PRECAUTIONS

In addition to Standard Precautions, use Droplet Precautions, or the equivalent, for patients known or suspected to be infected with pathogens transmitted by respiratory droplets (i.e., large particle droplets) that can be generated by the patient during coughing, sneezing, talking.

1. Patient placement.

   a. A single or private room is recommended to serve as an isolation space.

   b. If a single-patient room is in short supply, patients with excessive cough and sputum production may be prioritized for a single-patient room, patients infected/colonized with the same pathogen may be placed together in the same room (cohort patients), or decisions may need to be made on a case-by-case basis by considering options that balance infection risks to other patients while minimizing the potential adverse psychological impact on the infected or colonized patient.

   c. If it becomes necessary to place patients who require Droplet Precautions in a room with a patient who does not have the same infection, avoid placing with patients who have increased risk of adverse outcomes (e.g., immunocompromised), ensure that patients are physically separated (i.e., >3 feet apart, curtain drawn), and change protective attire and perform hand hygiene between contact with patients.

2. Use of PPE.

   a. Mask: don a mask upon entry into the patient room.

   b. There is no recommendation for routinely wearing eye protection (e.g., goggle or face shield), in addition to a mask, for close contact with patients who require Droplet Precautions. This is an unresolved issue.

   c. For patients with suspected or proven SARS, or other specific conditions, refer to the CDC website for the most recent recommendations.

3. Patient transport.

   a. Limit transport and movement of patients outside of the room to medically-necessary purposes.

   b. If transport or movement is necessary, instruct the patient to wear a mask and follow respiratory hygiene/cough etiquette procedures. No mask is required for persons transporting patients on Droplet Precautions.

AIRBORNE PRECAUTIONS

Use Airborne Precautions, or the equivalent, for patients known or suspected to be infected with infectious agents transmitted person-to-person by airborne route (i.e., particles that remain suspended in the air and that can be dispersed widely by air currents within a room or over a long distance).

1. Patient placement.

   a. Place patients who require Airborne Precautions in an airborne infection isolation room (AIIR) constructed in accordance with current guidelines:

      (1) Provide at least 6–12 air changes per hour.

      (2) Direct exhaust of air to the outside. If it is not possible to exhaust air from an AIIR directly to the outside, the air may be returned to the air-handling system or adjacent spaces if all air is directed through HEPA filters.

      (3) Monitor air pressure daily with visual indicators (e.g., smoke tubes, flutter strips), regardless of the presence of differential pressure sensing devices.

   b. Keep the AIIR door closed when not required for entry and exit.

   c. When an AIIR is not available, transfer the patient to a facility that has an available AIIR.

   d. In the event of an outbreak or exposure involving large numbers of patients who require Airborne Precautions, infection control professionals should be consulted before patient placement to determine the safety of an alternative room that do not meet engineering requirements for an AIIR.

2. Use of PPE.

   a. Wear a fit-tested N95 or higher level respirator for respiratory protection when entering the room or home of a patient when specific diseases (i.e., infectious pulmonary or laryngeal tuberculosis, smallpox) are suspected or confirmed, which can be found on the CDC's website.

   b. The CDC may routinely provide updates for PPE for specific diseases (e.g., there are current recommendations on face protection for measles).

   c. No recommendation is made regarding the type of personal protective equipment (i.e., surgical mask or respiratory protection with a N95 or higher respirator) to be worn by susceptible or presumed-immune healthcare personnel who must have contact with patients with known or suspected measles, chickenpox or disseminated herpes zoster. This is an unresolved issue.

3. Patient transport.

   a. Limit transport and movement of patients outside of the room to medically-necessary purposes.

   b. If transport or movement is necessary, instruct the patient to wear a surgical mask and follow respiratory hygiene/cough etiquette procedures.

   c. For patients with skin lesions or draining lesions associated with certain airborne-transmitted diseases (e.g., varicella, smallpox, tuberculosis), cover the affected areas to prevent aerosolization or contact with the infectious agent in skin lesions.

   d. Health care personnel transporting patients who are on Airborne Precautions do not need to wear a mask or respirator during transport if the patient is wearing a mask and infectious skin lesions are covered.

Reference: Centers for Disease Control and Prevention. (2023, July 11). Infection control: Isolation precautions. https://www.cdc.gov/infectioncontrol/guidelines/isolation/index.html

References

American Occupational Therapy Association. (2017). AOTA's societal statement on health literacy. American Journal of Occupational Therapy, 71(Suppl. 2), 7112410065. https://doi.org/10.5014/ajot.2017.716S14.

American Occupational Therapy Association. (2018). Reference manual of the official documents of the American Occupational Therapy Association (23rd ed.). AOTA Press.

American Occupational Therapy Association. (2020). Occupational therapy practice framework: Domain and process (4th ed.). 7412410010p1–7412410010p87.

American Occupational Therapy Association. (2021). Standards of practice for occupational therapy. American Journal of Occupational Therapy, 75(Suppl. 3), 7513410030. https://doi.org/10.5014/ajot.2021.75S3004

Asher, I. E. (2014). Occupational therapy assessment tools: An annotated index (4th ed.). AOTA Press.

Boyt Schell, B., & Schell, J.W. (2008). Clinical and professional reasoning in occupational therapy. Wolters Kluwer/Lippincott and Wilkins.

Braveman, B. (2016). Leading and managing occupational therapy services: An evidence-based approach (2nd ed.). F.A. Davis.

Brown, C., Stoffel, V., & Munuz, J.P. (2019). Occupational therapy in mental health: A vision for participation. (2nd ed.). F.A. Davis.

Centers for Disease Control and Prevention. (2023, July 11). Infection control: Isolation precautions. https://www.cdc.gov/infectioncontrol/guidelines/isolation/index.html

Cole, M., & Donohue, M. (2011). Social participation in occupational contexts: In schools, clinics, and communities. Slack.

George, A. H. (2018). Infection control and safety issues in the clinic. In W. Schultz-Krohn & H.M. Pendleton (Eds.), Pedretti's occupational therapy: Practice skills for physical dysfunction (8th ed., pp. 141–154). Elsevier.

Gutman, S., Mortera, M., Hinojosa, J., & Kramer, P. (2007). The issue is: Revision of the occupational therapy Practice Framework. American Journal of Occupational Therapy, 61, 119–126.

Hansen, R. A. (1990). Lesson 10: Ethical considerations. In C. B. Royeen (Ed.), AOTA self study series. Assessing function. American Occupational Therapy Association.

Hemphill-Pearson, B. J. (1999). Assessments in occupational therapy mental health: An integrative approach. Slack.

Hinojosa, J., & Kramer, P. (2014). Evaluation in occupational therapy: Obtaining and interpreting data (4th ed.). AOTA Press.

Jacobs, K., & MacRae, N. (2017). Occupational therapy essentials for clinical competence (3rd ed.). Slack.

Jimmo v. Sebelius settlement agreement fact sheet. (2013). Retrieved from http://www.cms.gov/Medicare/Medicare-Fee-for-Service-Payment/SNFPPS/Downloads/Jimmo-FactSheet.pdf.

Mailloux, Z., May-Benson, T. A., Summers, C. A., Miller, L. J., Brett-Green, B., Burke, J. P., & Schoen, S. A. (2007). The Issue Is—Goal attainment scaling as a measure of meaningful outcomes for children with sensory integration disorders. American Journal of Occupational Therapy, 61, 254–259.

Matuska, K. M. (Ed.). (2020). Ways of living: Intervention strategies to enable participation (5th ed.). AOTA Press.

Mosey, A. C. (1996). Psychosocial components of occupational therapy. Raven Press.

Moyers, P., & Dale, L. (2007). The guide to occupational therapy practice. AOTA Press.

Mulligan, S. (2014). Occupational therapy evaluation for children. Wolters Kluwer /Lippincott and Wilkins.

National Board for Certification in Occupational Therapy. (2022). 2022 Occupational Therapist Registered (OTR®) examination content outline. https://www.nbcot.org//media/PDFs/2022_OTR_Content_Outline.pdf.

O'Brien, J. C. (2017). Introduction to occupational therapy (5th ed.). Elsevier Health Sciences.

O'Brien, J.C., & Kuhaneck, H. (Eds.). (2020). Case-Smith's Occupational therapy for children and adolescents (8th ed.). Elsevier Mosby

Ottenbacher, K. J., & Cusick, A. (1990). Goal attainment scaling as a method of clinical service evaluation. American Journal of Occupational Therapy, 44, 519–525.

Runyen, M., & Benner, M. (2020). Enhancing health management by adapting technology and addressing electronic health literacy. American Journal of Occupational Therapy, 74(4_Suppl. 1), 7411505174p1. https://doi.org/10.5014/ajot.2020.74S1-PO5730

Scaffa, M., & Reitz, M. (Eds.). (2020). Occupational therapy in community and population health practice. F.A. Davis.

Schell, B., & Gillen, G. (Eds.). (2018). Willard and Spackman's occupational therapy (13th ed.). Wolters Kluwer Health.

Trombly, C. (1995). Eleanor Clarke Slagle Lecture Occupation: Purposefulness and meaningfulness as therapeutic mechanisms. American Journal of Occupational Therapy, 49, 960–972.

VanPuymbrouck, L., Carey, J., Draper, A., & Follansbee, L. (2021). Recognizing inequity: A critical step of health literacy for people with disability. American Journal of Occupational Therapy, 75, 7504180100. https://doi.org/10.5014/ajot.2021.04549

Chapter 3

Review Questions

Following are seven questions about key content covered in this Chapter. These questions are not inclusive of the entirety of content about the occupational therapy process that you must know for success on the NBCOT® exam. These questions are provided to help you "jump start" the thought processes you will need to apply your studying of content to the answering of exam questions; hence they are not in the NBCOT® exam format. Exam items in the NBCOT® format that cover the depth and breadth of content you will need to know to pass the NBCOT® exam are provided in the three online practice exams that accompany this text. The answers to the following questions are provided in Appendix 2.

1. An occupational therapist is preparing to evaluate a client. What contextual considerations should the therapist take into account when determining the assessments that will be appropriate to use with the client?

2. An occupational therapist owns and operates a preschool facility for children with developmental, intellectual, and physical disabilities. When should the therapist instruct the facility staff members to use standard precautions? What policies and procedures should the therapist implement for the use of standard precautions in this practice setting?

3. An occupational therapist is integrating health literacy into the home program for a client living with multiple sclerosis (MS). The client's MS has progressed to the point that they now need to use a wheelchair for all activities. The client has established a goal to learn how to perform wheelchair pushups and lateral leans to prevent decubiti. What learning principles should the therapist use to inform their intervention planning? What teaching methods are best for the therapist to use when implementing intervention?

4. An occupational therapist provides services in a community-based setting which offers individual and group interventions. What factors should the therapist consider when determining if it is best to use an individual intervention versus a group intervention with a client?

(Continued)

Review Questions

5. An occupational therapist working in a long-term care facility co-leads a discharge planning group with a social worker. What are the advantages to this co-leadership? What issues may arise to impede effective co-leadership that the therapist should be prepared to address?

6. An occupational therapist provides services to a group of parents of infants and toddlers. Each parent recently incurred a disability. The therapist plans to use a thematic and a topical group with the clients to address goals related to their parental role. What would be appropriate foci and relevant activities for these groups?

7. An occupational therapist is working with a client who is living with amyotrophic lateral sclerosis (ALS). The client is covered by Medicare and has attained their maximum level of function. The client and family are concerned that the client will be discharged from therapy and unable to maintain their current level of function and that their skill level will deteriorate. What information should the therapist provide to the client and family?

4

Competency and Practice Management

RITA P. FLEMING-CASTALDY AND MARLENE MORGAN

Professional Ethics

Code of Ethics Overview

1. Developed by the American Occupational Therapy Association (AOTA) as a statement to the public to identify the values and principles used to promote and maintain high standards for the behavior of occupational therapy (OT) practitioners.
2. A set of principles that apply to all levels of OT personnel.
3. Actions that are in violation of the purpose and spirit of the AOTA's Code of Ethics are considered unethical by the AOTA (AOTA, 2020a).
4. All OT practitioners are obligated to uphold these standards for themselves and their colleagues.
5. The *Occupational Therapy 2020 Code of Ethics* was written to address the ethical concerns that most typically arise in OT education, research, and practice.
6. This ethical code has two main purposes. These are to:
   a. Provide "aspirational Core Values that guide occupational therapy personnel toward ethical courses of action in professional and volunteer roles" (AOTA, 2020a, p. 1).
   b. Delineate "ethical Principles and enforceable Standards of Conduct that apply to AOTA members" (AOTA, 2020a, p. 1).

> **EXAM HINT:** The NBCOT® OTR® content outline identifies knowledge of the "application of ethical decision-making and professional behaviors guided by the NBCOT Practice Standards and Code of Conduct" (NBCOT®, 2022, p. 4) as essential for competent practice. Knowing how the AOTA Code of Ethics is used to guide OT practice can help you determine the correct answer for NBCOT® Domain 4 Competency and Practice Management exam items related to ethical practice.

Occupational Therapy Code of Ethics

1. "Principle 1. Beneficence. Occupational therapy personnel shall demonstrate a concern for the well-being and safety of persons" (AOTA, 2020a, p. 3).
2. "Principle 2. Nonmaleficence. Occupational therapy personnel shall refrain from actions that cause harm" (AOTA, 2020a, p. 3).
3. "Principle 3. Autonomy. Occupational therapy personnel shall respect the right of the person to self-determination, privacy, confidentiality, and consent" (AOTA, 2020a, p. 3).
4. "Principle 4. Justice. Occupational therapy personnel shall promote equity, inclusion, and objectivity in the provision of occupational therapy services" (AOTA, 2020a, p. 4).
5. "Principle 5. Veracity. Occupational therapy personnel shall provide comprehensive, accurate, and objective information when representing the profession" (AOTA, 2020a, p. 4).
6. "Principle 6. Fidelity. Occupational therapy personnel shall treat clients (persons, groups, or populations), colleagues, and other professionals with respect, fairness, discretion, and integrity" (AOTA, 2020a, p. 4).

Ethics in Practice

1. Ethics guide the behavior and decision-making of OT practitioners to help them determine the morally right course of action.
   a. Refer to Table 4-1 for examples as to how each ethical principle can be used to guide OT practice.
2. Occupational therapy practitioners are often faced with issues and events that challenge their personal values and beliefs and professional ethics.
3. NBCOT® exam items may include practice scenarios that reflect ethical distress or ethical dilemmas.
   a. Ethical distress.
      (1) When a practitioner knows the correct action to take but an existing barrier prevents the practitioner from taking this course of action.
         (a) For example, an admissions policy to a day treatment program excludes persons with substance abuse histories, yet this program would provide appropriate intervention for a client who is mentally ill and has a substance use disorder.
   b. Ethical dilemmas.
      (1) When there are two or more potentially morally correct ways to solve a problem. However, these solutions are exclusive; therefore, choosing one course of action prohibits acting on the other choices.
         (a) For example, a group of OT private practitioners can bid on a lucrative contract for the provision of services in a school system. However, none of the practitioners has pediatric experience. Their options may include

Chapter 4

Chapter 4

Table 4-1

Ethics in Practice Examples

Beneficence: An OT practitioner protects the rights of others, promotes good, prevents harm, demonstrates concern for people's safety and well-being and offers services that benefits service recipients by:
- providing evaluation and intervention services that best meets a service recipients' needs.
- ensuring they have the education and training to competently provide services within their scope of practice.
- engaging in professional development activities to ensure and maintain competency.
- conducting research in an ethical manner (e.g., obtaining informed consent and disclosing potential risks).
- defending and protecting the rights and safety of others and acting to remove people from dangerous situations.

Nonmaleficence: An OT practitioner avoids actions that can cause harm, injury, or wrongdoing to others by:
- not engaging in relationships or situations that can inflict harm or injury, are exploitive, and/or do not maintain clear professional boundaries and/or objectivity.
- ensuring that a service recipient is provided with needed services and that essential transitions are provided when services are being terminated for any reason.
- not following directives that violate practice, ethical, and legal standards (e.g., falsifying documentation to meet unrealistic productivity standards).
- not engaging in any activities that may impair their ability to be safe and competent.
- recognizing and taking needed action to remedy personal problems and situations that might cause harm to service recipients.

Autonomy: An OT practitioner recognizes and respects the opinions, values, self-agency, confidentiality, and privacy of service recipients and stakeholders by:
- establishing a collaborative relationship with and honoring the wishes of service recipients and stakeholders to enable shared decision making and self-determination.
- addressing communication barriers (e.g., cultural, language, and/or literacy differences and/or receptive, expressive, or global aphasia) to enable comprehension and participation.
- obtaining informed consent after disclosing essential information and answering questions to ensure voluntary participation in evaluation, intervention, and/or research.
- respecting the person's right to question and/or refuse services, even when the practitioner believes the refusal may result in a poor outcome.

Justice: An OT practitioner provides fair, respectful, inclusive, equitable, impartial, and needed services to all persons regardless of age, race, religion, origin, gender identity, sexual orientation, socioeconomic status, degree of ability, or any other attributes by:
- working to remove participation barriers and create and sustain an equitable society in which all are fully included and able to participate in meaningful occupations in their environments of choice.
- ensuring that documentation complies with applicable laws, regulations, and guidelines, and that billing is fair, reasonable, and accurate.
- not participating in any action that violates privacy, copyright, civil rights, disability rights, and scope of practice laws and regulations.
- reporting persons that are engaging in illegal and/or unethical actions to the authorities that have jurisdiction over the person and/or the area of concern.

Veracity: An OT practitioner ensures that all information they provide in their professional role is objective, comprehensive, and accurate and that recipients of this information is able to understand it by:
- recording and reporting practice or academic information in a timely and accurate manner that adheres to established documentation standards and applicable regulations.
- accurately representing their education, training, credentials, qualifications, experience, competencies, and contributions in all forms of communication.
- providing employees, supervisees, and students with timely, honest, and fair feedback on their performance in a respectful and fact-based manner.
- not conveying, using, or participating in any form of communication to service recipients, research participants, employers, payers, or public entities that contains unfair, misleading, false, or fraudulent information.
- giving credit and recognition to others when using their work and ideas in any format (i.e., oral, electronic, or written).

Fidelity: An OT practitioner demonstrates their commitment to treating others respectfully and fairly and with integrity and discretion by:
- addressing workplace conflicts in a proactive manner to ensure that positive professional relationships and competent service provision are maintained.
- taking action to address unethical, incompetent, exploitative, illegal, or impaired practice in others or self.
- recognizing and respecting the scope of practice and roles of interprofessional team members to promote a collaborative relationship, ensure safety and quality care, and fully address clients' needs.
- ensuring that all of their communications and actions are civil, courteous, inclusive, respectful, sensitive, and fair and not intimidating, hostile, biased, discriminatory, derogatory, or abusive.
- following organizational policies to address self-identified conflicts with service provision due to a personal, cultural, or religious values.
- not using a position of power to exert influence on others or engage in exploitive relationships or conflicts of interest.

Adapted from American Occupational Therapy Association. (2020). AOTA 2020 Occupational therapy Code of Ethics. American Journal of Occupational Therapy, 74(Suppl. 3, pp. 5–9). https://doi.org/10.5014/ajot.2020.74S3006

not bidding on the contract or bidding on the contract and if the contract is won, incurring the expense of hiring pediatric-trained practitioners.

4. Decisions about what are the right or wrong courses of action to take to resolve ethical distress or dilemmas are based on the profession's Code of Ethics.

Patient/Client Abuse and Neglect

1. Definition of abuse.
   a. Abuse is deliberately hurting a person physically, mentally, or emotionally.
   b. Neglect is deliberately withholding services that are necessary to maintain an individual's physical, mental, and emotional health.
   c. Definitions may vary from state to state.
2. Determination of abuse and/or neglect.
   a. Individuals' self-report of abuse and/or neglect must be documented and reported in accordance with setting and state-specific guidelines.
   b. Signs of patient/client abuse.
      (1) Box 4-1 outlines the psychosocial and physical signs of patient/client abuse.

BOX 4-1 ▷ Signs of Patient/Client Abuse

- **Psychosocial Signs**
  - The person:
    - is passive, withdrawn, and their behavior is emotionless.
    - complains of pain without obvious injury.
    - fears being alone with caretakers.
    - begs for food, water, or assistance (especially in regard to toileting).
    - is left unattended for long periods.
- **Physical Signs**
  - The person has:
    - frequent unexplained injuries.
    - burns or bruises suggesting the use of instruments, cigarettes, etc.
    - bedsores and skin lesions.
    - no reaction to pain.
    - unexplained difficulty in sitting or walking.
    - a sexually transmitted diseases or injury to the genital area.
    - obvious malnutrition.
    - poor personal cleanliness.
    - torn or dirty clothes.
    - obvious fatigue and listlessness.
    - an observable need for medical and/or dental care.

EXAM HINT: The occupational therapy Code of Ethics states "occupational therapy personnel shall demonstrate a concern for the well-being and safety of persons" (AOTA, 2020a, p. 3) and the NBCOT® OTR® exam content outline identifies the task of incorporating "risk management techniques at the individual and practice setting levels to protect clients . . . from injury or harm" (NBCOT®, 2022, p. 13). Therefore, it is likely that the NBCOT® exam will include items about the OT practitioner's role in identifying and responding to patient/client abuse. The application of knowledge about the signs of patient/client abuse and neglect described above and the following information about the role of OT practitioners in addressing patient/client abuse and neglect can help you determine the correct answer to items about patient/client abuse.

3. Role of OT practitioners.
   a. It is an ethical responsibility of all OT practitioners to report any observed or suspected incidents of patient/client abuse or neglect.
      (1) The party to whom reporting is required varies from state to state, as do the penalties for not reporting.
         (a) Minimum reporting standards require reporting to one's immediate supervisor.
   b. OT practitioners should also provide interventions to survivors of abuse and/or neglect. These can include:
      (1) Treatment for physical and emotional injuries.
      (2) Development of a trusting relationship.
      (3) Provision of support to family and loved ones.
      (4) Referral to appropriate disciplines and agencies.
      (5) Contributor to staff training programs to prevent abuse.
      (6) Refer to Chapter 14 for additional information about the role of the OT practitioner in screening for and responding to domestic abuse.

Ethical Decision-Making

EXAM HINT: The application of knowledge about the following guidelines for ethical decision-making can help you determine the correct answer for NBCOT® Domain 4 Competency and Practice Management exam items related to ethical practice.

1. The OT practitioner should use the following steps to guide their decision-making.
   a. Identify the ethical issues and potential dilemmas.
   b. Gather relevant information.
      (1) Identify all individuals affected by the issue.
      (2) Determine prior history of the issue.

(3) Analyze the dynamics and culture of the setting(s).

(4) Ask open-ended questions to obtain descriptive data.

c. Determine conflicting values and areas of agreement.

  (1) A commitment to a person's autonomy versus the principles of beneficence and nonmaleficence may need to be considered.

d. Identify as many relevant alternative courses of action as possible.

  (1) Consider who would take these actions and when these actions would need to occur.

e. Determine all possible positive and negative outcomes for each possible action.

  (1) Include outcomes for all participants in the dilemma. An ethical dilemma never involves just one person.

  (2) It can take time and thought to identify all those who may possibly have a 'stake' or will be touched by a specific decision.

f. Weigh, with care, the consequences of each outcome.

  (1) This step includes the process of reordering or rearranging parts of different decisions to arrive at a new alternative which may be the best possible course of action.

g. Seek input from others (i.e., supervisors).

  (1) Provide information in an anonymous fashion which enables the individual to give advice in a more objective manner and to provide recommendations that cannot be construed to be biased or prejudicial.

h. Apply best professional judgment to choose the action(s) to recommend.

i. Contact any and all agencies that have jurisdiction over a practitioner if there are questions about potential ethical violations that could cause harm or have the potential to cause harm to a person.

j. Determine desired and/or potential outcome of filing an ethical complaint.

Ethical Jurisdiction of Occupational Therapy

American Occupational Therapy Association (AOTA)

1. The profession's official membership organization that develops, publishes, and disseminates the field's ethical code.
2. The AOTA's Code of Ethics is a statement to the public that identifies the values and principles used to develop, endorse, and sustain high standards of behavior for OT practitioners.
3. These ethical standards are often the guide by which other bodies judge professional behaviors to determine if malpractice has occurred.
4. As a voluntary membership organization, the AOTA has no direct authority over practitioners (occupational therapists and OT assistants [OTAs]) who are not members, and no direct legal mechanism for preventing nonmembers who are incompetent, unethical, or unqualified from practicing.
5. Ethics Commission.
  a. The component of the AOTA that is responsible for the Code of Ethics and the Standards of Practice of the profession.

  b. The Ethics Commission is responsible for informing and educating members about current ethical issues, upholding the practice and education standards of the profession, monitoring the behavior of members, and reviewing allegations of conduct that violate the profession's standards of conduct (AOTA, 2020a).

    (1) Ethical complaints filed with the Ethics Commission initiate an extensive, confidential review process according to the AOTA's established enforcement procedures for the OT Code of Ethics (AOTA, 2021b).

      (a) The Ethics Commission enforces the profession's Standards of Conduct according to these enforcement procedures.

National Board for Certification in Occupational Therapy (NBCOT®)

1. The national credentialing agency that certifies qualified persons as occupational therapists, registered

(OTR®s) and certified occupational therapy assistants (COTA®s).

   a. Initial certification is obtained by successfully passing the NBCOT® exam for the entry-level OTR® or COTA®.

   b. NBCOT® also maintains the OTR® and COTA® certifications through a voluntary certification renewal program.

2. As a voluntary credentialing agency, NBCOT® has no direct authority over OT practitioners who are not certified by NBCOT®, and no direct legal mechanism for preventing uncertified practitioners who are incompetent, unethical, or unqualified from practicing.

3. NBCOT® has developed investigatory and disciplinary action procedures for NBCOT® certified practitioners whose practices raise concern due to incompetence, unethical behavior, and/or impairment.

State Regulatory Boards (SRBs)

1. Public bodies created by state legislatures to assure the health and safety of the citizens of that state.

   a. Their specific responsibility is to protect the public from potential harm that might be caused by incompetent or unqualified practitioners.

   b. All states, the District of Columbia, Puerto Rico, and Guam require OT practitioners to be licensed in their respective jurisdiction to practice as an occupational therapist or an OTA.

   c. Each jurisdiction has legal guidelines that specify the scope of practice of the profession, and the qualifications that must be met to practice in that state.

     (1) For state-specific licensure information refer to NBCOT Occupational Therapy Regulatory Body Contact List by State.

2. Ethical jurisdiction.

   a. SRBs usually provide a description of ethical behavior. In many instances, SRBs have adopted or modified the AOTA's Code of Ethics for this purpose.

   b. By the very nature of their limited jurisdiction (i.e., only over practitioners practicing in their state), SRBs can monitor a profession closely.

   c. SRBs have the authority by law to discipline members of a profession if the public is determined to be at risk due to malpractice.

   d. SRBs also intervene in situations in which the practitioner has been convicted of an illegal act that is directly connected with professional practice (i.e., fraud or misappropriation of funds through false billing practices).

   e. Since SRBs are primarily concerned with the protection of the public from harm, they will typically limit their review of complaints to those involving such a threat.

Disciplinary Actions for Ethical Violations and Professional Misconduct

1. When the AOTA, the NBCOT®, and/or an SRB determine that a person has violated their standards for ethical practice, different actions can be used as a disciplinary measure.

   a. The nature of disciplinary actions is based on an agency's internal investigations to determine the severity of an infraction. These are described in Box 4-2.

2. All disciplinary actions (except for reprimand) are made public by the respective agencies.

   a. Disciplinary actions that are made public by one agency (e.g., NBCOT®) can trigger an investigation into a practitioner's professional conduct by other practice jurisdictions (e.g., an SRB).

3. As independent entities, the AOTA, the NBCOT®, and SRBs have control over different jurisdictions and varying power with respect to the actions they can in response to complaints that a practitioner is incompetent, unethical, or unqualified.

   a. Refer to Table 4-2.

BOX 4-2 ◗ Types of Disciplinary Actions

- **Reprimand**: the private communication of the respective agency's disapproval of a practitioner's conduct.
- **Censure**: a public statement of the respective agency's disapproval of a practitioner's conduct.
- **Ineligibility**: the removal of eligibility for membership, certification, or licensure by the respective agency for an indefinite or specific time period.
- **Probation**: the requirement that a practitioner meet certain conditions (e.g., further education, extensive supervision, individual counseling, participation in a substance abuse rehabilitation program) to retain membership, certification, or licensure by the respective agency.
- **Suspension**: the loss of membership, certification, or licensure for a specific time period; suspended persons may be required to submit a new application to regain membership, certification, or licensure.
- **Revocation**: the permanent loss of membership, certification, or licensure.

Chapter 4

Table 4-2

ENTITY	JURISDICTION	LEGAL AUTHORITY
Comparison of Entities that Enforce Ethical OT Practice		
AOTA: a voluntary membership organization.	AOTA members; the AOTA has no direct authority over occupational therapists and OTAs who are not AOTA members. • The AOTA can notify the NBCOT® about ethical violations committed by AOTA members.	None
NBCOT®: the national credentialing agency for OT practitioners.	COTA®s and OTR®s and those eligible for NBCOT® certification; The NBCOT®: has no direct authority over OT practitioners who are not certified by the NBCOT®. • The NBCOT® can notify SRBs about ethical violations committed by NBCOT® certificants.	None
SRBs: public boards that enforce state OT practice acts and regulations.	All OT practitioners licensed by the specific SRB.	Yes

Common Law Related to Professional Misconduct and Malpractice

1. Common law evolves from legal decisions and can impact OT practitioners.
   a. Malpractice suits can be filed by individuals and/or their caregivers if the OT practitioner is viewed to be personally responsible for negligence or other acts that resulted in harm to a client.
      (1) Negligence.
         (a) Failure to do what other reasonable practitioners would have done under similar circumstances.
         (b) Doing what other reasonable practitioners would not have done under similar circumstances.
      (c) The end result was harm to the individual.
      (d) Every individual (occupational therapist, student occupational therapist, OTA or student OTA) is liable for their own negligence.
   b. Supervisors or superiors may also assume the liability of their workers if they provided faulty supervision or inappropriately delegated responsibilities.
   c. The institution usually assumes liability if an individual was harmed as a result of an environmental problem.
      (1) Falls resulting from slippery floors, poorly lit areas, lack of grab bars.
   d. The institution is also liable if an employee was incompetent or not properly licensed.
   e. Personal malpractice insurance is advisable for all levels of OT practitioners.

OT Practitioner Roles

General Information

1. OT practitioners include occupational therapists and OTAs.
   a. Due to the implementation of the voluntary NBCOT® certification renewal program, all occupational therapists may not be OTR®s and all OTAs may not be COTA®s.
2. OT aides have an important role but are not considered OT practitioners.
3. Over the course of their careers, OT practitioners can assume a variety of roles including entry- to advanced-level practitioner, peer and/or consumer educator, fieldwork educator, supervisor, administrator, consultant, fieldwork coordinator, faculty member, academic program director, researcher/scholar, and/or entrepreneur.
4. Role development and advancement depends on practitioner's experience, education, practice skills, and professional development activities (i.e., self-study, continuing education, advanced degrees).
   a. Refer to subsequent section in this Chapter about professional development.

OTA/COTA® Information

1. OTAs are graduates of Accreditation Council for Occupational Therapy Education (ACOTE) accredited educational programs, which are at an associate or baccalaureate degree level.
   a. COTA®s are certified by the NBCOT® and participate in the NBCOT® certification renewal program.
2. OTAs/COTA®s can contribute to the evaluation process by completing assessments with supervision from an occupational therapist.
3. OTA's/COTA®'s primary role is to implement treatment.
   a. OTAs/COTA®s can contribute to development and implementation of an intervention plan and the monitoring and documenting of the individual's response to intervention with the occupational therapist's supervision.
   b. OTAs/COTA®s can contribute to intervention review and discharge planning with the occupational therapist's supervision.
      (1) OTAs/COTA®s can provide pre-discharge client and caregiver education and training with the occupational therapist's supervision.
4. OTAs/COTA®s can expand their role by establishing service competency.
   a. Service competency is the ability to complete the specified task in a safe, effective, and reliable manner, (i.e., the OTA/COTA® and occupational therapist can perform the same or equivalent procedure and obtain the same results).
   b. OTAs/COTA®s who establish service competency cannot practice independently; they need to continue to work with the supervision of an occupational therapist.
5. Refer to Chapter 3 for more information about the role of OTAs/ COTA®s throughout the OT process.

> **EXAM HINT:** The application of knowledge about the standards for service competence can help you determine the correct answer for exam items about an OTA's/COTA®'s ability to perform a task that is beyond entry-level OTA/COTA® practice. If the exam item does not provide information establishing the OTA's/COTA®'s service competence, the correct answer to an NBCOT® exam item cannot have the OTA/COTA® performing the given task.

6. OTA/COTA®s can be activities directors in skilled nursing facilities (SNFs) and can supervise OT aides.

> **EXAM HINT:** The NBCOT® OTR® exam content outline identifies the task of providing "occupational therapy services in accordance with laws regulations, (and) state occupational therapy practice acts . . . to protect consumers and meet applicable reimbursement requirements related to the service delivery setting" (NBCOT®, 2022, p. 4) as essential for competent practice. Performance of this task requires knowledge of "licensing and credentialing (and) supervisory role under state practice acts" (NBCOT®, 2022, p. 4). The application of knowledge about the role of the OTA/COTA® as previously described and the role of OT aides described as follows can help you determine the correct answer to NBCOT® Domain 4 Competency and Practice Management exam items about an occupational therapist's role as a supervisor.

OT Aide Roles

1. Although OT aides are not considered OT practitioners, the use of OT aides has increased in response to changes in the health-care system (i.e., pressures to control costs have resulted in the delegation of nonskilled tasks to aides).
2. Occupational therapy aides can be trained by OTAs/COTA®s or occupational therapists to perform specific nonskilled tasks.
3. The occupational therapist and OTA/COTA® are responsible for the determination and delegation of the client and nonclient tasks an aide performs and the outcome of these activities.
   a. Nonskilled nonclient tasks aides may perform include routine maintenance and clerical activities (e.g., preparation of the clinic area for intervention, organizing supplies).
   b. Nonskilled client tasks (e.g., contact guarding a client during transfers) can only be delegated to an OT aide after the occupational therapist has determined that specific conditions have been met.
   c. Box 4-3 outlines the criteria that should be used to determine if a task can be performed by an aide.
4. Tasks performed by OT aides must be supervised by an OTA/COTA® or occupational therapist.
   a. This supervision must be documented.

> **EXAM HINT:** The delegation of a nonskilled client-related task to an OT aide that adheres to the conditions described in Box 4-3 will be the correct answer for an NBCOT® exam item. Conversely, an answer choice that includes delegating a skilled task to an OT aide would be an incorrect answer.

BOX 4-3 ▷ **Criteria to Determine if a Task Can be Performed by an Aide**

- The anticipated result of the delegated task is known.
- The performance of the delegated task is clearly established, predictable, and will not require the aide to make any interpretations, adaptations, and/or judgment calls.
- The client's situation and the practice environment are stable and will not require the aide to make any interpretations, adaptations, and/or judgment calls.
- The aide has been appropriately trained in the competent performance of the task and is able to demonstrate service competency in task performance.
- The aide has received specific instructions on task implementation relevant to the specific client with whom the aide will be performing the delegated task.
- The aide knows the precautions of the designated task and client signs and symptoms that could indicate the need to seek assistance from the OTA/COTA® or occupational therapist.

 # Supervisory Guidelines for OT Personnel

General Supervision Information

1. Supervision is the process in which two or more individuals collaborate to establish, maintain, promote, or enhance a level of performance and quality of service.
2. It is a mutually respectful joint effort between supervisor and supervisee.
3. It promotes professional growth and development and facilitates mentoring.
4. It ensures appropriate training, education, and use of resources for safe and effective service provision.
5. Supervision facilitates innovation, supports creativity, and provides encouragement, guidance, and support while working toward attainment of a shared goal.
6. Only OT practitioners can supervise OT practice; OT aides cannot supervise OT practice.
7. Occupational therapists can practice autonomously and do not require any supervision to provide OT services.
   a. Occupational therapists are responsible and accountable for all aspects of OT service delivery.
   b. To develop best practice competencies and foster professional growth, occupational therapists should use supervision and mentorship.
8. OTAs/COTA®s must be supervised by occupational therapists for all aspects of the OT service delivery process (AOTA, 2020b).

Methods of Supervision

1. Direct: face-to-face contact between supervisor and supervisee.
   a. Includes co-treatment, observation, instruction, modeling, discussion, and video teleconferencing.
2. Indirect: no face-to-face contact between supervisor and supervisee.
   a. Includes electronic, written, and telephone communications.

The Supervision Continuum

1. Supervision occurs along a continuum that includes close, routine, general, and minimum.
   a. Close: daily, direct contact at the site of work.
   b. Routine: direct contact at least every two weeks at the site of work, with interim supervision occurring by other methods such as telephone or written communication (e.g., email).
   c. General: at least monthly direct contact with supervision available as needed by other methods.
   d. Minimal: provided only on a needed basis and may be less than monthly.
2. Formal supervision can be supplemented by functional supervision, which is the provision of information and feedback to co-workers and the sharing of expertise.

3. The degree, amount, and pattern of supervision required can vary depending on the following factors.
   a. The practitioner's knowledge and skills (e.g., entry-level versus advanced).
   b. The type of work the practitioner will be performing (e.g., routine, predictable, and repetitive work versus complex, unpredictable, and constantly changing work).
   c. Complexities of client needs and caseload characteristics and demands (e.g., a caseload of clients recovering from hip replacement surgery versus a caseload of clients recovering from traumatic brain injuries).
   d. Practice setting type and facility procedures (e.g., a SNF versus a high school).
   e. State laws, licensure requirements, and other regulatory mandates (e.g., direct supervision must be provided once per month for an entry-level OTA/COTA®; notes written by an OTA/COTA® must co-signed by an occupational therapist).

> **EXAM HINT:** Know that the supervising occupational therapist is the one who determines the appropriate level of supervision, not the supervisee, administrator, or employer.

4. Ethically, the OT supervisor must ensure that the type, amount, and pattern of supervision match the supervisee's level of role performance.
5. OT aide supervision may be intermittent or continuous depending on the task being performed.
   a. Intermittent supervision is sufficient for tasks that are not related to direct service provision. It requires periodic discussion, demonstration, or contact between the supervisor and aide on at least a monthly basis.
   b. Continuous supervision is required for client-related tasks. A supervisory OTA/COTA® or occupational therapist must be within auditory and/or visual contact in the immediate area of the aide during the aide's task performance.

Specific OT Roles and Supervisory Guidelines

1. Occupational therapist.
   a. Functions to provide quality OT services (i.e., assessment, intervention, program planning and implementation, discharge planning, related documentation and communication).
   b. Can be direct, indirect, or consultative in nature, and can range from entry-level to advanced-level depending on experience, education, and practice skills.

   c. The occupational therapist has ultimate responsibility for service provision.
   d. Entry-level occupational therapists who do not have access to formal supervision are advised to seek mentoring to facilitate professional growth and develop best practice skills.
   e. Occupational therapists who are certified by the NBCOT® and participate in the NBCOT® certification renewal program use the designation of OTR®.
2. Occupational therapy assistant (OTA).
   a. Functions to provide quality OT services to assigned individuals with the supervision of, and in partnership with, an occupational therapist.
   b. Can range from entry level to advanced level depending on experience, education, and practice skills.
   c. Development from entry level to advanced level is dependent upon the development of service competency.
   d. OTAs who are certified by the NBCOT® and participate in the NBCOT® certification renewal program use the designation of COTA®.
3. Clinical fieldwork educator.
   a. Functions as the manager of Level I and/or II fieldwork in a practice setting, providing students with opportunities to practice and implement practitioner competence.
      (1) Entry-level occupational therapists/OTR®s and OTAs/COTA®s may supervise Level I fieldwork students.[1]
      (2) Occupational therapists/OTR®s with one year of practice-based experience may supervise Level II OT students.
      (3) OTAs/COTA®s with one year of practice experience may supervise OTA Level II fieldwork students.
      (4) Three years of experience are recommended for individuals supervising programs with multiple students and multiple supervisors.
4. Supervisor.
   a. Functions as the manager of the overall daily operation of OT services in defined practice area(s).
   b. Can be an occupational therapist or an OTA/COTA®.
   c. Experienced OTAs/COTA®s may supervise other OTAs/COTA®s administratively as long as service protocols and documentation are supervised by an occupational therapist.

---

[1] According to ACOTE standards, currently licensed and professionally credentialed personnel may supervise Level I fieldwork students. This standard includes occupational therapists and OTAs/COTA®s and non-OT personnel such as nurses, nurse practitioners, psychologists, vocational counselors, physician assistants, recreation therapists, teachers, speech therapists, social workers, and physical therapists.

Chapter 4

Chapter 4

5. Administrator.
   a. Functions to manage department, program, services, or agency providing OT services.
   b. Can be an occupational therapist with a graduate degree or continuing education relevant to management and experience appropriate to the size and scope of department and program(s), (i.e., a minimum of three to five years of experience).
6. Consultant.
   a. Functions to provide OT consultation to individuals, groups, or organizations.
   b. Can be an occupational therapist or an OTA/COTA® at the intermediate or advanced practice level.
   c. The occupational therapist and OTA/COTA® are responsible for obtaining the appropriate level of supervision to meet regulatory and professional standards.
7. Academic fieldwork coordinator.
   a. Functions to manage fieldwork within the OT academic setting.
   b. Can be an occupational therapist or an OTA/COTA® with a recommended three years of practice experience and experience in supervising fieldwork students.
   c. General supervision by the OT academic program director is recommended.
   d. Close to routine supervision is recommended for new faculty.
8. Academic faculty member.
   a. Functions to provide formal academic education to occupational therapist or OTA students.
   b. Can be an occupational therapist or an OTA/COTA® with an appropriate advanced professional degree and intermediate to advanced skills in teaching.
   c. General supervision is recommended by the OT academic program director.

   d. Close to routine supervision for new, adjunct, and part-time faculty by the OT program director.
9. Program director (academic setting).
   a. Functions to manage the occupational therapist or OTA education program with an appropriate advanced professional degree, experience as a faculty member, and experience or continuing education in academic management.
   b. General to minimal administrative supervision from a designated administrative officer (e.g., the Academic Dean).
10. Researcher/scholar.
   a. Functions to perform scholarly work of the profession, i.e., examining, developing, refining, and/or evaluating the profession's theoretical base, philosophical foundations, and body of knowledge.
   b. Can be an occupational therapist or an OTA/COTA® with additional self-study, continuing education, experience, and formal education related to research and scholarly activities.
   c. OTAs/COTA®s can contribute to research process.
   d. Additional academic qualifications are needed for OTAs/COTA®s to be principal investigators.
   e. Supervision needs range from close to minimal depending on skills of the researcher/scholar and the scope of the project.
11. Entrepreneur.
   a. Functions as a partially or fully self-employed individual who provides OT services.
   b. Can be an occupational therapist/OTR® or an OTA/COTA® who meets state regulatory requirements.
   c. OTAs/COTA®s who provide direct service have the responsibility to obtain appropriate supervision from an occupational therapist/OTR®.

Team Roles and Collaboration

Overview

1. A team is a group of equally important individuals with common interests collaborating to develop shared goals and build trusting relationships to achieve these shared goals.
2. Members of the team include the service recipient, their family, significant others, and/or caregivers; health-care professionals; and the payer's gatekeepers.
   a. Service recipients are typically called patients in medical model settings (e.g., hospitals), clients in community-based settings (e.g., outpatient clinics),

consumers in recovery-oriented programs (e.g., clubhouses), and residents in residential settings (e.g., group homes, SNFs).
3. Professional members on a team will vary according to practice setting.
4. The service recipient, family, significant other, and/or caregiver role on the team has become increasingly important. Collaboration with these individuals is even mandated by law (e.g., Omnibus Budget Reconciliation Act [OBRA], Individuals with Disabilities Education Act [IDEA]. Refer to this Chapter's section on legislation.

Team Collaboration

1. Factors that can influence the efficacy of team collaboration.
   a. Member skill and knowledge.
   b. Membership stability.
   c. Commitment to team goals.
   d. Effective communication.
   e. Membership composition.
   f. A shared philosophy.
   g. Facilitative leadership.
2. Recognize that all members of the team are equally important.
   a. No one's opinion or area of competence takes precedence over the other.
      (1) Facility chain of command guidelines will determine who is ultimately responsible for the team's decision.
3. Understand the principles of effective team collaboration and that correct exam answers will adhere to these principles.
4. Know the different types of teams and their respective limits and benefits for team efficacy.
5. Know all potential team members and their respective role responsibilities.
6. Recognize that OT practitioners are competent in many domains of concern, but our scope of practice does have its limits.
   a. Be prepared to recognize these limits.

Types of Teams

1. Multidisciplinary.
   a. Professionals from different disciplines conduct assessments and implement interventions independent from one another.
   b. Ongoing communication between team members should occur routinely via formal meetings and documentation to coordinate services, avoid duplication of services, and attain shared primary goals.
      (1) Informal communications should also occur on an as needed basis, (e.g., when there is a significant change in status, to ensure safety).
   c. If interdisciplinary communication is limited, a lack of understanding of different perspectives and difficulty attaining goals can occur.
   d. Resources and responsibilities are individually allocated between disciplines; therefore, competition among team members may develop if discipline-specific role responsibilities and boundaries are unclear.
   e. Multidisciplinary teams are most effective when the service recipient's needs are distinct and best met by discipline-specific interventions and when the roles and scope of practice of each discipline are well defined and recognized by all team members.
2. Interdisciplinary/interprofessional.
   a. Professionals from different disciplines collaborate to work together and coordinate care.
      (1) Members are directed toward a common goal and not bound by discipline-specific roles and functions.
   b. All members of an interdisciplinary team contribute to an interdisciplinary care plan via an interactive decision-making process that attains group consensus.
      (1) A formalized structure for sharing information and a culture that supports frequent informal communication enables a high level of interdisciplinary collaboration.
      (2) Because there is increased communication between members, there is a greater understanding of each profession's unique perspective.
   c. Evaluation and intervention can be conducted independently within the defined areas of each profession's expertise or jointly (e.g., the assessment of the motor skills of a person who incurred a stroke can be completed by an OT practitioner and a physical therapist, an intervention session to develop a student's ability to effectively use a communication board can be conducted by an OT practitioner and a speech language pathologist).
   d. Members tend to use group process skills effectively (e.g., during team treatment planning meetings to obtain consensus).

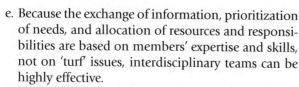

Chapter 4

e. Because the exchange of information, prioritization of needs, and allocation of resources and responsibilities are based on members' expertise and skills, not on 'turf' issues, interdisciplinary teams can be highly effective.

3. Transdisciplinary.
   a. Professionals from different disciplines work together with no discipline-specific boundaries beyond those regulated by state scope of practice laws.
      (1) The blurring of roles between disciplines is accepted with members providing services that are traditionally provided by disciplines other than their own.
      (2) All members retain responsibility to ensure that the services provided that relate to their area of expertise are high quality.
   b. Transdisciplinary teams are structured to facilitate collaborative evaluation and intervention planning with member sharing their discipline-specific expertise with each other via observation and consultation.
   c. One or two team members assume primary responsibility for implementing the evaluation and intervention plan and collaborating with the service recipient (and their caregivers, if needed) throughout service delivery.
      (1) In early intervention (EI) and schools, this team member (or members) will be the child's parents' and/or caregivers' primary contact.
   d. Members support and enhance service provision by sharing their knowledge and skills with each other to provide coordinated, integrated, and comprehensive services.
   e. Members are committed to ongoing communication, collaboration, and shared decision-making for service recipients' benefit.
   f. Ongoing training, support, supervision, cooperation, and consultation among disciplines are important to this model, ensuring that professional integrity and quality of care are maintained.

Lay Team Members and Role Responsibilities

1. Service recipient.
   a. The most important and primary member of the team.
   b. The service recipient's occupations, values, interests, and goals must be determined and used in all treatment planning.
      (1) If the service recipient and the OT practitioner do not share a common language, an interpreter must be used.
2. Family/primary caregiver.
   a. The family's/primary caregiver's sociocultural background, socioeconomic status, and caregiving

tasks, needs, and skills must be considered as they can impact on the outcome of intervention.
   (1) If the family/primary caregiver and the OT practitioner do not share a common language, an interpreter must be used.

Paraprofessional Team Members and Role Responsibilities

1. Personal care assistants/attendants (PCAs)/home health aides (HHAs).
   a. Individuals who provide primary care to enable a person with a disability or serious medical condition to remain in their own home.
   b. Most states require some minimum training and certification as a PCA/HHA. Standards and educational requirements can vary greatly from state to state.
   c. Responsibilities.
      (1) Personal care such as bathing, grooming, dressing, and feeding.
      (2) Home management such as shopping, cleaning, and cooking.
      (3) Supervision of home programs as directed by a health-care professional (e.g., therapist, nurse).
   d. Due to the tremendous importance this role has in maintaining a person with a disability or serious medical condition in their own home, OT practitioner collaboration with PCAs/HHAs is critical.
   e. OT practitioner can educate and train service recipients and/or their family members/caregivers on the hiring, training, and supervision of PCAs/HHAs.

Professional Team Members and Role Responsibilities

EXAM HINT: The NBCOT® OTR® exam content outline identifies knowledge of the "roles and responsibilities among interprofessional teams when coordinating client care and providing services" (NBCOT®, 2022, p. 6) as essential for competent practice. Some examples include "referral to and consultation with other services, interprofessional communication methods, (and) scope of practice" (NBCOT®, 2022, p. 6). The application of knowledge about the role responsibilities of the professional team members described in the following can help you determine the correct answer for NBCOT® exam items about interprofessional coordination and collaboration.

1. Alternative practitioners.
   a. May include massage therapists, acupuncturists, Reiki practitioners, and others.
   b. Training and licensure requirements vary greatly.

c. The roles and tasks of alternative practitioners will be determined by state practice regulations and payer's guidelines.

2. Athletic trainer.
   a. An allied health professional.
   b. Assesses athletes' risk for injury, conducts injury prevention programs, and provides treatment and rehabilitation under the supervision of a physician when athletic trauma occurs.

3. Assistive technology professional (ATP).
   a. Refer to Chapter 16.

4. Audiologist.
   a. A professional who is a graduate of an educational program in audiology.
   b. Administers assessments to determine an individual's auditory acuity, level of hearing impairment, and damage site(s) in the auditory system.
   c. Provides recommendations for assistive devices (e.g., hearing aids) and/or special training to enhance residual hearing and/or adapt to hearing loss.

5. Biomedical engineer.
   a. A graduate of an engineering program who specializes in the biomedical application of engineering theory and technology.
   b. Serves as a technical expert to recommend commercial products, adapt available devices, and/or modify existing environments.
   c. Develops, designs, and fabricates customized equipment, devices, and techniques.

6. Chiropractor.
   a. A professional who is a graduate of an educational program in chiropractic who is usually licensed by state boards.
   b. Assesses mechanical disorders of the musculoskeletal system and intervenes to restore and maintain health, decrease and eliminate pain, and prevent disability.

7. Dietician/clinical nutritionist.
   a. A licensed professional who is a graduate of an accredited educational program.
      (1) Practitioners who meet specific credentialing requirements can be credentialed as a registered dietician (RD), dietician technician, registered (DTR), or certified nutrition specialist (CNS®) depending on type and level of education.
   b. Evaluates individuals' nutritional status and dietary needs.
   c. Provides customized nutritional programs and counseling to prevent, manage, and treat diseases (e.g., diabetes) and conditions (e.g., obesity) for which proper diet and nutrition are important.

8. Driver rehabilitation specialist (DRS).
   a. Refer to Chapter 16.

9. Expressive/creative arts therapist.
   a. Professionals who are graduates of specialized education programs.

b. Depending on the state, they may or may not be licensed or registered.
   c. Includes art, dance/movement, music, horticulture, and poetry therapists.
   d. Conducts individual and/or group interventions that use select expressive modalities to facilitate self-expression, self-awareness, social skills, symptom reduction, and management.

10. Job coach.
    a. Provides on-site, one-on-one training to employees with disabilities to help them learn to perform their jobs accurately, efficiently, and safely, and acclimate to the work environment.
    b. Performs job analyses at work sites to match people with optimal positions.
    c. Conducts assessments, develops jobs, and provides counseling, travel and mobility training, and other services required to retain employment.
    d. The job coach's degree of involvement with the employee decreases over time as the employee masters the job with follow-up services provided as needed.

11. Nurse practitioner (NP).
    a. An advanced practice nurse who has completed post-professional graduate education to obtain a master's or a doctoral degree in nursing.
    b. NPs are nationally certified in specific areas of specialty (e.g., pediatrics, geriatrics, family practice, acute care).
    c. Depending on a state's scope of practice act, NPs can serve as primary care providers, prescribe medications, and complete referrals for OT and other rehabilitative services.
    d. Diagnoses, treats, and manages acute and chronic medical conditions.

12. Nurse, registered (RN).
    a. A licensed professional who is a graduate of an accredited nursing education program.
    b. Serves as the primary liaison between the individual and physician.
       (1) Often serves as the primary case manager.
    c. Monitors vital signs, symptoms, and behaviors.
    d. Dispenses medications and assists the physician with the titration of medications.
    e. Performs or supervises bedside care and assists with activities of daily living (ADL) in collaboration with the occupational therapist.
    f. Conducts group and individual interventions related to wellness and prevention and disease and symptom management (e.g., medication education).
    g. Performs patient/client, family, and caregiver education to facilitate recovery and maximize quality of life.
    h. Supervises and is assisted by licensed practical nurses (LPNs), certified nursing assistants (CNAs), and aides.

(1) Due to the major role LPNs, CNAs, and aides have in providing direct care to individuals. OT collaboration with these team members is essential.

13. Optometrist/vision specialist.
    a. A professional who is a graduate of an educational program in optometry.
    b. Examines the eye to determine visual acuity, level of visual impairments, and damage to or disease in the visual system.
    c. Prescribes assistive devices (e.g., corrective lenses) and prescribes other appropriate interventions (e.g., visual-motor training, the use of an eye patch for double vision).
    d. Optometrists can refer individuals to outpatient OT.

14. Orientation and mobility specialist.
    a. Refer to Chapter 15.

15. Orthotist.
    a. Evaluates the need for orthotic equipment (i.e., orthoses, braces).
    b. Designs, fabricates, and fits orthoses for individuals to enable performance of functional tasks, decrease pain, increase or restrict range of motion, prevent contractures, prevent or or correct deformities, protect bones, joints, and soft tissue and support body parts weakened by injury, disease, or congenital deformity.
    c. Educates the client on the purpose(s) of an orthotic, its recommended care, and wearing schedule.
    d. May be an occupational therapist, a physical therapist, or other individual with specialized training and certification.

16. Pastoral care.
    a. Serves as the spiritual advisor to the individual, their family, caregivers, and the team.
    b. Provides individual, couple, and family counseling in a nondenominational manner.

17. Physiatrist.
    a. A physician who specializes in physical medicine and rehabilitation and is certified by the American Board of Physical Medicine and Rehabilitation.
    b. Leads the rehabilitation team and works directly with occupational, speech, and physical therapy practitioners and others to maximize rehabilitation outcomes for persons with physical disorders.
    c. Diagnoses and medically treats individuals with musculoskeletal, neurological, cardiovascular, pulmonary, and/or other body systems disorders.

18. Physical therapist.
    a. A licensed professional who is a graduate of an accredited physical therapy (PT) education program at a baccalaureate, graduate, or doctoral level.
    b. Evaluates clients' physical motor skills and functional skills related to movement.
    c. Develops plan of care, and administers or supervises treatment to develop, improve and/or maintain client's physical motor skills, alleviate pain,

improve a person's respiratory function, correct or minimize physical deformity, and prevent disability.
    d. Supervises physical therapist assistants in the implementation of portions of the treatment program.
    e. Supervises and directs supportive staff (i.e., PCAs, HHA, CNAs, aides) in designated tasks.
    f. Reevaluates and adjusts plan of care as appropriate.
    g. Performs and documents final evaluation and establishes discharge and follow-up plans.

19. Physical therapist assistant (PTA).
    a. A skilled allied health-care technologist, usually with a two-year associate's degree.
       (1) To be licensed as a PTA, most states require a passing grade on a state-administered national exam.
    b. Must work with the supervision of a physical therapist.
       (1) If the supervisor is off-site, delegated responsibilities must be safe and legal practice with ready access to the supervisor.
       (2) In home health, required periodic joint on-site visits or treatments with physical therapist.
    c. Able to adjust treatment procedures in accordance with the client's status.
    d. May not evaluate, develop, or change plan of care, or write discharge plan or summary.

20. Physician's assistant.
    a. A professional who is a graduate of an accredited physician's assistant educational program and who has passed a national certification exam.
    b. Performs routine diagnostic, therapeutic, preventative, and health maintenance services.
    c. Specializations can include family medicine, geriatrics, pediatrics, obstetrics, orthopedics, psychiatry, and emergency care.
    d. Must work under the direction of and be supervised by a physician.

21. Primary care physician (PCP).
    a. Provides primary health-care services and manages routine medical care.
       (1) The PCP is the professional who most often first diagnoses a person's illness or condition.
    b. PCPs can be a doctor of medicine (MD) or a doctor of osteopathic medicine (DO).
       (1) DOs undergo a similar education as MDs with the addition of specific training in osteopathic medicine techniques.
    c. Makes referrals, as needed, to other health-care providers and services including specialty tests and exams, and rehabilitation services including OT.
    d. In managed health-care systems, the PCP serves as the 'gatekeeper' for service recipients.

22. Prosthetist.
    a. Evaluates the need for a prosthesis.

b. Designs, fabricates, and fits the prosthesis for an individual to ensure proper fit and to promote functional abilities.

c. Educates the client and/or caregiver(s) about the use and care of the prosthesis.

d. Works directly with OT practitioners, physical therapists, and physicians.

23. Psychiatrist.

a. A physician who specializes in mental health and psychiatric rehabilitation.

b. Leads the rehabilitation team and works directly with OT practitioners, psychologists, social workers, and others to maximize rehabilitation outcomes for persons with psychiatric disorders.

c. Diagnoses and medically treats individuals with psychiatric disorders.

d. Responsible for ordering transfers to long-term care settings and for determining competence and the need for involuntary treatment.

24. Psychologist.

a. A professional with a PhD in psychology.

b. Evaluates the psychological, emotional, cognitive, and behavioral status of a person.

c. Provides individual, couple, family, and group supportive therapy and cognitive retraining,

d. In EI programs and schools, psychologists can assist with the development, implementation, and evaluation of individualized education programs (IEPs), including positive behavior support plans.

25. Recreational therapist/therapeutic recreation specialist.

a. A professional who is a graduate of a baccalaureate or graduate-level recreation therapy education program.

b. Conducts individual and/or group interventions to develop leisure interests and skills; to facilitate community, social, and recreational integration; to manage stress and symptoms; and to adjust to disability.

c. May be called an activities therapist, but the two positions are not synonymous. Activities therapists may only have on-the-job training.

26. Respiratory therapy technician, certified.

a. A technically trained professional with an associate degree who has passed a national certification exam.

b. Administers respiratory therapy as prescribed and supervised by a physician.

c. Performs pulmonary function tests and intervenes through oxygen delivery, aerosols, and nebulizers.

27. Social worker.

a. A licensed/registered professional who is a graduate of an accredited educational social work program at a baccalaureate level (BSW) or at a Master's level (MSW).

b. Upon passing a national certification exam, a social worker is eligible to use the credentials certified social worker (CSW).

(1) In states with licensure requirements, a social worker may have the credential of licensed clinical social worker (LCSW).

c. Assesses client's social history and psychosocial functioning via clinical interviews and structured assessments.

d. Assists clients, families, and caregivers with accessing social support services (e.g., home care, support groups) and obtaining needed reimbursement for services (e.g., Medicare) and funding to meet essential needs (e.g., food stamps) through the completion of the required application processes and active advocacy.

e. Provides individual, couple, and family counseling.

f. Serves as a primary care manager, enabling individuals to function optimally and maintain quality of life.

g. Provides crisis intervention and recommendations for additional services.

h. Contributes to the discharge plan and completes tasks needed for implementation of discharge orders (e.g., application to a SNF).

i. Supervises and is assisted by social work assistants.

28. Special education teacher.

a. A professional teacher certified to provide education to children with special needs including visual and/or hearing impairments, emotional and psychosocial disabilities, physical and sensorimotor disabilities, developmental disabilities, and learning and cognitive disabilities.

b. Assesses and monitors student learning, plans and implements instructional activities, and addresses the special developmental and educational needs of each student.

c. Collaborates with other members of the education team. including OT practitioners, to develop and implement IEPs.

d. Advanced training in instructional methods for teaching children with special needs to develop to their fullest educational potential is required.

(1) Additional training in teaching children with multiple disabilities is often needed.

e. May be assisted by teacher aides who provide direct care and 'hands-on' support to students in the classroom.

(1) Collaboration with aides is required for effective follow-through of OT programming in school settings.

29. Speech-language pathologist (SLP) or speech therapist (ST).

a. A professional who is a graduate of an accredited educational program in speech-language pathology.

b. Assesses language, speech, and communication abilities and impairments.

c. Develops and conducts intervention programs to restore, improve, or augment the communication of persons with speech and/or language impairments.

d. Addresses cognitive deficits as they relate to communication.

e. Determines the need for augmentative communication devices and assistive technology (AT), selects appropriate devices and AT, and trains the person in their use in collaboration with OT practitioners and ATPs.

f. May receive advanced training and specialize in oral-motor functioning (e.g., the evaluation and treatment of dysphagia).

30. Substance abuse counselor.

a. A professional who may come from a diversity of educational backgrounds (psychology, social work, OT) who has completed a specialized training program.

b. Provides individual and/or group intervention.

c. Certified Alcohol Counselor (CAC) and Certified Alcohol and Drug Counselor (CADC) are the two main credentials designating this specialized role.

31. Vision rehabilitation therapist.

a. Refer to Chapter 16.

32. Vocational rehabilitation counselor.

a. A professional who is a graduate of an educational program in vocational rehabilitation.

b. If certified, the counselor can use the credential of Certified Rehabilitation Counselor (CRC).

c. Evaluates prevocational skills and vocational interests and abilities via standardized and non-standardized assessments to determine an individual's employability.

d. Provides counseling to maximize the individual's vocational potential.

e. Refers individual to appropriate vocational programming and/or job placement.

f. Serves as liaison between the individual and state educational and vocational departments for persons with disabilities to obtain funding for needed services.

The US Health-Care System

Overview

1. Health care in the United States is decentralized and overwhelmingly insured and delivered by privately owned companies.

2. Relatively small federal and state governmental programs work in conjunction with a large private sector; however, the government pays for a large portion of these private-sector services through Medicare and Medicaid reimbursement.

3. The Patient Protection and Affordable Care Act (ACA) expanded access to private health insurance for previously uninsured Americans and expanded Medicaid coverage to persons with low incomes.

4. Decentralization of health care in the United States results in overlap in some areas and competition in others; therefore, health care is primarily a business that is market driven.

a. Patients and clients are viewed as consumers due to this economic focus.

b. Cost containment while maintaining quality of service is a delicate balancing act that is not always achieved.

5. Primary care physicians serve as the first line for evaluation and intervention and the referral source for specialized and/or ancillary services.

Health-Care Regulations

1. Health care is a highly regulated industry with most established practices mandated by federal and state laws.

> **EXAM HINT:** Due to the great variance in state laws and regulations, the NBCOT® exam will likely only contain exam items that require knowledge of federal laws and regulations. Subsequent sections in this Chapter provide essential information about key legislation.

2. The Center for Medicare and Medicaid Services (CMS) is the federal agency that develops rules and regulations pertaining to federal laws governing the Medicare and Medicaid programs.

a. Facilities that participate in Medicare and/or Medicaid programs are monitored regularly for compliance with CMS guidelines by federal and state surveyors.

b. Facilities that repeatedly fail to meet CMS guidelines lose their Medicare and/or Medicaid certification(s).

c. Long-term settings (e.g., SNFs) are strongly influenced by CMS regulations since Medicare and/or Medicaid pays for all or most of the expense of long-term care.

3. Standards related to safety are set forth and enforced by the Occupational Safety and Health Administration (OSHA), a division of the US Department of Labor.
   a. Structural standards and building codes are established and enforced by OSHA to ensure the safety of structures.
   b. The safety of employees and consumers is regulated by OSHA standards for handling infectious materials and blood products, controlling blood-borne pathogens, operating machinery, and handling hazardous substances.
4. State accreditation to obtain licensure for a health-care facility is mandatory. Individual states develop their own requirements, with state agencies enforcing these regulations.
5. Local city or county entities also develop regulations pertaining to health-care institutions (e.g., physical plant safety features such as fire, elevator, and boiler regulations).

Voluntary Accreditation

1. Voluntary accreditation is sought by most health-care organizations, e.g., hospitals, SNFs, home health agencies, accountable care organizations (ACOs), preferred provider organizations (PPOs), rehabilitation centers, health maintenance organizations (HMOs), behavioral health (including mental health and chemical dependency) facilities, physicians' networks, hospice care, long-term care facilities, and others.
2. Accreditation is a status awarded for compliance with established standards; therefore, most health-care organizations have self-imposed compliance policies and procedures to attain and maintain accreditation.
3. Accreditation ensures the public that a health-care facility is adequately equipped, meets high standards for care, and employs qualified professionals and competent staff.
4. Accreditation affirms the competence of practitioners and the quality of health-care facilities and organizations.
5. Accreditation through an accrediting agency is voluntary; however, it is mandatory to receive third-party reimbursement and to be eligible for federal government grants and contracts.
6. CMS and many states accept certain national accreditations as meeting their respective requirements for participation in the Medicare and Medicaid programs and for a license to operate.
7. Voluntary accrediting agencies include the Joint Commission (JCAHO), Healthcare Facilities Accreditation Program (HFAP), Commission on Accreditation of Rehabilitation Facilities (CARF), the Council on Quality and Leadership (CQL), and others.

EXAM HINT: The NBCOT® OTR® exam content outline identifies the task of providing "occupational therapy services in accordance with . . . accreditation guidelines to protect consumers and meet applicable reimbursement requirements related to the service delivery setting" (NBCOT®, 2022, p. 4) and knowledge of "accreditation guidelines related to service delivery across occupational therapy practice settings (including) . . . accreditation organizations" (NBCOT®, 2022, p. 4) as essential for competent and safe practice. The application of knowledge about the accreditation information provided in this section and the following may help you determine the correct answer for NBCOT® Domain 4 Competency and Practice Management exam items about the OT practitioner's role in the accreditation process.

The Accreditation Process

1. Accreditation is initiated when the organization applies for review or survey by the accrediting agency.
2. A self-study or self-assessment is conducted to examine the organization based on the accrediting agency's standards.
3. An on-site review is conducted by an individual reviewer or surveyor or a team visiting the organization.
4. The accreditation and the reaccreditation processes involve all staff. Tasks include document preparation, hosting the site visit team, and interviews with accreditors.
5. Once accredited, the organization undergoes periodic review, typically every three years.

Value of Accreditation to Occupational Therapy

1. Self-study and self-assessment can be an opportunity to identify areas of strength, validate competence, and promote excellence.
2. Areas needing improvement can be identified (e.g., procedures can be streamlined, additional resources can be obtained, team communication can be enhanced).
3. Program goals are clarified.
4. Practice is defined and documented.
5. Accreditors can share information regarding best practices.
6. An increased recognition of OT's contributions to the agency and identification of occupational outcomes can result in increased visibility for OT and increased referrals.

Payment for Occupational Therapy Services²

Payment Models and Approaches

1. Box 4-4 describes the major payment models and approaches that are used in the US healthcare system.

> **EXAM HINT:** An increased emphasis on coordinated, high quality care rather than volume of care has resulted in a shift towards value-based payment models and away from volume-driven fee-for-service (FFS) healthcare. Therefore, NBCOT® exam items about payment for OT services will likely reflect this trend. However, it is important to recognize that even though the current healthcare system is moving away from the FFS model, it is still being used in some insurance plans (e.g., Medicare Part B). As a result, some exam items about OT services being reimbursed according to the FFS model may still be on the NBCOT® exam.

Key Payment Terms

1. Beneficiary: a person receiving services.
2. Coinsurance: the percentage of a total charge for a service that must be paid by a service recipient out of pocket; this is typically paid via a post-service bill.
3. Copayment: a fixed monetary amount to be directly paid by a service recipient to the service provider; typically requested at the time of service delivery.
4. Deductible: the amount a service recipient must pay to a provider before the insurance benefits will pay; usually expressed as an annual dollar amount.
5. Denial: the refusal by a payer to reimburse a provider for services rendered.
   a. Possible reasons for denial include benefits exhausted, duplication of services, all required documentation is not submitted, illegible documentation, vague justification of medical necessity and/ or the services not indicated.
6. Diagnosis code: a code that describes a service recipient's disease or medical condition that requires health service and is used for billing as part of the International Classification of Diseases (ICD).
   a. Physicians provide the medical diagnosis and therapists provide the treatment diagnosis based on functional limitations (AOTA, 2023).

---

² Kari Inda PhD, OTR, CEAS and Helene Lohman OTD contributed to this section on payment for OT services.

> **EXAM HINT:** Because the ICD is regularly updated, the NBCOT® exam will likely not include specific codes.

7. Diagnosis related groups (DRGs): the descriptive categories established by CMS to reimburse hospitals for inpatient stays based on the patient's diagnosis and the care provided.
   a. Hospitals are paid a fixed a per case rate for each patient based on the DRG assigned to the patient.
8. Out of pocket maximum: the most money a service recipient must pay during a specific time period (usually annually) before the insurance company pays 100 percent of the cost of provided services.
9. Premium: the amount of money that an insurance company charges a service recipient to obtain and maintain their insurance coverage.
10. Procedure codes: codes that describe specific services performed by health professionals. Refer to subsequent section on documentation.
11. Provider: the entity responsible for the delivery and quality of services. Providers bill the insurer and/or the service recipient for services rendered.
12. Third-party payers: agencies and companies who are the primary payers for health care in the United States (e.g., Blue Cross, Aetna). Health maintenance organizations (HMOs) and preferred provider organizations (PPOs) are also third-party payers.
13. Usual and customary rate (UCR): the average cost of specific health-care procedures in a geographic area. This is the maximum amount the insurer will pay for a service and covered expense.
14. Vendor/supplier: the entity that supplies services.
15. Refer to Box 4-4 for additional terms that are used for the major US healthcare system payment models and approaches.

Private Commercial Insurance

1. Largest source of insurance payment in the United States.
   a. These plans can be managed by for-profit or not-for-profit companies, organizations, and/or networks.
   b. There are broad variations among plans and plan options. Box 4-4 describes the different payment models and approaches that are used by private commercial insurers.
   c. In 2010, the ACA established the health insurance marketplace to allow consumers to compare the cost of insurance plans in their area.
      (1) Also known as health-care exchanges.

BOX 4-4 ▷ Payment Models and Approaches

- **Alternative Payment Models (APMs)**: a payment approach that gives added incentive payments to the providers of cost-efficient and high-quality care.
  - APMs can apply to a population, specific clinical condition, or a single care episode.
  - Types of APM include:
    - Episode payment model: includes all health care provider costs associated with a single episode of care for a person; rather than paying for each individual test, procedure, or treatment, costs are 'bundled' into one sum total.
      - Also known as bundled payments.
    - Value-based payment model: payments for care delivery are based on the value of care provided; providers are rewarded for quality, efficiency, and cost-effectiveness.
- **Capitation**: a payment system under which the provider prospectively (e.g., monthly) pays a set fee for each member of a specific population (e.g., health plan members)
  - Payment does not change even if no covered health care is delivered or if extensive care is delivered.
  - Payment is typically determined on a per member per month (PMPM) rate.
  - The provider retains more of the total PMPM payment with healthier enrollees and fewer services used.
- **Fee for Service Payment Models**: the payment system under which the provider is paid the same type of rate per unit of service.
  - Traditionally, the payer pays 80% and the service recipient or provider is responsible for the remaining 20%.
- **Health Maintenance Organization (HMO)**: the managed care payment approach that limits coverage to care from providers who work for or contract with the HMO. Referrals are required before seeking specialty or ancillary care and out-of-network care is typically not covered, except in an emergency.
  - OT practitioners can join HMOs.
- **Health Savings Account (HSA)**: a federal program that allows a person to contribute to a savings account on a pre-tax basis and use these funds to pay for qualified medical expenses (e.g., deductibles, copayments). Only persons with a high deductible health plan are eligible to set up an HSA.
- **High Deductible Health Plan (HDHP)**: a traditional insurance plan for which the purchaser pays a lower monthly premium, but more out-of-pocket expenses due to a higher deductible. Persons with HDHPs are eligible to open and use HSAs.
- **Managed Care Organization**: a system that is used by insurers to control the use of health care services by negotiating reduced fees from providers and requiring pre-approval for hospitalizations and specialized services.
- **Out-of-Pocket Payment**: the payment a service recipient directly pays to a service provider when services are rendered.
- **Patient-Driven Payment Model (PDPM)**: the Medicare payment system for skilled nursing facilities that uses a case-mix classification based on a service recipient's clinically relevant characteristics. Refer to subsequent section on Medicare.
- **Patient-Driven Grouping Model (PDGM)**: the Medicare payment system for home health that uses a case-mix classification based on a service recipient's clinically relevant characteristics. Refer to subsequent section on Medicare.
- **Per-Diem**: a negotiated, per hour/per day fee for service that is paid to an individual provider.
  - Typically used to pay for additional care in inpatient hospitals and SNFs.
- **Preferred Provider Organization (PPO)**: a managed care system that is similar to HMOs, but usually a greater choice of providers is offered. However, as choices increase, the percentage of payment decreases.
  - OT practitioners can join PPOs.
- **Private Payment**: the individual receiving services is responsible for payment.
- **Prospective Payment System (PPS)**: a payment approach in which the price of a service is predetermined and fixed based on a classification system (e.g., per diagnostic codes, per procedure, per diem).
- **Quality Payment Program (QPP)**: a payment system that encourages providers to provide quality care by awarding bonuses for meeting quality measures and charging penalties for failure to meet these in future provider payments.
- **Retrospective payment**: a payment approach that pays the provider after the delivery of services.

2. Many private insurers contract with Medicare to serve as fiscal intermediaries to handle the day-to-day operations of Medicare. Refer to subsequent Medicare section.
3. Private insurers offer many insurance products including PPOs and HMOs.
4. Coverage cannot be assumed based on the name of plan alone.
   a. Coinsurance, deductibles, and co-payments are common.
   b. Most plans cover OT in hospitals.
   c. Outpatient OT coverage varies greatly.

d. Total number of visits and/or type and amount of services per diagnosis are limited.

5. Under the ACA, federal regulations were established for essential benefits that private commercial insurers must provide to their customers.

 a. Key requirements are outlined in Box 4-5.

6. States can set their own requirements and regulations for insurers who operate within their borders.

> **EXAM HINT:** Because the NBCOT® exam is a national exam, it will likely not ask specific questions about private commercial insurers or state-specific reimbursement regulations; however, the application of knowledge about the industry trends described in this Chapter, the different payment models and approaches outlined in Box 4-4, and the ACA mandated benefits outlined in Box 4-5 can help you determine the correct answer for NBCOT® Domain 4 Competency and Practice Management exam items.

BOX 4-5 ▷ ACA Mandates for Private Insurance Coverage

- Under the ACA, commercial insurers must provide the following.
  - Emergency, inpatient, and outpatient services, including maternity and newborn care.
  - Rehabilitative and habilitative services.
    - Rehabilitative and habilitative services are those that help people acquire, maintain, or improve the skills necessary for daily functioning.
  - Mental health, substance abuse, and behavioral health treatment and care.
  - Preventative and wellness services.
  - Chronic disease management.
  - Continued coverage of young adults until their 26th birthday under their parents' plans, *if* these plans cover dependents.
- Under the ACA, commercial insurers *cannot* do the following.
  - Refuse coverage to persons with pre-existing conditions.
  - Raise insurance premiums based on a person's occupation, gender, preexisting condition, health status, or claim history.
  - Set caps on annual and lifetime coverage.

Workers' Compensation

1. Designed to compensate employees who have job-related illness or injuries.

2. Funded jointly by individual employers or groups of employers and state governments.

3. Each state has a workers' compensation commission board that determines regulations for employer participation, benefit provision, employee coverage, and insurance administration.

4. Administration can be through contract with private insurance companies or through individual employers or groups of employers who administer their own programs. This is known as self-insuring.

5. Coverage varies from state to state, with many states initiating cost-containment measures including limits on choice of providers, use of set fee schedules, utilization review, and managed care.

6. Workers' compensation programs include cash benefits and medical benefits. OT services may be included.

7. Rehabilitation and disability management to return the person to gainful employment is a primary focus.

Personal Payment, 'Pro Bono', Philanthropic Care, and Grants

1. Individuals whose health insurance has discontinued coverage of OT services may elect to pay for these services personally, providing that benefit can be derived from continued services.

2. Individuals without health insurance or with no coverage for rehabilitative services may also choose to personally pay for OT services.

3. The services of OT practitioners practicing in non-medical settings (e.g., wellness and prevention programs) are generally not covered by insurers, so their clients must personally pay.

4. 'Pro Bono' or free or reduced-rate care may be supported by the individual practitioner's personal donation of services or through philanthropic donations.

5. Grants and/or philanthropic donations can be used to support programs not typically covered by insurance (e.g., an adaptive yoga program for persons with disabilities, a lifestyle redesign program for persons aging in place).

Medicare and Medicaid[3]

Chapter 4

EXAM HINT: The NBCOT® OTR® exam content outline identifies the task of providing "occupational therapy services in accordance with laws (and) regulations . . . (to) meet applicable reimbursement requirements related to the service delivery setting" (NBCOT®, 2022, p. 14) as essential for effective practice and states that performance of this task requires knowledge of the "influence of reimbursement policies and guidelines on occupational therapy service delivery" (NBCOT®, 2022, p. 14). Since Medicare is a federal program and the major national payer for OT services, specifics about Medicare will likely be tested on the NBCOT® exam. Therefore, the application of knowledge about the following Medicare information will be required to determine the correct answer to NBCOT® exam questions about reimbursement.

Medicare General Coverage Information

1. Largest single payer for OT services.
2. Administered by CMS through the use of Medicare Administrative Contractors (MACs).
   a. MACs are private health insurers within a specific multistate or regional geographic area that contract with Medicare to process claims and payments for Medicare Parts A and B.
      (1) MACs perform other duties such as education and responding to inquiries.
3. Persons eligible for Medicare medical coverage for health-care services include the following.
   a. Persons 65 years or older.
   b. Individuals of all ages with end-stage renal disease/permanent kidney failure that may require dialysis treatment or a kidney transplant.
   c. Persons with a long-term disability (e.g., amyotrophic lateral sclerosis [ALS], multiple sclerosis [MS]) who have received government-funded disability benefits for 24 months may be eligible.
   d. Retired railroad workers.
4. Medicare beneficiaries can have physical and/or psychiatric diagnoses. There are no diagnostic restrictions for coverage.
5. Medicare Part A coverage: Refer to Box 4-6.
6. Medicare Part B coverage: Refer to Box 4-7.

---

[3] Kari Inda PhD, OTR, CEAS and Helene Lohman OTD contributed to the section on Medicare.

BOX 4-6 ▷ Medicare Part A

- Medicare Part A pays for inpatient services in a hospital, SNF, or rehabilitation facility and for home health and hospice services.
  - Part A is automatically provided to all who are covered by the Social Security System that meet Medicare coverage criteria.
  - Inpatient Part A coverage requires services for a minimum of five days per week.
  - Services provided in acute care hospitals receive a prospective, predetermined rate based on DRGs.
    - The DRG per case rate covers all services including OT.
    - It is a fixed dollar amount for patient care for each diagnosis regardless of length of stay (LOS) or number of services provided.
  - Treatment supplies (i.e., adaptive equipment, splints) are included in this per case rate.
  - Individual hospitals determine the combination of services a patient will receive.
- Part A covered services have specific time limits and also require deductible and coinsurance payments by the beneficiary.
  - Annual deductible fees must be paid by the patient.
  - Twenty percent of home health care must be paid for by the patient.

Refer to https://www.cms.gov/medicare/eligibility-and-enrollment/origmedicarepartabeligenrol

---

BOX 4-7 ▷ Medicare Part B

- Medicare Part B pays for outpatient Part B services for medical appointments, home health, and care from other health providers including OT services provided by independent practitioners when provided under a certified therapy plan of care.
  - Outpatient services can be provided in outpatient hospital departments, physician's offices, outpatient rehabilitation facilities, comprehensive outpatient rehabilitation facilities (CORF), private practice, and home health agencies.
  - Part B is considered a Supplemental Medical Insurance Program and therefore must be purchased by the beneficiary, usually as a monthly premium.
  - Part B typically covers three days per week of outpatient services.
  - Part B services have no specific time limit and require 20% co-payment.

Refer to https://www.cms.gov/medicare/eligibility-and-enrollment/origmedicarepartabeligenrol

7. Medicare Parts A and B do not cover long-term supportive care or all medical expenses incurred when ill.
8. Medicare Part C: private insurance plans which combine Medicare Part A and Part B; typically called Medicare Advantage.
   a. Many plans offer more benefits than traditional Medicare plans (e.g., prescription drug coverage, vision care).
      (1) Therapy benefits may vary based on the plan.
   b. Most Part C plans are run under a form of managed care (i.e., HMOs, PPOs).

Criteria for Medicare Coverage of OT Services

1. Need-based services must be provided under an established written physician or nonphysician provider (NPP) plan of care (POC) and payment is contingent on certification or dated signature of this plan.
   a. Nonphysician providers are defined by state practice acts; they can be a nurse practitioner, a clinical nurse specialist, or a physician assistant.
2. Payment is contingent on the certified POC from the physician or NPP.
   a. A physician's referral (order) for OT services is not required by Medicare.
      (1) However, a documented physician's order provides evidence that a physician is involved in overseeing a person's care and is available to certify a POC (CMS, 2023a, p. 12).
3. The POC must be established before intervention begins and require the skills of a licensed occupational therapist (not an OTA) to establish the intervention program and long-term goals that address the "type, amount, duration and frequency of therapy services" (CMS, 2023a, p. 12).
4. Services must be reasonable, and necessary according to evidence-based standards for treatment of the individual's injury, illness, or condition.
5. Services must be at a skilled level of complexity that requires the expertise of a licensed occupational therapist, or an OTA/COTA® with the supervision of an occupational therapist, to provide safe, appropriate, and effective intervention.
   a. Skilled services can be provided to improve a person's condition, prevent complications, slow deterioration, maintain current status, and/or maximize function.
6. Re-evaluations are not routine and are completed only if there is a noteworthy change in the person's condition, a new clinical finding, or if the person is not meeting the established POC.
7. Refer to subsequent section on documentation standards for reimbursement of OT services.

Inpatient Rehabilitation Coverage Specifics

1. In inpatient rehabilitation hospitals, Medicare regulations require that intensive rehabilitative services be provided by members of the interdisciplinary team at a minimum of three hours per day for five days a week.
2. The Inpatient Rehabilitation Facility Patient Assessment Instrument (IRF-PAI) is used to collect assessment data which contributes to quality indicators to pay for Medicare Part A and C (CMS, 2023b).
3. Patients are expected to benefit and improve in function from the intensive rehabilitative services provided by the interdisciplinary team.

Maintenance Plan and Program Coverage Specifics

1. Medicare covers a therapist's design of an individualized maintenance plan to be implemented by the person, a family member or care giver, and/or direct care staff (e.g., CNAs, HHAs, PCAs) and the occasional reevaluation of this plan's effectiveness., if the patient's condition requires the skilled expertise and knowledge of the therapist to develop and follow through with the plan.
   a. Reimbursement is not provided for an OT practitioner to carry out a maintenance plan that does *not* provide skilled services.
2. Since 2013, Medicare policy has covered skilled therapy services to maintain a person's functional status and quality of life.
   a. The restorative potential of a person is *not* the sole payment criteria for skilled therapy services.
   b. Therapy services to prevent or slow deterioration and maintain a person at their highest possible functional level are recognized as skilled and covered if these services are reasonable and necessary.
      (1) If maintenance services can be performed safely and effectively by unskilled personnel, coverage for skilled therapy services is not mandated (CMS, 2013).
3. Evaluation and training of caregivers are considered part of the design and reevaluation of a maintenance plan.
   a. The competence of caregivers to carry out the maintenance plan must be documented prior to discharge from OT.
4. Refer to subsequent section on documentation standards for reimbursement of maintenance services.

Skilled Nursing Facility Coverage Specifics

1. In SNFs, the Patient Driven Payment Model (PDPM) is the Medicare reimbursement system used to pay for services.
2. Reimbursement according to the PDPM is based on the client's characteristics regardless of the amount or type of provided services.
   a. Occupational therapy services are covered if the person requires skilled nursing or skilled rehabilitation (i.e., OT, PT, SLP).
   b. To be reimbursed under PDPM, OT practitioners need "to clearly articulate the value of their services" (Amini & Furniss, 2019, p. CE-2).
3. With the PDPM, a per-diem (each day) payment rate is established from coding of the Minimum Data Set (MDS).
   a. Data collected from the MDS is based on the five service components of nursing, OT, PT, SLP, and non-therapy ancillary (NTA) services and used to determine the specific needs of the patient and the daily payment rate.
      (1) Payment for all five service components is taken from the daily rate.
   b. There is a variable per diem adjustment that changes the per diem rate over the patient's stay.
4. Classification for OT is based on the patient's functional score in Section GG of the MDS along with the primary diagnosis.
   a. Patients for therapy are classified into four clinical categories of 1. joint replacement or spinal surgery, 2. other orthopedic surgery, 3. non-orthopedic surgery and acute neurological, and 4. medical management.

Home Care Coverage Specifics

1. Home care OT services are covered by Medicare Part A if the individual is homebound and received intermittent skilled nursing care, PT, or ST before OT began.
   a. Individuals with medical, physical, cognitive, and psychiatric conditions are eligible for Medicare homecare services if the person meets Medicare homebound status criteria.
      (1) Box 4-8 outlines Medicare homebound status criteria.
   b. OT services can continue after the need for skilled nursing, PT, or ST has ended.
2. Home health agencies are reimbursed under the Patient-Driven Groupings Model (PDGM),

---

BOX 4-8 ▷ Medicare Homebound Status Criteria

- An individual is considered home bound and confined to their home if the following two criteria are met.
- **Criteria One**
  - Because of illness or injury, the person needs to use an assistive device (e.g., a walker), special transportation, or the assistance of another person to leave their home.

    OR

  - Leaving the home is medically contraindicated.
- **Criteria Two**
  - The person is normally unable to leave their home.

    AND

  - "leaving home requires a considerable and taxing effort" (CMS, 2022a, p. 24).
  - Both points in Criteria Two *MUST* be met.
  - The need to attend adult daycare programs does *not* disqualify a person from receiving home health care.
  - A person can also maintain homebound status if they leave their home infrequently and for a short duration.
  - Acceptable short-term and infrequent trips can include medical appointments, health care treatments (e.g., kidney dialysis), religious services, and other unique or infrequent events (e.g., a funeral, graduation, or wedding; a trip to a barber/hair stylist).

Refer to https://www.medicare.gov/coverage/home-health-services

---

a prospective payment system based on a pre-established payment rate for 30 days.
   a. The PDGM is the home health case-mix system which considers patient characteristics (case-mix) and categorizes patients into 432 home health resource groups (HHRGs) to determine an episode payment rate.
   b. The per episode, 30 days of care, payment rate applies to all home health services including all forms of therapy and medical supplies.
      (1) Durable medical equipment is excluded.
3. An initial assessment visit and a comprehensive assessment using the Outcome and Assessment Information Set (OASIS) must be completed to verify the person's eligibility for Medicare home health benefits, to verify the continuing need for home care, and to plan for the person's nursing, medical, social, rehabilitative, and discharge needs.
   a. The initial assessment visit must be completed within 48 hours of referral or within 48 hours of the person's return home.

b. The OASIS is required to be completed within five days of the start of service (SOS).

4. When only rehabilitation services are ordered by the physician or NPP, the initial assessment is completed by the most suitable rehabilitation professional.

   a. Occupational therapists can open a home care case by completing the initial OASIS if OT is ordered along with PT or SLP.

5. As for all Medicare reimbursable services, OT services must be provided according to a signed POC, be reasonable and necessary for the patient's condition, and at a skilled level.

6. Occupational therapists can conduct follow-up, transfer, and discharge evaluations.

   a. OTAs can contribute information to the evaluations but cannot conduct them.

7. The AOTA is actively working to change federal legislation to have OT identified as an initial qualifying service for home health care. As a result, barriers to OT home health services may be removed in the future.

Additional Medicare Coverage Information

1. Occupational therapy in hospice care is provided to persons who are certified as terminally ill (i.e., medical prognosis of fewer than six months to live).

   a. Occupational therapy hospice services are provided to enable a person to manage symptoms, maintain occupational performance, and enhance quality of life.

2. Occupational therapy services can be covered if provided by a Medicare-certified occupational therapist in an independent private practice when services are provided in the therapist's office or in the person's home.

3. Occupational therapy services provided at a physician's office or in a physician-directed clinic can be covered if the following criteria are met.

   a. The occupational therapist or OTA/COTA® is employed by the physician or clinic.

   b. The service is furnished under physician's direct supervision, and the services are directly related to the condition for which the physician is treating the patient.

   c. OT service fees are included on the physician's bill to Medicare.

4. Criteria for coverage of Partial Hospitalization Program (PHP) services affiliated with a hospital or a community mental health psychiatric day program include the following.

a. The beneficiary would otherwise have required inpatient psychiatric care.

b. OT services are covered under general Medicare guidelines (i.e., a physician's POC, reasonable and necessary, function expected to improve, and an individualized intervention plan).

c. Active treatment incorporating an individualized multidisciplinary intervention plan to attain measurable, time-limited, medically necessary, functional goals directly related to the reason for admission must be provided.

   (1) Psychosocial programs that provide structured diversional, social, and/or recreational services or vocational rehabilitation do not meet the criteria for active treatment in a PHP and are not reimbursable under Medicare.

> **CAUTION:** All of the standards described in this section on Medicare can change when and if new federal legislative guidelines are passed for Medicare.

Medicare Coverage of Durable Medical Equipment

> **EXAM HINT:** The NBCOT® OTR® exam content outline identifies the task of selecting "durable medical equipment to enable participation in occupation" (NBCOT®, 2022, p. 11) and knowledge of the "influence of reimbursement policies and guidelines on occupational therapy service delivery" (NBCOT®, 2022, p. 14) as essential for competent practice. The application of knowledge about the Medicare DME reimbursement criteria described in the following and Box 4-9 can help you determine a correct answer to NBCOT® exam items about service recipients who rely on Medicare to pay for their medical expenses. For example, a three-in-one commode would be the correct answer for an exam item that identifies a client's need for equipment to safely and independently toilet; whereas a raised toilet seat and/or grab bars would be an incorrect answer. The former will be covered by Medicare because a three-in-one commode is not considered useful to persons without an illness or disability; the latter would not be covered by Medicare since a raised toilet seat and grab bars are considered useful to persons without an illness or disability and are not medically necessary.

1. Rental or purchase expenses for durable medical equipment (DME) are covered if used in beneficiary's home and if necessary and reasonable to treat an illness or injury or to improve functioning.
   a. A physician's prescription is needed and must include diagnosis, prognosis, and reason for DME need.
2. Under Medicare, reimbursable DME includes medial products, functional mobility devices (e.g., walkers wheelchairs, power scooters), orthotics and prosthetics, pressure-reducing devices, and hearing aid services.
   a. Refer to Chapter 6 for information about orthotics and prosthetics. Chapters 11 and 12 provide additional information about orthoses for specific clinical conditions.
   b. Refer to Chapter 9 for information about the three categories CMS uses to describe pressure-reducing devices (e.g., cushions, mattresses, beds) for reimbursement purposes.
   c. Refer to Chapter 16 for information about mobility aides and equipment.
      (1) Functional mobility devices are only covered if they are needed to enable functional mobility in the home. If the device is mainly intended to help with functional mobility outside the home, it is not covered.
3. Criteria for DME. Refer to Box 4-9.

Medicaid

1. A state/federal health insurance program for persons who have an income that is below an established threshold and/or have a disability.
2. States administer the program but receive at least 50% of their funding from the federal government.
   a. Under the ACA, states receive increased federal contributions to expand their Medicaid programs.
3. Includes federally mandated services and state optional services.
   a. Mandated services must be provided if a state receives federal funds.
      (1) Box 4-10 lists the federally mandated services.
   b. Occupational therapy services are included in the mandated early periodic screening diagnosis, and treatment (EPSDT) services.
      (1) All students (not just those with IEPs), who are Medicaid beneficiaries, are eligible to receive OT services under the EPSDT mandate.
         (a) Local Education Agencies (LEAs) can bill for any service provided to students that would otherwise be eligible for reimbursement by Medicaid.
   c. Coverage of optional services varies greatly from state to state.
4. Under the ACA, Medicaid must provide the same minimum essential benefits that are provided in the insurance exchanges established by the ACA.
   a. Refer to prior information on the ACA and Box 4-5.

BOX 4-9 ▷ Medicare Durable Medical Equipment Criteria

- DME that is reimbursable by Medicare includes items that meet the following criteria.
  - Repeated use can be withstood.
  - Primarily and customarily used for medical purpose (e.g., a wheelchair or walker).
  - Primarily used in the home.
  - Generally, not useful to a person in the absence of injury or illness.
  - Can be expected to last at least 3 years.
- DME that is *NOT* reimbursable by Medicare includes items that meet the following criteria.
  - Other people can use the item.
  - The item is used for comfort or convenience.
  - The item is not medically necessary.
- As a result of Medicare DME reimbursement criteria, self-help items (e.g., reachers, sock aids), bathroom grab bars, transfer/tub benches, shower chairs, and raised toilet seats are *NOT* reimbursable.

Refer to https://www.cms.gov/medicare/payment/fee-schedules/dmepos/center

---

BOX 4-10 ▷ Federally Mandated Medicaid Services

- Inpatient and hospital services.
- Outpatient services.
- Laboratory and x-ray services.
- Transportation to medical care.
- Skilled nursing facilities.
  - SNFs receiving Medicaid must provide skilled rehabilitation services (including OT) to residents who require them.
- Physician's services.
- Rural health clinic services.
- Federally qualified health center services.
- Home health services.
- Family planning services and nurse midwife services.
- Tobacco cessation counseling for pregnant women.
- Certified pediatric and family nurse practitioner services.
- Early periodic screening diagnosis, and treatment (EPSDT) services for persons 21 years old and younger.

Refer to https://www.medicaid.gov/medicaid/index.html

Occupational Therapy Documentation Guidelines[4]

Purposes of Documentation

1. Provides a legal, serial record of a service recipient's condition, evaluation and possible re-evaluation results, the intervention plan formulated based on these results, the course of therapeutic intervention, the response to intervention from referral to discharge, and discharge plans.
2. Justifies the necessity of skilled services to payers by providing a rationale for service provision.
3. Serve as an information resource for client care.
   a. An OT practitioner can use this documentation to inform their work with a client if the occupational therapist and/or OTA/COTA® who has been working with the person is absent.
4. Enhances communication among healthcare or educational team members.
5. Provides data for use in intervention, program evaluation, research, and education.
6. Electronic medical records (EMRs)/electronic health records (EHRs) provide digital versions of paper charts.

General Documentation Standards and Guidelines

1. All documentation must be relevant, current, and accurate.
2. The client's name and ID number should be on every page.
3. The type of documentation (i.e., initial note, evaluation, progress note, discharge plan) should be identified.
4. The complete date (i.e., day, month, and year) must be provided.
5. Legible handwriting and black or blue ink must be used for handwritten documentation.
   a. Illegible notes can result in miscommunication and possible Medicare denial.
6. Documentation for an EMR/EHR must adhere to all established documentation standards.
7. Correct grammar and spelling are required.
   a. Errors detract from a professional presentation.

8. Concise but complete information should be recorded.
   a. If it is not recorded, it does not exist and never happened.
   b. Nonimportant, extraneous details (i.e., color of clothing) should be left out.
9. Objective statements, with clear distinctions between facts and opinions, behavioral data and interpretations, are required.
10. Standard, well-recognized abbreviations (i.e., ROM, MMT) should be the only ones used.
    a. Avoid alphabet soup.
    b. Write in functional terms using uniform terminology consistent with the AOTA's Standards of Practice, Practice Framework, and state practice acts.
11. Person-first language should always be used (e.g., "a parent with schizophrenia," or "the student with an intellectual disability").
12. The blocking out or deletion of information is unacceptable.
    a. If notes are handwritten, errors must be crossed out with one line, initialed, and dated.
13. A full signature (first and last name with professional designations) should directly follow documentation content with no space left between the content and signature.
14. Countersignature by an occupational therapist on documentation written by an OTA/COTA® or a student, if required by law or the facility.
15. Institution and/or program guidelines, as well as commercial insurers'/third-party payers' guidelines must be followed.
16. Occupational therapy notes and records are legal documents; thus, all documentation may be subject to subpoena.
    a. Adherence to documentation standards is a must.

> CAUTION: Compliance with confidentiality standards is mandated (e.g., do not put other service recipients' names in a note).

> RED FLAG: Informed consent for treatment can only be given by a competent adult. Minors or adults determined to be incompetent must have written consent provided by a parent, legal guardian, person with power of attorney, or proxy.

---

[4] Christina Gavalas-Valdivia MS, OTR/L and Helene Lohman OTD contributed to this section on occupational therapy documentation guidelines.

Prescription Documentation Guidelines

1. A valid prescription to provide OT services may be required from a physician or NPP.
   a. Some state licensure acts may not allow a DO to prescribe OT.
2. The required elements on a prescription can be as basic as "OT eval and treat," while certain prescriptions may include diagnoses (sometimes with an accompanying ICD code), modalities, prescribed interventions, and physician-recommended frequency and duration.

> **EXAM HINT:** States can have different rules regarding referring physician and prescription criteria (e.g., the provider must be in the same state). However, the NBCOT® exam is a national exam; therefore, state-specific information is not tested.

> **CAUTION:** Always check for accuracy in a physician's orders, as an incorrect diagnosis or rehabilitative service ordered (i.e., the prescription ordered physical therapy instead of OT) can result in denial or delay of payment for OT services.

3. Specific to Medicare, a POC approved by a physician or a NPP signature is required to certify therapy services and to ensure that service provision is being overseen by a physician or NPP.
   a. In some settings, the POC can take the place of the prescription from the physician.
      (1) The requirements of a POC vary by setting, but generally it includes the person's diagnosis, type of rehabilitative therapy service (e.g., OT, PT, ST), long-term goals, and therapy frequency and duration.

> **CAUTION:** Always check that there are no 'technical' reasons for possible denials such as an unsigned POC.

4. If after the evaluation of a client, the occupational therapist determines that there is a discrepancy between the client needs they have identified for OT services and the ones the physician has outlined in the prescription or POC, the therapist should contact the physician to discuss the intervention plan and/or revise the prescription or POC as needed.

Initial Documentation Guidelines

1. Initial documentation should include the following.
   a. Referral source and reason for referral (e.g., the client's chief complaint relevant to OT's domain of concern).
   b. Identification and background information.
      (1) Name, age, gender, date of admission, treatment diagnosis, and case number if one exists.

> **CAUTION:** Whenever possible, make sure diagnoses are acute or an acute change in a chronic long-term condition that requires skilled intervention; not a condition with no need for skilled intervention from an occupational therapist or OTA/COTA®. If a person has a progressive or terminal diagnosis, skilled services can be justified if they can improve, maintain, or prevent deterioration of the person's condition. For example, an individual with a progressive disorder or terminal illness may require skilled therapy services to address ADL, functional mobility, and/or safety.

   c. For existing conditions, the onset date for when the current functional decline occurred must be provided.
      (1) For example, instead of documenting "rheumatoid arthritis (RA) x10 years", document the current functional decline that occurred and warranted the current need for skilled OT services by stating "an acute exacerbation of RA with an onset date of 10/14/2023 with a need for skilled intervention to address ADL limitations."
   d. Pertinent history that indicates prior levels of function and support systems, including applicable developmental, educational, vocational, socioeconomic, and medical history.
      (1) This can be brief.
   e. Secondary problems or pre-existing conditions that may affect function or treatment outcomes.
   f. Precautions, risk factors and contraindications, medications, surgery dates.

Evaluation Documentation Guidelines

1. Evaluation documentation should include the following.
   a. Assessments (preferably evidenced-based measures) administered and the results.
   b. Summary and analysis of assessment findings.
      (1) Use measurable, functional terms.
      (2) Use sufficient baseline objective data.
   c. References to other pertinent reports and information including relevant psychological, social, and environmental data.
   d. OT problem list that is specific and sufficient to develop an intervention plan.
   e. Recommendation(s) for OT services or a statement that no OT services are indicated.

f. Client's understanding of their status and their subjective complaints.

g. Client's interest and desire to participate in therapy.

Intervention Plan Documentation Guidelines

1. The documentation of an intervention plan should include the following.
   a. A clear reason for skilled therapeutic intervention.
   b. A prioritized problem list based on the evaluation results.
   c. Short- and long-term goals related to the problem list that indicate the potential for functional improvement.
      (1) Long-term goals must indicate the final desired functional outcome before discharge, regardless of LOS.

> **EXAM HINT:** The time identified for the attainment of goals must be relevant to the setting's LOS (e.g., in acute care, goals are measured in days, whereas in long-term care, weekly or monthly goals are relevant).

   d. The type, amount, frequency, and duration of intervention needed to accomplish goals.
      (1) Type is the specific description of intervention (e.g., the activities, modalities, procedures and/or methods) that will be used to address the stated problems and established goals.
      (2) Amount is the number of times in a day; if not delineated, it typically means one time per day.
      (3) Frequency is the number of times in a week; if not delineated, it typically means one treatment.
      (4) Duration is the number of weeks or treatment sessions.

   e. An explanation of the intervention plan to the client and the provision of goal statements in the client's words.

2. Goal statements should include the following.
   a. The identification of the person who will develop/exhibit the skill identified in the goal.
      (1) Almost always written as "the patient/client will." However, the caregiver, family member, and/or teacher may be the focus of the goal.
   b. The desired functional behavior that is to be demonstrated or increased as the outcome of intervention.
   c. The underlying factors (e.g., performance skill deficits) that must be remediated to achieve functional outcome.
   d. The circumstances under which the behavior must be performed or the conditions necessary for the behavior (e.g., independent, with cueing, with assistance).
   e. The degree at which the behavior is exhibited (e.g., three out of four times, minimum number of repetitions).
   f. The time anticipated to attain a goal.

3. Table 4-3 outlines four standardized documentation formats and their acronyms that are often used to structure and document OT intervention goals.

4. The POC is the individual written intervention plan required by Medicare for all patients.
   a. Changes to the POC are made in writing and signed by the person responsible for the patient's care (i.e., the physician, NPP, occupational therapist).
      (1) A physician or NPP can change the POC established by the occupational therapist, but the occupational therapist cannot significantly change a plan established by the physician/NPP without authorization.

Table 4-3

Documentation Formats Typically Used for Occupational Therapy Intervention Goals

SMART	RUMBA	COAST	FEAST
S = Specific: focus is clear and explicit, not general.	**R = Relevant:** related to the client's status, roles, and contexts.	**C = Client:** the client is identified.	**F = Function:** the focus and purpose of the goal.
M = Measurable: number of times or a percentage.	**U = Understandable:** easily understood by others.	**O = Occupation:** the occupation that will be addressed is identified.	**E = Expectation:** the outcome that is expected to occur.
A = Attainable: what can be realistically achieved; e.g., 100% return is unlikely.	**M = Measurable:** how the goal will be measured; e.g., duration, frequency.	**A = Assist Level:** the level and type of assistance that the client will use to successfully complete the goal.	**A = Action:** the task/behavior that the client will perform.
R = Relevant: related to the client's status, roles, and contexts.	**B = Behavioral:** client's observable behavioral outcome.	**S = Specific Condition:** the conditions (e.g., cueing, using adaptive equipment) under which performance will be done.	**S = Specific Conditions:** the conditions (e.g., using adaptive equipment, assistance level) that the goal will require for completion.
T = Time-allotted: the time anticipated to attain goals.	**A = Achievable:** realistic and attainable given the client's capabilities.	**T = Time Bound:** time in which the goal is expected to be completed.	**T = Timeline:** time anticipated to attain the goal.

Intervention Implementation Documentation Guidelines

1. Document honestly, but not over-optimistically. Medicare and commercial insurance reviewers are interested in determining the need for continued intervention.
2. The content must indicate that the intervention provided is skilled.

> **EXAM HINT:** Skilled intervention (also known as skilled therapy services) are at a level of complexity and sophistication that requires the judgment, knowledge, and skills of a licensed OT practitioner to address service needs of the person.

> **CAUTION:** Services must be unique to OT and not sound like PT or SLP. Medicare and commercial insurers do not pay for the duplication of services.

3. A clear description of the skilled intervention is mandatory.
   a. The description of the skilled care rendered must be appropriate for the client's diagnosis/diagnoses and presenting problems and the physician's order.
      (1) Inadequate documentation of the specific skilled care provided to a client is a major cause of denials for coverage of OT services.

> **CAUTION:** Notes must clearly document the skilled therapeutic intervention(s). For example, documenting that an intervention session focused on helping a person dress does not indicate that skilled therapeutic interventions were provided. Documenting that an intervention session focused on decreasing extensor tone, increasing bilateral integration, and/or training the person to use adaptive strategies and equipment to enable independent dressing does indicate that skilled interventions were provided.

4. The documentation of intervention implementation should include the following as relevant to the intervention provided.
   a. The activities, procedures, and modalities used.
   b. The client's response to treatment and the progress toward goal attainment as related to problem list.
   c. Goal modification when indicated by the client's response to treatment.
      (1) The rationale for changes in the focus of a goal and/or the anticipated time to achieve a goal must be provided.
   d. The client's attendance and participation in an intervention session (attendance can be a check format) or a statement of the reason(s) a client missed an intervention session.
   e. A description of the assistive/adaptive equipment, orthoses, and prostheses if issued or fabricated, and specific instructions for the application and/or use of the item, including their wearing schedule and care.
   f. Client-related conferences and communication with physicians, commercial insurers/third-party payers, case manager, team members.
   g. Caregiver education/training completed with the client.
      (1) For Medicare reimbursement, the client must be present during caregiver education and training.
   h. Home programs developed and taught to the client and/or along with their caregiver(s).
      (1) For Medicare reimbursement, the client must be present during caregiver education and training.
   i. Client's and/or caregiver's/caregivers' understanding of the home program and their intent to implement the program.
5. For Medicare, daily treatment notes are required to justify intervention and billing.
   a. Daily Medicare notes must include the actual minutes of service and the OT practitioner's signature.
   b. There is no specific Medicare documentation format requirements (e.g., an intervention grid) for intervention implementation notes.
   c. Daily notes can be used to inform the progress notes that Medicare requires to be completed every 10th treatment day.
      (1) For Medicare, progress notes must be written by the occupational therapist, not an OTA.
         (a) OTAs can contribute to Medicare progress notes.

Re-evaluation Documentation Guidelines

1. Re-evaluations are completed to ensure a service recipient is progressing towards their goals; however, they may not be routinely completed as many insurers follow Medicare guidelines.
   a. For Medicare, formal re-evaluations are only completed when there are significant changes in a client's functional status, new findings/diagnosis/diagnoses, and/or the person requires a new POC.
      (1) The significant changes in the client's status that warrant a re-evaluation must be documented by the practitioner.
2. Re-evaluation documentation content should include the following.
   a. The re-evaluation findings as compared to the initial evaluation findings.

b. Improvement with a clear description of the functional change(s).

c. If a person has improved but can benefit from further intervention, a clear explanation as to why continued treatment is medically necessary,

(1) Behavioral observations and evaluation results (ideally from evidence-based assessments) that substantiate the need for further intervention must be provided.

d. If improvements are not observed and/or progress is slower than expected, a clear explanation of the reason(s) for the lack of progress including extenuating circumstances and/or limiting factors (e.g., a secondary diagnosis).

3. The frequency of re-evaluations will vary based on the practice setting and the payer type.

a. Re-evaluations may be required at a specific frequency during a person's LOS to obtain insurance authorization for coverage of additional services.

(1) For example, a commercial insurer may authorize six visits and require that a re-evaluation be completed to request additional visits, if clinically indicated.

4. The frequency of POC re-certifications required by Medicare vary by practice setting.

a. For example, an outpatient setting is required to have the physician recertify for a significant change in POC at least once every 90 days, while a home health agency must have the physician recertify a POC at least once every 60 days.

(1) A POC can and should be recertified prior to the "expiration" date if a significant change is made to the one that is already approved (i.e., a long-term goal is added or modified).

Maintenance Program Documentation Guidelines

1. Occupational therapy practitioners can continue to be reimbursed for services they provide to persons not expected to improve *if* they adequately substantiate the need for skilled services.

2. Documentation of an occupational therapist's design of a maintenance plan that will be implemented by others (e.g., CNAs, HHAs, PCAs) and the periodical reevaluation of its effectiveness must clearly substantiate that the skill of an occupational therapist was required to design and reevaluate the plan.

3. Documentation of an OT practitioner's implementation of an individualized maintenance plans must adequately substantiate that the provided services are skilled and require a high level of complexity.

a. Skilled interventions to slow the deterioration of function, prevent complications, and maximize function are viewed as justifiable and covered by Medicare.

b. The goals established for individualized maintenance programs should address needs that require the expertise of an OT practitioner.

c. Medicare coverage of maintenance programs will be denied if there is inadequate documentation substantiating the need for skilled services.

Home Care Documentation Guidelines

1. A person's homebound status due to functional limitations must be documented according to Criterion One and Criterion Two for Medicare reimbursement.

a. Box 4-8 outlines these homebound criteria.

2. If a person's diagnosis may not render them homebound, documentation must explain why they are homebound.

> CAUTION: Documentation should not give a reviewer any doubt that a person does not meet Medicare homebound criteria (e.g., do not state a client was not at home when you arrived; rather state there was no answer to a locked door).

3. Because commercial insurers often use Medicare reimbursement guidelines to inform their own standards for payment, it is advisable to use Medicare standards for all home care documentation.

Discharge Plan Documentation Guidelines

1. If a client has met their goals and/or is no longer making significant functional gains, this must be documented and the client *may* need to be discharged from services.

a. If improvement is not made or expected, justifiable interventions to prevent deterioration and maximize function can be covered in settings *other than inpatient rehabilitation.*

(1) Refer to prior sections on maintenance plan and program coverage and documentation.

b. If there is no medical justification or skilled need for continued treatment, the person must be discharged in a timely fashion.

2. The documentation of a discharge plan should include the following.
   a. A summary of the evaluation and intervention.
   b. A comparison of the person's initial or last progress report and discharge status.
      (1) Medicare discharge documentation only requires a summary of the intervention period from the last progress report to discharge.
         (a) However, providing documentation that requires the practitioner to review the person's total progress during the complete course of intervention is an effective way to represent the episode of care to reviewers. This process also enables the practitioner to assess the outcomes of their interventions with the beneficiary.
   c. The specific number of sessions provided, the goals achieved, and the client's functional outcome.
   d. The reason(s) for discharge can vary. These can include the following.
      (1) Goals have been attained.
      (2) The client no longer requires skilled services because maximum benefit has been achieved and/or the services to maintain them at their highest level of function are not considered skilled.
      (3) The client chooses to no longer participate in therapy or does not follow the intervention plan.
      (4) The client moves to another location.
      (5) An exacerbation of an illness or a medical crisis requires discharge to a higher level of care.
      (6) The client's allotted length of stay (LOS) in the setting has expired and an extension of their LOS is not possible.
   e. The home programs to be followed after discharge.
   f. Client and family education provided.
   g. Equipment provided and/or ordered.
   h. Follow-up plans/recommendations with rationales.
   i. Referral(s) to other health-care providers and community agencies.

Specific Documentation Formats

1. Problem Oriented Medical Record (POMR): a system of providing structure for progress note writing that is based on a list of problems based on assessment.
2. Goal statements: refer to prior section on intervention plan documentation and Table 4-3.
3. SOAP notes.
   a. Subjective: information reported by the client, family, or significant other.
   b. Objective: the client's diagnosis, medical information and history, and measurable, observable data obtained through formal assessments.
   c. Assessment: the practitioner's interpretation and clinical reasoning based on objective data includes an analysis of the client's status and goals and a prioritized problem list.
   d. Plan: the practitioner's specific plan of intervention to resolve identified problems and meet stated goals.
4. Consultation reports: meetings and/or phone conversations with team members, other professionals, the individual, and their caregivers.
5. Critical incident reports: significant, out of the norm events that may occur during OT evaluation or intervention (e.g., a person slips during a transfer).
6. All of these must comply with general documentation standards and contain all fundamental components of documentation.

OTA/COTA® Documentation Guidelines

1. OTAs/COTA®s are qualified to write notes in medical charts and other documentation formats although there are some exceptions such as OTAs/COTAs® cannot write or sign off on the plan of care (POC), progress, or discharge notes although they can contribute data to them.
2. OTA/COTA® notes are not required to be co-signed by an occupational therapist by the AOTA, but state and federal governments may mandate co-signing as a tangible way to demonstrate compliance with OTA/COTA® supervisory laws and regulations.
3. Any documentation completed by OT practitioners are legal documents and are subject to subpoena.

EXAM HINT: The NBCOT® OTR® exam content outline identifies knowledge of "accountability processes and procedures for justifying, tracking, and monitoring outcomes...(including) relevant practice terminology (and) documentation guidelines" (NBCOT®, 2022, p. 14). The application of knowledge about the documentation standards and considerations described in above sections, the goal writing formats outlined in Table 4-3, and the documentation reimbursement standards described in the following can help you successfully analyze answer options for NBCOT® exam items. Correct answers will adhere to these standards and guidelines, incorrect answers will not.

Documentation for Reimbursement

EXAM HINT: Federal legislation and CMS policy decisions have shifted health-care reimbursement from a focus on the quantity of services provided to a focus on the quality of service outcomes. As this paradigm shift becomes embedded in practice, it will likely be reflected in the NBCOT® exam. Thus, correct answers to NBCOT® exam items about documentation for reimbursement should substantiate the distinct value of OT and the efficacy of OT outcomes.

1. Documentation in all settings and for all types of service should explicitly justify that a *skilled* level of OT intervention is necessary to improve, maintain or prevent deterioration of the person's condition.
2. Documentation must include essential content and adhere to established documentation standards and guidelines to receive payment for services.
   a. Noncompliance with established standards and guidelines can result in services and/or payment being denied.
      (1) Refer to the preceding sections on general documentation standards and guidelines and the specific documentation standards and guidelines for OT prescriptions, initial notes, evaluations, intervention plans, intervention implementation, reevaluation, and discharge and home care and maintenance programs. These standards and guidelines must be followed to obtain reimbursement.
3. OT practitioners should always be mindful of the terminology they use in documentation.
   a. The terms used can infer a level of rehabilitation potential that can impact coverage of OT services in certain settings (e.g., inpatient rehabilitation facilities).
      (1) For clients with diagnoses in which improvement is expected, terminology to highlight their rehabilitation potential should be used.
   b. Including certain words and/or terms that indicate a questionable need for skilled intervention or a limited potential to positively benefit from OT services can result in delayed/limited approval or denial of OT services for these clients.
      (1) Box 4-11 outlines terms that should be carefully considered or avoided in documentation for clients who are receiving rehabilitative services (not maintenance services) because they may reflect limited potential for progress and limited participation in intervention. Box 4-11 also outlines terms that should be avoided in all documentation because they are subjective, vague, and/or reflect bias.

BOX 4-11 ▷ Terminology to Carefully Consider or Avoid in Documentation

- Terms that reflect limited expectation for improvement when the objective is for rehabilitation or restoration of function, not maintenance.
  – Chronic/long-term condition.
  – Maintaining.
  – Little or no change in status.
  – Plateau.
  – Custodial care needed.
  – Poor rehabilitation potential (in this case, expected barriers to rehabilitation should be listed).
- Terms that are subjective or vague that do not justify medical necessity.
  – Unconfirmed.
  – Undecided, not sure.
  – Less or more pain.
  – Feeling better, feeling worse.
  – Doing well, not doing well.
- Terms that should be avoided or carefully considered, as they may infer undue bias or reflect limited participation in intervention.
  – Uncooperative.
  – Unmotivated.
  – Noncompliant with recommendations or home exercise program.
  – Dislikes therapy.

EXAM HINT: Answer choices for NBCOT® exam items about documentation that have any of the terms identified in Box 4-11 will likely be an incorrect answer. Conversely, correct answers for an exam item will likely not contain these words.

CAUTION: Terminology indicating limited rehabilitation potential or poor response to intervention should only be included in documentation *if they are true and accurate representations of a client's status.* Refer to prior section on documentation guidelines for Medicare reimbursable maintenance services for persons who are not expected to improve or who have progressive conditions but need skilled services.

RED FLAG: Documentation should never be falsified to indicate a better rehabilitation potential or response to intervention than is truly expected.

4. Coding and billing for services.
   a. To be reimbursed, OT services must be properly coded and billed, as required by payers.

b. Practitioners must represent their services in terms of diagnosis and procedure codes.

c. Diagnosis codes describe a person's condition or medical reason for requiring services.
  (1) The ICD is the most frequently used diagnosis-coding system in the United States.
    (a) Each service, procedure, supply, or piece of equipment must be related to a current ICD code.

d. Physicians determine the medical diagnostic code and therapists select appropriate intervention codes based on the patient's performance deficits which relate to the medical diagnosis.

e. Procedure codes describe the specific services provided by health-care professionals.
  (1) HCFA Common Procedure Coding System (HCPCS) is most widely used and are included on the Medicare Physician Fee Schedule (MPFS).
    (a) HCPCS includes the Current Procedural Terminology (CPT).
  (2) Specific codes that most closely describe the service(s) provided should be used.
    (a) Each procedure, modality, and/or treatment should be coded.

> **EXAM HINT:** The most current HCPCS and CPT codes must be used in practice. However, because they are often updated, the NBCOT® exam will likely not include specific codes.

5. Medicare certification is required for reimbursement.
  a. Certification is required from a physician or a NPP as defined by state practice acts.
    (1) Certification can vary and include as a physician or a NPP order, a signed POC, or a signed progress note.
  b. The signed POC must include the following.
    (1) A dated signature on the POC indicating physician or NPP approval of the therapy plan within 30 days of initial treatment.
    (2) A diagnosis, LT goals and type, frequency, and duration of services as established independently by each discipline and under acceptable standards of practice.
      (a) LT goals are developed for the episode of care, are measurable, and are related to functional impairment. A therapist can choose to also establish ST goals.
  c. Skilled care rendered must match the diagnosis and the physician's order.
    (1) Refer to prior sections on the documentation of intervention planning and implementation.
  d. If there is no medical justification for continued treatment, the person should be discharged in a timely fashion.
    (1) Refer to prior section on discharge documentation.

 ## Federal Legislation Related to Occupational Therapy

Overview

1. Federal laws establish numerous standards and provide funding for health benefits, medical services, rehabilitation, EI, education, vocational programming, professional training, and research.
2. These laws directly affect the profession of OT by establishing practice guidelines and reimbursement standards.
3. Historically, the opportunities available to and the roles afforded to persons with disabilities have been influenced by federal legislation.
4. Major social movements that have precipitated federal legislation and/or have resulted from federal legislation include deinstitutionalization, EI, mainstreaming, and full inclusion.
5. State laws also influence OT practice but, due to their variability, would not be included in a national exam.
6. Information about the ACA is included in prior section on payment for OT services and Box 4-5.

> **EXAM HINT:** The NBCOT® OTR® exam content outline identifies the task of providing "occupational therapy services in accordance with laws (and) regulations . . . to protect consumers" (NBCOT®, 2022, p. 14) as essential for competent and safe practice. The application of knowledge about the following laws can help you determine the correct answer for NBCOT® Domain 3 Select and Manage Interventions exam items.

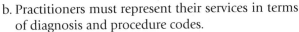

Health Insurance Portability and Accountability Act (HIPAA)

1. Sets standards and safeguards to assure the individual's right to continuity in health-care coverage and to ensure privacy and security of health-care records.
2. All persons must be informed of the setting's privacy policies and a good faith effort must be made to obtain written acknowledgement from each person about their attainment of this knowledge.
   a. If the person refuses to sign, the provider should document the efforts made; failure to obtain written acknowledgement is not a violation of the rule.
   b. Written consent must be obtained from a person before any personal health information is used or disclosed in the provision of treatment, obtainment of payment, or the carrying out of any health-care-related operations.
      (1) Exemptions to the written notification/acknowledgement are allowed if the attainment of this will prevent or delay timely care (i.e., emergency care). Written acknowledgement must be obtained as soon as possible.
      (2) If language barriers preclude signed acknowledgement, treatment can occur if the physician believes consent is implied.
3. Prior to discussing a person's status with a family member/significant other or other provider, the provider must obtain the person's permission, or give the person the opportunity to object.
   a. Providers can use their clinical judgment to determine whether to discuss the person's case with others if the person cannot give permission or objects.
      (1) Documentation for this decision is essential (e.g., person is at risk of harming self due to lack of judgment; consultation with a specialist is essential to ensure quality of care).
   b. All information used or disclosed about a person's status must be limited to the minimum needed for the immediate purpose.
4. The HIPAA Privacy Rule requires that all providers protect the confidentiality of service recipients in all forms (i.e., oral, written, and electronic) and implement appropriate physical, technical, and administrative safeguards to assure this privacy.
   a. Settings must reduce the physical identifiability of service recipient's information (e.g., door tags and whiteboards can only list last names, no diagnoses or treatment procedures may be listed).
   b. Charts and any documentation with service recipients' names or other identifiers must be stored out of public view and in secure locations.
   c. Opaque covers should be used for clipboards that contain paperwork with service recipient information.
   d. All computers that are used to record, document, or transmit service recipient information should be equipped with monitor privacy screens.
   e. All faxes must contain cover sheets noting confidentiality of accompanying information and be sent only to dedicated fax machines in secure locations.
   f. All e-mails must use password protection and encryption if going over the Internet.
   g. All faxes and computer printouts must be immediately destroyed or placed in the person's chart, as most appropriate.
   h. All conversations regarding a person's health status must be done in private areas, in low tones, and with minimal disclosure.
5. An individual has the right to access all of their records.
   a. Providers can charge reasonable copying costs and have 30–60 days to respond.
   b. Individuals have the right to request that information in their record be amended.
      (1) The provider can refuse the request, providing their rationale.
      (2) The provider can comply with the request by documenting the request and the reason for compliance. The original documentation should not be removed/excised.
6. HIPAA does not exclude treatment from occurring in group settings or open clinics.
   a. Discussion regarding treatment should be done quietly and, if possible, behind a screen/room divider.
7. HIPAA does not require a guarantee of 100% confidentiality; it does require reasonable and vigilant safeguards.
8. HIPAA guidelines for research are complex, but they are congruent with the established guidelines for human subject research and Institutional Review Board (IRB) standards.
   a. A limited data set that does not include any identifiable personal information can be used in research without participant approval (e.g., diagnosis, age, LOS).
9. The Administrative Simplification rules also provide standardization of codes and formats for medical data.
10. HIPAA does not override state laws that further restrict privacy and it defers to state laws governing minors.

Substance Use-Disorder Prevention that Promotes Optimal Recovery and Treatment (SUPPORT) for Patients and Communities Act (HR6)

1. Required the CMS to develop acute care practice guidelines for nonpharmacological pain management and opioid use disorder prevention.
   a. These guidelines were developed with input from health-care professionals, including OT practitioners.
2. Promoted Medicaid coverage for nonpharmacological therapies for the management of pain, including coverage of OT services.
3. Required training programs about pain care for health professionals to include information about nonpharmacological alternatives for pain management.
4. Expanded National Institutes of Health research on pain to include nonpharmacological interventions.
5. Refer to Chapters 6 and 7 for more information about OT evaluation of and intervention for pain.

Key Legislation Related to Overall Disability Rights

1. Medicare Title 18-PL 89-97.
   a. Established Medicare and Supplemental Security Income (SSI).
   b. SSI enables persons with disabilities to receive a monthly income enabling them to live in the community.
2. Rehabilitation Act of 1973.
   a. Prohibits discrimination on the basis of disability in any program or activity that receives federal assistance.
   b. Required all federal agencies to develop action plans for the hiring, placement, and advancement of persons with disabilities.
   c. Required contractors who received federal contracts over a pre-set amount to take affirmative action to employ persons with disabilities.
3. Fair Housing Act.
   a. Prohibits discrimination on the bases of disability, religion, sex, color, race, national origin, and familial status.
   b. Required owners of housing to make reasonable exceptions to their standard tenant policies to allow individuals with disabilities equal housing

opportunities (e.g., allowing a seeing eye or service dog in a 'no-pets' apartment).
   c. Required that tenants with disabilities be allowed to make reasonable modifications to common use areas and to their private living space to enable access.
      (1) The housing owner is not required to fund these modifications.
   d. Required that newly constructed multifamily residences (four or more apartments) be built to meet established accessibility standards.
4. Omnibus Budget Reconciliation Act (OBRA) of 1981.
   a. Affirmed application of Section 504 of the Rehabilitation Act of 1973, which prohibits discrimination in federally funded programs to a diversity of services (i.e., Head Start programs, block grant programs, community development programs).
   b. Provided Medicaid financing for community-based services for people with developmental disabilities when services were demonstrated to be less expensive than institutional care.
5. Americans with Disabilities Act (ADA) of 1990.
   a. Prohibits discrimination against qualified persons with disabilities in employment, transportation, accommodations, telecommunications, and public services.
   b. Criteria for classifying an individual as disabled.
      (1) A person with a physical or mental impairment that substantially limits one or more major life activities.
      (2) A person having a record of such an impairment.
      (3) A person regarded as having such an impairment.
   c. Individuals who are actively abusing substances or compulsively gambling or persons who have kleptomania, pyromania, or sexual behavior disorders are not protected by ADA.
   d. Title I—Employment.
      (1) Prohibits employers from discriminating against persons with disabilities in any aspect or phase of employment including recruitment, hiring, working conditions, hours, promotion, training opportunities, termination, social activities, and other privileges of employment.
      (2) Allows questions about one's ability to perform a job but prohibits inquiries as to whether one has a disability.
      (3) Prohibits employment tests that tend to screen out people with disabilities.
      (4) A "qualified individual with a disability" means a person with a disability who is able to perform the "essential functions" of a job (that

is, the tasks fundamental to the position) with or without reasonable accommodations.

(5) "Reasonable accommodations" must be provided by businesses with 15 or more employees to persons with disabilities to enable them to perform essential job functions unless such accommodations would impose an "undue" hardship on the business.

    (a) Undue hardship is defined as action that would be significantly difficult or overly expensive given the financial resources of the employer, its size, and major functions.

    (b) Box 4-12 outlines reasonable accommodations and auxiliary aids and services that can be provided under ADA.

    (c) Refer to Table 15-11 for specific accommodations to support psychosocial and cognitive abilities and address limitations that can impact work performance.

(6) The US Government, Indian Tribes, and/or private tax-exempt membership clubs are exempt from ADA employer guidelines.

e. Title II—Public Services.

(1) Mandates that state and local governments and their departments, agencies, and/or component parts may not discriminate against, exclude, or deny persons with disabilities participation in or benefit from the services, programs, or activities of these public entities.

    (a) This includes transportation, public education, employment, recreation, social services, health care, courts, town meetings, and voting.

f. Title III—Public Accommodations and Services operated by Public Entities.

(1) Mandates that places of public accommodation (e.g., hospitals, health-care providers' offices, schools, day care centers, restaurants, theatres, and other places of accommodation) may not discriminate against persons with disabilities with respect to their participation in or ability to benefit from the service, goods, facility, use, or other programming aspects.

(2) Public places operated by private entities must be designed, constructed, and altered to comply with accessibility standards.

    (a) All new construction of public accommodations must be accessible.

    (b) Physical barriers in existing facilities must be removed if removal is able to be carried out without much difficulty or expense.

    (c) The US Government, Indian Tribes, religious organizations, and/or private tax-exempt membership clubs are exempt from ADA accessibility standards.

(3) Private services that serve the public (e.g., restaurants, stores, and theaters) cannot discriminate in the provision of services.

(4) Public transportation systems must be accessible.

(5) Private transportation systems must be accessible and nondiscriminatory (e.g., livery services, taxis, tour bus companies).

g. Title IV—Telecommunications.

(1) All televisions must include closed captioning.

(2) Telephone companies must provide telecommunications relay services (TRS) to persons with hearing or speech impairments 24 hours per day, seven days per week.

6. ADA Amendments Act (ADAAA) of 2008.

a. Enacted to rectify the problems resulting from post-ADA Supreme Court decisions, which drastically narrowed the ADA definition of disability and substantially limited ADA protections.

b. Reaffirmed that a disability is the actual presence of a disorder or condition that impairs participation in one or more major life activities, a record of a limiting impairment, or being regarded as having an impairment.

(1) The use of "mitigating measures" (e.g., wheelchairs, hearing aids, taking insulin) to address a disability or the remediation of a condition (e.g., recovery from cancer, a repetitive stress disorder, or schizophrenia) does *not* negate the person's ability to be protected by the ADA.

BOX 4-12 ▷ Title I – ADA Reasonable Accommodations

• **Types of Reasonable Accommodations**

  – Acquisition or modification of equipment or devices.

  – Modifications or adjustments to exams, training materials, or publications.

  – Provision of ancillary aids or services.

  – Modified or part-time work schedules, job restructuring, or reassignment to a vacant position.

  – Improvement of existing facilities used by employees so they are usable by and accessible to persons with disabilities and/or other similar accommodations.

• **Types of Auxiliary Aids and Services**

  – Taped texts, qualified readers, or other methods that can effectively make visually delivered materials accessible to persons with visual impairments.

  – Qualified interpreters or other methods that can effectively make aurally delivered materials accessible to persons with hearing impairments.

  – Modification or acquisition of devices or equipment.

  – Similar actions or services that increase accessibility.

c. Redefined major life activities to include major body functions and organ operations performing basic and instrumental activities of daily living, completing physical movements and manual activities, sleeping, working, reading, learning, communicating and interacting, and thinking and concentrating.

d. Broadened the interpretation of a "substantially limited" impairment to include the inability to perform one major life activity as it is typically performed by the general population.

Key Legislation Related to Work

1. Work Investment Act (WIA) of 1998
   a. Established a federally sponsored national employment and vocational training system.
   b. Established a "One-Stop" delivery system for all adults aged 18 or older seeking access to employment and training services. This means traditionally separate unemployment offices and vocational rehabilitation services are now available at a One-Stop Center.
      (1) Availability of all employment and training services at a One-Stop Center is aimed to allow for universal access for person with disabilities, a core principle of WIA.
      (2) The categories of One-Stop services are described in Box 4-13.
      (3) The One-Stop system of services is provided through a network in each state. The names of these systems can vary from state to state.

BOX 4-13 ▷ Categories of One-Stop Services

- **Core Services**: provided to all service recipients. These can include outreach, intake and orientation; initial assessment; eligibility determination for services; assistance with job search and placement; job market information and career counseling.

- **Intensive Services**: provided to individuals who do not attain successful employment after receipt of core services. These can include comprehensive assessments of service needs and skill level, development of individualized plans for employment, case management, and counseling.

- **Training Services**: provided to individuals who do not attain successful employment after receipt of core and intensive services. These services are typically provided off-site from the One-Stop Center and can include adult education and literacy training, on-the-job training, and individualized vocational training.

---

c. Persons determined to be eligible for WIA services receive an Individual Training Account (ITA) which is used to obtain services from any approved provider. Specific ITA procedures can vary from state to state.

d. Services for youth (aged 14–21) with disabilities to successfully transition from school to work are also provided in the WIA and TWIIA.

2. Ticket to Work and Work Incentives Improvement Act (TWWIIA) of 1999.
   a. Strove to make it more realistic and easier for a person with a disability to work.
   b. Removed a major disincentive to work by allowing individuals with disabilities to maintain their Medicare or Medicaid health-care benefits.
      (1) Allowed an individual with a disability to keep Medicare benefits for an additional 54 months after starting work.
      (2) Eliminated limits on Medicaid 'buy-in' options.
   c. Enabled consumers to have a choice in their service provider beyond public assistance programs.
   d. Established community-based vocational planning and assistance programs.
   e. Increased consumer choices for accessing employment support services.
   f. Allowed all states can design their own program.

3. Workforce Innovation and Opportunity Act (WIOA) of 2014.
   a. Required states to strategically align and coordinate their core workforce development programs to improve access to career services, education, and training through the one-stop service delivery system.
   b. Sought to more effectively meet the needs of employers and job seekers including persons with significant barriers to employment (e.g., veterans, individuals with disabilities, out-of-school and at-risk youth).
   c. Mandated the measurement and public reporting of the performance of education and training programs to help those seeking services make informed choices about which provider to use.

Key Legislation Specific to Technology

1. Assistive Technology (AT) Act of 2004.
   a. Improved access to and acquisition of AT by funding direct services to support individuals with all types of disabilities and all ages, in all environments including school, work, home, and leisure.

2. Technology Related Assistance for Individuals with Disabilities Act.
   a. Funded the development of technology and technologic aids for persons with disabilities to improve

communication, mobility, self-care, transportation, and education.

3. Title IV—Telecommunications of the ADA. Refer to Section on the ADA.
4. Telecommunications Act of 1996.
   a. Required providers of telecommunications systems and manufacturers of telecommunications equipment to make services (e.g., caller ID, operator assistance) and equipment (e.g., cell phones) usable by and accessible to individuals with disabilities, if at all possible.

Legislation Specific to Children and Youth

1. Child Abuse Prevention and Treatment Act (CAPTA).
   a. Defined child abuse and neglect as mental or physical injury, negligent treatment, maltreatment, or sexual abuse of a child less than 18 years of age by a person responsible for the child's welfare under circumstances that indicate that a child's welfare or health is being threatened or harmed.

> **RED FLAG:** Healthcare and education professionals, including OT practitioners, are ethically bound *and legally mandated* to report any suspected abuse or neglect to law enforcement officials.

   b. OT practitioners can serve as child welfare advocates.
   c. Direct OT intervention may be needed to remediate the emotional or physical disorders that result from abuse.
      (1) Refer to Chapter 5 for further information about child abuse and neglect.
2. Early Intervention and Education Acts.
   a. Multiple acts have provided the foundation for current EI and education services. These include:
      (1) Mandated free and appropriate education (FAPE) for all students regardless of ability or disability (aged 3–21), in the least restrictive environment.
         (a) Mainstreaming (i.e., integrating students with disabilities into classrooms) was the means to ensure education is provided in the least restrictive environment.
      (2) Requirements for public schools to provide OT to special education students if OT is needed for the student to benefit from the special education.
      (3) The designation of OT as a primary EI service.
      (4) Funding for family support services and programs to train professionals in EI.

      (5) Recommendations for states to develop infant and toddler programs (birth to three years).
         (a) Programs are voluntary and vary from state to state but all states participate to some degree.
         (b) OT is considered a primary developmental service.
3. Reauthorization and Amendment of Individuals with Disabilities Education Act.
   a. Clarified early intervention services and systems.
      (1) Mandated an Individual Family Service Plan (IFSP) for children birth through two years of age.
      (2) OT is identified as a primary early intervention service.
   b. Emphasized that the purpose of the IEP is to address each student's unique needs as related to their disability and decide how these needs can be served so that students with disabilities have full access to the general education curriculum and can participate in the general education classroom.
   c. Maintained the established definition of related services (including OT).
   d. Clarified that the IEP can include consideration of assistive technology and behavioral interventions, strategies, and supports (an area in which OT can offer a great deal).
   e. Stated that the IEP planning team is open to related personnel at the request of the parent or school, in addition to the regular education teacher, if the student is in a regular education class.
   f. Asserted that the education the student receives should prepare them for independent living and employment in adult life.
      (1) Transitional planning begins at the age of 14 (or younger if indicated) to help the student plan a course of study that will lead to post-school goals.
      (2) Transition services begin at the age of 16 (or younger if indicated) to provide student with a coordinated set of services to attain post-school goals.
         (a) These services can include community experience, specific instruction, and/or ADL and vocational assessment and intervention.
      (3) The student must be invited to attend IEP meetings that discuss their transition planning and services to allow for self-advocacy and self-determination.
      (4) This transition plan must be updated annually with appropriate service revision provided.
   g. Expanded orientation and mobility services by broadly interpreting them to include all students with disabilities.

h. Established that students with disabilities may be punished in the same manner as other students for serious offenses (i.e., carrying illicit drugs or a weapon). However, disciplinary prevention measures are stressed.

   (1) If disciplined students are removed to an alternative placement, they must still receive educational and related services.

4. Individuals with Disabilities Education Improvement Act.

a. Allowed each state to define developmental delay criteria to determine if an infant or toddler is eligible for early intervention in that state.

   (1) Typically, states define developmental delays quantitatively (e.g., a percentage of delay according to a standardized developmental assessment).

b. Required that an IFSP be completed to include the following.

   (1) The infant's or toddler's developmental level.

   (2) Family priorities, concerns, and resources.

   (3) The infant's or toddler's natural environments.

   (4) Measurable outcomes.

   (5) Projected, length, frequency, and duration of research-based services.

   (6) Transition plans to pre-school or other services, as appropriate.

c. Clarified the role of the parent and IFSP team in determining the site for service provision.

   (1) Requires states to maximize the provision of early intervention services in the infant's or toddler's natural environments, as appropriate.

d. Required states to establish procedures for the referral of infants and toddlers who are victims of abuse and/or neglect to early intervention services.

   (1) This provision was also included in the Keeping Children and Families Safe Act.

e. Clarified that a screening done by a specialist is not equivalent to an evaluation for eligibility for IDEA services.

f. Directly addressed the student's functional performance along with academic performance.

   (1) Required that evaluations for IDEA eligibility include relevant functional and developmental information, not just academic achievement data.

   (2) Expanded the IEP's annual goals to include academic *and* functional goals.

   (3) Specified that accommodations must be provided as needed to measure the functional performance and academic achievement of all students with disabilities.

   (4) Enabled services to be provided to students as soon as learning needs become apparent via a Response to Intervention (RtI) approach.

     (a) For more information about RtI services, refer to this Chapter's subsequent section on OT service provision in schools.

g. Provided for the piloting of a multi-year (not to exceed three years) IEP to allow for long-term planning and to coincide with a student's 'natural' transitions (e.g., pre-school to elementary school, middle school to high school).

   (1) This plan was made optional for parents.

h. Provided for increased flexibility in IEP meetings.

   (1) Allowed IEP team members to be excused from IEP meetings if their area of concern is not being addressed or modified at the meeting or if a written report is submitted prior to the meeting.

     (a) Required district and parental approval for a team member's absence. Parental approval must be in writing.

   (2) Allowed IEP revisions and/or amendments to be made by parents and districts after an annual IEP meeting.

     (a) Parents must be provided with a written copy of the revised/amended IEP.

   (3) Allowed the use of technological alternatives to face-to-face IEP meetings (i.e., videoconferences, conference calls).

i. Required that recommendations for early intervention, special education, related, and supplementary services and aids be made based on peer-reviewed research to the extent that this is practical.

j. Required that all students with disabilities be assessed in compliance with the Elementary and Secondary Education Act (ESEA) commonly known as No Child Left Behind Act.

   (1) The IEP team determines if the student should take an alternative assessment or the standard assessment with or without accommodations.

k. Provided for early coordinated intervening services for general education students from kindergarten through 12th grade who do not require special education services but who do need additional supports to succeed in school. Refer to prior section on RtI.

l. Clarified that the purpose of the IDEA is to prepare children with disabilities for further education, employment, and independent living.

m. Allowed school personnel to individually consider each case of a student with a disability who violates the school's code of conduct.

   (1) Students with disabilities who are disciplined must:

     (a) Be provided with services to continue to progress toward achieving their IEP goals.

(b) Receive appropriate functional behavioral assessments and interventions, and service modifications as needed to address their conduct violation(s).

5. Every Student Succeeds Act (ESSA).
   a. Reauthorized the No Child Left Behind (NCLB) act, which was formerly called the Elementary and Secondary Education Act (ESEA).
   b. A general education law that emphasizes standards-based education with a focus on improving the educational opportunities and outcomes for children from lower-income families.
   c. Considers OT practitioners to be specialized instructional support personnel (SISP).
   d. Requires schools to provide accommodations, if needed by students, for mandated tests.
      (1) OT practitioners can recommend testing alternatives and/or classroom accommodations.

Legislation Specific to Older Adults

1. Age Discrimination in Employment Act.
   a. Prohibited employment practices that discriminate or unfairly affect workers 40 years and older.
   b. Prohibited mandatory retirement of older workers.
      (1) Employers cannot fix a retirement age.
2. Freedom to Work Act.
   a. Amended the Social Security Act to enable Americans receiving retirement Social Security (SS) benefits to be able to work without affecting their SS income.
      (1) There are no income restrictions in this amendment.
3. Omnibus Budget Reconciliation Act (OBRA) of 1990.
   a. Applied to all nursing homes that receive federal money for Medicare or Medicaid patients.
   b. Emphasized attending to resident rights, autonomy, and self-determination; providing quality of care; and enhancing quality of life within nursing homes.
   c. Mandated a comprehensive resident assessment system, the Minimal Data Set (MDS), which is administered upon admission and thereafter on an annual basis, unless there is a significant change in the resident's condition.
      (1) MDS is coordinated by an RN. Occupational therapists can contribute information.
   d. Psychosocial well-being and activity pursuit patterns must be considered along with the resident's physical condition and cognitive abilities.
      (1) This has broadened OT's role in nursing homes.
   e. Mandated that the evaluation and treatment of conditions found during the MDS follow specific guidelines called the Resident Assessment Protocols (RAP).
      (1) The structured approach to assessment is called the Resident Assessment Instrument (RAI).
      (2) Individualized care plans must be established within specific time frames.
   f. The enhancement of quality of life through restraint reduction and the provision of restraint-free environments are strongly emphasized.
      (1) Nursing homes must show evidence of consultation by an occupational or physical therapist for consideration of interventions that are less restrictive than restraints.
      (2) Refer to Chapter 16 for a description of OT restraint reduction interventions.
   g. Aimed to guarantee that residents have the right to choose how they want to receive care and live their lives.
      (1) Residents should have a choice in determining their ADL, and community participation activities.
      (2) Residents should be able to function as independently as possible.
   h. Asserted that post-discharge plans must meet specific criteria including client or caregiver education.

Service Delivery Models

Overview

1. The major service delivery models that are used in the United States are medical, education, community, and telehealth.
   a. Box 4-14 describes key features of each model.
2. Criteria for determining a service delivery model.
   a. The type of setting.
   b. The philosophy and mission of the particular setting and department.
   c. The role the OT practitioner plays as a team member within that particular setting.
   d. The needs, goals, and current and expected environment of the person.

BOX 4-14 ▷ Service Delivery Models

- **Medical model**
  - Views the individual with a disability and/or illness as a person who has incurred a physiological insult that has resulted in reduced functional capacity.
  - Focus is placed on identifying the deficits and limitation caused by disease or dysfunction.
  - Intervention addresses the disease, dysfunction, client factors, and/or performance skill deficits that contribute to decreased function.
  - OT frames of reference that address the pathological process of the disease and/or resulting dysfunction (e.g., biomechanical, neurodevelopmental, cognitive disabilities) are typically used in this model.

- **Education Model**
  - Views the individual with a disability and/or illness as needing knowledge and/or skills.
  - Focus is placed on identifying the gaps in knowledge and skills that hinder successful engagement in desired roles and environments.
  - Intervention focuses on the acquisition of knowledge, the learning of strategies and skills, and the development of competencies to successfully participate in the environment and desired roles.
  - OT frames of reference that are based on learning theories to facilitate adaptation in the environment (e.g., role acquisition, cognitive remediation, psychoeducational) are typically used in this model.

- **Community Model**
  - Views the individual with a disability and/or illness as lacking the skills, resources, and supports needed for community participation.
  - Focus is placed on identifying and developing the skills needed to engage in one's chosen environment; educational approaches are used.
  - If skills cannot be developed, community resources and supports are identified and developed to enable participation within the person's chosen environment(s).
  - OT frames of reference promote development of performance skills and/or engagement in desired occupational roles within the individual's unique performance contexts (e.g., lifestyle performance, occupation adaptation).

- **Telehealth Model**
  - A service delivery model that can include features of the previous models by providing medical, rehabilitative, and/or educational services via information and communication technologies (ICT) to clients who are in a different physical location than the practitioner.
  - Services can be provided in a synchronous manner (i.e., delivered in real time via ICT) or in an asynchronous manner (i.e., storing and forwarding information).
  - Telemedicine is the term used when telehealth is provided within the medical model.

(1) Chapters 11-16 describe OT frames of reference and evaluation and intervention methods that are used in a diversity of service delivery models.

3. As a result of legislative initiatives and health-care system changes, service delivery is evolving from medical-based models and settings to more community- and home-based models and settings (e.g., IDEA has solidified schools as a practice setting; legislation enacted and practices initiated during the COVID-19 epidemic have demonstrated the efficacy of telehealth).

4. Implications for OT practice.
   a. Fewer practitioners may work in hospitals and long-term care facilities.
   b. More practitioners may work in community- and home-based settings (e.g., primary care, day treatment, home care, school settings).

EXAM HINT: The NBCOT® OTR® exam content outline identifies knowledge of the "considerations for selecting, preparing, and adapting the intervention environment to support optimal engagement and promote goal achievement . . . (including) ensuring privacy during telehealth sessions" (NBCOT®, 2022, p. 8) and the "application of federal regulations . . . related to service delivery across occupational therapy practice settings . . . (including) health care legislation" (NBCOT®, 2022, p. 14) as essential for competent and safe practice. Therefore, correct answers to NBCOT® exam items will be HIPAA compliant, regardless of the service delivery model that is presented in the exam item scenario.

▶ Institutional Practice Settings

Acute Care Hospitals

1. Admission is for a medical or psychiatric diagnosis that cannot be treated on an outpatient basis.
   a. Initial onset of a new illness or major health problem.
   b. Acute exacerbation of a chronic illness.
   c. In psychiatry, a person may be involuntarily admitted to an acute unit if they are considered to be a danger to self or others, or as having a grave disability.
2. LOS is determined by diagnosis and presenting symptoms.
   a. LOS can be limited to one to seven days.
   b. Longer LOS requires significant documentation to justify need for further hospitalization.
   c. Ongoing need for care frequently results in discharge to another setting.
3. OT evaluation process focuses on quick and accurate screening of major difficulties impeding function (e.g., cognitive status, home safety skills).
4. OT intervention focus.
   a. Stabilization of client's status.
   b. Engagement of the client in the therapeutic relationship and purposeful activities/meaningful occupations so that they can see that change is possible, thereby increasing motivation to pursue follow-up.
   c. Discharge planning and after-care referrals.
   d. Family, caregiver, and consumer education.
5. The role of an acute care OT practitioner can be a generalist or a specialist (e.g., neonatology).

> **EXAM HINT:** The NBCOT® exam is designed to test entry-level OT competencies; thus, specialized practice roles that require advanced knowledge and skills will not be evaluated on the NBCOT® exam.

Subacute Care/Intermediate-Care Facilities (ICFs)

1. Admission is for a medical or psychiatric diagnosis that has progressed from an acute stage but has not stabilized sufficiently to be treated on an outpatient basis.
   a. Service recipients are able to participate in longer skilled therapy services than those in acute care.
2. LOS is determined by diagnosis and presenting symptoms.
   a. LOS can range from 5–30 days.
   b. Longer LOS requires significant documentation to justify need for further hospitalization.

   c. Ongoing need for intervention or long-term care frequently results in discharge to another setting.
3. OT evaluation can include more in-depth assessments and more thorough observations of client's functional performance.
4. OT intervention focus.
   a. Functional improvements in performance skills and areas of occupation.
   b. Active engagement of the client in the treatment planning, implementation, and reevaluation process.
   c. Discharge planning to expected environment.
5. Subacute care and ICFs can be housed in hospitals or SNFs.

Long-Term Acute Care Hospitals

1. Admission is for chronic or catastrophic illnesses or disabilities that require extensive medical care and/or dependency on life support or ventilators.
   a. Patients often have multiple diagnoses with major complications.
2. The average LOS is greater than 25 days to maintain Medicare certification.
3. OT evaluation and intervention are often limited by the population's severe and complex medical needs.
   a. For all patients, evaluation and intervention are concerned with palliative care and the prevention and treatment of complications (e.g., positioning to prevent decubiti and contractures).
   b. For individuals who are cognitively intact, the focus of evaluation and intervention is mastery of the environment and the attainment of client-centered goals.

Rehabilitation Hospitals

1. Admission is for a disability that is medically stable but that has residual functional deficits requiring skilled rehabilitation services.
2. LOS is determined by presenting deficits and rehabilitation potential.
   a. LOS can range from a week to months.
   b. Documentation requirements supporting the need for an extended LOS are dependent on institutional, state, and third-party payer guidelines.
   c. LOS ends when coverage is expended. The client is then discharged to the appropriate environment.
      (1) A SNF.
      (2) A supportive community residence.
      (3) Home/independent living.

3. OT evaluation can be extensive and focus on all performance skills and patterns, areas of occupation, and occupational roles that will be required in the expected environment.
   a. Environmental assessments of planned discharge environment must be completed.
4. OT intervention focus.
   a. Functional improvement in performance skills and patterns, areas of occupation, and occupational roles.
   b. Development of compensatory strategies for residual deficits and client factors.
   c. Provision of adaptive equipment and training in use of the equipment to promote independent function.
   d. Modification of the discharge environment, as needed, to enhance function.
   e. Education of the individual, family, and caregivers on abilities, limitations, compensatory techniques, and advocacy skills.

Long-Term Hospitals

1. Admission is for a medical or psychiatric diagnosis that is chronic with the presence of symptoms that cannot be treated on an outpatient basis.
2. LOS is determined by diagnosis and presenting symptoms.
   a. LOS can range from a month to years.
   b. Documentation requirements supporting a need for increased LOS are dependent upon institutional, third-party payer, and/or state guidelines.
   c. LOS in private long-term hospitals is determined by insurance coverage. When coverage is expended, an alternative discharge environment is needed for the client.
      (1) A state-run long-term hospital.
      (2) A SNF.
      (3) Home or supportive residence.
3. OT evaluation can be extensive due to increased LOS.
4. OT intervention focus.
   a. Functional improvements in performance skills and patterns and areas of occupation.
   b. Development of compensatory strategies for residual deficits and client factors.
   c. Maintenance of quality of life.
   d. Development of skills for discharge to the least restrictive environment.

Skilled Nursing Facilities (SNFs)

1. Admission is for a medical or psychiatric condition that is stable with no acute symptoms but residual symptoms and/or functional limitations require skilled 24-hour care.

2. Due to payer constraints on acute hospital stays, many individuals with potential to improve are admitted to SNFs for medical care and rehabilitation.
3. LOS can range less than a month to the individual's lifetime. Several factors influence LOS.
   a. The progression of an illness.
   b. Availability of family and/or community supports.
   c. Insurance coverage.
   d. The recovery of function that results in the person no longer requiring 24-hour skilled care.
4. OT evaluation and intervention is guided by Medicare standards.
   a. For individuals with rehabilitation potential, the focus of evaluation and intervention is the same as identified in this Chapter's section on rehabilitation hospitals.
   b. For individuals without rehabilitation potential, evaluation and intervention is more concerned with maintenance of quality of life as identified in this Chapter's section on palliative care.

Forensic Settings

1. Admission is due to engagement in criminal activity by a person. The person can be remanded to a variety of settings depending on the nature of the crime and if a psychiatric diagnosis has been made.
   a. Jail: a city or county facility that is the individual's first entry into the criminal justice system and the placement for those convicted of crimes with sentences of less than a year.
   b. Prison: a state or federal facility for individuals found guilty of crimes with sentences greater than a year.
   c. Forensic psychiatric hospital or unit: a specialized hospital or unit within a hospital which provides inpatient psychiatric care for individuals convicted of a crime and found guilty but mentally ill or not guilty by reason of insanity.
2. LOS is determined by court-ordered directives and criminal sentences.
3. The availability and quality of services vary greatly from none in most jails to extensive in some forensic hospitals.
4. Due to serious gaps in mental health and social services, the incarceration rate of persons with mental illness is significant (e.g., a homeless person with schizophrenia who steals food due to hunger is arrested instead of receiving services to directly address homelessness and hunger).
5. OT evaluation and intervention focus.
   a. Determination of an individual's competency to stand trial, in forensic psychiatry settings.
   b. Areas similar to those described under rehabilitation hospitals to develop community living skills

needed for successful community reintegration upon release.

c. Facilitation of skills and provision of structured programs to enable the person to function at their highest level within their current environment

since discharge may be delayed or not possible, depending on the nature of the crime.

d. Restoration of competency to stand trial in forensic psychiatry settings.

Community-Based Practice Settings

Early Intervention Programs

1. Acceptance criteria for an early intervention evaluation are based on 'at-risk' status of the infant or toddler who is under the age of three. This can include the following.
   a. Birth complications.
   b. Suspected delays in development.
   c. Failure to thrive.
   d. Maternal substance abuse during pregnancy.
   e. Birth to an adolescent/teen mother.
   f. Established disability/diagnosis.
2. Acceptance criteria for early intervention services are based on the following criteria.
   a. The extent of the developmental delay (typically a 33% delay in one area of development or a 25% delay in two areas).
   b. An established diagnosis/disability.
3. Length of service provision.
   a. If the infant/child qualifies for services, an IFSP is completed by the service coordinator after a review of all assessments and in collaboration with the family and early intervention team.
      (1) Refer to this Chapter's prior section on legislation specific to children for more information about the IFSP.
   b. Six-month reviews are submitted by all professionals to determine if services should continue.
4. OT evaluation.
   a. Assessment of five developmental areas.
      (1) Cognitive.
      (2) Physical.
      (3) Communication.
      (4) Social-emotional.
      (5) Adaptive.
   b. Determination of the effects of current development on the occupational areas of play and activities of daily living.
   c. Evaluations need to be written in a strength-oriented manner.

d. Functional goals must be written in family friendly terms and include levels of functioning, unique needs, and recommended services.
5. OT intervention process.
   a. Development of cognitive/process, psychosocial/communication/interaction, and sensorimotor skills.
   b. Development of play and activities of daily living skills.
   c. Provision of family education.
   d. Provision of advocacy and advocacy training.
   e. Transition planning from early intervention to preschool is essential.
6. Discharge from or discontinuation of EI services.
   a. Children can be discharged from EI services if their goals have been met and no additional needs have been identified.
   b. A child ages out of EI at three years of age and can be referred to an outpatient sensory clinic and/or the IU for additional services depending on needs identified.

Schools

1. Acceptance criteria for OT services as a related service in an educational setting.
   a. The child requires special education services and OT will enable the child to benefit from special education.
   b. Occupational therapy will facilitate the child's participation in educational activities and enhance the child's functional performance.
   c. Referrals are received from the previous agency that provided early intervention services, the child's teacher, and/or school's child study team.
   d. The school reviews the referral and, if indicated, recommends an OT evaluation.
      (1) If an OT evaluation has already been completed, the need for OT intervention services is discussed.

(2) The frequency, length of sessions, and duration of the intervention are also determined.

2. Length of services is dependent on the impact of OT services on the child's abilities and prevention of loss of abilities.

   a. If OT services can improve the child's ability to participate in education-related activities and allow full access to the general education curriculum, services can be continued.

   b. A review of services and progress made toward the child's individualized education plan (IEP) is conducted on an annual basis.

3. OT evaluation.

   a. Assess client factors, performance skills and patterns, and areas of occupation that impact on the educational and functional performance of the child within the school.

     (1) Findings are used to contribute to the IEP, in which goals and objectives are formulated to address the overall educational needs of the student.

   b. Assess the child's functional and developmental level to contribute to the Functional Behavioral Analysis.

4. OT intervention focus.

   a. Based on an educational model versus a medical model.

   b. Addresses the student's functional performance along with academic performance.

   c. Activities are utilized to address the goals and objectives documented in the IEP using both corrective and compensatory methods.

   d. Assistive technology and transition services, in accordance with the regulations of IDEA, are provided.

   e. Performance skill deficits and client factors (i.e., sensorimotor, cognitive/process, and psychosocial/communication/interaction) are treated to improve the child's ability to participate in and perform education-related activities within a school setting.

   f. Skills in the occupations of ADL, school, and play are developed to improve the child's ability to participate in and perform education-related activities within a school setting.

   g. Skills for adult life post-school are developed in accordance with the student's transition plan.

5. Transition planning for post-secondary life.

   a. Addresses skills for life after school including post-secondary education, vocational training, employment, and independent living.

   b. Begins at age 14 or 15.

   c. Student active participation in their transition planning should be encouraged.

     (1) As per the Reauthorization and Amendment of IDEA students must be invited to their IEP meetings during which their transition plans are being discussed.

6. The OT practitioner needs to know the school district's and state's funding sources, and regulations and interpretations of the federal laws regarding education. Refer to this Chapter's section on legislation.

7. The role of OT practitioners in school-based practice has expanded beyond education-related services to include programs that address students' psychosocial needs and prevent school violence.

   a. School-wide Positive Behavioral Supports (SWPBS), Response to Intervention (RtI) and Early Intervening Services (EIS) may be a component of school-based OT service provision.[5]

     (1) SWPBS is a program that is designed to create a positive school environment to improve behavioral, emotional, social, and academic outcomes for all students.

       (a) Potentially problematic situations are prevented and de-escalated before problem behaviors occur.

       (b) Table 4-4 describes the tenets of SWPBS and provides examples as to how these tenets can be actualized in practice. for each.

       (c) For students with chronic misbehaviors, individualized support plans are developed.

     (2) RtI is an evidence-based, structured multi-tiered intervention approach that uses EIS to address academic difficulties and PBS to address behavioral problems early in a child's education. Table 4-5 describes the three intervention tiers of RtI and provides an intervention example for each tier.

       (a) An RtI is designed to meet the needs of children who are having difficulty learning without requiring a full evaluation as required for an IEP.

       (b) The provision of classroom modifications (e.g., the use of a therapy ball as a seat instead of a standard desk chair) and the use of educational strategies (e.g., incorporating movement into class lessons) can positively impact children's ability to learn.

       (c) If the RtI approach is not effective, the occupational therapist can recommend the completion of a comprehensive evaluation and the development and implementation of an IEP.

---

[5] Karen Gualtieri MS, OTR/L contributed to this section on SWPBS and RtI.

Chapter 4

Table 4-4

Key Tenets of School-wide Positive Behavioral Support (SWPBS)

TENET	PRACTICE EXAMPLES
Clearly and consistently communicate behavioral expectations.	• Conduct assembly for all students at the beginning of the year to set clear expectations. • Hang posters and other visuals in hallways and classrooms to provide daily reminders. • Discuss the different behavioral expectations for different settings (e.g., behavior on the playground has different expectations than the behavior in the library).
Teach positive behaviors through specific, pre-determined strategies.	• Strategies to teach positive behaviors can be school specific, subject/classroom specific, and/or child specific depending on need. • They can include modeling positive behaviors, verbally praising positive behavior, and/or using a token-based reward system. • School-wide reward systems are individualized and include strategies that work for the students and teachers.
Provide consistent consequences and procedure for handling misbehaviors.	• Consequences should be consistent and explicitly discussed as part of the behavioral system. • If misbehaviors consistently occur with the same student or with several students within the same setting, a behavioral analysis should be conducted to determine if change to the setting, change to the expectations, or individualized behavioral plans to support positive behavior outcomes are needed.
Identify and acknowledge positive behaviors.	• The school's culture should have a primary focus on identifying positive behaviors. – Research suggests that five positive interactions for every behavior correction leads to an overall increase in positive behavior (Cook et al., 2017).

Table 4-5

Response to Intervention (RtI) Intervention Tiers

INTERVENTION TIERS	LEVEL OF SUPPORT	INTERVENTION EXAMPLE
Tier 1: Universal Instruction	Early screening, social, and behavioral supports provided for the entire student population throughout the school year.	An OT practitioner visits kindergarten classrooms during the first week of school to demonstrate the opening of lunch containers and snack bags and facilitate practice of these tasks by the kindergarten students to enable their independence during lunch and snack time.
Tier 2: Targeted Intervention	Services provided in the classroom or in a small group setting that address the specific needs of the students.	An OT practitioner conducts a weekly lunch group to develop the self-esteem and social interaction skills of a small group of students who self-referred themselves to the group or were recommended to the group by teachers or other staff.
Tier 3: Intensive Interventions	Designed to meet the specific needs of individual students and typically provided in a 1:1 intensive service model.	An OT practitioner provides one on one intervention to address an individual student's specific sensory processing and emotional regulation needs to develop the skills they need to effectively navigate the school day.

Supported Education Programs

1. Participant criteria include adolescents or adults who require intervention to develop skills that are needed to succeed in secondary and/or postsecondary education.
   a. The person may have never developed these skills or lost them due to a psychiatric disability or mental health problems.
2. LOS is determined by the agency's funding and the person's attainment of goals.
   a. Discharge is upon entry into, or completion of, an educational program or the attainment of a graduate equivalency degree (GED).

3. OT evaluation is focused on the individual's client factors and performance skills and patterns that impact on the occupational role of student.
4. OT intervention focus.
   a. Improvement in performance skills and patterns that are needed for the occupational role of student (e.g., time management and task prioritization).
   b. Education and training in compensatory strategies to support academic performance (e.g., studying in a quiet room).
   c. Exploration of participant's educational interests and aptitudes to ensure self-determined engagement in a school, college, technical training program, or community-based adult-education class(es).

Prevocational and Vocational Programs

1. Prevocational programs.
   a. Participant criteria include adolescents or adults who require intervention to develop skills that are prerequisite to work.
      (1) The person may have never developed these skills due to developmental delays, environmental insufficiencies, illness, or disability.
      (2) The person may have lost these skills due to illness or disability.
   b. LOS is determined by the agency's funding and the person's attainment of goals.
      (1) Discharge is usually to a vocational program.
      (2) Discharge to a work setting can occur if sufficient abilities are developed.
   c. OT evaluation is focused on the individual's task skills, social interaction skills, work habits, interests, and aptitudes.
   d. OT intervention focus.
      (1) Improvement in task skills and social skills that are prerequisite to vocational training or work.
      (2) Development of work habits and abilities.
      (3) Exploration of work interests and aptitudes to ensure discharge to a relevant vocational training program, school, or work setting.
2. Vocational programs.
   a. Acceptance is for the development of specific vocational skills.
      (1) Person has the prerequisite abilities to work (e.g., good task skills and work habits) but requires training for a specific job and/or ongoing structure, support, and/or supervision to maintain employment.
      (2) Person has to develop their work capacities to a level acceptable for competitive employment (e.g., strength and endurance).
   b. LOS is determined by the agency's funding and the person's attainment of goals.
      (1) In some supported employment programs, (e.g., rehabilitation [sheltered] workshops) and discharge is not always a goal.
         (a) Maintenance of the person in these structured work environments can be the desired objective for some individuals while others will be discharged to other programs or to work.
      (2) Transitional employment programs (TEPs) are generally time limited (three to six months) with discharge to competitive employment, supported employment programs, or rehabilitation workshops.
   c. OT evaluation is focused on the individual's functional skills and deficits related to work in their current and expected vocational environment.
   d. OT intervention focus.
      (1) Remediation of underlying performance skill deficits and compensation for client factors that affect work performance.
      (2) Development of general work abilities and specific job skills.
      (3) Consultation to and/or supervision of vocational direct care staff.
      (4) Identification and implementation of reasonable accommodations in accordance with the ADA.
      (5) Referral to state offices of vocational and educational services (i.e., One-Stop Centers) for persons with disabilities for further evaluation, education, and training.

Residential and Transitional Living Programs

1. Acceptance criteria can include the following.
   a. A developmental, medical, or psychiatric condition that has resulted in functional limitations that impede independent living; however, these are not severe enough to require hospitalization.
   b. Homeless or eminent risk for homelessness.
   c. Survivor of domestic/intimate partner violence.
   d. Impending release from a prison to the community.
2. The type of residential or transitional living program that a person is eligible for will depend on the above acceptance criteria.
   a. Residential programs for persons who have functional limitations that impede their ability to live independently are on a continuum that ranges from 24-hour supervised group homes and quarter way houses, to halfway houses with primarily evening and weekend staff, to supportive apartments with weekly or biweekly "check-in" appointments with a case manager.
      (1) The person's functional abilities and limitations determine the residential level of care needed.
   b. Homeless shelters are specifically for persons who are homeless.
      (1) Homeless shelters typically have specific additional parameters for acceptance (e.g., gender, age, no active substance use, unaccompanied adults with no children in their care, families).
      (2) Some shelters have active programs to help a person obtain transitional and/or permanent housing.

(a) Because untreated mental illness and substance abuse disorders often contribute to homelessness, some shelters adopt a treatment first approach that requires the homeless person to effectively address their substance use and/or mental illness prior to receiving housing and to remain in recovery to maintain their housing.

(b) The Housing First approach does not require a homeless person to have recovered from their mental illness and/or a substance use disorder prior to obtaining housing. This approach also does not require a person to be actively engaged in treatment to maintain housing.

- Housing First programs offer services to help residents attain and maintain housing stability, health, and well-being, but participation is not required.
- Housing First proponents hold that treatment is more effective and outcomes more sustainable when a person has a secure, safe, supportive place to live.

c. Domestic violence shelters are specifically for survivors of domestic/intimate partner violence.

(1) Domestic violence shelters may have additional parameters for acceptance (e.g., gender, unaccompanied adults with no children in their care, parents with children, older adults).

(2) Most domestic violence shelters have active programs to help survivors develop the skills they need to be safe and live a self-directed life. Refer to chapter 14 for information about domestic/intimate partner violence and OT services for survivors.

d. Residential reentry centers are specifically for persons who are transitioning from prisons to community.

(1) The services provided in these centers can range from comprehensive and coordinated to limited and fragmented.

3. LOS for transitional living programs (e.g., shelters, quarter way and halfway house programs) is determined by the mission and objectives of the program and/or by the program's funding source,

a. Long-term and permanent housing options (i.e., group homes and supportive apartments) are available and are typically funded through the individual's social service benefits.

4. OT evaluation is focused on assessment of the individual's skills for living in the community and determination of the social and environmental resources and supports needed to maintain the individual in their current and expected living environment.

5. OT intervention focus.

a. Consultation to and/or supervision of residential program staff.

b. Remediation of underlying performance skill deficits and compensation for client factors that affect independent living skills.

c. ADL training, activity adaptation, and environmental modifications to facilitate community living skills.

d. Referral to appropriate residential services along the continuum of care as individual's functional level improves.

e. Education about the ADA, the Fair Housing Act, and Section 8 Housing.

Partial Hospitalization and Day Hospital/Day Treatment Programs

1. Admission is for a medical or psychiatric condition that has been sufficiently stabilized to enable an individual to be discharged home or to a community residence (e.g., a halfway house or supported apartment); however, the individual still has symptoms remaining which require active treatment.

2. Treatment is up to five days per week with multiple interventions scheduled each day.

3. LOS is determined by diagnosis, presenting symptoms, and response to intervention.

a. LOS can vary from one week to six months, it is usually shorter for partial hospital programs (PHPs).

b. Documentation requirements supporting the need for an extended LOS are dependent on institutional, state, and/or third-party payer guidelines.

c. Once LOS is expended, discharge is usually to a less intensive community day program.

4. OT evaluation is focused on the individual's functional skills and limitations in their performance areas and the occupational roles that are required in their current and expected environment(s).

5. OT intervention focus.

a. Functional improvement in areas of occupation and occupational role functioning.

b. Remediation of underlying performance skill deficits and compensation for client factors that affect functional performance.

c. Development of skills for community living and identification of community supports for independent living, health management, and community participation.

Clubhouse Programs

1. Membership is open to adults and older adults with a current mental illness or a history of mental illness.
   a. All members have equal access to all clubhouse functions and opportunities regardless of functional level or diagnosis.
   b. Individuals who pose a significant and direct threat to the safety of the clubhouse community are the only persons excluded.
2. Services are provided by staff and members with the responsibilities of operating the clubhouse shared equally by staff and members under the oversight of a director.
   a. Due to this role equality, it can be difficult to distinguish between members and paid staff.
   b. Staff's main role is to engage membership, provide needed support and structure, and enable recovery.
3. Individual schedules will vary to meet each person's unique needs and interests.
   a. Clubhouses are open at least five days per week. Many are open seven days per week.
   b. The daily schedule is organized around the 'work-ordered' day, which parallels typical working hours to engage members and staff in the running of the clubhouse.
   c. Evening and weekend schedules are focused on avocational interests and recreational pursuits.
   d. Additional services that can be provided include literacy and education programs, transitional employment programs and placements, independent competitive employment assistance, community support and outreach services, housing programs, and legal and financial advisement.
4. LOS is indefinite and members can exit and reenter a clubhouse community at will.
5. OT evaluation and intervention are not provided in a formalized manner.
   a. The role of the OT practitioner is integrated into the clubhouse model which has staff acting as generalists who contribute to the development and enrichment of members' abilities and the promotion of their recovery.

Adult Day Care

1. Admission is for adults and elders with chronic physical and/or psychosocial impairments, and/or for individuals who are frail but semi-independent.

2. Services are provided in a congregate or group setting.
3. Individual schedules will vary.
   a. Flexibility in scheduling is provided to address daily caregiver needs and allow for planned respite.
   b. Schedules can range from one afternoon per week to five full days.
4. LOS is indefinite.
   a. Ongoing services are provided to individuals with chronic conditions who might otherwise be institutionalized or to individuals who are frail and need ongoing support (e.g., cooked meals, socialization opportunities).
5. OT evaluation is focused on the individual's functional skills and deficits in the areas of occupation, their home environment, and the adult day center's environment.
6. OT intervention focus.
   a. Maintenance of the healthy, functional aspects of the individual and facilitation of adaptation to impairments.
   b. Engagement in purposeful activities that provide appropriate stimulation, reflect lifelong interests, develop new interests, and foster a sense of community with other participants.
   c. Caregiver education, support groups, home visits, consultations, and referrals to community resources.
   d. Modifications to the day care center's environment and the individual's home environment to maximize the person's comfort in, and mastery and control of, these environments.

Outpatient Ambulatory Care

1. Acceptance criteria for outpatient ambulatory care.
   a. A medical or psychiatric condition that requires skilled evaluation and intervention but it is not serious enough to warrant hospitalization.
   b. A medical or psychiatric condition that has sufficiently stabilized to enable the individual to be discharged from a hospital, but their remaining symptoms require active treatment.
2. Outpatient services are provided in private clinics, medical offices, and/or hospital satellite centers.
3. Intervention is usually provided in short 30- to 60-minute sessions once a day for up to five days a week.
4. LOS is determined by diagnosis, presenting symptoms, response to treatment, and insurance coverage or ability to pay a fee for service.
5. The client is actively engaged in the intervention planning, implementation, reevaluation, and discharge process.

6. OT evaluation is focused on the individual's client factors and functional assets and deficits in their performance skills and patterns, areas of occupation, and their home, work, and leisure environments.
7. OT intervention focus.
   a. Remediation of underlying performance skill deficits that affect functional occupational performance.
   b. Functional improvements in performance areas and occupational roles.
   c. Compensatory strategies for remaining performance skill deficits and client factors.
   d. Health promotion and prevention.
   e. Consumer, family, and caregiver education.

Home Health

1. Acceptance criteria for home health services.
   a. Presence of a medical or psychiatric condition that is not serious enough to warrant hospitalization or for a condition that has sufficiently stabilized to enable the individual to be discharged from a hospital but that still has remaining symptoms requiring active treatment.
   b. Reimbursers can have strict and variable criteria for qualifying for home health care. Refer to prior section on Medicare and third-party reimbursement.
2. Treatment is usually provided in 60-minute sessions, once a day for up to five days a week, as determined by insurance coverage.
3. LOS is determined by diagnosis, presenting symptoms, response to treatment, insurance coverage, or ability to pay a fee for service.
4. OT evaluation is focused on the individual's client factors and functional skills and deficits in their performance skills and patterns, areas of occupation, and the occupational roles that are required in the current and expected environment(s).
5. OT intervention focus.
   a. Active engagement of the client, family, and caregivers in the treatment planning, and other places of accommodation, implementation, and reevaluation processes.
   b. Functional improvement in areas of occupation and occupational role functioning within the home.
   c. Remediation of underlying performance skill deficits and compensation for client factors that affect functional performance within the home.
   d. Education of the family, caregivers, and/or home health aides to provide appropriate care and/or assistance as needed.
   e. Environmental modifications and activity adaptations that maintain optimal functioning and improve quality of life.

   f. Increasing ability to resume occupational roles outside of the home.
   g. Prevention of hospitalization and avoidance or delay of residential institutional placement.

Hospice and Palliative Care

1. Hospice.
   a. Acceptance criteria for hospice services.
      (1) Terminal illness that has a life expectancy of six months or less.
   b. Services are most often provided in the home with the type and quantity of services determined by the needs of the individual, their family, significant others, and caregivers.
      (1) Hospice services may also be provided in an independent facility or in a special unit of a SNF or a hospital.
   c. LOS is determined by the person's terminal outcome.
   d. OT evaluation is focused on determining the individual's occupational functioning and their physical, psychosocial, spiritual, and environmental needs that are most important to them.
   e. OT intervention focus.
      (1) Maintenance of the individual's control over their life.
      (2) Facilitation of engagement in meaningful occupations and purposeful activities that are consistent with the individual's roles, values, choices, interests, aspirations, abilities, and hopes and that contribute to a satisfactory quality of life.
      (3) Reduction or removal of distressing symptoms and pain.
      (4) Environmental modifications and activity adaptations that maintain optimal functioning and improve quality of life.
      (5) Caregiver and family education and support to maintain optimal functioning and improve quality of life for all.
2. Palliative care.
   a. Acceptance criteria for palliative care services.
      (1) A serious illness that affects a person's functional abilities and quality of life, regardless of their age, stage of illness, or life expectancy.
   b. Services are most often provided in the home with the type and quantity of services determined by the needs of the individual, their family, significant others, and caregivers.
      (1) Palliative care services can be provided along with curative treatment services.
   c. LOS is indefinite.
   d. OT evaluation and intervention foci are the same as hospice.

Case Management Programs

1. There are two different focuses to case management programs: one is clinical and one is administrative.
   a. Clinical case management provides individualized support and intervention to a client with a serious illness which significantly limits their ability to access and/or engage in existing community services and/or therapeutic programs, ensuring that the person is able to remain in the community and not be rehospitalized.
   b. Administrative case management connects a person with a serious illness to the appropriate and needed community services and/or therapeutic programs, overseeing this service provision to ensure that quality of care in a cost-effective manner is achieved.
2. Services can be provided in an office and/or in the individual's home and community.
3. LOS is determined by the individual's ability to independently access needed services and by funding availability.
4. OT evaluation is focused on the individual's client factors and functional skills and deficits in their performance skills and patterns, areas of occupation, and the occupational roles that are required in their current and expected environment.
   a. Assessment of the individual's supports and barriers for community integration is critical.
5. Case management interventions can be purely referral-based in the administrative model or encompass the full range of interventions in the clinical model, (e.g., one-on-one counseling, family education, ADL training, community reentry).
   a. Both models aim to prevent regression and rehospitalization and promote optimal functioning and quality of life.
   b. Both models actively engage the individual and family in the intervention planning, implementation, and re-evaluation processes.
   c. Both models plan discharge, if appropriate, to an environment that will best serve an individual's needs.

Wellness and Prevention Programs

1. Acceptance is most often by an individual's self-referral to meet a personal need or by an institution's provision of a program to its members or employees (e.g., a parenting skills class for pregnant teens in a school).
2. Programs have been developed to serve populations considered at risk and are held in offices or individual's residences and/or at community sites.
3. LOS is determined by the individual. It is usually influenced by program's planned length (e.g., a six-week joint protection program) or by individual's achievement of a desired outcome (e.g., smoking cessation).
4. OT evaluation focuses on risk factors for illnesses and disabilities and the individual's functional skills and deficits in the occupational roles that are required in their current and expected environment.
5. OT intervention focus.
   a. Disease prevention and health promotion.
   b. Interventions can range from the traditional domain of OT (e.g., home safety and environmental modifications), to contemporary areas of concern (e.g., stress management, smoking cessation, life coaching).
   c. Refer to Chapter 3 for definitions of and specific interventions for primary, secondary, and tertiary prevention.

Private/Independent Practice

Overview

1. In any and all of the previously mentioned community and institutional settings, the OT practitioner can work in an entrepreneurial manner by negotiating a fee-for-service agreement and/or a long-term contract.

2. Private practitioners can also open their own free-standing clinics.
3. A provider number is required for a private practitioner to receive third-party payment.
4. Private practitioners must abide by all state and third-party payer regulations for evaluation, intervention, and documentation.

Service Management

Chapter 4

Management Principles, Functions, and Strategies

1. The use of different management styles (i.e., the manager's characteristic way of performing management tasks) has a significant impact on quality, change, and growth. Refer to Chapter 3's section on leadership styles.
2. Box 4-15 outlines key characteristics of effective managers.
3. Administrative functions of management include program development, fiscal and personnel management, and program evaluation.
   a. Subsequent chapter sections provide specific information about each of these major functions.

Program Development

1. Purposes of developing specific programs.
   a. To directly meet the needs of a specific population(s) or group(s).
   b. To clearly focus evaluation and intervention efforts and activities.

c. To increase visibility and use of available services (e.g., offering an outpatient cardiac rehabilitation program is more visible than individual referrals, resulting in increased recognition and utilization of this service).
   d. To convert an idea into a practice reality.
2. The four basic steps of program development include needs assessment, program planning, program implementation, and program evaluation.
3. Needs assessment is a systematic process.
   a. Table 3-1 in Chapter 3 describes how needs assessment is a component of the evaluation process for populations.
   b. Box 4-16 describes the steps of a needs assessment.
   c. Needs assessment methods.
      (1) Survey, interview, or self-report of target population. A representative sample is required.
      (2) Key informant, which involves the surveying of specific individuals who are knowledgeable about the target population needs.
      (3) Community forums (e.g., public meetings, focus groups or panels to engage with and obtain
      (4) Review of existing secondary quantitative data. This can include service utilization records and

---

BOX 4-15 ▷ Characteristics of Effective Managers

- Effective managers:
  - support open communication, team building, decentralization of resources, and the sharing of power.
  - understand and apply motivation theories to facilitate relevant and effective responses to situations, foster program efficacy, and promote employee satisfaction.
  - collaborate with their team to determine a mission, establish goals, quantify measurable objectives, establish specific time frames for the accomplishment of objectives, and evaluate program outcomes.
  - provide staff training and resources to ensure goal attainment.
  - keep abreast of, critically review, and evaluate the reliability, validity, quality, and relevance of information that may have an impact on service delivery and service recipients.
    - synthesize and disseminate this information to key stakeholders (i.e., administrators, team members).
  - recognize the challenges that hinder the translation of knowledge into practice and provide supports and resources to implement and sustain evidence-based practice.
  - utilize strategic thinking and a systems model to respond proactively to market demands and changes.

BOX 4-16 ▷ Needs Assessment Steps

- Describe the community; its physical, social, cultural, and economic factors; and populations at risk.
- Describe the target population's demographics, disorder(s), functional level(s), and presenting problem(s).
- Identify specific needs of the target population.
  - Perceived needs of the population as reported by others (e.g., family, physicians, other professionals).
  - Felt needs as stated by the individual members of the target population.
  - Real needs, which are the actual disabilities and functional limitations of the target population as determined by an evaluation.
- Determine discrepancies and consistencies between real, perceived, and felt needs.
- Establish unmet needs according to priority.
- Identify resources available for program implementation.
  - Formal or institutional resources such as staff, supplies, money, and space.
  - Informal resources such as family, friends, cultural or religious figures, and self-help/consumer groups.

reports, census data and public health records (e.g., demographics, socioeconomic status, prevalence of disease or disability).

    (5) Analysis of social indicators to identify social, cultural, environmental, and/or economic factors that can predict problems.

4. Program planning uses a systematic approach.
   a. Table 3-1 in Chapter 3 describes how program planning is a component of intervention for groups and populations.
   b. Box 4-17 describes the steps of program planning.
5. Program implementation.
   a. Initiate program according to timetable and steps set forth in the program plan.
   b. Document program activities, procedures, and use.
   c. Communicate and coordinate with other programs within the system.
   d. Promote the program to ensure it reaches the target population.
   e. Table 3-1 in Chapter 3 describes how program implementation is a component of intervention for groups and populations.

6. Program evaluation. Refer to this Chapter's section on program evaluation and quality improvement.

Fiscal/Financial Management

1. Purposes of fiscal/financial management.
   a. To ensure quality services and programs are planned and implemented in a cost-effective manner.
   b. To meet the demands of a managed health-care system and the press for cost-containment.
   c. To remain competitive in a market-driven practice environment.
2. Major fiscal/financial management tasks.
   a. Develop a financial plan including revenue and expense projections.
   b. Use cost-effective charging procedures and fee structures.
   c. Develop and manage payroll and staffing budgets.
   d. Schedule staff in a cost-effective manner that meets quality standards.
   e. Plan for short- and long-term program needs including capital expenses.

BOX 4-17 ▷ Program Planning Steps

- Define a focus for the program based on the needs assessment results.
  - Problem areas, functional limitations, and unmet needs that are relevant to the majority of the target population are the priority focus.
  - Program level of difficulty as determined by the range of the population's functional levels and the level required by the current and expected environment.
- Adopt a frame or frames of reference that are most likely to successfully address and meet the needs that are the program's focus/foci.
- Establish objectives and goals of the program specifically related to its primary focus.
  - Individual goals that will be met by the program are set.
  - Programmatic goals that establish standards for program evaluation are determined.
- Describe integration of the program into existing system(s) of care.
  - Establish a realistic timetable for program implementation.
  - Define staff roles, responsibilities, and assignments.
  - Identify methods for professional collaboration.
  - Determine the physical setting and space requirements.
  - Consider potential barriers to program implementation.
  - Develop methods to effectively deal with identified obstacles before program implementation.
- Develop a system of referral for entry into, completion of, and discharge from the program.
  - Evaluation protocols to standardize information to be obtained from each person referred to the program and to assess the type of program services needed.
  - Criteria for acceptance into the program and for movement through program levels.
  - Discharge criteria to determine when an individual has achieved maximum gain from the program, usually defined as the achievement of program goals.
- Describe the fiscal implications of program plan.
  - Determine projected volume or service demand to estimate revenue.
  - Identify resource utilization and projected expenses to estimate costs.
  - Directly compare estimated revenue and estimated expenses to determine financial viability of program.

f. Manage general, administrative, and operating expenses.

g. Meet organization's revenue expectations.

3. Budget terms and concepts.

a. A budget financially projects, for a specified time period, the costs of managing a program and the anticipated revenue from service provision.

b. Budget periods vary from multiyear (5–10 years) for capital expenses to annual for personnel and supply expenses.

c. Budget revisions may be needed as program(s) or service(s) change due to ongoing program evaluation.

d. Capital expense budget.

(1) Permanent or long-term purchases such as an ADL kitchen or for new facilities, such as a new wing for a work hardening program.

(2) Typically, any item or action above a fixed amount (e.g., $500.00) with a lifespan of more than a year is considered a capital expense.

(3) Capital items are separated from other expenses due to depreciation of value and possible tax credits for purchases and investments.

e. Operating expense budget.

(1) The daily financial activity of a program or service.

(2) Information on revenue and volume, and direct, indirect, fixed and variable expenses. Box 4-18 describes these expenses.

f. Full-time equivalent (FTE).

(1) The amount of time a full-time staff employee works; in the United States, eight hours/day, five days/week.

(2) A budget formula used to determine the number of personnel providing direct care.

(a) Two practitioners who do administrative tasks half of the day and direct care half of the day would equal one FTE.

(b) Three part-time employees would equal 1.5 FTEs.

BOX 4-18 ▷ Operating Budget Expenses

• Direct expenses include costs directly related to OT service provision:

  – Salaries and benefits (e.g., vacation and sick time)

  – Office supplies (e.g., ink, paper)

  – Treatment equipment (e.g., ADL materials).

• Indirect expenses are not related to service delivery; they include costs shared by the setting as a whole such as rent, utilities, housekeeping, and marketing.

  – Sometimes called operating expenses.

• Fixed expenses remain at the same level even when there are changes in the number of services provided (e.g., rent).

• Variable expenses change in direct proportion to the amount of services provided (e.g., splinting materials).

---

g. Productivity standards.

(1) Establishes the amount of direct care and reimbursable service(s) each practitioner is to provide per day.

(2) Although Medicare has adopted the PDPM and PDGM reimbursement systems to pay for services based on the client's characteristics, not the amount or type of provided services, many insurers continue to reimburse based on the amount of services provided. As a result, the high productivity expectations that are set in some practice settings can lead to ethical dilemmas and/or ethical distress.

h. Break-even analysis.

(1) Also called cost-volume-profit analysis.

(2) Determines the volume of services needed to be provided for revenues to equal cost and profits to equal zero.

i. Accounts payable.

(1) The debts within a budget.

(2) Indicates payments that are due for purchases or services rendered (e.g., to an equipment supplier, to a landlord).

j. Accounts receivable.

(1) The assets within a budget.

(2) Indicates payments that are owed to the program, setting, or institution (e.g., insurance reimbursement, consultation fees).

Personnel Management

1. The oversight of OT practitioners and support personnel and the services they provide.

2. Purposes of personnel management.

a. To serve as the link between the individuals working for an organization and the larger organizational structure.

b. To attain best practice from personnel.

3. Major personnel management tasks.

a. Design work roles and write job descriptions.

b. Recruit, select, and orient personnel to perform the roles.

c. Supervise and evaluate personnel to ensure adequate role performance and the attainment of organizational goals.

d. Support personnel's ongoing professional development.

e. Deal with difficult personnel issues as they arise.

4. Job description: a statement of the job's expectations, duties, and purpose and its supervisory relationships. It should include the following.

a. Position's title and department.

b. Skilled and nonskilled requirements of the job including education, special training, experience, physical demands, and licensure requirements.

c. Specific responsibilities, duties, and performance standards in detail.

d. Supervisor(s) and supervisory relationships: decision-making authority and degree of autonomy.

5. Recruitment: the process of determining staffing needs, predicting turnover and vacancies, and identifying and recruiting potential replacements to maintain the staffing levels required to meet program objectives.

a. Identify the position available and determine its job description.

b. Attract potential qualified applicants.
   (1) Network internally within one's own organization and externally at local, state, and/or national OT meetings and conferences and through established OT contacts.
   (2) Conduct open houses, job fairs, and workshops.
   (3) Email or post mail recruitment information directly to OT practitioners.
   (4) Use employment websites, placement agencies, and online recruitment tools.
   (5) Advertise in trade publications, state and national OT association newsletters, and/or online.
   (6) Train and educate fieldwork students.

c. Screen interested applicants for an interview.
   (1) Review applications and resumes.
   (2) Check references.

d. Interview screened applicants to determine their suitability for the position.
   (1) Obtain information about relevant experience and career goals.
   (2) Verify their knowledge and skills.
   (3) Use open-ended semi-structured questions to facilitate discussion.
   (4) Ask the same questions of every candidate.
   (5) Take notes of applicants' responses.
   (6) Questions to the applicant that violate civil rights legislation or ADA should not be asked.
      (a) Age.
      (b) Sexual orientation.
      (c) Marital status or family composition.
      (d) Race or national origin, religion, or political beliefs.
      (e) Physical, mental, or cognitive disabilities.
   (7) Share information about the position's salary, benefits, work hours, job description, and advantages and limitations of the organization.

e. Make the job offer.
   (1) Contact selected applicant to offer position.
   (2) Upon applicant's acceptance of the position, confirm the terms of employment, the starting date, salary, and licensure requirements.

6. Orientation of staff.
   a. The process of providing specific information to a new employee to increase the ease and effectiveness of their transition into their new position.
      (1) Introduce key co-workers, managers, and department heads.
      (2) Provide specific information about the organization's and department's mission, policies, and procedures.
      (3) Distribute manuals, checklists, and/or handouts with recommended standards on how to perform required tasks competently.
      (4) Tour the facility and department to learn locations of resources, support services, equipment, and materials.

7. Supervision of personnel. Refer to this Chapter's section on supervision.

8. Performance appraisal.
   a. The process of formally evaluating staff performance according to established performance expectations and providing feedback to employees about the outcomes of this evaluation.
      (1) This typically occurs once per year in most organizations.
   b. Effective performance appraisal should be based on a foundation of ongoing feedback that has been provided during supervision.
   c. Steps in performance appraisal.
      (1) Articulate specific and clear expectations for performance related to programmatic needs, service delivery, and professional development.
      (2) Document positive performance to substantiate quality care and to support recommendations for merit pay, raises, bonuses, and/or promotions.
      (3) Document substandard performance to identify areas requiring quality improvement, further training, increased supervision, and/or disciplinary action.
      (4) Meet privately with each employee to discuss their self-assessment of their performance and the formal written performance appraisal. To maximize the efficacy of a performance appraisal, this meeting should include the following.
         (a) The opportunity for the employee to provide feedback about the manager's performance appraisal.
         (b) The establishment of mutually agreed upon goals that build on an employee's strengths and address performance concerns.
         (c) The development of a professional development plan and a remediation plan (if needed) that includes SMART goals and specific action steps for goal attainment. Refer to subsequent section on professional development for information about activities that can be included in this plan.

(5) Conduct intermittent reviews to monitor employee's progress, recognize accomplishments, and /or address continued concerns.

    (a) If an employee does not follow through on addressing areas of concern that were documented in the performance appraisal, disciplinary action may be indicated.

9. Disciplinary action.

  a. The process of informing an employee that their job performance is unacceptable, the organization's procedures for an administrative review of disciplinary actions, and the organization's employee grievance procedures.

  b. Criteria for fair disciplinary action.

    (1) Written documentation of problem behaviors and expectations for improvement.

    (2) Referral to counseling and/or other services needed to improve performance.

    (3) Clear and documented warnings of consequences for unremediated behavior.

    (4) Consequences that are impersonal, immediate, and consistent.

    (5) Continuous documented monitoring of the employee's behavior until they achieve satisfactory job performance, resign voluntarily, or are terminated.

10. Retention and motivation of staff.

  a. The process of identifying understanding, and meeting employees' needs, expectations, and desired rewards.

  b. Refer to Box 4-19 for a description of motivating job characteristics.

11. Staff development.

  a. The process of continually upgrading employees' knowledge and skills to provide competent, current, and caring OT services in changing and challenging delivery systems.

BOX 4-19 ▷ Motivating Job Characteristics

- A fair and competitive salary and benefits package.
- Job security, realistic performance expectations, and fair employment policies.
- A good working environment with a relaxed, friendly atmosphere, adequate physical space, and sufficient current equipment and supplies.
- Challenging, satisfying work and diverse caseloads.
- Competent supervision with adequate feedback on job performance.
- Active mentorship and support for professional development.
- Tuition reimbursement and financial support for conferences, workshops, and/or post professional education.
- Recognition of contributions and achievements.

---

  b. Staff development steps.

    (1) Assess employees' development needs and interests.

    (2) Assess organization's strategic plan to identify existing and new areas planned for OT service that may require staff training.

    (3) Provide mentorship and supervision.

    (4) Provide educational in-services, workshops, and practical on-site experiences.

    (5) Support self-directed learning, such as journal reviews, self-study courses, online networking, teleconferencing, off-site workshops, and/or post-professional education.

Program Evaluation and Quality Improvement

1. The systematic review and analysis of care provided to determine if this care is at an acceptable level of quality.

2. Table 3-1 in Chapter 3 describes how program evaluation is a component of intervention for groups and populations.

> **EXAM HINT:** The NBCOT® OTR® exam content outline identifies knowledge of the "methods for applying continuous quality improvement processes and procedures to occupational therapy service delivery . . . including program evaluation (and) outcome measures (NBCOT®, 2022, p. 13) as essential for competent practice. The application of knowledge about the following purposes, types, and terms of program evaluation and quality improvement can help you determine the correct answer for NBCOT® Domain 4 Competency and Practice Management exam items related to quality improvement.

3. Purposes of program evaluation.

  a. To gather information on the implementation of the program implementation.

  b. To measure the effectiveness of a program; that is, were program goals accomplished.

  c. To measure the program's impact.

  d. To meet external accreditation standards (refer to this Chapter's section on voluntary accreditation).

  e. To identify program problems/limitations and to resolve them.

  f. To use information obtained in the evaluation to improve services and assure quality.

4. Major types and terms. Refer to Table 4-6.

  a. Risk management, an integral part of program evaluation, is described in a subsequent section.

Table 4-6

Program Evaluation and Quality Improvement

Concurrent review: the evaluation of an ongoing intervention program during inpatient, outpatient, or home care service provision.
- Method to ensure appropriate care is being delivered.
- Often a component of a QI or PAI system.

Goal attainment scaling (GAS): an evaluation tool that attains clients' goals for intervention and measures goal attainment and intervention outcomes after a specified time period.
- Refer to Chapter 14.

Performance assessment and improvement (PAI): a systematic method to evaluate the quality and appropriateness of services.
- Utilization of an interdisciplinary systems focus.
- A client-centered approach that focuses on the rights, assessment, care, and education of the person.
- Organizational ethics, improved organizational performance, leadership, and management are emphasized.

Prospective review: the evaluation of a proposed intervention plan that specifies how and why care will be provided.
- Used by third-party payers to approve a proposed OT intervention program.

Quality improvement (QI): a system-oriented approach that views limitations and problems proactively as opportunities to increase quality.
- Prevention is emphasized.
- Blame is not attributed to persons; problems are related to organizational improvement needs.
- A prospective viewpoint is used.
Current services are critically reviewed and improvements that can enhance the efficacy of future service delivery are identified and implemented.

Retrospective review: audits of medical records after intervention was rendered.
- Method to ensure appropriate care was given.
- A UR tool for third-party payers that can be time consuming and costly.

Statistical utilization review: reimbursement claims data are analyzed to determine the most efficient and cost-effective care.

Total quality management (TQM): the creation of an organizational culture that enables all employees to contribute to an environment of continuous improvement to meet or exceed consumer needs.

Utilization review (UR): a plan to review the use of resources within a facility.
- Determination of medical necessity and cost efficiency.
- Often a component of a QI or PAI system.

5. Methods of program evaluation.
  a. Describe program objectives and goals to determine program outcome criteria.
  b. Identify measurable indicators based on objectives and goals.
  c. Describe population, staff, services provided, intervention methods, scope of care, and length of treatment.
  d. Design an evaluation study.
  e. Select methods to collect data. These can include the following.
    (1) Direct observation and/or review of client charts.
    (2) Safety checklists, incident reports, and/or client/family complaints.
    (3) Surveys of clients, families and/or staff.
    (4) Review of treatment sessions and missed treatments.
    (5) Initial, discharge, and follow-up assessments.
    (6) Review of statistics on costs and service volume.
  f. Collect and organize data.
  g. Evaluate and analyze results and limitations of the study.

  h. Report results, highlighting information to determine program's efficacy.
  i. Use results to initiate appropriate program actions.
    (1) Continue and/or expand programs that have demonstrated good efficacy/positive outcomes.
    (2) Change or modify programs that have demonstrated limited efficacy/satisfactory outcomes.
    (3) Discontinue programs that have demonstrated poor efficacy/unsatisfactory outcomes.
  j. Evaluate effectiveness of actions.

Marketing/Promotion

1. A managerial process that analyzes consumer need(s), plans and designs a service or product to meet the identified market need(s), and implements strategies and actions to promote consumer use of the service or product.
2. Major marketing tasks.
  a. Analyze market opportunities.
    (1) Conduct a self-audit to assess the strengths and weaknesses of oneself and/or one's organization.

(2) Conduct a consumer analysis to determine consumer need(s) and desire(s) for services or products.

(3) Identify potential competitors to clarify areas of service overlap/product similarity and to identify areas that are underserved or unserved.

(4) Assess the environment to determine political, sociocultural, economic, and/or demographic factors that may impact on the product(s) or service(s).

b. Analyze the market to be targeted for purchase of product(s) or service(s).

(1) Research selected target market(s) to determine validity of perceived market needs and wants.

(2) Divide market into segments to identify groups of consumers with similar characteristics, interests, and needs that will influence their purchase of the product(s) or service(s).

c. Develop marketing strategies to address the five Ps (i.e., product, price, place, promotion, and position) of a market plan for the OT service.

(1) Product: the service or product that is being offered to the market (e.g., a work hardening program, adaptive equipment).

(2) Price: the financial, physical, and psychological cost of doing business.

(3) Place: the location of service delivery and/or the distribution method for providing the target market with access to the service or product.

(4) Promotion: all efforts to communicate information about the service or product to the target market or market segment that makes the product or service visible and desirable.

(5) Position: the place the service or product holds in relation to similar products or services available in the marketplace.

d. Implement and evaluate the marketing plan.

(1) The implementation and evaluation of marketing efforts must always consider ethics (i.e., truth in advertising).

(2) Undifferentiated marketing: the use of the same marketing strategies and activities with the complete market (e.g., promoting the OT profession to the general public).

(3) Differentiated marketing: the design and use of marketing strategies and activities for different market segments (e.g., promoting OT specialties to different consumer self-help groups).

(4) Concentrated marketing: the design and use of specific marketing strategies and activities to concentrate on one market segment (e.g., older adults).

(5) Ongoing assessment and periodic review is needed to determine a market plan's effectiveness and to modify it, as needed.

3. Methods

a. Marketing instruments that can be employed to address the 5 Ps include the following.

(1) Advertising and publicity releases.

(2) Sales promotions, discounts, and bonuses.

(3) Personal contact selling and networking.

(4) Word-of-mouth recommendations.

Fieldwork Education

1. A key service management function is to develop, implement, and support clinical fieldwork education for occupational therapists and OTA students.

a. ACOTE guidelines for Level I and Level II fieldwork education are to be followed.

b. Supervisory qualifications and guidelines for fieldwork educators are provided in this Chapter's section on OT practitioner roles and supervision.

2. Fieldwork education managerial tasks.

a. Collaboration with the academic education program to develop specific fieldwork learning objectives and activities consistent with the facility's and school's philosophies and missions.

b. Development of professional development plans and activities for the students' clinical supervisors to ensure adequate fieldwork supervision.

c. Establishment of departmental policies and procedures for a student program and its supervision.

d. Assurance of quality care provided by student(s) according to established program standards and professional ethics.

e. Evaluation and supervision of students' performance and completion of ACOTE's evaluation tool.

f. Completion of cost-benefit analysis to collect data for institutional support of clinical education.

Risk Management

Overview and General Guidelines

> **EXAM HINT:** The NBCOT® OTR® exam content outline identifies the task of incorporating "risk management techniques at the individual and practice-setting levels to protect clients, self, staff, and others from injury or harm" (NBCOT®, 2022, p. 13) and knowledge of "infection control procedures and universal precautions for reducing transmission of contaminants . . . (including) PPE, isolation precautions, (and) cleaning equipment . . . (and) preventive measures for minimizing risk and promoting safety . . . (including) proper body mechanics, . . . equipment maintenance, emergency preparedness, (and) personal safety in the client's environment (NBCOT®, 2022, p. 13) as essential for competent and safe practice. Thus, the application of knowledge about the guidelines provided in this section can help you determine the correct answer to NBCOT® OTR® Domain 4 exam items about the OT practitioner's role in managing risks.

1. Risk management: a process that identifies, evaluates, and takes corrective action against risk and plans, organizes and controls the activities and resources of OT services to decrease actual or potential losses.
   a. Potential risks are client or employee injury and property loss or damage with resulting liability and financial loss.
   b. Risk management is an integral part of program evaluation.
2. Effective communication with team members and service recipients (e.g., informed consent) is required.
3. Staff education and training to prevent and manage risks are required. This training should include the following.
   a. Adherence to laws and regulations that govern practice (e.g., CAPTA mandatory reporting, HIPAA privacy rules) and ensure safety (e.g., fire regulations)
   b. The use of standard and transmission-based precautions.
      (1) Refer to Appendix 3A and Appendix 3B in Chapter 3.
   c. The proper maintenance of equipment and a safe treatment environment.

   d. Adherence to manufacturer guidelines for the storage and use of materials that can be potentially hazardous (e.g., varnish, paint)
   e. The location and effective use of first aid kits, emergency equipment (e.g., defibrillator, fire extinguisher, evacuation wheelchairs).
   f. The prevention of staff and client accidents and injuries.
      (1) Refer to Chapter 11 for information about principles of body mechanics.
      (2) Refer to Chapter 11 for information about the contraindications for the use of physical agent modalities (PAMs).
      (3) Refer to Chapter 16 for information about safe transfers and fall prevention.
         (a) Box 16-4 provides information about strategies to reduce fall risk factors in clinical settings.
   g. Recognition of serious risk factors and prevention of client complications. Refer to the next section about specific conditions and potential incidents.
   h. Precautions that should be taken when using intervention equipment and modalities.
      (1) Refer to Chapter 11 for information about the precautions for the use of PAMs.
   i. Procedures for handling medical emergencies and client and staff injuries.
      (1) Refer to next section on risk management for specific conditions and potential incidents and the subsequent section on first aid.
   j. The warning signs of professional burnout and strategies to prevent burnout. Refer to subsequent section on professional burnout.
4. Managers need to advocate for the inclusion of 'difficult' topics such as suicide in all practice settings and the development of protocols for OT employees' response to suicide risks. These should include the following.
   a. Education in suicide risks factors and suicide prevention.
   b. Training in screening for suicide risk and intervention to prevent suicide.
5. If risk management fails and an incident occurs, completion of an incident report according to setting's standards is required.

EXAM HINT: Throughout this text, CAUTION boxes highlight intervention precautions, contraindications, and risk factors that can result in potential harm. **RED FLAG** boxes identify unsafe actions, contraindications, and serious risk factors that are known to cause harm and situations that require an immediate response to ensure a person's safety and well-being. The application of knowledge about the information provided in these boxes can help you successfully analyze answer options for NBCOT® exam items about risk management. Correct answers to exam items will adhere to all precautions, consider all risk factors and contraindications, and follow established procedures for handling medical emergencies and injuries. Incorrect answers will not.

Risk Management for Specific Conditions and Potential Incidents

EXAM HINT: The NBCOT® OTR® exam content outline identifies knowledge of "responses to adverse reactions . . . and emergency situations" (NBCOT®, 2022, p. 13) as essential for competent and safe practice. Diabetic reactions and seizures are listed as examples. The application of knowledge about the following specific conditions and potential incidents can help you determine the correct answer for managing these risks.

1. To effectively manage risks, the OT practitioner must be able to recognize the warning signs of dangerous clinical conditions and medical complications and know how to prevent and/or respond to these in a timely manner.
   a. Information about conditions and complications that can endanger a person's health and well-being and/or place their life at risk and the response that is needed to address these are provided in the Clinical Conditions section of this text.
   b. The following outlines some of the major conditions and complications that may be on the NBCOT® exam and the specific chapter in which information about these is located.
      (1) Neurological conditions and complications including concussion, transient ischemic attack (TIAs), strokes, deep vein thrombosis (DVT), autonomic dysreflexia, blocked and infected shunts, myasthenic crisis, and seizures. Refer to Chapter 7.
      (2) Cardiopulmonary conditions and complications including COVID emergency warning

signs, angina, myocardial infarction, cardiac arrest. Refer to Chapter 8.
      (3) Wounds and pressure/decubitus ulcers decubiti. Refer to Chapter 9.
      (4) Dysphagia and aspiration. Refer to Chapter 9.
      (5) Diabetic reactions including hypoglycemia and hyperglycemia. Refer to Chapter 9.
      (6) Heat exhaustion and heat stroke. Refer to Chapter 9.
      (7) Self-injurious behavior and suicide. Refer to Chapter 14.

First Aid

EXAM HINT: The NBCOT® OTR® exam content outline identifies knowledge of "responses to adverse reactions, minor injuries, and emergency situations" (NBCOT®, 2022, p. 13) as essential for competent and safe practice. Minor cuts and burns are listed as examples. The application of knowledge about the following first aid techniques can help you determine the correct answer for exam items about responding to situations that require the OT practitioner to administer first aid (e.g., a person accidentally incurs a cut during a cooking activity).

1. External bleeding.
   a. Minor bleeding.
      (1) Usually clots within 10 minutes.

CAUTION: If a person is taking aspirin or nonsteroidal anti-inflammatory drugs (NSAIDS), clotting may take longer.

   b. Severe bleeding characteristics.
      (1) Blood spurting from a wound.
      (2) Blood fails to clot even after measures to control bleeding have been taken.
      (3) Arterial bleed: high pressure, spurting, red.
      (4) Venous bleed: low pressure, steady flow, dark red or maroon blood.
      (5) Capillary bleed: low pressure, oozing, dark red blood.
   c. Controlling external bleeding. Refer to Box 4-20.
2. Internal bleeding.
   a. The possible result of a fall, blunt force trauma, or a fracture rupturing a blood vessel or organ.

RED FLAG: Severe internal bleeding may be life threatening. Knowledge of the following signs/characteristics of severe internal bleeding is essential to effectively manage internal bleeding and ensure emergency medical care is obtained, if needed.

BOX 4-20 ▷ Controlling External Bleeding

- Use standard precautions such as wearing gloves.
  - Refer to Appendix 3-A in Chapter 3.
- Apply gauze pads using firm pressure. If no gauze is available, use a clean cloth, towel, a gloved hand, or the person's own hand. If blood soaks through, do not remove any gauze, add additional layers.
- Elevate the part if possible unless it is anatomically misaligned or it causes significant pain when elevated.
- Apply a pressure bandage, such as roller gauze, over the gauze pads.
- If necessary, apply pressure with the heel of your hand over pressure points. The femoral artery in the groin and the brachial artery in the medial aspect of the upper arm are two such points.
- Monitor A, B, Cs and overall status of the patient. Administer supplemental oxygen if nearby. Seek more advanced care as necessary.

BOX 4-21 ▷ Severe Internal Bleeding Signs/Characteristics

- Ecchymosis (black and blue) in the injured area.
- Body part, especially the abdomen, may be swollen, tender, and firm.
- Skin may appear blue, gray, or pale and may be cool or moist.
- Respiratory rate is increased.
- Pulse rate is increased and weak.
- Blood pressure is decreased.
- Patient may be nauseated or vomit.
- Patient may exhibit restlessness or anxiety.
- Level of consciousness may decline.

b. Severe internal bleeding signs/characteristics. Refer to Box 4-21.
c. Management of internal bleeding.
  (1) If minor, follow RICE procedure: rest, ice, compression, elevation.
  (2) Major internal bleeding.
    (a) Summon advanced medical personnel.
    (b) Monitor A, B, Cs and vital signs.
      • A = Airway: clear the airway.
      • B = Breathing: after airway is clear, make sure the person is breathing. If not, give rescue breaths.
      • C = Chest compressions to restore circulation.
    (c) Keep the person comfortable and quiet. Keep the person from getting chilled or overheated.

    (d) Reassure the person.
    (e) Administer supplemental oxygen if available and nearby.
3. Shock (hypoperfusion).
  a. Failure of the circulatory system to perfuse (i.e., supply) vital organs.
  b. At first, blood is shunted from the periphery to compensate.
    (1) The victim may lose consciousness as the brain is affected.
    (2) The heart rate increases, resulting in increased oxygen demand.

> **RED FLAG:** Organs ultimately fail when deprived of oxygen. Heart rhythm is affected, ultimately leading to cardiac arrest and death. Knowledge about the types, causes, signs, and symptoms of shock is essential to effectively recognize shock, provide needed care, and obtain emergency medical care.

  c. Types and causes of shock. Refer to Box 4-22.
  d. Signs and symptoms. Refer to Box 4-22.
  e. Care for shock.
    (1) Obtain history, if possible.
    (2) Examine the person for airway, breathing, circulation, and bleeding.

BOX 4-22 ▷ Types, Causes, Signs and Symptoms of Shock

- **Types and Causes**
  - Hemorrhagic: severe internal or external bleeding.
  - Psychogenic: emotional stress causes blood to pool away from the brain.
  - Metabolic: loss of body fluids from heat, severe vomiting, or diarrhea.
  - Anaphylactic: allergic reaction to drugs, food, or insect stings.
  - Cardiogenic: MI or cardiac arrest results in pump failure.
  - Respiratory: respiratory illness or arrest results in insufficient oxygenation of the blood.
  - Septic: severe infections cause blood vessels to dilate.
  - Neurogenic: traumatic brain injury (TBI), spinal cord injury (SCI), or other neural trauma causes disruption of autonomic nervous system resulting in disruption of blood vessel dilation/constriction.
- **Signs and Symptoms**
  - Pale, gray, or blue, cool skin.
  - Increased, weak pulse.
  - Increased respiratory rate.
  - Decreased blood pressure.
  - Irritability or restlessness.
  - Diminishing level of consciousness.
  - Nausea or vomiting.

(3) Assess level of consciousness.
(4) Determine skin characteristics and perform capillary refill test of fingertips.
  (a) Capillary refill test: squeeze fingernail for two seconds.
  (b) In healthy individuals, the nail will blanch and turn pink when pressure is released.
  (c) If nail bed does not refill and turn pink within two seconds, the cause could be that blood is being shunted away from the periphery to vital organs to maintain core temperature.

(5) Treat specific conditions if possible, e.g., control bleeding, provide an orthosis for a fracture, use an EpiPen for anaphylaxis.
(6) Keep the person from getting chilled or over-heated.
(7) Elevate the legs 12 inches unless there is suspected spinal injury or painful deformities of the lower extremities.
(8) Reassure the person and continue to monitor A, B, Cs.
(9) Administer supplemental oxygen if nearby.

Research

Purposes of Research

1. Critical evaluation and consumption of research literature enhances one's theoretical and philosophical foundations, improves clinical reasoning and critical thinking, increases professional knowledge and skills, and facilitates evidence-based decision-making.
2. Application of research literature ensures practice is current, meaningful, and competent, which ultimately improves the quality of life of individuals receiving OT services.
3. Knowledge of research provides opportunities to address questions that arise daily in professional practice.
4. The development and implementation of research projects that test and establish the efficacy of OT evaluation and intervention is essential to the provision of evidence-based practice (EBP).
   a. Establishment of the relevance and efficacy of OT can influence public health, social, and educational policy, thereby impacting on the delivery of OT services.
   b. Recent legislation (e.g., IDEA 2004 and NCLB) place increase emphasis on the provision of EBP.
   c. Table 4-7 provides an outline of the steps for EBP.
5. Acquisition of scientific knowledge can provide answers to practice questions and help solve problems encountered in practice.

Table 4-7

Steps in Evidence-Based Practice	
Step 1	A clinical problem is identified, and an answerable research question is formulated. • The question is clearly defined and related to a clinical decision (e.g., whether to use a therapeutic, preventive, or diagnostic intervention). • The question is focused to clarify the target of the literature search.
Step 2	A systematic literature review is conducted and best evidence is collected. • Sources of evidence include books, journals, clinical protocols, colleagues. • Stronger sources of evidence include a systematic review using an electronic search of the medical literature; refer to Electronic Medical Databases. • Articles are selected that are most likely to provide valid results (e.g., randomized controlled trials [RCTs]).
Step 3	The research evidence is summarized and critically analyzed. • The type (design) of the study is identified. • Study methods are identified (e.g., Were all patients who entered the trial properly accounted for and attributed at the conclusion of the study? Were appropriate samples of patients used? What are the inclusion and exclusion criteria?). • Statistical methods and analysis are identified (e.g., Are results presented clearly? Statistically significant?).
Step 4	The research evidence is synthesized and applied to clinical practice. • Best evidence is available and applied to clinical practice using clinical decision analysis.

6. Development of a body of professional research contributes to the science of a profession and provides a body of knowledge to guide practitioners.

7. Participation in research to evaluate program outcomes is a requirement of most practice settings and accrediting bodies.

> **EXAM HINT:** The NBCOT® OTR® exam content outline identifies knowledge of the "methods for locating, reviewing, interpreting, and critically appraising scholarly research to guide practice-relevant decision-making (including) defining a clinical question (and) determining the clinical bottom line" (NBCOT®, 2022, pp. 12–13) as essential for competent practice. The application of knowledge about the purposes of research previously described and the quantitative and qualitative research methods described in the following sections can help you determine the correct answer for NBCOT® Domain 4 Competency and Practice Management exam items about research and evidence-based practice.

Quantitative Methodology/ Design Types

1. True-experimental: the classic two-group design which includes random selection and assignment into an experimental group that receives treatment or a control group that receives no treatment. All other experiences are kept similar.
   a. The two levels of treatment (some and none) together constitute the independent variable being manipulated.
   b. The comparison of their status on some variable (i.e., the outcome) that might be influenced by treatment constitutes the dependent variable.
   c. A cause-and-effect relationship between the independent and dependent variable is examined.
   d. In human subject research, it is often difficult to design a pure experimental design.

2. Quasi-experimental: an independent variable is manipulated to determine its effect on a dependent variable but there is a lesser degree of researcher control and/or no randomization.
   a. Used often in health-care research in which it is unethical to control or withhold treatment.
   b. Used to study intact groups created by events or natural processes.

3. Nonexperimental/correlational: there is no manipulation of independent variable; randomization and researcher control are not possible.
   a. Used to study the potential relationships between two or more existing variables (e.g., attendance at a day program and social interaction skills).

b. Describes relationships, predicts relationships among variables without active manipulation of the variables.
   c. Limitations.
      (1) Cannot establish cause-and-effect relationships; limits interpretation of results.
      (2) May fail to consider all variables that enter into a relationship.
   d. Degree of a relationship is expressed as a correlational coefficient, ranging from –1.00 to +1.00.
   e. Examples of correlation research.
      (1) Retrospective: investigation of data collected in the past.
      (2) Prospective: recording and investigation of present data.
      (3) Descriptive: investigation of several variables at once; determines existing relationships among variables.
      (4) Predictive: used to develop predictive models.
   f. Can be "ex post facto" (after the fact) research, because variables may be studied after their occurrence (e.g., postdiagnosis adjustment).

4. Table 4-8 outlines the levels of evidence and grades of recommendation for quantitative research.

Qualitative Methodology/ Design Types

1. A form of descriptive research that studies people, individually or collectively, in their natural social and cultural context.

2. A systematic, subjective approach to describe real-life experiences and give them meaning.

3. It is rich in verbal descriptions of people and phenomena based on direct observation in naturalistic settings.

4. The process of the study is considered as important as the specific outcome data.

5. Types of qualitative research.
   a. Phenomenological: a study of one or more persons and how they make sense of their experience.
      (1) Minimal interpretations by the investigator.
      (2) Meanings can only be ascribed by participants.
   b. Ethnographic: patterns and characteristics of a cultural group, including values, roles, beliefs, and normative practices, are intensely studied.
      (1) Extensive field observations, interviews, participant observations, the examination of the culture's literature and artifacts, and cultural immersion are used.
      (2) Used in health care to understand an insider's perspective to develop meaningful services (e.g., a study of a nursing home).

Chapter 4

Chapter 4

Table 4-8

Levels of Evidence and Grades of Recommendation

LEVEL	DESCRIPTION
I	Evidence is based on SR of high-quality RCTs (or meta-analyses) with adequate size to ensure low risk of bias, substantial agreement of size and direction of treatment effects; or individual RCT with narrow confidence level, treatment effects precisely defined, and low risk of bias; prospective studies.
II	Evidence is based on SR lesser-quality RCT, e.g., too small to provide Level I evidence; weaker diagnostic criteria and reference standards, improper randomization; < than 80% follow-up of subjects enrolled in study or SR of cohort studies with homogeneity; prospective studies.
III	Evidence is based on SR of nonrandomized, controlled cohort studies or individual case-control study; retrospective studies.
IV	Evidence is based on case series studies and poor-quality cohort or case-control studies (comparison groups not adequately defined, exposures and outcomes not measured objectively, lack of control for confounders, insufficient follow up—cohort studies only).
V	Evidence is based on expert opinion without critical appraisal, or based on physiology, bench research.

GRADES OF RECOMMENDATION BASED ON	STRENGTH OF EVIDENCE
A—Strong evidence	A preponderance of Level I and/or Level II studies support the recommendation. This must include at least one Level I study.
B—Moderate evidence	A single, high-quality RCT or a preponderance of Level II studies support the recommendation.
C—Weak evidence	A single Level II study or a preponderance of Level III and IV studies, including statements of consensus by content experts support the recommendation.
D—Conflicting evidence	Higher-quality studies conducted on this topic that disagree on conclusions. The recommendation is based on these conflicting studies.
E—Theoretical/ foundational evidence	A preponderance of evidence from animal or cadaver studies, from conceptual models/principles, or from basic sciences/bench research support this conclusion.
F—Expert opinion	Best practice based on the clinical experience of the guidelines development team.

RCT = randomized controlled trials; SR = systematic review

Grades of recommendation adapted from Knee Pain and Mobility Impairments: Meniscal and Articular Cartilage Lesions. Clinical Practice Guidelines linked to the International Classification of Functioning, Disability, and Health from the Orthopedic Section of the American Physical Therapy Association, Summary of Recommendations. JOSPT 6(40): A30, 2010.

c. Heuristic: complete involvement of the researcher in the experience of the subject(s) to understand and interpret a phenomenon.
   (1) Aim is to understand human experience and its meaning.
   (2) Meanings can only be understood if personally experienced.
d. Case study: a single subject or a group of subjects is investigated in an in-depth manner.
   (1) Purpose can be description, interpretation, or evaluation.
   (2) This method is easy to use in most practice settings.
6. To attain rigor in qualitative research, the trustworthiness of a study should be critiqued, and strategies to increase trustworthiness should be employed.
   a. Box 4-23 identifies and defines the criteria for determining the trustworthiness of a qualitative

study and describes methods to enhance the trustworthiness of each criterion.

EXAM HINT: Correct answers to NBCOT® exam items about the development and/or implementation of a qualitative research project will include the use of strategies to enhance the study's trustworthiness according to the criteria outlined in Box 4-23.

Essentials of the Research Process

1. Formulation of a philosophical foundation to reflect researcher's view of, and assumptions about, learning, human behavior, and other phenomena related to health and human services.

BOX 4-23 ▷ Qualitative Research Trustworthiness Criteria

- **Credibility**: the researcher's level of confidence that their findings truthfully reflect the reality of a study's participants and the study's context.
  - Credibility is attained when the researcher does not have preconceived notions about a study and allows for multiple truths to emerge from the findings, as revealed by the participants.
  - Credibility can be enhanced by extended and varied field experience, reflexivity via completion of a field journal, sampling, triangulation of data, interview techniques, and member checks.
- **Transferability**: how well other researchers can fit a study's findings into similar contexts; the "goodness of fit" between the contexts of two studies.
  - Transferability is evident when a researcher provides sufficient descriptive data to allow comparison by other researchers.
    - Transferability can be enhanced by use of a nominated sample, comparison of sample characteristics to available demographic data, and dense description of the study's participants and contexts.
- **Dependability**: the inclusion of the full range of data, including outlier or atypical findings.
  - Dependability is attained when all participants' experiences/perspectives are considered important and reported.
    - Dependability can be enhanced by a dependability audit, triangulation of data, comprehensive description of research methods, peer review, member check, code-recode procedures, and step-wise replication.
- **Confirmability**: the degree to which a study's conclusions are based on the data.
  - Confirmability is attained when data is truthful.
    - Confirmability can be enhanced by a confirmability audit, member check, researcher reflexivity, and triangulation of data.

(4) Critically evaluate literature reviewed according to established standards (refer to 3b).

(5) Recognize that the literature may need to be revisited and/or re-searched as the study progresses and/or when its results are analyzed.

b. Critique of published research.

(1) Analyze the purpose, relevance, and meaningfulness of the study.

(2) Assess the comprehensiveness of the study's literature review.

(3) Examine the congruence between the purpose, literature, methodology, findings, and conclusions.

(4) Assess the adequacy of the research procedures to address the study's question or focus.

(5) Analyze the comprehensiveness of data analyses, interpretation, conclusions, and limitations.

4. Utilization of a theoretical base to frame the research problem or area of concern to ensure that the resulting research contributes to, or builds upon, theory.

5. Development of a specific question or focus for research.

a. In quantitative/experimental research this is specific, detailing the exact variables to be studied.

b. In qualitative/naturalistic research, this is a broad question called a "query" that will develop specificity over the course of the study.

6. Selection of a research design.

a. In quantitative/experimental research, the design is highly standardized.

b. In qualitative/naturalistic research, the design is more fluid.

7. Formulation of methodology (refer to section on research design types).

8. Determination of the study's length.

9. Identification of the study's participants/population sample.

a. Based on a literature review, the study's hypothesis, and goals, determine a target population's desired characteristics.

b. Describe criteria for selecting a sample of the population to be study's participants.

c. Determine sampling method.

(1) Random: individuals are selected through the use of a table of random numbers.

(2) Systematic: individuals are selected from a population list by taking individuals at specified intervals (e.g., every 10th name).

(3) Stratified: individuals are selected from a population's identified subgroups based on some predetermined characteristic (e.g., by diagnosis) that correlates with the study.

(4) Purposive: individuals are purposefully and deliberately selected for a study (e.g., all consumers of a program for a QI study).

2. Identification of a broad issue, topic, or problem of interest and relevance that warrants scientific investigation.

3. Review and synthesis of research literature related to identified area of interest.

a. Conduct a comprehensive and systematic literature search.

(1) Define the parameters and boundaries of the literature search according to the research question's main concepts and constructs.

(2) Use databases, indices, and abstracts along with the support of a reference librarian.

(3) Organize literature obtained according to relevance and concepts and take notes to summarize content.

(5) Convenience: individuals are selected who meet population criteria based upon availability to the researcher.

(6) Network/snowball: study subjects identify other individuals who can meet study criteria and be recruited to participate.

d. Obtain informed consent from all participants.

10. Collection of data using established principles for collecting research information.

a. Information obtained must be relevant and sufficient to answer the specific research question or query.

b. The method of data collection selected must be realistic given the practical limitations of the researcher, the type of research design, and the nature of the research problem.

c. Use of a combination of data collection methods can be useful and more fully answer a research question or query.

11. Methods of data collection.

a. Methods range along a continuum from unstructured observations to highly structured, fixed choice questionnaires.

(1) Measurement scales used to collect data include ordinal, nominal, interval, and ratio.

Table 4-9 describes these scales and provides a practice example for each.

b. Most methods are used in both qualitative and quantitative research.

c. Most methods are used in conjunction with other data collection techniques.

d. Observation.

(1) In quantitative research, observations are structured and formalized.

(2) In qualitative research, observations are unstructured and ever-changing according to the contexts and results of the observations.

(3) Observations may be made of nonhuman objects, such as equipment, or human subjects during actual performance or via videotapes.

e. Interview.

(1) Used to gather information in ethnographic and survey research.

(2) In survey research, interviews can be face-to-face or by telephone or electronic media (e.g., Zoom).

(3) In ethnographic research, interviews are always face-to-face.

f. Written questionnaires.

(1) In quantitative research, questionnaires must be structured.

Table 4-9

Types of Measurement Scales

MEASUREMENT TYPE	EXAMPLE
Ordinal: a measurement scale used to depict the order of variables, and not the difference between each of the variables. An ordinal scale contains qualitative data. It places variables in order/rank, only permitting measurement of the value as higher or lower.	A client satisfaction survey used a Likert scale (an ordinal measurement) to measure clients' opinions of their OT services. Questions were answered using the 5-point scale of 1 = very dissatisfied, 2 = dissatisfied, 3 = neither dissatisfied or satisfied, 4 = satisfied, 5 = very satisfied). Respondents chose the option that best described how they felt about the various OT services they received.
Nominal: a measurement scale, in which numbers serve as "tags" or "labels" only to identify or classify a category. The numbers have no value, but they are useful for inputting data into a statistical analysis program for data analysis.	A study that examined the use of evidence-based research to inform practice surveyed a sample of occupational therapists. A nominal scale was used to collect information about the participants' practice area (i.e., 1 = acute care, 2 = rehabilitation, 3 = home care, 4 = school-based, 5 = mental health).
Interval: a measurement scale that has equal distances between adjacent values. The distances are "intervals". There is no true zero on an interval scale, which is what distinguishes it from a ratio scale. On an interval scale, zero is an arbitrary point not a complete absence of the variable. Interval measurement allows the researcher to calculate the mean and median of variables.	A thermometer is used by a therapist to measure the water temperature of a hydrocollator prior to its use with a client. A thermometer has equal distances between values (degrees), but there is no true "zero". A thermometer can record below "zero" water temperatures. The hydrocollator is designed to maintain a constant temperature between 160° F–165° F. As a component of hydrocollator maintenance, an OT aide also uses a thermometer to record the temperature daily on the hot pack temperature log. The mean (average temperature) and median (middle of the temperature range) are calculated weekly (e.g., a weekly mean of 163° and median of 164° would indicate that the hydrocollator is operating safely).
Ratio: a quantitative measurement scale where there is a true zero and equal intervals between neighboring points. Unlike on an interval scale, a zero on a ratio scale means there is a total absence of the variable being measured. The measurement is not arbitrary. Ratio data is the most sophisticated level of measurement. Variables can be added, subtracted, multiplied, divided.	A therapist used a stopwatch to measure the time it took for an average, healthy adult to complete the 9-hole Peg Test. The finding of 17 seconds with the right hand is a ratio measurement. At zero on the stopwatch, the client had not started the test. The client's score reflects the number of seconds the client needed to complete the test; it is not arbitrary. The therapist can compare the client's score to the norm (the average score of 17.8 seconds).

(2) In qualitative research, questions may be unstructured.

(3) Distribution may be by mail, email, or in person, with instructions to complete at that moment or at respondent's convenience and with directions to return the completed questionnaire to researcher by a specific date.

(4) Surveys are a major type of questionnaire used in research.

g. Survey instruments.

(1) Surveys are nonexperimental instruments designed to measure specific characteristics.

(2) Survey questions can be open-ended questions or closed-ended questions.

(a) Box 4-24 describes the different types of questions that can be used on a survey measure.

(3) Survey design research typically uses large samples through mail, telephone, or face-to-face contact.

(4) Benefits of survey research.

(a) The ability to obtain a large number of participants at a relatively low cost.

(b) The ability to measure numerous variables with one instrument.

(c) The ability to use the data obtained in multiple ways through statistical manipulation during data analysis.

(5) Disadvantages and limitations of survey research.

(a) Limited or poor response rate.

(b) Missing or inaccurately completed data.

(c) The response rate issues and data collection problems of survey research can be minimized with the development and use of a good survey instrument; therefore, it is advisable for all researchers to carefully critique and pilot their study measure before its use in a research study.

(d) Due to sampling limitations and potential respondent bias, the generalizability of survey research is limited.

h. Artifact and record review.

(1) Used to gather information in all types of research.

(2) May be the sole data collection method in historical research.

(3) A review of written records can include medical records, publications, letters, and/or minutes of meetings and conferences.

(4) A review of artifacts may include physical items such as personal objects in a person's home, adaptive equipment, and/or audiovisuals.

i. Hardware instrumentation.

(1) Mechanical or physical instruments with established reliability and validity that measure independent variables (e.g., goniometers).

j. Tests and assessments.

(1) Used to measure independent variables, (e.g., performance components, interests, and values).

(2) Published tests with established reliability and validity are preferred.

(3) If there are no existing tests or assessments available to collect information sought by the research, an instrument can be constructed in accordance with established test construction guidelines.

(4) Refer to Chapter 3 for the psychometric characteristics of evaluations and definitions of assessments.

12. Analysis and interpretation of data using descriptive statistics.

a. Measures of central tendency: a determination of average or typical scores.

(1) Mean: the arithmetic average of all scores.

(a) The most frequently used measure of central tendency; appropriate for interval or ratio data.

(2) Median: the midpoint, 50% of scores are above the median and 50% of scores are below; appropriate for ordinal data.

(3) Mode: the most frequently occurring score; appropriate for nominal data.

b. Measures of variability: a determination of the spread of a group of scores.

(1) Box 4-25 describes the different types of variability measures.

BOX 4-24 ▶ Types of Survey Questions

- **Semantic differential**: a point scale with opposing adjectives at two extremes, measuring affective meaning.

- **Likert scale**: respondents indicate their level of agreement, usually on a five-point scale.

- **Guttmann scale rank ordering**: the respondent places a number alongside a list of items, indicating their order of importance. Sometimes only two to three items are asked for, other times a whole list may be prioritized. It is difficult (and irrelevant) to prioritize more than ten.

- **Multiple choice**: a statement is provided, sometimes in a question format, and the respondent selects the item most reflective of their opinion. Used to elicit opinions or attitudes.

- **Incomplete sentences**: a phrase is provided to indicate a certain domain of concern and the respondent completes the sentence. Used to find out opinions, attitudes, knowledge, styles of behavior, personality traits.

BOX 4-25 ▷ **Measures of Variability**

- **Range**: the difference between the highest score and the lowest score.
- **Standard deviation (SD)**: a determination of variability of scores (difference) from the mean.
  - The most frequently used measure of variability.
  - Appropriate with interval or ratio data.
- **Normal distribution**: a symmetrical bell-shaped curve indicating the distribution of scores; the mean, median, and mode are similar.
  - Half the scores are above the mean and half the scores are below the mean.
  - Most scores are near the mean, approximately 68% of scores fall within +1 or −1 SD of the mean.
  - Frequency of scores decreases further from the mean.
- **Skewed distribution**: scores are not symmetrical; they are extreme; clustered at one end or the other; the mean, median, and mode are different.
- **Percentiles and quartiles**: describe a score's position within the distribution, relative to all other scores.
  - Percentiles: data is divided in 100 equal parts; position of score is determined.
  - Quartiles: data is divided into four equal parts, and position of score is placed accordingly.

---

13. Analysis and interpretation of data using inferential statistics.
    a. Determines how likely the results of a study of a sample can be generalized to the whole population.
    b. Standard error of measurement: an estimate of expected errors in an individual's score; a measure of response stability or reliability.
    c. Tests of significance: an estimation of true differences, not due to chance; a rejection of the null hypothesis.
       (1) Alpha level: preselected level of statistical significance.
           (a) Most commonly .05 or .01: indicates that the expected difference is due to chance, e.g., at .05, only five times out of every 100 or a 5% chance, often expressed as a value of p.
           (b) There are true differences on the measured dependent variable.
       (2) Degrees of freedom: based on number of subjects and number of groups; allows determination of level of significance based on consulting appropriate tables for each statistical test.
       (3) Errors.
           (a) Standard error: expected chance variation among the means, the result of sampling error.
           (b) Type I error: the null hypothesis is rejected by the researcher when it is true, e.g., the means of scores are concluded to be truly

different when the differences are due to chance.
           (c) Type II error: the null hypothesis is not rejected by the researcher when it is false, e.g., the means of scores are concluded to be due to chance when the means are truly different.
    d. Parametric statistics: testing is based on population parameters; includes tests of significance based on interval or ratio data.
       (1) Table 4-10 describes these tests and provides research examples.
    e. Nonparametric statistics: testing not based on population parameters; includes tests of significance based on ordinal or nominal data.
       (1) Used when parametric assumptions cannot be met; less powerful than parametric tests, more difficult to reject the null hypothesis.
       (2) Table 4-11 describes these tests and provides research examples.

Table 4-10

Specific Parametric Statistical Tests

STATISTICAL TEST	RESEARCH EXAMPLE
T test: a parametric test of significance used to compare two group means and identify a difference at a selected probability level (e.g., .05).	The mean of the practice exam scores obtained by a cohort of graduate students before the completion of a certification exam preparation course are compared to the mean of practice exam scores obtained by this cohort after the completion of a certification exam preparation course.
Analysis of variance (ANOVA): a parametric test used to compare two or more treatment groups or conditions at a selected probability level.	The effectiveness of a dynamic seating system for improving attention to task among second-grade students is researched. Measures of executive function, behavioral regulation, and metacognition collected pre and post intervention are compared. Students assigned to the treatment group used a dynamic cushion throughout the school day. Students assigned to the control group did not. Teachers completed a behavior rating inventory for each participant before and after the intervention. ANOVA identified differences in the attention to task before and after the intervention for the treatment group as compared to the control group.
Analysis of covariance (ANCOVA): a parametric test used to compare two or more treatment groups or conditions while also controlling for the effects of intervening variables (covariates).	Two groups of subjects are compared on the basis of upper extremity functional reach using two different types of assistive devices; subjects in one group have longer arms than subjects in the second group; arm length then becomes the covariate that must be controlled during statistical analysis.

Table 4-11

Specific Nonparametric and Correlation Statistical Tests	
STATISTICAL TEST	**RESEARCH EXAMPLE**
Chi square test: a nonparametric test of significance used to compare data in the form of frequency counts occurring in two or more mutually exclusive categories.	Occupational therapists were surveyed about their use of evidence-based practice (EBP). Participants provided demographic characteristics (i.e., their highest academic degree, region of practice, clinical experience, practice area, and research experience). They also responded to questions about EBP variables (i.e., resource use, time, skills, administrative support). Demographic characteristics defined mutually exclusive categories. The frequency of responses to EBP variables were calculated. Chi-square tabulations were calculated between demographics and EBP variables and the frequency of resource use was found to be associated with the highest academic degree obtained and research experience.
Pearson product-moment coefficient (r): used to correlate interval or ratio data.	A study identified the correlation between caregiver burden and quality of life reported by the caregivers of stroke survivors. Participants completed caregiver burden and quality of life questionnaires. The questionnaires were designed to collect ratio data. Correlations between variables (caregiver burden and quality of life) were analyzed using Pearson's product-moment coefficient.
Spearman's rank correlation coefficient (rs): a nonparametric test used to correlate ordinal data.	The relationship between the degree of community integration and life satisfaction was determined for persons with traumatic brain injury (TBI). Participants completed community integration and life satisfaction questionnaires. Questions were designed to allow participants to rank or order their responses in order of importance with 1 = the most important item to 10 = the least important item. Data analysis using Spearman's rank order correlation coefficients determined the associations between two ranked variables of community integration and life satisfaction.
Intraclass correlation coefficient (ICC): a reliability coefficient based on an analysis of variance.	A study examined whether the Purdue Pegboard Test (developed more than 40 years ago) should continue to be used in current OT practice. Teams of raters administered the test. Inter-rater reliability was measured using ICC for the mean of all of the rating teams and was found to be above 0.99. This study reported inter-rater reliability (the first step in answering the practice question) but validity testing is needed to bring the psychometrics of the Purdue Pegboard Test up to date to be generalized for current use by occupational therapists.

f. Correlational statistics: used to determine relationships between two variables; e.g., compare progression of radiologically observed joint destruction in rheumatoid arthritis and its relationship to demographic variables (gender, age), disease severity, and exercise frequency.
   (1) Table 4-11 describes these tests and provides research examples.
   (2) Strength of relationships: positive correlations range from 0.00 to +1.00; indicates as variable X increases, so does variable Y.
      (a) High correlations: 0.70 to +1.00.
      (b) Moderate correlations: 0.35 to 0.69.
      (c) Low correlations: 0 to 0.34.
      (d) 0 means no relationship between variables.
      (e) Negative correlations range from –1.00 to 0.00: indicates as variable X increases, variable Y decreases; an inverse relationship.
   (3) Common variance: a representation of the degree that variation in one variable is attributable to another variable.
14. Report of research findings.
   a. Results section.
      (1) In quantitative/experimental research, report all factual data with no interpretation.
      (2) In quantitative/experimental research report all findings with no bias toward reporting only results supportive of the study's hypothesis.

      (3) In qualitative/naturalistic research, results, conclusions, and interpretation are discussed in an integrated manner.
         (a) Descriptions, illustrative quotations, and brief examples are used.
         (b) Writing format used depends on the qualitative/naturalistic design of the study.
   b. Conclusions section.
      (1) Interpretation of the results.
      (2) Comparison of study's findings to those presented in the literature review.
      (3) Analysis of findings supportive and not supportive of the hypothesis.
   c. Summary.
      (1) Major contributions, practical or theoretical implications that can be drawn from the study.
      (2) Brief suggestions for improvements to the study's design and procedures.
      (3) Proposals for new research based on the study's findings.
15. Dissemination of research.
   a. Research outcomes that contribute to the profession's body of knowledge and advance the provision of evidence- and occupation-based practice should be disseminated.
   b. Dissemination efforts should be consciously planned to target relevant audiences (e.g., consumers, OT practitioners, professionals from

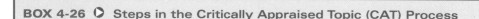

Chapter 4

BOX 4-26 ▷ **Steps in the Critically Appraised Topic (CAT) Process**

1. **Background:** state the rationale for the CAT and explain the importance of the question being asked.
2. **Question:** a succinct question usually written in a PICO format.
   a. P = Population.
   b. I = Intervention.
   c. C = Comparison.
   d. O = Outcome.
3. **Inclusion criteria:** describe which studies will be included (i.e., date of publication, language, types of studies, study design, measurements, outcome, and context).
4. **Search strategy:** the search conducted should use relevant databases and be transparent, verifiable, and reproducible. The search process should be clearly documented and identify the search terms that were used to conduct the search, the strategies used to combine search terms, and the number of studies found at each step.
5. **Study selection:** verify that studies meet the inclusion criteria by first reviewing the abstracts and then the full study.
6. **Data extraction:** collate the results of the included studies.
7. **Critical appraisal:** assess the reliability, validity, and trustworthiness of each study according to established levels of evidence. Refer to Table 4-3.
8. **Results or synthesis:** summarize the findings of the critical appraisal.
9. **Conclusion:** construct a concise statement on the primary findings of the CAT.
10. **Limitations:** describe any limitations and discuss their potential impact on the findings of the CAT.
11. **Implications and recommendations:** report on the specific recommendations for practice based on the evidence.

Reference: The Center for Evidence-Based Management. (2017). Guideline for Critically Appraised Topics in Management and Organizations. Retrieved from https://cebma.org/wp-content/uploads/CEBMa-CAT-Guidelines-vs-2.0.pdf

---

other disciplines, administrators, payers, and policy makers).

c. Research dissemination can be oral (e.g., an in-service to professional colleagues, a conference panel, or poster presentation) and/or written (e.g., publication of a critically appraised topic [CAT], critically appraised paper [CAP], or peer-reviewed journal article).[6]

(1) A CAT is a short summary of the best available evidence on a topic of interest, usually focused on a clinical question.

(a) It is a shorter and less rigorous version of a systematic review. Refer to Box 4-26 for an outline of the CAT process.

(b) The AOTA publishes CATs online in the "Evidence-Based Practice Tools and Resources" section, organized by practice area.

(2) A CAP is the summary of the methods, findings, and study limitations of a selected individual article. Refer to Box 4-27 for an outline of steps to complete a CAP according to the AOTA format.

(a) The AOTA publishes CAPs in the online "Evidence Exchange" section.

BOX 4-27 ▷ **Steps in Completing A Critically Appraised Paper (CAP)**

1. Provide APA formatted citation (including DOI number).
2. Describe the clinical bottom line.
3. Describe the study's objective(s) and level of evidence.
4. Describe the study's design.
   a. Participant/sample selection, inclusion criteria, and exclusion criteria.
   b. Intervention and control groups (i.e., the number and characteristics of participants in each group).
   c. Interventions (i.e., what, how, who, setting, frequency, and duration).
   d. Outcome measures (name, brief description, reliability, and validity of outcome measure.
5. Report study findings.
6. Describe study limitations.
   a. Intervention biases.
   b. Measurement biases.
   c. Additional limitations (i.e., appropriateness of analysis methods and statistics, consideration of participant attrition).
7. Provide conclusions.

Reference: American Occupational Therapy Association. (2018). AOTA's Evidence Exchange: Critically Appraised Paper (CAP) guidelines [PDF].

---

[6] Christina Gavalas-Valdivia MS, OTR/L contributed to this section on CATs and CAPs.

Ethical Considerations

> **EXAM HINT:** The NBCOT® OTR® content outline identifies knowledge of the "application of ethical decision-making and professional behaviors guided by the NBCOT Practice Standards and Code of Conduct" (NBCOT®, 2022, p. 4) as essential for competent practice. The application of knowledge about the following ethical considerations for research can help you determine the correct answer for NBCOT® Domain 4 Competency and Practice Management exam items related to ethical research practices.

1. Participants must be provided with full disclosure of study's purpose, methodology, and the nature and scope of expected participation.
2. Participants must be informed of any potential risk or discomforts and a plan to remediate risk or discomfort must be developed and provided to participants.

3. Participation in the study must be voluntary.
   a. Participants' right to withdraw from a study must be protected.
   b. Participants' refusal to answer certain questions and/or participate in a specific procedure must be respected and honored.
4. Confidentiality of all participants identifying information must be ensured at all times.
5. Institutional Review Board (IRB) approval must be obtained for all human subject research.
   a. IRBs (or Human Subjects Boards) are mandated by the government to be established at all institutions that are involved in research. This includes educational and health-care settings.
   b. IRB approval is required to receive federal (and most other) research grants.
   c. Proposals for research must be submitted to, and approved by, an IRB prior to implementation of the research study.
   d. IRBs review research proposals to ensure that all of the previously mentioned ethical standards for research have been considered by the researcher.

Service Competence and Professional Development

> **EXAM HINT:** The NBCOT® OTR® exam content outline identifies the task of engaging "in professional development and competency assessment activities relevant to the job role, practice setting, scope of practice, and professional certification standards" (NBCOT®, 2022, p. 14) as essential for competent practice. The application of knowledge about the following professional development and competency assessment activities can help you determine the correct answer for NBCOT® Domain 4 Competency and Practice Management exam items.

Overview

1. All OT practitioners have an ethical responsibility to engage in activities that maintain and enhance their competence and ability to provide client-centered, occupation-based, and evidence-based practice.
2. Professional development activities are required to develop advanced and specialized knowledge and skills beyond entry-level competencies.

3. Supervisory feedback, performance appraisals, peer review, and active self-reflection should be used to identify professional development needs and establish professional development goals.
4. Practitioners should seek and participate in professional development activities that are relevant to their practice setting, client population, job responsibilities, and professional goals.
   a. Refer to subsequent section and Box 4-28.
5. Professional development tools (PDTs) are available to guide the self-assessment of professional development needs and interests and develop a professional development plan.
6. Most state regulatory boards (SRBs) and the NBCOT® require evidence of participation in professional development activities to maintain licensure and certification, respectfully.
   a. The amount and nature of these requirements vary between different jurisdictions.
      (1) It is the practitioner's responsibility to ensure that all professional development requirements are fulfilled within the required time frame (e.g., every two to three years) and that

Chapter 4

all documentation (e.g., proof of continuing education units [CEUs] earned) is available for review upon request by an SRB or the NBCOT®.
   (a) The use of professional portfolio is an effective means to track and document professional development activities.

a. Box 4-28 outlines activities that are typically used to ensure service competence and support professional development.
3. The use of professional portfolio is an effective means to track and document professional development activities.

Professional Development Tools and Activities

1. Professional development tools (PDTs) can guide the self-assessment of service competence and professional development needs and interests, inform the development of a plan to meet these needs and interests, and monitor progress on meeting service competency and professional development goals.
2. Practitioners should seek and participate in professional development activities that are relevant to their practice setting, client population, job responsibilities, and professional goals.

> **BOX 4-28 ▷ Service Competence and Professional Development Activities**
>
> - Research.
> - Mentorship.
> - Clinical reasoning.
> - Independent study.
> - Facility-based training.
> - Participation in professional association(s).
> - Professional presentations and publications.
> - Continuing education via participation in conferences, workshops, webinars and/or post-professional education.

Professional Burnout and Prevention

Overview

1. Burnout is a work-related stress syndrome resulting from chronic exposure to job stress.
   a. Feelings of burnout can be experienced by healthcare professionals, including OT practitioners.
2. Common workplace issues that can contribute to burnout among OT practitioners include the following.
   a. High workload.
   b. Unrealistic demands on time.
   c. Lack of resources.
   d. Dissatisfaction with income.
   e. Pressure to adopt a generalist approach.
   f. Under recognized value of the profession.
   g. Lack of collaboration from colleagues.
   h. Pressure to use non-occupation-based interventions.
3. Potential consequences of burnout can include the following.
   a. Impaired quality of care.
   b. Lower client satisfaction.
   c. Job dissatisfaction.
   d. Service delivery errors.
   e. Malpractice suits.

Characteristics and Signs of Burnout

1. Healthcare providers who experience burnout may exhibit the following.
   a. Lower empathy.
   b. Decreased responsivity to clients' needs.
   c. Diminished creativity.
   d. Professional self-doubt.
   e. Poor professional identity.
   f. Role conflict.
   g. Physical exhaustion.
   h. Mental exhaustion.
   i. Uncharacteristic irritability.
   j. Cynicism.
   k. Reduced professional efficacy.
   l. Decreased sense of personal accomplishment.

> CAUTION: Due to the potential negative impact burnout can have on service provision, OT practitioners have an ethical responsibility to recognize the signs of burnout and take actions to prevent it.

2. The self-assessment of the signs of burnout is the essential first step in burnout prevention and management.
   a. Table 4-12 outlines the five stages of burnout a healthcare professional may experi-ence at work and their characteristics.
3. Awareness of these characteristics and self-reflection when they are experienced and their relationship to burnout is an important component of professional development.

> **EXAM HINT:** The NBCOT® OTR® exam content outline states that the task of incorporating "risk management techniques at the individual and practice-setting levels to protect clients (and) self . . . from injury or harm" (NBCOT®, 2022, p. 13) and knowledge of "strategies and resources to prevent professional burnout . . . (including) assessment of personal needs, self-advocacy regarding workload, and stress management" (NBCOT®, 2022, p. 14) are essential for competent and safe practice. The application of knowledge about the characteristics and signs of burnout described in the above section and the following burnout prevention strategies and resources can help you determine the correct answers for NBCOT® Domain 4 exam items about profes-sional burnout.

Burnout Prevention and Management

1. Burnout can be addressed by the individual, supervisor(s), and workplace administrator(s).
   a. Box 4-29 outlines concrete actions and proactive strat-egies that individuals, supervisors, and administrators can take to prevent and manage work-related burnout.
2. The intentional use of the actions and strategies to prevent burnout outlined in Box 4-29 and the infor-mation provided in this Chapter's prior section on professional development can provide effective guideposts to develop and sustain a rewarding career as an occupational therapist.

Table 4-12

Stages of Burnout

STAGE	CHARACTERISTICS AND SIGNS
Stage 1 **Honeymoon Phase**	The practitioner experiences a feeling of satis-faction by taking on new tasks. If stress is experienced, it is expected and the practi-tioner has good coping skills to manage it.
Stage 2 **Onset of Stress**	The practitioner experiences the onset of stress that is unexpected and/or less manageable. The first signs of stress show up emotionally and physically (e.g., anxiety, fatigue, and distraction).
Stage 3 **Chronic Stress**	The practitioner experiences increased stress, Stress levels rise and become more frequent. Fatigue is deeper and anxiety more pronounced. Increased irritability, poor deci-sion making, and lower mood are evident. Physical symptoms increase in severity.
Stage 4 **Burnout**	The practitioner experiences burnout. The situation is now critical with all the above symptoms of chronic stress. Behavioral changes, negative mindset, sense of isola-tion and depressive thoughts also develop. Physical symptoms worsen.
Stage 5 **Habitual Burnout**	The practitioner experiences habitual burnout. The above symptoms of burnout are a constant presence and additional physical and emotional symptoms may become chronic and life threatening.

> **BOX 4-29** ▷ **Individual, Supervisory and Administrative Actions and Strategies to Prevent Burnout**
>
> - **Individual**: to prevent work-related burnout OT practitioners can:
>   - engage in ongoing self-assessment and reflection. about personal and professional needs and goals.
>   - practice mindfulness and relaxation techniques.
>   - use coping and stress management strategies.
>   - set limits between work and personal life.
>   - advocate to obtain a reasonable workload and a fair salary.
>   - proactively use supervision.
>   - participate in an employee assistance program.
>   - engage in professional networks (e.g., special interest sections, state and local OT associations) that support a strong OT professional identity and ethical practice.
> - **Supervisor**: to prevent supervisee burnout, supervisors can:
>   - provide support, supervision, and opportunities for professional development.
>   - advocate for fair salaries and reasonable workloads.
>   - weigh priorities and clearly convey these to employees.
>   - solicit ideas and empower people to move them forward.
>   - make all employees feel they belong and are an important part of the organization.
>   - recommend the use of employee assistance programs.
> - **Administrators**: to prevent employee burnout, adminis-trators can develop and sustain a workplace culture that:
>   - enables proactive supervision.
>   - provides fair salaries.
>   - ensures reasonable workloads.
>   - makes all employees feel they belong and are an important part of the organization.
>   - offers onsite opportunities for professional development (e.g., mentorship, on-site seminars).
>   - financially supports participation in external professional development activities (e.g., continuing and/or post-professional education, conference participation).
>   - funds and supports an effective employee assistance program.

References

Ainsworth, E., & DeJonge, D. (2019). Legislation, regulations, codes and standards influencing home modifications. In E. Ainsworth & D. DeJonge (Eds.), An occupational therapist's guide to home modification practice (pp. 63–82). Slack.

American Occupational Therapy Association. (2018a). AOTA's Evidence Exchange: Critically appraised paper (CAP) guidelines [PDF].

American Occupational Therapy Association. (2018b). Occupational therapy included in new law to address opioid epidemic. https://www.aota.org/advocacy/advocacy-news/legislative-issues-update/occupational-therapy-included-new-law-opioid-epidimic-pain-management

American Occupational Therapy Association. (2018c). Telehealth in occupational therapy. American Journal of Occupational Therapy, 72(Suppl. 2), 7212410059. https://doi.org/10.5014/ajot.2018.72S219

American Occupational Therapy Association. (2020a). AOTA 2020 Occupational therapy Code of Ethics. American Journal of Occupational Therapy, 74(Suppl. 3), 7413410005. https://doi.org/10.5014/ajot.2020.74S3006

American Occupational Therapy Association. (2020b). Guidelines for supervision, roles, and responsibilities during the delivery of occupational therapy services. American Journal of Occupational Therapy, 74(Suppl. 3), 7413410020. https://doi.org/10.5014/ajot.2020.74S3004

American Occupational Therapy Association. (2020c). Occupational therapy practice framework: Domain and process (4th ed.). American Journal of Occupational Therapy, 74(Suppl. 2), 7412410010. https://doi.org/10.5014/ajot.2020.74S2001

American Occupational Therapy Association. (2020d). Standards of practice for occupational therapy. American Journal of Occupational Therapy, 75(Suppl. 3), 7513410030. https://doi.org/10.5014/ajot.2021.75S3004.

American Occupational Therapy Association. (2021a). AOTA 2021 standards for continuing competence in occupational therapy. American Journal of Occupational Therapy, 75(Suppl. 3), 7513410040. https://doi.org/10.5014/ajot.2021.75S3009

American Occupational Therapy Association. (2021b). Enforcement procedures for occupational therapy Code of Ethics. American Journal of Occupational Therapy, 75(Suppl. 3), 7513410040. https://doi.org/10.5014/ajot.2021.75S3006

Amini, D., & Furniss, J. (2018, October). The occupational therapy practice framework: A foundation for documentation. OT Practice, CE-1–CE-8.

Barends, E., Rousseau, D., & Briner, R. (2017). Guideline for critically appraised topics in management and organizations. Center for Evidence-Based Management.

Bausch, M. E., Mittler, J. E., Hasselbring, T. S., & Cross, D. P. (2005). The Assistive Technology Act of 2004: What does it say and what does it mean? Physical Disabilities: Education and Related Services, 23(2), 59–67.

Bogenrief, J. (2019, January). New patient-driven groupings model will change HH PPS payment. OT Practice, 24(1), 10–11.

Boyt Schell, B. A., & Gillen G. (Eds.). (2018). Willard and Spackman's occupational therapy (13th ed.). Wolters Kluwer.

Braveman, B. (2022). Roles and functions of managers: Planning, organizing, and staffing, directing, and controlling. In B. Braveman (Ed.), Leading and managing occupational therapy services (3rd ed., pp. 187–216). F.A. Davis.

Braveman, B. (2022). Professional teams, interprofessional education, and collaborative practice. In B. Braveman (Ed.), Leading and managing occupational therapy services (3rd ed., pp. 269–286). F.A. Davis.

Braveman, B. (2022). Financial planning, management, and budgeting. In B. Braveman (Ed.), Leading and managing occupational therapy services (3rd ed., pp. 331–351). F.A. Davis.

Braveman, B. (2022). Developing evidence-based occupational therapy programming. In B. Braveman (Ed.), Leading and managing occupational therapy services (3rd ed., pp. 463–498). F.A. Davis.

Cahill, S. (2022, January). Research brief: Occupational therapy and palliative care. OT Practice, 31–32.

Centers for Medicare and Medicaid Services. (2013). Jimmo v. Sebelius Settlement Agreement (cms.gov)

Centers for Medicare and Medicaid Services. (2019a). Design and development of the Diagnosis Related Group (DRG). (cms.gov)

Centers for Medicare & Medicaid Services. (2019b). Medicare claims processing manual: Chapter 1 - Inpatient hospital services covered under Part A. https://www.cms.gov/Regulations-and-Guidance/Guidance/Manuals/downloads/bp102c01.pdf

Centers for Medicare & Medicaid Services. (2020). Billing and coding: Therapy evaluation, re-evaluation and formal testing. https://www.cms.gov/medicare-coverage-database/view/article.aspx?articleid=53309

Centers for Medicare & Medicaid Services. (2022a). Medicare claims processing manual: Chapter 7 – Home health services. Retrieved September 24, 2023 from https://www.cms.gov/Regulations-and-Guidance/Guidance/Manuals/Downloads/bp102c07.pdf

Centers for Medicare and Medicaid Services. (2022b). Medicare & Your Mental Health Benefits.

Centers for Medicare & Medicaid Services. (2023a). Billing and coding: Outpatient physical and occupational therapy services. Retrieved September, 24, 2023 from https://www.cms.gov/medicare-coverage-database/view/article.aspx?articleid=57067&ver=25&=

Centers for Medicare & Medicaid Services. (2023b). Inpatient Rehabilitation Facility Patient Assessment Instrument (IRF-PAI) and IRF-PAI manual. https://www.cms.gov/medicare/quality-initiatives-patient-assessment-instruments/irf-quality-reporting/irf-pai-and-irf-pai-manual

Chapter 4

Centers for Medicare & Medicaid Services. (2023c). Mental health care (partial hospitalization). https://www.medicare.gov/coverage/mental-health-care-partial-hospitalization

Centers for Medicare & Medicaid Services. (2023d). Parts of Medicare. https://www.medicare.gov/basics/get-started-with-medicare/medicare-basics/parts-of-medicare#:~:text=Part%0A%20(Hospital%20Insurance)%3A,Outpatient%20care

Clark, G. (2008, January). The infants and toddlers with disabilities program (Part C of IDEA). OT Practice, 13(1), CE-1–CE-8.

Clifton, D. (2004, December). Workers' Comp: A plethora of opportunities. Rehab Management, 32, 34–36.

Code of Federal Regulations (2023, March 14). Part 484-Home health services: 484.55 Condition of participation: Comprehensive assessment of patients. https://www.ecfr.gov/current/title-42/chapter-IV/subchapter-G/part-484

Cole, M. (2000). Learning through reflective practice: A professional approach to effective continuing professional development among healthcare professionals. Research in Post-Compulsory Education, 5(1), 23–38.

Cook, C. R., Grady, E. A., Long, A. C., Renshaw, T., Codding, R. S., Fiat, A., & Larson, M. (2017). Evaluating the impact of increasing general education teachers' ratio of positive-to-negative interactions on students' classroom behavior. Journal of Positive Behavior Interventions, 19(2), 67–77. https://doi.org/10.1177/1098300716679137

De Hert, S. (2020). Burnout in healthcare workers: Prevalence, impact and preventative strategies. Local and regional anesthesia, 171–183.

DeLany, J., Demchick, B., & Crabtree, L. (2020). From school to community transition services. In M. Scaffa & A. Reitz (Eds.), Occupational therapy in community-based practice settings (2nd ed., pp. 178–197). F.A. Davis.

DePoy, E., & Gitlin, L. N. (2015). Introduction to research: Understanding and applying multiple strategies (5th ed.). Elsevier.

Doherty, R. F., & Peterson, E. W. (2022). Responsible participation in a profession: Fostering professionalism and leading for moral action. In B. Braveman (Ed.), Leading and managing occupational therapy services (3rd ed., pp. 559–591). F.A. Davis.

Doll, J., & Domina, A. (2020). Program design and implementation. In M. Scaffa & A. Reitz (Eds.), Occupational therapy in community-based practice settings (2nd ed., pp. 94–113). F.A. Davis.

Doresy, J., Ehrenfreid, H., Finch, D., & Jaegers, L. (2018). Work. In B. A. Boyt Schell & G. Gillen (Eds.), Willard and Spackman's occupational therapy (13th ed., pp. 779–804). Wolters Kluwer.

Edelstein, J., Walker, R., Middleton, A., Reistetter, T., Gary, K. W., & Reynolds, S. (2022). Higher frequency of acute occupational therapy services is associated with reduced Hospital readmissions. American Journal of Occupational Therapy, 76(1), 1–9. 7601180090. https://doi.org/10.5014/ajot.2022.048678

Finlayson, M., & Braveman, B. (2022). Engaging in evidence-based management. In B. Braveman (Ed.), Leading and managing occupational therapy services (3rd ed., pp. 45–69). F.A. Davis.

Flecky, K., Doll, J., & Scaffa, M. (2020). Community-based and population health program development. In M. Scaffa & A. Reitz (Eds.), Occupational therapy in community-based practice settings (2nd ed., pp. 73–93). F.A. Davis.

Fleming-Castaldy, R. (2020). Community mental health programs. In M. Scaffa & A. Reitz (Eds.), Occupational therapy in community-based practice settings (2nd ed., pp. 351–379). F.A. Davis.

Garcia, C. D. L., Abreu, L. C. D., Ramos, J. L. S., Castro, C. F. D. D., Smiderle, F. R. N., Santos, J. A. D., & Bezerra, I. M. P. (2019). Influence of burnout on patient safety: Systematic review and meta-analysis. Medicina, 55(9), 553.

George, A. H. (2018). Infection control and safety issues in the clinic. In W. Schultz-Krohn & H.M. Pendleton (Eds.), Pedretti's occupational therapy: Practice skills for physical dysfunction (8th ed., pp. 141–154). Elsevier.

Grossman, J., & Bortone, J. (2000). Program development. In R. P. Cottrell (Ed.), Proactive approaches in psychosocial occupational therapy (pp. 39–45). Slack.

Henry, T., & Braveman, B. (2022). Assessing and promoting clinical and managerial competency. In B. Braveman (Ed.), Leading and managing occupational therapy services (3rd ed., pp. 379–410). F.A. Davis.

International Center for Clubhouse Development. (2016). STANDARDS FOR CLUBHOUSE PROGRAMS (clubhouse-intl.org)

Jacobs, K. (2000). Innovation to action: Marketing occupational therapy. In R. P. Cottrell (Ed.), Proactive approaches in psychosocial occupational therapy (pp. 505–507). Slack.

Jacobs, K., & McCormack, G. (2019). The occupational therapy manager (6th ed.). AOTA Press.

Job Accommodation Network. (2009). Accommodation and compliance series: The ADA Amendments Act of 2008. Accommodation_and_Compliance_Series_The_ADA_Amendments_Act_of_2008.pdf

Johnson, K. V. (2000, September). Home health PPS: The new payment system. OT Practice, 5(16), CE1–CE8.

Kielhofner, G. (2006). Research in occupational therapy: Methods of inquiry for enhancing practice. F. A. Davis.

Kornblau, B. (2015, May). The Americans with Disabilities Act in 2015: Implications for Practice. OT Practice, 20(9), CE1–CE4.

Kornblau, B., & Burkhardt, A. (2012). Ethics in rehabilitation: A clinical perspective (2nd ed.). Slack.

Koverman, B., & Braveman, B. (2022). Roles and functions of supervisors. In B. Braveman (Ed.), Leading and managing occupational therapy services (3rd ed., pp. 217–247). F.A. Davis.

Kreftling, L. (1991). Rigor in qualitative research: The assessment of trustworthiness. American Journal of Occupational Therapy, 45, 214–222.

Kurian, S., Kramer, J., O'Rourke, B., Rocco, C., & Newman, R. (2022, January). Making meaning while living with life-threatening illness. OT Practice, 15-18.

Leary, D. A., & Mardirossian, J. (2000, September 11). Ethical knowledge = collaborative power. OT Practice, 5(16), 19–22.

Lindstrom-Hazel, D. K., & VanderVlies Veenstra, N. (2015). Examining the Purdue pegboard test for occupational therapy practice. Open Journal of Occupational Therapy, 3(3), 5.

Loeffler, H., & Crystal Simpson, C. (2015). Certifying patients for the Medicare home health benefit. https://www.cms.gov/Outreach-and-Education/Outreach/NPC/Downloads/2014-12-16-HHBenefit-HL.pdf

MacEwan Dysart, A., & Tomlin, G. S. (2002). Factors related to evidence-based practice among US occupational therapy clinicians. American Journal of Occupational Therapy, 56(3), 275–284.

Mckinnon, A. L. (2000). Client values and satisfaction with occupational therapy. Scandinavian Journal of Occupational Therapy, 7(3), 99–106.

Meinert, V. (2017). How to prevent employee burnout. HR Magazine. https://www.shrm.org/hr-today/news/hr-magazine/0817/pages/how-to-prevent-employee-burnout.aspx

Moyers, P., & Dale, L. (2007). The guide to occupational therapy practice. American Occupational Therapy Association.

Murer, C. (2007, October). Psychiatric partial hospitalization: An overview. Rehabilitation Management, 48–49.

Nastasi, J., & Braveman, B. (2022). Marketing occupational therapy services. In B. Braveman (Ed.), Leading and managing occupational therapy services (3rd ed., pp. 443–462). F.A. Davis.

National Alliance to End Homelessness. (2022). Housing first. Housing First - National Alliance to End Homelessness.

National Board for Certification in Occupational Therapy (NBCOT®). (2022). 2022 Occupational Therapist Registered (OTR®) examination content outline. https://www.nbcot.org/-/media/PDFs/2022_OTR_Content_Outline.pdf

National Board for Certification in Occupational Therapy (NBCOT®). (2023a). Code of Conduct (nbcot.org).

National Board for Certification in Occupational Therapy (NBCOT®). (2023b). Procedures for Enforcement (nbcot.org).

Nellis, P. (2015). Enabling successful practice through application of business foundations. In C. Christensen, C. Baum, & J.M. Bass (Eds.), Occupational therapy performance, participation and wellbeing (pp. 549–563). Slack.

Nicholson, J., & Salinas, J. (2022). Occupational therapist/occupational therapy assistant partnership: Supervision and collaboration. In B. Braveman (Ed.), Leading and managing occupational therapy services (3rd ed., pp. 249–267). F.A. Davis.

Nissen, R. (2020). Telehealth. In M. Scaffa & A. Reitz (Eds.), Occupational therapy in community-based practice settings (2nd ed., pp. 488–502). F.A. Davis.

O'Brien, J. C., & Kuhaneck, H. (2019). Case-Smith's occupational therapy for children and adolescents (8th ed.). Elsevier.

Opp, A. (2007, September 27). Reauthorizing No Child Left Behind: Opportunities for OT. OT Practice, 12(17), 9–13.

Oxford Grice, K., Vogel, K. A., Le, V., Mitchell, A., Muniz, S., & Vollmer, M. A. (2003). Adult norms for a commercially available Nine Hole Peg Test for finger dexterity. American Journal of Occupational Therapy, 57(5), 570–573.

Ottenbacher, K. J., & Cusick, A. (1990). Goal attainment scaling as a method of clinical service evaluation. American Journal of Occupational Therapy, 44, 519–525.

Pfeiffer, B., Henry, A., Miller, S., & Witherell, S. (2008). Effectiveness of Disc 'O'Sit cushions on attention to task in second-grade students with attention difficulties. American Journal of Occupational Therapy, 62(3), 274–281.

Reitz, S. M., Scaffa, M., & Chromiak, S. B. (2020). Health professional well-being. In M. Scaffa & A. Reitz (Eds.), Occupational therapy in community-based practice settings (2nd ed., pp. 318–349). F.A. Davis.

Robinson, M., & Fisher, G. (2022). Understanding healthcare systems and practice contexts. In B. Braveman (Ed.), Leading and managing occupational therapy services (3rd ed., pp. 73–118). F.A. Davis.

Rogers, A. T., Bai, G., Lavin, R. A., & Anderson, G. F. (2017). Higher hospital spending on occupational therapy is associated with lower readmission rates. Medical Care Research and Review: MCRR, 74(6), 668–686. https://doi.org/10.1177/1077558716666981

Saffer, A. (2023, June 5). New Medicaid guidance for school-based services, new opportunities. https://www.aota.org/advocacy/advocacy-news/2023/new-medicaid-guidance-for-school-based-services-new-opportunities

Scaffa, M. E., & Reitz, A. M. (2020). Occupational therapy in community-based practice settings (2nd ed.). F.A. Davis.

Schindler, V. P. (2000). Occupational therapy in forensic psychiatry. In R. P. Cottrell (Ed.), Proactive approaches in psychosocial occupational therapy (pp. 319–325). Slack.

Shadish, W., Cook, T., & Campbell, D. (2002). Experimental and quasi-experimental designs for generalized causal inference. Houghton Mifflin.

Shin, J., McCarthy, M., Schmidt, C., Zellner, J., Ellerman, K., & Britton, M. (2022). Prevalence and predictors of burnout among occupational therapy practitioners in the United States. American Journal of Occupational Therapy, 76(4).

Triller, M., Motzi, A., & Harper, G. (2022). Continuous quality improvement. In B. Braveman (Ed.), Leading and managing occupational therapy services (3rd ed., pp. 411–444). F.A. Davis.

US Government Printing Office. (2011). Code of Federal Regulations, Title 42, Volume 5. https://www.govinfo.gov/content/pkg/CFR-2011-title42-vol5/pdf/CFR-2011-title42-vol5.pdf

United States Department of Health and Human Services. (2021). HIPAA for Professionals. https://www.hhs.gov/hipaa/for-professionals/index.html

Vance, K., McGuire, M. J., & Nanof, T. (2009, August). Medicare coverage of occupational therapy in the home and community. OT Practice, 14(13), CE-1–CE-8.

Wilmarth, C. (2009, November 9). Using aides to provide therapy. OT Practice, 14(20), 8.

Wooster, D., & Baxter, A. (2020). Early intervention programs. In M. Scaffa & A. Reitz (Eds.), Occupational therapy in community-based practice settings (2nd ed., pp. 153–177). F.A. Davis.

Chapter 4

Review Questions

Competency and Practice Management

Following are eight questions about key content covered in this Chapter. These questions are not inclusive of the entirety of content on occupational therapy professional standards and responsibilities that you must know for success on the NBCOT® exam. These questions are provided to help you "jump-start" the thought processes you will need to apply your studying of content to the answering of exam questions; hence, they are not in the NBCOT® exam format. Exam items in the NBCOT® format that cover the depth and breadth of content you will need to know to pass the NBCOT® exam are provided in the three online practice exams that accompany this text. The answers to the following questions are provided in Appendix 2.

1. You are working in a skilled nursing facility. An administrator asks you to actively treat a new resident who is very frail with multiple medical complications. Upon admission, you had evaluated the resident and determined that the resident would not be able to tolerate occupational therapy services. During the evaluation, the resident had stated that chronic pain has made all activities very difficult. Pain relief and rest were the only things the resident identified as personally desired. How should you respond to the administrator's request? Which principles of the AOTA's Code of Ethics should you use to guide your response? Explain how these principles relate to this situation.

2. A large regional health-care system provides occupational therapy services across the continuum of care. Settings in which occupational therapy services are provided include an acute care hospital, an outpatient clinic, a subacute rehabilitation unit, a skilled nursing facility (SNF), a palliative care unit, and a home health agency. All settings employ occupational therapists and OTAs/COTA®s. What factors should be considered when determining the level of supervision that the occupational therapist should provide to the OTAs/COTA®s? What is a key determinant for deciding if an OTA/COTA® can ethically be given more responsibility?

3. An occupational therapist is opening a private practice. What procedures should the therapist implement to ensure full compliance with the Health Insurance Portability and Accountability Act (HIPAA)?

(Continued)

Review Questions

4. You are beginning a new job as an occupational therapist for a Medicare-certified home health agency. Most of your clients will have limited independence or be dependent in activities of daily living. What are key Medicare guidelines for home-based occupational therapy services you must consider when working with these individuals and their caregivers?

5. You are employed by a school system to provide direct services to students with disabilities. Your caseload includes middle and high school students. Which federal legislative mandates can help guide your interventions with these students? Describe major regulations and their relationship to the provision of school-based occupational therapy services.

6. You have been hired by a behavioral health organization to develop a partial hospital program (PHP) for an adult population. Describe the major focus of a PHP and the specific occupational therapy program components you need to include.

7. You are developing a new driver rehabilitation program. What are important issues for you to consider as you develop your budget and fiscal management plan?

8. You are starting a new job in a practice area that has high demands on your time and challenges your approach to occupation-based practice. What signs of stress should you be sure to address if you experience them? If you begin to experience the early signs of burnout, what strategies can you incorporate into your daily routine to prevent its progression?

Review>Practice>Motivate>Analyze>Apply

5

Human Development Across the Lifespan

RITA P. FLEMING-CASTALDY, MARLENE MORGAN,
GERALDINE HEALY MARINI, KAREN GUALTIERI,
and CHRISTINA GAVALAS-VALDIVIA[1]

[1] Marge E. Moffett Boyd, Jan G. Garbarini, Linda Kahn D'Angelo, and Susan B. O'Sullivan contributed to this Chapter in prior editions of this text.

Human Development

Definition

1. Sequential changes in the function of the individual.
   a. Qualitative or quantitative.
   b. Influenced by biologic determinants and biopsychosocial environmental experiences.

> **EXAM HINT:** The NBCOT® OTR® exam content outline identifies knowledge of the "impact of typical development and aging on occupational performance, health, and wellness across the life span" (NBCOT®, 2022, p. 3) as essential for competent and safe practice. The application of knowledge about the developmental information provided in this Chapter is required to correctly answer NBCOT® exam items about working with persons of all ages throughout the occupational therapy (OT) process.

Developmental Milestone Guidelines

1. In 2022, the Centers for Disease Control and Prevention (CDC) published revised versions of their Developmental Surveillance Milestone Checklists.
   a. The checklists were developed during a 15-year process which included evidence-informed methodology and criteria provided by the American Academy of Pediatrics.
   b. Table 5-1 describes the benefits and limitations of these checklists and their relationship to OT practice.
      (1) For more information about these guidelines refer to the CDC resource "Learn the Signs. Act Early."
   c. Because these checklists have limitations, they cannot replace the need for OT practitioners to use their extensive knowledge about development to screen, evaluate, plan and implement intervention for, and monitor the progress of children.
      (1) Refer to https://www.aota.org/practice/practice-essentials/cdc-guidelines-faq for further information about the relevance of the CDC guidelines to OT.
2. The developmental milestone information provided in this Chapter is based on well-regarded OT textbooks including those identified on the NBCOT® publication reference list as being most commonly used in OT education programs. This list is used by the NBCOT®'s exam item writers to inform the development, verification, and validation of certification exam items (NBCOT®, 2020).

Table 5-1

CDC Developmental Surveillance Milestone Checklists and Their Relevance to OT Practice

Benefits: These checklists:
- provide parents/caregivers with a trajectory of expected developmental milestones from birth to 5 years.
- decrease the use of a "wait and see" approach for screenings or evaluation by OT and other related services when a delay is identified.
- place milestones at an age that 75% or more of children exhibit them to make missing a single milestone more likely to prompt the need for a screening.

Limitations: These checklists cannot:
- be used as screening or diagnostic tools.
- be used to establish necessity for the initiation, continuation, or termination of OT services.
- provide a standard for the average or median age of achievement of the developmental milestones for children.
- include all of the milestones that a child may achieve.

Relevance to OT Practice: OT practitioners can use these checklists to:
- provide a resource for parents/caregivers to monitor a child's development and identify a delay.
- determine need for further screening or evaluation for OT services.

References
https://www.aota.org/practice/practice-essentials/cdc-guidelines-faq.
https://www.cdc.gov/ncbddd/actearly/about.html#points

> **CAUTION:** The NBCOT® asks their item writers "to cross-reference their content expertise with current and frequently used occupational therapy references" (NBCOT®, 2020, p.4); therefore, only studying the CDC Milestones Checklists will not provide you with sufficient information to ensure certification exam success. Whereas, mastering this Chapter's content will ensure that you have acquired the depth and breadth of knowledge about development that is based on OT professional publications and needed for NBCOT® exam success.

> **EXAM HINT:** Because this Chapter's developmental milestone content summarizes the information that is provided in the publications identified on the NBCOT®'s reference list, it is comprehensive. When studying this content, it is important to recognize that the NBCOT® exam items will test your knowledge of typical developmental patterns and the most commonly reported age at which a skill is developed. Therefore, the time and effort you spend to master this content will be well spent. Correct answers to exam items will adhere to these guidelines; incorrect answers will not.

Sensorimotor Development

Prenatal and Development of Sensorimotor Integration

1. Prenatal period: the gestational period; from conception to birth.
   a. Table 5-2 outlines the development of sensorimotor integration that typically occurs during the prenatal period.
2. Infancy: the earliest period of postnatal life; the time from a child's birth through their first year.
   a. The first year of life is often subdivided into 2–3-month periods described as early infancy (birth to 3 months), middle infancy (4–6 months), late infancy (7–9 months), and transitional infancy (10–12 months).

   (1) The first month of early infancy is also called the neonatal period.
   b. Table 5–2 outlines the development of sensorimotor integration that typically occurs during infancy.

Post-Infancy and Early Childhood Development of Sensorimotor Integration

1. The first five years of life after infancy is often subdivided divided into the stages of emerging toddler (13–24 months), toddler (2–3 years of age), and preschool/early childhood (3–5 years of age).
   a. Table 5–3 outlines the development of sensorimotor integration that typically occurs after infancy and during early childhood.

Chapter 5

Table 5-2

Prenatal and Infant Development of Sensorimotor Integration

Prenatal Period (from conception to birth)
- All neonatal reflexes are present at 29 weeks gestation, although they are not fully developed.
- Innate tactile, proprioceptive, and vestibular reactions are present.
- Responses to tactile stimuli begin as early as 5.5 weeks after conception.
- Responses to sound begin at 24 weeks gestation.

Early Infancy (birth to 3 months)
- Tactile, proprioceptive, and vestibular systems begin to integrate and be refined.
  - Input from these systems impact the infant's arousal level, are critical for the development of body scheme, and help the infant feel more organized and content.
- The visual system continues to develop as the infant responds to human faces and items of high contrast placed up to approximately 10 inches from their face.
- The auditory system develops as the infant orients to inputs that are typically voices but may be other sounds.
- The integration of primitive oral motor reflexes results in effective feeding.
- The integration of motor skills allows for head righting and turning the head from side to side.
- At this stage, changes in sensory input may easily overstimulate infants.

Middle Infancy (4–6 months)
- Tactile and proprioceptive systems continue to be refined, laying the foundation for the somatosensory skills.
  - This results in increased awareness of and interest in the world.
- Vestibular, proprioceptive, and visual systems integrate laying the foundation for postural control and facilitating a stable visual field.
- Visual and tactile systems become integrated as the infant reaches for objects and uses a primitive grasp, laying the foundation for eye-hand coordination.
- Play at the midline begins, which is important for the development of bilateral coordination.
- Infant movement patterns progress from reflexive to voluntary and goal directed.

Late Infancy (7–9 months)
- Vestibular, visual and somatosensory responses increase in quality and quality as the infant becomes more mobile.
- Tactile and proprioception perceptions become more refined allowing for the development of fine motor skills and motor planning.

Transitional Infancy (10–12 months)
- Tactile and proprioceptive responses improve and lead to the development of midline skills and the ability to cross the midline.
- Auditory, tactile, and proprioception perceptions are heightened allowing for development of sounds for the purpose of communication.
- Tactile, proprioceptive, gustatory, and olfactory perceptions are integrated, allowing for primitive self-feeding.

References

May-Benson, T. A. (2017). Introduction to sensory integration. In A. Wagenfeld, J. Kaldenberg, & D. L. Honaker (Eds.), Foundations of pediatric practice for the occupational therapy assistant (2nd ed., pp. 162–196). Slack.

Smet, N., Lucas, C. B., Parham, D., & Mailloux, Z. (2020). Occupational therapy view of child development. In J. C. O'Brien & H. Kuhaneck (Eds.), Case-Smith's occupational therapy for children and adolescents (8th ed., pp. 76–121). Elsevier.

5. Refer to Figures 5-1 to 5-9 for pictures of some key reflexes.

Table 5-3

Post-infancy and Early Childhood Sensorimotor Integration Development

Emerging Toddler (13–24 months)
- Tactile perceptions become more precise allowing for the localization and discrimination of skills.
- Balance and dynamic posture control become stronger as a result of increased sensory integration.
- Further integration of all systems promote the development of complex motor planning as the toddler's repertoire of movement patterns expand.
- Increased motor planning abilities contribute to the toddler's self-concept as they begin to master the environment.
- Symbolic gesturing and vocalization promote ideation, indicating the ability to conceptualize.

Toddler (2–3 years of age)
- The vestibular, proprioceptive, and visual systems further develop and refine, resulting in improved balance and postural control.
- Tactile discrimination and localization skills further develop leading to improved fine motor skills.
- Motor planning and praxis ideation further develop leading to an increase in planned actions and the sequencing of play.

Preschool/early childhood (3–5 years of age)
- The child challenges and develops sensorimotor competencies by engaging in roughhouse play, playground activities, games, sports, music, dancing, arts and crafts, household chores, and school tasks.
- These activities also provide opportunities to promote social development and self-esteem.
- This is a period of refinement as the vestibular, proprioceptive, and visual systems further develop, leading to improved balance and postural control, and therefore independence in mobility.
- Further development of tactile discrimination and localization lead to improved fine motor skills.
- Motor planning and praxis ideation also progress during this period.

References

May-Benson, T. A. (2017). Introduction to sensory integration. In A. Wagenfeld, J. Kaldenberg, & D. L. Honaker (Eds.), Foundations of pediatric practice for the occupational therapy assistant (2nd ed., pp. 162–196). Slack.

Smet, N., Lucas, C.B., Parham, D., & Mailloux, Z. (2020). Occupational therapy view of child development. In J. C. O'Brien & H. Kuhaneck (Eds.), Case-Smith's occupational therapy for children and adolescents (8th ed., pp. 76–121). Elsevier.

Reflex Development and Integration

1. Predictable motor response elicited by tactile, proprioceptive, or vestibular stimulation.
2. Primitive reflexes are present at or just after birth and typically integrate throughout the first year.
3. The persistence or re-emergence of these primitive reflexes is indicative of central nervous system (CNS) dysfunction that may interfere with motor milestone attainment, patterns of movement, musculoskeletal alignment, and function.
4. Refer to Tables 5-4 and 5-5 for reflex timetables, stimuli, responses, and functional significance.

EXAM HINT: A child's occupational performance can be enhanced or inhibited based on their sensorimotor integration, reflex development and integration, and motor development. Therefore, knowledge of the developmental sequence for sensorimotor integration and reflex development and integration that is described in this and previous sections and the following information about motor development will be required to correctly answer NBCOT® exam items about working with children with typical and atypical development. Correct answers to exam items will be consistent with these developmental milestones incorrect answers will not.

Motor Development

1. The development of motor skills is needed for the child to effectively move their body, use objects, interact with the environment, and sustain performance (American Occupational Therapy Association [AOTA], 2020).
   a. For example, crossing the midline to reach for a desired toy for play, propelling a scooter around a playground.
2. General principles of typical motor development.
   a. Occurs in a cephalocaudal/proximal to distal direction.
   b. Progresses from gross to fine movement.
   c. Progresses from stability to controlled mobility.
   d. Occurs in a spiraling manner, with periods of equilibrium and disequilibrium.
   e. Sensitive periods occur when the infant/child is affected by environmental input.
3. Table 5-6 outlines the typical sensorimotor developmental sequence of stability in key positions (i.e., prone, supine, sitting).
4. Table 5-7 outlines the typical sensorimotor developmental sequence of major gross motor mobility activities (i.e., rolling, creeping, walking, stair climbing, jumping and hopping).
5. Important aspects in the development of upper extremity function.
   a. Head and trunk control.
   b. Eye/hand interaction, sensory-perceptual interaction.
   c. Shoulder-scapular stability/mobility.
   d. Humeral control.
   e. Elbow control.
   f. Forearm control.
   g. Wrist control.
   h. Thumb opposition and stability.
   i. Palmar arches of hand.
   j. Isolated finger control.

Table 5-4

Reflexes that Integrate During Typical Development

REFLEX	STIMULUS	RESPONSE	FUNCTIONAL SIGNIFICANCE	ONSET AGE	INTEGRATION AGE
Rooting	Stroke the corner of the mouth, upper lip, and lower lip	Movement of the tongue, mouth, and/or head during the stimulus	Helps the baby locate the feeding source to begin feeding	28 weeks' gestation	3 months
Suck-swallow	Place examiner's index finger inside infant's mouth with head in midline	Strong, rhythmical sucking	Facilitates nutritive sucking for the ingestion of liquid	28 weeks' gestation	2–5 months
Traction	Grasp infant's forearms and pull-to-sit	Complete flexion of upper extremities	Promotes momentary grasp to enable the child to hold onto mother when being pulled	28 weeks' gestation	2–5 months
Moro	Rapidly drop infant's head backward	First phase: arm extension/abduction, hand opening Second phase: arm flexion and adduction	Protective response to 'stress;' helps develop extensor tone during a period when flexor tone is dominant	28 weeks' gestation	4–6 months
Plantar grasp	Apply pressure with thumb on the infant's ball of the foot	Toe flexion	Increases input to sole of foot; integration is associated with readiness for independent gait	28 weeks' gestation	9 months
Galant	Hold infant in prone suspension, gently scratch or tap alongside the spine with finger, from shoulders to buttocks	Lateral trunk flexion and wrinkling of the skin on the stimulated side	Enhances trunk stabilization by facilitating lateral trunk movement	32 weeks' gestation	2 months
Asymmetric tonic neck	Fully rotate infant's head and hold for 5 seconds	Extension of extremities on the face side, flexion of extremities on the skull side	Promotes visual attention to upper extremity; decreases incidence of rolling	37 weeks' gestation	4–6 months
Palmar grasp	Place a finger in infant's palm	Finger flexion; reflexive grasp	Increases palmar tactile input; prepares muscles for voluntary grasp	37 weeks' gestation	4–6 months
Tonic labyrinthine - Supine	Place infant in supine	Increased extensor tone	Facilitates full-body extensor tone; allows posture to adapt to that of the head	> 37 weeks' gestation	6 months
Tonic labyrinthine - Prone	Place infant in prone	Increased flexor tone	Facilitates full-body flexor tone; allows posture to adapt to that of the head	> 37 weeks' gestation	6 months
Landau	Hold infant in horizontal prone suspension	Complete extension of head, trunk, and extremities	Regulates tone; promotes prone extension to manage flexor tone	3–4 months	12–24 months
Symmetric tonic neck	Place infant in the crawling position and extend the head	Flexion of hips and knees	Facilitates quadruped position in preparation for crawling; breaks up total-body extension	4–6 months	8–12 months
Neck righting (on body) (NOB)	Place infant in supine and fully turn head to one side	Log rolling of the entire body to maintain alignment with the head	Facilitates rolling; maintains body orientation in response to cervical position changes	4–6 months	5 years
Body righting (on body) (BOB)	Place infant in supine, flex one hip and knee toward the chest and hold briefly	Segmental rolling of the upper trunk to maintain alignment	Promotes trunk and spinal rotation to facilitate sitting and quadruped positions	4–6 months	5 years

Table 5-5

Reflexes that Persist Throughout Life

REFLEX	STIMULUS	RESPONSE	FUNCTIONAL SIGNIFICANCE	ONSET AGE
Labyrinthine/optical (head) righting	Hold infant suspended vertically and tilt slowly (about 45°) to the side, forward, or backward	Upright positioning of the head	Basis for head management and postural stability; orients head in space vertically	Birth–2 months
Downward parachute (protective extension downward)	Rapidly lower infant toward supporting surface while suspended vertically	Extension of the lower extremities	Prepares lower extremities for surface contact (i.e., standing); breaks a fall	4 months
Forward parachute (protective extension forward)	Suddenly tip infant forward toward supporting surface while vertically suspended	Sudden extension of the upper extremities, hand opening, and neck extension	Places upper extremities in anticipation of surface contact to break a fall; supports prop sitting	6–9 months
Sideward parachute (protective extension sideward)	Quickly but firmly tip infant off-balance to the side while in the sitting position	Arm extension and abduction to the side	Unilaterally supports body for use of opposite arm; prevents falls	7 months
Backward parachute (protective extension backward)	Quickly but firmly tip infant off-balance backward	Backward arm extension or arm extension to one side spinal rotation	Protects from backwards falls	9–10 months
Prone tilting	After positioning infant in prone, slowly raise one side of the supporting surface	Curving of the spine toward the raised side (opposite to the pull of gravity); abduction/extension of arms and legs	Facilitates postural adjustments to maintain center of gravity	5 months
Supine tilting and Sitting tilting	After positioning infant in supine or sitting, slowly raise one side of the supporting surface	Curving of the spine toward the raised side (opposite to the pull of gravity); abduction/extension of arms and legs	Facilitates postural adjustments to maintain center of gravity; promotes sitting balance	7–8 months
Quadruped tilting	After positioning infant on all fours, slowly raise one side of the supporting surface	Curving of the spine toward the raised side (opposite to the pull of gravity); abduction/extension of arms and legs	Facilitates postural adjustments to maintain center of gravity and preserve positioning in quadruped	9–12 months
Standing tilting	After positioning infant in standing, slowly raise one side of the supporting surface	Curving of the spine toward the raised side (opposite to the pull of gravity); abduction/extension of arms and legs	Facilitates postural adjustments to maintain center of gravity and balance during standing and walking	12–21 months

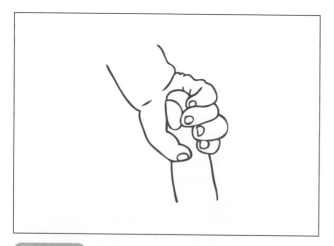

Figure 5-1   **Palmar Grasp Reflex.**

Groenweghe, Marisa with permission.

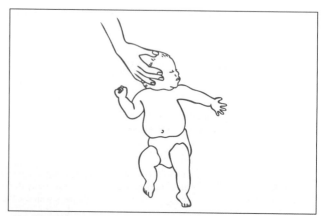

Figure 5-2   **Asymmetric Tonic Neck Reflex (ATNR).**

Groenweghe, Marisa with permission.

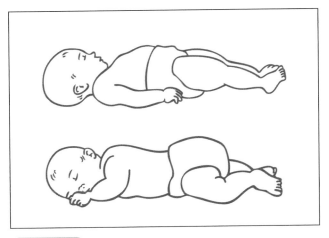

Figure 5-3   **Tonic Labyrinthine Reflex (TLR).**
Groenweghe, Marisa with permission.

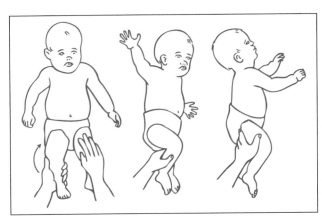

Figure 5-6   **Body Righting Reaction on Body (BOB).**
Groenweghe, Marisa with permission.

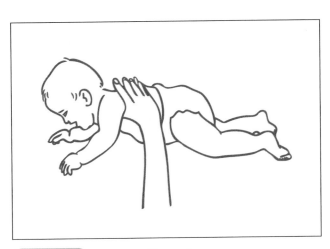

Figure 5-4   **Landau Reaction.**
Groenweghe, Marisa with permission.

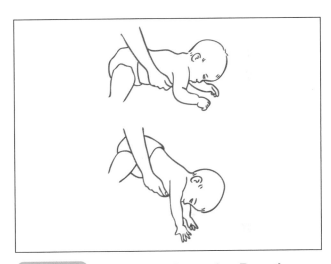

Figure 5-7   **Protective Extension Reaction Forward.**
Groenweghe, Marisa with permission.

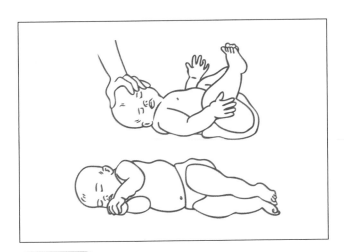

Figure 5-5   **Neck on Body (NOB).**
Groenweghe, Marisa with permission.

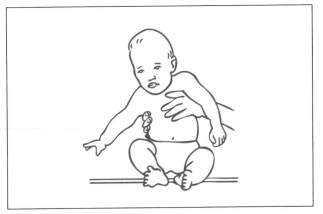

Figure 5-8   **Protective Extension Reaction Sideward.**
Groenweghe, Marisa with permission.

Chapter 5

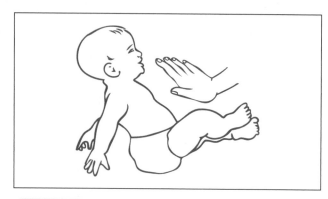

Table 5-6

Sensorimotor Development for Stability

TYPICAL AGE RANGE	STABILITY SKILLS DEVELOPED
Prone	
0–4 months	The infant: • lifts their head momentarily. • turns their head from side to side. • lifts their head and sustains it in midline. • rotates their head freely when their head is supported. • bends their hips with their bottom in air. • can bear weight on their forearms. • can tuck their chin and gaze at their hands in a forearm prop. • attempts to shift weight on their forearms, resulting in the shoulders collapsing.
5–6 months	The infant: • bears weight and shifts weight on their extended arms. • shifts weight on their forearms and reaches forward. • lies prone with their hips and legs extended. • has equilibrium reactions.
6–8 months	The infant: • lifts their chest and thighs off of a surface. • exhibits airplane posturing in a prone position. • pivots in the prone position. • moves from a prone position to sitting.
9 months	The infant: • begins to dislike the prone position.
Supine	
0–3 months	The infant: • holds their head to one side. • can turn their head from side to side.
3–4 months	The infant: • holds their head in midline. • tucks their chin and extends their neck. • brings their legs together in midline. • can flatten their head, back and pelvis against the supporting surface.

Table 5-6

Sensorimotor Development for Stability (*Continued*)

TYPICAL AGE RANGE	STABILITY SKILLS DEVELOPED
4–5 months	The infant: • no longer has head lag when pulled to a sitting position. • begins to play with hands in midline away from the body.
5–6 months	The infant: • lifts their head independently. • can actively kick their legs. • brings their feet to their mouth. • brings their hands to their feet. • can reach for a toy with one or both of their hands. • maintains thumb and finger extension with an open palm.
7 months	The infant: • has equilibrium reactions.
Sitting	
0–3 months	When the infant is held in sitting, the infant: • bobs their head and moves it side to side. • can right their head. • has a rounded back. • sits with their hips apart, turned out, and bent. • can hold their head steady. • tucks their chin and is able to gaze at floor. • sits with less support. • has hips bent with their shoulders in front of their hips.
5–6 months	When the infant supports themself in sitting, the infant: • sits alone momentarily. • has increased back extension. • sits by propping forward on their arms. • sits with a wide base with their legs bent.
7–8 months	The infant: • has equilibrium reactions. • can rotate their upper body while their lower body remains stationary. • has protective responses when falling to the side.
8–10 months	The infant: • sits well without support. • sits with their legs closer together. • has a full upright position with their knees straight. • has an increased variety of sitting positions, including "w" sitting and side sitting. • plays in a sitting position. • independently gets to a sitting position from a prone position. • may return to a wide base of support when engaged in difficult fine motor tasks.
10–12 months	The infant: • exhibits protective extension backwards, first with their elbows bent then with their elbows straightened. • can move in and out of a sitting position into other positions. • has fully developed trunk control and equilibrium responses in the sitting position. • can assume an increased variety of positions.

Chapter 5

Table 5-6

Sensorimotor Development for Stability (*Continued*)

TYPICAL AGE RANGE	STABILITY SKILLS DEVELOPED
11–24 months +	The infant/toddler: • rises from supine by first rolling to their side then pushing up into the sitting position.
Standing	
0–3 months	The infant: • takes some weight on their legs when held in a standing position (0–3 months). • when held in a standing position, their legs may give way (2–3 months).
3–4 months	The infant: • bears some weight on their legs but must be held proximally. • can hold their head up at midline with no chin tuck. • aligns their pelvis and hips behind their shoulders. • turns their legs outward and brings them apart.
5–6 months	The infant: • demonstrates increased capability to bear weight. • needs less support; may be held by the arms or hands. • continues to stand with their legs outward and apart. • bounces in the standing position.
6–9 months	The infant: • pulls to a standing position using furniture for assistance. • rotates their trunk over their lower extremities. • when pulling to a standing position, their lower extremities are more active. • pulls to a standing position by kneeling, then half-kneeling.
9–12 months	The infant: • pulls to a standing position with their legs only, they no longer need their arms. • stands alone momentarily. • will display evidence of equilibrium reactions. • can shift their body weight onto one leg while side stepping with the opposite leg.

References

Mulligan, S. (2014). Occupational therapy evaluation for children: A pocket guide (2nd ed.). Wolters Kluwer. Lippincott Williams & Wilkins.

Smet, N., Lucas, C.B., Parham, D., & Mailloux, Z. (2020). Occupational therapy view of child development. In J. C. O'Brien & H. Kuhaneck (Eds.), Case-Smith's occupational therapy for children and adolescents (8th ed., pp. 76–121). Elsevier.

Zubler, J. M., Wiggins, L. D., Macias, M. M., et al. (2022). Evidence-informed milestones for developmental surveillance tools. Pediatrics.

Table 5-7

Sensorimotor Development for Mobility

TYPICAL AGE RANGE	MOBILITY SKILLS DEVELOPED
Rolling	
3–4 months	The infant: • accidentally rolls from the prone position to their side because of poor control of weight shift. • rolls from the supine position to the side.
5–6 months	The infant: • rolls from the prone to the supine position. • rolls from the supine position to the side with their right and left legs performing independent movements. • rolls from the supine to the prone position with their right and left legs performing independent movements. • can roll sequentially across a room.
6–14 months	The infant: • rolls segmentally with the roll initiated by their head, shoulder, or hips.
Creeping	
7 months	The infant: • crawls forward on their belly.
7–10 months	The infant: • reciprocally creeps.
10–11 months	The infant: • creeps on their hands and feet.
11–12 months	The infant: • creeps well. • can creep on a variety of surfaces. • can creep up and down inclines.
Cruising and Walking	
5–6 months	The infant: • periodically uses the "high guard" position (i.e., walking with a wide-based gait and arms extended). • has protective responses when falling to the front.
8 months	The infant: • cruises sideways.
9–10 months	The infant: • cruises around furniture, turning slightly in the intended direction.
10–12 months	The infant/toddler: • stoops and recovers in play. • walks purposefully when one of their hands held by an adult or adolescent. • reaches for furniture out of reach when cruising. • cruises in either direction with no hesitation.
12–15 months	The toddler: • walks independently. • uses a wide-based gait to walk. • can start and stop walking.

(*Continued*)

Chapter 5

Table 5-7

Sensorimotor Development for Mobility (Continued)

TYPICAL AGE RANGE	MOBILITY SKILLS DEVELOPED
15–18 months	The toddler: • falls frequently. • runs stiffly with eyes on the ground. • uses a wide-based gait to walk.
Climbing onto Surfaces	
15–18 months	The toddler: • climbs on and off surfaces.
Stair Climbing	
15 months	The toddler: • creeps up stairs.
18–24 months	The toddler: • walks up stairs while holding on. • walks down stairs while holding on. • creeps backwards down stairs.
2–2½+ years	The child: • walks up stairs without support while taking their time bringing one foot up to the next step, then bringing the second foot up to it. • walks down stairs without support while taking their time, bringing one foot down to the next step, then bringing the second foot down to it.
2½–3 years	The child: • walks up stairs, alternating their feet.
3–3½ years	The child: • walks down stairs, alternating their feet.
Jumping and Hopping	
2 years	The child: • jumps down from a step.
3 years	The child: • jumps off the floor with both feet.
3–4 years	The child: • gallops, leading with one foot and transferring weight smoothly and evenly.
4–5 years	The child: • jumps over objects. • hops on one foot.
5 years	The child: • hops in a straight line.
5–6 years	The child: • skips on alternating feet, maintaining balance.

References

Mulligan, S. (2014). Occupational therapy evaluation for children: A pocket guide (2nd ed.). Wolters Kluwer. Lippincott Williams & Wilkins.

Smet, N., Lucas, C.B., Parham, D., & Mailloux, Z. (2020). Occupational therapy view of child development. In J. C. O'Brien & H. Kuhaneck (Eds.), Case-Smith's occupational therapy for children and adolescents (8th ed., pp. 76–121). Elsevier.

Zubler, J. M., Wiggins, L. D., Macias, M. M., et al. (2022). Evidence-informed milestones for developmental surveillance tools. Pediatrics.

6. Important components in the development of hand skills and their age of development.
   a. Reaching skills.
      (1) Table 5-8 outlines the typical developmental sequence of reaching skills.

Table 5-8

Development of Reaching Skills

TYPICAL AGE RANGE	REACHING SKILLS DEVELOPED
Birth–2 months	The infant: • has visual regard accompanied by swiping/batting at objects with their closed hand while supine.
3–4 months	The infant: • begins to direct their arm movements while supine; one side may be preferred. • bring their hands together at midline for bilateral reaching while supine.
5 months	The infant: • successfully reaches a desired object and uses both hands to secure and hold the object against their body in midline while supine. • develops the ability to move their arms and hands further away from their body and to approach a desired object with an indirect reach while supine. • weight shifts to one side while prone and reaches for and moves the desired object towards their body with the opposite upper extremity using a closed fist; many attempts to obtain the desired object are unsuccessful.
6 months	The infant: • has increased dissociation of body sides, allowing for more effective unilateral reaching. • uses a more open hand. • has a more direct reach and successfully grasps a desired object while supine. • weight shifts to one side while prone to successfully reach and grasp a desired object with the opposite upper extremity.
7 months	The infant: • weight shifts while on their hands and knees to reach for and grasp a desired object with one upper extremity while their opposite upper extremity and knees support their body weight.
9 months	The infant: • reaches with one or two hands while prone and on their hands and knees with increased accuracy and efficiency.

References

Dorich, J. M., & Harpster, K. (2020). Pediatric hand therapy. In J. C. O'Brien & H. Kuhaneck (Eds.), Occupational therapy for children and adolescence (8th ed., pp. 702–727). Elsevier.

McCoy-Powlen, J. D., Gallen, D. B., & Edwards, S. J. (2017). Hand development. In A. Wagenfeld, J. Kaldenberg, & D. L. Honaker (Eds.), Foundations of pediatric practice for the occupational therapy assistant (2nd ed., pp. 282–299). Slack.

Mulligan, S. (2014). Occupational therapy evaluation for children: A pocket guide (2nd ed.). Wolters Kluwer. Lippincott Williams & Wilkins.

b. Grasping skills according to Erhardt Prehension Developmental Levels and their age of development.
   (1) Grasp of the cube.
       (a) Table 5-9 outlines the typical developmental sequence of these grasp skills.
       (b) Figure 5-10 provides pictures of the developmental levels for the grasp of a cube.

Table 5-9

Sensorimotor Development of Grasp Skills

TYPICAL AGE RANGES	SKILLS DEVELOPED
Grasping a Cube	
Birth–1 month	The infant: • displays visual attention to an object. • has a reflexive grasp.
3 months	The infant: • visually attends to an object and may swipe at it. • may have sustained voluntary grasp upon contact. • uses the ulnar side of their hand with no thumb involvement and a flexed wrist.
4 months	The infant: • demonstrates primitive squeeze grasp. • visually attends to an object and approaches the object within one inch from themselves. • upon contact with an object, they pull the object back in their hand to squeeze it unsteadily against their other hand or body. • has no thumb involvement in their grasp.
4–5 months	The infant: • begins to progress toward a palmar grasp. • starts to adduct their thumb with their fingers pressed against the ulnar side of their palm, progressing in the direction of the center of their palm toward a palmar grasp. • This is sometimes referred to as an ulnar-palmar grasp.
5 months	The infant: • develops a palmar grasp. • places their fingers on the top surface of an object and presses it into center of their palm with their thumb adducted.
6–7 months	The infant: • develops a radial-palmar grasp: • presses their fingers on the far side of an object against their opposed thumb and the radial side of their palm (6 months), with the wrist straight (7 months).
8–9 months	The infant: • develops the radial-digital grasp: an object is held with the opposed thumb and fingertips, space is visible between (8 months) with wrist extended (9 months).

Table 5-9

Sensorimotor Development of Grasp Skills (Continued)

TYPICAL AGE RANGES	SKILLS DEVELOPED
Grasping a Pellet	
Birth–1 month	The infant: • has no voluntary grasp or visual attention to a pellet-sized object.
3 months	The infant: • visually attends to a pellet-sized object without attempting to grasp it.
6 months	The infant: • begins swiping/raking and contacting a pellet-sized object.
7 months	The infant: • develops an inferior-scissors grasp; raking a pellet-sized object into their palm with an adducted, totally flexed thumb and all flexed fingers, or two partially extended fingers.
8 months	The infant: • develops scissors grasp: between the thumb and side of a curled index finger, distal thumb joint slightly flexed, proximal thumb joint extended.
9 months	The infant: • develops an inferior pincer grasp: between the ventral surfaces of their thumb and index finger, distal thumb joint extended, beginning of thumb opposition.
10 months	The infant: • develops a pincer grasp: between the distal pads of their thumb and index finger, the distal thumb joint is slightly flexed, the thumb is opposed.
12 months	The infant: • develops a fine pincer grasp: between their fingertips or fingernails, the distal thumb joint is flexed.

References

Erhardt, R. P. (1994). The Erhardt Developmental Prehension Assessment. Erhardt Developmental Products.

Mandich, M. B. (2016). Infancy. In A. Cronin & M. B. Mandich (Eds.), Human development and performance throughout the lifespan (2nd ed., pp. 200–226). Cengage.

McCoy-Powlen, J. D., Gallen, D. B., & Edwards, S. J. (2017). Hand development. In A. Wagenfeld, J. Kaldenberg, & D. L. Honaker (Eds.), Foundations of pediatric practice for the occupational therapy assistant (2nd ed., pp. 282–299). Slack.

Mulligan, S. (2014). Occupational therapy evaluation for children: A pocket guide (2nd ed.). Wolters Kluwer. Lippincott Williams & Wilkins.

Smet, N., Lucas, C.B., Parham, D., & Mailloux, Z. (2020). Occupational therapy view of child development. In J. C. O'Brien & H. Kuhaneck (Eds.), Case-Smith's occupational therapy for children and adolescents (8th ed., pp. 76–121). Elsevier.

Chapter 5

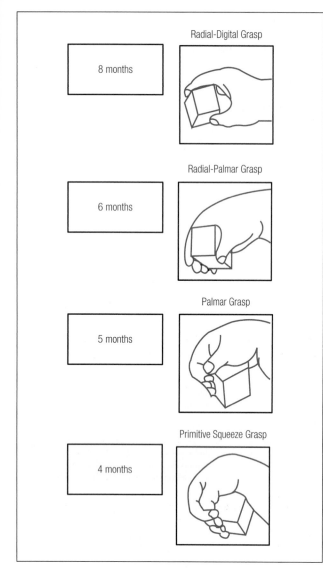

Figure 5-10 **Developmental Levels: Grasp of the Cube.**

Illustrations from The Erhardt Developmental Prehension Assessment, copyright 1994 by Rhoda P. Erhardt. Published by Erhardt Developmental Products, 2379 Snowshoe Court, Maplewood, MN 55119, (651) 730-9004. Reprinted with permission.

(2) Grasp of the pellet (prone or sitting).
(a) No voluntary grasp or visual attention to the object (natal).
(b) Table 5-9 outlines the typical developmental sequence of these grasp skills.
(c) Figure 5-11 provides pictures of the developmental levels for the grasp of a pellet.
c. Mature grasping skills are needed to complete functional activities.
(1) These grasp patterns are used to perform activities that require precision and/or power.
(2) Refer to Table 5-10.

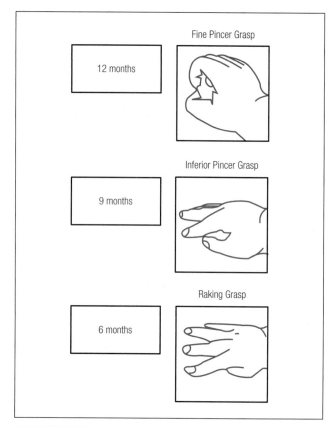

Figure 5-11 **Developmental Levels: Grasp of the Pellet.**

Illustrations from The Erhardt Developmental Prehension Assessment, copyright 1994 by Rhoda P. Erhardt. Published by Erhardt Developmental Products, 2379 Snowshoe Court, Maplewood, MN 55119, (651) 730-9004. Reprinted with permission.

d. Releasing skills: development progresses from no release (0–1 month) to involuntary release (1–4 months) to two-stage transfer (5–6 months) to one-stage transfer (6–7 months) to voluntary release (7–9 months).
(1) Table 5-11 further describes the transfer skills used to release objects.
(2) By 9 months, release is by full arm extension.
(3) Refinement of release continues up to age four with the attainment of graded release.
e. Carrying skills: involves a combination of movements of the shoulder, body, and distal joints of the wrist and hand to hold an item and making appropriate adjustments as necessary to maintain this hold.
f. Bilateral hand use: asymmetric movements prevail until three months, and then symmetric movements emerge until 10 months.
(1) By 12–18 months, the infant uses both hands for different functions.
(2) At 18–24 months, manipulation skills emerge.

Table 5-10

Mature Grasping Patterns Used in Functional Activities

GRASP PATTERN	FUNCTIONALITY	DESCRIPTION
Power grasp	Used to control tools or other objects. Used when hand strength is required in activity	The object is help obliquely in the hand; ulnar fingers are flexed; radial fingers are less flexed. Thumb is in extension and adduction. The child stabilizes the object with the ulnar side of the hand and controls the object using the radial side of the hand.
Hook grasp	Used to carry objects such as a purse or briefcase	The transverse metacarpal arch is flat; the fingers are adducted with flexion at the interphalangeal (IP) joints. The metacarpophalangeal (MCP) joints may be flexed or extended.
Spherical grasp	Used to hold a small ball	The wrist is extended, fingers abducted, with some flexion at the MCP and IP joints. Stability of the longitudinal arch is needed to use this pattern to grasp a larger ball. The hypothenar eminence assists in cupping the hand for control of the object.
Cylindrical grasp	Used to hold a glass, cup, or can with hand around the object	The transverse arch is flattened to allow the fingers to hold against the object. The fingers are only slightly abducted, and IP and MCP joint flexion is graded according to the size of the object. When additional force is required, more of the palmar surface of the hand contacts the object.
Disk grasp	Used to hold a disk such as a jar lid	Thee fingers hold the disk with extension of the MCP joints and flexion of the IP joints. The wrist flexes and thumb extends when objects are larger, and only the pads of the fingers contact the object. This pattern involves dissociation of flexion and extension movements and use of a combination of wrist flexion with MCP extension and IP flexion.
Lateral pinch	Used to exert power on or with a small object	The index finger is slightly flexed and the thumb is flexed and adducted. The pad of the thumb is placed against the radial side of the index finger at or near the distal interphalangeal (DIP) joint.
Pincer grasp	Used to hold and handle small objects and precision tools (e.g., a pencil)	The thumb is opposed to the index finger pad and the object is held within the finger pads. The ulnar fingers are often flexed.
Three-jaw chuck or tripod grasp	Used to hold and manipulate a writing utensil or eating utensil	The thumb is simultaneously opposed to the index and middle finger pads. These fingers provide stability for prehension of a tool. The thumb forms an oval or modified oval shape with the fingers. When using a tripod grasp on a tool, the forearm is slightly supinated.
Tip pinch	Used to prehend and hold tiny objects	The thumb is opposed with thumb tip meeting index finger tip, forming a circle. All joints of the index finger and thumb are partly flexed.

Reference: Case-Smith, J., & Exner, C. E. (2015). Hand function evaluation and intervention. In J. Case-Smith, & J. C. O'Brien (Eds.), Occupational therapy for children and adolescents (7th ed., p. 224). Elsevier. Reprinted with permission.

Table 5-11

Development of Object Manipulation and Release Skills

TYPICAL AGE RANGE	SKILLS DEVELOPED
2–3 months	An object is held in the palm and visualization occurs by moving the wrist. An object is moved towards and away from the face to change perspective; e.g., the object's size.
3–4 months	A grasped object is moved by flexing the elbow. A bilateral hold is used to grasp and manipulate objects with both hands. An object can be held in one hand and another object can be held in the other hand.
5–7 months	Coordinated movements are used to manipulate an object with one hand holding the object and the other one performing movement. Coordinated movements are used to manipulate multiple objects. A two-stage transfer is used to release an object; i.e., the taking hand grasps the object before the releasing hand lets go.
7–9 months	Sequential actions are done to achieve a goal. A one-stage transfer is used to release an object; i.e., the taking hand and the releasing hand perform actions simultaneously (6–7 months). A voluntary release develops (7–9 months).
9–15 months	Voluntary release is refined and progresses from the clumsy release of an object into a large container to a precise, controlled release into a small container.
15 months–2 years	Finger-to-palm translation is used to complete a linear movement of an object from the fingers to the palm of the hand; e.g., picking up coins. The complexity of the manipulation of objects increases; e.g., the bilateral manipulation of more than one object at the same time.

Chapter 5

(Continued)

Chapter 5

Table 5-11

Development of Object Manipulation and Release Skills (*Continued*)

TYPICAL AGE RANGE	SKILLS DEVELOPED
2–2½ years	Palm-to-finger translation with stabilization is used to complete a linear movement of an object from the palm of the hand to the fingers; e.g., placing coins in a slot. Simple rotation is used to turn or roll an object held at the finger pads approximately 90° or less; e.g., unscrewing a small bottle cap.
3–6 years	Shift is used to perform a linear movement of an object on the finger surfaces to allow for the repositioning of the object relative to the finger pads; e.g., separating two pieces of paper, turning book pages, rolling a piece of clay into a ball, shifting on marker or pencil.
6–7 years	Complex rotation is used to rotate an object 360°; e.g., turning a pencil over to erase. In-hand manipulation with stabilization is used to hold several objects in the hand and manipulate one object while simultaneously stabilizing the other objects; e.g., picking up coins with the thumb and forefinger while storing them in the ulnar side of the same hand.

References

Mandich, M. B. (2016). Infancy. In A. Cronin & M. B. Mandich (Eds.), Human development and performance throughout the lifespan (2nd ed., pp. 200–226). Cengage.

McCoy-Powlen, J. D., Gallen, D. B., & Edwards, S. J. (2017). Hand development. In A. Wagenfeld, J. Kaldenberg, & D. L. Honaker (Eds.), Foundations of pediatric practice for the occupational therapy assistant (2nd ed., pp. 282–299). Slack.

Mulligan, S. (2014). Occupational therapy evaluation for children: A pocket guide (2nd ed.). Wolters Kluwer. Lippincott Williams & Wilkins.

Smet, N., Lucas, C.B., Parham, D., & Mailloux, Z. (2020). Occupational therapy view of child development. In J. C. O'Brien & H. Kuhaneck (Eds.), Case-Smith's occupational therapy for children and adolescents (8th ed., pp. 76–121). Elsevier.

(3) The ability to use two different hands for two very different functions emerges at age 2½ years.
  g. Manipulating skills.
    (1) Table 5-11 outlines the typical developmental sequence of manipulating skills.

  h. Prewriting and writing skills.
    (1) Table 5-12 outlines the typical developmental sequence of prewriting and writing skills.
    (2) Figure 5-12 provides pictures of the developmental grasps and postures used to hold writing tools.

Table 5-12

Development of Prewriting and Writing Skills

TYPICAL AGE RANGE	SKILLS DEVELOPED
8–12 months	Mouths writing utensils. Crinkles paper.
12–18 months	Scribbling emerges. Table 5–14 provides further information about the development of drawing skills. Grasps writing utensil first with a cylindrical grasp (12–16 months), then with a palmar-supinate grasp (12–18 months). The writing tool held is with fisted hand with wrist slightly flexed and slightly supinated away from mid-position. The arm moves as a unit.
2–3 years	Digital-pronate grasp: writing tool held with fingers, wrist neutral with slight ulnar deviation, and forearm pronated; arm moves as a unit.
3½–4 years	Static tripod posture: writing tool held with crude approximation of thumb, index, and middle fingers, ring and little fingers only slightly flexed, grasped proximally with continual adjustments by other hand, no fine localized movements of digit components; hand moves as a unit.
4½–6 years	Dynamic tripod posture: writing tool held with precise opposition of distal phalanges of thumb, index, and middle fingers, ring and little fingers flexed to form a stable arch, wrist slightly extended, grasped distally, MCP joints stabilized during fine, localized movements of proximal interphalangeal (PIP) joints. Copies some letters and numbers, and possibly their name (4–5 years). Can write their name using upper and lowercase letters (5–6 years).

References

Mulligan, S. (2014). Occupational therapy evaluation for children: A pocket guide (2nd ed.). Wolters Kluwer. Lippincott Williams & Wilkins.

Smet, N., Lucas, C.B., Parham, D., & Mailloux, Z. (2020). Occupational therapy view of child development. In J. C. O'Brien & H. Kuhaneck (Eds.), Case-Smith's occupational therapy for children and adolescents (8th ed., pp. 76–121). Elsevier.

Van Gorder, L. (2017). Handwriting. In A. Wagenfeld, J. Kaldenberg, & D. L. Honaker (Eds.), Foundations of pediatric practice for the occupational therapy assistant (2nd ed., pp. 300–319). Slack.

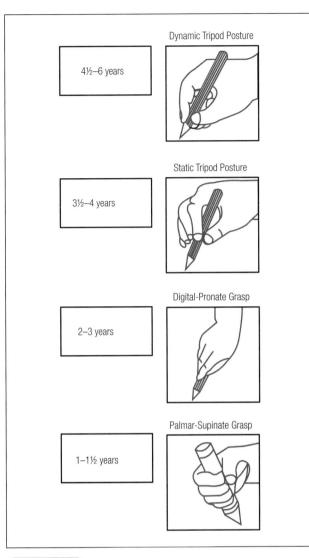

Dynamic Tripod Posture
4½–6 years

Static Tripod Posture
3½–4 years

Digital-Pronate Grasp
2–3 years

Palmar-Supinate Grasp
1–1½ years

Figure 5-12 **Developmental Levels: Prewriting Skills.**

Illustrations from *The Erhardt Developmental Prehension Assessment,* copyright 1994 by Rhoda P. Erhardt. Published by Erhardt Developmental Products, 2379 Snowshoe Court, Maplewood, MN 55119, (651) 730-9004. Reprinted with permission.

i. Scissor skills.
   (1) Table 5-13 outlines the typical developmental sequence of scissor skills.
j. Drawing skills.
   (1) Table 5-14 outlines the typical developmental sequence of drawing skills.

Table 5-13

Development of Scissor Skills

TYPICAL AGE RANGE	SCISSOR SKILLS
1–2 years	None are evident.
2–3 years	Shows an interest in scissors. Holds and snips with scissors. Opens and closes scissors in a controlled fashion.
3–4 years	Starts to cut with jagged snips across an average size paper. Able to cut straight and curve lines with a guide. Cuts simple circles using helper hand.
4.5–5 years	Cuts simple geometric shapes (e.g., squares, triangles).
5.5–7 years	Cuts a variety of shapes and progressively more complex shapes.

References
Klein, M. (1987). Pre-scissor skills (rev. ed.). Therapy Skill Builders.
Mulligan, S. (2014). Occupational therapy evaluation for children: A pocket guide (2nd ed.). Wolters Kluwer. Lippincott Williams & Wilkins.
Smet, N., Lucas, C.B., Parham, D., & Mailloux, Z. (2020). Occupational therapy view of child development. In J. C. O'Brien & H. Kuhaneck (Eds.), Case-Smith's occupational therapy for children and adolescents (8th ed., pp. 76–121). Elsevier.
Van Gorder, L. (2017). Handwriting. In A. Wagenfeld, J. Kaldenberg, & D. L. Honaker (Eds.), Foundations of pediatric practice for the occupational therapy assistant (2nd ed., pp. 300–319). Slack.

Chapter 5

Table 5-14

Development of Drawing Skills

TYPICAL AGE RANGE	DRAWING SKILLS
1–2 years	Scribbles haphazardly and without intent to draw something specific.
2–3 years	Scribbles in an intentional, repetitive manner (e.g., round and round, back and forth). Imitates and crudely/unevenly copies vertical and horizontal lines and circles.
3–4 years	Scribbles and starts to draw forms that include recognizable simple shapes (e.g., circles, squares, crosses). Draws a human figure with one to three human features. Interpretations of drawings are made after the drawing is finished.
4.5–5 years	Intentionally draws a picture to represent what they want to produce. The elements and shapes of their pictures are noticeable and distinct but they may have some mistakes (e.g., inaccurate sizing). Draws a human figure with more complete human features.
5.5–7 years	Intentionally draws a picture with multiple details that reflects their interests and experiences. Draws pictures with human figures that have numerous distinct human features (e.g., blue eyes, brown hair, red fingernails) and additional unique characteristics (e.g., wearing a hat, holding a flower).

References

Mulligan, S. (2014). Occupational therapy evaluation for children: A pocket guide (2nd ed.). Wolters Kluwer. Lippincott Williams & Wilkins.

Smet, N., Lucas, C.B., Parham, D., & Mailloux, Z. (2020). Occupational therapy view of child development. In J. C. O'Brien & H. Kuhaneck (Eds.), Case-Smith's occupational therapy for children and adolescents (8th ed., pp. 76–121). Elsevier.

Wagenfeld, A., Kaldenberg, J., & Honaker, D. L. (Eds.). (2017). Foundations of pediatric practice for the occupational therapy assistant (2nd ed.). Slack.

Psychosocial Development and Major Theorists

EXAM HINT: The NBCOT® exam will likely not ask specific questions about psychosocial developmental theories. However, the OTR® exam content outline states that the task of recognizing "the influence of development . . . on occupational performance" (NBCOT®, 2022, p. 3) is essential to entry-level practice. Therefore, the application of knowledge about major psychological theories can help you determine a developmentally correct answer to NBCOT® exam items about working with persons across the lifespan. For example, knowing that the typical crisis experienced during the teen years, as described by Erikson, is self-identity versus role confusion can be relevant to answering a question about the development of a transition program in a high school. An answer choice that includes an exploration of students' unique interests and personal aspirations would be correct. Similarly, the application of Maslow's hierarchy of needs can help you determine the correct answer to an NBCOT® item about an occupational therapist designing a program in a homeless shelter. According to Maslow, the therapist would first focus on meeting the participants' physiological and safety needs. Subsequent interventions would address participants' love and belonging, and self-esteem needs followed by referrals to resources and programs that would support the attainment of self-actualization.

Erik Erikson

1. Erikson proposed that the ego is a positive force that creates a self-identity which is the center of an individual's personality.
   a. Ego adaptation is the adaptive response of the ego in the development of the personality.
   b. The ego helps an individual adapt to difficult situations and life crises while maintaining their personal identity.
2. Erickson identified eight stages of psychosocial development that occur from infancy through older adulthood.
   a. Each stage includes a critical personal-social crisis that when resolved by the individual results in the acquisition of a personality quality.
      (1) Box 5-1 describes the crisis that is associated with each psychosocial developmental stage and the trait that is integrated into the personality if the stage is successfully resolved.
         (a) Successful resolution of these crises results in the individual feeling complete and satisfied that their life has meaning.
         (b) If a person is not able to successfully resolve the crisis of one stage, their ability to resolve crisis in subsequent stages is limited and unhealthy personality traits and a poor sense of self develops.

BOX 5-1 ▷ Erikson's Eight Stages of Psychosocial Development

- **Stage 1 - Basic Trust versus Mistrust:** the infant/baby realizes that survival and comfort needs will be met; hope is integrated into the personality (birth to 18 months).
- **Stage 2 - Autonomy versus Doubt and Shame:** the child realizes that they can control bodily functions; self-controlled will is integrated into the personality (2–4 years).
- **Stage 3 - Initiative versus Guilt:** the child gains social skills and a gender role identity; a sense of purpose is integrated into the personality (preschool age).
- **Stage 4 - Industry versus Inferiority:** the child gains a sense of security through peers and gains mastery over activities of their age group; a feeling of competency is integrated into the personality (elementary school age).
- **Stage 5 - Self-identity versus Role Confusion:** the teenager begins to make choices about adult roles, and with the resolution of this identity crisis a sense of fidelity or membership with society is integrated into the personality (adolescence).
- **Stage 6 - Intimacy and Solidarity versus Isolation:** the young adult establishes an intimate relationship with a partner and family; the capacity to love is achieved (young adulthood).
- **Stage 7 - Generativity versus Self-absorption:** the adult finds security in the contribution of their chosen personal/ professional roles; the capacity to care is achieved (middle adulthood).
- **Stage 8 - Integrity versus Despair:** the mature adult reflects on their own value and shares with the younger generation the knowledge gained; wisdom is acquired (maturity, older adulthood).

Lawrence Kohlberg

1. Stages of moral development.
   a. Level 1, preconventional morality: occurs from three or four years up to about eight years.
      (1) Stage 1, punishment and obedience: the child is obedient in order to avoid punishment.
      (2) Stage 2, instrumental relativism: the child makes moral choices based on the benefit to self and sometimes to others.
   b. Level 2, conventional morality: occurs at about 9 or 10 years of age.
      (1) Stage 1, social conformity: the child desires to gain the approval of others.
      (2) Stage 2, law and order: rules and social norms are internalized.
   c. Level 3, postconventional morality: age range can vary, and not all will achieve this level.
      (1) Social contracts: the young adult has social awareness and an awareness of the legal implications of decisions/actions.

Abraham Maslow

1. Maslow developed a hierarchy of basic human needs, proposing that if the lower-level needs are not met, the individual is unable to work on higher-level pursuits.
   a. Physiological: basic survival needs (i.e., food, water, rest, warmth).
   b. Safety: the need for physical and physiologic security.
   c. Love and belonging: the need for affection, emotional support, and group affiliation.

d. Self-esteem: the need to believe in one's self as a competent and valuable member of society.
e. Self-actualization: After attaining all of the psychosocial developmental milestones an individual's development of creativity, morality, spontaneity, lack of prejudice, acceptance of facts and problem-solving becomes integrated at this highest level of individual capability.

Ryan and Deci

1. Ryan and Deci's self-determination theory examines how self-determination can enhance or weaken intrinsic motivation, self-regulation, and well-being.
2. The key elements of self-determination are competence, autonomy, and relatedness.
   a. Competence promotes children's desire to continue engaging in an activity with the belief that they will succeed.
      (1) Success leads to continued engagement, and additional success.
      (2) Children who consistently fail during engagement in activities tend to discontinue engaging, due to a perceived sense of failure.
   b. Autonomy promotes intrinsic motivation, which leads children to enthusiastic, self-directed behaviors and a desire to explore.
      (1) These characteristics are associated with a high level of self-esteem and well-being.
      (2) External pressures to engage can result in decreased initiative and learning.
   c. Relatedness, which is dependent on secure relationships, promotes motivation for increased engagement, exploration autonomy, and success.

Cognitive Development

Jean Piaget

1. Described the process of cognitive development from birth to adolescence.
2. Major constructs.
   a. Adaptation: responding to environmental challenges as they occur.
   b. Mental schemes: organizing experiences into concepts.
   c. Operations: the cognitive methods used by the child to organize schemes and experiences to direct subsequent actions.
   d. Adapted intelligence or cognitive competence.
   e. Equilibrium: the balance between what the child knows and can act on and what the environment provides.
   f. Assimilation: the ability to take a new situation and change it to match an existing scheme or generalization.
   g. Accommodation: the development of a new scheme in response to the reality of a situation, or discrimination.

> **EXAM HINT:** The following information about the developmental sequence of cognitive development and cognitive milestones provides foundational knowledge for answering NBCOT® exam items about working with children with typical and atypical cognitive development. For example, the correct answer to an exam item that asks how best to present an activity to a child at the developmental level of a five-year-old would include demonstration. At this age, the child is at the phase of the preoperational cognitive level, during which children will imitate what they see and hear.

3. Hierarchical development of cognition.
   a. Refer to Table 5-15 for an outline of this hierarchy.
4. Piaget stated that maturation of cognition is dependent on the following tasks.
   a. Organic growth, especially the maturation of the nervous system and endocrine glands.
   b. Experience in the actions performed on objects.
   c. Social interaction and transmission.
   d. A balance of opportunities for both assimilation and accommodation.

Major Milestones in Cognitive Development

1. Early object use.
   a. Child focuses on action performed with objects; e.g., banging, shaking (3–6 months).
   b. Child explores characteristics of objects and expands the range of schemes; e.g., pulling, turning, poking, tearing (6–9 months).
   c. Child combines objects in relational play, such as placing objects in containers (8–9 months).
   d. Child notices the relation between complex actions and consequences such as opening doors, placing lids on containers, and differential use of schemes based on the toy being played with; e.g., pushing a train or rolling a ball (9–12 months).
   e. Child acts on objects with a variety of schemes (12 months +).
   f. Child links schemes in simple combinations; e.g., placing a baby in carriage and then pushing the carriage (12–15 months).
   g. Child links multischeme combinations into a meaningful sequence; e.g., putting food in a bowl, scooping the food using a spoon, and feeding a doll (24–36 months).
   h. Child links schemes into a complex script (36–42 months).
2. Problem-solving skills.
   a. 6–9 months.
      (1) Child finds object after watching it disappear; e.g., toy covered by cloth.
      (2) Child uses movement as a means to an end; e.g., rolling to secure toy.
      (3) Child anticipates movement of objects in space; e.g., looking toward trajectory of object circling the child's head.
      (4) Child attends to consequences of actions; e.g., banging a toy and realizing it makes noise.
      (5) Child repeats actions to repeat consequences; e.g., banging a toy to hear noise.
   b. 9–12 months.
      (1) Child is able to use a tool after demonstration, e.g., using a stick to secure a toy that is out of reach.
      (2) Child's behavior becomes more goal directed.
      (3) Child performs an action to produce a response.

Table 5-15

Piaget's Hierarchical Development of Cognition

Sensorimotor Period: ages birth to 2 years.
During this period, the child uses their sensorimotor skills to develop an understanding of the world and progress from reflexive activity to the ability to use cognitive functions to combine and manipulate objects in play. This progression includes the following.
- Reflexive stage: action schemes (e.g., sucking, grasping) begin in response to reflexes (1 month).
- Primary circular reactions: the child learns about cause and effect as a result of reflexive sensorimotor patterns that are repeated for enjoyment (2–4 months).
- Secondary circular reactions: voluntary movement patterns emerge as the coordination of vision and hand function and an early awareness of cause and effect develop (5–8 months).
- Coordination of secondary schemata: voluntary movement in response to stimuli that cannot be seen (i.e., object permanence) and early development of de-centered thought development (9 to 12 months).
- Tertiary circular reactions: the child seeks out new schemes with improved gross and fine motor abilities; tool use begins (12 to 18 months).
- Inventions of new means through mental combinations: the child demonstrates insight and purposeful tool use and explores problem-solving options. The ability to represent concepts without direct manipulation emerges (18 months to 2 years).

Preoperational Period: ages 2–7 years.
During this period, the child progresses from dependence on perception and having an egocentric orientation to the use of logical thought to solve problems. The child develops the ability to engage in and enjoy symbolic and verbal play.
The preoperational period is divided into two phases.
- Preconceptual: the child expands vocabulary and symbolic representations (2–4 years).
- Intuitive thought phase: the child imitates, copies, or repeats what is seen or heard and bases conclusions on what the child believes to be true rather than on logic. Inductive reasoning denotes a transition to the next stage (4–7 years).
The cognitive skills that are developed during this period include the following.
- Classification: categorizing objects according to similarities and differences.
- Seriation: the relationship of one object or classification of objects to another.
- Conservation: the end product of the preoperational period. The child is able to recognize the continuities of an object or class of objects despite apparent changes.

Concrete Operations: ages 7 to 11 years.
During this period, the child develops the ability to use logical thinking on observed or mentally represented objects and enjoy games with rules which help the child adjust to social demands.
The cognitive skills that are developed during this period include the following.
- Reversibility: an expansion of conservation, leads to increased spatial awareness.
- Rules: as rules are better understood, they are also applied.
- Empirical-inductive thinking: the child solves problems with the information that is obvious and present.

Formal Operations: ages 11 through the teen years.
During this period, the child develops the ability to use logic to hypothesize many ways to solve problems and can draw from past and present experiences to imagine what can influence future situations.
The hypothetical-deductive cognitive skills that are developed during this period include the following.
- Abstract thinking and the ability to analyze, plan, and envision the outcome of particular actions.
- The capacity to formulate hypotheses and systematically test them to arrive at an answer to a problem.
- The ability to understand mathematical problems and complete mathematical calculations.

Chapter 5

c. 12–15 months.
 (1) Child recruits the help of an adult to achieve a goal.
 (2) Child attempts to activate a simple mechanism.
 (3) Child turns and inspects objects.
 (4) Child uses a trial and error approach to new challenges.
d. 18–21 months.
 (1) Child attends to shapes of things and uses them appropriately.
 (2) Child begins to think before acting.
 (3) Child uses a tool to obtain a favored object.
 (4) Child begins to replace trial and error with a thought process in order to attain a goal.
 (5) Child can operate a mechanical toy; e.g., an on-off switch.
 (6) Child can predict effects or presume causes.

e. 21–24 months.
 (1) Child recognizes operations of several mechanisms.
 (2) Child matches circles, squares, triangles, and manipulates objects into small openings; e.g., shape sorters.
f. 24–27 months.
 (1) Child discriminates sizes.
g. 24–30 months.
 (1) Child can build with blocks horizontally and vertically.
h. 27–30 months.
 (1) Child begins to relate experiences to one another, based on logic and knowledge of previous experiences.
 (2) Child can make a mental plan of action without acting it out.

Chapter 5

(3) Child can see relationships between experiences; e.g., if the balloon is popped, it will make a loud noise.
  i. 36–48 months.
    (1) Child can build a tower of nine cubes, demonstrating balance and coordination.
    (2) Child can organize objects by size and build a structure from a mental image.

j. 48–60 months.
    (1) Child can build involved structures combining various planes, along with symmetrical designs.
    (2) Child is able to utilize spatial awareness, cause-and-effect, and mental images in problem-solving.
3. Symbolic play.
    a. Refer to the following section.

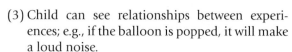

Development of Play

EXAM HINT: The NBCOT® OTR® exam content outline states that the task of implementing "occupation-based strategies to support participation in . . . play" (NBCOT®, 2022, p. 8) is essential to entry-level practice and that performance of this task requires knowledge of "interventions for supporting . . . play" (NBCOT®, 2022, p. 8). The following developmental information about play provides foundational knowledge for determining correct answers for NBCOT® exam items about interventions to enable play. For example, the correct answer to an NBCOT® exam item about working with a child at the developmental level of a three-year-old would include symbolic parallel play, while an option that included creative cooperative play would be the correct answer to an NBCOT® exam item about working with a child at the developmental level of a six-year-old.

Categories of Play

1. Exploratory play, zero to 2 years.
   a. Child engages in play experiences through which the child develops a body scheme.
   b. Sensory integrative and motor skills are also developed as the child explores the properties and effects of actions on objects and people.
   c. Child plays mostly with parents/caregiver(s).
2. Symbolic play.
   a. 12–18 months.
     (1) Basic "make-believe" play, primarily involving self; e.g., eating, sleeping.
     (2) Child can project "make-believe" play on objects and others.
     (3) Child uses a variety of schemes in imitating familiar activities.

   b. 18–24 months.
     (1) Child increases the use of non-realistic objects in pretending; e.g., substituting a block for a train.
     (2) Child has inanimate objects perform familiar activities, e.g., a doll washing itself.
   c. 2–4 years.
     (1) Child engages in play experiences through which the child formulates, tests, classifies, and refines ideas, feelings, and combined actions.
     (2) This form of play is associated with language development.
     (3) Objects that are manageable for the child in terms of symbolization, control, and mastery are preferred by the child.
     (4) Child is mostly involved in parallel play with peers and begins to become more cooperative over time.
3. Creative play, 4–7 years.
   a. Child engages in sensory, motor, cognitive, and social play experiences in which the child refines relevant skills.
   b. Child explores combinations of actions on multiple objects.
   c. Child begins to master skills that promote performance of school- and work-related activities.
   d. Child participates in cooperative peer groups.
4. Games, 7–12 years.
   a. Child participates in play with rules, competition, social interaction, and opportunities for development of skills.
   b. Child begins to participate in cooperative peer groups with a growing interest in competition.
   c. Friends become important for validation of play choices and performance, while parents and caregivers assist and validate in the absence of peers.

Development of Activities of Daily Living Skills

Feeding

1. Oral-motor development: Box 5-2 outlines the typical developmental sequence of oral-motor skills.
2. Self-feeding development: Table 5-16 outlines the typical developmental sequence of self-feeding skills.

> **EXAM HINT:** The NBCOT® OTR® exam content outline identifies knowledge of "impact of typical development . . . . (and) body functions and body structures on occupational performance" (NBCOT®, 2022, p. 3) and the "intervention strategies and techniques used to facilitate oral motor skills for drinking, eating, and swallowing" (NBCOT®, 2022, p. 9) as essential for competent practice. Thus, the application of knowledge about oral-motor development outlined in Box 5-2, the developmental sequence of self-feeding described in Table 5-16, and the evaluation and intervention approaches described in the following can help you determine the correct answer for NBCOT® exam items about working with children to develop the oral motor skills needed for drinking, eating, and swallowing.

3. Evaluation of oral-motor and feeding skills.
   a. Parent interview including parent's concerns, feeding history, behavior during feeding, weight gain or loss.
   b. Medical and developmental history.
   c. Observation of feeding including postural control; oral sensitivity; motor control of the jaw, lip, tongue, and cheek; and coordination and endurance of all.
   d. Recommendation for videofluoroscopy swallow study, especially if the child has a high risk of aspiration (refer to Chapter 9).

> **EXAM HINT:** The NBCOT® OTR® exam outline identifies knowledge of the "roles and responsibilities among interprofessional teams when coordinating client care and providing services" (NBCOT®, 2022, p. 6) as essential for competent and safe practice. While the evaluation of oral motor and feeding skills and interventions to develop these are within the scope of OT practice, OT practitioners frequently collaborate with speech-language pathologists (SLPs) while providing these services. Therefore, a correct answer to an exam item about an OT practitioner working with a child with an oral motor deficit may include their collaboration with an SLP.

4. Intervention for oral motor control and feeding.
   a. Appropriate positioning to allow for neutral pelvic alignment and trunk stability either in the caregiver's lap or in a chair, infant seat, or wheelchair.

> **CAUTION:** Avoid head extension to prevent asphyxiation as a result of closing of the airway.

   b. Hand positioning of the caregiver: place the index finger longitudinally under the child's lip, middle finger under the jaw, and place the thumb on the lateral end of the mandible.

BOX 5-2 ▷ Oral-Motor Development

- **Prior to 33 weeks of gestation:** an infant is fed by non-oral means.
- **35 weeks of gestation or after:** jaw and tongue movements are strong enough to allow for feeding.
- **40 weeks of gestation and up to 4 months:** rooting, gag, and cough reflexes are present, protecting the airway and decreasing the chances of aspiration.
- **1 month:** rhythmic sucking.
- **4–5 months:** strong sucking, good lip closure, tongue moves up and down, munching occurs (consists of a phasic bite and release of a soft cookie).
- **6 months:** efficient sucking, strong up and down movement of the tongue, good lip closure.
- **7–8 months:** beginning of mastication of soft and mashed foods with diagonal jaw movement.
- **9 months:** lateral tongue movements make mastication of soft and mashed food effective, able to drink from a cup but jaw is not firm.
- **12 months:** jaw is firm; rotary chewing allows for a good bite on a hard cookie.
- **18 months:** tongue movements increase to include elevation, rotary chewing is well coordinated, biting is sustained.
- **24 months:** able to chew most foods (including meats and raw vegetables) with a well-graded and sustained bite, drinks from a cup with a firm jaw.

Chapter 5

Table 5-16

Developmental Continuum in Self-Feeding and Associated Component Areas

AGE (MONTHS)	EATING AND FEEDING PERFORMANCE	CONCURRENT CHANGES IN PERFORMANCE COMPONENTS		
		SENSORIMOTOR	COGNITION	PSYCHOSOCIAL
5–7	Takes cereal or poured baby food from spoon.	Has good head stability and emerging sitting abilities; reaches and grasps toys; explores and tolerates various textures (e.g., fingers, rattles); puts objects in mouth.	Attends to effect produced by actions, such as hitting or shaking.	Plays with caregiver during meals and engages in interactive routines.
6–8	Attempts to hold bottle but may not retrieve it if it falls; needs to be monitored for safety reasons.		Object permanence is emerging and infant anticipates spoon or bottle.	Is easily distracted by stimuli (especially siblings) in the environment.
6–9	Holds and tries to eat cracker but sucks on it more than bites it; consumes soft foods that dissolve in the mouth; grabs at spoon but bangs it or sucks on either end of it.	Good sitting stability emerges; able to use hands to manipulate smaller parts of rattle; guided reach and palmer grasp applied to hand-to-mouth actions with objects.	Uses familiar actions initially with haphazard variations; seeks novelty and is anxious to explore objects (may grab at food on adult's plate).	Recognizes strangers; emerging sense of self.
9–13	Finger-feeds self a portion of meals consisting of soft table foods (e.g., macaroni, peas, dry cereal) and food if fed by an adult.	Uses various grasps on objects of different sizes; able to isolate radial fingers on smaller objects.	Has increased organization and sequencing of schemes to do desired activity; may have difficulty attending to events outside visual space (e.g., position of spoon close to mouth).	Prefers to act on objects than be passive observer.
12–14	Dips spoon in food, brings spoonful of food to mouth, but spills food by inverting spoon before it goes into mouth.	Begins to place and release objects; likely to use pronated grasp on objects like crayon or spoon.	Recognizes that objects have function and uses tools appropriately; relates objects together, shifting attention among them.	Has interest in watching family routines.
15–18	Scoops food with spoon and brings it to mouth.	Shoulder and wrist stability demonstrate precise movements.	Experiments to learn rules of how objects work; actively solves problems by creating new action solutions.	Internalizes standards imposed by others for how to play with objects.
24–30	Demonstrates interest in using fork; may stab at food such as pieces of canned fruit; proficient at spoon use and eats cereal with milk or rice with gravy with utensil.	Tolerates various food textures in mouth; adjusts movements to be efficient (e.g., forearm supinated to scoop and lift spoon).	Expresses wants verbally; demonstrates imitation of short sequence of occupation (e.g., putting food on plate and eating it).	Has increasing desire to copy peers; looks to adults to see if they appreciate success in an occupation; interested in household routines.

Shepherd, J. (2005). Activities of daily living and adaptations for independent living. In J. Case-Smith (Ed.), Occupational therapy for children (5th ed., p. 489). Elsevier Mosby. Reprinted with permission.

c. Facilitate lip closure by applying slight upward pressure of the index finger under the child's lip.

d. Facilitate jaw closure by firm upper pressure of the middle finger under the jaw.

e. Hand positioning of the index and middle fingers to assist in inhibiting tongue thrust.
   (1) Press bowl of spoon downward and hold onto tongue.

f. Facilitate swallow by lip closure and by placing the spoon on the middle aspect of the tongue while applying slight downward pressure.

g. Facilitate chewing by placing foods, such as long soft cooked vegetables, between the gum and teeth.

h. Integrate preventive measures to address atypical patterns.

(1) If a tonic bite reflex is present, provide firm downward pressure, using a spoon, on the middle of the tongue.

(2) Prevent tongue retraction to avoid choking.

(3) Facilitate lip closure for a tongue thrust that can result in loss of liquid and food, drooling, and failure to thrive.

(4) Decrease tactile sensitivity prior to feeding as well as at other times, by providing firm pressure; encourage sucking/chewing on a cloth; rub gums, palate, and tongue; promote oral exploration of toys; use a NUK toothbrush; and vary the texture of foods, gradually introducing mashed potatoes mixed with other vegetables and soft meats.

  i. Consider the child's feeding difficulties and the texture of foods appropriate to use to address these.

(1) Thick foods are easier to swallow and manage, especially if a tongue thrust is present.

  j. A major role of the OT practitioner is to assist the caregiver in considering and promoting a pleasant social atmosphere for feeding by utilizing positioning and handling techniques to promote eye contact and bonding in a relaxed environment.

  k. Consider the developmental sequence of self-feeding skills and associated component areas as outlined in Table 5-16.

EXAM HINT: The NBCOT® OTR® exam content outline identifies knowledge of the "clinical decision-making for assessing and adapting the intervention plan and prioritizing goals based on client response to intervention (including) developmental needs" (NBCOT®, 2022, p. 7) as essential for competent practice. The application of knowledge about the developmental sequence for all areas of occupation outlined in this Chapter's text and tables can help you determine the correct answer for NBCOT® exam items about working with typically and atypically developing children.

Development of Toileting Skills

1. When a child has consistent patterns of bowel movements and urination, they are typically ready for toilet training.
2. Table 5-17 outlines the typical developmental sequence of toileting skills.
  a. Very active children who are less likely to stop their play to toilet may have a delayed toilet training.

Development of Dressing Skills

1. Table 5-18 outlines the typical developmental sequence of dressing skills.

Table 5-17

Developmental Sequence for Toileting

TYPICAL AGE RANGES	TOILETING
1–2 years	The child: • knows that they are wet or soiled. • cooperates with routine diaper changes. • exhibits emotional distress and discomfort when wet or soiled. • has regular bowel movements.
2–2½ years	The child: • has regular urination patterns, bowel accidents are rare. • begins to show interest in toilet training. • knows whether they need to urinate or have a bowel movement. • tells someone when they need to use the bathroom. • may need reminders about the need to toilet. • cooperates (for a limited time) when placed on a toilet or potty chair. • if not using a potty chair, they may need help getting on and off a standard toilet. • may have occasional accidents; needs nighttime diapers. • typically needs assistance with wiping and reminders about the need to wash hands and flush. • may need help with clothing.
3–4 years	The child: • can toilet on their own. • may need help with wiping and clothing with fasteners. • may need reminders about the need to flush and wash hands. • has less frequent accidents.
4–5 years	The child: • has daytime and nighttime control. • can independently toilet, wipe self, and pull up clothing. • may need help with difficult clothing fasteners. • remembers to flush and wash hands. • may have a few accidents (particularly while sleeping).
5–6 years	The child: • is completely independent in all aspects of toileting.

References

Kaldenberg, J., & Wagenfeld, A. (2017). Self-care. In A. Wagenfeld, J. Kaldenberg, & D. L. Honaker (Eds.), Foundations of pediatric practice for the occupational therapy assistant (2nd ed., pp. 246–267). Slack.

Mulligan, S. (2014). Occupational therapy evaluation for children: A pocket guide (2nd ed.). Wolters Kluwer. Lippincott Williams & Wilkins.

Smet, N., Lucas, C.B., Parham, D., & Mailloux, Z. (2020). Occupational therapy view of child development. In J. C. O'Brien & H. Kuhaneck (Eds.), Case-Smith's occupational therapy for children and adolescents (8th ed., pp. 76–121). Elsevier.

Chapter 5

Table 5-18

Developmental Sequence for Dressing

TYPICAL AGE RANGES	DRESSING
1 year	The child: • cooperates with the person dressing/undressing them. • puts their arms up for donning and doffing shirts. • extends their legs to get socks and pants on. • removes their socks.
1½–2 years	The child can do all of the above plus: • removes slip-on or untied shoes. • removes unfastened jackets, coats, and sweaters. • removes mittens. • helps pull pants down. • pushes their arms through the armholes in a pullover shirt when the shirt is placed above their head.
2½–3 years	The child can do all of the above plus: • attempts to don slip-on shoes. • assists in pulling up socks. • pulls down and removes elastic waist pants. • dons and doffs pullover shirts with some assistance. • dons open front jackets or shirts but cannot zipper or button them. • unbuttons large buttons and unsnaps snaps. • unzips and zips zippers that are placed on track.
3½–4 years	The child can do all of the above plus: • dons slip-on slippers and shoes; initially may be on wrong feet. • dons elastic waist pants. • recognizes the front and back of clothing. • dons and doffs pullover shirts. • buttons large buttons. • buttons a series of three or four buttons. • zips zippers. • snaps front snaps. • fastens front hooks. • unbuckles belt. • dons mittens.
4½–5 years	The child can do all of the above plus: • independently dresses and undresses their upper and lower body. • pulls a belt through belt loops and buckles the belt buckle. • may need minimal assistance with difficult fasteners and tying shoes.
5–6 years	The child can do all of the above plus: • ties and unties shoelaces and bows. • buttons small buttons. • can close back fasteners. • zips back zippers.

References

Kaldenberg, J., & Wagenfeld, A. (2017). Self-care. In A. Wagenfeld, J. Kaldenberg, & D. L. Honaker (Eds.), Foundations of pediatric practice for the occupational therapy assistant (2nd ed., pp. 246–267). Slack.

Mulligan, S. (2014). Occupational therapy evaluation for children: A pocket guide (2nd ed.). Wolters Kluwer. Lippincott Williams & Wilkins.

Smet, N., Lucas, C.B., Parham, D., & Mailloux, Z. (2020). Occupational therapy view of child development. In J. C. O'Brien & H. Kuhaneck (Eds.), Case-Smith's occupational therapy for children and adolescents (8th ed., pp. 76–121). Elsevier.

Development of Home Management Skills

1. Table 5-19 outlines the typical developmental sequence for the performance of common household chores and other instrumental activities of daily living (IADL) tasks.

   a. The household chores and IADL tasks that a family expects a child to complete and when they set this expectation will depend on the family's culture.

Developmental Sequence for Household Chores and Other IADL Tasks

TYPICAL AGE RANGE	HOUSEHOLD CHORES AND IADL TASKS
2–3 years	The child can: • imitate household chores (e.g., sweeping, vacuuming, mowing a lawn, raking leaves). • follow directions to pick up items and put them in a designated space (e.g., toys in a toy chest, dirty clothes in laundry basket, books on bookshelves). • wipe up spills and pick up fallen objects. • fill a pet's food dish with food provided in the proper amount.
4–5 years	The child can do all of the above plus: • prepare simple cold meals and snacks (e.g., yogurt with fruit, a sandwich, cheese and crackers). • set a table for meals and clear it after the meal. • empty a dishwasher; sort cutlery and put it away. • sort laundry and match socks. • make a bed (with imperfections accepted). • dust, sweep, and rake leaves. • water houseplants and gardens. • feed pets. • throw trash away and place items for recycling in their proper receptacle.
6–7 years	The child can do all of the above plus: • help make and pack lunch for school. • help with meal preparation (e.g., peel vegetables). • wash and dry unbreakable dishes, cups, and cookware. • tidy up their room. • collect and bring in mail, newspapers, and delivered packages.
8–9 years	The child can do all of the above plus: • prepare hot meals and snacks (e.g., baking cookies, making scrambled eggs). • load the dishwasher. • wash and dry breakable dishes, cups, and cookware. • put away groceries. • fold laundry and put it away. • mop and vacuum floors. • walk pets.
10–11 years	The child can do all of the above plus: • clean the kitchen and bathroom(s). • help find items while shopping. • change bed linens.
12+ years	The child can do all of the above plus: • plan and prepare complete hot and cold meals. • do laundry and iron clothes. • independently manage household machines (e.g., dishwasher, washing machine, and dryer). • grocery shop using a list. • wash a car. • complete simple home repairs (e.g., paint walls, change lightbulbs).

References

Kaldenberg, J., & Wagenfeld, A. (2017). Self-care. In A. Wagenfeld, J. Kaldenberg, & D. L. Honaker (Eds.), Foundations of pediatric practice for the occupational therapy assistant (2nd ed., pp. 246–267). Slack.

Mulligan, S. (2014). Occupational therapy evaluation for children: A pocket guide (2nd ed.). Wolters Kluwer. Lippincott Williams & Wilkins.

Smet, N., Lucas, C.B., Parham, D., & Mailloux, Z. (2020). Occupational therapy view of child development. In J. C. O'Brien & H. Kuhaneck (Eds.), Case-Smith's occupational therapy for children and adolescents (8th ed., pp. 76–121). Elsevier.

Chapter 5

Occupational Therapy Developmental Evaluation

EXAM HINT: In the NBCOT® OTR® exam content outline, Domain 1 Evaluation and Assessment comprises 23% of the exam and knowledge of the "administration, purpose, indications, advantages, and limitations of standardized and nonstandardized screening and assessment tools" (NBCOT®, 2022, p. 4) is identified as essential for competent and safe practice. Thus, the application of knowledge about the following overall components of a developmental evaluation and specific standardized assessments can help you correctly answer Domain 1 exam items about the evaluation of infants and children.

Overall Components

1. Information regarding the mother's pregnancy and specifics of birth history.
    a. Apgar score of the infant's heart rate, respiration, reflex irritability, muscle tone, and color is measured at one, five, and 10 minutes after birth; each item receives a rating of 0, 1 or 2. The highest score possible is 10 points indicating a newborn's well-being.
    b. Number of weeks premature, adjusted age.
    c. Number of days/weeks in incubator, intubated and/or on ventilator, or nasogastric tube.
2. Medical history: admissions and length of hospitalizations for illness, disease, surgery, and medications.
3. Developmental history: important developmental milestones, their time of achievement, and any difficulties or problems surrounding their attainment.
4. Parent interview to address the above and the parent's perspective on their child's developmental progress and/or concerns, home situation, family history, school history, and support systems.

Assessment of the Newborn, Infant, and Child

1. Neurobehavioral organization: signs of stress or stability.
    a. Neurobehavioral subsystems: based on synactive theory of development (i.e., subsystems continuously interact with each other and with the environment as evidenced by the infant's levels of stress or stability).
        (1) Autonomic system: physiological instability or stability.

(2) Motor system: fluctuating tone with uncontrolled activity or consistent tone with controlled activity.
        (3) Emotional state: disorganized, calm, alert.
        (4) Attention-interaction: stress signals upon attempts at attending to stimuli, difficulty shifting attention, focused responsiveness to stimuli, and fluid shifting of attention.
        (5) Self-regulation: ability to self-organize and balance of subsystems.
    b. Reflex testing. Refer to Tables 5-2 and 5-3.
    c. Muscle tone.
2. Musculoskeletal status.
    a. Skeletal status including extremity and spine deformities.
    b. Range of motion status.
    c. Posture at rest and posture during active movement (see neuromotor assessments).
    d. Refer to Chapter 6 for information about the evaluation of and intervention for musculoskeletal dysfunction.
3. Developmental assessments.
    a. There are many published tools that measure neonate, infant, and child development.
    b. As of the publication of this text, NBCOT® has not made public the names of the specific assessments that may be on the exam.
        (1) The assessments included in this Chapter are based on the authors' review of NBCOT® self-assessment tools, major OT textbooks, and feedback obtained from OT practitioners regarding developmental measures used in practice.

EXAM HINT: The NBCOT® OTR® exam may include the names of specific evaluation tools; therefore, knowing the following assessments can help you determine the correct answer for NBCOT® Domain 1 exam items that address the evaluation of typical and atypical development.

Developmental Assessments of Neonates

1. Assessment of Preterm Infants' Behavior (APIB).
    a. Focus: assesses the infant's pattern of developing behavioral organization in response to increasing sensory and environmental stimuli.
        (1) An extension and refinement of the Neonatal Behavioral Assessment Scale (NBAS).

b. Method: a behavior checklist and scale.

c. Scoring and interpretation.

  (1) Scores are obtained prior to administration for a baseline, during administration, and following administration.

  (2) Scores reflect the degree of facilitation provided by the examiner.

  (3) Eye movements and asymmetry of performance are measured.

  (4) Function and integration of the physiological, motor, state, attentional/interactive, and regulatory systems are determined.

  (5) Interpretation of scores allows the therapist to plan interventions, measure outcomes, and plan follow-up.

d. Population: preterm and full-term infants.

2. Neurological Assessment of Preterm and Full-term Newborn Infant (NAPFI).

a. Focus: a rating scale consisting of a brief neurological examination incorporated into routine assessment.

  (1) Can be used with newborns in an incubator and/or on a ventilator if handling can be tolerated.

  (2) Habituation, movement and tone, reflexes, and neurobehavioral responses including state transition, level of arousal and alertness, auditory and visual orientation, irritability, consolability, and cry are assessed.

b. Method: items are administered in a sequence; first in a quiet or sleep state, followed by items not influenced by state, then during the awake state.

c. Scoring and interpretation.

  (1) The infant's state is recorded, based on six gradings of state, for each item.

  (2) Interpretation of scores allows the therapist to document a pattern of responses to reflect neurological functions and identify deviations for diagnosis.

  (3) A comparison of preterm with full-term infant behavior is provided.

d. Population: preterm and full-term newborn infants.

Overall Development Assessments

1. Bayley Scales of Infant Development, 3rd Edition (BSID-III).

a. Focus: standardized rating scales that assess multiple areas of development to attain a baseline for intervention and to monitor progress.

  (1) Evaluates five domains: cognitive, language, and motor, which are performance-based tasks, and social-emotional and adaptive behavior skills.

b. Method.

  (1) Age-appropriate items are selected from items on the different domain scales.

  (2) Involves parent(s) completing two questionnaires.

c. Scoring and interpretation.

  (1) Composite scores yield qualitative descriptors and performance levels for each domain.

  (2) Results are used to plan interventions for any delays.

d. Population: one to 42 months.

2. Developmental Assessment of Young Children (DAY-C).

a. Focus: a standardized developmental assessment that measures the basic skills of young children across the five domains of cognitive, communication, social-emotional, and physical development.

  (1) The communication development domain has the subdomains of receptive and expressive language, and the physical development domain has the subdomains of fine and gross motor.

b. Method: the DAY-C should be administered by a practitioner familiar with the assessment.

  (1) Domains can be administered separately.

  (2) Assessed items can be scored through observation of the child, a structured interview of the caregiver, or by direct assessment.

c. Scoring and interpretation: each assessed item is scored as either "passed" or "not passed." Passed items earn 1 point; items not passed are scored 0.

  (1) The raw score is converted to a standard score. Standard scores, percentiles, and age equivalents are provided for each domain.

  (2) When all domains are administered and scored, a general developmental index (GDI) of overall performance is obtained.

  (3) Interpretation of the DAY-C scores can identify a child with significant delays in one or more of the subdomain categories, monitor a child's progress, and inform intervention planning.

d. Population: birth to 5 years, 11 months.

3. Denver Developmental Screening Test II.

a. Focus: standardized task performance and observation screening tool for early identification of children at risk for developmental delays in four areas including personal-social, fine motor-adaptive, language, and gross motor skills.

b. Method.

  (1) Test includes 125 test items.

  (2) Test items below the child's chronological age level are administered with sequential progression toward higher-level chronological items until the child fails three items.

  (3) Behaviors observed during the screening are marked on a checklist.

(4) Questionnaires for home screening of environments and pre-screening of development are available to administer to parents/caregivers.

c. Scoring and interpretation.

(1) Each item is scored as a Pass (the child successfully does the item or the caregiver reports the child does the item), Fail (the child does not successfully do the item or the caregiver reports the child does not do the item), No Opportunity (the child does not have the opportunity to do the item due to external constraints) or Refuses (the child refuses to do the item).

(2) The test is discontinued when three items are failed.

(3) Each item scored indicates the chronological age at which it is expected to be performed. The child's score on that item is compared to determine whether the child's performance is age appropriate, advanced, or delayed and is marked as pass or fail.

(4) The screening allows for the interpretation of a child's performance in terms of being normal, suspect, or untestable in personal-social, fine motor-adaptive, language, and gross motor abilities.

(5) Interpretation of findings must be considered in the context of other pertinent information and with ongoing observations.

d. Population: 1 month to 6 years.

4. FirstSTEP Screening Test for Evaluating Preschoolers.

a. Focus: a checklist and rating scale that identifies preschool students at risk and in need of a more comprehensive evaluation.

b. Method.

(1) It assesses five areas/domains as identified by the Individuals with Disabilities Education Act, which include cognition, communication, physical, social and emotional, and adaptive functioning.

(a) Tabletop tasks are administered while sitting across from the child; additional space is needed for gross motor tasks.

(2) An optional Social-Emotional Rating Scale is rated by the examiner based on the child's behavior during testing.

(3) An optional Adaptive Behavior Checklist is rated by the examiner according to the information obtained from a parent or caregiver interview regarding daily functioning.

(4) An optional Parent-Teacher Scale provides additional information not obtained during the testing.

c. Scoring and interpretation.

(1) Each item has criteria for grading and scores for each domain are totaled.

(2) Total domain scores are converted to composite scores to determine whether the child's performance is within an acceptable level or if the child is at risk.

(3) The determination of a child's strengths and areas needing improvement guide treatment planning.

d. Population: 2 years, 9 months to 6 years, 2 months.

5. Goal-Oriented Assessment of Lifeskills (GOAL).

a. Focus: A standardized assessment that measures the functional motor abilities that are needed to complete seven daily goal-related activities that are typically performed by school-aged children.

(1) The seven activities are divided into 54 individual steps that are intended to be fun and motivating for the participant with an emphasis on accuracy, independence, and speed of performance.

(2) The seven activities are organized into two subtests of gross motor activities and fine motor activities. Box 5-3 outlines these subtests.

b. Method.

(1) Items are administered by a practitioner, familiar with the GOAL's administration, who observes the child's functional behavior as they perform the seven activities.

c. Scoring and interpretation.

(1) Provides raw scores of each step, standard scores for each subtest, and progress scores.

(2) Scoring is based on accuracy, independence, and speed of the task completion.

d. Population: 7 years to 17 years.

6. Hawaii Early Learning Profile, Revised (HELP).

a. Focus: non-standardized scale of developmental levels. An educational curriculum-referenced test that assesses six areas of function including cognitive, language, gross motor, fine motor, social-emotional, and self-help.

BOX 5-3 ▷ Goal-Oriented Assessment of Lifeskills (GOAL) Subtests

- **Fine Motor**
  - Utensils: using a knife, fork, and spoon to cut, spear, and scoop
  - Locks: opening keyed and combination padlocks
  - Paper Box: coloring, cutting, folding, and taping a paper construction project
  - Notebook: organizing and filling a three-ring binder
- **Gross Motor**
  - Clothes: putting on and taking off a T-shirt and shorts
  - Ball Play: bouncing and kicking a ball
  - Tray Carry: carrying a loaded tray and avoiding obstacle

b. Method.
   (1) Administered in the child's natural environment and in the context of the family during typical routines.
   (2) Developmentally appropriate items are administered according to established protocols.
   (3) A protocol using a warm-up period, structured play, and snack time is recommended.

c. Scoring and interpretation.
   (1) Developmental age range levels of skills in each of the six areas can be approximated.
   (2) Specification of skills noted on a chart can be transferred to a checklist for analysis of expected skills that are absent.
   (3) A description of behavior and possible causes of difficulty, all within the context of the family and environment, can be obtained.
   (4) Developmental structuring of skills is provided in the form of a sequence of conceptual strands, so skills needed as a foundation for more advanced skills are provided.

d. Population: children from birth to three years, with developmental delay, disabilities, or at risk. HELP for Preschoolers is available for children ages three to six years, with and without delays.

7. Pediatric Evaluation of Disability Inventory (PEDI).
   a. Focus: a standardized, comprehensive assessment that assesses capabilities and performance in the three domain areas of self-care, functional mobility, and social function to determine mastery in functional performance skills, monitor treatment progress, and determine limitations to inform treatment planning and intervention.
   b. Method.
      (1) Administered by clinical observation of the child, professional judgement of a teacher or therapist familiar with the child, a structured parent/caregiver interview, or a parent/caregiver written report.
         (a) A combination of these methods can be used.
      (2) Consists of three measurement sections.
         (a) Part I Functional Skills: a checklist of child's current capabilities in functional skills.
         (b) Part II Caregiver Assistance: measures the extent of help required by the caregiver for routine daily task performance.
         (c) Part III Modifications Scale: identifies the modifications and adaptive equipment needed to perform a task.
   c. Scoring and interpretation.
      (1) The score forms include the areas of functional skills, caregiver assistance, and modifications.
         (a) The three sections are scored separately.
         (b) All items need to be scored.
      (2) Identifies children with patterns of delay.

(3) Progress and outcomes can be monitored.
   d. Population: six months to 7.5 years.
8. Pediatric Evaluation of Disability Inventory-Computer Adaptive Test (PEDI-CAT):
   a. Focus: a standardized computer-based behavior checklist and rating scale that assesses the child's abilities in the three domains of daily activities, mobility, and social/cognitive skills to determine their developmental level, monitor their progress, and/or complete an evaluation.
      (1) A Responsibility domain measures the level of responsibility the child or parent/caregiver take to manage complex multi-step life tasks.
   b. Method: a parent/caregiver familiar with the child's performance completes the computer-based assessment. The computer program analyses item responses to determine the ease or difficulty of the next question.
   c. Scoring and interpretation: instant scoring provides normative standard scores (provided as age percentiles and T scores) and scaled scores; available for 21 age groups (provided in intervals of one year).
      (1) Progress and outcomes can be monitored.
   d. Population: birth–21 years of age.

Motor Assessments

1. Bruininks-Oseretsky Test of Motor Proficiency (2nd ed.) (BOT-2).
   a. Focus: a standardized test that assesses and provides an index of a child's overall motor proficiency; fine and gross motor composites, including consideration of speed, duration, and accuracy of performance, and hand and/or foot preferences.
   b. Method.
      (1) There is a long and short form with eight subtests: fine motor precision, fine motor integration, manual dexterity, bilateral coordination, balance, running speed and agility, upper limb coordination, and strength.
         (a) Hand and foot preference is initially determined.
   c. Scoring and interpretation.
      (1) A total motor composite score consists of four motor areas: fine manual control, manual coordination, body coordination, and strength and agility.
      (2) Age equivalency and descriptive categories, and performance scores indicate motor strengths and weaknesses.
      (3) Scores may be used as a basis for determining intervention goals and to evaluate change.
   d. Population: four to 21 years.

2. Erhardt Developmental Prehension Assessment (EDPA) Revised and Short Screening Form (EDPA-S).
   a. Focus: observation checklist based on performance which assesses three clustered areas including involuntary arm-hand patterns; voluntary movements of approach; and prewriting skills.
      (1) EDPA allows for charting and monitoring of prehensile development.
      (2) EDPA-S identifies developmental gaps in prehensile development and the need for further assessment.
   b. Method.
      (1) Test is administered in sections according to the appropriate age level for the child.
      (2) There are 341 test components in the EDPA categorized according to involuntary arm-hand patterns, voluntary movements, and prewriting skills.
      (3) The EDPA-S contains 128 components.
   c. Scoring and interpretation.
      (1) Part One: right- and left-hand scores are scored as normal or well-integrated, not present or emerging, or abnormal.
      (2) Part Two: scores are placed into a developmental level for each cluster.
      (3) Part Three: function is determined for involuntary arm-hand patterns, voluntary movements, and prewriting skills.
      (4) Gaps in hand skills and developmental levels can be determined.
         (a) Intervention can be planned and provided depending on individual needs.
   d. Population: children of all ages and cognitive levels with neurodevelopmental disorders.
3. Miller Function and Participation Scales (M-FUN).
   a. Focus: a standardized, developmental performance measure that assesses the child's visual-motor, fine motor, and gross motor skills while they perform hands-on activities.
      (1) The assessment also includes three behavioral checklists for the home, school, and testing environments.
   b. Method.
      (1) Test items include the subtests of visual-motor, fine motor, and gross motor activities that are presented as games in which a child would naturally participate.
      (2) The M-FUN should be administered by a professional familiar with the testing materials.
      (3) Home and School Observation Checklists should be completed by teachers, caregivers, or other individuals familiar with the child's participation in these specific settings.
      (4) The Testing Observation Checklist should be completed by the evaluator at the time of testing.

   c. Scoring and interpretation.
      (1) Normative and scaled scores for each individual subtest and a composite score of the combined subtests can be generated.
      (2) Identifies children with mild, moderate, or severe motor delays.
   d. Population: Two years, 6 months to 7 years, 11 months.
4. Peabody Developmental Motor Scales (2nd ed.) (PDMS-2).
   a. Focus: a standardized rating scales of gross and fine motor development.
   b. Method.
      (1) Gross and fine motor subtests measure the child's reflexes, sustained control, locomotion, object manipulation, grasping, and visual motor integration.
      (2) Test items are administered one level below the child's expected motor age in order to obtain a baseline age level.
      (3) The test is discontinued with three consecutive scores of zero.
   c. Scoring and interpretation.
      (1) A developmental profile of gross and fine motor skills is provided.
      (2) Standard scores are provided.
      (3) Strengths and weaknesses are indicated once the percentile ranks are grafted.
      (4) A motor activity program useful for planning and implementing training is provided.
   d. Population: children from birth to six years, with motor, speech-language, and/or hearing disorders.
5. Toddler and Infant Motor Evaluation (TIME).
   a. Focus: assesses the child's quality of movement.
   b. Method.
      (1) Five primary subtests assess the child's mobility, stability, motor organization, social/emotional abilities, and functional performance.
      (2) Quality rating, component analysis, and atypical positions can be assessed by clinicians with advanced training.
   c. Scoring and interpretation.
      (1) Cut-off scores are indicative of moderate or significant motor delays.
      (2) Subtests give more specific information.
   d. Population: birth to three years and six months.

Visual Motor and Visual Perception Assessments

1. Beery-Buktenica Developmental Test of Visual-Motor Integration-VMI, 6th edition.
   a. Focus: assesses visual motor integration.
      (1) Can be used as a classroom screening tool.

(2) If there is a need to obtain additional information about the child's area(s) of difficulty after the VMI has been administered, two optional supplemental tests can be used to further assess their visual perceptual and visual motor skills.

    (a) The Visual Perception Test: only tests perceptual skills.

    (b) The Visual Motor Coordination Test: only tests motor skills.

    (c) One or both of these tools can be administered as needed. Both are timed tests and administered in a particular order.

b. Method.

  (1) The child copies 24 geometric forms that are sequenced according to level of difficulty.

  (2) Once the child fails to meet grading criteria for three consecutive forms, the test is discontinued.

c. Scoring and interpretation.

  (1) Raw score can be translated to percentile ranks, standard score, and age equivalency.

  (2) Average scores fall between 80 and 120 and average percentiles fall between 25 and 75.

d. Population: two years to 100 years.

  (1) The revised edition provides new norms for ages two through 18 years.

    (a) The adult norms for ages 19 and older have not been updated.

2. Developmental Test of Visual Perception (2nd Edition) (DTVP-2) and Developmental Test of Visual Perception—Adolescent and Adult (DTVP-A).

a. Focus: assesses visual perceptual skills and visual motor integration for levels of performance and for designing interventions and monitoring progress.

b. Method.

  (1) The DTVP-2 is composed of eight subtests including eye-hand coordination, copying, spatial relations, visual-motor speed, position in space, figure-ground, visual-closure, and form-constancy.

  (2) The DTVP-A is composed of four subtests of visual motor integration, composite index, and motor-reduced visual perception composite index.

c. Scoring and interpretation.

  (1) Raw scores, age equivalents, percentiles, subtest standard scores, and composite quotients are provided.

  (2) Three indexes and provided.

    (a) General visual perceptual.

    (b) Motor-reduced visual perception.

    (c) Visual motor integration.

d. Population: children aged four to 10 years for the DTVP-2; adolescents and adults aged 11 to 74 years for the DTVP-A.

3. Erhardt Developmental Vision Assessment (EDVA) and Short Screening Form (EDVA-S).

a. Focus: a behavior rating scale to determine visuomotor development that assesses involuntary visual patterns including eyelid reflexes, pupillary reactions, doll's eye responses, and voluntary patterns including fixation, localization, ocular pursuit, and gaze shift.

b. Method.

  (1) There are 271 test items organized developmentally into seven clusters.

  (2) The clusters are presented and items are sequenced developmentally.

  (3) Upon administration of each item, a response is scored for each eye.

  (4) Models for assessment and management, and items required for testing are provided.

c. Scoring and interpretation.

  (1) Responses are scored as normal, well-integrated, emerging, or not present.

  (2) A developmental level is provided for each cluster and a final developmental level is estimated.

  (3) EDVA-S includes 67 components of permanent vision patterns and is scored in the same manner as EDVA.

    (a) If a test item is scored emerging or not present, a full evaluation using EDVA is indicated.

  (4) Baseline levels allow for the identification of delays and also determine the sequenced developmental items that have not been attained.

    (a) A baseline also allows progress to be tracked and interventions to be established.

  (5) Findings will determine indications for an ophthalmic evaluation.

d. Population: birth to six months. Since the six-month level is considered the norm, the EDVA-S can be used for assessing older children.

4. Miller Function and Participation Scales (M-FUN).

a. See prior section on motor assessments.

5. Preschool Visual Motor Integration Assessment (PVMIA).

a. Focus: a standardized norm-referenced assessment that evaluates visual motor integration and visual perceptual skills of preschoolers, including perception in space, awareness of spatial relationships, color and space discrimination, matching two attributes simultaneously, and the ability to reproduce what is seen and interpreted.

b. Method: two performance subtests and two behavioral observation checklists.

  (1) The Drawing subtest requires the child to recognize and reproduce lines and shapes that increase in level of complexity.

(2) The Block Patterns subtest requires the child to recognize color and shape and reproduce block patterns and match block pictures using three-dimensional blocks.

(3) It has a section that first predetermines that the child has the requisite skills to continue with the test items.

(4) The behavioral observation checklists are completed during testing by the administrator to document observed behaviors in an orderly manner to be used in test interpretation.

c. Scoring and interpretation.

(1) The child's fine motor skills and visual perceptual abilities are examined separately, to the extent possible.

(2) Each task has specific criteria listed on the score sheet.

(3) To attain the precision needed to accurately score the child's final products, templates and a ruler are provided to be used when scoring each subtest.

(4) Raw scores are converted to standard scores and percentile ranges for both subtests and for the total test.

(a) Impairments are indicated by standard scores below 80 and percentile scores below 25.

(5) The evaluator's recorded behavioral observations of the child during the testing are not included in the score. These observations are used in test interpretation and subsequent intervention planning.

(6) Interpretation of the child's performance and current emerging abilities are made based on the combination of numerical scores, behavioral observations, and error analysis.

d. Population: preschoolers aged 3½ to 5½ years old.

6. Motor-Free Visual Perception Test (MVPT-4).

a. Focus: a standardized, quick evaluation to assess visual perception (excludes motor components) in five areas including spatial relationships, visual discrimination, figure-ground, visual closure, and visual memory.

b. Method.

(1) The number of items administered depends on the child's age.

(a) For children aged 4 to 10 years, items 1–40 are administered; for persons aged 10 years or older, items 14–65 are administered.

c. Scoring and interpretation.

(1) Raw scores are translated into perceptual ages and perceptual quotients.

(2) Average performance is determined as a standard score of 80–120 and percentile ranks of 25–75.

d. Population: children and adults aged four to 95 years.

7. Motor-Free Visual Perception Test, Vertical (MVPT-V).

a. Focus: an evaluation of individuals with spatial deficits, due to hemi-field visual neglect or abnormal visual saccades.

b. Method: thirty-six items vertically placed are used to assess spatial relationships, visual discrimination, figure ground, visual closure, and visual memory (excluding motor components).

c. Scoring and interpretation.

(1) Provides perceptual ages and perceptual quotients.

(2) Inadequate performance is determined as a score of 85 or less.

d. Population: children and adults with visual field cuts or without visual impairments.

(1) Appropriate for individuals with brain injury since it reduces confounding variables.

8. Test of Visual-Motor Skills (TVMS) and Test of Visual-Motor Skills: Upper Level (TVMS-UL).

a. Focus: assesses eye-hand coordination skills for copying geometric designs.

b. Method.

(1) The individual copies and draws geometric designs that become sequentially more complex.

(a) There are 23 geometric forms in the TVMS which are scored for eight possible errors and 16 in the TVMS: UL which are scored for 9–22 possible errors in motor accuracy, motor control, motor coordination, and psychomotor speed.

(2) Test behavior is also documented.

c. Scoring and interpretation.

(1) The resulting score can be translated into a motor age, standard score, and percentile rank.

(2) Characteristics and errors of the drawings are examined and provide clinical information.

(3) Information is used to establish an intervention plan.

d. Population.

(1) TVMS: two–13 years.

(2) TVMS- UL: twelve–40 years.

9. Test of Visual Perceptual Skills (4th Edition) (TVPS4).

a. Focus: assesses visual perceptual skills and differentiates these from motor dysfunction, as a motor response is not required.

b. Method.

(1) Seven visual perceptual skills including visual discrimination, visual memory, visual-spatial relationships, visual form constancy, visual sequential memory, visual figure-ground, and visual closure are assessed.

(2) Test items are presented in a multiple-choice format and are sequenced in complexity.

(a) If subjects have three consecutive errors, the test is discontinued.

(3) The individual looks at the test item and then selects the correct choice among all possible responses on the test plate.

(4) Behavior observed during testing is also recorded.

c. Scoring and interpretation.

(1) Indications of visual perceptual problems are determined by standard scores below 80 and percentile ranks below 25.

(2) Information is used to establish an intervention program to address deficits that impact on learning.

d. Population: four to 19 years.

Assessment of Motor and Process Skills (AMPS)

1. The AMPS was a standardized assessment that was administered to persons three years of age and older regardless of diagnoses by evaluators who had completed AMPS training.

2. At the time of this text's publication, the AMPS training course and online materials were placed on an indefinite hold; thus, there is no further training of the standardized AMPS.

3. Fisher and Griswold published a non-standardized administration method for the AMPS in 2019.

a. The non-standardized AMPs can be used with any population aged two years or older.

b. Refer to Chapter 15 for a description of the non-standardized AMPs' method, materials, scoring, and interpretation.

Sensory Processing Assessments

1. Sensory Profile (SP): Infant/Toddler Sensory Profile.

a. Focus: measures the infant's/toddler's reactions to daily sensory experiences.

b. Method.

(1) Obtains the caregiver's judgment and observation of a child's sensory processing, modulation, and behavioral and emotional responses in each sensory system via a caregiver questionnaire.

c. Scoring and interpretation.

(1) Cut-off scores indicate typical performance and probable, definite, and significant differences.

(a) Differences indicate which sensory system is hindering performance.

(b) Can be used for intervention planning.

d. Population.

(1) Infants and toddlers from birth to 36 months.

2. Sensory Profile (SP): Adolescent/Adult Sensory Profile.

a. Focus: allows adolescents and adults to identify their personal behavioral responses and develop strategies for enhanced participation.

b. Method.

(1) A questionnaire measures the individual's reactions to daily sensory experiences.

c. Scoring and interpretation.

(1) Cut-off scores indicate typical performance and probable, definite, and significant differences.

(a) Differences indicate which sensory system is hindering performance.

(b) Can be used for intervention planning.

d. Population: individuals from 11 to 65 years old.

e. Refer to Chapter 14 for additional information.

3. Sensory Processing Measure (SPM).

a. Refer to Chapter 7.

4. Sensory Integration and Praxis Tests (SIPT).

a. Refer to Chapter 7.

Psychological and Cognitive Assessments

1. Childhood Autism Rating Scale (CARS).

a. Focus: determines the severity of autism (i.e., mild, moderate, or severe) and distinguishes children with autism from children with developmental delays who do not have autism.

b. Method.

(1) An observational tool is used to rate behavior.

(a) Fifteen descriptive statements include characteristics, abilities, and behaviors that deviate from the norm.

c. Scoring and interpretation.

(1) Scores below 30 = no autism.

(2) Scores of 31–36.5 = mild to moderate autism.

(3) Scores of 37–60 = severe autism.

d. Population: children over two years of age who have mild, moderate, or severe autism.

2. Coping Inventory and Early Coping Inventory.

a. Focus: assesses coping habits, skills, and behaviors, including effectiveness, style, strengths, and vulnerabilities to develop intervention plans for coping skills.

b. Method.

(1) Coping Inventory: a questionnaire that assesses coping with self and coping with the environment according to three categories of coping styles; i.e., productive, active, and flexible.

(2) Early Coping Inventory: a questionnaire assesses the effectiveness of behaviors according to sensorimotor organization, reactive behavior and self-initiated behavior.

c. Scoring and interpretation.
   (1) Determines the level of adaptive behavior and whether or not intervention is needed.
   (2) A coping profile can be drafted for each dimension.
d. Population.
   (1) Coping Inventory: 15 years and above.
   (2) Early Coping Inventory: four to 36 months.

> **EXAM HINT:** In the NBCOT® OTR® exam content outline, knowledge of the "administration, purpose, indications, advantages, and limitations of standardized and nonstandardized screening and assessment tools" (NBCOT®, 2022, p. 4) is identified as essential for competent practice. Thus, the application of knowledge about the visual motor and visual perception, sensory processing, and psychological and cognitive assessments described in the preceding sections and the play and leisure, prevocational and vocational interest, and social participation assessments described in the following can help you correctly answer NBCOT® exam items about the evaluation of children's occupational performance.

Play and Leisure Assessments

1. Interest Checklist.
   a. Focus: an assessment of a person's level of interest in 80 leisure activities, additional leisure interests, and their perspective on how leisure interests and involvement has evolved over time.
   b. Chapter 15 provides information about the Interest Checklist's method and scoring and interpretation.
2. Leisure Diagnostic Battery (LDB).
   a. Focus: the measurement of an individual's leisure experience, and motivational and situational issues that influence leisure (e.g., perceived barriers to leisure and knowledge of leisure opportunities).
   b. Chapter 15 provides information about the LDB's method and scoring and interpretation.
3. Play History.
   a. Focus: assesses a child's or adolescent's developmental level and the adequacy of their play behavior and play opportunities.
   b. Method.
      (1) The evaluator conducts a semi-structured interview with the primary caregiver of the child/adolescent being evaluated.
      (2) Information is gathered in the three categories of general information, previous play experience, and actual play that occurs over three days of play.
   c. Scoring and interpretation.
      (1) Previous play experiences and actual play, consisting of nine aspects that address the form and content of behavior, are analyzed according to materials, action, people, and setting.
      (2) Values are assigned to the interview information according to manual standards.
         (a) A description of play is obtained and play dysfunction is determined.
      (3) Knowledge of a child's/adolescent's play history and play environments can increase understanding of current play behaviors.
         (a) An intervention plan can be developed based on the identified strengths and limitations.
   d. Population: children and adolescents.
4. Revised Knox Preschool Play Scale (RKPPS).
   a. Focus: observations of play skills to differentiate developmental play abilities, strengths and weakness, and interest areas.
   b. Method.
      (1) Administered in a natural indoor and outdoor environment with peers.
         (a) Two 30-minute periods of observations are completed indoors and outdoors.
      (2) Observations are organized according to six-month increments up to age three.
      (3) Four dimensions of play including space management, material management, pretense/symbolic (including imitation), and participation are assessed.
   c. Scoring and interpretation.
      (1) The four dimensions of play are described.
         (a) Each dimension contains behavioral descriptions/factors.
      (2) The mean scores of all four dimension scores provide a play age score indicative of the child's play maturity.
      (3) The effectiveness of intervention can also be determined.
   d. Population: zero through six years.
      (1) It is useful with children for whom standardized testing may not be appropriate.
5. Test of Playfulness (ToP) Revised Version 4.0.
   a. Focus: assesses a child's playfulness based on observations according to four aspects of play.
   b. Method.
      (1) An infant, child, or adolescent is observed for 15 minutes in a familiar play setting.
      (2) Observed behaviors are rated according to intrinsic motivation, internal control, freedom from unnecessary constraints of reality, and framing.
   c. Scoring and interpretation.
      (1) Items are scored on a 4-point scale, ranging from 0 (low frequency of the behavior, low intensity, or unskilled) to 3 (high frequency of the behavior, high intensity, or skillful).

(2) A high score on the ToP indicates greater playfulness of the child. Scores in the 25 percentile or below indicate the need for intervention.

d. Population: six months to 18 years.

6. Transdisciplinary Play-Based Assessment (TPBA).
   a. Focus: measures a child's development, learning style, interaction patterns, and behaviors to determine need for services.
   b. Method.
      (1) Non-standardized play assessment employing team observations based on six phases.
      (2) Observations are categorized into the developmental domains of cognitive, social-emotional, communication and language, and sensorimotor.
   c. Scoring and interpretation.
      (1) A program plan is developed and can include developmental levels, family assessment, intervention services, and strategies to promote an appropriate activity environment.
      (2) A curriculum is available to address particular needs.
   d. Population: infancy to six years.

7. Refer to Chapter 15 for additional information on the evaluation of play.

Prevocational and Vocational Interest Assessments

1. Jacob's Prevocational Assessment (JPVA).
   a. Focus: assessment of work-related skills in 14 major areas (e.g., cognitive-perceptual skills, motor skills) in adolescents and preadolescents with learning disabilities.
   b. Chapter 15 provides information about the JPVA's method and scoring and interpretation.

2. McCarron-Dial Systems (MDS).
   a. Focus: assessment of the prevocational, vocational, and educational abilities of individuals with disabilities and/or sociocultural disadvantages in five main areas.
   b. Chapter 15 provides information about the MDS's method and scoring and interpretation.

3. Reading-Free Vocational Interest Inventory (RFVII).
   a. Focus: identification of vocational areas of interest and/or patterns of interest in a number of vocational areas (e.g., animal care, automotive, housekeeping, clerical work).
   b. Chapter 15 provides information about the RFVII's method and scoring and interpretation.

4. Vocational Interest Inventory–Revised (VII-R).
   a. Focus: measurement of student interest in eight employment areas for adolescents who are unclear about their vocational interests.
   b. Chapter 15 provides information about the VII-R's method and scoring and interpretation.

5. Vocational Interest, Temperament, and Aptitude System (VITAS).
   a. Focus: assessment of vocational interests, temperament, and aptitudes to assist with career guidance and vocational placement.
   b. Chapter 15 provides information about the VITAS's method and scoring and interpretation.

Social Participation Assessments

1. Adolescent Role Assessment.
   a. Focus: assesses the development of internalized roles within family, school, and social settings.
   b. Method: a semistructured interview that follows an interview guide to generate discussion in the areas of family, school performance, peer interactions, occupational choice, and work.
   c. Scoring and interpretation: scoring indicates behavior that is appropriate, marginal, or inappropriate.
   d. Population: adolescents aged 13–17 years.

2. Participation Scale (P Scale) (Version 6.0).
   a. Focus: a measure of restrictions in social participation related to community mobility, access to work, recreation, and social interaction with family, peers, neighbors, etc.
   b. Method.
      (1) An 18-item questionnaire addressing the nine domains of participation identified in the International Classification of Function, Disability, and Health.
      (2) Self-care, mobility, and social function and their functional subunits are assessed.
         (a) The score forms include the areas of functional skills, caregiver assistance, and modifications.
   c. Scoring and interpretation.
      (1) Scores above 12 on the scale (ranging from 0 to 90) indicate the need for intervention.
   d. Population: 15 years and older with physical disabilities.

3. Pediatric Activity Card Sort.
   a. Focus: measures a child's occupational performance and engagement.
   b. Method: the evaluator shows the child pictures of children engaged in typical childhood occupations to determine their level of occupational performance and engagement.
      (1) There are 83 cards depicting 75 activities organized into the four life domains of personal care, school/productivity, hobbies/social activities, and sports.
      (2) The child is shown each card individually and asked whether they have participated in the depicted activity in the past year.

(3) Next, the child is asked to identify the five activities that are the most important to them and the five activities that they would like to do.

  c. Scoring and interpretation: the therapist calculates participation percentages for each of the four domains.

  d. Population: children aged six to 12.

4. School Function Assessment (SFA).

  a. Chapter 15 provides information about the SFA's focus, method and scoring and interpretation.

Additional Assessments

1. Several assessments that are used with adults are also used with children and adolescents. Box 5-4 lists these and describes their focus and population age range.

  a. Chapters 14 and 15 provide information about the method, scoring, and interpretation of these assessments.

BOX 5-4 ◗ Additional Assessments Used with Children and Adolescents

- **Barth Time Construction (BTC)**
  - Focus: assesses time usage, roles, and underlying skills and habits.
  - Population: adolescents through older adults.

- **Beck Depression Inventory**
  - Focus: measures the presence and depth of depression.
  - Population: 13–80 years.

- **Canadian Occupational Performance Measure (COPM)**
  - Focus: identifies the individual's perception of satisfaction with performance and changes over time in the areas of self-care, productivity, and leisure.
  - Population: individuals over the age of seven or parents of small children.

- **Goal Attainment Scaling (GAS)**
  - Focus: facilitates active participation in the goal-setting process by having the individual and/or caregivers identify desired intervention outcomes for the client that are personally relevant to them.
  - Population: older children, adolescents, and adults and caregivers of younger children.

- **Model of Human Occupation Screening Tool (MOHOST)**
  - Focus: provides ratings on the person's volition, habituation, communication and interaction skills, motor skills, process skills, and the environment to provide an overview of their occupational functioning.
  - Population: adolescents to older adults.

- **Occupational Performance History Interview-II (OPHI-II)**
  - Focus: gathers information about an individual's life history, past and present occupational performance, and the impact of the incidence of disability, illness, or other traumatic event in the person's life.
  - Population: adolescents to older adults.

- **Role Checklist**
  - Focus: assesses self-reported role participation and the value of specific roles to the individual.
  - Population: adolescents through older adults.

- **Kohlman Evaluation of Living Skills (KELS)**
  - Focus: determines an individual's knowledge and/or performance of 13 basic living skills needed to live independently in five main areas.
  - Population: adolescents and adults.

- **Klein-Bell Activities of Daily Living Scale (K-B Scale)**
  - Focus: assesses independent functioning in ADL according to 170 items in six areas.
  - Population: individuals from six months to older adults.

Lifespan Developmental Theory and Frame of Reference

Overview

> **EXAM HINT:** The NBCOT® OTR® exam content outline identifies knowledge of the "impact of typical development and aging on occupational performance, health, and wellness across the life span" (NBCOT®, 2022, p. 3) and "resources and considerations for acquiring information about the client's current condition and occupational performance . . . (including) theoretical approach and frame of reference" (NBCOT®, 2022, p. 4) as essential for competent practice. While the NBCOT® exam will likely not ask specific questions about lifespan developmental theories or OT frames of reference, the application of this knowledge can be used to correctly answer exam items. Understanding that development occurs in many dimensions throughout the lifespan, with specific tasks being considered typical for each life stage, can help you determine developmentally appropriate answers for exam items.

Havighurst

1. Proposed that people need to develop certain skills at different ages to meet social standards.
2. Believed that these developmental tasks rely on biological, psychological, and sociological conditions.
   a. Proposed that there are certain sensitive periods, when biological, psychological, and sociological conditions are optimal for the accomplishment of a developmental task.
   b. Described "teachable moments," referring to the sensitive periods when conditions are optimal for integration of previous knowledge and the accomplishment of new developmental tasks with assistance.
3. Six stages of development are described along with specific developmental tasks for each stage.
4. In current society, the tasks of some stages may occur later than described by Havighurst.
5. Tasks of infancy and childhood.
   a. Walk.
   b. Take solid food.
   c. Talk.
   d. Control elimination of body wastes.
   e. Develop sex differences and sexual modesty.
   f. Develop physiologic stability.
   g. Understand concepts of social and physical reality.
   h. Develop emotional ties with parents, siblings, and others.
   i. Understand right from wrong, conscience evolves.
6. Tasks of middle childhood.
   a. Develop physical skills needed for games.
   b. Establish healthy self-concept.
   c. Make friends with children of the same age.
   d. Read, write, and calculate.
   e. Acquire a fund of information necessary for everyday life.
   f. Develop morality and values.
   g. Formulate opinions about social groups and institutions.
7. Tasks of adolescence.
   a. Establish relationships with male and female friends of same age, increasing in quantity and quality.
   b. Develop a gender social role.
   c. Become comfortable with and respect one's changing body.
   d. Decrease emotional reliance on parents/other adults.
   e. Prepare for marriage and family life.
   f. Prepare for economic career.
   g. Develop a value system to shape behavior or develop one's own philosophy.
   h. Behave in a socially responsible manner.
8. Tasks of early adulthood.
   a. Choose a partner.
   b. Adjust to a partner.
   c. Start a family.
   d. Raise children.
   e. Manage a home.
   f. Pursue an occupation.
   g. Develop civic responsibility.
   h. Join/form a compatible social group.
9. Tasks of middle adulthood.
   a. Guide adolescents toward becoming responsible and well-adjusted adults.
   b. Engage in adult civic and social responsibility.
   c. Progress in an occupational career.
   d. Pursue leisure-time activities.
   e. Relate to partner as a person.
   f. Deal with and accept physiologic changes of middle age.
   g. Accept aging parents.

10. Tasks of later adulthood.
    a. Cope with decreasing physical strength and health.
    b. Adjust to retirement and reduced income.
    c. Adjust to death of a spouse/partner.
    d. Affiliate with one's age-group.
    e. Change social roles.
    f. Arrange for the most appropriate and appealing living environment.

Anne Mosey

1. Recapitulation of ontogenesis frame of reference.
    a. The development of adaptive skills, essential learned behaviors, is considered critical for successful participation in occupational performance.
2. Six major adaptive skills along with subskills are delineated.
    a. Sensory integration of vestibular, proprioceptive, and tactile information for functional use.
        (1) Integration of the tactile subsystems (0–3 months).
        (2) Integration of primitive postural reflexes (3–9 months).
        (3) Maturation of righting and equilibrium reactions (9–12 months).
        (4) Integration of two sides of the body, awareness of body parts and their relationship, and motor plan gross movements (1–2 years).
        (5) Motor plan fine movements (2–3 years).
    b. Cognitive skill: ability to perceive, represent, and organize sensory information to think and problem-solve.
        (1) Utilization of inborn behavioral patterns for environmental interaction (0–1 month).
        (2) Interrelation of visual, manual, auditory, and oral responses (1–4 months).
        (3) Early exploration of the environment and interest in outcomes of actions: remembers action responses, believes that own actions cause responses, and has an awareness of the relation of these actions and events (4–9 months).
        (4) Utilization of deliberate actions to achieve a goal: object permanence begins, anticipation of familiar events, imitation, interest in sizes/shapes, and perception of other objects as partially causal (9–12 months).
        (5) Utilization of a trial-and-error approach to problem-solving: tool use, begins to realize that alternate routes can be used, remembers the order of a simple sequence, and realizes that others can cause events to happen (12–18 months).

        (6) Formulation of mental pictures: pretends, early cause and effect, manipulates objects in space, has a clearer understanding that others can manipulate the environment (18 months–2 years).
        (7) Representation of objects in terms of felt experiences: understands that there are consequences to actions, that others cannot read your mind, and recognizes that events have causes (2–5 years).
        (8) Representation of objects by name: begins to understand that other people may have differing opinions (6–7 years).
        (9) Comprehension that different labels can be used for the same object, use of formal logic and speculation (11–13 years).
    c. Dyadic interaction skill: the ability to participate in a variety of dyadic relationships.
        (1) Family relationships (8–10 months).
        (2) Playmate relationships (3–5 years).
        (3) Superior/authority relationship interactions (5–7 years).
        (4) Friend relationships (10–14 years).
        (5) Peer-superior relationships (15–17 years).
        (6) Intimate/sharing/committed relationships (18–25 years).
        (7) Caring/unselfish relationships (20–30 years).
    d. Group interaction skill: the ability to engage in a variety of primary groups.
        (1) Parallel group: minimal awareness of or interaction with others (18 months–2 years).
        (2) Project group: limited in duration, cooperation, and sharing (2–4 years).
        (3) Egocentric group: cooperation, competition, longer in duration, builds self-esteem (5–7 years).
        (4) Cooperative group: compatible group, members concerned with meeting the needs of fellow members (9–12 years).
        (5) Mature group: differing roles, concerned with completion of task as well as meeting the needs of fellow members (15–18 years).
    e. Self-identity skill: the ability to perceive the self as a relatively autonomous, holistic, and acceptable person who has permanence and continuity over time.
        (1) Self as a valued person (9–12 months).
        (2) Assets and limitations of the self (11–15 years).
        (3) Self as self-directed (20–25 years).
        (4) Self as a productive, contributing member of a society (30–35 years).
        (5) Self-identity as an independent individual (35–50 years).
        (6) Understanding the aging process of oneself and eventual death as part of the life cycle (45–60 years).

f. Sexual identity skill: the ability to feel comfortable about one's sexual nature and to engage in continued sexual relationship that takes into account mutual satisfaction of sexual needs.
   (1) Act on the basis of one's pregenital sexual nature (4–5 years).
   (2) Sexually mature as a positive growth experience (12–16 years).
   (3) Give and receive sexual gratification (18–25 years).
   (4) Sustain sexual relationship with mutual satisfaction of sexual needs (20–30 years).
   (5) Accept sex-related physiological changes that occur as a natural part of the aging process (40–60 years).

CAUTION: Since the publication of the lifespan theory and frame of reference described above, there have been significant social, cultural, and demographic changes in the United States. Thus, before applying these conceptual frameworks to an NBCOT® exam item, you should carefully consider the social, cultural, and demographic information that is provided in an exam scenario to determine a correct answer. For example, an exam item scenario may describe an older adult who incurred a concussion and multiple fractures due to a skiing accident. Correct answers about the foci of the OT evaluation would include assessing the effect of these injuries on the roles, occupations, and activities identified in the scenario.

Child Abuse and Neglect

Definition and Types

1. The federal Child Abuse Prevention and Treatment Act (CAPTA) defines child abuse and neglect as "any recent act or failure to act on the part of a parent or caregiver that results in death, serious physical or emotional harm, sexual abuse, or exploitation, or an act or failure to act that presents an imminent risk of serious harm" (CAPTA Reauthorization Act of 2010).
2. Child abuse can include the following.
   a. Physical abuse: intentional behaviors (e.g., hitting, kicking, biting, burning) that causes physical injury to a child and/or results in a physical impairment.
   b. Emotional and mental abuse: intentional behaviors (e.g., berating, yelling, mocking) that damages the child's emotional stability and sense of self and/or results in a mental disorder (e.g., anxiety, depression, conduct disorder).
   c. Sexual abuse: the trafficking, exploitation, molestation, prostitution, and rape of or incest with a child; forcing, enticing, or persuading a child to engage in or simulate sexually explicit behavior.
   d. Neglect: the failure of a parent or a caregiver to provide a child with the basic necessities (e.g., shelter, food, clothing, medical and mental health care, education, supervision) that are required for the child's safety, health, and well-being.

Facts

1. In the United States, child abuse is a major social justice and health care crisis.

   a. A report of child abuse is made every 10 seconds in the United States.
   b. Every year, more than four million referrals are made to child protection agencies.
   c. In the United States, an average of five children die every day as the result of child abuse and neglect.
   d. Refer to https://www.childhelp.org/child-abuse-statistics/ for more information.
2. Child abuse can occur in any family. It is evident at all socioeconomic and educational levels and in all ethnicities, cultural groups, and religions.
3. The effects of child abuse and neglect continue into adulthood and may become intergenerational.

EXAM HINT: The above facts are provided to support the critical need for all OT practitioners to be vigilant about recognizing the signs of child abuse and neglect in all interactions with children and adult survivors. These specifics will not be on the NBCOT® exam. However, the principle of beneficence in the AOTA's Code of Ethics requires OT personnel to "demonstrate a concern for the safety and well-being of persons" (AOTA, 2020, p. 3). State licensure boards have similar standards and the federal Child Abuse Prevention and Treatment Act (CAPTA) requires mandated reporting by health care and education professionals including OT practitioners. Therefore, it is very likely that the NBCOT® exam will include items about the OT practitioner's role in identifying and responding to child abuse. The application of knowledge about the types, signs, and symptoms of child abuse and the role of OT in addressing cases of abuse as described in the following can help you determine the correct answer to these exam items.

Signs of Abuse

1. General signs of abuse.
   a. Withdrawal.
   b. Nightmares.
   c. Running away.
   d. Anxiety or depression.
   e. Guilt.
   f. Mistrust of adults.
   g. Fear.
   h. Aggressiveness.
2. Signs and symptoms of physical abuse.
   a. The child reports being physically mistreated.
   b. Unexplained injuries.
   c. Repeated injuries.
   d. Abrasions and lacerations.
   e. Small circular burns such as cigarette or cigar burns.
   f. Burns with a "doughnut" shape on the buttocks that may indicate scalding, or any burn that shows the pattern of an object used to inflict injury, such as an iron.
   g. Friction burns such as those from a rope.
   h. Unexplained fractures.
   i. Denial, unlikely explanations, or delays in treatment on the part of the caregiver.
3. Signs and symptoms of emotional and mental abuse.
   a. The child reports being verbally and/or emotionally mistreated.
   b. Defensive appearance, aggressive or acting out behavior such as lying or stealing.
   c. Shy, withdrawn, dependent, anxious, or depressed appearance and behaviors.
   d. Verbally abuses others with language that appears to have been directed toward them.
4. Signs and symptoms of sexual abuse.
   a. The child reports being inappropriately approached, touched, and/or assaulted.
   b. Abuse may be physical (e.g., touching), nonphysical (e.g., indecent exposure), or violent (e.g., rape), so signs may include emotional and physical indicators.
   c. Precocious sexual behavior or knowledge.
   d. Copying adult sexual behavior.
   e. Inappropriate sexual behavior (e.g., putting tongue in other's mouth when kissing).
   f. Soreness or injury around the genitals.
   g. Reluctance or refusal to let caregivers wash parts of the body.
   h. Sexual play.
5. Signs and symptoms of neglect.
   a. Poorly nourished appearance or inadequately clothed.
   b. Consistently tired or listless behavior.
   c. Inconsistent attendance at school.
   d. Poor hygiene or obsession with cleanliness.
   e. Left alone in dangerous situations, for long periods of time and/or at an inappropriate young age.
   f. Unable to relate well to adults or form friendships.

Role of Occupational Therapy

1. Mandatory reporting.
   a. The federal Child Abuse Prevention and Treatment Act (CAPTA) defined child abuse and neglect and established mandates for professionals to report abuse and neglect to law enforcement officials.
   b. All states must have child abuse and neglect reporting laws to qualify for federal funding under CAPTA.
   c. All states require reporting of known or suspected cases of child abuse or neglect by health-care providers.
      (1) Standards for reporting may vary.
      (2) Reporting to the therapist's direct supervisor may/may not be sufficient.
         (a) The therapist should immediately report any and all concerns to their supervisor but must be prepared to follow-up as necessary.
   d. Failure to report suspected child abuse may be considered a crime.
   e. In most states, good faith reporting is immune from liability.
   f. All states require reporting to be made to a law enforcement agency or child protective services.

> **EXAM HINT:** The NBCOT® OTR® exam content outline identifies the task of providing "occupational therapy services in accordance with laws, regulations, (and) state occupational therapy practice acts . . . to protect consumers" (NBCOT®, 2022, p. 14) as essential for competent practice. The application of knowledge about the above federal and state mandates for the reporting of child abuse and the following descriptions of OT intervention to address child abuse and neglect can help you determine the correct answer to NBCOT® Domain 4 Competency and Management exam items related to abuse and neglect.

2. Occupational therapy intervention.
   a. Treat physical injuries, emotional injuries, and developmental delays.
   b. Develop a trusting relationship with child and non-abusive caregivers.
   c. Provide support to non-abusive caregivers.
   d. Refer to appropriate disciplines and agencies.

Aging

General Concepts and Definitions

1. Aging: the process of growing old.
   a. Describes a wide array of physiological changes in the body systems.
   b. A complex and variable process.
   c. Common to all members of a given species.
   d. Aging is developmental, occurs across the lifespan.
   e. Progressive with time.
   f. Evidence of aging.
      (1) Decline in homeostatic efficiency.
      (2) Decline in reaction time.
         (a) Increased probability that reaction to injury will not be successful.
   g. Varies among and within individuals.

> **EXAM HINT:** The NBCOT® OTR® exam content outline identifies knowledge of the "impact of . . . aging on occupational performance, health, and wellness across the life span" (NBCOT®, 2022, p. 3) as essential for competent and safe practice. The application of knowledge about the information provided in this section can help you correctly answer NBCOT® exam items about working with older adults throughout the OT process.

2. Aging changes.
   a. Cellular changes.
      (1) Increase in size; fragmentation of Golgi apparatus and mitochondria.
      (2) Decrease in cell capacity to divide and reproduce.
      (3) Arrest of DNA synthesis and cell division.
   b. Tissue changes.
      (1) Accumulation of pigmented materials, lipofuscins.
      (2) Accumulation of lipids and fats.
      (3) Connective tissue changes: decreased elastic content, degradation of collagen; presence of pseudoelastins.
   c. Organ changes.
      (1) Decrease in functional capacity.
      (2) Decrease in homeostatic efficiency.
3. Gerontology: the scientific study of the factors impacting the normal aging process and the effects of aging.
4. Geriatrics: the branch of medicine concerned with the illnesses of old age and their care.

5. Agism: discrimination and prejudice leveled against individuals on the basis of their age.
   a. Isolates older adults socially.
   b. Permits attitudes and policies that discourage older adults from full participation in work, leisure, and other meaningful occupations.
   c. Perpetuates fears of aging.
   d. Diminishes quality of life.

Demographics, Mortality, and Morbidity

1. Lifespan: maximum survival potential, the inherent natural life of the species; in humans 110–120 years.
2. Senescence: the weakening of the body at a gradual but steady pace during the last stages of adulthood through death.
3. Life expectancy: the number of years of life expectation from year of birth.
   a. Overall life expectancy is 78.7 years in United States; women live five years longer than men (81 versus 76 years).
   b. For decades, the following trends have contributed to increased life expectancy.
      (1) Advances in health care, improved infectious disease control.
      (2) Advances in infant/child care, decreased infant/child mortality rates.
      (3) Improvements in nutrition and sanitation.
4. Categories of older adults.
   a. Young-old: ages 65–74.
   b. Middle-old: ages 75–84.
   c. Very old: ages > 85.
5. Persons over 65 years: represents a rapidly growing segment with lengthening of life expectancy.
   a. Persons 65 and older accounted for 16.5% of the U.S. population in 2019.
   b. By 2040, it is expected that there will be 82 million people over age 65 years, which is 21.7% of the U.S. population.

> **EXAM HINT:** The above demographics and the following characteristics of older adults are provided to emphasize that there is a significant need for OT practitioners to work with older adults in a manner that recognizes their lived experiences. Correct answers to NBCOT® exam items about OT evaluation and intervention for older adults will reflect these realities.

6. Social and economic characteristics of older adults.
   a. Approximately 31% of all older women are widows, which is triple the widow rate for older men.
   b. The educational level of older adults is increasing. Approximately 86% of older persons have completed high school, and 31% have a bachelor's degree or higher.
   c. About 3% of persons over 65 reside in nursing homes; the percentage of institutionalized older adults increases with age (i.e., 9% of persons over 85).
      (1) The number of older adults residing in institutional settings has been decreasing as more people choose to age in place and more community-based living options have become available.
   d. The need for caregiving increases with age. About one-third of older adults need assistance with personal care.
   e. Most noninstitutionalized older adults live in a family setting, usually with their spouse. About 28% of older adults live alone.
   f. Approximately 34% of older adults report at least one disability.
   g. Most older adults live on fixed incomes.
      (1) Social security is the major source of income.
      (2) Poverty rate for persons over 65 years is 9.7%.
      (3) Increasing age is related to increasing poverty levels.
   h. In 2019, about 20% of older adults were working, comprising ~6% of the U.S. labor force.
7. Leading causes of death (mortality) in persons over 65, in order of frequency are as follows.
   a. Coronary heart disease (CHD), accounts for 25% of deaths.
   b. Cancer, accounts for 21% of deaths.
   c. Chronic lower respiratory disease and stroke, account for 6.5% of deaths.
   d. Alzheimer's disease, the incidence of death increases with age from 5.7% to 9.1% for those over 85 years of age.
8. Leading causes of disability/chronic conditions (morbidity) in persons over 65 years, in order of frequency (National Council on Aging 2021).
   a. Hypertension, 58%.
   b. Hyperlipidemia, 47%.
   c. Arthritis, 31%.
   d. Heart disease, 29%.
   e. Diabetes, 27%.

f. Most older persons (80%) report having one or more chronic conditions.
9. Health-care costs.
   a. Older persons account for 14% of population and 34.5% of total health-care expenditures.
   b. Older persons account for 27% of all hospital stays.
   c. 95% of non-institutionalized adults are covered by Medicare.

Theories of Aging

1. Overview: aging theories attempt to explain the phenomenon of aging as it occurs over the lifespan.
   a. They include biological, psychological, and sociological theories of aging. Refer to Table 5-20.

> **EXAM HINT:** The NBCOT® OTR® exam content outline identifies knowledge of the "resources and considerations for acquiring information about the client's current condition and occupational performance . . . (including) theoretical approach and frame of reference" ((NBCOT®, 2022, p. 3) as essential for competent practice. The application of knowledge about the theories of aging provided in Table 5-20 can help you determine a correct answer to NBCOT® exam items about working with older adults.

Integration of the Theories of Aging to Client-Centered OT Practice

1. An integrated model of aging assumes aging is a complex, multifactorial phenomenon in which some or all of the previous processes may contribute to the overall aging of an individual.
   a. Aging is not adequately explained by any single theory.
2. All theories focus on function, which is identified and described in many ways; from cellular to social participation.
3. The definition of function in the International Classification of Functioning, Disability and Health (ICF) is instructive to OT.
   a. In ICF the term "functioning" refers to all "bodily functions, activities and participation" (World Health Organization, 2002, p. 2).

Table 5-20

Theories of Aging

CATEGORY AND FOCUS	THEORY TYPES AND MAIN HYPOTHESES/APPROACHES
Biological: addresses aging at the cellular, molecular, and organism levels.	Stochastic ("insults") Theory: proposes that genetic damage leads to functional failure and death. Developmental/Genetic Theory: proposes that aging is genetically programmed. Evolutionary Theory: proposes that genetic errors/accidents over time lead to aging.
Psychological: addresses changes in cognitive, personality, and social development in the middle and later years of life.	Lifespan Development Theory: proposes that development is both biologically and socially constituted. Refer to this Chapter's section on lifespan and occupational therapy developmental theories. Selective Optimization with Compensation Theory: outlines a strategy for improving health and well-being. Recommends that older adults select and optimize their best abilities and most intact functions while compensating for declines and losses. Socioemotional Selectivity Theory: proposes that older adults are motivated to systematically hone their social networks to satisfy their emotional needs. Cognition and Aging Theories: propose that selected cognitive changes are a component of normal aging. Personality and Aging Theories: propose that personality is stable (for most individuals) over time.
Sociological: considers the context in which aging occurs.	Life Course Perspective Theory: applies a multidisciplinary approach that incorporates life span and life stage concepts to develop an understanding of the mental, physical, and social health of individuals that determine their health trajectory. Social Exchange Theory: proposes that social behavior is the result of an exchange process designed to weigh the potential benefits and risks of social relationships to maximize benefits and minimize costs. Political Economy of Aging Theory: examines how resources are allocated to older adults and how the treatment and status of older adults are impacted by public policy, social structures, and economic trends. Critical Perspectives of Aging Theory: focuses on the trends in social gerontology (i.e., the political economy of aging, theories of diversity, and humanistic gerontology).

Chapter 5

EXAM HINT: The NBCOT® OTR® exam content outline states the task of identifying "the influence of development . . . body functions and body structures . . . on occupational performance" (NBCOT®, 2022, p. 3) is essential to entry-level practice and states that knowledge of the impact of "aging on occupational performance, health, and wellness across the life span" (NBCOT®, 2022, p. 3) is required for competent and safe practice. Thus, knowing the following body system changes that occur with aging and understanding how these affect functional abilities can help you correctly answer NBCOT® exam items about the best approach to use to enable the occupational performance, health, and wellness of older adults.

Muscular System Changes and Adaptation in the Older Adult

1. Age-related changes.
   a. Changes may be due more to decreased activity levels (hypokinesis) and disuse than from the aging process.
   b. Loss of muscle strength: peaks at age 30, remains fairly constant until age 50, after which there is an accelerating loss; 20%–40% loss by age 65 in the non-exercising adult.
   c. Loss of power (force/unit time): significant decline due to losses in speed of contraction and changes in nerve conduction and synaptic transmission.
   d. Loss of skeletal muscle mass (atrophy): both size and number of muscle fibers decrease, 33% of skeletal muscle mass is lost by age 70.
   e. Changes in muscle fiber composition: selective loss of Type II, fast-twitch fibers, with increase in proportion of Type I fibers.
   f. Changes in muscular endurance: muscles fatigue more readily.
      (1) Decreased muscle tissue oxidative capacity.
      (2) Decreased peripheral blood flow, oxygen delivery to muscles.
      (3) Altered chemical composition of muscle: decreased myosin ATPase activity, glycoproteins, and contractile protein.
      (4) Collagen changes: denser, irregular due to cross-linkages, loss of water content and elasticity; affects tendons, bone, and cartilage.
2. Clinical implications.
   a. Movements become slower.
   b. Increased complaints of fatigue.
   c. Connective tissue becomes denser and stiffer.
      (1) Loss of range of motion: highly variable by joint and individual's activity level.

> **CAUTION:** Increased risk of muscle sprains, strains, and tendon tears and increased tendency for fibrinous adhesions and contractures.

   d. Decreased functional mobility, limitations to movement.
   e. Gait may become unsteady due to changes in balance and strength, increased need for assistive devices.

> **RED FLAG:** Increased risk of falls.

3. Strategies to slow, reverse, and/or compensate for age-related muscular system changes.
   a. Refer to Box 5-5.
     (1) The implementation of some of the strategies in Box 5-5 will require the OT practitioner to refer the person and/or their caregivers to a physician, nurse practitioner, or dietician/clinical nutritionist.
   b. Refer to Chapter 6 for additional information on muscular system disorders and Chapter 11 for more information on biomechanical evaluation and intervention approaches.

Skeletal System Changes and Adaptations in the Older Adult

1. Age-related changes.
   a. Cartilage changes: decreased water content, becomes stiffer, fragments, and erodes; by age 60 more than 60% of adults have degenerative joint changes, cartilage abnormalities.
   b. Loss of bone mass and density: peak bone mass at age 40; between 45 and 70 bone mass decreases (women by about 25%; men 15%); decreases another 5% by age 90.
     (1) Loss of calcium, bone strength: especially trabecular bone.
     (2) Decreased bone marrow red blood cell production.
   c. Intervertebral discs: flatten, less resilient due to loss of water content (30% loss by age 65 years) and loss of collagen elasticity; trunk length and overall height decreases.
   d. Senile postural changes.
     (1) Forward head.
     (2) Kyphosis of thoracic spine.
     (3) Flattening of lumbar spine.

BOX 5-5 ▷ Strategies to Slow, Reverse, and/or Compensate for Age-related Muscular System Changes

- Improve health.
  - Correct medical problems that may cause weakness.
  - Improve nutrition.
  - Address substance use disorders.
- Increase levels of physical activity.
  - Emphasize engagement in functional activities.
  - Implement activity programs.
  - Gradually increase intensity of activities to avoid injury.
  - Plan and include adequate warm-ups and cool downs.
  - Teach appropriate pacing and provide rest periods.
- Provide strength training to increase and/or maintain muscle strength.
  - Significant increases in strength are noted in older adults with isometric and progressive resistive exercise regimes.
  - High-intensity training programs (70%–80% of one-repetition maximum) produce quicker and more predictable results than moderate intensity programs; both have been successfully used with the older adults.
  - Age is not a limiting factor; significant improvements have been noted in 80- and 90-year-old older adults who were frail and institutionalized.
  - Improvements in strength can improve functional abilities and occupational performance.
  - Maintain newly gained and existing strength by incorporating into functional activities.
- Provide flexibility and range of motion exercises to increase range of motion.
  - Utilize slow, prolonged stretching, maintained for 20–30 seconds.
  - Tissues heated prior to stretching are more distensible, e.g., warm pool.
  - Maintain newly gained range by incorporating into functional activities.
  - Mobility gains are slower with older adults.

CAUTION: With prolonged sitting, the tendency to develop hip and knee flexion contractures increases.

2. Clinical implications.
   a. Maintenance of weightbearing is important for cartilaginous/joint health and mobility.

RED FLAG: Increased risk of falls and fractures.

3. Strategies to slow, reverse, and/or compensate for age-related skeletal system changes.
   a. Refer to Box 5-6.
      (1) The implementation of some of the strategies in Box 5-6 will require the OT practitioner to refer the person and/or their caregivers to a physician, nurse practitioner, or dietician/clinical nutritionist.
   b. See Chapter 6 for additional information on skeletal system disorders and Chapter 16 for information on fall prevention.

BOX 5-6 ▷ Strategies to Slow, Reverse, and/or Compensate for Age-related Skeletal System Changes

- Postural exercises: stress components of good posture.
- Weight-bearing (gravity-loading) exercise can decrease bone loss in older adults (e.g., walking, stair climbing, all activities that are performed in standing).
- Nutritional, hormonal, and medical therapies.

Neurological System Changes and Adaptations in the Older Adult

1. Age-related changes.
   a. Atrophy of nerve cells in cerebral cortex: overall loss of cerebral mass/brain weight of 6%–11% between ages of 20 and 90; accelerating loss after age 70.
   b. Changes in brain morphology.
      (1) Gyral atrophy: narrowing and flattening of gyri with widening of sulci.
      (2) Ventricular dilation.
      (3) Generalized cell loss in cerebral cortex: especially frontal and temporal lobes, association areas (prefrontal cortex, visual).
      (4) Presence of lipofuscins, senile or neuritic plaques, and neurofibrillary tangles (NFT): significant accumulations associated with pathology, e.g., neurocognitive disorder.
      (5) More selective cell loss in basal ganglia (substantia nigra and putamen), cerebellum, hippocampus, locus coeruleus; brain stem minimally affected.
   c. Decreased cerebral blood flow and energy metabolism.
   d. Changes in synaptic transmission.
      (1) Decreased synthesis and metabolism of major neurotransmitters, e.g., acetylcholine, dopamine.
      (2) Slowing of many neural processes, especially in polysynaptic pathways.
   e. Changes in spinal cord/peripheral nerves.
      (1) Neuronal loss and atrophy: 30%–50% loss of anterior horn cells, 30% loss of posterior roots (sensory fibers) by age 90 years.
      (2) Loss of motoneurons results in increase in size of remaining motor units (development of macro motor units).
      (3) Slowed nerve conduction velocity: sensory greater than motor.
      (4) Loss of sympathetic fibers: may account for diminished autonomic stability, increasing incidence of postural hypotension in older adults.
   f. Age-related tremors (essential tremor [ET]).
      (1) Occur as an isolated symptom, particularly in hands, head, and voice.
      (2) Characterized as postural or kinetic, rarely resting.
      (3) Benign, slowly progressive; in late stages may limit function.
      (4) Exaggerated by movement and emotion.

2. Clinical implications.
   a. Effects on movement.
      (1) Overall speed and coordination are decreased; increased difficulties with fine motor control.
      (2) Slowed recruitment of motoneurons contributes to loss of strength.
      (3) Both reaction time and movement time are increased.
      (4) Older adults are affected by the speed/accuracy trade-off.
         (a) The simpler the movement, the less is the change.
         (b) More complicated movements require more preparation, leading to longer reaction and movement times.
         (c) Faster movements decrease accuracy, increase errors.
      (5) Older adults typically shift in motor control processing from open to closed loop: e.g., demonstrate increased reliance on visual feedback for movement.
      (6) Demonstrate increased cautionary behaviors, an indirect effect of decreased capacity.
   b. General slowing of neural processing: learning and memory may be affected.
   c. Problems in homeostatic regulation: stressors (heat, cold, excess exercise) can be harmful, even life threatening.

3. Strategies to slow, reverse, and/or compensate for age-related neurological system changes.
   a. Refer to Box 5-7.
      (1) The implementation of some of the strategies in Box 5-7 will require the OT practitioner to refer the person and/or their caregivers to a physician, nurse practitioner, or dietician/clinical nutritionist.
   b. Refer to Chapter 7 for additional information on neurological system disorders and Chapter 12 for more information on intervention approaches for neurological disorders.

BOX 5-7 ▷ Strategies to Slow, Reverse, and/or Compensate for Age-related Neurological System Changes

- Correct medical problems; improve cerebral blood flow.
- Improve health; promote good nutrition and smoking cessation.
- Increase levels of physical activity: this encourages neuronal branching, slows the rate of neural decline, and improves cerebral circulation.
- Provide effective strategies to improve motor learning and control.
  - Allow for increased reaction and movement times; this can improve engagement and the accuracy of movements.
  - Allow for limitations of memory; avoid long sequences of movements.
  - Allow for increased cautionary behaviors by providing adequate explanations and demonstration when teaching new movement skills.
  - Stress familiar, well-learned skills and repetitive movements.

Sensory Systems Changes and Adaptations in the Older Adult

1. Age-related changes: older adults experience a loss of function of the senses.
   a. May lead to sensory deprivation, isolation, disorientation, confusion, appearance of senility and depression.
   b. May strain social interactions and decrease ability to interact socially and with the environment.
   c. Alters quality of life.

CAUTION: May lead to decreased functional mobility and increased risk of injury.

2. Visual system changes, conditions, and clinical implications.
   a. Age-related changes: there is a general decline in visual acuity; gradual prior to sixth decade; rapid decline between ages 60 and 90; visual loss may be as much as 80% by age 90. These changes include the following.
      (1) Presbyopia: visual loss in middle and older ages characterized by inability to focus properly and blurred images; due to loss of accommodation, diminished elasticity of lens.
      (2) Decreased ability to adapt to dark and light.
      (3) Increased sensitivity to light and glare.
      (4) Loss of color discrimination, especially for blues and greens.
      (5) Decreased pupillary responses, size of resting pupil increases.
      (6) Decreased sensitivity of corneal reflex: less sensitive to eye injury or infection.
      (7) Oculomotor responses diminished: restricted upward gaze, reduced pursuit eye movements; ptosis may develop.
   b. Additional vision loss associated with pathology.
      (1) Low vision: a visual impairment that standard eyeglasses, contact lenses, medication, or surgery cannot correct.
         (a) Persons with low vision have some usable vision, but impairments are severe enough to make it difficult to perform everyday activities.
         (b) One in 28 Americans over the age of 40 years qualify as having low vision.
         (c) Four chronic, progressing eye diseases are the main conditions contributing to the development of low vision: i.e., age-related macular degeneration (AMD), diabetic retinopathy, glaucoma, and cataracts.
      (2) Age-related macular degeneration (AMD).
         (a) Affects the macula, the part of the eye that allows you to see fine detail.
         (b) Appears as a "blank spot" in the central visual field, blurring details and the sharp/central vision needed for many daily activities.
         (c) AMD can be dry (80%–90% of cases) or wet (10%–20% of cases). In dry AMD, drusen block vision; in wet AMD, hemorrhagic bleeding on the macula blocks vision. Dry AMD can progress to wet AMD.
         (d) There is no treatment available for dry AMD; however, wet AMD can progress quickly, and medical treatment (i.e., eye injections) is available.
         (e) The affected area on the macula is called a scotoma. Scotomas can be relative (e.g., some vision can be processed with increased light) or dense (no vision despite light changes).
         (f) All scotomas are not the same; they can be in different sizes, different shapes, and different locations. Variations may also exist between the two eyes.

> **CAUTION:** Use of magnifiers is *not* indicated for certain scotomas because it may enlarge images into the nonseeing portion of the macula.

(g) Less common symptoms of AMD include metamorphopsia, which is the appearance of spinning and swirling of images, and Charles Bonnet syndrome (also known as "phantom vision"), which leads to visual hallucinations that the individual knows are not real.

(h) Affects occupational performance such as reading, driving, managing medication, and watching television.

(3) Diabetic retinopathy.

(a) A complication of diabetes that affects the eyes. This is caused by damage to the blood vessels of the light-sensitive tissue at the back of the eye, the retina.

(b) This condition affects central and peripheral vision, causing blurred or hazy vision in affected areas.

(c) Can develop in anyone who has type 1 or type 2 diabetes.

(d) There are two types of diabetic retinopathy: nonproliferative and proliferative.

- Nonproliferative diabetic retinopathy is the early stage of the disease, in which symptoms will be mild or not apparent, leaving more vision intact. This form can progress to proliferative.
- Proliferative diabetic retinopathy is a more advanced form of the disease, characterized by new blood vessel growth in the retina and leakage of blood vessels, which causes scar formation and possibly retinal detachment.

> **RED FLAG:** This can lead to total blindness.

(e) Maintaining control of blood glucose levels helps prevent vison loss.

(4) Glaucoma.

(a) Chronic elevated pressure in the eye that may cause optic nerve atrophy and loss of peripheral vision. This is more prevalent in persons over 40 years old.

(b) Vision loss starts peripherally and moves toward central vision (also referred to as "tunnel vision").

(c) Symptoms include difficulty scanning the environment and decreased visual acuity, contrast sensitivity, light sensitivity, and sensitivity to glare. Orientation and mobility within the environment are often affected, especially with dim illumination and at night.

(d) Medical intervention is available to decrease the intraocular pressure. Glaucoma can also be prevented with eye drops.

(e) This condition is painless and is often detected too late when the person experiences vision deficits. At that point, the goal is to decrease further vision loss.

(5) Cataracts.

(a) Opacity of the lens, including protein changes and lens hardening/thickening, which results in diminished visual acuity and gradual loss in vision.

(b) Field of vison is not affected.

(c) Vision is overall hazy and blurry, especially in glaring light or when reading printed materials.

(d) Central vision is predominantly affected because of the glare, haziness, and decrease in contrast sensitivity.

(e) If surgery is indicated, the lens is removed and an intraocular lens (plastic implant) is inserted to correct visual deficits.

(6) Neurological injuries (e.g., cerebrovascular accident [CVA], traumatic brain injury [TBI], and brain tumors) can also lead to irreversible vision damage.

(a) With neurological diagnoses, the structures of the eye remain functionally intact; impairment depends on where damage in the visual pathway occurs.

(b) Aspects of vision that may be affected include visual acuity, visual fields, oculomotor control, binocularity, contrast sensitivity, visual attention, visual scanning, vision perception, and visual memory.

(c) Homonymous hemianopsia: a visual field deficit in which half of the visual field is lost in each eye (i.e., nasal half of one eye and temporal half of other eye); occurs after neurological injury, especially CVA. This results in an inability to receive information from right or left sides, corresponding to the side of sensorimotor deficit.

c. Strategies to slow, reverse, and/or compensate for age-related visual system changes.

(1) Refer to Box 5-8 for intervention strategies.

(a) The implementation of some of the strategies in Box 5-8 will require the OT practitioner to refer the person and/or their caregivers to a physician (i.e., ophthalmologist).

(2) Visual deficits: visual acuity, visual fields, contrast sensitivity, light and dark adaptation, depth

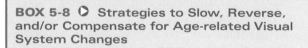

BOX 5-8 ▷ Strategies to Slow, Reverse, and/or Compensate for Age-related Visual System Changes

- Maximize visual function: assess for need for magnification and/or environmental adaptations.
- Allow extra time for visual discrimination and response; sensory thresholds are increased with age.
- Work in adequate light, increase intensity, reduce glare; avoid abrupt changes in light, for example, from light to dark.
- Use large, high-contrast print for written materials.
- Provide magnifying glasses (either portable or attached to a stand/worktable) to view objects and complete tasks.
  – Magnification level must be prescribed by an ophthalmologist.
- Provide an eye patch for diplopia.
  – Some state OT licensure practice acts do not allow OT practitioners to give clients eye patches. In these states, the occupational therapist should refer the person to an ophthalmologist.
- Decreased peripheral vision can negatively impact social interactions; therefore, the OT practitioner should stand directly in front of the person at eye level when communicating with them.
- Assist in color discrimination: use warm colors (i.e., yellow, orange, red) for identification and color coding.
- Provide other sensory cues when vision is limited (e.g., verbal descriptions to new environments, sighted guide techniques, touching to communicate you are listening, and 'talking' clocks and watches).
- Provide safety education; reduce fall risk. Refer to Chapter 16.

---

perception, diplopia, eye fatigue, and eye pain should be assessed and outcomes addressed.

(3) When considering visual compensatory strategies, consider other factors that may impact function; e.g., tremors, decreased range of motion and/or strength, diminished sensation, impaired cognition, hearing loss, and cognitive perceptual deficits.

(4) Refer to Chapter 16 for additional information about evaluation methods and intervention approaches for low vision.

3. Auditory system changes, conditions, and clinical implications.
   a. Hearing aging changes: occur as early as the fourth decade; affect a significant number of older adults (33% of individuals aged 65–74 have hearing impairments and 50% over age 75 have hearing loss; rate of loss in men is twice the rate of women, also starts earlier).
      (1) Outer ear: buildup of cerumen (earwax) may result in conductive hearing loss; common in older men.

(2) Middle ear: minimal degenerative changes of bony joints.

(3) Inner ear: significant changes in sound sensitivity, understanding of speech, and maintenance of equilibrium may result with degeneration and atrophy of cochlea and vestibular structures, loss of neurons.

   b. Types of hearing loss.
      (1) Conductive: mechanical hearing loss from damage to external auditory canal, tympanic membrane, or middle ear ossicles; results in hearing loss (all frequencies); tinnitus (ringing in the ears) may be present.
      (2) Sensorineural: central or neural hearing loss from multiple factors; e.g., noise damage, trauma, disease, drugs, arteriosclerosis, etc.
      (3) Presbycusis: sensorineural hearing loss associated with middle and older ages; characterized by bilateral hearing loss, especially at high frequencies at first, then all frequencies; poor auditory discrimination and comprehension, especially with background noise; tinnitus.

   c. Additional hearing loss with pathology.
      (1) Otosclerosis: immobility of stapes results in profound conductive hearing loss.
      (2) Paget's disease.
      (3) Hypothyroidism.

   d. Strategies to slow, reverse, and/or compensate for age-related auditory system changes.
      (1) Refer to Box 5-9 for intervention strategies.
      (2) Hearing acuity, speech discrimination/comprehension; tinnitus, dizziness, vertigo, pain should be assessed and outcomes addressed.
         (a) Determine use of hearing aids; check for proper functioning.

BOX 5-9 ▷ Strategies to Slow, Reverse, and/or Compensate for Age-related Auditory System Changes

- Minimize auditory distractions, work in a quiet environment.
- Speak slowly, clearly, and directly in front of the person at eye level.
- Use nonverbal communication to reinforce your message; e.g., gesturing, demonstrating.
- Provide written and demonstrated directions/guidelines for activities.
- Orient persons to the topic of a conversation to decrease isolation and prevent paranoia if they cannot completely hear the conversation.
- Provide assistive devices to compensate for the functional effects of hearing loss and to ensure the person's safety (e.g., vibrating and flashing smoke alarms, telephones, doorbells, and clocks).

4. Vestibular system changes, conditions, and clinical implications.
   a. Vestibular/balance changes: decreased number of vestibular neurons; vestibular ocular reflex decline begins at age 30; at ages 55–60 there is accelerating decline which results in diminished vestibular sensation.
      (1) Diminished acuity, delayed reaction times, longer response times.
      (2) Reduced function of vestibular ocular reflex; affects retinal image stability with head movements, produces blurred vision.
      (3) Altered sensory organization: older adults more dependent upon somatosensory inputs for balance.
      (4) Less able to resolve sensory conflicts when presented with inappropriate visual or proprioceptive inputs due to vestibular losses.
      (5) Postural response patterns for balance are disorganized: characterized by diminished ankle torque, increased hip torque, increased postural sway.

   > RED FLAG: Increased incidence of falls in older adults.

   b. Additional loss of vestibular sensitivity with pathology.
      (1) Ménière's disease: episodic attacks characterized by tinnitus, dizziness, and a sensation of fullness or pressure in the ears; may also experience sensorineural hearing loss.
      (2) Benign paroxysmal positional vertigo (BPPV): brief episodes of vertigo (less than one minute) associated with position change; the result of degeneration of the utricular otoconia that settle on the cupula of the posterior semicircular canal; common in older adults.
      (3) Medications: antihypertensives (postural hypotension); anticonvulsants; tranquilizers, sleeping pills, aspirin, nonsteroidal anti-inflammatory drugs.
      (4) Cerebrovascular disease: vertebrobasilar artery insufficiency (transient ischemic attacks, strokes); cerebellar artery stroke, lateral medullary stroke.
      (5) Cerebellar dysfunction: hemorrhaumors (acoustic neuroma, meningioma); degenerative disease of brain stem and cerebellum; progressive supranuclear palsy.
      (6) Migraine.
      (7) Cardiac disease.
   c. Strategies to slow, reverse, and/or compensate for changes.
      (1) Refer to Chapter 16 for information on fall prevention.

5. Somatosensory system changes, conditions, and clinical implications.
   a. Age-related changes.
      (1) Decreased sensitivity of touch associated with decline of peripheral receptors, atrophy of afferent fibers, lower extremities more affected than upper.
      (2) Proprioceptive losses, increased thresholds in vibratory sensibility, beginning around age 50: greater in lower extremities than upper extremities, greater in distal extremities than proximal.
      (3) Loss of joint receptor sensitivity; losses in lower extremities and/or cervical joints may contribute to loss of balance.
      (4) Cutaneous pain thresholds increase; greater changes in upper body areas (upper extremities, face) than in lower extremities.
   b. Additional loss of sensation with pathology.
      (1) Diabetes, peripheral neuropathy.
      (2) CVA, central sensory losses.
      (3) Peripheral vascular disease, peripheral ischemia.
   c. Strategies to slow, reverse, and/or compensate for age-related somatosensory system changes.
      (1) Refer to Box 5-10 for intervention strategies.
      (2) Assess for increased thresholds to stimulation, sensory losses by modality and/or area of body and address outcomes.
      (3) Allow extra time for responses with increased thresholds.
      (4) Refer to Chapters 15 and 16 for further information on assistive devices and environmental modifications.

BOX 5-10 ▷ Strategies to Slow, Reverse, and/or Compensate for Age-related Somatosensory System Changes

- Use touch to communicate, maximize physical contact (e.g., rubbing, stroking, tapping).
- Provide augmented feedback through appropriate sensory channels (e.g., using kitchen utensils with wide textured grips may be easier than narrow, smooth handles).
- Teach compensatory strategies to prevent injury to anesthetic limbs.
- Provide assistive devices and environmental modifications as needed for fall prevention.
- Provide biofeedback devices as appropriate (e.g., limb load monitor).

---

6. Gustatory and olfactory system changes, conditions, and clinical implications.
   a. Taste and smell age-related changes.
      (1) Gradual decrease in taste sensitivity.

(a) As a result, older adults frequently increase their use of taste enhancers (e.g., salt and/or sugar).

(b) Decreased taste can diminish the enjoyment of food and contribute to a poor diet and inadequate nutrition.

(2) Decreased smell sensitivity.

(a) Decreased home safety can result (e.g., the inability to detect gas leaks or smoke).

b. Conditions resulting in additional loss of gustatory and olfactory sensations.

(1) Smoking.

(2) Chronic allergies, respiratory infections.

(3) Dentures.

(4) CVA, involvement of hypoglossal nerve.

c. Strategies to slow, reverse, and/or compensate for age-related gustatory and olfactory system changes.

(1) Assess for identification of odors, tastes (i.e., sweet, sour, bitter, salty); somatic sensations (i.e., temperature, touch).

Cognitive Changes and Adaptations in the Older Adult

1. Age-related cognitive changes, conditions, and clinical implications.

a. No uniform decline in intellectual abilities throughout adulthood.

(1) Cognitive changes do not typically show up until mid-60s; significant declines affecting everyday life do not show up until early 80s.

(2) Most significant decline in measures of intelligence occurs in the years immediately preceding death (termed "terminal drop").

b. Tasks involving perceptual speed show early declines (by age 39); require longer times to complete tasks.

c. Numeric ability (tests of adding, subtracting, and multiplying): abilities peak in the mid-40s, well maintained until the 60s.

d. Verbal ability: abilities peak at age 30, well maintained until the 60s.

e. Memory.

(1) Impairments are typically noted in short-term memory; long-term memory retained.

(2) Impairments are task dependent; e.g., deficits primarily with novel conditions, new learning.

f. Learning: all age groups can learn. Factors affecting learning in older adults include the following.

(1) Increased cautiousness.

(2) Anxiety.

(3) Sensory deficits

(4) Pace of learning: fast pace is problematic.

(5) Interference from prior learning.

g. Table 10-4 in Chapter 10 describes the reversible causes of mental confusion that should be assessed and ruled out prior to concluding that a person has a cognitive impairment.

2. Clinical implications.

a. Older adults utilize different strategies for memory; i.e., context-based strategies versus memorization that is typically used by young adults.

3. Strategies to slow, reverse, and/or compensate for age-related cognitive changes.

a. Refer to Box 5-11.

(1) The implementation of several of these strategies will require the OT practitioner to refer the person and/or their caregivers to a physician.

b. Refer to Chapters 10, 13, and 14 for additional information about cognitive disorders and intervention approaches for cognitive disorders.

BOX 5-11 ▷ Strategies to Slow, Reverse, and/or Compensate for Age-related Cognitive System Changes

- Improve health.
  - Correct medical problems; address imbalances between oxygen supply and demand to the CNS (e.g., cardiovascular disease, hypertension, diabetes, and hypothyroidism).
  - Address possible pharmacological issues by re-evaluating medications, decreasing the use of multiple drugs, and closely monitoring for medication interactions and drug toxicity.
  - Reduce use of tobacco and alcohol.
  - Correct nutritional deficiencies.
- Increase physical activity.
- Increase mental activity.
  - Keep mentally engaged, 'use it or lose it' (e.g., chess, crossword puzzles, book discussion groups, reading to children).
  - Maintain an engaged lifestyle: socially active (e.g., clubs, travel, work, volunteerism; allow for personal choice in activity).
  - Use cognitive training activities.
- Provide multiple sensory cues to compensate for decreased sensory processing and sensory losses and to maximize learning (e.g., provide visual demonstrations, written instructions, verbal cues).
- Provide a stimulating, 'enriching' environment that is not overstimulating.
- Avoid environmental dislocation and if it occurs address its impact (e.g., hospitalization or institutionalization can produce disorientation and agitation).
- Reduce stress; provide counseling and family support.

Cardiopulmonary System Changes and Adaptations in the Older Adult

1. Cardiovascular age-related changes.
   a. Changes due more to inactivity and disease than aging.
   b. Degeneration of heart muscle with accumulation of lipofuscins (characteristic brown heart); mild cardiac hypertrophy of left ventricular wall.
   c. Decreased coronary blood flow.
   d. Cardiac valves thicken and stiffen.
   e. Changes in conduction system: loss of pacemaker cells in SA node.
   f. Changes in blood vessels: arteries thicken, less distensible; slowed exchange capillary walls; increased peripheral resistance.
   g. Resting blood pressures rise: systolic greater than diastolic.
   h. Decline in neurohumoral control: decreased responsiveness of end-organs to ß-adrenergic stimulation of baroreceptors.
   i. Decreased blood volume, hemopoietic activity of bone.
   j. Increased blood coagulability.
2. Clinical implications for cardiovascular changes.
   a. Changes at rest are minor: resting heart rate and cardiac output relatively unchanged; resting blood pressures increase.
   b. Cardiovascular responses to exercise: blunted, decreased heart rate acceleration, decreased maximal oxygen uptake and heart rate; reduced exercise capacity, increased recovery time.
   c. Decreased stroke volume due to decreased myocardial contractility.
   d. Maximum heart rate declines with age.
   e. Cardiac output decreases, 1% per year after age 20: due to decreased heart rate and stroke volume.
   f. Orthostatic hypotension: common problem in older adults due to reduced baroreceptor sensitivity and vascular elasticity.
   g. Increased fatigue; anemia common in older adults.
   h. Systolic ejection murmur common in older adults.
   i. Possible electrocardiogram changes: loss of normal sinus rhythm; longer PR and QT intervals; wider QRS; increased arrhythmias.
3. Pulmonary system age-related changes.
   a. Chest wall stiffness, declining strength of respiratory muscles increases the work of breathing.
   b. Loss of lung elastic recoil, decreased lung compliance.
   c. Changes in lung parenchyma: alveoli enlarge, become thinner; fewer capillaries for delivery of blood.
   d. Changes in pulmonary blood vessels: thicken, less distensible.
   e. Decline in total lung capacity: residual volume increases, vital capacity decreases.
   f. Forced expiratory volume (airflow) decreases.
   g. Altered pulmonary gas exchange: oxygen tension falls with age (at a rate of 4 mm Hg/decade; PaO_2 at age 70 is 75, versus 90 at age 20).
   h. Blunted ventilatory responses of chemoreceptors in response to respiratory acidosis: decreased homeostatic responses.
   i. Blunted defense/immune responses: decreased ciliary action to clear secretions, decreased secretory immunoglobulins, alveolar phagocytic function.
4. Clinical implications for pulmonary changes.
   a. Respiratory responses to exercise: similar to younger adult at low and moderate intensities; at higher intensities, responses include increased ventilatory cost of work, greater blood acidosis, increased likelihood of breathlessness, and increased perceived exertion.
   b. Clinical signs of hypoxia are blunted; changes in mentation and affect may provide important cues.
   c. Cough mechanism is impaired.
   d. Gag reflex is decreased, increased risk of aspiration.
   e. Recovery from respiratory illness: prolonged in older adults.
   f. Significant changes in function with chronic smoking, exposure to environmental toxic inhalants.
5. Strategies to slow, reverse, and/or compensate for age-related changes in cardiopulmonary systems.
   a. Complete a cardiopulmonary assessment prior to commencing an exercise program.

> CAUTION: This is essential in older adults due to the high incidence of cardiopulmonary pathologies.

   (1) Select an appropriate graded exercise testing protocol.
   (2) Standardized test batteries and norms for older adults are not available.

> CAUTION: Many older adults cannot tolerate maximal testing; submaximal testing commonly used.

   (3) Testing and training modes should be similar.
   b. Box 5-12 outlines intervention strategies to slow, reverse, and/or compensate for age-related changes in cardiopulmonary systems.
   c. Refer to Chapter 8 for additional information on cardiovascular and pulmonary system disorders and cardiopulmonary evaluation and intervention approaches.

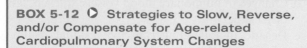

BOX 5-12 ◑ Strategies to Slow, Reverse, and/or Compensate for Age-related Cardiopulmonary System Changes

- An individualized exercise prescription is essential.
  - The choice of a training program is based on the person's fitness level, presence or absence of cardiovascular disease, musculoskeletal limitations, and their goals, roles, and activity interests.
  - Prescriptive elements (i.e., frequency, intensity, duration, mode) are the same for older adults as for younger adults.
  - Walking, chair and floor exercises, yoga, tai-chi, and modified strength/flexibility calisthenics are well-tolerated by most older adults.
  - Pool programs (e.g., exercises, tai-chi, walking, swimming) are effective for persons with musculoskeletal and neurological impairments.
  - Multiple modes of exercise on alternate days can help maintain interest and reduce the likelihood of muscle injury, joint overuse, pain, fatigue, and boredom.
- Aerobic training programs can significantly improve cardiopulmonary function in older adults. These programs:
  - Decrease heart rate at a given submaximal power output.
  - Improve maximal oxygen uptake (VO_2 max).
  - Improve peripheral adaptation and muscle oxidative capacity.
  - Improve recovery heart rates.
  - Decrease systolic blood pressure, this may produce a small decrease in diastolic blood pressure.
  - Increase maximum ventilatory capacity, improve vital capacity.
  - Reduce breathlessness, lower perceived exertion.
  - Improve sense of well-being and self-image.
  - Improve functional capacity.
- Improve overall daily activity levels for independent living.
  - Lack of exercise/activity is an important risk factor in the development of cardiopulmonary diseases.
  - Lack of exercise/activity contributes to problems of immobility and disability in older adults.

Other Systems Changes and Adaptations in the Older Adult

1. Integumentary changes.
   a. Changes in skin composition.
      (1) Dermis thins with loss of elastin.
      (2) Decreased vascularity; vascular fragility results in easy bruising (senile purpura).
      (3) Decreased sebaceous activity and decline in hydration.

      (4) Appearance: skin appears dry, wrinkled, yellowed, and inelastic; aging spots appear (clusters of melanocyte pigmentation); increased with exposure to sun.
      (5) General thinning and graying of hair due to vascular insufficiency and decreased melanin production.
      (6) Nails grow more slowly, become brittle and thick.
   b. Loss of effectiveness as protective barrier.
      (1) Skin grows and heals more slowly, less able to resist injury and infection.
      (2) Inflammatory response is attenuated.

> **CAUTION:** Decreased sensitivity to touch and diminished perception of pain and temperature can contribute to increased risk for injury from concentrated pressures or excess temperatures.

> **CAUTION:** Decreased sweat production with loss of sweat glands results in decreased temperature regulation and homeostasis.

2. Gastrointestinal changes.
   a. Decreased salivation, taste, and smell along with inadequate chewing (tooth loss, poorly fitting dentures); poor swallowing reflex may lead to poor dietary intake, nutritional deficiencies.
   b. Esophagus: reduced motility and control of lower esophageal sphincter; acid reflux and heartburn, hiatal hernia common.
   c. Stomach: reduced motility, delayed gastric emptying; decreased digestive enzymes and hydrochloric acid; decreased digestion and absorption; indigestion common.
   d. Decreased intestinal motility; constipation common.
3. Renal, urogenital changes.
   a. Kidneys: loss of mass and total weight with nephron atrophy, decreased renal blood flow, decreased filtration.
      (1) Blood urea rises.
      (2) Decreased excretory and reabsorptive capacities.
   b. Bladder: muscle weakness; decreased capacity causing urinary frequency; difficulty with emptying causing increased retention.
      (1) Urinary incontinence common (affects over 10 million adults; over half of nursing home residents and one-third of community-dwelling older adults); affects older women with pelvic floor weakness and older men with bladder or prostate disease.
      (2) Increased likelihood of urinary tract infections.

Nutrition and Older Adults

Overview and Contributing Factors to Poor Nutrition

1. Many older adults have primary nutrition problems.
   a. Nutritional problems in older adults are often linked to health status and poverty rather than to age itself.
      (1) Chronic diseases alter the overall need for nutrients, the abilities to take in and utilize nutrients, energy demands, and overall activity levels (e.g., neurocognitive disorders, CVA, and diabetes).
      (2) Limited, fixed incomes severely limit food choices and availability.
2. There is an age-related slowing in basal metabolic rate and a decline in total caloric intake; most of the decline is associated with a concurrent reduction in physical activity.
   a. Both undernourishment and obesity exist in older adults and contribute to decreased levels of vitality and fitness.
3. Contributing factors to poor dietary intake.
   a. Decreased sense of taste and smell.
   b. Poor teeth or poorly fitting dentures.
   c. Reduced gastrointestinal function.
      (1) Decreased saliva.
      (2) Gastromucosal atrophy.
      (3) Reduced intestinal mobility; reflux.
   d. Loss of interest in foods.
   e. Isolation, lack of social support, no socialization during meals, loss of spouse, loss of friends.
   f. Lack of functional mobility.
      (1) Inability to get to a grocery store to shop.
      (2) Inability to prepare foods.

Outcomes of Poor Nutrition

1. Dehydration is common in older adults, resulting in fluid and electrolyte disturbances.
   a. Thirst sensation is diminished.
   b. May be physically unable to acquire/maintain fluids.

> RED FLAG: Environmental heat stresses can contribute to dehydration (e.g., having no air conditioning during a summer heat wave) which can be life threatening and should be treated as medical emergencies.

2. Diets are often deficient in nutrients, especially vitamins A and C, B12, thiamine, protein, iron, calcium, vitamin D, folic acid, and zinc.

3. Increased use of alcohol or taste enhancers (e.g., salt and sugar) influences nutritional intake.
4. Drug/dietary interactions influence nutritional intake (e.g., reserpine digoxin, antitumor agents, and excessive use of antacids).

Assessment of Nutrition

1. Dietary history: patterns of eating, types of foods.
2. Psychosocial: mental status, desire to eat, depression, grief, social isolation, social supports.
3. Body composition.
   a. Weight/height measures.
   b. Skinfold measurements: triceps/subscapular skinfold thickness.
   c. Upper arm circumference.
4. Olfactory and gustatory sensory function.
5. Dental and periodontal diseases, fit of dentures.
6. Ability to feed self: mastication, swallowing, hand/mouth control, posture, physical weakness and fatigue.
7. Integumentary: skin condition, edema.
8. Compliance to special diets.
9. Functional assessment: basic activities of daily living, feeding; overall exercise/activity levels, amount and type of social participation.

Goals and Interventions

1. Assist in monitoring adequate nutritional intake.
2. Assist in maintaining nutritional support.
   a. Refer to dietitian, nutritional consultants, and/or nutritional education programs as needed.
   b. Make recommendations for a home health aide, personal care assistant, and/or family member to assist with grocery shopping and meal preparation.
   c. Refer to older adults' food programs: home delivered meals, i.e., meals-on-wheels; congregate meals/senior center daily meal programs; federal food stamp programs.
3. Maintain physical function and promote adequate activity levels.
4. Maintain independence in food preparation and self-feeding.
   a. Teach work simplification and energy conservation techniques to maximize function.
   b. Modify the environment and adapt activities to enhance mastery and ensure safety.
   c. Refer to Chapters 15 and 16 for more details.

Elder Abuse

Facts and Statistics

1. Statistics for elder abuse are difficult to accurately assess due to limited reporting.
   a. In the United States, the abuse of vulnerable and older adults is a social justice and health-care crisis.
   b. According to the best available estimates, in the United States, five million older adults (age 65 or older) are victims of abuse, neglect, and/or exploitation.
   c. Elder and vulnerable adult abuse is underreported; approximately one in 14–24 cases is reported to authorities.
   d. Two-thirds (67%) of reported elder abuse victims were female.
   e. The vast majority (86%) of reported elder abuse is committed by someone familiar to the victim.
2. Definitions vary; however, there are three basic categories.
   a. Domestic elder abuse.
   b. Institutional elder abuse.
   c. Self-neglect or self-abuse.

> **EXAM HINT:** The above facts are provided to support the critical need for OT practitioners to be vigilant about the potential of elder abuse, neglect, and exploitation in all interactions with vulnerable and older adults. These statistics will not be on the NBCOT® exam. However, the principle of beneficence in the AOTA's Code of Ethics requires OT personnel to "demonstrate a concern for the safety and well-being of persons" (AOTA, 2020, p. 3). State licensure boards have similar standards. Therefore, it is likely that the NBCOT® exam will include items about the OT practitioner's role in identifying and responding to elder abuse. The application of knowledge about the signs and symptoms of elder abuse and the role of OT in addressing cases of abuse can help you determine the correct answer to these items.

Signs and Symptoms of Elder Abuse

1. Physical abuse signs and symptoms.
   a. An older adult's report of being physically mistreated.
   b. Bruises, black eyes, welts, and/or lacerations.
   c. Rope marks and/or other signs of restraint.
   d. Bone and skull fractures, sprains, and/or dislocations.
   e. Open wounds, cuts, and untreated injuries in various stages of healing.
   f. Internal injuries/bleeding.
   g. Broken eyeglasses.
   h. Under- or overdosing of prescribed drugs.
   i. A sudden change in behavior.
   j. The caregiver's refusal to allow visitors to see an older adult alone.
2. Sexual abuse signs and symptoms.
   a. An older adult's report of sexual assault or rape.
   b. Bruises around the breasts or genital area.
   c. Unexplained venereal disease or genital infection.
   d. Unexplained vaginal or anal bleeding.
   e. Torn, stained, or bloody underclothing.
3. Emotional/psychological abuse signs and symptoms.
   a. An older adult's report of being verbally or emotionally mistreated.
   b. Emotionally upset or agitated behavior.
   c. Extremely withdrawn and noncommunicative or nonresponsive behavior.
   d. Unusual behavior such as sucking, biting, or rocking.
4. Neglect signs and symptoms.
   a. An older adult's report of being mistreated.
   b. Dehydration, malnutrition, untreated bedsores, and poor personal hygiene.
   c. Unattended or untreated health problems.
   d. Hazardous or unsafe living conditions.
5. Financial or material exploitation signs and symptoms.
   a. An older adult's report of financial exploitation.
   b. Sudden changes in bank account or banking practice.
   c. The inclusion of additional names on an older adult's bank signature card.
   d. Unauthorized withdrawal using an ATM card.
   e. Abrupt changes in a will or other financial documents.
   f. Substandard care or unpaid bills despite the availability of funds.
   g. Discovery of a forged signature.
   h. Sudden appearance of relatives claiming rights to decisions, money, or possessions.
   i. Unexplained transfer of funds.
   j. The provision of unnecessary services.

Role of Occupational Therapy

1. Mandatory reporting.
   a. Elder abuse per se may or may not be designated as a specific crime in a state; however, most physical, sexual, and financial/material abuse are crimes in all states.
   b. Health-care workers are required to report suspected or observed cases of elder abuse.
   c. Failure to report may be considered a crime.
   d. In most states, Adult Protective Services, the area Agency on Aging, or the county Department of Social Services is designated to provide investigation and services.
2. OT intervention.
   a. Treat for physical and emotional injuries.
   b. Develop a trusting relationship.
   c. Assist in developing a support system.
   d. Refer to appropriate disciplines and/or agencies.

References

Administration on Aging (2020). 2019 Profile of older Americans. https://acl.gov/sites/default/files/Aging%20and%20Disability%20in%20America/2019ProfileOlderAmericans508.pdf

American Occupational Therapy Association. (2020). Occupational therapy practice framework: Domain and process (4th ed.). 7412410010p1–7412410010p87.

American Occupational Therapy Association. (2022). FAQ: CDC developmental surveillance milestone checklists. https://www.aota.org/practice/practice-essentials/cdc-guidelines-faq.

Amini, D. A. (2014). Motor and praxis assessments. In I. E. Asher (Ed.), Occupational therapy assessment tools: An annotated index (4th ed., pp. 441–499). AOTA Press.

Anzalone, M. E., & Lane, S. J. (2012). Sensory processing disorder. In S. J. Lane & A. C. Bundy (Eds.), Kids can be kids: A childhood occupations approach (pp. 437–459). F.A. Davis.

Asher, I. E. (2014). An annotated index of occupational therapy evaluation tools (4th ed.). AOTA Press.

Bengtson, V. L., & Settersten, R. (2016). Handbook of theories of aging (2nd ed.). Springer.

Berkow, R., & Beers, R. (Eds.). (2000). The Merck manual of geriatrics (3rd ed.). Merck.

Bonder, B., Taylor, R., & Popova, E. (2018). Theories of aging: A multidisciplinary review for occupational and physical therapists. In B. R. Bonder & V. Dal Bello-Hass (Eds.), Functional performance in older adults (pp. 20–26). F.A. Davis.

Bundy, A. C., & Murray, E. A. (2002). Sensory integration: A. Jean Ayres' theory revisited. In A. C. Bundy, S. J. Lane, & E. A. Murray (Eds.), Sensory integration: Theory and practice (2nd ed., pp. 3–33). F.A. Davis.

CAPTA Reauthorization Act of 2010 (P.L. 111-320), 42 U.S.C. § 5101, Note (§ 3) PUBL320.PS (congress.gov)

Case-Smith, J., & Humphry, R. (2020). Assessment and treatment of feeding, eating, and swallowing. In J. Case-Smith (Ed.), Occupational therapy for children (8th ed., pp. 212–238). Elsevier.

Centers for Disease Control and Prevention (2021). National Center for Health Statistics. https://www.cdc.gov/nchs/data/hestat/life-expectancy/life-expectancy-2018.htm

Centers for Disease Control and Prevention. (2023). Developmental surveillance resources for healthcare providers. https://www.cdc.gov/ncbddd/actearly/hcp/index.html.

Centers for Medicare and Medicaid Services. (2018, December 6). NHE fact sheet. https://www.cms.gov/research-statistics-data-and-systems/statistics-trends-and-reports/nationalhealthexpenddata/nhe-fact-sheet.html.

Child Welfare Information Gateway. (2022). Definitions of child abuse and neglect. U.S. Department of Health and Human Services, Administration for Children and Families, Children's Bureau. https://www.childwelfare.gov/topics/systemwide/laws-policies/statutes/define/

Child help. (2021, October 25). National child abuse statistics. https://www.childhelp.org/child-abuse-statistics/

Child Welfare Information Gateway. (2019). Mandatory Reporters of Child Abuse and Neglect. https://www.childwelfare.gov/topics/systemwide/laws-policies/statutes/manda/

Christenson, M., & Taira, E. (2013). Aging in the designed environment. Routlege.

CRE Care. (2018). PEDI-CAT. https://www.pedicat.com/.

Crist, P. A. (2014). Emotional regulation and psychological assessments. In I. E. Asher (Ed.), Occupational therapy assessment tools: An annotated index (4th ed., pp. 501–551). AOTA Press.

D'Amico, M., & Mortera, M. H. (2007). Assessments of coping and adaptive behaviors. In I. E. Asher (Ed.), Occupational therapy assessment tools: An annotated index (3rd ed., pp. 633–671). AOTA Press.

D'Amico, M., & Mortera, M. H. (2007). Assessments of disability status. In I. E. Asher (Ed.), Occupational therapy assessment tools: An annotated index (3rd ed., pp. 673–707). AOTA Press.

Deitchman, G., & Puttkammer, C. (2001). Preschool Visual Motor Integration Assessment (PVMIA). Therapro.

Dorich, J. M., & Harpster, K. (2020). Pediatric hand therapy. In J. C. O'Brien & H. Kuhaneck (Eds.), Occupational therapy for children and adolescence (8th ed., pp. 702–727). Elsevier.

Dunbar, S. B. (2007). Theory, frame of reference and model: A differentiation for practice considerations. In S. B. Dunbar (Ed.), Occupational therapy models for intervention with children and families (pp. 1–9). Slack.

Erhardt, R. P. (1994). The Erhardt Developmental Prehension Assessment. Erhardt Developmental Products.

Eriksson, G., Lilja, M., Jonsson, H., Petersson, I., & Tatzer, V. C. (2015). Occupations of elderhood. In C. Christensen, C. Baum, & J. M. Bass (Eds.), Occupational therapy performance, participation and well-being (4th ed., pp. 169–183). Slack.

Gench, B., Hinson, M., & McNurlen, G. (1996). Human reflexes and reacting resource cards. Eddie Bowers.

Haley, S., Coster, W., Ludlow, L., Haltiwanger, J., & Andrellos, P. (1998). Pediatric Evaluation of Disability Inventory (PEDI) Development, Standardization and Administration Manual. Trustees of Boston University.

Haynes, C. J., & Anderson, M. D. A. (2014). Sensory-perceptual assessments. In I. E. Asher (Ed.), Occupational therapy assessment tools: An annotated index (4th ed., pp. 363–441). AOTA Press.

Heron, M. (2021). Deaths leading causes for 2018. National Vital Statistics Report. https://www.cdc.gov/nchs/data/nvsr/nvsr70/nvsr70-04-508.pdf

Hollenbeck, J. (2017). Childhood occupations and play. In A. Wagenfeld, J. Kaldenberg, & D. L. Honaker (Eds.), Foundations of pediatric practice for the occupational therapy assistant (2nd ed., pp. 222–245). Slack.

Humphry, R., & Womack, J. (2012). Transformations of occupations: A life course perspective. In B. A. B. Schell, G. Gillen, & M. E. Scaffa (Eds.), Willard and Spackman's occupational therapy (12th ed., pp. 60–71). Lippincott Williams & Wilkins.

Jaffe, L., Cosper, S., & Fabrizi, S. (2020). Working with families. In J. C. O'Brien & H. Kuhaneck (Eds.), Occupational therapy for children and adolescence (8th ed., pp. 46–75). Elsevier.

Kaldenberg, J., & Wagenfeld, A. (2017). Self-care. In A. Wagenfeld, J. Kaldenberg, & D. L. Honaker (Eds.), Foundations of pediatric practice for the occupational therapy assistant (2nd ed., pp. 246–267). Slack.

Kaplan, H. I., & Sadock, B. J. (2021). Synopsis of clinical psychiatry: Behavioral sciences/clinical psychiatry (12th ed.). Lippincott Williams & Wilkins.

Klein, M. (1987). Pre-scissor skills (rev. ed.). Therapy Skill Builders.

Knox, S. (2008). Development and current use of the Knox Preschool Play Scale. In L. D. Parham & L. S. Fazio (Eds.), Sensory integration: Theory and practice (2nd ed., pp. 55–70). Elsevier.

Korth, I., &. Maune, N. C. (2020). Assessment and treatment of feeding, eating, and swallowing. In J. C. O'Brien & H. Kuhaneck (Eds.), Occupational therapy for children and adolescents (8th ed., pp. 212–238). Elsevier.

Kuhaneck, H. (2020). Autism spectrum disorder. In J. C. O'Brien & H. Kuhaneck (Eds.), Occupational therapy for children and adolescence (8th ed., pp. 786–813). Elsevier.

Lane, S. J. (2002). Sensory modulation. In A. C. Bundy, S. J. Lane, & E. A. Murray (Eds.), Sensory integration: Theory and practice (2nd ed., pp. 101–122). F.A. Davis.

Lane, S. J. (2002). Structure and function of the sensory systems. In A. C. Bundy, S. J. Lane, & E. A. Murray (Eds.), Sensory integration: Theory and practice (2nd ed., pp. 35–68). F.A. Davis.

Leech, S. W. M. (2014). Play assessments. In I. E. Asher (Ed.), Occupational therapy assessment tools: An annotated index (4th ed., pp. 319–328). AOTA Press.

Lewis, C., & Bottomley, J. (2007). Geriatric rehabilitation: A clinical approach (3rd ed.). Prentice Hall.

Linder, T. (2008). Transdisciplinary play-based assessment (rev. ed.). Paul H. Brookes.

Mandich, M. B. (2016). Infancy. In A. Cronin & M. B. Mandich (Eds.), Human development and performance throughout the lifespan (2nd ed., pp. 200–226). Cengage.

Mandich, A., Wilson, J., & Carmichael, K. (2020). Cognitive interventions. In J. C. O'Brien & H. Kuhaneck (Eds.), Occupational therapy for children and adolescence (8th ed., pp. 431–450). Elsevier.

Martin, L. M. (2014). Social participation assessments. In I. E. Asher (Ed.), Occupational therapy assessment tools: An annotated index (4th ed., pp. 335–360). AOTA Press.

May-Benson, T. A. (2017). Introduction to sensory integration. In A. Wagenfeld, J. Kaldenberg, & D. L. Honaker (Eds.), Foundations of pediatric practice for the occupational therapy assistant (2nd ed., pp. 162–196). Slack.

McCoy-Powlen, J. D., Gallen, D. B., & Edwards, S. J. (2017). Hand development. In A. Wagenfeld, J. Kaldenberg, & D. L. Honaker (Eds.), Foundations of pediatric practice for the occupational therapy assistant (2nd ed., pp. 282–299). Slack.

Miller, L. J. (2014). Sensational kids: Hope and help for children with sensory processing disorder (SPD) (rev. ed.). G. P. Putnam & Sons.

Mosey, A. C. (1996). Psychosocial components of occupational therapy. Lippincott-Raven.

Mulligan, S. (2014). Occupational therapy evaluation for children: A pocket guide (2nd ed.). Wolters Kluwer. Lippincott Williams & Wilkins.

Myers, C. T., & Cason, J. (2020). Early intervention services. In J. C. O'Brien & H. Kuhaneck (Eds.), Occupational therapy for children and adolescents (8th ed., pp. 601–626). Elsevier.

National Board for Certification in Occupational Therapy (NBCOT®). (2020). 2020 OTR® Curriculum Textbook and Peer-Reviewed Journal Report (nbcot.org).

National Board for Certification in Occupational Therapy (NBCOT®). (2022). 2022 Occupational Therapist Registered (OTR®) examination content outline. https://www.nbcot.org/-/media/PDFs/2022_OTR_Content_Outline.pdf

National Center on Elder Abuse. (2013). Elder abuse and its impact: What you must know. http://eldermistreatment.usc.edu/wp-content/uploads/2016/10/Elder-Abuse-and-Its-Impact-What-You-Must-Know-2013.pdf

National Council on Aging. (2021). The top 10 most chronic conditions in older adults. https://www.ncoa.org/article/the-top-10-most-common-chronic-conditions-in-older-adults

National Institute on Deafness and Other Communication Disorders. (2018, July 17). Age-related hearing loss. https://www.nidcd.nih.gov/health/age-related-hearing-loss.

O'Brien, J.C., & Kuhaneck, H. (2020). Case-Smith's occupational therapy for children and adolescents (8th ed.). Elsevier.

Parham, D., & Mailoux, Z. (2020). Sensory integration. In J. C. O'Brien & H. Kuhaneck (Eds.), Occupational therapy for children and adolescents (8th ed., pp. 516–549). Elsevier.

Parks S. (2007). HELP Strands. VOTT Corp.

Participation Scale Development Team. (2010). Participation Scale v6.0.

Pearson Assessments. (2023). Pediatric Evaluation of Disability Inventory- Computer Adaptive Test. https://www.pearsonassessments.com/store/usassessments/en/Store/Professional-Assessments/Behavior/Pediatric-Evaluation-of-Disability-Inventory-Computer-Adaptive-Test/p/100002037.html.

Polatajko, H. J., Mandich, A. D., Miller, L. T., & Macnab, J. J. (2001). Cognitive orientation to daily occupational performance (CO-OP): Part II—The evidence. Physical and Occupational Therapy in Pediatrics, 20, 83–106.

Rafeedie, S. (2018). Special needs of the older adult. In H. M. Pendleton & W. Schultz-Krohn (Eds.), Pedretti's occupational therapy: Practice skills for physical dysfunction (8th ed., pp. 1142–1165). Elsevier.

Reeves, G. D., & Cermak, S. A. (2002). Disorders of praxis. In A. C. Bundy, S. J. Lane, & E. A. Murray (Eds.), Sensory integration: Theory and practice (2nd ed., pp. 71–100). F.A. Davis.

Rodger, S., & Liu, S. (2008). Cognitive orientation to (daily) occupational performance: Changes in strategy and session time use over the course of intervention. OTJR: Occupation, Participation and Health, 38, 168–179.

Rodger, S., Springfield, E., & Polatajko, H. J. (2007). Cognitive orientation for daily occupational performance approach for children with Asperger's syndrome: A case report. Physical and Occupational Therapy in Pediatrics, 27, 7–22.

Rodger, S., Ziviani, J., & Lim, S. M. (2015). Occupations of childhood and adolescence. In C. Christensen, C. Baum, & J. M. Bass (Eds.), Occupational therapy performance, participation and well-being (4th ed., pp. 129–155). Slack.

Rogers, S. (2005). Common conditions that influence children's participation. In J. Case-Smith (Ed.), Occupational therapy for children (5th ed., pp. 160–215). Elsevier Mosby.

Schneck, C. M., & O'Brien, S. P. (2020). Assessment and treatment of educational performance. In J. C. O'Brien & H. Kuhaneck (Eds.), Occupational therapy for children and adolescents (8th ed., pp. 374–394). Elsevier.

Schultz-Krohn, W. (2014). Occupational performance assessments. In I. E. Asher (Ed.), Occupational therapy assessment tools: An annotated index (4th ed., pp. 27, 29–64). AOTA Press.

Shapiro, B. K., & Batshaw, M. L. (2013). Developmental delay and intellectual disability. In M. L. Batshaw, N. J. Roizen, & G. R. Lotrecchiano (Eds.), Children with disabilities (7th ed., pp. 291–306). Paul H. Brookes.

Shepherd, J., & Ivey, C. (2020). Assessment and treatment of activities of daily living, sleep, rest, and sexuality. In J. C. O'Brien & H. Kuhaneck (Eds.), Occupational therapy for children and adolescence (8th ed., pp. 267–314). Elsevier Mosby.

Skard, G., & Bundy, A.C. (2008). Test of Playfulness. In L.D. Parham & L.S. Fazio (Eds.), Play in occupational therapy for children (2nd ed., pp. 71–93). Mosby.

Smet, N., Lucas, C.B., Parham, D., & Mailloux, Z. (2020). Occupational therapy view of child development. In J. C. O'Brien & H. Kuhaneck (Eds.), Occupational therapy for children and adolescence (8th ed., pp. 76–121). Elsevier.

U. S. Census Bureau. (2020, June 25). 65 and older population grows rapidly as baby boomers age [Press Release]. https://www.census.gov/newsroom/press-releases/2020/65-older-population-grows.html

U.S. Census Bureau. (2021, May). Quick facts United States. https://www.census.gov/quickfacts/fact/table/US/PST045219

U.S. Department of Health and Human Services, The Administration for Community Living. (2018). 2017 profile of older Americans. https://acl.gov/sites/default/files/Aging%20and%20Disability%20in%20America/2017OlderAmericansProfile.pdf.

U.S. Department of Health & Human Services, Administration on Children, Youth and Families, Children's Bureau. (2021). Child Maltreatment 2019. https://www.acf.hhs.gov/sites/default/files/documents/cb/cm2019.pdf

Van Gorder, L. (2017). Handwriting. In A. Wagenfeld, J. Kaldenberg, & D. L. Honaker (Eds.), Foundations of pediatric practice for the occupational therapy assistant (2nd ed., pp. 300–319). Slack.

Wagenfeld, A., Kaldenberg, J., & Honaker, D. L. (Eds.). (2017). Foundations of pediatric practice for the occupational therapy assistant (2nd ed.). Slack.

Western Psychological Services. (n.d.). (Beery VMI). Beery-Buktenica Developmental Test of Visual-Motor Integration, 6th edition. https://www.wpspublish.com/beery-vmi-beery-buktenica-developmental-test-of-visual-motor-integration-sixth-edition?utm_term=&utm_campaign=Search+%7C+Occupational+Therapy+%26+Sensory+Processing&utm_source=adwords&utm_medium=ppc&hsa_net=adwords&hsa_tgt=dsa-437115340933&hsa_ad=500120071122&hsa_acc=6243382947&hsa_grp=88861386955&hsa_mt=b&hsa_cam=1687564793&hsa_kw=&hsa_ver=3&hsa_src=g&gclid=Cj0KCQjw7pKFBhDUARIsAFUoMDZ5J6BZJu64A7ydMYNygJ5TUf0bQpftgcP-qrhCHJKQI6JgW9v9mR8aAqtmEALw_wcB

World Health Organization. (2021). International Classification of Functioning, Disability and Health (ICF). (who.int)

Zubler, J. M., Wiggins, L. D., Macias, M. M., et al. (2022). Evidence-informed milestones for developmental surveillance tools. Pediatrics.

Review Questions

Following are eight questions about key content covered in this Chapter. These questions are not inclusive of the entirety of content about human development across the lifespan and pediatric through geriatric considerations for occupational therapy practice that you must know for success on the NBCOT® exam. These questions are provided to help you "jump-start" the thought processes you will need to apply your studying of content to the answering of exam questions; hence, they are not in the NBCOT® exam format. Exam items in the NBCOT® format that cover the depth and breadth of content you will need to know to pass the NBCOT® exam are provided in the three online practice exams that accompany this text. The answers to the following questions are provided in Appendix 2.

1. A 16-month-old toddler is brought to occupational therapy for an evaluation. The parents are concerned with the frequency of the toddler's falls which result in bangs to the head. The child demonstrates delayed motor skills. You notice that the toddler has not yet integrated primitive reflexes. Which primary primitive reflex is most likely absent in this toddler? Explain its relevance to the toddler's health status, safety, and its impact on occupational performance.

2. A 26-month-old child is referred to occupational therapy to address feeding challenges. The parents report that their child met all feeding milestones without difficulty, but when introducing foods that needed to be chewed well, like small pieces of meat or crunchy items, the child pockets the food in their cheek and tries to spit the food out of their mouth. The child is now refusing to accept these food items due to a recent gagging episode. What skills does the child need to master to independently manage these foods?

3. A 4-year-old child is referred to your occupational therapy clinic due to a limited food repertoire that includes French fries, yogurt, and apple sauce. The child has an aversion to any lumps in food items and will refuse these food items. What challenges do you think this child has and what assessments would you use for evaluation?

4. A new student in second grade is referred to occupational therapy to screen for potential developmental delays. The therapist observes the child in the classroom and notes that the child uses a static tripod grasp during writing tasks and can cut circles and squares with scissors, but they cannot cut more complex shapes. During recess, they jump over objects and hop on one foot. When the child's shoes become untied, they cannot independently tie them. Do these observations warrant further evaluation? What rationale would you provide to the teacher and the student's parents to support your decision to evaluate this student or to not evaluate them?

(Continued)

Review Questions

5. You are part of an intraprofessional screening team to determine children's readiness for kindergarten. A five-year-old child whom you are evaluating has performed at or above level on every aspect of the screening and has not demonstrated any fine motor, visual motor, or gross motor delays. The child has no cognitive deficits. The child performed well on the Beery-Buktenica Developmental Test of Visual-Motor Integration. Given the child's performance so far, which of Erhardt's developmental levels of prewriting skills would you expect the child to use for writing tasks? Explain your answer.

6. A typically developing child with no developmental delays independently creates a building made of blocks from a mental image. Identify the child's age range and describe the skills the child would use during this play activity.

7. A 15-year-old has a group of friends who have recently become involved in experimenting with drugs, alcohol, and other risky behaviors. The teen is torn between wanting to remain friends with this group and not wanting to join them in these behaviors. They decide to join a competitive youth soccer league so that they can meet new people and develop a new group of friends. According to Erikson's eight stages of man, what stage of development is the teenager undergoing? Describe the characteristics of this stage.

8. You provide wellness and prevention services to older adults who attend a community-based senior center. What strategies to slow, reverse, and/or compensate for age-related changes to their muscular, skeletal, and neurological systems can you can share with these older adults?

6

Musculoskeletal System Disorders

COLLEEN MAHER

Anatomy of the Musculoskeletal System

Relationship to the Examination

1. It is not likely that the NBCOT® exam will ask direct questions about anatomy or physiology.
2. As a result, this Chapter does not provide a complete anatomy and physiology review.

> **EXAM HINT:** The NBCOT® OTR® exam content outline identifies knowledge of the "impact of body functions and body structures on occupational performance" (NBCOT®, 2022, p. 3) as essential for competent and safe practice. The application of knowledge about the major structures and functions of the musculoskeletal system can help you correctly answer NBCOT® exam items about the *functional implications* of damage to this system. For example, damage to the opponens pollicis would result in the need to engage in activities that do not require thumb opposition.

Anatomy of the Hand

1. Intrinsic muscles innervated by the median nerve (Figure 6-1).
   a. Abductor pollicis brevis.
      (1) Function: palmar abduction.
   b. Opponens pollicis.
      (1) Function: opposition.
   c. Flexor pollicis brevis: superficial head.
      (1) Function: thumb metacarpophalangeal (MCP) flexion, deep head innervated by ulnar nerve.
   d. Lumbricals (radial side).
      (1) Function: MCP flexion and extension of interphalangeal (IP) joints of digits II and III.
2. Intrinsic muscles innervated by the ulnar nerve (Figure 6-2).
   a. Abductor digiti minimi.
      (1) Function: abduction of the fifth digit.
   b. Opponens digiti minimi.
      (1) Function: opposition of the fifth digit.
   c. Flexor digiti minimi.
      (1) Function: flexion of MCP joint and opposition of the fifth digit.
   d. Adductor.
      (1) Function: adducts carpometacarpal (CMC) joint of thumb.
   e. Lumbricals (ulnar side).
      (1) Function: MCP flexion and extension of IP joints of digits IV and V.
   f. Palmar interossei.
      (1) Function: adduction and assistance with MCP flexion and extension of IP joints of digits II through V.
   g. Dorsal interossei.
      (1) Function: abduction and assists with MCP flexion and extension of IP joints of digits II through V.

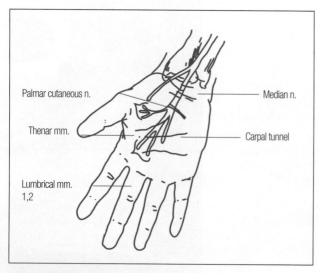

Figure 6-1 Median Nerve.

Malick, M., & Kasch, M. (1984). Manual on management of specific hand problems. AREN. Reprinted with permission.

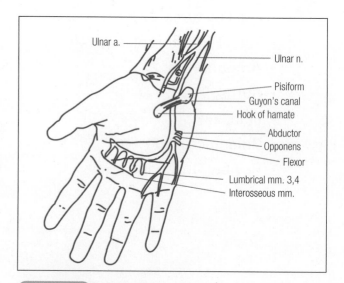

Figure 6-2 Ulnar Nerve.

Malick, M., & Kasch, M. (1984). Manual on management of specific hand problems. AREN. Reprinted with permission.

3. Extrinsic flexor muscles of the hand innervated by the median nerve (Figure 6-3).
   a. Flexor digitorum superficialis (sublimis) (FDS).
      (1) Function: flexion of proximal interphalangeal (PIP) joints.
   b. Flexor digitorum profundus (FDP).
      (1) Function: flexion of distal interphalangeal (DIP) joints to digits II and III. (Refer to ulnar nerve for digits IV and V.)
   c. Flexor pollicis longus (FPL).
      (1) Function: flexion of IP joint of thumb.
4. Extrinsic flexors of the hand innervated by the ulnar nerve (Figure 6-4).

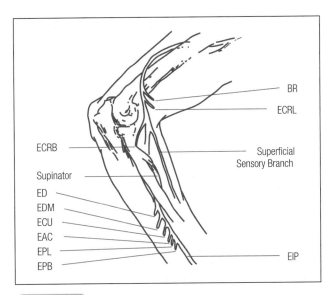

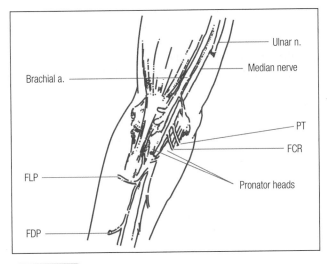

Figure 6-3   **Median Nerve.**

   a. Flexor digitorum profundus.
      (1) Function: flexion of DIP joints to digits IV and V.
5. Extrinsic extensor muscles of the hand innervated by the radial nerve (Figure 6-5).
   a. Extensor digitorum communis (EDC).
      (1) Function: extension of MCP joints and contributes to extension of the IP joints.
   b. Extensor digiti minimi (EDM).
      (1) Function: extension of MCP joint of the fifth digit and contributes to extension of the IP joints.
   c. Extensor indicis proprius (EIP).
      (1) Function: extension of MCP joint of the second digit and contributes to extension of the IP joints.
   d. Extensor pollicis longus (EPL).
      (1) Function: extension of IP joint of thumb.
   e. Extensor pollicis brevis (EPB).
      (1) Function: extension of MCP and CMC joints of thumb.
   f. Abductor pollicis longus (APL).
      (1) Function: abduction and extension of CMC joint.

Anatomy of the Wrist

1. Wrist flexors innervated by the median nerve (Figure 6-3).
   a. Flexor carpi radialis (FCR).
      (1) Function: flexion of wrist and radial deviation.
   b. Palmaris longus (PL).
      (1) Function: flexion of wrist.

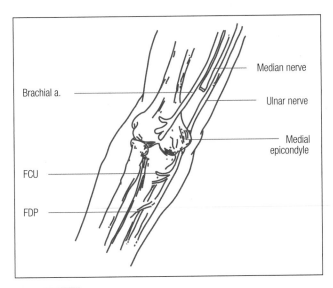

Figure 6-4   **Ulnar Nerve.**

2. Wrist flexors innervated by the ulnar nerve (Figure 6-4).
   a. Flexor carpi ulnaris (FCU).
      (1) Function: flexion of wrist and ulnar deviation.
3. Wrist extensors innervated by the radial nerve (Figure 6-5).
   a. Extensor carpi radialis brevis (ECRB).
      (1) Function: extension of wrist and radial deviation.
   b. Extensor carpi radialis longus (ECRL).
      (1) Function: extension of wrist and radial deviation.
   c. Extensor carpi ulnaris (ECU).
      (1) Function: extension of wrist and ulnar deviation.

Anatomy of the Forearm

1. Volar forearm muscles innervated by the median nerve.
   a. Pronator teres.
      (1) Function: forearm pronation.
   b. Pronator quadratus.
      (1) Function: forearm pronation.
2. Dorsal forearm muscles innervated by the radial nerve.
   a. Supinator.
      (1) Function: forearm supination.

Anatomy of the Elbow

1. Elbow flexion: biceps and brachialis innervated by musculocutaneous nerve; brachioradialis innervated by radial nerve.
   a. Biceps.
      (1) Function: elbow flexion with forearm supinated.
   b. Brachialis.
      (1) Function: elbow flexion with forearm pronated.
   c. Brachioradialis.
      (1) Function: elbow flexion with forearm neutral.
2. Elbow extension: triceps and anconeus innervated by radial nerve.
   a. Triceps.
      (1) Function: elbow extension.
   b. Anconeus.
      (1) Function: elbow extension.

Anatomy of the Shoulder

1. Rotator cuff muscles.
   a. Subscapularis innervated by the subscapular nerve.
      (1) Function: internal rotation.
   b. Supraspinatus innervated by the suprascapular nerve.
      (1) Function: abduction and shoulder elevation.
   c. Infraspinatus innervated by the suprascapular nerve.
      (1) Function: external rotation.
   d. Teres minor innervated by the axillary nerve.
      (1) Function: external rotation.
2. Shoulder flexion muscles.
   a. Anterior deltoid innervated by axillary nerve.
   b. Coracobrachialis innervated by the musculocutaneous nerve.
3. Shoulder abduction muscles.
   a. Middle deltoid innervated by the axillary nerve.
   b. Supraspinatus.
4. Horizontal abduction muscle.
   a. Posterior deltoid innervated by the axillary nerve.
5. Horizontal adduction muscle.
   a. Pectoralis major innervated by the lateral pectoral nerve.
6. Shoulder extension muscles.
   a. Latissimus dorsi innervated by the thoracodorsal nerve.

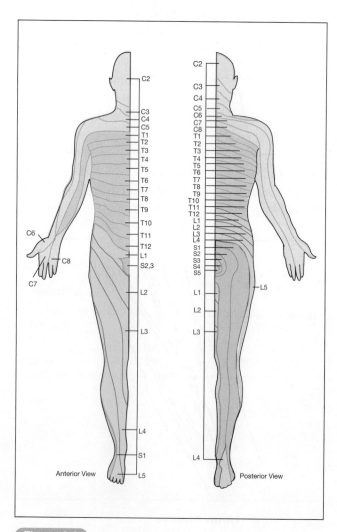

Figure 6-6 **Dermatomes.**

b. Teres major innervated by the subscapular nerve.
c. Posterior deltoid.

Anatomy of the Scapula

1. Upward rotation muscles.
   a. Trapezius (upper, middle, and lower) innervated by the spinal accessory nerve (CNXI).
   b. Serratus anterior innervated by the long thoracic nerve.
2. Downward rotation muscles.
   a. Levator scapulae innervated by C3–C4 nerves.
   b. Rhomboids (major and minor) innervated by the dorsal scapular nerve.
   c. Serratus anterior.
   d. Latissimus dorsi.

3. Scapula adduction muscles.
   a. Middle trapezius.
   b. Rhomboid major.
4. Scapula abduction muscles.
   a. Serratus anterior.
5. Scapula elevation muscles.
   a. Trapezius (upper).
   b. Levator scapulae.
6. Scapula depression muscles.
   a. Trapezius (lower).

Dermatome Distribution

1. Refer to Table 11-4.
2. Refer to Figure 6-6.

▶ Hand and Upper Extremity Disorders and Injuries

EXAM HINT: The NBCOT® OTR® exam content outline identifies knowledge of the "expected patterns, progressions, and prognoses associated with conditions that limit occupational performance" (NBCOT®, 2022, p. 3) as essential for competent and safe practice. The application of knowledge about the musculoskeletal system disorders described in this Chapter will be required to correctly answer NBCOT® exam items about working with people with these conditions.

EXAM HINT: In the NBCOT® OTR® exam content outline, Domain 3 Select and Manage Interventions comprises 38% of the NBCOT® exam. This domain is defined as the selection and implementation of "interventions to promote healing and enhance engagement in occupation-based activities" (NBCOT®, 2022, p. 7). The application of knowledge about the diagnostic-specific interventions described for each condition in this section can help you correctly answer NBCOT® Domain 3 exam items about intervention management for persons with hand and upper extremity disorders and injuries.

Dupuytren's Disease

1. Disease of the fascia of the palm and digits.
   a. The fascia becomes thick and contracted. Develops cords and bands that extend into the digits.

   b. Results in flexion deformities of the involved digits (Figure 6-7).
2. Etiology: unknown.
3. Conservative treatment with no surgery (e.g., the use of orthotics) has not been successful.
4. Medical treatments.
   a. Collagenase enzymatic injection (nonsurgical): no wound care or scar management is required.
   b. Fasciotomy small incision to weaken the diseased fascia.
   c. Aponeurotomy (using a needle): perforates the diseased tissue to weaken it with a needle.
   d. Fasciectomy is the most common (better results); removal of diseased tissue.
   e. McCash procedure (open palm); type of fasciectomy.

Figure 6-7   **Dupuytren's Contractures.**

Adapted from Magee, D. J. (1992). Orthopedic physical assessment (2nd ed.). W.B. Saunders.

5. OT intervention post-surgery.
   a. Wound care: dressing changes.
   b. Edema control: elevation above the heart.
   c. Hand-based extension orthosis: remove for range of motion (ROM) and bathing.
      (1) This orthosis can be dorsal or volar.

> CAUTION: The ideal orthosis is full extension; however, this is not always possible due to the severity of a contracture and the quality of the tendon and nerves. The occupational therapist should consult with the surgeon to obtain clarification.

   d. Active range of motion (AROM)/passive range of motion (PROM); progress to strengthening (usually at four weeks) when wounds are healed.
   e. Scar management: massage, scar pad/gel sheeting, and compression garment.
   f. Purposeful and occupation-based tasks that emphasize flexion (gripping) and extension (release) (DeHerder, 2015).

Skier's Thumb (Gamekeeper's Thumb).

1. Rupture of the ulnar collateral ligament of the MCP joint of the thumb.
2. Etiology: most common cause is a fall while skiing with the thumb held in a ski pole.
3. OT intervention.
   a. Conservative treatment (if a partial tear) includes a thumb orthosis (can be hand based or forearm based with IP joint free). Refer to Figure 6-8.

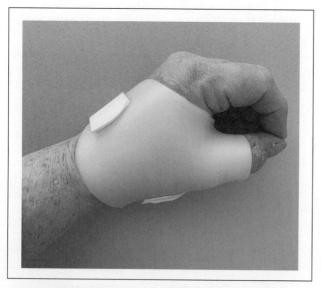

Figure 6-8 **Skier's Thumb Orthosis**
Photo Courtesy of Colleen Maher, OTD, OTR/L, CHT.

b. Begin with AROM.
   (1) Await for physician's orders to begin gentle AROM, usually at 2–4 weeks.
   (2) When approved by the physician, progress to active assistive range of motion (AAROM) and lateral pinch strengthening, usually at 6 or more weeks.

> CAUTION: Palmar abduction should be performed very cautiously as it puts direct stress on the repaired site; keep it pain free. Because of this stress, the physician may delay this AROM movement.

c. Focus on activities of daily living (ADL) that require opposition and pinch strength.
   (1) Strengthening is often delayed 6–12 weeks post injury starting with lateral pinch,
   (2) The physician will guide initiation of strengthening.
d. Postoperative treatment includes the following.
   (1) Thumb orthosis for 6–12 weeks (hand or forearm based).
   (2) Edema management (elevation is a must) followed by removing the orthosis for AROM (4–6 weeks).
   (3) Strengthening, when approved by the physician, beginning with lateral pinch (Solomon, 2020; Amini, 2021).

Complex Regional Pain Syndrome (CRPS)

1. Formerly known as reflex sympathetic dystrophy (RSD).
2. Vasomotor dysfunction as a result of an abnormal reflex.
3. It can be localized to one specific area or spread to other parts of the extremity.
4. Etiology: may follow trauma (e.g., Colles' fracture) or surgery, but actual cause is unknown.
5. Symptoms include severe pain (beyond what is expected for the injury), edema, discoloration, osteoporosis, sudomotor changes (sweating), blotchy/shiny skin, temperature changes, trophic changes (skin, nail, and fingertip appearance), and vasomotor instability.
6. OT intervention.
   a. Modalities to decrease pain and decrease hypersensitivity (desensitization, warm fluidotherapy or hot packs). TENS can be used to address pain prior to AROM or during ADL.
   b. Edema management: elevation, manual edema mobilization, compression glove.
   c. AROM to involved joints.
   d. ADL to encourage pain-free active use.

e. Stress loading: weightbearing and joint distraction activities, including scrubbing and carrying activities.

f. Orthotics to prevent contractures and enable ability to engage in occupation-based activities.

g. Encourage self-management.

h. Interventions to avoid or to proceed with caution are those that increase pain such as PROM, passive stretching and joint mobilization (Walsh & Chee, 2018).

Fractures

1. Types of fractures.
   a. Intra-articular versus extra-articular.
   b. Closed versus open.
   c. Dorsal displacement versus volar displacement.
   d. Midshaft versus neck versus base.
   e. Complete versus incomplete.
   f. Transverse versus spiral versus oblique.
   g. Comminuted.
2. Medical treatment.
   a. Closed reduction: types of stabilization include short arm cast (SAC), long arm cast (LAC), orthosis, sling, or fracture brace.
   b. Open reduction internal fixation (ORIF): types include nails, screws, plates, or wire.
   c. External fixation.
   d. Arthrodesis: fusion.
   e. Arthroplasty: joint replacement.
3. Most common upper extremity fractures.
   a. Colles' fracture: fracture of the distal radius with dorsal displacement.
   b. Smith's fracture: fracture of the distal radius with volar displacement.
   c. Carpal fractures: most common is scaphoid fracture (60% of carpal fractures). The proximal scaphoid has a poor blood supply and may become necrotic.
   d. Metacarpal fractures: classified according to location (head, neck, shaft, or base). A common complication is rotational deformities.
      (1) A Boxer's fracture is a fracture of the fifth metacarpal (requires an ulnar gutter orthosis).
   e. Proximal phalanx fractures: most common with the thumb and the index finger. A common complication is loss of PIP AROM/PROM.
   f. Middle phalanx fractures: not commonly fractured.
   g. Distal phalanx fracture: most common finger fracture; may result in mallet finger (which involves terminal extensor tendon).
   h. Elbow fracture: involvement of the radial head may result in limited rotation of the forearm.
   i. Humerus fractures: nondisplaced versus displaced fractures.
      (1) Etiology: a fall onto an outstretched upper extremity.
      (2) Fractures of the greater tuberosity may result in rotator cuff injuries.
      (3) Humeral shaft fractures may cause injury to the radial nerve resulting in wrist drop.
4. OT evaluation.
   a. Occupational profile.
   b. History should include the mechanism of injury and fracture management.
   c. Results of special tests (x-rays, magnetic resonance imaging, and computed tomography scan).
   d. Edema.
   e. Pain.
   f. AROM.
      (1) Do not assess PROM or strength until ordered by a physician.
      (2) Exceptions are humerus fractures that often begin with PROM or AAROM.
   g. Sensation.
   h. Engagement in occupations, ADL, and activities related to roles.
5. OT intervention.
   a. Immobilization phase: stabilization and healing are the goals.
      (1) AROM of joints above and below the stabilized part.
      (2) Edema control: elevation, manual edema mobilization, gentle retrograde massage, and compression garments.
      (3) Light ADL and role activities with no resistance, progress as tolerated.
         (a) If the person is in a sling, shoulder immobilizer, LAC, fracture brace, or ORIF, they should be instructed in one-handed techniques.
   b. Mobilization phase: consolidation is the goal.
      (1) Edema control: elevation, manual edema mobilization, gentle retrograde massage, contrast baths, and compression garments (e.g., Tubigrip™, Isotoner™ glove).
      (2) Some persons will require an orthosis for protection.
      (3) AROM.
         (a) Progress to AA/PROM when approved by physician.
         (b) Exceptions are humerus fractures that often begin with PROM or AAROM.
      (4) Light purposeful or occupation-based activities.
      (5) Pain management: positioning and physical agent modalities.
      (6) Strengthening: when approved by the physician.

Cumulative Trauma Disorders (CTDs)

1. Also known as repetitive strain injuries (RSIs), overuse syndromes, and/or musculoskeletal disorders.
2. Risk factors: repetition, static position, awkward postures, forceful exertions, and vibration. Refer to Figure 15-1.
3. Nonwork risk factors: acute trauma, pregnancy, diabetes, arthritis, and wrist size and shape.
4. Most common types.
   a. de Quervain's.
      (1) Stenosing tenosynovitis of the abductor pollicis longus (APL) and the extensor pollicis brevis (EPB) (Figure 6-9).
      (2) Pain and swelling over the radial styloid.
      (3) Positive Finkelstein's test.
      (4) Conservative treatment.
         (a) Thumb spica orthosis (IP joint free).
         (b) Activity/work modification.
         (c) Ice massage over radial wrist.
         (d) Gentle AROM of wrist and thumb to prevent stiffness.
      (5) Postoperative treatment.
         (a) Thumb spica orthosis and gentle AROM (0–2 weeks).

   (b) Strengthening, ADL, and role activities (2–6 weeks).
   (c) Unrestricted activity (6 weeks).
   b. Lateral epicondylitis
      (1) Degenerative changes of the tendon's origin as a result of repetitive microtrauma.
      (2) Overuse of wrist extensors, especially the extensor carpi radialis brevis. Also called tennis elbow.
      (3) Conservative treatment.
         (a) Elbow strap (counter force strap), wrist orthosis.
         (b) Ice and deep friction massage.
         (c) Stretching.
         (d) Activity/work modification.
         (e) As pain decreases, add strengthening. Focus on proximal strengthening. Begin with eccentric exercises for the wrist extensors (Amini, 2021).
   c. Trigger finger.
      (1) Tenosynovitis of the finger flexors: most commonly is the A1 pulley.
      (2) Caused by repetition and the use of tools that are placed too far apart.
      (3) Conservative treatment.
         (a) Hand- or finger-based trigger finger orthosis (MCP extended, IP joints free). Refer to Figure 6-10.
         (b) Scar massage.
         (c) Edema control.
         (d) Tendon gliding. Refer to Figure 11-2.

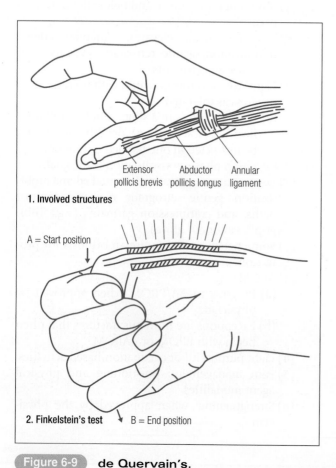

Extensor pollicis brevis   Abductor pollicis longus   Annular ligament

1. Involved structures

A = Start position

2. Finkelstein's test   B = End position

Figure 6-9   **de Quervain's.**

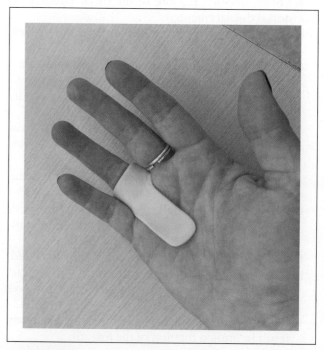

Figure 6-10   **Trigger Finger Orthosis.**
Photo Courtesy of Megan Deiling.

(e) Activity/work modification: avoid repetitive gripping activities and using tools with handles too far apart.

d. Nerve compressions: refer to section on peripheral nerve injuries.

Tendon Repairs

1. Rationale for early mobilization.
   a. Prevents adhesion formation.
   b. Facilitates wound/tendon healing.
2. OT goals.
   a. Increase tendon excursion.
   b. Improve strength at repair site.
   c. Increase joint ROM.
   d. Prevent adhesions.
   e. Facilitate resumption of meaningful roles, occupations, and activities.
3. Early passive mobilization programs for flexor tendons.
   a. Duran protocol: passive flexion and extension of digits.
      (1) 0–4 weeks: dorsal blocking orthosis.
         (a) Wrist is positioned in 10°–30° of flexion, MCP joints in 40°–60° of flexion and IP joints extended. Note: there may be slight variations in degrees depending on the surgeon (Amini, 2021; DeHerder, 2015).
         (b) Exercises in the orthosis include passive flexion of PIP joint, DIP joint and to DPC within confines of dorsal blocking orthosis. Refer to Figure 6-11.
      (2) At 2½ weeks: passive place/active hold exercises may be approved by the physician (DeHerder, 2015).
         (a) During this time period, manage edema with elevation.
         (b) When the incision is healed, massage scar to prevent adherence.
      (3) 4–6 weeks: AROM that includes wrist AROM with fingers relaxed and tendon gliding.
      (4) 6–8 weeks: gentle strengthening.
      (5) 12 weeks: return to regular functional activity (Amini, 2021 & DeHerder, 2015).
   b. Kleinert protocol: not commonly used.
      (1) Passive flexion using rubber band traction and active extension to the hood of the dorsal blocking orthosis.
      (2) 3–4 weeks: out of orthosis and rubber band traction attached to wrist band
      (3) 6 weeks: AROM.
4. Early active mobilization (multiple protocols) for flexor tendons.
   a. Requires a minimum of four strands or more used in surgical procedure.
   b. Close communication with surgeon is critical.
   c. Requires an experienced therapist who is knowledgeable in treating flexor tendon repairs.
   d. Dorsal blocking orthosis: position of wrist (usually neutral) and digits will depend on the protocol prescribed by the surgeon. Another approach uses the tenodesis orthosis.
   e. Exercises and protocol to be followed will be determined by the surgeon.
      (1) Under close supervision of the therapist, the person may complete the following.
         (a) Place and active hold in flexion.
         (b) Tenodesis with place hold flexion.
         (c) Partial finger flexion with wrist in extension.
         (d) Tendon gliding.
   f. 6 weeks: may begin light ADL.
   g. 8 weeks: gentle strengthening (Walsh &Chee, 2018; Klein, 2020).

CAUTION: The above are guidelines only. Ultimately, the surgeon will guide the occupational therapist as to the progression of exercises; beginning with the least amount of tension on the repaired tendon. Some protocols initiate active flexion immediately after surgery; others delay it until post-op week four or until the surgeon determines the tendon can begin active exercise. The occupational therapist should consult with the surgeon to obtain clarification.

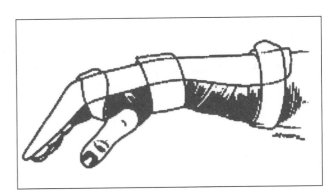

Figure 6-11   **Dorsal blocking orthosis used for "modified Duran" protocol. Wrist and MP joints are flexed, and fingers are strapped in IP joint extension when not exercising.**

Hunter, J. M., MacKin, E. J., & Callahan, A. D. (1995). Rehabilitation of the hand: Surgery and therapy (4th ed., p. 448). Mosby. Reprinted with permission.

5. Early mobilization programs for extensor tendons.
   a. Zones I and II.
      (1) Mallet finger deformity.
      (2) 0–8 weeks: DIP extension orthosis.
      (3) 6–8 weeks: gentle AROM.
         (a) Some surgeons will have ROM restrictions on how much DIP flexion will be allowed. Monitor for a lag.
      (4) Orthotic should be worn at night and in between exercises.
   b. Zones III and IV.
      (1) Boutonniere deformity.
      (2) 0–6 weeks: PIP extension orthosis (DIP free).
         (a) AROM of DIP while in orthosis (Amini, 2021; DeHerder, 2015).
   c. Zones V, VI, and VII.
      (1) Types of orthosis and protocols vary. One example includes wrist extension orthosis that also includes MCPs in slight flexion and IP joints in full extension.
         (a) As per the physician, the orthosis is adjusted to allow for IP AROM, then progresses to freeing the MCPs to allow for AROM (with wrist in extension).
         (b) Progression continues to full flexion to DPC with wrist in extension.
         (c) The incorporation of EDC exercises is important.
         (d) Strengthening will begin when approved by the physician (DeHerder, 2015).

Peripheral Nerve Injuries

1. Three major nerves: median, ulnar, and radial.
2. Two common types of nerve injuries.
   a. Compression or nerve entrapment.
   b. Laceration or avulsion injury.
3. Carpal tunnel syndrome (CTS): a median nerve compression.
   a. Etiology: narrowing of the carpal canal due to swelling/pregnancy, inflammation, hypertrophy and anatomical anomalies. Cumulative trauma causes include repetition, awkward sustained postures, and vibration.
   b. Symptoms: numbness and tingling of the thumb, index, middle, and radial half of the ring fingers.
      (1) Paresthesias usually occur at night (most characteristic).
      (2) The person will complain of dropping things.
      (3) Positive Tinel's sign at wrist. Positive Phalen's sign.
      (4) Advanced stage of CTS can result in muscle atrophy of the thenar eminence.
   c. Conservative treatment.
      (1) Wrist orthosis in neutral: should be worn at night and during the day if performing repetitive activity. Refer to Figure 11-4.

      (2) Median nerve gliding exercises (gentle sliding, should not place tension on the nerve) and differential tendon gliding exercises.
      (3) Activity modification: avoid activities with extreme positions of wrist flexion, wrist flexion with repetitive finger flexion, and wrist flexion with a static grip.
      (4) Ergonomics: appropriate workstation design. CTS is the most common work-related injury of the upper extremity. Refer to Chapter 15.
   d. Surgical intervention: carpal tunnel release (CTR); open or endoscopic.
   e. Postoperative treatment of CTR.
      (1) Edema control: elevation, AROM, ice pack, retrograde massage, compression garment, and/or contrast bath.
      (2) AROM: Wrist and tendon gliding. Refer to Figure 11-2.
      (3) Scar management: scar pad with compression garment.
      (4) Nerve and tendon gliding exercises. Refer to Figure 11-2.
      (5) Sensory re-education or desensitization.
      (6) Strengthening of thenar muscles (usually six weeks postoperative).
      (7) Ergonomic/work/activity modification (Amini, 2021).
4. Cubital tunnel syndrome: an ulnar nerve compression at the elbow. Can present with sensory and/or motor problems.
   a. Etiology: second most common compression; pressure at the elbow (leaning on the elbow) and extreme elbow flexion.
   b. Symptoms.
      (1) Numbness and tingling along ulnar aspect of forearm and hand.
      (2) Pain at elbow with extreme position of elbow flexion.
      (3) Weakness of power grip.
      (4) Special tests, Froment's sign, elbow flexion test and positive Tinel's sign at elbow.
      (5) Advanced stages can lead to atrophy of FCU, FDP to digits IV and V, and ulnar nerve–innervated intrinsic muscles of the hand. Results in claw hand deformity.
   c. Conservative treatment.
      (1) Elbow orthosis at 30° of flexion to prevent positions of extreme flexion (especially at night).
      (2) Elbow pad to decrease compression of nerve when leaning on elbows.
      (3) Ulnar nerve glides
      (4) Activity/work modification: avoid activities that have repetitive elbow flexion and static elbow flexion postures (Amini, 2021).
   d. Surgical intervention: decompression or transposition.
   e. Postoperative treatment.

(1) Edema control.
(2) Scar management.
(3) AROM and nerve gliding (2 weeks postoperative).
(4) Strengthening (4 weeks postoperative).
(5) MCP flexion anticlaw orthosis if clawing noted.

5. Radial nerve palsy: a radial nerve compression.
   a. Etiology: Saturday night palsy, a term used to describe sleeping in a position that places stress on the radial nerve. Also, compression as a result of a humeral shaft fracture.
   b. Symptoms: weakness or paralysis of extensors to the wrist, MCPs, and thumb; wrist drop.
   c. Conservative treatment.
      (1) Dynamic wrist and MCP extension orthosis.
      (2) Work/activity modification.
      (3) Strengthening wrist and finger extensors when motor function returns.
   d. Surgical intervention: decompression.
   e. Postoperative treatment.
      (1) AROM.
      (2) Strengthening: 6–8 weeks postoperative.
      (3) ADL and meaningful role activities.

> **CAUTION:** Avoid combined forearm pronation, elbow extension, and wrist flexion, as this can place tension on the nerve.

6. Median nerve laceration.
   a. Sensory loss.
      (1) Central palm: thumb to radial half of ring finger.
      (2) Palmar surface of thumb, index, middle, and radial half of ring fingers.
      (3) Dorsal surface of index, middle, and radial half of ring fingers (middle and distal phalanges).
   b. Motor loss for a low lesion at the wrist.
      (1) Lumbricals I and II (MCP flexion of digits II and III).
      (2) Opponens pollicis (opposition).
      (3) Abductor pollicis brevis (abduction).
      (4) Flexor pollicis brevis (flexion of thumb MCP).
   c. Motor loss for a high lesion at or proximal to the elbow.
      (1) All of the above in b.
      (2) FDP to index and middle fingers, and FPL (flexion of tip of index, middle fingers, and thumb).
      (3) FCR (inability to flex to radial aspect of wrist).
   d. Deformity.
      (1) Flattening of thenar eminence
      (2) Clawing of index and middle fingers for a low lesion, but not that obvious.
   e. Functional loss.
      (1) Loss of thumb opposition.
      (2) Weakness of pinch.
   f. OT intervention.
      (1) Dorsal protection orthosis with wrist positioned in 30° flexion if a low lesion (the physician may approve for digits to be left free). Include elbow (90° flexion) if a high lesion.

(2) Begin A/PROM of digits with wrist in flexed position in orthosis at 5–7 days post repair.
(3) Scar management when incision is healed.
(4) AROM of wrist out of orthosis when approved by the physician (usually around 4 weeks post repair); include elbow if a high lesion.
(5) Begin strengthening when approved by the physician (usually around 6–8 weeks post repair).
   g. Orthotic considerations to prevent deformity and promote function.
      (1) Web spacer orthosis to prevent thumb adduction contracture.
      (2) Opponens orthosis to improve functioning.
   h. Sensory reeducation: educate on the safe use of the hand using vision. Many programs on sensory reeducation use different/graded textures, particles, and vibration.
      (1) Repetition throughout the day and with eyes open/eyes closed seem to be most effective (DeHerder, 2015; Walsh & Chee, 2018).

7. Ulnar nerve laceration.
   a. Sensory loss.
      (1) Ulnar aspects of palmar and dorsal surfaces.
      (2) Ulnar half of ring and little fingers on palmar and dorsal surfaces.
   b. Motor loss: low lesion at the wrist.
      (1) Palmar and dorsal interossei: adduction and abduction of MCP joints.
      (2) Lumbricals III and IV: MCP flexion of digits 4 and 5.
      (3) FPB and adductor pollicis: flexion and adduction of thumb.
      (4) ADM, ODM, FDM: abduction, opposition, and flexion of fifth digit.
   c. Motor loss: high lesion wrist or above.
      (1) Same as above, including FCU: flexion toward ulnar wrist.
      (2) FDP IV and V: flexion of DIPs of ring and little fingers.
   d. Deformity.
      (1) Claw hand.
      (2) Flattened metacarpal arch.
      (3) Positive Froment's sign: assessment of thumb adductor while laterally pinching paper.
   e. Functional loss.
      (1) Loss of power grip.
      (2) Decreased pinch strength.
   f. OT intervention.
      (1) Refer to median nerve repair.
      (2) Orthotic consideration: MCP flexion block orthosis.
      (3) Sensory re-education: same as median nerve.

8. Radial nerve injury.
   a. Sensory loss: high lesions at the level of the humerus.
      (1) Medial aspect of dorsal forearm. Radial aspect of the dorsal palm, thumb, and index, middle and radial half of ring phalanges.

b. Motor loss: low lesion at the level of the forearm.
  (1) Loss of wrist extension due to absent or impaired innervation to ECU.
  (2) EDC, EI, EDM: MCP extension.
  (3) EPB, EPL, APL: thumb extension.
c. Motor loss: high lesion at the level of the humerus.
  (1) All of the above, including ECRB, ECRL, and brachioradialis.
  (2) If level of axilla, loss of triceps: elbow extension.
d. Functional loss.
  (1) Inability to extend digits to release objects.
  (2) Difficulty manipulating objects.
e. Deformity.
  (1) Wrist drop (Figure 6-12).
f. OT intervention.
  (1) Dynamic extension orthosis.
  (2) ROM.
  (3) Sensory re-education if needed.
  (4) Instruct in home program.
  (5) Activity modification.
  (6) Neuromuscular electrical stimulation (NMES) to aide in muscle re-education.

Rotator Cuff Tendonitis

1. Anatomy of the rotator cuff.
  a. Supraspinatus.
    (1) Function: abduction and flexion.
  b. Infraspinatus and teres minor.
    (1) Function: external rotation.
  c. Subscapularis.
    (1) Function: internal rotation.
  d. The rotator cuff functions together to control the head of the humerus in the glenoid fossa.

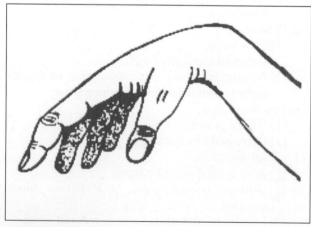

Figure 6-12 **Wrist Drop: Due to injury of the radial nerve.**

Darlington, Vicki, OTR/L, CHT. Reprinted with permission.

e. Site of impingement: coracoacromial arch (acromion, coracoacromial ligament, and coracoid process).
2. Etiology.
  a. Repetitive overuse.
  b. Curved or hook acromion.
  c. Weakness of the rotator cuff.
  d. Weakness of the scapula musculature.
  e. Ligament and capsule tightness.
  f. Trauma.
3. OT conservative intervention.
  a. Activity modification: avoid above shoulder level activities until pain subsides.
  b. Educate in sleeping posture: avoid sleeping with arm overhead or combined adduction and internal rotation.
  c. Decrease pain: positioning, modalities, and rest.
  d. Restore pain-free ROM.
  e. Strengthening: below shoulder level.
  f. Occupation- and role-specific training.
4. Surgical interventions.
  a. Arthroscopic surgery.
  b. Open repair: small, medium, large, and massive tears.
5. OT postoperative intervention.
  a. Begin with PROM (may be initiated anytime from 0 to 6 weeks); progress to AAROM/AROM (commonly initiated from 6–8 weeks).
    (1) Patients will be placed in a sling or abduction orthosis to be worn in between exercises.

> **CAUTION:** The surgeon will determine when exercise should begin based on the size of the tear and tension of the repair site. The occupational therapist must communicate with the surgeon about when exercise can be initiated and what types of exercise should be used.

  b. Decrease pain: begin with ice, progress to heat.
  c. Strengthening: begin with isometrics, progress to isotonic; below shoulder level usually begins 8–10 weeks.
  d. Activity modification: light ADL and meaningful role activities; progress as tolerated.
  e. Leisure and work activities at 12 weeks postoperative (Maher & Mendonca, 2021).

Adhesive Capsulitis

1. Also known as frozen shoulder.
2. Stages.
  a. Freezing: shoulder becomes painful at end ranges.
  b. Frozen: less pain, but loss of motion; develops capsular pattern.
  c. Thawing: pain subsides and ROM gradually returns.

3. Restricted passive shoulder range of motion.
   a. Capsular pattern: greatest limitation is external rotation, then abduction, internal rotation, and flexion.
4. Anatomy: glenohumeral ligaments and joint capsule.
5. Etiology.
   a. Inflammation and immobility.
   b. Linked to diabetes mellitus and Parkinson's disease.
6. OT conservative intervention.
   a. Freezing stage.
      (1) Address pain through ice packs, E-Stim, and positioning.
      (2) Gentle pain free A/PROM: try to maintain functional movements such as reaching to small of back or behind head.
      (3) Educate in a home exercise program (HEP) that includes gentle exercises such as table glides and pain free functional movements.
   b. Frozen stage.
      (1) Can use hot packs to begin session and then conclude with ice.
      (2) Continue A/PROM and can begin gentle pain-free stretching.
      (3) Continue HEP to increase ROM (e.g., functional tasks, cane exercises, wall walking, table glides).
   c. Thawing stage.
      (1) Continue as above with more emphasis on stretching.
      (2) Focus is on restoring ROM and function (Butler, 2020).
7. Surgical interventions: manipulation and arthroscopic surgery.
8. OT postoperative intervention.
   a. PROM immediately following surgery.
   b. Pain relief: use of modalities.
   c. Encourage use of extremity for all ADL and role activities.

Shoulder Dislocations

1. Anterior dislocation most common.
2. Etiology.
   a. Trauma.
   b. Repetitive overuse.
3. OT intervention.
   a. Regain ROM: avoid combined abduction and external rotation with anterior dislocation.
   b. Pain-free ADL and role activities.
   c. Strengthen rotator cuff.

 ## Arthritis

Definition

1. An inflammation of a joint or joints.

Types

1. Rheumatoid arthritis (RA).
   a. Systemic, symmetrical, and affects many joints.
      (1) Most commonly attacks the small joints of the hands.
      (2) Characterized by remissions and exacerbations.
      (3) Begins in the acute phase as an inflammatory process of the synovial lining.
   b. Etiology is unknown, but there are two main theories.
      (1) Infection theory.
      (2) Autoimmune theory.
   c. Symptoms.
      (1) Pain.
      (2) Stiffness.
      (3) Limited range of motion.
      (4) Fatigue.
      (5) Weight loss.
      (6) Limited ADL status, diminished ability to perform role activities.
      (7) Inflammation/swelling.
      (8) Social isolation.
      (9) Deformities.
   d. Types of deformities common with RA.
      (1) Ulnar drift and subluxation of the MCP joints.
      (2) Boutonniere deformity: flexion of the PIP joint and hyperextension of DIP joint (Figure 6-13).
      (3) Swan neck deformity: hyperextension of the PIP joint and flexion of DIP joint (Figure 6-14).
      (4) Zig zag deformity (Deshaies, 2018).
2. Osteoarthritis (OA).
   a. Degenerative joint disease.
      (1) Not systemic but wear and tear.
      (2) Commonly affects large weightbearing joints.
      (3) Attacks hyaline cartilage.
   b. Etiology.
      (1) Genetic.
      (2) Trauma.

Chapter 6

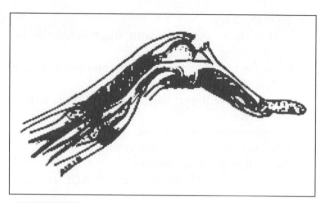

Figure 6-13   Boutonniere Deformity.

Darlington, Vicki, OTR/L, CHT. Reprinted with permission.

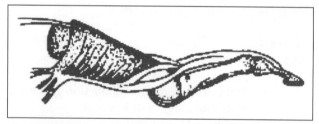

Figure 6-14   Swan Neck Deformity.

Darlington, Vicki, OTR/L, CHT. Reprinted with permission.

    (3) Cumulative trauma.
    (4) Endocrine and metabolic diseases.
  c. Symptoms.
    (1) Pain.
    (2) Stiffness.
    (3) Limited ROM.
    (4) Bone spurs.
  d. Types of bone spurs.
    (1) Heberden's nodes at the DIP joints.
    (2) Bouchard's nodes at the PIP joints.

Occupational Therapy Evaluation

> **EXAM HINT:** The NBCOT® OTR® exam content outline states that the task of identifying the "impact of body functions and body structures on occupational performance" (NBCOT®, 2022, p. 3) is essential to entry-level practice. Thus, the application of knowledge about the presenting symptoms of RA and OA described previously and the following assessment approaches will be required to correctly answer NBCOT® exam items about the evaluation of persons with arthritis.

1. Occupational profile.
2. ROM.
  a. Gentle AROM and/or PROM: no pain.
  b. Note deformities and nodules.
3. Muscle strength.
  a. Avoid muscle testing unless requested by the physician.
  b. Document strength in relation to function.
4. Grip strength: use sphygmomanometer or bulb dynamometer.
5. ADL and role activities: document if ADL and role activity deficits are related to pain, limitation in motion, deformity, weakness, or fatigue.
6. Pain: complete a pain profile.
7. Edema: volumeter or tape measure.
8. Chapter 11 provides detailed information about the above biomechanical evaluation methods.

Occupational Therapy Intervention

> **EXAM HINT:** The NBCOT® OTR® exam content outline identifies the task of incorporating "preparatory techniques, activities, and modalities as an adjunct to interventions to promote healing and enhance engagement in occupation-based activities" (NBCOT®, 2022, p. 7) and knowledge of "adaptive and preventive strategies for supporting optimal engagement in occupation . . . (including) . . . joint protection, task simplification (and) energy conservation" (NBCOT®, 2022, p. 9) and the "types and functions of immobilization, mobilization, and restriction orthoses for managing specific conditions and congenital anomalies across the life span" (NBCOT®, 2022, p. 10) as essential for competent and safe practice. The application of knowledge about the following interventions can help you correctly answer NBCOT® Domain 3 exam items about intervention management for persons with arthritis.

1. Orthotics.
  a. Resting hand orthosis in the acute stage.
  b. Wrist orthosis only if arthritis specific to the wrist.
  c. Ulnar drift orthosis to prevent ulnar drift deformity of the MCP joints.
  d. Swan neck deformity: silver rings, 3-point oval 8 orthosis™, or digital dorsal orthosis in slight PIP flexion.
  e. Boutonniere deformity: silver rings, 3-point oval 8 orthosis™, or PIP extension orthosis.

f. Dynamic MCP extension orthosis with radial pull for postoperative MCP arthroplasties.
   (1) Some surgeons may order a night resting orthosis.
g. Hand base thumb orthosis for CMC arthritis.

2. Joint protection techniques.
3. Energy conservation techniques.
4. Pain management.
5. ROM.
   a. Gentle AROM and/or PROM, depending on the person's joint stability, deformity, and pain.

> **CAUTION:** All exercises should be pain free.

6. Physical agent modalities.
   a. Physical agent modalities are effective in decreasing pain and swelling.
   b. Fluidotherapy and hot packs can be used before exercise but avoid using them during the inflammatory stage.
   c. Paraffin is recommended for the hands.

d. Cold packs can be used during inflammatory stage. They are effective for decreasing pain and swelling; however, many individuals have difficulty tolerating the cold (Crites & Samuel, 2021).

7. Strengthening.
   a. Avoid during inflammatory stage.
   b. Gentle strengthening while avoiding positions of deformity.
   c. Strengthen through functional activities.
8. Chapter 11 provides detailed information about these biomechanical intervention approaches.
9. Purposeful and occupation-based activities.
   a. Joint protection and energy conservation techniques should be incorporated. Refer to Chapter 11.
   b. Adaptive equipment should be provided to prevent deformity, decrease stress on small joints, and extend reach. Refer to Chapter 15.
   c. Chapter 15 provides detailed information about intervention approaches to enable occupational performance.

Osteogenesis Imperfecta (OI)[1]

Etiology and Prognosis

1. Disorder caused by the dysfunction of one of several genes responsible for producing collagen for the development of bone structure and strength.
2. Present at birth and a lifelong condition without a cure.
3. The severity of OI can vary greatly.
   a. OI can be a mild disorder or a serious one with severe complications.

Signs and Symptoms

1. Malformed bones.
   a. Bowing of the long bones.
   b. Short stature and/or small body.
   c. Triangular shaped face.
   d. Barrel-shaped rib cage and co-morbid breathing difficulty.

   e. Curvature of the spine.
   f. Deformity of the hip joint (coxa vera).
2. Brittle bones that fracture easily.
   a. Frequently broken bones, mostly before puberty.
3. Developmental growth problems.
4. Loose joints.
5. Whites of the eyes (sclera) look blue, purple, or gray.
6. Brittle, misshapen, or discolored teeth.
7. Hearing loss.

Classification

1. OI is classified as types I to VIII which include mild, moderate, and severe manifestations.
   a. Skeletal anomalies and co-morbidities vary between types.
2. The eight main types of OI are classified by the genes that are involved.
   a. Type I: mild symptoms.
   b. Types IV, V, and VI: moderate symptoms.
   c. Types II, III, VII, and VIII: severe symptoms; type II is the most severe.

---

[1] Cynthia H August and Marge E. Moffett Boyd contributed this section on osteogenesis imperfecta.

Diagnosis

1. Family and medical history.
2. Results from a physical examination and medical tests including bone density, x-rays, and blood tests.

Medical Management

1. Care for broken bones.
   a. Refer to this Chapter's section on the medical treatment of fractures.
2. Dental care for brittle teeth.
3. Medication for pain.
4. Surgery.
   a. Fix bone malformations.
   b. Prevent bone malformations.
   c. "Rodding" in which metal rods are put inside the long bones.

Occupational Therapy Evaluation

1. Developmental evaluation of childhood occupations and occupational performance (ADL, play, education).
2. Environmental risk factors.
3. Strength and endurance.
4. Joint flexibility and range of motion.
5. Refer to this Chapter's sections on OT evaluation for fractures and the assessment of pain.

Occupational Therapy Intervention

1. Family, caregiver, and teacher education about proper handling, positioning, activity adaptations, environmental modifications, and the need to observe all safety precautions.
2. Activity adaptation and assistive device prescription and fabrication to facilitate safe participation in daily occupations. Refer to Chapter 15.
3. Environmental modifications to maintain safety. Refer to Chapter 16.
4. Preventive positioning and protective splinting/padding. Refer to Chapter 11.
5. Weightbearing activities to facilitate bone growth and activities to increase muscle strength (e.g., exercise: swimming/aquatic therapy, walking). Refer to Chapter 11.
6. Health education to promote a healthy lifestyle.
7. Developmental activities associated with childhood occupations.
8. Refer to this Chapter's section on OT intervention for fractures and musculoskeletal pain.

> **EXAM HINT:** In the NBCOT® OTR® exam content outline Domain 3 Select and Manage Interventions comprises 38% of the exam. This domain focuses on the therapist's responsibility for selecting and implementing "interventions to promote healing and enhance engagement in occupation-based activities" (NBCOT®, 2022, p. 7). The application of knowledge about the above interventions for children with osteogenesis imperfecta and the interventions described in the following section for children with arthrogryposis multiplex congenita can help you effectively determine the correct answers to Domain 3 exam items that address intervention management for children with these conditions.

 # Arthrogryposis Multiplex Congenita (AMC)[2]

Diagnosis and Etiology

1. Arthrogryposis refers to congenital joint contractures. When there are two or more joints with congenital contractions, a child may be diagnosed with AMC.
   a. AMC can be detected in utero via ultrasound or at birth.

2. The specific causes of AMC are not fully known.
   a. AMC is thought to be related to decreased movement during fetal development which may be caused by low amniotic fluid and/or inadequate room in utero.
   b. AMC is not a discrete diagnosis; it can be a component of other conditions and disorders with diverse causes that have the common feature of multiple congenital joint contractures.

---

[2] Cynthia H August and Rita P. Fleming-Castaldy contributed to this section on arthrogryposis multiplex congenita.

Signs and Symptoms

1. The presence of multiple joint contractures affecting two or more areas of the body at birth.
2. Because AMC can result from many different medical conditions, the signs and symptoms associated with AMC can vary greatly in severity and range depending on the underlying condition. They can include the following.
    a. Weakness: muscles of affected limbs may be atrophied or underdeveloped.
    b. Limited or no ROM in affected joints.
        (1) Persons with this condition typically have limited functional use of their hands and digits.
    c. Position of rest for the upper extremities tends to be shoulders internally rotated, elbows extended, and wrists flexed.
    d. Position of rest for the lower extremities tends to be internally rotated, flexed hips and clubfeet.
3. Related problems include congenital heart defects, spinal defects, torticollis, and involvement of the diaphragm.
    a. Scoliosis that is not typically responsive to bracing often develops during childhood.
4. AMC signs and symptoms may be stable, mildly progressive, or may improve depending on the person's response to therapy.
5. Persons with AMC often have typical cognitive development.

Medical Management

1. AMC is non-progressive and cannot be reversed or cured; therefore, medical management is mostly limited to non-invasive therapies such as physical and occupational therapy to increase and/or maintain joint ROM.
2. Orthopedic surgeries are used conservatively to release tendons, lengthen limbs, and reduce joint contractures.

Occupational Therapy Evaluation

1. Range-of-motion and functional muscle strength.
2. Mobility, positioning, and movement.
3. Ability to participate in occupations at home and in school, work, and community settings including the assessment of the person's environmental contexts.
4. Comprehensive developmental assessment.

Occupational Therapy Intervention

1. Gentle range-of-motion and weight bearing exercise to maintain joint integrity and build muscle strength.
2. Environmental modifications and adaptations that enable access to occupations.
    a. For example: provide a child who has limited upper extremity use, but sufficient agility with their feet, sufficient space to access and handle utensils, writing tools, and other educational tools and materials with their feet.
3. Training in the use of mobility devices as necessary to maximize participation in all contexts.
4. Caregiver education in the use of modifications and adaptations that maximize the child's independence and participation.

 # Hip Fractures

Etiology

1. Trauma.
2. Osteoporosis.
3. Pathological fractures (i.e., cancer).

Types

1. Femoral neck fracture.
2. Intertrochanteric fracture.
3. Subtrochanteric fracture.

Medical Management

1. Closed reduction for minimally displaced fractures.
2. ORIF.
3. Joint replacement.

Occupational Therapy Evaluation

1. Review precautions and weightbearing status before initiating evaluation.
2. Occupational role requirements and expectations.

3. ADL: focus on dressing, bathing, and transfers.
4. ROM and strength of upper extremities.
5. Conduct other assessments as needed (e.g., cognitive).
6. Chapters 11–16 provide detailed information about evaluation methods and approaches.

> **EXAM HINT:** In the NBCOT® OTR® exam content outline, knowledge of "the impact of body functions and body structures on occupational performance" (NBCOT®, 2022, p. 3) and the task of synthesizing "assessment results to . . . establish a client-centered intervention plan" (NBCOT®, 2022, p. 5) are identified as essential for competent and safe practice. The application of knowledge about the previous evaluation foci and the following intervention foci can help you effectively determine the correct answers to NBCOT® exam items about working with persons with hip fractures.

Occupational Therapy Intervention

1. Bed mobility and bedside ADL. Refer to Chapter 15.
2. Upper extremity strengthening. Refer to Chapter 11.

3. Functional ambulation and transfers with appropriate weightbearing status and appropriate ambulation device (i.e., walker, crutches). Refer to Chapter 16.
   a. The type of ambulation device is determined by the person's weightbearing status.
4. Instruct in and practice use of assistive devices for use in the home (e.g., shower chair, elevated commode seat). Refer to Chapters 15 and 16.
5. Practice occupation-based activities (e.g., small meal preparation) using proper weightbearing status and ambulatory device. Refer to Chapter 15.

> **CAUTION:** Weightbearing status, the amount of ROM allowed at the hip, and time frames for beginning OT intervention will be determined by the surgeon (Maher & Mendonca, 2021).

Complications

1. Avascular necrosis.
2. Nonunion.
3. Degenerative joint disease.

Total Hip Arthroplasty

Etiology

1. Trauma, from hip fracture.
2. Disease, most often arthritis; surgery is then elective.

Types

1. Total hip joint implant: replaces acetabulum and femoral head.
2. Hemiarthroplasty: partial hip replacement. Replaces femoral head.
3. Refer to Figure 6-15.

Surgical Procedures

1. Cemented or uncemented.
2. Anterolateral or posterolateral.

Occupational Therapy Evaluation

> **CAUTION:** Review precautions and weightbearing status before initiating evaluation.

1. Complete an occupational profile.
2. Assess ADL; focus on dressing, bathing, and transfers. Refer to Chapter 15.
3. Assess ROM and strength of upper extremities. Refer to Chapter 11.
4. Conduct other assessments as needed (e.g., cognitive).
5. Chapters 11–16 provide detailed information about evaluation methods and approaches.

> **EXAM HINT:** In the NBCOT® OTR® exam content outline, knowledge of the "expected patterns, progressions, and prognoses associated with conditions that limit occupational performance . . . (including) secondary complications" (NBCOT®, 2022, p. 3) and "considerations for selecting, preparing, and adapting the intervention technique . . . and environment . . . to support optimal engagement and promote goal achievement" (NBCOT®, 2022, p. 8) are identified as essential for competent and safe practice. The application of knowledge about the above evaluation foci and the following interventions can help you effectively determine the correct answers to NBCOT® exam items about working with persons with total hip replacements.

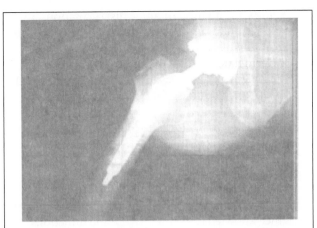

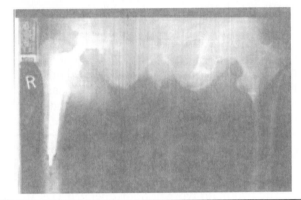

Figure 6-15   **Hybrid cemented total hip arthroplasty (Biomet Integral Design, Warsaw, IN).**

From Maxey, L., & Magnusson, J. (2006). Rehabilitation for the postsurgical orthopedic patient (p. 173). Mosby Publications. Reprinted with permission.

Occupational Therapy Intervention

1. Educate the individual in hip precautions. Refer to Box 6-1.

> **RED FLAG:** If the posterolateral precautions are not followed, a dislocation could result.

2. Instruct in and practice use of long-handled equipment. Refer to Chapter 15.
3. Provide transfer training. Refer to Chapter 16.
   a. Practice with tub bench, raised toilet seat.
   b. Practice car transfers.
   c. Practice bed-to-chair transfers.
4. Practice occupation-based activities (e.g., small meal preparation) using proper weightbearing status and ambulatory device (Maher & Mendonca, 2021).
   a. Refer to Chapter 15.

BOX 6-1 ▷ Hip Precautions

- **Posterolateral**
  - Do not flex beyond 90°.
  - Do not adduct or cross legs.
  - Do not internally rotate.
  - Do not pivot at hip.
  - Sit only on raised chair and raised toilet seat.
  - Transfer sit to stand by keeping operated hip in slight abduction and extended out in front.
- **Anterolateral**
  - Do not externally rotate.
  - Do not extend hip.
  - Precautions vary for anterior total hip arthroplasty (THA).
  - Some surgeons follow a no restriction protocol.

 Amputations

Etiology

1. Congenital, peripheral vascular disease, trauma, cancer, and infection.

Classification of Amputations

1. Upper extremity level of amputation.
   a. Forequarter: loss of clavicle, scapula, and entire upper extremity.
   b. Shoulder disarticulation: loss of entire upper extremity.
   c. Transhumeral short.
   d. Transhumeral long.
   e. Elbow disarticulation: amputation of the upper extremity distal to the elbow joint.
   f. Transradial short.
   g. Transradial long.
   h. Wrist disarticulation: amputation distal to the wrist joint. Loss of entire hand.
   i. Transmetacarpal.

j. Finger amputation: amputation of digit(s) at any level.

k. Refer to Figure 6-16.

2. Lower extremity (LE) level of amputation.

a. Hemipelvectomy: amputation of half of pelvis and entire LE.

b. Hip disarticulation: amputation at the hip joint. Loss of the entire LE.

c. Above-knee amputation (transfemoral): amputation above knee at any level on the thigh.

d. Knee disarticulation: amputation at the knee joint.

e. Below-knee amputation (transtibial): amputation below knee at any level on the calf. This is the most common.

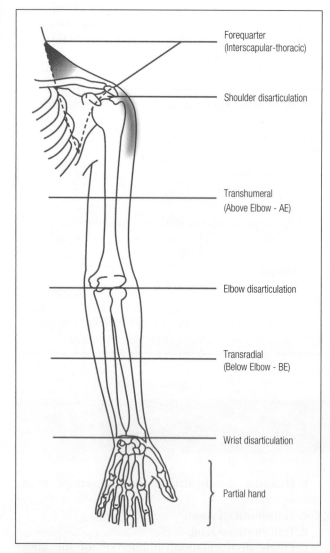

Figure 6-16 **Levels of Upper Extremity Amputation.**

Walters, L.S. (2021). Amputation and prosthetics. In D.P. Dirette & S.A. Gutman (Eds.), Occupational therapy for physical dysfunction (8th ed., p. 923). Wolters Kluwer. Reprinted with permission.

f. Syme's amputation or ankle disarticulation.

g. Ray amputation (amputation of the entire digit from the metatarsal and distal).

h. Transmetatarsal amputation.

i. Complete phalanges: amputation of toe(s) (Orr, et al., 2018; Walters, 2021).

Prostheses and Prosthetic Terminal Devices (TDs)

EXAM HINT: In the NBCOT® OTR® exam content outline, knowledge of the "types and functions of prosthetic devices for upper and lower extremity amputations" (NBCOT®, 2022, p. 11) is identified as essential for competent and safe practice. The application of knowledge about the different types of prosthetics and terminal devices described in this section can help you determine the correct answer for NBCOT® exam items about working with individuals who can benefit from and desire a prosthetic.

1. Body-powered prostheses: use specific muscles to place tension on the cable that opens or closes the TD.

a. The two main types of body-operated TDs are the hook and the prosthetic hand.

(1) Both hooks and hands are operated in one of two ways.

(a) Voluntary closing (VC): hook remains opened until tension is placed on cable and then it closes.

(b) Voluntary opening (VO): hook remains closed until tension is placed on cable and then it opens. This is prescribed more than the VC (Walters, 2021).

(2) Hook TDs: used to perform functional activities. Types include the following.

(a) A hook with slanted fingertips: easier for the user to see during functional tasks.

(b) A lyre shape hook: allows for a cylindrical grasp.

(c) Aluminum: less weight, used mainly for lighter functional tasks.

(d) Stainless steel: sturdier, better for heavier outdoor work.

(3) Hand TDs: used for cosmetic appearance and have limited pinch force (Orr et al., 2018).

b. Control of body-powered prostheses.

(1) Transradial prosthesis: uses humeral flexion and scapular abduction.

(2) Transhumeral prosthesis: uses humeral flexion and scapular abduction and scapula depression, shoulder extension, and abduction to lock and unlock elbow.

(3) Shoulder disarticulation: uses chest expansion to control the TD.

(4) Refer to Table 6-1.

c. Box 6-2 outlines the advantages and disadvantages of body-powered prostheses.

2. Myoelectric (electrically powered) prostheses: muscle contractions of two different muscle groups are used to control the TD.

a. The types of terminal devices are the hook and hand.

(1) The electric hook allows for pinch and fine motor manipulations including opposition.

(2) Hands are used for cosmetic appearance. Main types include the following.

(a) The Sensor Hand can open and close and has 3-point pinch.

(b) Multi-articulating hands have multiple grasp patterns that allow for increased functional use.

b. Control of myoelectric/electrically powered prostheses.

(1) Transradial prosthesis: uses wrist flexors and extensors.

(2) Transhumeral prosthesis: uses biceps and triceps.

(3) Shoulder disarticulation: uses pectoralis major or infraspinatus.

c. Box 6-3 outlines the advantages and disadvantages of myoelectric prostheses.

3. Hybrid prosthesis: combination of body powered and electrically powered.

a. Most common for elbow or above elbow amputations.

b. Box 6-4 outlines the advantages and disadvantages of hybrid prostheses.

4. Passive prosthesis: static.

a. Used for cosmetic appearance; can be passively adjusted to assist with carrying and grasping items.

Table 6-1

Amputation

LEVEL	TERMINAL DEVICE OR DIGIT OPERATION	ELBOW COMPONENT OPERATION
Partial finger	PIP or MP flexion and extension	NA
Partial hand	Wrist flexion or extension	NA
Wrist disarticulation and transradial amputation	Humeral flexion and scapular protraction	NA
Elbow disarticulation and transhumeral	Humeral flexion and unilateral or biscapular protraction. Incorporating chest expansion may be used if necessary.	Combination of scapular depression, and humeral extension and abduction to lock/unlock elbow.

*MP, metacarpophalangeal; NA, not applicable; PIP, proximal interphalangeal

Reference: Walters, L.S. (2021). Amputations and prosthetics. In D. P. Dirette & S. A. Gutman (Eds.), Occupational therapy for physical dysfunction (8th ed., p. 932). Wolters Kluwer. Reprinted with permission.

BOX 6-2 ○ Body-Powered Prostheses: Advantages and Disadvantages

- **Advantages**
  - Durable and can be exposed to environmental conditions (e.g., water and dirt).
  - Provides proprioceptive feedback.
  - Lower maintenance costs than myoelectric prostheses.

- **Disadvantages**
  - Restrictive harness.
  - Decreased grip force compared to myoelectric options.
  - Force is exerted on the residual limb.
  - Can be difficult to control for high levels of amputations.

Reference: Orr, A. E., Glover, J.S., & Cook, C.L. (2018). Amputations and prosthetics. In H. M. Pendleton & W. Schultz-Krohn (Eds.), Pedretti's occupational therapy: Practice skills for physical dysfunction (8th ed., p. 1090). Elsevier. Reprinted with permission.

BOX 6-3 ○ Myoelectric Prostheses: Advantages and Disadvantages

- **Advantages**
  - Improved cosmesis.
  - Increased and proportional grip force.
  - Minimal or no harnessing.
  - Provides a larger functional work envelope for use.
  - Minimal effort needed to control.
  - Can be fitted early in rehabilitation phase.

- **Disadvantages**
  - Increased cost.
  - Frequency of maintenance and repair for battery.
  - Lack of sensory feedback.
  - Susceptible to interference from moisture or other environmental factors.
  - Increased overall weight.

Reference: Orr, A. E., Glover, J.S., & Cook, C.L. (2018). Amputations and prosthetics. In H. M. Pendleton & W. Schultz-Krohn (Eds.), Pedretti's occupational therapy: Practice skills for physical dysfunction (8th ed., p. 1091). Elsevier. Reprinted with permission.

b. Box 6-5 outlines the advantages and disadvantages of passive prostheses.

5. Activity-specific prosthesis: no harness or control cable.
   a. Designed to be used for specific work and leisure tasks.
   b. Can be used interchangeably with a body powered or myoelectric prosthesis.
   c. Box 6-6 outlines the advantages and disadvantages of activity-specific prostheses.

BOX 6-4 ▶ Hybrid Prostheses: Advantages and Disadvantages

- **Advantages**
  - Simultaneous control of elbow and wrist or terminal device.
  - Less weight than an entirely electrically powered prosthesis.
  - Increased grip force.
- **Disadvantages**
  - Harness is required for operation of elbow.
  - May be difficult to operate with a short transhumeral or higher amputation because of the force required to operate the elbow.

Reference: Orr, A. E., Glover, J.S., & Cook, C.L. (2018). Amputations and prosthetics. In H. M. Pendleton & W. Schultz-Krohn (Eds.), Pedretti's occupational therapy: Practice skills for physical dysfunction (8th ed., p. 1091). Elsevier. Reprinted with permission.

BOX 6-5 ▶ Passive Prosthesis: Advantages and Disadvantages

- **Advantages**
  - No harnessing or control cables.
  - Provides cosmetic restoration and positive body image.
  - Low maintenance.
  - Lightweight.
  - Digits can be positioned for static grasp or opposition.
- **Disadvantages**
  - Does not provide active grasping function.
  - Cosmetic covers made of latex or polyvinyl chloride (PVC) can stain easily.

Reference: Orr, A. E., Glover, J.S., & Cook, C.L. (2018). Amputations and prosthetics. In H. M. Pendleton & W. Schultz-Krohn (Eds.), Pedretti's occupational therapy: Practice skills for physical dysfunction (8th ed., p. 1091). Elsevier. Reprinted with permission.

BOX 6-6 ▶ Activity-Specific Prostheses: Advantages and Disadvantages

- **Advantages**
  - Allows enhanced function and task-specific participation in a variety of activities.
  - Minimal harness or cabling.
  - Durable and low maintenance.
  - Reduces wear and tear on primary prosthesis.
- **Disadvantages**
  - Does not provide active grasp.
  - Appropriate for specific tasks only, not for a broad range of functions.

Reference: Orr, A. E., Glover, J.S., & Cook, C.L. (2018). Amputations and prosthetics. In H. M. Pendleton & W. Schultz-Krohn (Eds.), Pedretti's occupational therapy: Practice skills for physical dysfunction (8th ed., p. 1092). Elsevier. Reprinted with permission.

Complications of Amputations

CAUTION: The occurrence of the following complications can negatively impact a person's health, impede function, and compromise the safe and effective use of prosthetic devices.

1. Neuromas: nerve endings adhered to scar tissue.
   a. These can be very painful and hypersensitive.
2. Skin breakdown.
3. Phantom limb syndrome: sensation of the presence of the amputated limb.
4. Phantom limb pain: sensation of the presence of the amputated limb but is also painful.
5. Infection.
6. Knee flexion contractures in transtibial amputation.
7. Psychological impairments due to shock/grief (Walters, 2021).

Preprosthetic Intervention

1. Change of dominance activities, if needed.
2. ROM of uninvolved joints.
3. Strengthening of joints proximal to the amputation.
4. Prepare limb for a prosthesis.
5. Desensitization.
6. Wrapping to shape and shrink the residual limb. Refer to Figure 6-17.
   a. Wrap distal to proximal.
   b. Tension should decrease with proximal wrapping.
7. ADL training, including education in skin care.

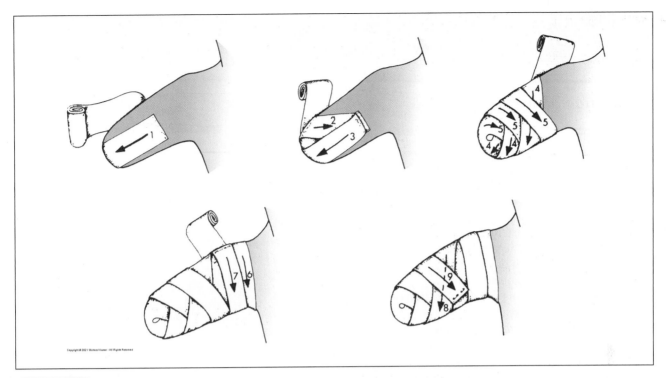

Figure 6-17 **Wrapping Technique for Transhumeral Amputation.** Repeat diagonal turns as necessary to cover the limb with no constriction.

Walters, L.S. (2021). Amputations and prosthetics. In D. P. Dirette & S. A. Gutman (Eds.), Occupational therapy for physical dysfunction (8th ed., p. 929). Wolters Kluwer. Reprinted with permission.

8. Education in decubiti prevention (e.g., weight shifting). Refer to Chapter 9.
9. Supportive counseling to facilitate adjustment.
10. Individualize treatment to enhance physical and psychological adjustment.
   a. Determination of the most appropriate prosthesis and TD is based on the person's age, amputation level, cognitive ability, interests, roles, and functional goals.
   b. The earlier a person is fitted for a prosthesis, the better is their acceptance and functional use of the device (Orr et al., 2018; Walters, 2021).

Prosthetic Interventions

EXAM HINT: The NBCOT® OTR® exam content outline identifies knowledge of "client-centered education and training methods for the safe and effective use of . . . prosthetic devices" (NBCOT®, 2022, p. 11) as essential for competent and safe practice. Based on this requirement, it is likely that the NBCOT® exam will include items about the occupational therapist's role in prosthetic training.

1. Functional training with prosthesis.
   a. Practice engagement in activities of interest and occupational role activities.

2. Donning and doffing the prosthesis: residual limb sock, prosthetic liner, prosthetic socket and/or harness.
3. Increase prosthetic wearing tolerance: starts out 15–30 minutes 3x daily and increases as tolerated.
4. Most important is teaching the person to do skin checks before and after wearing the prosthesis.
   a. Have the person watch for excessive perspiration and clean residual limb daily.
5. Individualize treatment to enhance physical and psychological adjustment (Orr et al., 2018).

Treatment for LE Amputations

1. Wrapping to shape the residual limb and decrease swelling.
   a. The alternative is using different size shrinkers.
2. Desensitization.
3. Strengthening of the UE with the focus on the triceps.
4. Transfer (stand pivot) training and functional ambulation (often using a walker).
5. ADL training; LE dressing is the most difficult.
6. Standing tolerance.
7. Wheelchair mobility and residual limb support (to prevent knee flexion contracture).
8. Chapters 11–16 provide detailed information about the above intervention methods and approaches (Orr et al., 2018).

Burns

Classification

1. Superficial: involves the superficial epidermis only.
   a. Minimal pain and edema, but no blisters.
   b. Healing time is three to seven days (e.g., sunburn).
2. Superficial partial-thickness burn.
   a. Involves the epidermis and upper portion of dermis (e.g., severe sunburn or radiation burn).
   b. Appearance: red, blistering, and wet.
   c. Painful, no grafting necessary, heals on its own.
   d. Healing time is 7–14 days.
3. Deep partial-thickness burn.
   a. Involves the epidermis and deep portion of dermis, hair follicles, and sweat glands.
   b. Appearance: red, blotchy and white.
   c. Severe pain at burn site.
   d. Sensation may be impaired.
   e. Healing time is 21–35 days. May require skin grafts to hasten healing and minimize hypertrophic scarring.
   f. Because of the depth of the burn and the potential for hypertrophic scarring, deformities may develop.

> CAUTION: Potential to convert to full-thickness burn due to infection.

4. Full-thickness burn.
   a. Epidermis and dermis are completely damaged; hair follicles, sweat glands, and nerve endings also involved.
   b. Appearance: white, waxy, leathery, and nonelastic.
   c. Sensation is absent.
   d. Hypertrophic scar.
   e. Healing time can take months.
   f. Full-thickness burns require surgery; i.e., skin grafts (Kurakazu & Hira, 2018; Ozlie, 2021).
5. Full-thickness burns with complications: electrical burns involve destruction of nerve(s) along their pathway and damage to fat, muscle, and bone.
6. The rule of nines is a method for assessing burn wound size.
   a. Refer to Figure 6-18.

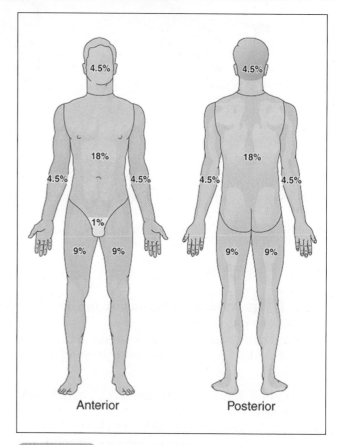

Figure 6-18   **Rule of Nines.**

Occupational Therapy Evaluation and Intervention

> EXAM HINT: In the NBCOT® OTR® exam content outline, the task of identifying the "impact of body functions and body structures on occupational performance" (NBCOT®, 2022, p. 3) and knowledge of "considerations for selecting, preparing, and adapting the intervention technique to support optimal engagement and promote goal achievement" (NBCOT®, 2022, p. 8) are identified as essential for competent and safe practice. The application of knowledge about the following evaluation and intervention foci can help you effectively determine the correct answers to NBCOT® exam items about working with persons with burns.

1. The focus of occupational therapy evaluation and intervention depends on the phase of burn recovery.
2. Emergent phase: from initial burn injury to 72 hours later.

a. The focus during this stage is medical management to stabilize the patient.

b. Occupational therapy may not be included in this phase.

  (1) OT may be ordered for positioning and orthotic fabrication. Refer to subsequent section and Table 6-2.

    (a) Pillows for elevation to decrease swelling of the distal upper extremities can also be used.

3. Acute phase: follows the emergent phase and continues until wounds are closed.

a. Depending on the severity of the burns and the number of grafting surgeries this phase can last from 1 week to months.

b. The period after surgery for a skin graft is known as the perioperative period.

c. Occupational therapy evaluation includes the following.

  (1) Occupational profile.

  (2) ROM.

  (3) Cognitive screen.

  (4) Pain.

  (5) Sensation, when wounds are healed.

  (6) Strength, when wounds are healed.

  (7) ADL, when possible.

d. Occupational therapy intervention includes the following.

  (1) Fabrication of anti-deformity orthoses as needed (e.g., for skin grafted areas). Refer to subsequent section and Table 6-2.

    (a) The person stays immobilized in the orthosis/orthoses for 5–14 days (as per the surgeon and graft type).

  (2) ROM is contraindicated during this period. ROM is resumed when the surgeon/burn team determine the stability of the graft.

  (3) Wound care may require debridement, sterile whirlpool, and dressing changes. Refer to Chapter 9.

  (4) Gentle AROM and PROM to the individual's tolerance. AROM is preferred, and can be addressed using functional activities.

> **CAUTION:** ROM is contraindicated following a skin graft and if exposed tendons or fractures are present.

  (5) Edema control: elevation and AROM.

  (6) ADL: not the focus at this stage due to the need to prioritize medical issues.

    (a) Basic ADL, such as feeding with a built-up utensil, may be started.

  (7) Patient and family education (Ozelie, 2021).

4. Rehabilitation phase: follows the acute phase and continues until scar maturation.

a. Occupational therapy evaluation: refer to the acute phase.

b. Occupational therapy intervention: the focus is to return the person to their prior level of functioning and includes the following.

  (1) Pain free A/PROM to prevent contractures. Passive stretching to end range (blanching and no pain).

> **CAUTION:** Overstretching can lead to tearing of tissue/skin.

  (2) Strengthening: using therapeutic exercises and functional, purposeful, occupation-based activities.

  (3) Scar management: once burns/wounds heal they are at risk for developing hypertrophic scar.

    (a) Hypertrophic scar is disorganized collagen that can raise up, appear red, inelastic, and can develop cords; can be very disfiguring.

      • Scarring can continue for 1–2 years after wounds heal.

    (b) A routine for scar management should include the following.

      • Massage: performed several times daily to improve cosmetic appearance and elasticity of the scar.

      • AROM to reorganize disorganized scar tissue.

      • Pressure therapy: refer to Box 6-7.

  (4) Orthotics: continue to monitor orthoses for any needed modifications.

  (5) Sensation: with skin grafts and as wounds heal, the person may experience hypersensitivity.

    (a) Desensitization techniques as described in Chapter 11 should be implemented.

  (6) Occupational role activities and ADL.

  (7) Psychosocial: select activities that are meaningful and that the person will be able to successfully achieve.

    (a) Group therapy for social support (Ozelie, 2021).

BOX 6-7 ⊙ Guidelines for Pressure Therapy

- Once wounds are healed compression can be applied using Tubigrip™ (stockinette with elastic), elastic bandage wraps, Isotoner gloves™ and Coban™ wrap.

- Wearing schedule should start out in two hour intervals and increase as tolerated until wearing is tolerated 23 hours daily.

- Therapy then can progress to the use of custom-made garments.
  - These garments are worn at all times except for bathing.
  - The person should have two sets.

- Custom-made garments are worn for 1–2 years until scars have matured.

- Otoform™ and/or certain foams can be used in areas where the garment is not flush against the skin such as the axilla and web spaces.

- Silicone gel sheets and other silicone products (Ozelie, 2021).

Antideformity Positions Following Burn Injury

1. Refer to Table 6-2.

Hand Orthoses

EXAM HINT: The NBCOT® OTR® exam content outline states that the task of "select, fabricate, and modify orthotic devices, and provide training in the use of orthotic . . . devices to support functional outcomes" (NBCOT®, 2022, p. 10) is essential to entry-level practice and that performance of this task requires knowledge of the "types and functions of immobilization, mobilization, and restriction orthoses for managing specific conditions . . . across the life span" (NBCOT®, 2022, p. 10). The application of knowledge about the following orthoses will be required to determine the correct answer to the NBCOT® exam items about the occupational therapist's role in the selection and fabrication of orthotics for persons with burns.

1. Burns to the hand or dorsal hand.
   a. Wrist in 20°–30° extension.
   b. MCP joints in 70° flexion.
   c. IP joints in full extension.
   d. Thumb abducted and extended (Hock & DeMott, 2021).
2. Burns to the volar surface of the hand which result in flexion contractures: palmar extension orthosis.
   a. Wrist in 0°–30° extension.
   b. MCP joints in neutral to slight extension and abducted (monitor collateral ligaments).
   c. IP joints in full extension.
   d. Thumb abducted and extended.
3. Web space burn.
   a. Web spacer orthosis.

Table 6-2

Anticontracture Positioning by Location of Burn

LOCATION OF BURN	CONTRACTURE TENDENCY	ANTICONTRACTURE POSITIONING AND/OR TYPICAL SPLINT*
Anterior neck	Neck flexion	Remove pillows; use half-mattress to extend the neck; neck extension splint or collar
Axilla	Adduction	120° abduction with slight external rotation; axilla splint or positioning wedges; watch for signs of brachial plexus strain
Anterior elbow	Flexion	Elbow extension splint in 5°–10° flexion
Dorsal wrist	Wrist extension	Wrist support in neutral
Volar wrist	Wrist flexion	Wrist cockup splint in 5°–10° extension
Hand dorsal	Claw hand deformity	Functional hand splint with MP joints 70°–90°, DIP joints fully extended, first web open, thumb in opposition (safe position)
Hand volar	Palmar contracture cupping of hand	Palm extension splint MPs in slight hyperextension
Hip-anterior	Hip flexion	Prone positioning; weights on thigh in supine; knee immobilizers
Knee	Knee flexion	Knee extension positioning and/or splints; prevent external rotation, which may cause peroneal nerve compression
Foot	Foot drop	Ankle at 90° with foot board or splint; watch for signs of heel ulcer

*At the time of publication of this original table, the term splint was used instead of the term orthosis. Orthosis is currently the recognized terminology by the NBCOT® at the time of publication of this book.

MP = metacarpophalangel; DIP = distal interphalangeal.

Pessina, M.A., & Ellis, S.M. (1997). Burn management rehabilitation. The Nursing Clinics of North America, 32(2), 367. Reprinted with permission.

Pain

Definition

1. Personal sensation of hurt that can significantly affect an individual's quality of life.

Types of Pain

1. Acute pain has a recent onset and usually lasts for a short duration.
2. Chronic pain is of a long duration and can lead to depression and prescription drug misuse. Refer to Chapter 7.
3. Myofascial pain is specific to muscles, tendons, or fascia.
   a. Myofascial pain syndrome (MPS).
      (1) Persistent, deep aching pains in muscle, nonarticular in origin.
      (2) Characterized by well-defined, highly sensitive tender spots (trigger points).
4. Fibromyalgia syndrome (FMS) is a musculoskeletal pain and fatigue disorder that can vary in intensity.
   a. Widespread pain accompanied by tenderness of muscles and adjacent soft tissues.
   b. A nonarticular rheumatic disease of unknown origin.
5. Low back pain.
   a. Most common work-related injury.
   b. Location: lumbar lordosis.
   c. Etiology.
      (1) Poor posture: seated and standing.
      (2) Repetitive bending using poor body mechanics.
      (3) Heavy lifting.
      (4) Sleeping with poor posture.
   d. Symptoms.
      (1) Pain.
      (2) Difficulty with self-care activities and other role activities (especially LE activities).
      (3) Difficulty sleeping.

> **EXAM HINT:** In the NBCOT® OTR® exam content outline, the tasks of identifying the "impact of body functions and body structures on occupational performance" (NBCOT®, 2022, p. 3) is identified as essential for competent and safe practice. The application of knowledge about the previously described types, causes, and symptoms of pain and the following assessment foci can help you effectively determine the correct answers to NBCOT® Domain 1 exam items about the evaluation and assessment of pain.

Assessment of Pain

1. When assessing a person with a pain diagnosis and/or a history of chronic pain, a comprehensive pain profile including the following points should be completed.
2. Determine location of pain.
   a. Localized or diffuse.
3. Evaluate intensity of pain.
   a. Pain intensity scale of 0–10 is most commonly used.
   b. Identify the time of day the pain is most intense.
4. Determine the onset and duration of pain.
   a. Gradual or sudden onset.
   b. The length of time pain has been experienced.
5. Description of pain.
   a. Common descriptors include sharp, throbbing, tender, burning, and shooting.
6. Functional assessment of pain.
   a. Pain scales that commonly address function.
      (1) McGill Pain Questionnaire.
      (2) Pain Disability Index.
      (3) Functional Interference Estimate.
7. Refer to pain management section in Chapter 7.

Occupational Therapy Intervention

> **EXAM HINT:** The NBCOT® OTR® exam content outline identifies the task of selecting and implementing "interventions for improving sensory, motor, neurological, and physiological status, considering client condition and current stage of recovery, to support occupational performance" (NBCOT®, 2022, p. 10) and knowledge of "techniques for . . . pain management" (NBCOT®, 2022, p. 10) as essential for competent and safe practice. Based on this requirement and the recognition of OT as a nonpharmacological intervention for pain, it is likely that the NBCOT® exam will include items about the following interventions for pain.

1. Utilize physical agent modalities and massage in preparation for functional activities.
2. Teach proper positioning techniques.
3. Use gentle ROM.
4. Teach relaxation exercises.
5. Utilize proper body mechanics during self-care, leisure, and work activities.
6. Correct environmental factors.

Chapter 6

7. Correct standing and seated posture.
8. Teach proper lifting techniques.
   a. Power and tripod: both for heavy objects.
   b. Golfer's lift: used for activities such as picking up objects off the floor and removing laundry from dryer.
9. Modify activities and provide ADL training and adaptive equipment, as needed.
10. Provide alternative exercise programs (e.g., aquatic therapy, tai chi).
11. Refer to pain management section in Chapter 7.

▶ References

American Society of Hand Therapists. (1992). Clinical assessment recommendations (2nd ed.). The Society, Chicago.

Amini, D. (2020). Hand impairment. In C. M. Wietlisbach (Ed.), Cooper's fundamentals of occupational therapy (3rd ed., pp. 895–921). Elsevier.

Batshaw, M. L., Roizen, N.J., & Lotrecchiano, G.R. (2013). Children with disabilities (7th ed.). Paul H. Brookes.

Bearden, M. D. (2017). Burns. In H. Smith-Gabai & S. E. Holm (Eds.), Occupational therapy in acute care (2nd ed., pp. 571–581). AOTA Press.

Butler, M. (2020). Common shoulder diagnoses. In C. M. Wietlisbach (Ed.), Cooper's fundamentals of occupational therapy (3rd ed., pp. 167–202). Elsevier.

Crites, A., & Samuel, P. S. (2021). Rheumatoid arthritis and osteoarthritis. In D. P. Dirette & S. A. Gutman (Eds.), Occupational therapy for physical dysfunction (8th ed., pp. 877–894). Wolters Kluwer.

De Herder, E. (2015). Evidence based hands and upper extremity protocol: A practical guide for therapists and physicians.

Deshaies, L. (2018). Arthritis. In H. M. Pendleton & W. Schultz-Krohn (Eds.), Pedretti's occupational therapy: Practice skills for physical dysfunction (8th ed., pp. 945–970). Elsevier.

Hock, N. S., & DeMott, L. (2021). Upper extremity orthosis. In D. P. Dirette & S. A. Gutman (Eds.), Occupational therapy for physical dysfunction (8th ed., pp. 431–465). Wolters Kluwer.

Johns Hopkins Medicine. (n.d.). Arthrogyrposis. https://www.hopkinsmedicine.org/health/conditions-and-diseases/arthrogryposis

Karakazu, D., & Hira, A. H. (2018). Burns and burn rehabilitation. In H. M. Pendleton & W. Schultz-Krohn (Eds.), Pedretti's occupational therapy: Practice skills for physical dysfunction (8th ed., pp. 1048–1082). Elsevier.

Klein, L. J. (2020). Evaluation of the hand and upper extremity. In C. M. Wietlisbach (Ed.), Cooper's fundamentals of occupational therapy (3rd ed., pp. 46–65). Elsevier.

Maher, C., & Mendonca, R. (2021). Orthopaedic conditions. In D. P. Dirette & S. A. Gutman (Eds.), Occupational therapy for physical dysfunction (8th ed., pp. 857–876). Wolters Kluwer.

National Board for Certification in Occupational Therapy (NBCOT®). (2022). 2022 Occupational Therapist Registered (OTR®) examination content outline. https://www.nbcot.org/-/media/PDFs/2022_OTR_Content_Outline.pdf.

National Institute of Health. (2021). Arthrogryposis multiplex congenita. Genetic and Rare Diseases Information Center (GARD) – an NCATS Program (nih.gov)

Neer, C. (1990). Shoulder reconstruction. Saunders.

Orr, A. E., Glover, J. S., & Cook, C. L. (2018). Amputations and prosthetics. In H. M. Pendleton & W. Schultz-Krohn (Eds.), Pedretti's occupational therapy: Practice skills for physical dysfunction (8th ed., pp. 1083–1116). Elsevier.

Ozelie, R. (2021). Burn injuries. In D. P. Dirette & S. A. Gutman (Eds.), Occupational therapy for physical dysfunction (8th ed., pp. 994–1013). Wolters Kluwer.

Solomon, G. (2020). Finger sprain and deformities. In C. M. Wietlisbach (Ed.), Cooper's fundamentals of occupational therapy (3rd ed., pp. 320–337). Elsevier.

Walsh, J. M., & Chee, N. (2018). Hand and upper extremity injuries. In H. M. Pendleton & W. Schultz-Krohn (Eds.), Pedretti's occupational therapy: Practice skills for physical dysfunction (8th ed., pp. 972–1003). Elsevier.

Walters, L. S. (2021). Amputations and prosthetics. In D. P. Dirette & S. A. Gutman (Eds.), Occupational therapy for physical dysfunction (8th ed., pp. 922–941). Wolters Kluwer.

Review Questions

Following are eight questions about key content covered in this Chapter. These questions are not inclusive of the entirety of content related to musculoskeletal system disorders that you must know for success on the NBCOT® exam. These questions are provided to help you "jump-start" the thought processes you will need to apply your studying of content to the answering of exam questions; hence, they are not in the NBCOT® exam format. Exam items in the NBCOT® format that cover the depth and breadth of content you will need to know to pass the NBCOT® exam are provided in the three online practice exams that accompany this text. The answers to the following questions are provided in Appendix 2.

1. You provide postoperative occupational therapy for clients who have undergone tendon repair surgery. You receive a referral for a client diagnosed with a Zone 1 extensor tendon repair. What is this diagnosis typically termed? According to established protocol, what is your diagnostic-specific intervention for the first six weeks? What are the overall goals for tendon repair surgeries that you will use to guide your intervention?

2. A client incurred a right Colles' fracture. One week ago, the client's cast was removed. You have worked with this client since the initial evaluation and during several intervention sessions. When arriving for the current therapy session, the client is tearful and holding the right arm in a protected position. The client reports that severe pain developed over the weekend in the wrist, hand, and shoulder and that it has not gone away. The right hand is swollen and skin is shiny. On a pain scale of 0–10, the client reports a 10+. The client describes an inability (over the past two days) to complete exercises and basic self-care activities due to the pain. What do you suspect is causing the client's increase in symptoms? How would you address the client's new presenting symptoms?

3. A client is referred to you with a diagnosis of (R) de Quervain's. The client's major complaint is pain when lifting (e.g., the client's newborn child, grocery bags). Pain is reported as 8/10. What findings will you expect upon formal evaluation? What interventions should you implement?

4. You receive a referral for a client with a third-degree burn to the dorsal hand which includes a prescription for an orthosis. What is the optimal antideformity position you should use to guide your orthotic construction? Explain your reasoning.

(Continued)

5. You receive a referral for a person with a diagnosis of carpal tunnel syndrome (CTS). What conservative treatment methods are indicated for this diagnosis?

6. A child with a diagnosis of osteogenesis imperfecta receives occupational therapy services. What should be the primary foci of occupational therapy intervention? Describe how safety precautions should be integrated into the treatment of a child with osteogenesis imperfecta.

7. A school-based occupational therapist has a third-grade student with arthrogryposis multiplex congenita assigned to their caseload. The student is meeting grade level expectations academically and does not need curricular or learning accommodations. What services would be relevant for the therapist to provide to this student?

8. A client recently sustained a left below elbow transradial amputation in a work-related incident. The client is right hand dominant. The plan is for the client to receive a body powered prosthesis. You are developing a pre-prosthetic intervention plan with the client. What interventions should you include in this plan?

7

Neurological System Disorders

DANIEL GELLER, GLEN GILLEN, AND CYNTHIA H. AUGUST[1]

[1] Susan B. O'Sullivan, Jan G. Garbarini, and Marge E. Moffet Boyd contributed to this Chapter in prior editions of this text.

Anatomy and Physiology of the Nervous System

Relationship to the Examination

1. It is not likely that the NBCOT® exam will ask direct questions about anatomy or physiology. As a result, this Chapter does not provide a complete anatomy and physiology review.

> **EXAM HINT:** The NBCOT® OTR® exam content outline identifies knowledge of the "impact of body functions body structures on occupational performance" (NBCOT®, 2022, p. 3) as essential for competent and safe practice. Thus, knowing the major structures and functions of the nervous system can help you correctly answer NBCOT® exam items about the *functional implications* of damage to the nervous system. For example, damage to the frontal lobe would affect executive functions, while damage to the cerebellum would impact the coordination of voluntary movement.

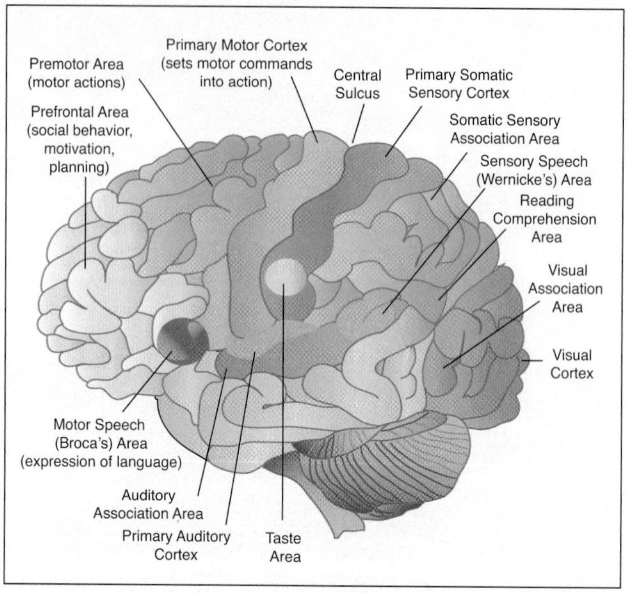

Figure 7-1 **Functional areas of the brain.**

Brain

1. Refer to Figure 7-1.
2. Cerebral hemispheres (telencephalon).
   a. Paired hemispheres, consisting of six lobes on each side: frontal, parietal, temporal, occipital, insular, and limbic.
   (1) Frontal lobe.
       (a) Precentral gyrus: primary motor cortex for voluntary muscle activation.
       (b) Prefrontal cortex: controls emotions, judgments, higher-order cognitive functions such as ideation and abstraction.
       (c) Premotor cortex related to planning of movements, includes Broca's area, which controls the motor aspects of speech.
   (2) Parietal lobe.
       (a) Postcentral gyrus: primary sensory cortex for integration of sensation.
       (b) Receives fibers conveying touch, proprioceptive, pain, and temperature sensations from opposite side of body.
   (3) Temporal lobe.
       (a) Primary auditory cortex: receives/processes auditory stimuli.
       (b) Associative auditory cortex: processes auditory stimuli.
       (c) Wernicke's area: language comprehension.
   (4) Occipital lobe.
       (a) Primary visual cortex: receives/processes visual stimuli.
       (b) Visual association cortex: processes visual stimuli.
   (5) Insula: deep within lateral sulcus, associated with visceral functions.
   (6) Limbic system.
       (a) Consists of the limbic lobe, hippocampal formation, amygdaloid nucleus, hypothalamus, and anterior nucleus of thalamus.
       (b) Phylogenetically oldest part of the brain, concerned with instincts and emotions contributing to preservation of the individual.
       (c) Basic functions: feeding, aggression, emotions, endocrine aspects of sexual response, and long-term memory formation.
   b. Subcortical white matter: myelinated nerve fibers located centrally.
   (1) Corpus callosum: connects hemispheres to allow communication.
   (2) Projection fibers: connect cerebral hemispheres with other portions of the brain and spinal cord.
   (3) Association fibers: connect different portions of the cerebral hemispheres (within the same hemisphere), allowing cortex to function as an integrated whole.

c. Basal ganglia.
  (1) Masses of gray matter deep within the cerebral hemispheres, including the corpus striatum, subthalamic nucleus, and the substantia nigra pars compacta.
  (2) Basic functions: initiates voluntary movement, controls postural adjustments, refines coordination, forms and stores motor plans, and produces dopamine.
  (3) Basil ganglia disorders.
    (a) Parkinson's Disease: reduced dopamine production.
    (b) Huntington's chorea: degeneration of caudate nucleus (Hamby, 2017).
3. Diencephalon.
  a. Thalamus.
    (1) Sensory nuclei: integrates and relays sensory information from body, face, retina, cochlea, and taste receptors to cerebral cortex and subcortical regions; smell (olfaction) is the exception.
    (2) Motor nuclei: relays motor information from cerebellum and globus pallidus to precentral motor cortex.
    (3) Other nuclei: assists in integration of visceral and somatic functions.
  b. Subthalamus: involved in control of several functional pathways for sensory, motor, and reticular function.
  c. Hypothalamus.
    (1) Integrates and controls the functions of the autonomic nervous system (ANS) and the neuroendocrine system.
    (2) Maintains body homeostasis: regulates body temperature, eating, water balance, anterior pituitary function/sexual behavior, and emotion.
  d. Epithalamus.
    (1) Habenular nuclei: integrate olfactory, visceral, and somatic afferent pathways.
    (2) Pineal gland: secretes hormones that influence the pituitary gland and several other organs; influences circadian rhythm.
4. Brain stem.
  a. Midbrain (mesencephalon).
    (1) Connects the pons to the cerebrum.
    (2) Basic function: acts as an important relay station for auditory, visual, and pupillary reflexes; contains endorphin-producing cells that are important for the suppression of pain.
    (3) Substantia nigra: a large motor nucleus connecting with the basal ganglia and cortex; important in motor control and muscle tone (Hamby, 2017).
  b. Pons.
    (1) Connects the medulla oblongata to the midbrain, allowing passage of important ascending and descending tracts.

    (2) Basic functions: assists in controlling autonomic functioning (modulating pain and controlling arousal); acts as a relay system between the cerebrum and cerebellum; initiates REM sleep; and acts as the center for horizontal gaze (Hamby, 2017).
  c. Medulla oblongata.
    (1) Connects the spinal cord with the pons.
    (2) Basic functions: acts as vital cardiac, respiratory, and vasomotor centers; controls reflex actions such as vomiting, swallowing, gagging, and coughing; and is important for the control of head movements and gaze stabilization (vestibulo-ocular reflex).
5. Cerebellum.
  a. Located behind the dorsal pons and medulla and divided into three lobes: anterior, posterior, and flocculonodular.
    (1) Anterior lobe basic functions: proprioceptive regulation, important in the maintenance of posture and voluntary movement.
    (2) Posterior lobe basic functions: motor planning, timing and coordination of multiple muscles.
    (3) Flocculodular lobe basic functions: concerned with trunk control, balance, equilibrium, and the regulation of muscle tone (Gutman, 2017).
    (4) Cerebellar disorders.
      (a) Friedreich's ataxia (FA): an autosomal recessive ataxia.
      (b) Spinocerebellar ataxia (SCA): a group of autosomal dominant ataxias that affect the cerebellum, but also the spinal cord, brain stem, and peripheral nerves.

Spinal Cord

1. General structure.
  a. Cylindrical mass of nerve tissue extending from the foramen magnum in skull to the conus medullaris.
  b. Divided into five distinct sections: cervical C1-C8, thoracic T1-T12, lumbar L1-L5, sacral S1-S5, and a few coccygeal segments.
2. Central gray matter contains: two anterior (ventral) and two posterior (dorsal) horns united by gray commissure with central canal. Refer to Figure 7-2.
  a. Anterior horns contain cell bodies that give rise to efferent (motor) neurons.
  b. Posterior horns contain afferent (sensory) neurons with cell bodies located in the dorsal root ganglia.
  c. Two enlargements, cervical and lumbosacral, for origins of nerves of upper and lower extremities, respectively.
  d. Lateral horn is found in the thoracic and upper lumbar segments for preganglionic fibers of the ANS.
3. White matter: anterior (ventral), lateral, and posterior (dorsal) white columns or funiculi.

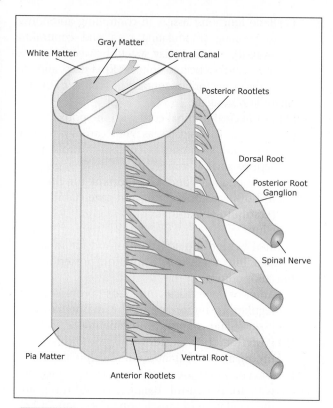

White Matter

Gray Matter

Central Canal

Posterior Rootlets

Dorsal Root

Posterior Root Ganglion

Spinal Nerve

Pia Matter

Ventral Root

Anterior Rootlets

Figure 7-2   **Spinal cord: Anterior cross section.**

a. Ascending fiber systems (sensory pathways): convey sensory information from the body up the spinal cord to the brain.
  (1) Dorsal columns/medial lemniscal system: convey sensations of proprioception, kinesthesia, vibration, pressure, and tactile discrimination to the somatosensory cortex.
  (2) Spinothalamic tracts: convey sensations of pain, temperature, (lateral) and crude touch (anterior).
  (3) Spinocerebellar tracts: convey unconscious proprioception, touch and pressure information from lower extremities to the cerebellum for the coordination of individual muscles (Gutman, 2017).
  (4) Spinoreticular tracts: convey deep and chronic pain to reticular formation of brain stem.
b. Descending fiber systems (motor pathways): convey motor information from brain down the spinal cord to the body.
  (1) Corticospinal tracts: arise from the primary motor cortex, descend in the brainstem, cross in the medulla (10% remain ipsilateral, 90% become contralateral), and synapse on motor spinal nerves that innervate skeletal muscles; important for voluntary motor control.

  (2) Vestibulospinal tracts: arise from the vestibular nucleus and descend to the spinal cord important for control of muscle tone, antigravity muscles, and postural reflexes.
  (3) Rubrospinal tract: arises in contralateral red nucleus and descends in lateral white columns to spinal gray; assists in motor function.
  (4) Reticulospinal tract: arises in the reticular formation of the brain stem and descends in both the ventral and lateral columns; can inhibit or stimulate motor activity; important for preparatory and movement related activities and postural control (Hamby, 2017).
  (5) Tectospinal tract: arises from the superior colliculus (midbrain) and descends to ventral gray; assists in head turning responses in response to visual stimuli.

> **EXAM HINT:** Applying knowledge of the anterior (ventral) and posterior (dorsal) spinal cord tracts can help you correctly answer NBCOT® exam items about the functional implications of incomplete spinal cord lesions and specific cord syndromes (e.g., anterior cord, central cord, and Brown-Sequard syndromes). Refer to Table 7-1.

4. Autonomic nervous system (ANS).
  a. Concerned with innervations of involuntary structures: smooth muscle, heart, glands; helps maintain homeostasis (constant internal body environment).
  b. Divided into two divisions: sympathetic and parasympathetic; both have afferent and efferent nerve fibers; preganglionic and postganglionic fibers.
    (1) Sympathetic (thoracolumbar) division: prepares the body for fight or flight, emergency responses, raises heart rate and blood pressure, constricts peripheral blood vessels, and redistributes blood; inhibits peristalsis.
    (2) Parasympathetic (craniosacral) division: conserves and restores homeostasis; slows heart rate and reduces blood pressure, increases peristalsis and glandular activity.
  c. Autonomic plexuses: cardiac, pulmonary, celiac (solar), hypogastric, pelvic.
  d. Modulated by brain centers.
    (1) Descending autonomic system: arises from the control centers in the hypothalamus and lower brain stem (cardiac, respiratory, vasomotor) and projects to preganglionic ANS segments in thoracolumbar (sympathetic) and craniosacral (parasympathetic) segments.
    (2) Cranial nerves: visceral afferent sensations via glossopharyngeal, and vagus nerves; efferent outflow via oculomotor, facial, glossopharyngeal, and vagus nerves.

Table 7-1

Spinal Cord Syndromes

LESION	CHARACTERISTICS
Complete Cord Lesion: UMN lesion	Complete bilateral loss of all sensory modalities Bilateral loss of motor function with spastic paralysis below level of lesion Loss of bladder and bowel functions with spastic bladder and bowel
Central Cord Lesion: UMN lesion	Cavitation of central cord in cervical section Loss of spinothalamic tracts with bilateral loss of pain and temperature Loss of ventral horn with bilateral loss of motor function: primarily upper extremities Preservation of proprioception and discriminatory sensation
Brown-Sequard Syndrome: UMN lesion	Hemisection of spinal cord Ipsilateral loss of dorsal columns with loss of tactile discrimination, pressure, vibration, and proprioception Ipsilateral loss of corticospinal tracts with loss of motor function and spastic paralysis below level of lesion Contralateral loss of spinothalamic tract with loss of pain and temperature below level of lesion; at lesion level, bilateral loss of pain and temperature
Anterior Cord Syndrome: UMN lesion	Loss of anterior cord Loss of lateral corticospinal tracts with bilateral loss of motor function, spastic paralysis below level of lesion Loss of spinothalamic tracts with bilateral loss of pain and temperature Preservation of dorsal columns: proprioception, kinesthesia, and vibratory sense
Posterior Cord Syndrome: UMN lesion	Loss of dorsal columns bilaterally Bilateral loss of proprioception, vibration, pressure, and epicritic sensations (stereognosis, two-point discrimination) Preservation of motor function, pain, and light touch
Cauda Equina Injury: LMN lesion	Loss of long nerve roots at or below L1 Variable nerve root damage (motor and sensory signs); incomplete lesions common Flaccid paralysis with no spinal reflex activity Flaccid paralysis of bladder and bowel Potential for nerve regeneration; regeneration often incomplete, slows and stops after about 1 year

LMN = lower motor neuron; UMN = upper motor neuron

Central Nervous System (CNS) Support Structures

1. Bony structure.
   a. Skull (cranium): rigid bony chamber that contains the brain and facial skeleton, with an opening (foramen magnum) at its base.
2. Meninges: three membranes, located between the skull and brain and over the spinal cord, which form a protective seal around the CNS.
   a. Dura mater: outermost layer, which is thick and tough.
   b. Arachnoid mater: Middle layer; delicate, vascular membrane.
   c. Subarachnoid space: beneath the arachnoid; contains cerebrospinal fluid and cisterns, major arteries.
   d. Pia mater: deepest layer; thin vascular membrane that covers the brain surface; forms tela choroidea of ventricles.
   e. Blood-brain barrier: consists of meninges, glial cells and capillary beds; selective restriction of blood borne substances from entering the CNS (Gutman, 2017).
3. Ventricles: four cavities or ventricles are filled with cerebrospinal fluid (CSF) and communicate with each other and the spinal cord canal.
   a. One pair of lateral ventricles (one in each hemisphere), a third and fourth ventricle.
   b. Cerebrospinal fluid: clear fluid, which provides mechanical support (i.e., cushions the brain), controls brain excitability by regulating ionic composition, aids in exchange of nutrients and waste products.
      (1) Normal pressure: 70–180 mm/H_2O.
      (2) Total volume: 125–150 cc.
      (3) Hydrocephalus: abnormal accumulation of cerebrospinal fluid in the ventricles, causing enlargement and pressure on the brain (Gutman, 2017).
4. Blood supply
   a. Carotid system: supplies a large area of brain and many deep structures.
   b. Vertebrobasilar system: supplies the brain stem, cerebellum, occipital lobe, and parts of thalamus.
   c. Circle of Willis: formed by the anterior communicating artery connecting the two anterior cerebral arteries and the posterior communicating artery connecting each posterior and middle cerebral artery.
   d. Venous drainage: includes the cerebral veins and the dural venous sinuses.

Neurons

1. Structure.
   a. Neurons vary in size and complexity.
      (1) Cell bodies (genetic center) with dendrites (receptive surface area to receive information via synapses).
      (2) Axons conduct impulses away from the cell body (one-way conduction).
      (3) Myelin: axons covered with myelin, which acts as an insulator, and increases speed of conduction across the axon.
         (a) Multiple sclerosis is a disease of the myelin.
      (4) Nodes of Ranvier: spaces between the myelin, whereby the nerve signal jumps from one node to the other during conduction.
      (5) Synapses allow communication between neurons; chemical neurotransmitters are released (chemical synapses) or electrical signals pass directly from cell to cell (electrical synapses).
         (a) Myasthenia gravis: disorder of the neuromuscular junction (the synapse. between motor neuron and muscle).
   b. Neuron groupings and types.
      (1) Nuclei are compact groups of nerve cell bodies; in the peripheral nervous system these groups are called ganglia.
      (2) Projection neurons carry impulses to other parts of the CNS.
      (3) Interneurons are short relay neurons.
      (4) Axon bundles are called tracts or fasciculi; in spinal cord, collections of tracts are called columns, or funiculi.
   c. Neuroglia: support cells that do not transmit signals; important for myelin and neuron production; maintenance of K+ levels and reuptake of neurotransmitters following neural transmission at synapses.
   d. Nerve fiber types.
      (1) A fibers: large, myelinated, fast conducting.
         (a) Alpha: proprioception, somatic motor.
         (b) Beta: touch, pressure.
         (c) Gamma: motor to muscle spindles.
         (d) Delta: pain, temperature, touch.
      (2) B fibers: small, myelinated, conduct less rapidly; preganglionic autonomic.
      (3) C fibers: smallest, unmyelinated, slowest conducting.
         (a) Dorsal root: pain, reflex responses.
         (b) Sympathetic: postganglionic sympathetics.

2. Upper and lower motor neurons.
   a. Upper motor neuron (UMN): carries motor messages from primary motor cortex to cranial nerve nuclei in brain stem and interneurons in the ventral horn.
   b. Lower motor neuron (LMN): carries motor messages from the motor cell bodies in the ventral horn to the skeletal muscles in the periphery (Gutman, 2017).
   c. Refer to Table 7-2.

Peripheral Nervous System

1. Peripheral nerves are referred to as lower motor neurons (LMN). Refer to Figure 7-3. Functional components include the following.
   a. Motor (efferent) fibers originate from motor nuclei (cranial nerves) or anterior horn cells (spinal nerves).
   b. Sensory (afferent) fibers originate in cells outside of the brain stem or spinal cord with sensory ganglia (cranial nerves) or dorsal root ganglia (spinal nerves).
   c. ANS fibers: sympathetic fibers at thoracolumbar spinal segments and parasympathetic fibers at craniosacral segments.

2. Cranial nerves: 12 pairs of cranial nerves, all nerves are distributed to the head and neck except C.N. X, which is distributed to the thorax and abdomen.
   a. C.N. I, II, VIII: pure sensory; carry special senses of smell (I), vision (II), hearing and equilibrium (VIII).
   b. C.N. III, IV, VI: pure motor; controlling eye movements (III, IV, VI) and pupillary constriction (III).
   c. C.N. XI, XII: pure motor; innervating sternocleidomastoid and trapezius (XI), and tongue (XII).
   d. C.N. V, VII, IX, X are mixed: motor and sensory; involved in chewing (V), facial expression (VII), swallowing (IX, X), vocal sounds (X), sensations from the head (V, VII, IX), alimentary tract, heart, vessels, lungs (IX, X), and taste (VII, IX, X).
   e. C.N. III, VII, IX, X involved in control of the smooth muscles of inner eye (III), salivatory and lacrimal glands (VII), parotid gland (IX), muscles of heart, lung, and bowel (X).
   f. Refer to Chapter 12 for additional information on cranial nerves.
3. Spinal nerves: 31 pairs of spinal nerves; spinal nerves are divided into groups (8 cervical, 12 thoraces, 5 lumbar, 5 sacral, coccygeal) and correspond to vertebral segments; each has a ventral root and a dorsal root.

Table 7-2

Differential Diagnosis: Comparison of Upper Motor Neuron (UMN) and Lower Motor Neuron (LMN) Syndromes

	UMN LESION	LMN LESION
Location of Lesion	Central nervous system	Peripheral nervous system
Structures Involved	Cortex, brainstem, corticospinal tracts, spinal cord	SC: anterior horn cell, spinal roots, peripheral nerves CN: cranial nerves
Disorders	Stroke, traumatic brain injury, spinal cord injury	Polio, Guillain-Barré, PNI, peripheral neuropathy, radiculopathy
Tone	Increased: hypertonia Velocity-dependent	Decreased or absent: hypotonia, flaccidity Not velocity dependent
Reflexes	Increased: hyperreflexia, clonus Exaggerated cutaneous and autonomic reflexes: + Babinski response	Decreased or absent: hyporeflexia Cutaneous reflexes decreased or absent
Involuntary Movements	Muscle spasms: flexor or extensor	With denervation: fasciculations
Strength	Stroke: weakness or paralysis on one side of the body Corticospinal lesions: contralateral if above decussation in medulla, ipsilateral if below Spinal cord lesions: bilateral loss below level of lesion	Limited distribution: segmental or focal pattern Root-innervated pattern
Muscle Bulk	Variable, disuse atrophy	Neurogenic atrophy: rapid, focal, severe wasting
Voluntary Movements	Impaired or absent: dyssynergic patterns, obligatory synergies	Weak or absent if nerve interrupted

Key: CN = cranial nerve; PNI = peripheral nerve injury; SC = spinal cord

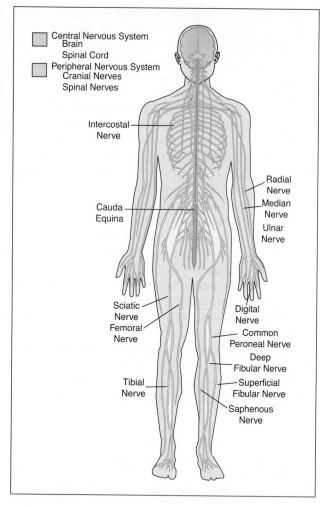

Figure 7-3   **Overview of nervous system.**

a. Ventral (anterior) root: efferent (motor) fibers to voluntary muscles (alpha motoneurons, gamma motoneurons) and to viscera, glands, and smooth muscles (preganglionic ANS fibers).

b. Dorsal (posterior) root: afferent (sensory) fibers from sensory receptors from skin, joints, and muscles.

c. The term dermatome refers to a specific segmental skin area innervated by sensory spinal axons. Refer to Chapter 11 and refer to Figure 6-6 and Table 11-4.

d. The term myotome refers to the skeletal muscles innervated by motor axons in a given spinal root.

e. Nerve roots exit from the vertebral column through intervertebral foramina.

   (1) In cervical spine, numbered roots exit above the corresponding vertebral body, with C8 exiting below C7 and above T1.

   (2) In the thoracic and lumbar segments, the roots exit below the corresponding vertebral body.

f. Spinal cord ends at the level of L1; below L1, nerve roots descend vertically to form the cauda equina.

Spinal Level Reflexes

1. Involuntary responses to stimuli; basic, specific, and predictable; dependent upon intact neural pathway (reflex arc).

   a. Reflexes may be monosynaptic or polysynaptic (involving interneurons).

   b. Provide the basis for unconscious motor function and basic defense mechanisms.

2. Stretch (myotatic) reflexes.

   a. Stimulus: muscle stretch.

   b. Functions to maintain muscle tone, support agonist muscle contraction, and to provide feedback about muscle length.

   c. Clinically, sensitivity of the stretch reflex and intactness of spinal cord segment are tested by applying stretch to the deep tendons.

   d. Reciprocal inhibition: via an inhibitory interneuron the same stretch stimulus inhibits the antagonist muscle.

   e. Reciprocal innervation: describes the responses a stretch stimulus can have on agonist (autogenic facilitation), antagonist (reciprocal inhibition), as well as on synergistic muscles (facilitation).

3. Inverse stretch (myotatic) reflex.

   a. Stimulus: muscle contraction.

   b. Functions to provide agonist inhibition, diminution of force of agonist contraction.

4. Gamma reflex loop.

   a. Stretch reflex forms part of this loop.

   b. Functions to allow muscle tension to come under control of descending pathways (reticulospinal, vestibulospinal, and others); thus, regulating the level of tension in the muscle.

5. Flexor (withdrawal) reflex.

   a. Stimulus: cutaneous sensory stimuli to largely flexor muscles.

   b. Functions as a protective withdrawal mechanism to remove a body part from a harmful stimuli.

6. Crossed extension reflex.

   a. Stimulus: noxious stimuli and reciprocal action of antagonists; flexors of one side are excited causing extensors on same side to be inhibited; opposite responses occur in opposite limb.

   b. Function: coordinates reciprocal limb activities such as gait.

> CAUTION: While stimuli are applied during testing to evoke reflex responses, any stimulus that evokes an abnormal response that hinders function should be avoided. For example, a quick stretch to a spastic muscle may in fact increase spasticity.

Stroke/Cerebral Vascular Accident (CVA)

Specific Types and Etiology

1. The term CVA or stroke is a disease of the cerebral vasculature in which there is a failure of blood and oxygen to the brain, causing brain death. It applies to clinical syndromes that accompany ischemic or hemorrhagic lesions.
   a. Transient ischemic attack (TIA).
      (1) A TIA, also known as a "mini-stroke," is a transitory stroke that for the most part lasts only a few minutes.
      (2) TIA symptoms, which usually occur suddenly, are similar to those of stroke but do not last as long. Most symptoms of a TIA disappear within an hour, although they may persist for up to 24 hours.
      (3) Symptoms can include numbness or weakness in the face, arm, or leg, especially on one side of the body; confusion or difficulty in talking or understanding speech; trouble seeing in one or both eyes; difficulty with walking, dizziness, and/or loss of balance and coordination.

> **RED FLAG:** TIAs are often warning signs that a person is at risk for a more serious and debilitating stroke. About one-third of those who have a TIA will have an acute stroke at some point in the future.

   b. Ischemic stroke: most common type of stroke and due to either embolism or thrombosis of the intra- or extracranial arteries.
   c. Hemorrhagic stroke: a bleed secondary to hypertension or aneurysm or arteriovenous malformation (AVM).
      (1) AVM: abnormal, tangled collections of dilated blood vessels that result from congenitally malformed vascular structures (Rief et al., 2021).

Symptoms of CVA

1. Abrupt onset of usually unilateral neurological signs (e.g., weakness, vision loss, sensory changes).
   a. The American Stroke Association has advocated for the universal use of the F.A.S.T. acronym to identify and respond to the possible occurrence of a stroke. Refer to Box 7-1.

2. Symptoms can progress over several hours to two days.
3. Specific symptoms are determined by the site of the infarct and the involved artery.
   a. Middle cerebral artery (MCA) stroke results in contralateral hemiplegia, hemianesthesia, and/or homonymous hemianopsia A MCA stroke can also cause the following.
      (1) Aphasia (most common from a left MCA).[2]
      (2) Unilateral neglect and/or spatial dysfunction (most common from a right MCA).
      (3) Bilateral apraxia (most common from a left MCA).
      (4) Left apraxia (most common from a right MCA).
   b. Internal carotid artery (ICA) stroke results in symptoms similar to those associated with MCA CVA.
   c. Anterior cerebral artery (ACA) stroke results in contralateral hemiplegia, grasp reflex, incontinence, confusion, apathy, and/or mutism.
   d. Posterior cerebral artery (PCA) stroke results in homonymous hemianopsia, thalamic pain, hemisensory loss, and/or alexia.

BOX 7-1 ○ Stroke Early Warning Signs: F.A.S.T

- **F = Face Drooping**
  - Initial Observations: is one side of the person's face drooping or numb?
  - Action and Response: ask the person to smile. The person smiles unevenly.
- **A = Arm Weakness**
  - Initial Observations: is one arm weak or numb?
  - Action and Response: ask the person to raise both arms. One arm drifts downward.
- **S = Speech Difficulty**
  - Initial Observations: is the person unable to speak? is speech slurred and/or hard to understand?
  - Action and Response: Ask the person to repeat a simple sentence (e.g., "It may rain tomorrow"). The person cannot repeat the sentence correctly or clearly.
- **T – Time to Telephone 911**

---

[2] Because language centers are typically in the left hemisphere, it is most common to get aphasia from a left CVA. However, there are a small portion of people who are left-handed who can have the language centers in the right hemisphere. Thus, if they have a stroke on right side, it could cause aphasia.

e. Vertebrobasilar system results in pseudobulbar signs (dysarthria, dysphagia, emotional instability), tetraplegia.

f. Refer to Table 7-3 for hemispheric specialization information, which is based on hemispheric lateralization in most individuals.

(1) Hemispheric asymmetry and functional localization can vary in individuals.

> **EXAM HINT:** When determining the correct answers to NBCOT® exam items about strokes/CVAs, be sure to consider the reported site of the infarct. For example, the correct answer to an exam item about an OT practitioner working with a person recovering from a left CVA will need to consider its impact on the person's communication abilities; whereas, the correct answer to an exam item about a person recovering from a right CVA will need to consider its impact on their ability to attend to the left side of the environment and body.

Risk Factors

1. Modifiable risk factors: hypertension, cardiac disease, atrial fibrillation, diabetes mellitus, smoking, alcohol abuse, hyperlipidemia, sedentary lifestyle, contraceptive with high doses of estrogen (Rief et al., 2021).

Table 7-3

LEFT HEMISPHERE	RIGHT HEMISPHERE
Movement of right side of body	Movement of left side of body
Processing of sensory information from right side of body	Processing of sensory information from left side of body
Visual reception from right field	Visual reception from left field
Visual verbal processing	Visual spatial processing
Bilateral motor praxis	Left motor praxis
Verbal memory	Nonverbal memory
Bilateral auditory reception	Attention to incoming stimuli
Speech	Emotional lability
Processing of verbal auditory information	Processing of nonverbal auditory information
	Interpretation of abstract information
	Interpretation of tonal inflections

Hemispheric Specialization*

*Based on hemispheric lateralization in most clients. It must be recognized that hemispheric asymmetry and functional localization varies in individuals.

2. Nonmodifiable risk factors: age, gender, race, ethnicity, and heredity.

a. Prevalence: higher for females than males, increases with age for both male and females, highest among African Americans and lowest among Asian Americans (American Heart Association, 2021).

Diagnosis

1. Usually diagnosed clinically using symptoms as a guide to lesion location.

2. Cerebrovascular imaging.

a. Computed tomography (CT).

(1) Standard for a person experiencing an acute onset of a stroke.

(2) Best to identify presence of hemorrhage and ruling out other conditions (e.g., tumors).

(3) May initially read as negative.

b. CT angiography: creates 3D reconstruction of blood flow in the brain to assess large vessel occlusions.

c. Magnetic resonance imaging (MRI): rule out other conditions, screen for acute bleeding, and detect small infarcts (Rief et al., 2021).

3. Diagnostic testing.

a. Transcranial and carotid Doppler for non-invasive visualization of plaque or occlusion of the cerebral vessels.

b. Electrocardiogram (ECG) to detect arrhythmias.

c. Echocardiography to evaluate presence of cardiac emboli and cardiac disease.

d. Blood work to rule out metabolic abnormalities.

Medical Management

1. Immediate care.

a. Airway maintenance.

b. Adequate oxygenation.

c. Nutritional intervention (IV fluids, alternative feeding routes).

d. Decubiti prevention.

e. Treatment of underlying cardiac dysfunction (dysrhythmias).

2. Pharmacologic therapies.

a. Antithrombotic therapy (antiplatelet and anticoagulation) is used for rapid recanalization and reperfusion of occluded vessels to reduce infarction area (e.g., aspirin, heparin).

b. Thrombolytic therapy is used in acute strokes to open occluded cerebral vessels and restore blood flow to ischemic areas (e.g., t-PA).

Trauma

Traumatic Brain Injury (TBI)

1. Etiology.
   a. Open TBI: damage results from penetration of the skull (e.g., a bullet).
   b. Closed TBI.
      (1) Rapid acceleration or deceleration of the brain whereby no direct impact is required (e.g., a restrained passenger coming to a sudden stop when a car hits a tree).
      (2) Blunt external force to head (e.g., a fall, an assault, getting hit in the head during football).
   c. Injury can result from other occurrences.
      (1) Skull fractures.
      (2) Traumatic injury to extracranial blood vessels.
      (3) Nerve tissues, blood vessels, and meninges are sheared, torn, or ruptured, resulting in hemorrhage, edema, and ischemia.
2. Symptoms.
   a. Concussion: characterized by post-traumatic loss of consciousness. Refer to subsequent section on concussion.
   b. Cerebral contusion/laceration/edema accompanied by surface wounds and skull fractures.
   c. Hemiplegia or monoplegia and abnormal reflexes.
   d. Decorticate or decerebrate rigidity.
   e. Fixed pupils.
   f. Coma.
   g. Changes in vital signs.
3. Diagnostic testing.
   a. Administration of the Glasgow Coma Scale.
      (1) A neurological scale, which provides an objective method to record the conscious state of a person.
      (2) It is used for initial evaluation and continuing assessment to determine a person's level of consciousness after head injury.
      (3) A client is assessed against the scale's criteria, which delineate a range of points for three tests: eye (E), verbal (V), and motor (M) responses.
         (a) The total score comprises the Glasgow Coma Score (or GCS).
         (b) Three individual scores are considered.
         (c) The highest total GCS is 15 (i.e., a fully conscious person).
         (d) The lowest possible total GCS is 3 (i.e., deep coma or death).
      (e) The GCS is interpreted as severe TBI with GCS < 8, moderate TBI with GCS 9–12, and mild TBI with GCS > 13.
      (4) Refer to Table 7-4.
      (5) Individual scores as well as the total GCS score are documented (e.g., "GCS 11 = E4 V3 M4 at 11:30 pm").
   b. Administration of the Rancho Los Amigos Levels of Cognitive Functioning Scale. Refer to Table 7-5.
   c. CT scan and MRI to visualize intracranial structure damage.

Table 7-4

Glasgow Coma Scale		
Best eye response (E)	Eyes opening spontaneously	4
	Eyes opening to speech	3
	Eyes opening in response to pain	2
	No eye opening	1
Best verbal response (V)	Oriented (patient responds coherently and appropriately to questions such as the patient's name and age, where they are and why, the year, month, etc.)	5
	Confused (patient responds to questions coherently but there is some disorientation and confusion)	4
	Inappropriate words (random or exclamatory speech, but not conversational exchange)	3
	Incomprehensible sounds (moaning but no words)	2
	None	1
Best motor response (M)	Obeys commands (the person does simple things as asked)	6
	Localizes to pain (purposeful movements towards changing painful stimuli)	5
	Withdraws from pain (pulls part of body away when pinched)	4
	Flexion in response to pain (decorticate response)	3
	Extension to pain (decerebrate response)	2
	No motor response	1

Acknowledgement: Copyright 1974 by Glasgow University and Sir Graham Teasdale.

Chapter 7

Table 7-5

Rancho Los Amigos Levels of Cognitive Functioning Scale

Level I - No Response: Total Assistance

- Complete absence of observable change in behavior when presented visual, auditory, tactile, proprioceptive, vestibular, or painful stimuli.

Level II - Generalized Response: Total Assistance

- Demonstrates generalized reflex response to painful stimuli.
- Responds to repeated auditory stimuli with increased or decreased activity.
- Responds to external stimuli with physiological changes generalized, gross body movement, and/or not purposeful vocalization.
- Responses noted above may be same regardless of type and location of stimulation.
- Responses may be significantly delayed.

Level III - Localized Response: Total Assistance

- Demonstrates withdrawal or vocalization to painful stimuli.
- Turns toward or away from auditory stimuli.
- Blinks when strong light crosses visual field.
- Follows moving object passed within visual field.
- Responds to discomfort by pulling tubes or restraints.
- Responds inconsistently to simple commands.
- Responses directly related to type of stimulus.
- May respond to some persons (especially family and friends) but not to others.

Level IV - Confused/Agitated: Maximal Assistance

- Alert and in heightened state of activity.
- Purposeful attempts to remove restraints or tubes or crawl out of bed.
- May perform motor activities such as sitting, reaching, and walking but without any apparent purpose or upon another's request.
- Very brief and usually nonpurposeful moments of sustained alternatives and divided attention.
- Absent short-term memory.
- May cry out or scream out of proportion to stimulus even after its removal.
- May exhibit aggressive or flight behavior.
- Mood may swing from euphoric to hostile with no apparent relationship to environmental events.
- Unable to cooperate with treatment efforts.
- Verbalizations are frequently incoherent and/or inappropriate to activity or environment.

Level V - Confused, Inappropriate, Nonagitated: Maximal Assistance

- Alert, not agitated but may wander randomly or with a vague intention of going home.
- May become agitated in response to external stimulation and/or lack of environmental structure.
- Not oriented to person, place, or time.
- Frequent brief periods, nonpurposeful sustained attention.
- Severely impaired recent memory, with confusion of past and present in reaction to ongoing activity.
- Absent goal-directed, problem solving, self-monitoring behavior.
- Often demonstrates inappropriate use of objects without external direction.
- May be able to perform previously learned tasks when structured and cues provided.
- Unable to learn new information.
- Able to respond appropriately to simple commands fairly consistently with external structures and cues.
- Responses to simple commands without external structure are random and nonpurposeful in relation to command.
- Able to converse on a social, automatic level for brief periods of time when provided external structure and cues.
- Verbalizations about present events become inappropriate and confabulatory when external structure and cues are not provided.

Level VI - Confused, Appropriate: Moderate Assistance

- Inconsistently oriented to person, time, and place.
- Able to attend to highly familiar tasks in nondistracting environment for 30 minutes with moderate redirection.
- Remote memory has more depth and detail than recent memory.
- Vague recognition of some staff.
- Able to use assistive memory aide with maximum assistance.
- Emerging awareness of appropriate response to self, family, and basic needs.
- Moderate assist to problem solve barriers to task completion.
- Supervised for old learning (e.g., self-care).
- Shows carryover for relearned familiar tasks (e.g., self-care).
- Maximum assistance for new learning with little or no carryover.
- Unaware of impairments, disabilities, and safety risks.
- Consistently follows simple directions.
- Verbal expressions are appropriate in highly familiar and structured situations.

Level VII - Automatic, Appropriate: Minimal Assistance for Daily Living Skills

- Consistently oriented to person and place, within highly familiar environments. Moderate assistance for orientation to time.
- Able to attend to highly familiar tasks in a nondistracting environment for at least 30 minutes with minimal assist to complete tasks.
- Minimal supervision for new learning.

Table 7-5

Rancho Los Amigos Levels of Cognitive Functioning Scale (*Continued*)

Level VII - Automatic, Appropriate: Minimal Assistance for Daily Living Skills (*Continued*)

- Demonstrates carryover of new learning.
- Initiates and carries out steps to complete familiar personal and household routine but has shallow recall of what he/she has been doing.
- Able to monitor accuracy and completeness of each step in routine personal and household ADL and modify plan with minimal assistance.
- Superficial awareness of his/her condition but unaware of specific impairments and disabilities and the limits they place on his/her ability to safely, accurately, and completely carry out his/her household, community, work, and leisure ADL.
- Minimal supervision for safety in routine home and community activities.
- Unrealistic planning for the future.
- Unable to think about consequences of a decision or action.
- Overestimates abilities.
- Unaware of others' needs and feelings.
- Oppositional/uncooperative.
- Unable to recognize inappropriate social interaction behavior.

Level VIII - Purposeful, Appropriate: Stand-By Assistance

- Consistently oriented to person, place, and time.
- Independently attends to and completes familiar tasks for one hour in distracting environments.
- Able to recall and integrate past and recent events.
- Uses assistive memory devices to recall daily schedule, recall "to do" lists, and record critical information for later use with stand-by assistance.
- Initiates and carries out steps to complete familiar personal, household, community, work, and leisure routines with stand-by assistance and can modify the plan when needed with minimal assistance.
- Requires no assistance once new tasks/activities are learned.
- Aware of and acknowledges impairments and disabilities when they interfere with task completion but requires stand-by assistance to take appropriate corrective action.
- Thinks about consequences of a decision or action with minimal assistance.
- Overestimates or underestimates abilities.
- Acknowledges others' needs and feelings and responds appropriately with minimal assistance.
- Depressed.
- Irritable.
- Low frustration tolerance/easily angered.
- Argumentative.
- Self-centered.
- Uncharacteristically dependent/independent.
- Able to recognize and acknowledge inappropriate social interaction behavior while it is occurring and takes corrective action with minimal assistance.

Level IX - Purposeful, Appropriate: Stand-By Assistance on Request

- Independently shifts back and forth between tasks and completes them accurately for at least two consecutive hours.
- Uses assistive memory devices to recall daily schedule, "to do" lists, and record critical information for later use with assistance when requested.
- Initiates and carries out steps to complete familiar personal, household, work, and leisure tasks independently and unfamiliar personal, household, work, and leisure tasks with assistance when requested.
- Aware of and acknowledges impairments and disabilities when they interfere with task completion and takes appropriate corrective action but requires stand-by assist to anticipate a problem before it occurs and take action to avoid it.
- Able to think about consequences of decisions or actions with assistance when requested.
- Accurately estimates abilities but requires stand-by assistance to adjust to task demands.
- Acknowledges others' needs and feelings and responds appropriately with stand-by assistance.
- Depression may continue.
- May be easily irritable.
- May have low frustration tolerance.
- Able to self-monitor appropriateness of social interaction with stand-by assistance.

Level X - Purposeful, Appropriate: Modified Independent

- Able to handle multiple tasks simultaneously in all environments but may require periodic breaks.
- Able to independently procure, create, and maintain own assistive memory devices.
- Independently initiates and carries out steps to complete familiar and unfamiliar personal, household, community, work, and leisure tasks but may require more than usual amount of time and/or compensatory strategies to complete them.
- Anticipates impact of impairments and disabilities on ability to complete daily living tasks and takes action to avoid problems before they occur but may require more than usual amount of time and/or compensatory strategies.
- Able to independently think about consequences of decisions or actions but may require more than usual amount of time and/or compensatory strategies to select the appropriate decision or action.
- Accurately estimates abilities and independently adjusts to task demands.
- Able to recognize the needs and feelings of others and automatically respond in appropriate manner.
- Periodic periods of depression may occur.
- Irritability and low frustration tolerance when sick, fatigued, and/or under emotional stress.
- Social interaction behavior is consistently appropriate.

Reprinted with permission from the author Chris Hagen.

EXAM HINT: NBCOT® exam items about working with a person recovering from a TBI may include behavioral descriptions that indicate a specific level on the Glasgow Coma or Rancho Los Amigos Levels of Cognitive Functioning Scale. Correct answers about the implementation of an OT intervention plan should consider the person's current capabilities and include treatment approaches that are designed to develop the person's abilities to progress to the next level on these scales.

4. Medical management.
   a. Resuscitation.
   b. Management of respiratory dysfunction.
   c. Cardiovascular monitoring.
   d. Surgical, pharmacologic, or mechanical means to decrease intracranial pressure.
   e. Neurosurgery to manage lacerated vessels and depressed skull fractures.
   f. Pharmacologic interventions.
      (1) Antibiotics.
      (2) Anticonvulsants.
      (3) Sedatives.
      (4) Antidepressants.

Concussion

1. A mild TBI.
   a. The terms concussion and mild TBI are often used interchangeably.
2. At least one of the following manifestations is required for a concussion diagnosis.
   a. Any loss of consciousness up to 30 minutes.
   b. Post traumatic amnesia (PTA) lasting no longer than 24 hours (e.g., any loss of memory for events immediately before or after incident).
   c. Any alteration in mental state at time of accident (e.g., feeling dazed, confused, disoriented).
   d. Transient neurological abnormalities (e.g., focal signs, seizures).
   e. GCS score 13 to 15 (Lohmann & Vas, 2021).
3. Other signs of concussion.
   a. Clumsy movements.
   b. Slow responses to questions.
   c. Mood, behavior, or personality changes.
   d. Vomiting.
4. Symptoms of concussion.
   a. Headache or pressure in head.
   b. Nausea or vomiting.
   c. Dizziness and/or blurry vision.
   d. Sensitivity to light or noise.
   e. Feeling sluggish, hazy, foggy, or groggy.
   f. Confusion, concentration, or memory problems.
   g. Just not "feeling right" or "feeling "down".

5. Severe concussion: activate emergency medical services (EMS). Seek immediate medical care if the person experiences any of the following:
   a. Drowsiness or inability to wake up.
   b. Loss of consciousness for longer than 30 seconds.
   c. One pupil larger than the other pupil.
   d. Repeat vomiting or nausea, convulsions, or seizures.
   e. Headache that gets worse with time.
   f. Slurred speech, numbness, or decreased coordination.
   g. Changes in behavior: irritability, restlessness, agitation.
6. Diagnostic testing.
   a. CT and/or MRI but findings are sometimes normal.

Post-concussion Syndrome

1. A set of symptoms that may continue for weeks, months, or a year or more after a concussion.
2. Symptoms.
   a. Concussion with or without loss of consciousness.
   b. A variety of symptoms can result. These can include headache, fatigue, cognitive impairments, dizziness, depression, anxiety, impaired balance, irritability, apathy, visual problems (e.g., blurry vision, light sensitivity), auditory sensitivity, mood and emotional regulation problems.
3. Further evaluation, in addition to the occupational therapy evaluation.
   a. Physical therapy evaluation (e.g., exercise testing such as treadmill exercise).

CAUTION: Concussion symptoms are typically exacerbated by exercise.

   b. Neuropsychiatric evaluation.
   c. Neuro-ophthalmologic evaluation.
   d. Vestibular evaluation.
   e. Speech evaluation.
4. Medical management.
   a. Prescribing a period of cognitive and physical rest.
   b. Cognitive behavioral therapy (CBT).
   c. Medications for depression, sleep deprivation, headaches, and attention problems.

Spinal Cord Injury (SCI)

1. Etiology.
   a. Trauma to the spinal cord as a result of compression, shearing force, contusion secondary to motor vehicle accident, diving accident, penetration wound (gunshot or knife), sports injury, or fall.
   b. Nontraumatic cord injuries may be a result of a tumor or progressive degenerative disease.

2. Classification of injury/signs and symptoms.
   a. Degree of impairment and severity of injury is graded using the American Spinal Injury Association (ASIA) Impairment Scale (AIS). Refer to Box 7-2.
3. Specific symptoms.
   a. Spinal shock (four to eight weeks), all reflex activity is obliterated below the level of the injury presenting as flaccid paralysis.
   b. Sensory deficits may be partial loss or complete.
   c. Loss of bowel/bladder control.
   d. Loss of temperature control below the lesion.
   e. Decreased respiratory function.
   f. Sexual dysfunction.
   g. Changes in muscle tone.
      (1) Spasticity in upper motor neuron lesions.
      (2) Flaccidity in lesions below L1.
   h. Loss of motor function resulting in tetraplegia (quadriplegia) or paraplegia; may be complete or incomplete. Refer to Table 7-6 for more information about the motor abilities and functional outcomes of different levels of SCI.
4. Clinical syndromes. Refer to Table 7-1.
   a. Central cord: caused by hyperextension injuries.
      (1) Presents with more upper extremity deficits than lower extremity deficits.
   b. Brown-Séquard: caused by a trauma (e.g., a gunshot wound, infectious process, or inflammatory disease), which results in a hemi-section of the spinal cord.
      (1) The result is ipsilateral paralysis, ipsilateral loss of proprioception and discriminative touch; contralateral loss of pain and thermal sense.
   c. Anterior cord: caused by flexion injuries.

   (1) The result is bilateral loss of motor function, pain, pinprick, and temperature sensation below the lesion while proprioception and light touch are preserved.
   d. Posterior cord: least frequent syndrome, caused by injury to the posterior columns.
      (1) The result is loss of proprioception; pain, temperature, and touch are preserved. Motor function is preserved to varying degrees.
   e. Conus medullaris: injury of the sacral cord and lumbar nerve roots.
      (1) The result is lower extremity motor and sensory loss and an areflexic bowel and bladder.
      (2) If the lesion is in the sacral segments, reflexes may be occasionally preserved.
   f. Cauda equina syndrome: injury at the L1 level and below.
      (1) The result is a LMN lesion; flaccid paralysis with no spinal reflex activity; an areflexic bowel and bladder.

> **EXAM HINT:** The NBCOT® OTR® exam content outline identifies knowledge of the "expected patterns, progressions, and prognoses associated with conditions that limit occupational performance . . . (including) . . . secondary complications" (NBCOT®, 2022, p. 3) as essential for competent and safe practice. The application of knowledge about the following potential complications of a SCI can help you determine the correct answer for NBCOT® exam items about working with a person living with a SCI who is at risk for these complications and/or experiencing them.

BOX 7-2 ▷ ASIA Impairment Scale (AIS)

- **A = Complete.** No sensory or motor function is preserved in the sacral segments S4-5.
- **B = Sensory Incomplete.** Sensory but not motor function is preserved below the neurological level and includes the sacral segments S4-5 (light touch [LT] or pin prick [PP] at S4-5 or deep anal pressure) AND no motor function is preserved more than three levels below the motor level on either side of the body.
- **C = Motor Incomplete.** Motor function is preserved at the most caudal sacral segments for voluntary anal contraction (VAC) OR the patient meets the criteria for sensory incomplete status (sensory function preserved at the most caudal sacral segments S4-5 by LT, PP, or DAP), and has some sparing of motor function more than three levels below the ipsilateral motor level on either side of the body. (This includes key or non-key muscle functions to determine motor incomplete status.) For AIS C – less than half of key muscle functions below the single NLI have a muscle grade ≥ 3.
- **D = Motor Incomplete.** Motor incomplete status as defined above, with at least half (half or more) of key muscle functions below the single NLI having a muscle grade ≥ 3.
- **E = Normal.** If sensation and motor function as tested with the ISNCSCI are graded as normal in all segments, and the patient had prior deficits, then the AIS grade is E. Someone without an initial SCI does not receive an AIS grade.
- **Using ND:** To document the sensory, motor and NLI levels, the ASIA Impairment Scale grade, and/or the zone of partial preservation (ZPP) when they are unable to be determined based on the examination results.

AIS = ASIA Impairment Scale; DAP = deep anal pressure; ISNCSCI = International Standards for Neurological Classification of Spinal Cord Injury; LT = light touch; NLI = neurological level of injury; PP = pin prick; SCI = spinal cord injury.

Reference: American Spinal Injury Association: International Standards for Neurological Classification of Spinal Cord Injury, revised 2019; Richmond, VA. Reprinted with permission.

5. Complications.
   a. Respiratory complications, decreased vital capacity, pneumonia.
   b. Decubitus ulcer formation: a serious health problem in debilitated and immobilized patients.
      (1) Prevention of decubitus ulcers.
         (a) Repositioning and pressure relief.
         (b) Keeping skin dry and clean.
         (c) Maintaining good and adequate nutrition.
         (d) Using pressure relief systems (e.g., mattress, wheelchair cushions).
      (2) Management of decubitus ulcers.
         (a) Wound care.
         (b) Surgical intervention.
      (3) Refer to the section on wounds and pressure/decubitus ulcers in Chapter 9 for more information about decubitus ulcers and their prevention and management.
   c. Orthostatic hypotension: an excessive fall in blood pressure upon assuming the upright position.
      (1) Prevention.
         (a) Decrease venous pooling in legs (e.g., abdominal binders, compression stockings).
         (b) Positioning to foster upright position (e.g., gradual increase of bed while sleeping, gradual increase in sitting upright in tilt-in-space or recliner wheelchair).
         (c) Adequate hydration and timing of meals (Budash, 2021).
      (2) Medical management.
         (a) Medications or managing medications that have hypotensive effects (Budash, 2021).
   d. Deep vein thrombosis (DVT): inflammation of a vein in association with the formation of a thrombus; usually occurs in lower extremities.
      (1) Refer to the section on peripheral vascular disease (PVD) in Chapter 8 for more information about the presenting symptoms of DVT.

> **RED FLAG:** Deep vein thrombosis can be life threatening as it can turn into a pulmonary embolism; thus, its presenting symptoms require immediate medical attention.

   e. Autonomic dysreflexia: an abnormal response to a noxious stimulus that results in an extreme rise in blood pressure, pounding headache, and profuse sweating.
      (1) Irritants that would normally cause pain to areas below the spinal injury specific to the bowel include bowel irritation or overdistention (e.g., constipation/impaction, distention during bowel program [digital stimulation], hemorrhoid infection or irritation).

      (2) Irritants specific to the bladder include bladder infection or overdistention (e.g., urinary tract infection [UTI], urinary retention, blocked catheter, overfilled urine collection bag, noncompliance with intermittent catheterization program).
      (3) Skin-related irritants can include any skin irritation below area of injury (e.g., decubitus ulcers, ingrown toenails, burns, tight or restrictive clothing or pressure to skin from clothing restrictions or wrinkles in clothing).
      (4) Sexual activity irritants can include overstimulation during sex, stimuli to the pelvic region that would be felt as pain if sensation were intact, menstrual cramps, labor and delivery.
      (5) Other irritants can include heterotopic ossification/myositis ossificans, skeletal fractures, and appendicitis.

> **RED FLAG:** Autonomic dysreflexia is a medical emergency if not reversed by quickly removing the irritating stimulus.

      (6) Prevention of autonomic dysreflexia.
         (a) Teach the person/caregiver pressure relief principles to prevent decubitus ulcers.
         (b) Ensure compliance with intermittent catheterization.
         (c) Practice well-balanced diet habits.
         (d) Ensure medication compliance.
         (e) Educate the person with the condition (and/or at risk) and caregivers on how to use prevention methods; recognize the cause, signs, and symptoms (i.e., sweating, headache); and initiate first aid procedures to deal effectively with the occurrence of this condition.
      (7) Management of autonomic dysreflexia.
         (a) Identify the offending stimulus and relieve the underlying issue immediately.
         (b) Medications, if no impact can be made by removing the irritant.
   f. Urinary tract infection.
   g. Heterotopic ossification, the formation of bone in abnormal anatomical locations.
6. Medical management.
   a. Prevention of further cord damage via stabilization.
   b. Traction and rest for unstable injuries.
   c. Surgery with internal or external fixation.
   d. Diuretic prescription to decrease inflammation.
   e. Bladder care.
   f. Decubiti prevention.
   g. Control of autonomic dysreflexia and orthostatic hypotension.
   h. Prevention of thrombus formation.
   i. Treatment for heterotopic ossification.

Table 7-6

Motor Abilities and Functional Outcomes of Spinal Cord Injury

SCI LEVEL	FUNCTIONALLY RELEVANT MUSCLES INNERVATED	POSSIBLE MOVEMENTS AND PHYSICAL ABILITIES	FUNCTIONAL CAPABILITIES [EQUIPMENT USED*]
C1-C3	Sternocleidomastoid, cervical paraspinal, and neck accessories	• Neck flexion, extension and rotation • Limited movement of head and neck	**Breathing** • Ventilator dependent, inability to clear secretions [suction equipment to clear secretions]. **Communication** • Can be difficult, very limited or impossible, however, can be independent with assistive technology. (AT) to direct care to personal care assistants (PCAs)/caregivers [mouth stick, computer, communication board for speech or typing]. **Daily Tasks** • Total assist for ADL and IADL. • AT for independence in reading a book, operating a phone, lights or tv [mouth stick, environmental control units (ECU)]. **Mobility** • Total assist for bed mobility and transfers. • Can independently use a power recline and/or tilt wheelchair by using head control, mouth stick, sip and puff for mobility and pressure relief [power or manual lift, electric bed or semi-electric hospital bed].
C4	All of the above and diaphragm, upper trapezius, cervical paraspinal	• All of above and scapular elevation and inspiration • Usually, head and neck control • May have shoulder shrug	**Breathing:** • May be able to breathe without a ventilator, unable to cough, low respiratory capacity reserve and limited endurance. **Communication:** • Normal and can self-direct PCAs and caregivers. **Daily Tasks:** • Total assist for most ADL and IADL. • Possible independence with eating [sandwich holder on gooseneck feeder, long straw for liquids]. • AT for independence in typing, writing, operating adjustable bed [ECU for bed control, mouth stick for typing]. **Mobility:** • Total assist for bed mobility and transfers. • Can independently use a power recline and/or tilt wheelchair by using head control, mouth stick, sip and puff for mobility and pressure relief [power or manual lift, electric bed or semi-electric hospital bed].
C5	All of the above and deltoids, biceps, brachialis, brachio-radialis, rhomboids, serratus anterior (partially innervated)	• All of above and shoulder flexion, abduction, extension; elbow flexion and supination • Typically head and neck control, some shoulder control • Can bend elbows and turn palms up	**Daily Tasks:** • Can be independfent with eating after set-up [dorsal hand splint with universal cuff and attachments for utensils, scoop plate, plate guard, long straw]. • Requires assistance for cough assist. • Can be independent with grooming after set-up [wash mitt for face, dorsal hand splint with universal cuff for attachment of toothbrush, comb, electric razor and/or make-up applicators]. • Can use adaptive equipment (AE) to assist a PCA/caregiver with upper body dressing and bathing [roll-in padded shower chair, padded transfer bench, wash mitt]. • Total assist for bowel [roll-in padded commode chair] and bladder [electric leg bag emptier] management. **Mobility:** • Total assist for bed mobility and transfers. • Can independently relieve pressure with a power tilt wheelchair. • Can independently use a power wheelchair with hand controls for functional mobility; may be able to push a manual wheelchair for short distances over level surfaces. • Can drive a modified van with a lift and specialized hand controls, but may still need assist with transportation.

Chapter 7

(Continued)

Table 7-6

Motor Abilities and Functional Outcomes of Spinal Cord Injury (Continued)

SCI LEVEL	FUNCTIONALLY RELEVANT MUSCLES INNERVATED	POSSIBLE MOVEMENTS AND PHYSICAL ABILITIES	FUNCTIONAL CAPABILITIES [EQUIPMENT USED*]
C6	All of the above and extensor carpi radialis longus and brevis, serratus anterior, latissimus dorsi	• All of above and wrist extension • Has movement in head, neck, shoulders arms and wrist; can shoulder shrug, bend elbows, turn palms up and extend wrist	**Daily Tasks:** • Can be independent with eating after set-up with a tenodesis splint and AE [universal cuff and attachments, built up utensils, scoop plate, long straw, plate guard]. • Can be independent with grooming after set-up with a tenodesis splint and AE [universal cuff and attachments, adapted electric razor or toothbrush]. • Can be independent with upper body dressing and some assistance with lower body dressing after set-up [dressing stick, leg lifter thigh straps, dressing hook splints, adapted clothing]. • Can use AE to assist a PCA/caregiver with upper body bathing [adapted loofah, long handled sponge with universal cuff]. • Some to total assist for bowel [digital stimulation splint device, enema insertion device] and bladder [catheter inserter, penis positioner, thigh spreader with mirror]. **Mobility:** • Can turn in bed with AE [bed ladder, thigh straps, bed rails, electric hospital bed]. • Can perform sliding board transfers to toilet, commode and/or shower/tub bench with some assistance from PCA/caregiver. • Can independently relieve pressure with a power tilt wheelchair. • Can perform forward and/or lateral lean pressure relief independently or with some assistance. • Can use an ultra-lightweight manual wheelchair for mobility on even surfaces [wheelchair pegs, wheelchair gloves, rubber tubing on wheels]; may prefer to use a power wheelchair for easier mobility over uneven terrain. • Can independently drive a vehicle with specialized equipment and vehicle modifications [modified van with lift, hand controls, tie downs].
C7-8	All of above plus triceps, flexor digitorum profundus and superficialis, extensor communis, pronator/flexor/extensor and abductor pollicis, lumbricals (partially innervated)	• All of the above with elbow extension and finger and thumb flexion/extension/abduction • Movement similar to C6 with added ability to straighten elbow (C7) and move hand (C8)	**Daily Tasks:** • Can be independent in many daily tasks with the use of a tenodesis grasp, AE, and/or tenodesis splint if needed or preferred. • Can be independent with eating with a tenodesis grasp, tenodesis splint, and/or AE [built up utensils, curved utensils, long straw, plate guard, adapted strategies for grasp]. • Can be independent with grooming with a tenodesis grasp, tenodesis splint, and/or AE [built up toothbrush, splint material added to devices]. • Can be independent with upper body dressing, but may need some assistance with lower body dressing and AE [dressing stick, leg lifter, zipper pull]. • Can use AE to assist a PCA/caregiver with lower body bathing [adapted loofah, long handled sponge]. • Some to no assist for bowel [digital stimulation splint device, enema insertion device, toileting aid] and bladder [catheter inserter, thigh spreader with mirror]. **Mobility:** • Can independently perform transfers with or without a sliding board on level surfaces. • Can independently complete wheelchair pushups and/or lateral leans to relieve pressure. • Can independently propel a manual wheelchair; some assistance may be required for uphill mobility and unlevel transfers. • Can independently drive with specialized equipment and vehicle modifications [hand controls]; may be able to load and unload wheelchair into and from a car. If not, a modified van with a lift is indicated.

Chapter 7

Table 7-6

Motor Abilities and Functional Outcomes of Spinal Cord Injury (*Continued*)

SCI LEVEL	FUNCTIONALLY RELEVANT MUSCLES INNERVATED	POSSIBLE MOVEMENTS AND PHYSICAL ABILITIES	FUNCTIONAL CAPABILITIES [EQUIPMENT USED*]
T1-T9	All of the above plus intrinsics of the hand including the thumb, lumbricals, internal and external intercostals, erector spinae	• Upper extremity fully intact • Limited upper trunk stability	**Daily tasks:** • Can independently perform all ADL including bowel and bladder management, AE may be used, if needed or preferred. **Mobility:** • Independent with bed mobility and transfer with or without equipment. • Can independently complete wheelchair pushups for pressure relief. • Can independently propel a wheelchair on even and uneven surfaces and up and down curbs. • Can independently drive with hand controls and load and unload a wheelchair into and from a car.
T10-L1	All of the above plus fully intact intercostals, external obliques, and rectus abdominis	• All of the above plus good trunk stability • Possible ambulation with braces and some assist	**Daily tasks:** • Can independently perform all ADL including bowel and bladder management, adaptive equipment may be used, if needed or preferred. **Mobility:** • Independent with bed mobility and transfer with or without equipment. • Can independently complete wheelchair pushups for pressure relief. • Can independently propel a wheelchair on even and uneven surfaces and up and down curbs. • Can possibly ambulate with the use of specialized leg braces [knee, ankle, foot orthosis (KAFO)] and assistive devices [forearm crutches or walker]; the functionality of ambulation depends on the person's lower extremity strength and range of motion, and the total distance that will be traversed. • Individuals may use a wheelchair for community mobility. • Can independently drive with hand controls and load and unload a wheelchair into and from a car.
L2-S5	All of the above plus fully intact abdominals and all other trunk muscles Depending on level some degree of hip flexors/extensors/abductors/adductors, knee flexors/extensors, ankle dorsi/plantar flexors	• All of the above plus partial to full control of lower extremities • Ambulation with or without braces	**Daily tasks:** • Can independently engage in all areas of occupation. **Mobility:** • Can ambulate with little to no bracing [KAFO or ankle foot orthosis (AFO)] with assistive devices [forearm crutches or cane as indicated].

*Equipment identified is not an all-inclusive list.

Cerebral Palsy (CP)

1. Etiology.
   a. Caused by malformation of brain structures and/or injury to brain structures during the prenatal, perinatal and/or postnatal periods and through the first two years of childhood.
   b. Common causes include genetic factors leading to malformation of the brain, premature birth with injury to the underdeveloped brain, low birth weight, multiple-gestation pregnancies, maternal and prenatal infections, intracranial hemorrhage, meningitis, encephalitis, and/or hypoxia.

2. Prognosis is dependent on the extent of brain malformation or severity and extent of injury to the brain. The location of malformation and injury are also factors in prognosis.
   a. The brain malformation and/or injuries are non-progressive.
      (1) In some cases, patterns of motor, sensory, and developmental challenges may change over time and can increase in severity as a child ages.
   b. Comorbidities can include respiratory problems, seizure disorders, scoliosis, contractors, and pressure sores.

c. Cognitive and language abilities vary in children with cerebral palsy and are dependent upon the extent and location of brain malformation and/or injury.

   (1) Motor impairments that lead to dysarthria typically impact verbal expressive skills and may lead to the false presumption of impaired cognition in a person with cerebral palsy.

     (a) Many children and adults with cerebral palsy have typical intellectual abilities.

3. Diagnosis.

  a. Typically diagnosed between 12 and 24 months of age.

  b. Early indicators of cerebral palsy.

   (1) Hypotonia in infancy.

   (2) The development of spasticity in the limbs with or without hypotonia in the trunk and proximal muscles.

   (3) Head lag when pulled to sit that is outside the range of typical motor development.

   (4) The persistence of primitive reflexes beyond typical developmental norms.

   (5) The absence of the development of protective responses.

   (6) The development of clonus, asymmetrical motor development, involuntary movements, and feeding difficulties due to oral motor impairments.

   (7) Cognitive, and other global delays may also develop over time.

  c. The location and severity of the brain malformation or injury determines the type of motor control present in cerebral palsy. Types include the following.

   (1) Spastic cerebral palsy: upper motor neuron dysfunction that causes increased muscle tone, which restricts movement.

     (a) Severe spasticity is present at rest and with voluntary movement and can result in impairments of range of motion leading to contractures of the joints.

   (2) Dyskinetic cerebral palsy: dysfunction in the basal ganglia that causes combinations of movement patterns and muscle tone impacting the whole body and presenting with wide fluctuations of tone and motor control. Dyskinetic movements occur at rest and with voluntary movement. Types of dyskinetic cerebral palsy include the following.

     (a) Chorea: rapid random jerking motions.

     (b) Athetosis: slow writhing movements.

     (c) Dystonia: twining movements and contortions in posture.

     (d) Choreo-athetosis: combined types of chorea and athetosis.

   (3) Ataxic cerebral palsy: dysfunction in the cerebellum causing movements to be poorly coordinated and characterized by overshooting and/or undershooting of the limbs during voluntary motor activities. Signs of ataxia include the following.

     (a) Wide-based and unsteady gait.

     (b) Motor control lacks precision in direction and aiming toward a target.

     (c) Most difficulties with motor control are present with voluntary movement versus at rest.

  d. Classification of severity is based on daily functional capacity to perform manual tasks; the ability to handle objects, walk, and use mobility devices; and the quality of movement. Tools used for classification are listed below.

   (1) The Gross Motor Functional Classification System (GMFCS). This tool delineates five levels of functional mobility from infancy to age 18. Walking and use of mobility devices are major components of this tool. Refer to Table 7-7.

   (2) The Manual Ability Classification System (MACS) for Children with Cerebral Palsy describes five levels of handling everyday objects placed within easy reach. These levels include amount of support and assistance needed for handling objects. Refer to Table 7-8.

  e. The distribution of the disorder in limbs is another form of classification.

   (1) Monoplegia involves one extremity.

   (2) Hemiplegia involves the upper and lower extremity on the same side.

   (3) Quadriplegia involves all extremities.

   (4) Tetraplegia involves all limbs and the head/neck.

   (5) Diplegia involves less upper extremity impairment and greater functional impairments of the lower extremities.

4. Complications and common comorbidities.

  a. Seizure disorders.

  b. Impairments of expressive and receptive speech and language development including dysarthria and aphasia.

  c. Cognitive impairments.

Table 7-7

Summary of Functional Motor Performance of Children with Cerebral Palsy

LEVEL	DESCRIPTION OF FUNCTIONAL MOTOR PERFORMANCE
For Each Level of the Gross Motor Functional Classification System	
I	Walks without limitations.
II	Walks with limitations.
III	Walks using a hand-held mobility device.
IV	Self-mobility with limitations; may use powered mobility.
V	Transported in a manual wheelchair.

Palisano, R., Rosenbaum, P., Bartlett, D., & Livingston, M. (2007). Gross motor function classification system: Expanded and revised. CanChild Centre for Childhood Disability Research Institute for Applied Health Sciences. McMaster University. https://canchild.ca/en/resources/42-gross-motor-function-classification-system-e-r. Reprinted with permission.

Table 7-8

Manual Ability Classification System for Children with Cerebral Palsy	
I	Handles objects easily and successfully.
II	Handles most objects but with somewhat reduced quality and/or speed of achievement.
III	Handles objects with difficulty; needs help to prepare and/or modify activities.
IV	Handles a limited selection of easily managed objects in adapted situations.
V	Does not handle objects and has severely limited ability to perform even simple actions.

Eliasson, A.C., Krumlinde Sundholm, L., Rösblad, B., Beckung, E., Arner, M., Öhrvall, A.M., & Rosenbaum, P. (2006). The Manual Ability Classification System (MACS) for children with cerebral palsy: Scale development and evidence of validity and reliability. Developmental Medicine and Child Neurology, 48, 549–554. Reprinted with permission.

d. Oral motor impairments resulting in difficulties with feeding and swallowing, which can lead to malnourishment and placement of a gastrostomy tube for feeding.

e. Various types of visual impairments are common in cerebral palsy.
   (1) Strabismus: deviation of how one eye aligns with the other (eyes crossing).
   (2) Nystagmus: a reflexive oscillating response of the eyes.
   (3) Refractive errors:
      (a) Myopia near-sightedness.
      (b) Hyperopia far-sightedness.
      (c) Presbyopia: difficulty in accommodation when focusing on objects nearby and when shifting focus from near to far.
   (4) Homonymous hemianopsia: loss of vision in one half of the visual fields of both eyes causing a visual field cut to the right or the left sides. Refer to Figure 13-1 in Chapter 13.

f. Impaired and inefficient cardiac and respiratory functions.

5. Management includes rehabilitative, medical, surgical, and developmental.
   a. Rehabilitative interventions include traditional occupational, physical, and speech therapy services as well as interventions such as hippotherapy and aquatic therapy.
   b. Medical management.
      (1) Medications to manage muscle tone (e.g., anti-spasticity medications such as benzodiazepines, baclofen, botulinum toxin), pain, seizures, and other co-morbidities, if present.
      (2) Orthopedic management to address the development of scoliosis and joint contractures. This includes use of splints, orthotics, and positioning devices.
      (3) Surgical interventions such as selective dorsal rhizotomy, deep brain stimulation, and releases of muscles and tendons to reduce joint contractures.
      (4) Dietary interventions and special feeding techniques.
6. Occupational therapy evaluation and intervention.
   a. Refer to Chapter 5: Human Development Across the Life Span.
   b. Refer to Chapter 12: Neurological Approaches: Evaluation and Intervention.
   c. Refer to Chapter 15: Evaluation and Intervention for Performance in Areas of Occupation.

> **EXAM HINT:** The NBCOT® OTR® exam content outline identifies knowledge of "expected patterns, progressions, and prognoses associated with conditions that limit occupational performance . . . (including the) signs and symptoms of disease, stages of disease, (and) secondary complications" (NBCOT®, 2022, p. 3) as essential for competent and safe practice. Thus, the application of knowledge about CVA, TBI, CP, and other trauma disorders described above and in prior sections and the following information about disorders of movement and neuromuscular diseases can help you determine the correct answer to exam items about working with persons with these conditions.

Disorders of Movement/Neuromuscular Diseases

Classification of Symptoms

1. Ataxia: describes a lack of coordination while performing voluntary movements. It may appear as clumsiness, inaccuracy, or instability. Movements are not smooth and may appear disjointed or jerky.

2. Chorea: brief, purposeless, involuntary movements of the distal extremities and face; usually considered to be a manifestation of dopaminergic overactivity in the basal ganglia.

3. Dyskinesias: involuntary, nonrepetitive, but occasionally stereotyped movements affecting distal, proximal,

Chapter 7

and axial musculature in varying combinations. Most dyskinesias are representative of basal ganglia disorders.

4. Dystonia: results in sustained abnormal postures and disruptions of ongoing movement resulting from alterations of muscle tone. Dystonias may be generalized or focal.

5. Hemiballismus: usually characterized by involuntary flinging motions of the extremities. The movements are often violent and have wide amplitudes of motion. They are continuous and random and can involve proximal and/or distal muscles on one side of the body.

6. Myoclonus: a brief and rapid contraction of a muscle or group of muscles.

7. Tics: brief, rapid, involuntary movements, often resembling fragments of normal motor behavior. They tend to be stereotyped and repetitive, but not rhythmic.

8. Tremor: rhythmic, alternating, oscillatory movements produced by repetitive patterns of muscle contraction and relaxation.
   a. Tremors are classified by rate, rhythm, and distribution.
   b. Tremors are identified as to whether they occur at rest (resting tremor) or during activity (action or intention tremor).

> **EXAM HINT:** Understanding how neuromuscular symptoms affect functional abilities can help you correctly answer NBCOT® exam items about the best approach to use to enable occupational performance. For example, the functional effects of intention tremors can be minimized by teaching the person to use the environment for proximal stability.

Parkinson's Disease

1. Etiology: a hypokinetic CNS movement disorder that is idiopathic, slowly progressive, and degenerative.
2. Onset is usually after 40 years of age, with increasing incidence in older age groups.
3. Symptoms.
   a. Begins insidiously with a resting "pill-rolling" tremor of one hand.
   b. Cardinal signs: tremor (T), rigidity (R), akinesia (A) and postural (P) instability (TRAP).
      (1) Postural instability may present as festinating gait, falling backward (retropulsion) or forward (propulsion), motoric "freezing" (Forwell, 2021).
   c. Other symptoms: resistance to passive motion that is not velocity dependent (cogwheel or lead pipe), micrographia, cognitive impairments, depression, apathy, fatigue, urinary and sexual dysfunction,

sensory symptoms, swallowing, and weight loss (Forwell, 2021).

4. Diagnostic testing.
   a. Presence of cardinal signs.
   b. Positive response to Sinemet (carbidopa/levodopa).
   c. Stage of disease progression is diagnosed using Hoehn and Yahr's five-stage scale. Refer to Box 7-3.

5. Medical management.
   a. Surgical interventions: thalamotomy, pallidotomy, fetal tissue transplant, deep brain stimulators.
   b. Pharmacology.
      (1) Used to compensate for loss of dopamine.
      (2) Medications.
         (a) Levodopa (the metabolic precursor of dopamine) also called L-dopa.
         (b) Carbidopa/levodopa (Sinemet): Carbidopa combined with levodopa to decrease side effects of levodopa, such as nausea, and delay conversion of levodopa to dopamine until it reaches the brain.
         (c) Dopamine agonists (mimics dopamine).
         (d) Anticholinergics (Benadryl, Artane, Cogentin) for rigidity and tremors.
         (e) Amantadine, an antiviral drug, helps decrease PD symptoms (National Institute of Neurological Disorders and Stroke [NINDS], 2020).
   c. Side effects are common when the disease is being managed pharmacologically.
      (1) During early treatment, side effects from carbidopa/levodopa therapy are usually not a major problem.
      (2) As the disease progresses, the drug works less evenly and predictably.
         (a) As a result, some people may experience involuntary movements (dyskinesia), primarily when the medication is having its peak effects.

BOX 7-3 ▷ Stages of Parkinson's Disease

- **Stage I:** unilateral tremor, rigidity, akinesia, minimal or no functional impairment.
- **Stage II:** bilateral tremor, rigidity or akinesia, with or without axial signs, independent with ADL, no balance impairment.
- **Stage III:** worsening of symptoms, first signs of impaired righting reflexes, onset of disability in ADL performance, can lead independent life.
- **Stage IV:** requires help with some or all ADL, unable to live alone without some assistance, able to walk and stand unaided.
- **Stage V:** unable to stand, walk, or perform ADL, a wheelchair and maximal assistance are required.

(b) The length of time for which each dose is effective may begin to shorten (wearing-off effect), leading to more frequent doses.

> CAUTION: The on-off effect of long-term carbidopa/levodopa usage may cause Parkinson's-related movement problems to appear and disappear suddenly and unpredictably.

    (3) Other side effects may include the following.
      (a) Hallucinations.
      (b) A drop in blood pressure when standing (orthostatic hypotension).
      (c) Nausea.
  d. Despite the above potential side effects, carbidopa/levodopa typically allows people with Parkinson's disease to extend the time that they can lead their lives as they would without PD, and in many cases is effective for a number of years.

Neural Tube Defects

1. Etiology.
  a. Complex interaction of environmental and genetic factors, which contribute to the malformation of the brain, vertebrae, and spinal cord.
    (1) Variations of neural tube defects include lack of brain development beyond the brain stem (anencephaly), malformation of the skull causing protrusion of the brain (encephalocele), and malformation of the vertebral arches causing protrusion of the spinal cord (spina bifida).
  b. Some studies suggest certain medications and a lack of folic acid may induce neural tube defects.
2. Onset and prognosis.
  a. Onset: prenatal (within 26 days of conception).
  b. In cases of anencephaly, about half of fetuses are spontaneously aborted. The majority of babies born with anencephaly die in early infancy.
  c. Babies born with encephalocele have better outcomes if the malformation is frontal versus occipital.
    (1) Co-morbid hydrocephalus and seizures impact outcomes and children may develop a range of cognitive impairments or learning disabilities.
  d. In spina bifida, the prognosis and degree of impairment is dependent on the level of the lesion, the extent of the neural tube defect, degree of malformation of the vertebral arches, and the extent to which the spinal column is enclosed in an external sac.
3. Diagnosis: detected prenatally through amniocentesis for levels of alpha-fetoprotein (AFP) and acetylcholinesterase, and ultrasound if indicated.
4. Classification of spina bifida is dependent on the level of the lesion and the extent of tissue involved.

  a. Spina bifida occulta: a bony malformation with separation of vertebral arches of one or more vertebrae with no external manifestations; may not be discovered until late childhood.
    (1) Occult spinal dysraphism (OSD): when external manifestations such as a red birthmark (hemangioma or flame nevus), patch of hair, a dermal sinus (opening in skin), a fatty benign tumor (lipoma), or dimple covering the site are present.
  b. Spina bifida cystica: an exposed pouch composed of the spinal cord and meninges.
    (1) Spina bifida with meningocele: protrusion of a sac through the spine, containing cerebral spinal fluid and meninges; however, it does not include the spinal cord.
    (2) Spina bifida with myelomeningocele: protrusion of a sac through the spine, containing cerebral spinal fluid and meninges as well as the spinal cord or nerve roots. Most commonly located in the lumbar region; however, it can occur at any point along the spinal column.
5. Specific symptoms.
  a. Spina bifida occulta usually does not result in any symptoms.
    (1) Occasionally slight instability and neuromuscular impairments, such as mild gait involvement and bowel or bladder problems may occur.
  b. Occult spinal dysraphism may result in the spinal cord being split (diplomyelia) or being tied down and tethered (diastematomyelia), which may lead to neurological damage and developmental abnormality as the child grows.
  c. Spina bifida meningocele usually does not present with symptoms impacting on function as the spinal cord itself is not entrapped. Occasionally slight instability and neuromuscular impairments, such as mild gait involvement and bowel or bladder problems may occur.
  d. Spina bifida with myelomeningocele results in sensory and motor deficits occurring below the level of the lesion and may result in lower extremity paralysis and/or deformities, bowel and bladder incontinence, decubitus ulcer, and DVT.
    (1) The level of lesions determines the impact on leg movements.
    (2) Lesions of S2–S4 results in bladder and bowel problems.
      (a) A neurogenic bladder impacts on the sensation to urinate and the control of the urinary sphincter.
      (b) Incomplete emptying of the bladder results; this often leads to infections.
      (c) A neurogenic bowel causes constipation and incontinence.

6. Tethered cord syndrome occurs in the tail end of the spinal cord when the cord is stretched as a result of compression, being trapped with a fatty mass or scar tissue, developmental abnormality, or injury.
   a. Visible signs include a hairy patch of skin, a hemangioma, and/or a dimple of the lower spine.
   b. Difficulties with bowel and bladder control, gait disturbances, deformities of the feet, low back pain, and/or scoliosis may result.
   c. May go undiagnosed until the above symptoms emerge.
   d. Symptoms may be exacerbated with pregnancy or with age due to spinal stenosis.
   e. In children and adolescents, symptoms may be exacerbated by growth spurts. During growth spurts, it is also possible for the spine to "re-tether" even after surgery has occurred, which may warrant additional surgery to correct.

7. Chiari Type II malformation: common among children with myelomeningocele. Displacement of the brainstem and cerebellum into the spinal canal causing compression on the spinal cord, cerebellum, and brain stem.
   a. Symptoms include trouble breathing, swallowing problems, weakness, and arching of the head backward.

8. Medical management.
   a. During the neonatal period precautions are taken to protect the sac from rupturing and from infection, which may result in meningitis. All or part of the sac may be removed 24–48 hours after birth.
   b. A ventriculoperitoneal or other type of shunt is indicated should the complication of hydrocephalus occur, in which the cerebral spinal fluid is not absorbed resulting in an increase in size of the ventricles and the infant's head.
      (1) Shunts can malfunction or become blocked or infected resulting in increased intracranial pressure, which can be life threatening. Signs and symptoms include the following.
         (a) During infancy, extreme head growth and often a soft spot on the forehead.
         (b) Severe headaches, vomiting, and/or irritability.
         (c) A change in the function of upper extremities and regression in developmental milestones.
         (d) A decline in school performance and/or cognitive function.
         (e) Impaired vision, double vision, and inability to direct gaze upward.
         (f) Onset of seizure disorders or increase in seizure activity.
         (g) Deterioration of physical skills and/or loss of balance.
      (2) Medical interventions for shunt malfunction or infection are critical and include the following.
         (a) Withdrawal of fluid or replacement of tubing.
         (b) Administration of intravenous antibiotics.
         (c) Medications to reduce cerebrospinal fluid production and intracranial pressure.

> **RED FLAG:** Early identification of blocked and infected shunts is vital, as these conditions are life threatening. Immediate notification of signs and symptoms to the child's/facility's neurosurgeon is required.

   c. Urological management, and if indicated intermittent catheterization.
   d. Orthopedic management for motor deficits.
   e. Surgical intervention may be indicated for tethered cord syndrome.

Muscular Dystrophies/Atrophies

1. Etiology: a group of degenerative disorders resulting in muscle weakness and decreased muscle mass due to a hereditary disease process.
   a. Muscular dystrophies are due to an absent muscle protein production called dystrophin. Dystrophin levels can be tested with a muscle biopsy.

2. Onset and prognosis.
   a. Muscular dystrophies/atrophies can begin in infancy, childhood, or adulthood.
   b. First symptoms may not be apparent until 2.5 years of age.
   c. Average age of diagnosis is five years, unless there is a known family history; whereby, earlier detection is more likely to occur.
   d. Progress may be rapid and fatal or may remain stable throughout life.
      (1) Those starting early in life tend to be more severe and to progress more rapidly.

3. Diagnosis.
   a. Detection is confirmed by blood tests for muscle enzymes or muscle proteins (e.g., high creatine kinase levels), nerve conduction velocity, electromyography, and, if indicated, muscle or nerve biopsy.
   b. Common symptoms include hypotonia, muscle weakness, and atrophy.

4. Major types.
   a. Duchenne's muscular dystrophy is the most common form of muscular dystrophy.
      (1) It is detected between three and five years of age.
      (2) Symptoms include pseudohypertrophy (enlargement of calf muscles), and at times enlargement of the forearm and thigh muscles, giving an appearance the child is muscular and healthy.
      (3) Weakness of the proximal joints progresses to the point that the child has significant functional mobility impairments. These include:
         (a) Ambulating with a Trendelenburg (i.e., waddling) gait with frequent falls.

(b) Difficulty getting up from the floor to a standing position; uses hands to crawl up the thighs to get to the standing position, known as Gower's sign.

(4) Weakness occurs in all voluntary muscles, including the heart and diaphragm.

(5) Behavioral and learning difficulties and delayed speech may occur.

(6) Individuals rarely survive beyond their early 20s due to respiratory problems, infections, and/or cardiovascular complications; however, advancements in supportive care enable some individuals to live longer.

b. Becker's muscular dystrophy.

(1) A variant of Duchenne's muscular dystrophy that is slower to progress, less severe, and less predictable.

(2) Presenting symptoms.

(a) Loss of motor function of the hips, thighs, pelvic area, and shoulders.

(b) Enlarged calves.

(c) Cardiac system can be involved.

(3) Survival can be into late adulthood.

(a) A normal life span can be attained if there is minimal cardiac involvement.

c. Limb-girdle muscular dystrophy.

(1) Onset begins between the first and third decades of life.

(2) Proximal muscles of the pelvis and shoulder are initially affected.

(3) Typically progresses slowly.

d. Fascioscapulohumeral muscular dystrophy.

(1) Occurs in early adolescence.

(2) Involves the face, upper arms, and scapular region, causing masking, weakness, decreased mobility of the face, and the inability to lift the arms above shoulder level.

(3) As it progresses, the weakness can extend to the abdominal muscles and sometimes the hip muscles.

(4) Progresses slowly and rarely affects the cardiac or respiratory systems; thus, life expectancy can be relatively normal.

e. Spinal muscular atrophy.

(1) Weakness of the voluntary muscles of the shoulders, hips, thighs, and upper back, which can result in spinal curvatures.

(2) Muscles for breathing and swallowing can be affected.

(3) The earlier the age of diagnosis, the greater the severity of functional deficits and the shorter the life expectancy.

f. Congenital myasthenia gravis.

(1) A disorder involving transmission of impulses in the neuromuscular junction.

(2) Onset starting near birth and occurring more frequently in males.

g. Charcot-Marie-Tooth disease.

(1) A disease involving the peripheral nerves marked by progressive weakness, primarily in peroneal (fibular) and distal leg muscles.

(2) Typically occurs in the teenage years or earlier.

h. Myopathies.

(1) Symptoms are similar to dystrophies; however, myopathies progress slowly, resulting in a better prognosis.

(2) Weakness of the face, neck, and limbs is characteristic.

5. Specific symptoms.

a. Low muscle tone and weakness contributes to abnormal movement patterns and delayed developmental milestones.

b. There may be difficulty with oral motor feeding, necessitating a nasogastric or gastrostomy tube.

c. Weakness contributes to deformities of the extremities and spine.

d. Difficulty with breathing may require tracheostomies or mechanical ventilators, and frequently results in death.

6. Medical management.

a. Prescribed medications to decrease pulmonary and cardiac complications and prolong life.

b. Nutritional management for difficulties with feeding and the tendency to gain weight secondary to inactivity.

c. Prevention of skin breakdown and decubitus ulcers.

d. Steroids to help delay or reverse muscle weakness; however, the undesirable side effects associated with steroids bring their use into question.

Progressive Supranuclear Palsy (PSP)

1. Rare brain disorder, which causes progressive problems with gait and balance, as well as complex eye movements and cognition.

2. Classic sign: inability to coordinate eye movements causing blurry vision.

3. Other symptoms: altered mood and behavior, depression, apathy, and progressive dementia (National Organization of Rare Disorders [NORD], 2021).

4. Can be confused with Parkinson's disease due to common symptoms such as stiffness and gait difficulties.

a. PSP is more rapidly progressive.

b. Tremors are rare in PSP.

c. People with PSP have "axial rigidity" (i.e., they stand very straight and tend to fall backward), while people with Parkinson's tend to lean forward.

d. Slowing or loss of eye movements, particularly in the downward direction.

Huntington's Chorea

1. Etiology: an autosomal dominant disorder.
2. Onset and prognosis.
   a. Begins in middle age.
   b. Onset of this disease process is insidious.
   c. Signs and symptoms are progressive until the end of life.
3. Symptoms.
   a. Characterized by choreiform movements and progressive intellectual deterioration.
   b. Psychiatric disturbances (e.g., personality change, manic-depressive symptoms, and schizophreniform illness) may precede the onset of the movement disorder.
   c. Impaired walking and balance.

Cerebellar/Spinocerebellar Disorders

1. Characterized by ataxia, dysmetria, dysdiadochokinesia, hypotonia, movement decomposition, intention tremors, dysarthria, and nystagmus.

Structural Cerebellar Lesions

1. Etiology: includes vascular lesions (stroke) and tumor deposits, producing symptoms and signs appropriate to their locus within the cerebellum.
   a. Demyelinating plaques of multiple sclerosis may also arise in the cerebellum white matter and give rise to cerebellar symptoms.
   b. Alcoholism and nutritional deprivation can cause degeneration of the vermis and anterior cerebellum.

Spinocerebellar Degenerations

1. A group of degenerative disorders, characterized by progressive ataxia due to the degeneration of the cerebellum, brain stem, spinal cord, peripheral nerves, and the basal ganglia.
2. Types: these disorders are grouped as spinal ataxias, cerebellar ataxias, and multiple system degeneration.
   a. Friedrich's ataxia.
      (1) Etiology: autosomal recessive inheritance.
      (2) Onset: occurs in childhood or early adolescence.
      (3) Symptoms: the prototype of spinal ataxia.
         (a) Gait unsteadiness, upper extremity ataxia, and dysarthria.
         (b) Tremor may be a minor feature.
         (c) Presentation also includes areflexia and loss of large fiber sensory modalities.
         (d) As the disease progresses, scoliosis and cardiomyopathy are common.
   b. Cerebellar cortical degeneration.
      (1) Etiology: pathologic changes are seen in the cerebellum and the inferior olives.
      (2) Onset begins between ages 30 and 50.
      (3) Symptoms: cerebellar symptoms are the only signs detectable.
   c. Multiple systems degeneration (olivopontocerebellar atrophies).
      (1) Etiology: characterized by spasticity, extrapyramidal, sensory, LMN, and autonomic dysfunction.
      (2) Onset occurs in young to middle life.
3. Medical management for movement disorders is limited in many cases.
   a. Pharmacologic intervention may be able to dampen effects of the movement disorders.
      (1) Agents utilized for this population include propranolol, clonazepam, clonidine, and anticholinergic agents depending upon symptomatology.

Disorders of the Peripheral Nervous System/ Neuromuscular Diseases

Amyotrophic Lateral Sclerosis (ALS)

1. Etiology: motor neuron disease of unknown etiology but believed that genetics and environment may play a role (Forwell, 2021).
2. Onset and prognosis.
   a. The disease is more prevalent in men than women.
   b. Onset occurs at an average age of 57.
   c. Death usually occurs in two to five years.
3. Symptoms.
   a. Muscle weakness and atrophy, often begins distally and asymmetrically.
   b. Cramps and fasciculations precede weakness.

c. Signs usually begin in the hands.

d. LMN signs are soon accompanied by spasticity, hyperactive deep tendon reflexes, and evidence of corticospinal tract involvement.

e. Dysarthria and dysphagia are evident.

f. Sensory systems, eye movements, and urinary sphincters are often spared.

g. Symptom severity is documented by scores on the Revised ALS Functional Rating Scale (ALSFRS-R) (Cederbaum et al., 1999).

(1) Symptoms that are quantified include speech, salivation, swallowing, handwriting, cutting food, dressing/hygiene, turning in bed, walking, climbing stairs, dyspnea, orthopnea, respiratory insufficiency.

(2) Lower scores indicating greater symptoms.

4. Diagnosis.

a. Usually clinical, with generalized motor involvement unaccompanied by sensory abnormalities.

b. Electromyography, nerve conduction, MRI, blood and urine analysis and spinal tap may support the diagnosis or rule out other conditions, such as spinal cord tumors and myopathies.

5. Medical management.

a. Two medications approved by the FDA

(1) Riluzole (Rilutek): taken orally and has been shown to slightly slow the disease course, but it has side effects such as dizziness, fatigue, and gastrointestional and liver issues.

(2) Edaravone (Radicava): intravenous infusion and has been shown to reduce daily functioning decline, but it has side effects such as swelling and shortness of breath (Forwell, 2021).

b. Treatment is aimed at treating secondary complications such as spasticity (treated with antispasmodics), prevention of aspirations (gastrostomy and modified diets), prevention of decubiti, prevention of contracture, and pain management.

Brachial Plexus Disorder

1. Etiology: secondary to traction during birth, invasion of metastatic cancer, post-radiation treatment secondary to fibrosis, or traction injury.

2. Symptoms.

a. Mixed motor and sensory disorders of the corresponding limb.

b. Rostral injuries produce shoulder dysfunction while caudal injuries produce dysfunction in the hand.

3. Diagnosis.

a. Made via CT scanning of the plexus in cases where a mass is present.

b. EMG/nerve conduction velocities are used to localize the plexus lesion.

4. Common injuries of the brachial plexus seen in children.

a. Erb's palsy: a paralysis of the upper brachial plexus including the fifth and sixth cervical nerves; C7 may also be involved in some cases.

(1) Muscles most often paralyzed include the supraspinatus and infraspinatus as well as the deltoid, biceps, brachialis, and subscapularis.

(2) The arm cannot be raised; elbow flexion is weakened and weakness in retraction and protraction of scapula may be noted.

(3) The arm grossly presents with the arm straight and wrist fully bent (the "waiter's tip" position).

(4) After the age of six months, contractures may begin to develop (adduction and internal rotation contractures).

(a) Supination deformity of the forearm may also develop from the imbalance between the supinator and the paralyzed pronator muscles.

(5) Positioning and ROM exercises are necessary to retain external rotation, abduction, and flexion at the shoulder as well as distal flexibility.

b. Klumpke's palsy: a paralysis of the lower brachial plexus including the seventh and eighth cervical and first thoracic nerves.

(1) Relatively rare when compared to the prevalence of Erb's palsy.

(2) It results in paralysis of the hand and wrist, often with ipsilateral Horner's syndrome (miosis, ptosis, and facial anhidrosis).

(3) Characteristic signs are that the hand is limp and the fingers do not move.

Peripheral Neuropathies

1. Etiology: peripheral neuropathy of a single nerve may be the result of trauma, pressure paralysis, forcible overextension of a joint, hemorrhage into a nerve, exposure to cold or radiation, or ischemic paralysis.

a. Multiple nerves may be affected in cases of collagen vascular disease, metabolic diseases (diabetes mellitus), or infectious agents (Lyme disease).

b. Other causes include nutritional deficiency, malignancy, microorganisms, exposure to toxic agents, and chronic alcohol abuse.

2. Diagnosis.

a. Focused on the cause of the symptoms.

b. Specific tests utilized include electromyography, nerve conduction velocity, muscle biopsy, and examinations to identify systemic disorders.

3. Symptoms.

a. A syndrome of sensory, motor, reflex, and vasomotor symptoms.

b. Symptoms include pain, weakness, and paresthesias in the distribution of the affected nerve.

4. Medical management.
   a. Guided by the underlying disease process, not the symptoms of the neuropathy.
   b. Treatment of the underlying systemic disorder (diabetes, tumor, multiple myeloma) may slow progression, although recovery is slow.

Guillain-Barré Syndrome

1. Etiology: the exact cause is unknown.
   a. Considered an autoimmune disease that may occur after an infection, surgery, or an immunization; however, little evidence linked to surgery and immunization.
   b. Acute and rapidly progressing demyelination of the peripheral nerves and spinal nerve roots (Hamby, 2017).
2. Onset and prognosis.
   a. It affects both sexes at any age.
   b. Onset of recovery is two to four weeks after first symptoms.
   c. Long-term prognosis:
      (1) 50% exhibit mild neurological deficits.
      (2) 15% exhibit residual functional deficits.
      (3) 80% are ambulatory in six months.
      (4) 5% die of complications.
3. Diagnosis.
   a. Diagnosis is based on clinical symptoms.
   b. Lumbar puncture reveals increased protein without cells in the cerebrospinal fluid.
   c. Electromyography and nerve conduction studies may support the diagnosis.
   d. Segmental demyelination is apparent and in severe cases, axonal degeneration accompanies the demyelination.
4. Symptoms.
   a. Acute, rapidly progressive form of polyneuropathy characterized by symmetric muscular weakness and mild distal sensory loss/paresthesias.
   b. Weakness is always more apparent than sensory findings and is at first more prominent distally, but it then progresses proximally.
   c. Relatively minor sensory signs and symptoms occur.
      (1) The person may complain of painful extremities.
      (2) Subjective and objective sensory disturbances are common initially.
         (a) Most commonly occurring in a distal (stocking-glove) distribution.
   d. Deep tendon reflexes are lost and sphincters are spared.
   e. Respiratory failure and dysphagia may be seen in some cases.
5. Medical management.
   a. Severe cases constitute a medical emergency requiring constant monitoring of vital signs.
   b. Respiratory support may be necessary in some cases.
   c. Plasmapheresis may be utilized to slow symptoms or halt progression.
   d. Intravenous immunoglobulin has been utilized effectively.

Myasthenia Gravis

1. Etiology: the disease is caused by an autoimmune attack on the acetylcholine receptor of the postsynaptic neuromuscular junction.
   a. This process is considered a disorder of neuromuscular transmission.
   b. The initiating event leading to antibody production is unknown.
2. Onset and prognosis.
   a. Occurs at any age but most often affects younger women and older men.
   b. Prognosis varies, but usually is a progressive disabling process.
   c. Death may occur from respiratory complications.
3. Diagnosis.
   a. Diagnosis is often missed because of the rarity of the disease and the vagueness of symptoms.
   b. Characterized by episodic muscle weakness, chiefly in muscles innervated by cranial nerves.
   c. The possibility of myasthenia gravis is suggested by any of the below symptoms and is confirmed by response to anticholinesterase drugs.
4. Symptoms.
   a. Common symptoms include ptosis, diplopia, muscle fatigue after exercise, dysarthria, dysphagia, and proximal limb weakness.
   b. Sensation and deep tendon reflexes are intact.
   c. Symptoms fluctuate over the course of the day.
   d. In relapsing periods, quadriparesis may develop.
   e. Life threatening respiratory muscle involvement may occur.
5. Medical management.
   a. Treatment includes cholinesterase inhibitors, corticosteroids, immunosuppressive agents, and plasmapheresis.
   b. The anticholinergics and plasmapheresis treat current symptoms.
   c. Corticosteroids and immunosuppressives may alter the disease course by interfering with autoimmune pathogenesis.

RED FLAG: The hallmark symptoms of a myasthenic crisis include progressive weakness, tachycardia, tachypnea, dysphagia, impaired speech, anxiety, restlessness, and decreased respiratory function, which necessitates hospitalization. About 15%–20% of patients are at high risk for respiratory decline, which may require ventilator support (Hamby, 2017).

Post-Polio Syndrome (PPS)

1. Etiology: some motor neurons infected with the polio virus die (leaving paralyzed muscle cells), others survive. Recovered motor neurons develop new terminal axon sprouts that reinnervate muscle cells. After years of stability, these motor units break down, causing new muscle weakness.
   a. Degeneration of the axon sprouts explains the new weakness and fatigue, but the mechanism remains controversial.
   b. A current explanation is related to the overuse of individual motor neurons over time.
2. Onset and prognosis.
   a. Onset is typically 15 years after recovery from polio.
   b. Progress is slow with a good prognosis unless breathing or swallowing difficulties occur.
3. Diagnosis.
   a. Based on clinical symptoms.
   b. Characterized by the onset of new muscle weakness after years of stable functioning.
   c. Disuse weakness should be ruled out.
4. Symptoms.
   a. New onset of weakness.
   b. Easily fatigued.
   c. Muscle pain.
   d. Joint pain.
   e. Cold intolerance.
   f. Atrophy.
   g. Loss of functional skills.
5. Medical management.
   a. Bracing with orthoses and pacing daily activity.
   b. Stretching programs.
   c. Exercise program.
   d. Low doses of tricyclic antidepressants to relieve muscle pain.
   e. Pyridostigmine to reduce fatigue and improve strength.

> **EXAM HINT:** The NBCOT® OTR® exam content outline identifies knowledge of "expected patterns, progressions, and prognoses associated with conditions that limit occupational performance . . . (including the) signs and symptoms of disease, stages of disease, (and) secondary complications" (NBCOT®, 2022, p. 3) as essential for competent and safe practice. Thus, the application of knowledge about disorders of the peripheral nervous system and neuromuscular diseases described above and in prior sections and the following information about multiple sclerosis can help you determine the correct answer to OTR® exam items about working with persons with these conditions.

Demyelinating Disease

Multiple Sclerosis (MS)

1. A slowly progressive CNS disease characterized by patches of demyelination in the brain and spinal cord.
   a. The myelin damage is probably mediated by the immune system.
   b. Postulated etiologies include infection by a slow or latent virus and the possibility of environmental factors contributing to the disease.
2. Onset, prevalence, and prognosis.
   a. Occurs most often between the ages of 20 and 50; it is most often diagnosed when persons are in their 30s.
   b. Overall prognosis is variable with an unpredictable disease course.
3. Diagnosis.
   a. Diagnosis is largely based on symptoms.
   b. Basic diagnostic criteria are evidence of multiple CNS lesions and evidence of at least two episodes of neurological disturbance in an individual between 10 and 59 years.
   c. Diagnostics may include MRI to detect lesions, evoked potentials to measure conduction along sensory pathways, and cerebrospinal fluid examination.
4. Symptoms.
   a. Multiple and varied neurologic symptoms and signs, usually with remissions and exacerbations.
   b. Onset of symptoms is usually insidious.
   c. Fatigue.
   d. Paresthesias in one or more extremities, on the trunk, or in the face.
   e. Weakness or clumsiness in the leg or hand is common.
   f. Visual disturbance (diplopia, partial blindness, nystagmus, eye pain, etc.).
   g. Emotional disturbances (lability, euphoria, and reactive depression).
   h. Balance loss and/or vertigo.
   i. Bowel and bladder dysfunction.
   j. Cognitive features may include apathy, memory loss, lack of judgment, and inattention.
   k. Spasticity, increased reflexes, ataxia, tremors, pain
   l. Sexual dysfunction.

m. The course of the symptoms is highly variable and may follow one of four patterns.
   (1) Relapsing remitting.
   (2) Secondary progressive.
   (3) Primary progressive.
   (4) Progressive relapsing.
5. Medical management is symptom specific.
   a. During acute exacerbation, anti-inflammatory drugs are used to control symptoms.
   b. Antispasmodics (Baclofen) may be effective to counteract spasticity.
   c. Management of bowel and bladder dysfunction may require pharmacologic intervention.
      (1) Catheterization (indwelling or intermittent) is necessary in many cases of bladder dysfunction.
   d. Disease-modifying drugs are used to slow progression.

Occupational Therapy Evaluation for Neurological System Disorders

EXAM HINT: The NBCOT® OTR® exam content outline states that the task of assessing "a client's functional skills, roles, prioritized needs and wants, and performance context to evaluate their occupational performance" (NBCOT®, 2022, p. 4) is essential to entry-level practice and that performance of this task requires knowledge of "resources and considerations for acquiring information about the client's current condition and occupational performance . . . (and) internal and external factors influencing a client's engagement in occupation" (NBCOT®, 2022, p. 4). The application of knowledge about the evaluation process and assessment methods described in this section can help you determine the correct answer for NBCOT® Domain 1 items about the evaluation of persons with neurological system disorders.

Occupational Profile

1. The initial step in the evaluation process that provides an understanding of "the client's occupational history and experiences, patterns of daily living, interests, values, needs, and relevant contexts" (American Occupational Therapy Association [AOTA], 2020, p. 80).
2. The person's concerns about performing occupations and daily life activities are identified and the person's priorities are determined.

Analysis of Performance in Areas of Occupation

1. Activities of daily living (ADL).
2. Instrumental activities of daily living (IADL).
3. Education.
4. Work.
5. Play and leisure.
6. Rest and sleep.
7. Social participation.
8. Health management.
9. Refer to Chapter 15 for more information on the evaluation of occupational performance.

Evaluation of Client Factors and Performance Skills

1. Determine neuromusculoskeletal and movement related strengths and limitations.
   a. Muscle strength: extent of paralysis/weakness.
   b. Muscle endurance: extent of sustainability of muscle contraction.
   c. Joint mobility: joint range of motion.
   d. Muscle tone: severity and distribution of spasticity.
   e. Control of voluntary movement: eye-hand coordination, gross and fine motor coordination, bilateral integration, oculomotor function.
   f. Postural control.
      (1) Limitations in neuromusculoskeletal and movement related functions will impact occupational performance (e.g., a person with limited arm strength and range of motion will have difficulty with dressing).
   g. Motor skills: small observable movements (e.g., reaches, bends, grips, moves, manipulates, walks, lifts) that are initiated and performed to enable engagement in a task.
      (1) Functional examples.
         (a) A person with hand manipulation problems will have difficulty buttoning a shirt or picking up small items.
         (b) A person with lifting problems will have difficulty lifting a cup to drink and/or placing groceries in the refrigerator (AOTA, 2020).
2. Determine sensory function strengths and limitations.
   a. Foundational visual function: acuity, visual fields, ocular range of motion, accommodation, pursuits, saccades.

(1) Functional examples.
  (a) A person with near visual acuity problems will have difficulty reading and/or working on a computer.
  (b) A person with visual fields problems may bump into objects when walking, may have difficulty driving.
b. Sensory functions: touch, pain, pressure, vestibular, proprioceptive, kinesthetic, temperature, taste, smell, hearing.
  (1) Functional examples.
    (a) A person with temperature function problems in their hands may burn their hands on the oven without realizing it.
    (b) A person with touch function problems in their hands will have difficulty manipulating objects.
    (c) A person with touch function problems in their feet will have difficulty walking.
3. Determine cognitive/perceptual strengths and limitations (AOTA, 2020).
  a. Global mental functions, such as orientation, energy, sleep (e.g., a person who has sleep deprivation will have difficulty engaging in all ADL, IADL, work, or education).
  b. Specific mental functions, such as attention, memory, thought, perception, and higher level cognition, (e.g., a person with higher level cognitive problems will have difficulty participating in work or school related tasks).
  c. Performance skills.
    (1) Process skills: actions that enable a person to select, initiate, organize, and perform activities (e.g., attending to a work task, organizing a pantry) and prevent problems (e.g., using a schedule to remember appointments, inquiring about medication side effects) (AOTA, 2020).
  d. Evaluate ability to self-direct care if needed.
4. Determine psychosocial strengths and limitations.
  a. Coping mechanisms.
  b. Adaptation to change in occupational role functioning or to difficulty in assuming occupational roles.
  c. Performance skills.
    (1) Social interaction skills: observable actions that enable communication and interaction with others (e.g., looking to make eye contact with a sales person, replying to a question, regulating behavior to be consistent with social norms). (AOTA, 2020).
  d. Impact of specific psychosocial deficits on occupational performance (e.g., lability, euphoria, apathy, depression, aggression, irritability, and frustration tolerance).
5. Refer to Chapters 10–14 for more information on the evaluation of client factors and performance skills.

Context Evaluation

1. Natural environment or human-made changes to environment.
  a. Physical geography (e.g., raised garden beds or steep terrain in the backyard or the urban setting).
  b. Light intensity (e.g., darkness inside or out, leading to falls).
  c. Weather (e.g., sunny day requiring sunglasses).
  d. Human caused events (e.g., architectural barriers).
2. Products and technology.
  a. Access to food or drugs (e.g., living in rural area or underserved community)
  b. General products and technology for daily living (e.g., electric toothbrush, household refrigerator).
  c. Indoor or outdoor mobility and transportation (e.g., walker, family car, elevator).
  d. Communication (e.g., hearing aid, cell phone).
  e. Virtual environments (e.g., cell phone, social media).
  f. Financial (e.g., the impact of lower socioeconomic status [SES] upon a person's and/or family's ability to purchase technology).
3. Support and relationships (i.e., practical or emotional support for the person).
  a. Immediate and extended family.
  b. Friends, peers, neighbors, colleagues.
  c. Health care professionals.
  d. Domesticated animals.
4. Attitudes (i.e., observable evidence of norms, values, beliefs, and customs according to culture, society, religious background of others).
5. Local, regional, national government systems, policies, services.
6. Home/school/work site evaluations (AOTA, 2020).
7. Refer to Chapter 16 for more information on the evaluation of environmental contexts.

Role of the Occupational Therapy Assistant (OTA)/ Certified Occupational Therapy Assistant (COTA®) in Evaluation

1. The OTA/COTA® contributes to the evaluation process.
  a. The OTA/COTA® can assist with the collection of data for the evaluation once service competency has been established.
  b. The level of supervision required will be determined by the OTA's/COTA®'s established service competency.
  c. The OTA/COTA® cannot independently evaluate or interpret evaluation results.

Chapter 7

Occupational Therapy Intervention for Neurological System Disorders

Types of Intervention

> **EXAM HINT:** Domain 2: Analysis, Interpretation, and Planning comprises 23% of the NBCOT® exam and Domain 3 Select and Manage Interventions comprises 38% of the exam. Domain 2 exam items focus on the therapist's ability to "formulate conclusions regarding client needs and priorities to develop and monitor an intervention plan throughout the occupational therapy process (NBCOT®, 2022, p. 5) and Domain 3 exam items focus on the therapist's selection and implementation of "interventions to promote healing and enhance engagement in occupation-based activities" (NBCOT®, 2022, p. 7). The application of knowledge about the diagnostic-specific interventions described for each condition in this Chapter and the following information about types of intervention can help you correctly answer NBCOT® Domains 2 and 3 exam items about developing, selecting, implementing, and monitoring interventions for persons with nervous system disorders.

1. Interventions to enable occupations and activities.
   a. Specific ADL, IADL training, retraining, adaptation, and/or compensation.
   b. Adults: work or school related tasks, work hardening programs, return to work or school.
   c. Children: play, school-related tasks, return to school.
   d. Management and self-direction of personal assistance for ADL and IADL.
   e. Adaptations and modifications to home and/or work/school environment(s) to enable participation.
   f. Community participation and integration.
   g. Refer to Chapters 15 and 16 for more information about interventions to enable occupational performance in chosen environments.
2. Interventions to support occupations.
   a. Orthotic devices.
      (1) To prevent contractures (e.g., Bobath finger spreader).
      (2) To enhance function (e.g., tenodesis orthosis).
      (3) Refer to Chapter 12 for specific orthotic interventions for neurological conditions.

   b. Adaptive equipment, assistive technology, and/or durable medical equipment for ADL, IADL, work, school (e.g., use of adaptive equipment for sexual expression and/or bowel/bladder training; augmentative communication to enable participation in school and/or work).
      (1) Refer to Chapters 15 and 16 for more information about adaptive equipment, assistive technology, and/or durable medical equipment.
   c. Positioning device prescription and training.
      (1) Seating and wheeled mobility.
      (2) Bed positioning.
      (3) Pressure reduction devices (e.g., wheelchair cushions) and pressure relief techniques (e.g., weight shifting).
      (4) Refer to Chapters 9 and 16 for more information about pressure relief and positioning interventions.
   d. Self-regulation: use of mindfulness, provision of sensory diets and sensory-friendly environments.
      (1) Refer to Chapter 14 for more information about self-regulation interventions.
3. Training to help the person acquire the concrete functional skills they need to meet their goals and successfully apply these skills in real-life situations.
   a. Postural control training for seated and standing activities.
   b. Sensory re-education, compensation, and safety training for those without return of sensation.
   c. Visual skills retraining and/or adaptation (e.g., visual occlusion for diplopia).
      (1) Refer to Chapters 5 and 15 for specific interventions to address vision deficits.
   d. Motor learning and control training or retraining/relearning for functional integration of affected limbs.
      (1) Refer to Chapter 12 for specific interventions to address motor recovery.
   e. Coping skills, assertiveness, and social skills training.
      (1) Refer to Chapter 14 for more information about psychosocial interventions
   f. Cognitive/perceptual training, retraining, and/or compensation.
      (1) Refer to Chapter 13 for specific interventions to address cognitive-perceptual functions.

EXAM HINT: The NBCOT® OTR® exam content outline identifies knowledge of "strategies for addressing and enhancing health literacy with the client and relevant others . . . . (including) caregiver training, teaching-learning models, (and) methods for making health information accessible" (NBCOT®, 2022, p. 6) as required for competent and safe practice. The application of knowledge about the education foci and methods described in the following can help you determine the correct answer for NBCOT® Domain 2 exam items about addressing and enhancing the health literacy of clients with nervous system disorders and their significant others.

4. Education to provide clients and/or family/caregivers with information about participation, occupations, health, and well-being and increase their knowledge about adaptive behaviors, and healthy habits and routines.
   a. Personal care device, adaptive equipment and durable medical equipment management and maintenance.
   b. Health management (e.g., symptom and condition management, skin care).
   c. Safety education (e.g., transfer training, pressure relief, passive range of motion, emergency response).
   d. Posture and ergonomics.
   e. For children, effective education requires the integration of services across medical providers, educators, and caregivers in the child's life.

5. Advocacy by the practitioner and the client and/or caregivers to acquire needed resources and essential services.

EXAM HINT: Understand that the prognosis of neurological system disorders must be considered during intervention planning and implementation. To determine correct answers for NBCOT® exam items about working with clients with these conditions, remember that compensatory approaches are best to use with people with progressive disorders (e.g., ALS, muscular dystrophy) while a combination of remediation and rehabilitative approaches are best for people with nonprogressive disorders (e.g., TBI, SCI).

Role of the OTA/COTA® in Intervention

1. The OTA/COTA® implements intervention with the supervision of the occupational therapist.
   a. The level of supervision required depends upon the OTA's/COTA®'s experience and established service competency.
   b. During the implementation of intervention, the OTA/COTA® informs the supervising therapist of any change in the individual's status and any other relevant information that may affect treatment.

 Pain

Definition

1. The sensory and emotional experience associated with actual or potential tissue damage.

Pain Pathways/Neurophysiology

1. Fast pain: transmitted over A delta fibers.
   a. Functions for localization, discrimination of pain.
2. Slow pain: transmitted over C fibers.
   a. Functions for diffuse arousal (protective/aversive reactions), affective, and motivational aspects of pain.
3. Intrinsic inhibitory mechanisms.
   a. Gate control theory: transmission of sensation at spinal cord level is controlled by balance between large fibers (A alpha, A beta) and small fibers (A delta, C).
      (1) Activity of large fibers at the level of first synapse can block activity of small fibers and pain transmission (counterirritant theory).
   b. Descending analgesic systems: endogenous opiates (endorphins, enkephalins) produced throughout CNS; can depress pain transmission at various sites through mechanisms of presynaptic inhibition.

Acute Pain

1. Pain provoked by noxious stimulation.
2. Associated with an underlying pathology (injury or acute inflammation/disease).
3. Signs include sharp pain and sympathetic changes (increased heart rate, increased blood pressure, pupillary dilation, sweating, hyperventilation, anxiety, protective/escape behaviors).

4. Normally resolves as tissues heal.
5. Acute pain control is associated with improved recovery time, mobility, reduced complications, reduced hospital length of stay and readmission, and overall patient satisfaction (Holm, 2017).

Chronic Pain

1. Pain that persists beyond the usual course of healing.
2. Symptoms present for greater than six months for which an underlying pathology is no longer identifiable or may never have been present.
3. Can be very debilitating and impede full participation in the rehabilitation process.
4. Effective treatment is a coordinated, interprofessional team approach (Holm, 2017).

Pain Syndromes

1. Neuropathic pain: pain as a result of lesions in some part of the nervous system (central or peripheral); usually accompanied by some degree of sensory deficit.
   a. Thalamic pain: continuous, intense pain occurring on the contralateral hemiplegic side; the result of a stroke involving the ventral posterolateral thalamus; poor rehabilitation potential.
   b. Complex regional pain syndrome type I (formerly known as reflex sympathetic dystrophy [RSD]): pain maintained by efferent activity of sympathetic nervous system.
      (1) Characterized by abnormal burning pain (causalgia), hypersensitivity to light touch, and sympathetic hyperfunction (e.g., coldness, sweating).
      (2) Usually associated with traumatic injury.
   c. Disorders of peripheral roots and nerves.
      (1) Complex regional pain syndrome type II (formerly known as neuralgia): pain occurring along the branches of a nerve; frequently paroxysmal.
      (2) Radiculalgia: neuralgia of nerve roots.
      (3) Paresthesias, allodynia: with nerve injury or transection.
   d. Herpes zoster (shingles): an acute, painful mononeuropathy caused by the varicella zoster virus.
      (1) Characterized by a rash most concentrated on the trunk with motor weakness in 5%–10% of cases.
      (2) Infection can last from 10 days to 5 weeks.
      (3) Pain may persist for months (postherpetic neuralgia).
   e. Phantom limb pain: pain in a limb following amputation of that limb; differentiated from far more common phantom limb sensation.
   f. Musculoskeletal pain: refer to Chapter 6.

g. Psychosomatic pain: the origin of the pain experience is due to mental or emotional disorders.
h. Headache and craniofacial pain (e.g., temporomandibular joint syndrome).
i. Referred pain: pain arising from deep visceral tissues that is felt in a body region remote from the site of pathology, resulting in tenderness and cutaneous hyperalgesia (e.g., medial left arm pain with heart attack, right subscapular pain from gallbladder attack).

Assessment of Chronic Pain

1. History: determine chief complaints, description of onset, and mechanism of injury.
2. Determine localization: chronic pain is poorly localized, not well defined.
3. Identify nature of pain: constant, intermittent.
4. Determine irritating stimuli/activities and time of day (e.g., night pain).
5. Determine subjective assessment using pain intensity rating scales.
   a. Simple descriptive scales: verbal report; e.g., select the words that best describe your pain.
   b. Semantic differentiation scales e.g., McGill Pain Questionnaire.
   c. Numerical rating scales: pain rating on a scale of 1 to 10; e.g., 8/10.
   d. Visual analog scale; e.g., bisect line where your pain falls, from mild to severe pain.
   e. Spatial distribution of pain: using drawings to plot location, type of pain.
   f. Visual scales; e.g., Wong-Baker FACES® Pain Rating Scale.
6. Physical examination: identification of underlying pathology (cause of pain); objective physical findings are usually not readily identified.
   a. Assess all systems: musculoskeletal, neurologic, and cardiopulmonary. Check for muscle guarding.
   b. Check for postural stress syndrome (PSS): chronic muscle lengthening and/or shortening that causes postural malalignment and stress to soft tissues.
   c. Check for movement adaptation syndrome (MAS): habituated movement dysfunction.
   d. Check for autonomic changes (sympathetic activity): typically present with acute pain but not with chronic pain.
   e. Assess for abnormal movements.
7. Assess degree of suffering.
   a. Verbal complaints are out of proportion to degree of underlying pathology and include emotional content.
   b. The person exhibits a stooped posture, antalgic gait.
   c. The person exhibits facial grimacing.

8. Assess for functional changes.
   a. Check for self-imposed limited activity; disrupted lifestyle; disuse syndrome.
   b. Check for avoidance of work, home management, leisure, social, and/or sexual activity.
9. Assess for consequences of pain, behavioral impact, and secondary gains.
   a. Monetary benefits (malingering, insurance claims).
   b. Sympathy and attention.
   c. Avoidance of undesirable tasks.
10. Assess for depression and anxiety. Refer to Chapter 14.
11. Assess for prescription drug misuse.
12. Assess for dependence on health-care system: multiple health-care providers, clinical services; "shopping around" behaviors.
13. Determine responsiveness of pain to physiological interventions/treatments: chronic pain is often unresponsive.
14. Determine motivational/affective components.
   a. Previous experience with pain.
   b. Learned responses to pain.
   c. Perception of control over pain.
   d. Ethnic/cultural aspects of pain.
   e. Familial response to pain behavior.
15. Role of the OTA/COTA® in evaluation.
   a. The OTA/COTA® can assist with the collection of data for the evaluation of pain once service competency has been established.
   b. The level of supervision required will be determined by the OTA's/COTA®'s experience and established service competency.
   c. The OTA/COTA® cannot independently evaluate or interpret evaluation results.

Occupational Therapy Intervention

EXAM HINT: The NBCOT® OTR® exam content outline identifies knowledge of "techniques for . . . pain management" (NBCOT®, 2022, p. 10) as essential for competent and safe practice. Based on this requirement and the recognition of occupational therapy as a nonpharmacological intervention for pain, it is likely that the NBCOT® exam will include items about the following interventions for pain.

1. Educate the individual about contributing factors.
2. Assist the individual in identifying and responding adaptively to pain behaviors.
   a. Remove behavioral reinforcers.
   b. Establish a behavioral contract.
   c. Provide positive reinforcers, educational support.
   d. Demonstrate change, allow person to experience success.
   e. Practice well behaviors.
3. Assist the individual in developing strategies and using techniques to manage pain.
   a. Teach coping skills, stress management, assertive communication.
   b. Provide relaxation training.
      (1) Progressive relaxation techniques (e.g., Jacobson's), deep breathing exercises.
      (2) Guided imagery.
      (3) Yoga, tai chi, ai chi, meditation, mindfulness.
      (4) Biofeedback.
4. Establish a realistic, person-directed daily activity program.
   a. Improve overall level of conditioning (e.g., implement a daily walking program).
   b. Improve overall functional capacity and functional mobility skills.
   c. Increase engagement in activities of daily living and meaningful occupations.
   d. Teach energy conservation techniques.
   e. Provide meaningful diversional activities.
5. Instruct in the use of assistive devices as needed.
6. Provide family education.
7. Postural education and ergonomics.
8. Role of the OTA/COTA® in intervention.
   a. The OTA/COTA® implements intervention with the occupational therapist's supervision.
      (1) The level of supervision required depends upon the OTA's/COTA®'s experience and established service competency.
      (2) During the implementation of intervention, the OTA/COTA® informs the supervising therapist of any change in the individual's status and any other relevant information that may affect treatment.
9. Refer to other professionals for direct pain/symptom control interventions.

Sensory Processing Disorders

Etiology

1. Unknown etiology.
2. Neither sensory processing disorder or sensory integrative disorder are officially recognized by the medical community as stand-alone disorders or diagnostic conditions.
   a. However, atypical behavioral responses to routine sensory stimuli are recognized as a component of other diagnostic conditions (i.e., autism spectrum disorder).
3. Dysfunctional behavioral responses to routine sensory stimuli begin to occur in early childhood.
   a. The child demonstrates difficulty regulating responses to multi-sensory systems and/or to particular isolated sensory systems.

Symptom Classification

1. Ayres Sensory Integration© model. Refer to Chapter 12.
2. Dunn's model: symptoms are classified according to the interaction of sensory stimuli that are needed to stimulate a behavioral response.
   a. There are two types of neurological threshold: high neurological threshold and low neurological threshold.
      (1) High neurological threshold: unfazed by immersion in highly stimulating sensory environment. Low level responsiveness to routine environmental stimuli. Stimuli that is unexpected or experienced over a prolonged time period may elicit a response.
      (2) Low neurological threshold: minimal stimulus facilitates a behavioral response, which may be perceived as an over-reaction compared to the average person.
   b. There are two types of behavioral responses.
      (1) Passive behavioral response: the individual makes no attempt to change the intensity or duration of sensory input.
      (2) Active behavioral response: the individual avoids or seeks to avoid sensory stimuli.
   c. Neurological thresholds and behavioral responses combine to form four categories.
      (1) Poor registration: high neurological thresholds and passive behavioral responses. This person may appear aloof or indifferent to the demands of the environment because of low levels of processing ordinary sensory experiences.
      (2) Sensory seeking: high neurological thresholds and active behavioral responses. This person actively engages in seeking sensory input and often seeks intense experiences.
      (3) Sensory sensitivity: low neurological thresholds and passive behavioral responses. This person responds to ordinary sensory input with agitation, being bothered, and is often considered hypersensitive.
      (4) Sensory avoiding: low neurological thresholds and active behavioral responses. This person is frequently in a state of "fight or flight" in response to ordinary sensory stimuli. Behavioral responses to stimuli can escalate quickly and seem unpredictable as the person may be triggered by ordinary sensory experiences.
3. Ecological Model of Sensory Modulation Disorder describes individuals' unique responses to interactions between external and internal dimensions of sensory processing in the context of their lives.
   a. External dimensions include culture, relationships, and chosen tasks.
   b. Internal dimensions include sensation, emotion, and attention.
   c. Difficulty with modulation can either result in:
      (1) Difficulties with social and environmental interactions.
      (2) Difficulties with self-regulation due to a mismatch between internal capabilities and external environment and activities.
4. Proposed sensory processing nosology classifies symptoms according to the below categories.
   a. Sensory modulation disorder (SMD) in any sensory system.
      (1) Sensory overresponsivity (SOR).
      (2) Sensory underresponsivity (SUR).
      (3) Sensory seeking/craving (SS).
   b. Sensory-based motor disorder (SBMD) includes underlying sensory discrimination disorder as well as possible sensory modulation disorder.
      (1) Dyspraxia (difficulty planning new movements).
      (2) Sensory-based postural disorders.
   c. Sensory discrimination disorder (SDD): The ability to distinguish sensations as different, i.e., visual, auditory, tactile, vestibular, proprioceptive, gustatory, and olfactory.

Presenting Signs and Symptoms

1. Fluctuating or extreme responsiveness while engaging in everyday activities (e.g., stress and frustration demonstrated in performance of everyday activities).
2. Difficulties in interacting with the environment in play, learning, and social situations, and while engaging in other developmental and health-promoting activities.
3. Difficulty with conceiving, planning, sequencing, or executing novel actions (dyspraxia). Tendency to avoid or reject simple motor challenges.
4. Poor initiation of activities as demonstrated in some children due to difficulty generating ideas (ideation).
5. Difficulty with goal-directed action on the environment, known as an adaptive response.
6. Responses may present along a continuum of under-responsivity to overresponsivity of multisensory processing and sensory seeking.
7. Tactile processing dysfunction manifestations.
   a. Deficits in modulation (regulation and organization).
   (1) Tactile defensiveness: overresponsivity to ordinary touch sensations.
      (a) The individual may demonstrate irritation and discomfort from a variety of textures such as clothing, sand, grass, glue, water, paint, and/or food.
      (b) The individual may dislike brushing their teeth or hair.
      (c) The individual may demonstrate various behavioral responses including distractibility, anger, hostility, temper tantrums, fear, and/or distress.
   (2) Underresponsivity to tactile stimuli as demonstrated by diminished sensory registration and responsiveness.
      (a) The individual may not respond to normal levels of tactile input and may seek disproportionate amounts of stimuli to gain environmental information (e.g., excessive touching of people and objects).
   b. Deficits in tactile discrimination.
   (1) Difficulty interpreting tactile information in a precise and efficient manner.
      (a) Contributes to impaired body scheme and somatodyspraxia (a disorder in motor planning due to poor tactile perception and proprioception).
      (b) Contributes to awkwardness in fine and gross motor tasks and impaired manipulation skills, visual perception, and eye-hand coordination.
      (c) Hinders ability to learn about properties and substances.
   (2) Difficulty with localizing tactile stimuli.
      (a) Impaired stereognosis and decreased fine motor and eye-hand coordination skills may be demonstrated in difficulties with writing and cutting with a scissors and knife.
8. Proprioceptive processing disorder manifestations.
   a. Deficits in modulation.
   b. Discrimination deficits demonstrated by poor awareness of position of body, body parts, and body schema.
   c. Clumsiness, awkwardness.
   d. Distractibility.
   e. Motor planning and movement difficulties.
   f. Reliance on visual cues or other cognitive strategies to motor plan, guide movements, and perform tasks.
   g. Use of too much or too little force (e.g., stomping when walking, breaking objects unintentionally).
   h. Poor awareness of personal space.
   i. Seeks heavy resistance and pressure.
9. Vestibular processing disorder manifestations.
   a. Deficits in modulation.
   (1) Hypersensitivity to movement, characterized by aversion to movement impacting on the sympathetic system.
   (2) Hyposensitivity to movement characterized by the individual seeking intense vestibular stimulation without complaints of feeling dizzy, and by a tendency to be a thrill seeker unaware of potential danger.
   (3) Gravitational insecurity characterized by excessive fear during typical activities, especially when the individual's feet are off the ground, when moving backward or upward in space, walking on uneven terrain, jumping, getting on/off elevators, using any playground equipment involving movement, and when handling even minimal heights.
   b. Vestibular discrimination deficits, characterized by the above symptoms; however, symptoms are demonstrated on a subtle level.
   c. Low muscle tone.
   d. Postural-ocular deficits.
   e. Decreased balance and equilibrium reactions.
   f. Deficits in bilateral coordination.
   g. Low endurance.
   h. Deficient motor planning and sequencing.
   i. Behavior responses include difficulty with attention, organization of behavior, communication.
10. Sensory-based motor disorder.
    a. Deficits in proprioceptive and vestibular systems.

b. Dyspraxia: difficulty with planning movements, particularly those that are complex or new.
c. Postural disorders: decreased muscle tone impacting on stability.

Medical Management

1. Possible pharmacology intervention to decrease activity level.

Occupational Therapy Evaluation

1. Parent/caregiver interview regarding medical and developmental history.
2. Teacher interview regarding school performance, play, and behaviors (e.g., Sensory Profile or Sensory Processing Measure [SPM]; refer to Chapters 5 and 12).
3. Formal assessment of sensory processing (e.g., the Sensory Profile; refer to Chapter 5).
4. Informal observations of performance and behavior in a variety of settings (e.g., classroom, playground, home, and work).
5. Formal assessment of clinical observations using Ayres' unpublished and nonstandardized tools. Refer to Chapter 12.
   a. Items to be observed include specific reflexes, crossing body midline, bilateral coordination, muscle tone.
6. Standardized tests for tactile processing, vestibular-proprioceptive processing, visual perception, practicability, and their impact on occupational functioning (e.g., SPM; refer to Chapter 12).

7. Role of the OTA/COTA® in evaluation.
   a. The OTA/COTA® contributes to the evaluation process.
      (1) The OTA/COTA® can assist with the collection of data for the evaluation once service competency has been established.
      (2) The level of supervision required will be determined by the OTA's/COTA®'s established service competency.
      (3) The OTA/COTA® cannot independently evaluate or interpret evaluation results.

Occupational Therapy Intervention

1. Refer to Chapter 12 for information on the sensory integration (SI) frame of reference and SI intervention approaches.
2. Role of the OTA/COTA®.
   a. The OTA/COTA® implements intervention with supervision of the occupational therapist.
      (1) The level of supervision required depends upon the OTA's//COTA®'s experience and established service competency.
      (2) During the implementation of intervention, the OTA/COTA® informs the supervising therapist of any change in the individual's status and any other relevant information that may affect treatment.

Seizure Disorders

Etiology

1. Seizure disorders are differentiated from epilepsy.
   a. Sources vary on when the presence of seizures becomes epilepsy.
      (1) Some sources suggest that two seizures within 24 hours is cause for a diagnosis of epilepsy and other sources indicate that epilepsy is a chronic state of recurrent seizures without specific definition of frequency of recurrence.
   b. Seizure disorder refers to a temporary disturbance in brain activity causing a group of nerve cells to fire excessively, interfering with normal brain function.

2. Seizures are typically idiopathic; they also can be hereditary.
3. Seizures are often associated with other conditions. These include the following.
   a. Oxygen deprivation (e.g., during childbirth).
   b. Severe head injuries or brain hemorrhage.
   c. Cerebral palsy.
   d. Stroke.
   e. Brain tumors.
   f. Other neurological disorders (e.g., neurocognitive disorders).
   g. Hydrocephalus.
   h. Metabolic disorders.
   i. Infections, meningitis, encephalitis, congenital infections.

Specific Classifications of Seizures and Presenting Signs and Symptoms

1. Two broad groups.
   a. Primary generalized seizures: seizures begin with widespread involvement of both sides of the brain.
   b. Partial seizures or focal seizures begin with involvement of a smaller, localized area within the brain.
      (1) The disturbance can still spread within seconds or minutes to widespread areas of the brain (known as secondary generalized seizure).
2. Generalized seizures.
   a. Tonic-clonic seizures (previously known as grand mal).
      (1) Motor and non-motor seizure presentation.
      (2) A brief warning/aura such as numbness, taste, smell, or other sensation occurs.
      (3) Tonic phase includes a loss of consciousness, stiffening of the body, heavy and irregular breathing, drooling, skin pallor, and occasional bladder and bowel incontinence for a few seconds before the clonic phase begins.
      (4) Clonic phase includes alternating rigidity and relaxation of muscles.
      (5) Postictal state follows the clonic phase, and includes a period of drowsiness, disorientation, or fatigue and can last minutes to hours.
   b. Myoclonic seizures are brief, involuntary jerking of the upper body and extremities.
   c. Atonic seizures (drop seizures) include a brief loss of postural tone and can cause a person to fall. This can include impaired consciousness during the seizure.
   d. Absence seizures (also known as petit mal).
      (1) Typically occur between ages of 3 and 12 years.
      (2) Episodes of brief impairments of consciousness without loss of muscle tone, involuntary body or extremity movements, or falling down.
      (3) Rapid blinking or staring into space.
      (4) The person does not recall the episode or any lapse in time.
      (5) Not followed by postictal confusion.
      (6) Often occurs in clusters.
3. Partial focal seizures.
   a. Focal seizure without loss of consciousness (simple partial).
      (1) May begin with an aura and/or unprovoked change in behavior.
      (2) Abnormal electrical impulses occur in a localized area of the brain, often in the motor strip of the frontal lobe.
      (3) Involuntary, repetitive jerking of the hand and arm occurs, but the individual can maintain interaction with their environment.
   b. Focal seizure with impaired consciousness (complex partial).
   c. Symptoms vary.
      (1) May begin with an aura, unprovoked change in behavior, or unusual sensory experiences.
      (2) There are alterations in consciousness and responsiveness.
      (3) May appear confused or dazed, unable to respond to questions or directions.
      (4) Automatisms or automatic motions, such as lip smacking, chewing, and swallowing, and nervous movement of the hands/fingers, and repetitive movements may occur.
4. Selected seizure syndromes.
   a. Infantile spasms or West syndrome.
      (1) Begins at three to seven months of age.
      (2) Brief flexor (head, arms, hips) or extensor (arm and trunk) contractions or spasms occur.
      (3) Seizures occur frequently throughout the day.
   b. Lennox-Gastaut syndrome.
      (1) Evolves out of infantile spasms.
      (2) Seizures of different types begin during the first three years of life and are difficult to control.
      (3) All children affected manifest intellectual disability associated with the seizure disorder.
   c. Landau-Kleffner syndrome or acquired epileptic aphasia.
      (1) Loss of language skills, which can lead to speech impairments.
      (2) Auditory agnosia (inability to distinguish different sounds).
5. Simple febrile seizures.
   a. Most common type of seizure that occurs in children under the age of five, precipitated by a fever.
   b. The seizure can be simple or complex and occur during acute illness or last through a spell of illness.
   c. These seizures usually do not cause damage and they do not lead to epilepsy.
6. Status epilepticus.
   a. A state of continuous seizure (lasting more than 5 minutes) or frequent recurring seizures without regaining full consciousness between episodes. This diagnosis can lead to brain damage or death.

Diagnostic Criteria

1. Clinical observations of the obvious manifestations associated with the specific seizure disorder.
2. The EEG alone is not sufficient to diagnose a seizure disorder since the disorder does not always show up on the EEG; conversely, abnormal EEG patterns may appear when there is no clinical evidence of seizures.

Impact on Occupational Performance

1. The seizure disorder and/or the anticonvulsive medication(s) prescribed to control the seizures may affect the individual's alertness and learning potential.
2. The amount of brain injury incurred by the seizures and associated conditions as well as the effects of medication can influence performance in all areas of occupation including play, social participation, education, work, health management, sleep, and ADL/IADL.
3. Depending on the severity, type, and frequency of seizures, children may experience significant disruptions to the acquisition of developmental milestones associated with motor and cognitive development.

> CAUTION: Seizures and epilepsy have long been considered a condition of unfit mental health and have even been associated with possession of evil spirits. While it is well known today that seizures and epilepsy are neurological conditions, the false narratives and misunderstandings previously associated with these conditions perpetuate a persistent stigma associated with seizures and epilepsy, which can negatively impact the person's occupational performance and quality of life.

Medical Management

1. A neurologist is most often required to medically manage seizures.
2. Seizure disorders are treated with anticonvulsive and other medications or interventions.

> EXAM HINT: The NBCOT® OTR® exam content outline identifies knowledge of "responses to adverse reactions . . . and emergency situations . . . (including) . . . seizures" (NBCOT®, 2022, p. 13) as essential for competent and safe practice. The application of knowledge about the first aid procedures for seizures, post-seizure care, and OT evaluation of and intervention for persons with seizures provided in the following section can help you determine correct answers to NBCOT® exam items about the management of seizures.

Intervention for Seizure Disorders

1. First aid procedures for seizures.
   a. Remain calm.

> RED FLAG: Status epilepticus can be life threatening; thus, it is a medical emergency, and immediate medical attention must be obtained.

   b. Remove dangerous objects from the area.
   c. Protect the individual from harm, without interfering with the individual's movements.
   d. If the person is in a hospital bed, raise the bed rails.
   e. Do not place anything in the mouth.
   f. Turn the individual on their side if there is a risk of aspiration (e.g., person is salivating or vomiting and could aspirate fluid).
   g. Allow the seizure to happen, protect the head and/or extremities if injury could occur from violent shaking.
   h. Once the clonus activity is over (for tonic-clonic type), place the person in the recovery position (side-lying).
   i. Monitor for improving mental state postictal.
   j. Do not be alarmed if the individual seems to stop breathing momentarily.
      (1) If breathing actually stops, use standard rescue breathing techniques.
   k. Call for medical attention during seizures:
      (1) If this is the individual's first seizure.
      (2) If the person has a seizure in water.
      (3) If the person has a second seizure.
      (4) If the individual does not regain consciousness within 5 or 10 minutes following the seizure.
      (5) If the seizure lasts five minutes or more.
      (6) If the individual is diabetic or pregnant.
2. Post-seizure care.
   a. Allow the individual to rest or sleep after the seizure.
   b. Call a physician if this is the individual's first seizure, if the seizure is followed by another seizure (status epilepticus), or if the seizure lasts more than five minutes.
   c. Notify the parents/guardians/caregivers or designated emergency contact person that a seizure has occurred.
   d. Observe safety precautions if the individual seems groggy, confused, or weak following the seizure.
3. Occupational therapy evaluation and intervention.
   a. Assess and intervene for developmental delays as necessary.
   b. Observe all medical and safety precautions.
   c. Document and report any seizure activity, medication side effects, or behavioral changes.
   d. Document and report any changes in skills, abilities, performance patterns, etc. after seizure events.
   e. Refer to Chapter 15 for information on evaluation and intervention for deficits in performance in areas of occupation.

References

Adamolekun, B. (2020, July). Seizure disorder. Merck Manual professional version. https://www.merckmanuals.com/professional/neurologic-disorders/seizure-disorders/seizure-disorders

American Heart Disease Association. (2021). Heart disease and stroke statistics-2021 update. Circulation, 143, e254–e743.

American Stoke Association. (2019). F.A.S.T. materials. https://www.stroke.org/en/help-and-support/resource-library/fast-materials

American Occupational Therapy Association. (2020). Occupational therapy practice framework: Domain and process (4th ed.). American Journal of Occupational Therapy, 74(2), Article 7412410010p1-7412410010.

Anzalone, M. E., & Lane, S. J. (2012). Sensory processing disorder. In S. J. Lane & A. C. Bundy (Eds.), Kids can be kids: A childhood occupations approach (pp. 437–459). F.A. Davis.

Arner, M., Eliasson, A-C., Rosblad, B., Rosenbaum, P., Beckung, E., & Krumlinde-Sundholm, L. (2010). The Manual Ability Classification System (MACS) for children with cerebral palsy 4–18 years. https://www.macs.nu/developers-of-macs.php

Boston Children's Hospital. (n.d.). Tethered spinal cord: Frequently asked questions. http://www.childrenshospital.org/conditions-and-treatments/conditions/t/tethered-spinal-cord/research-and-clinical-trials

Budash, D.E. (2021). Spinal cord injury. In D.P. Dirette & S.A. Gutman (Eds.), Occupational therapy for physical dysfunction (8th ed., pp. 812–838). Wolters Kluwer.

Bundy, A.C., & Lane, S.J. (2020). Sensory integration: A. Jean Ayres' theory revisited. In A.C. Bundy & S.J. Lane (Eds.), Sensory integration: Theory and practice (3d ed., pp. 2–20). F.A. Davis.

Cedarbaum, J.M., Stambler, N., Malta, E., Fuller, C., Hilt, D., Thurmond, B., & Nakanishi, A. (1999). The ALSFRS-R: A revised ALS functional rating scale that incorporates assessments of respiratory function. BDNF ALS study group (phase III). Journal of Neurological Sciences, 169(1–2), 13–21.

Centers for Disease Control and Prevention. (2020a, September 3). What is spina bifida? https://www.cdc.gov/ncbddd/spinabifida/facts.html

Centers for Disease Control and Prevention. (2020b, September 30). Epilepsy fast facts. https://www.cdc.gov/epilepsy/about/fast-facts.html

Centers for Disease Control and Prevention. (2020c, October 27). MD STARnet data and statistics. https://www.cdc.gov/ncbddd/musculardystrophy/data.html

Cermak, S. A., & May-Benson, T.A. (2020). Praxis and dyspraxia. In A. C. Bundy & S. J. Lane. (Eds.), Sensory integration: Theory and practice (3rd ed., pp. 115–150). F.A. Davis.

Coker-Bolt, P.C., Garcia, T., & Naber, E. (2015). Neuromotor: Cerebral palsy. In J. Case-Smith & J. Clifford O'Brien (Eds.), Occupational therapy for children and adolescents (7th ed., pp. 793–811). Elsevier.

Dirette, D.P., & Gutman, S. (Eds). (2021). Occupational therapy for physical dysfunction (8th ed.). Wolters Kluwer.

Eliasson, A.C., Krumlinde Sundholm, L., Rösblad, B., Beckung, E., Arner, M., Öhrvall, A.M., & Rosenbaum, P. (2006). The Manual Ability Classification System (MACS) for children with cerebral palsy: Scale development and evidence of validity and reliability. Developmental Medicine and Child Neurology, 48, 549–554.

Forwell, S.J., Hugos, L.L., & Ghahari, S. (2021). Neurodegenerative diseases. In D.P. Dirette & S.A. Gutman (Eds.), Occupational therapy for physical dysfunction (8th ed., pp. 789–811). Wolters Kluwer.

Gillen, G., & Nilsen D.M. (Eds.). (2021). Stroke rehabilitation: A function-based approach (5th ed.). Elsevier.

Gutman, S. A. (2017). Quick reference neuroscience for rehabilitation professionals: The essential neurologic principles underlying rehabilitation practice (3rd ed.). Slack.

Gutman, S. A., & Schonfeld, A. B. (2019). Screening adult neurologic populations: A step-by-step instruction manual (3rd ed.). AOTA Press.

Hamby, J.R. (2017). The nervous system. In H. Smith-Gabai & S.E. Holm (Eds.), Occupational therapy in acute care (2nd ed., pp. 293–391). AOTA Press.

Holm, S.E. (2017). Pain management. In H. Smith-Gabai & S.E. Holm (Eds.), Occupational therapy in acute care (2nd ed., pp. 673–685). AOTA Press.

Humphry, R., & Wakeford, L. (2006). An occupation-centered discussion of development and implications for practice. American Journal of Occupational Therapy, 60, 258–267. https://doi.org/10.5014/ajot.60.3.258

Johnson, T.L., Chin, E.M., & Hoon, A.H. (2019). Cerebral palsy. In M. L. Batshaw, N. J. Roizen, & L. Pellegrino (Eds.), Children with disabilities (8th ed., pp. 756–814). Paul H. Brookes.

Kandell, E. R., Schwartz, T. H., Jessel, T. M., Siegelbaum, S.A., & Hudspeth, A.J. (Eds.). (2013). Principles of neural science (5th ed.). McGraw-Hill.

Kang, P.B. (2019). Muscles, bones and nerves. In M. L. Batshaw, N. J. Roizen, & L. Pellegrino (Eds.), Children with disabilities (8th ed., pp. 287–321). Paul H. Brookes.

Lane, S. J. (2020). Sensory modulation functions and disorders. In A. C. Bundy, S. J. Lane, & E. A. Murray (Eds.), Sensory integration: Theory and practice (3rd ed., pp. 151–180). F.A. Davis.

Lane, S. J. (2020). Structure and function of the sensory systems. In A. C. Bundy, S. J. Lane, & E. A. Murray (Eds.), Sensory integration: Theory and practice (3rd ed., pp. 58–114). F.A. Davis.

Lane, S.J., & Reynolds, S. (2020). Sensory discrimination functions and disorders. In A. C. Bundy, S. J. Lane, & E. A. Murray (Eds.), Sensory integration: Theory and practice (3rd ed., pp. 181–205). F.A. Davis.

Liptak, G.S. (2013). Neural tube defects. In M.L. Batshaw, N.J. Roizen, & G.R. Lotrecchiano (Eds.), Children with disabilities (7th ed., pp. 451–472). Paul H. Brookes.

Lohmann, A.F., & Vas, A.K. (2021). Acquired brain injury. In D.P. Dirette & S.A. Gutman (Eds.), Occupational therapy for physical dysfunction (8th ed., pp. 765–788). Wolters Kluwer.

Mayo Clinic. (2021, October 18). Chiari malformation. https://www.mayoclinic.org/diseases-conditions/chiari-malformation/symptoms-causes/syc-20354010

Mayo Clinic. (2021, October 21). Epilepsy. https://www.mayoclinic.org/diseases-conditions/epilepsy/symptoms-causes/syc-20350093

Medline Plus. (n.d.). Duchenne and Becker muscular dystrophy. https://medlineplus.gov/genetics/condition/duchenne-and-becker-muscular-dystrophy/

Miller, L. J. (2014). Sensational kids hope and help for children with sensory processing disorders (SPD). Penguin Group.

Miller, L. S., Anzalone, M. E., Lane, S. J., Cermak, S. A., & Osten, E. T. (2007). Concept evolution in sensory integration: A proposed nosology for diagnosis. American Journal of Occupational Therapy, 61, 135–140. https://doi.org/10.5014/ajot.61.2.135

Missiuna, C., Polatajko, H., Pollock, N., & Cameron, D. (2012). Neuromotor disorders. In S. J. Lane & A. C. Bundy (Eds.), Kids can be kids: A childhood occupations approach (pp. 460–482). F.A. Davis.

Muscular Dystrophy Association. (2021). About neuromuscular diseases. http://www.mda.org/disease.

National Board for Certification in Occupational Therapy (NBCOT®). (2022). 2022 Occupational Therapist Registered (OTR®) examination content outline. https://www.nbcot.org/-/media/PDFs/2022_OTR_Content_Outline.pdf.

National Eye Institute. (2021, March 8). Refractive errors. https://www.nei.nih.gov/learn-about-eye-health/eye-conditions-and-diseases/refractive-errors

National Institutes of Neurological Disorders and Stroke. (2019, March 27). NINDS tethered spinal cord syndrome information page. https://www.ninds.nih.gov/Disorders/All-Disorders/Tethered-Spinal-Cord-Syndrome-Information-Page

National Institutes of Neurological Disorders and Stroke. (2020, April 29). Parkinson's disease information page. https://www.ninds.nih.gov/Disorders/All-Disorders/Parkinsons-Disease-Information-Page#disorders-r1

National Organization for Rare Disorders. (2021a). Duchenne muscular dystrophy. https://rarediseases.org/rare-diseases/duchenne-muscular-dystrophy/

National Organization for Rare Disorders. (2021b). Progressive supranuclear palsy. https://rarediseases.org/rare-diseases/progressive-supranuclear-palsy/

O'Brien, J. C., & Kuhaneck, H. (Eds.). (2015). Case-Smith's occupational therapy for children and adolescents (8th ed.). Elsevier.

Palisano, R., Rosenbaum, P., Bartlett, D., & Livingston, M. (2007). Gross motor function classification system: Expanded and revised. CanChild Centre for Childhood Disability Research Institute for Applied Health Sciences. McMaster University. https://canchild.ca/en/resources/42-gross-motor-function-classification-system-e-r

Patel, P., & Moshe, S.L. (2020). The evolution of the concepts of seizures and epilepsy: What's in a name? Epilepsia Open, 5(1), 22–35. https://doi.org/10.1002/epi4.12375

Parham, L. D., & Mailoux, Z. (2020). Sensory integration. In J. C. O'Brien & H.M. Kuhaneck (Eds.), Case Smith's occupational therapy for children and adolescents (8th ed., pp. 516–549). Elsevier.

Pendleton, H., & Schultz-Krohn, W. (Eds.). (2018). Pedretti's occupational therapy: Practice skills for physical dysfunction (8th ed.). Elsevier.

Rief, K., Bartels, M.N., Duffy, C.A., Beland, H.E., & Stein, J. (2021). Stroke diagnosis, acute treatment, prevention, and medical management. In G. Gillen & D.M. Nilsen (Eds.), Stroke rehabilitation: A function-based approach (5th ed., pp. 2–46). Elsevier.

Shaf, R., & Lane, S. (2009). Neuroscience foundations of vestibular, proprioceptive, and tactile sensory strategies. OT Practice, 14(22), CE1–CE8.

Schonberg, R.L., & Menzel, M.B. (2019). Birth defects and prenatal diagnosis. In M. L. Batshaw, N. J. Roizen, & L. Pellegrino (Eds.), Children with disabilities (8th ed., pp. 114–138). Paul H. Brookes.

Smith-Gabai, H., & Holm, S.E. (Eds.). (2017). Occupational therapy in acute care (2nd ed.). AOTA Press.

Spina Bifida Association. (2021). Infants & children. https://www.spinabifidaassociation.org/infants-children/

Spina Bifida Association. (n.d.). Spinal cord tethering. https://www.spinabifidaassociation.org/wp-content/uploads/Spinal-Cord-Tethering.pdf.

United Cerebral Palsy. (UCP). (2018). Cerebral palsy information. http://ucp.org.

Zelleke, T.G., Depositario-Cabacar, D.F.T., & Gaillard, W.D. (2019). Epilepsy. In M. L. Batshaw, N.J. Roizen, & L. Pellegrino (Eds.), Children with disabilities (8th ed., pp. 815–854). Paul H. Brookes.

Review Questions

Below are eight questions about key content covered in this Chapter. These questions are not inclusive of the entirety of content related to neurological disorders that you must know for success on the NBCOT® exam. These questions are provided to help you "jump start" the thought processes you will need to apply your studying of content to the answering of exam questions; hence they are not in the NBCOT® exam format. Exam items in the NBCOT® format that cover the depth and breadth of content you will need to know to pass the NBCOT® exam are provided in the three online practice exams that accompany this text. The answers to the below questions are provided in Appendix 2.

1. You will be evaluating two persons who have survived strokes. One incurred a left MCA stroke and one incurred a right MCA stroke. What symptoms might each person present during their respective evaluation session?

2. You are working on a spinal cord unit. You are about to evaluate a client who has an injury classified as ASIAA. The injury is at the C5 level. What is the expected sensory and motor status of your client?

3. You have just completed your first evaluation session with a patient who sustained a TBI two weeks ago. Your findings include that the patient was alert and in heightened state of activity (easily overstimulated) and attempting to pull out the IV and feeding tube. The patient could not remember directions exhibiting poor short-term memory. The patient screamed out for no reason several times during the session and was observed to be aggressive (e.g., attempting to hit you and the nurse). The patient required maximum assist for BADL. Your facility requires you to document each TBI patient's Rancho Los Amigos Levels of Cognitive Functioning Scale. What is the appropriate level for you to record?

4. A three-year old child is brought to an outpatient center for an occupational therapy evaluation. The parent reports that their child is always "on the go", loves playgrounds, and seems to take extraordinary physical risks (e.g., jumping off furniture, climbing onto cupboards and tables, swinging too high and fast on playground swings) without showing fear. The child also mouths toys, crayons, and pencils, and chews on their clothing. The parent states that their child does not attend to table-top tasks for long periods and often leaves the table during meals. How would you describe this child's pattern of sensory processing and what intervention activities would likely be helpful for this child and family?

(Continued)

5. During an occupational therapy evaluation of a toddler, you observe the child walking with the left foot in plantar flexion, the left arm flexed at the elbow and wrist, and the left hand in a fist position with the thumb tucked inside the palm. The child is able to move their right extremities with typical movement patterns. The parent reports that they have noticed a difference in the movement patterns of the two sides and that the difference has markedly increased since the child started walking. Based on this information, what neurological condition would you suspect this child has?

6. You are working with a child who is seated at a table completing activities in a coloring and writing workbook. You notice that on multiple occasions the child stares straight ahead for a few seconds and then returns to their work. You have also noticed that the staring episodes cannot be interrupted by waving your hand in front of their face or by calling their name. Given this information what can you surmise is happening? What actions should you take if you have never seen the child respond this way before when working with them?

7. You are working with a child who suddenly has a series of seizures that occur in rapid succession and are prolonged. When the parents are contacted, they report that they ran out of the child's medicine the day before. What type of seizure do these symptoms represent? How should you respond in this situation?

8. You receive a referral to evaluate a person with Parkinson's disease (PD). What are the cardinal signs of Parkinson's that you will want to be sure to consider during your evaluation? Upon reviewing the client's chart, you learn that their disorder has progressed to stage 3 on the Hoehn and Yahr's Parkinson's disease scale. Which functional limitations and abilities can you expect the person to demonstrate?

8

Cardiovascular and Pulmonary System Disorders

REGINA M. LEHMAN and RITA P. FLEMING-CASTALDY

▶ Cardiovascular System

Function

1. Delivers oxygen to organs and tissues.
2. Removes carbon dioxide and other by-products from the body.
3. Assists in the regulation of core body temperature.

Cardiovascular Anatomy and Physiology

1. Relationship to the NBCOT® exam.
   a. It is not likely that the NBCOT® exam will ask direct questions about anatomy and physiology.
   b. As a result, this Chapter does not provide a complete anatomy and physiology review.
   c. Major structures, functions, and related conditions are outlined and specific figures are provided; knowledge of these can increase understanding of cardiovascular function.

> **EXAM HINT:** The NBCOT® OTR® exam content outline identifies knowledge of the "impact of body functions and body structures on occupational performance" (NBCOT®, 2022, p. 3) as essential for competent and safe practice. While it is unlikely that *direct* questions about the structure of the cardiovascular system will be on the NBCOT® exam, knowing its major structures and functions can help you correctly answer NBCOT® exam items about the *functional implications* of cardiovascular conditions. This knowledge will improve your ability to understand pathology, presenting symptoms, medical interventions, and occupational therapy (OT) treatment rationales.
>
> For example, the left ventricle is the main pump of the heart, pumping blood from the heart to the rest of the body. This is usually the first area to be affected by a deficiency in coronary artery perfusion because it has a higher workload than the rest of the heart. Decreased function of the left ventricle can result in left-sided congestive heart failure (CHF) with tachycardia, shortness of breath, decreased endurance, weakness, and fatigue.

The Heart and Circulation

1. Heart tissue.
   a. Damage to heart tissue has an impact on function; cardiac conditions and complications can occur.
   b. Table 8-1 outlines the functional implications and related conditions that can result from damaged heart tissue.
      (1) Comprehensive information about the conditions listed in Table 8-1 are provided in subsequent sections in this Chapter.
2. Heart chambers and blood flow.
   a. Four chambers arranged in pairs, functioning as two pumps working in sequence. Refer to Figure 8-1.
      (1) Table 8-2 provides a description of the mechanism of each chamber.

> **EXAM HINT:** Understanding the mechanism of blood flow through the heart can help you understand what systems and structures could be affected by damage in a specific area. Interruption of blood flow through the heart can result in a myocardial infarction.

   b. Damage to any of the four chambers of the heart can impact function; cardiac conditions and complications, including heart failure, can occur.
      (1) Refer to Table 8-3: Possible Clinical Manifestations of Cardiac Failure.
3. Valves and related conditions: valves ensure unidirectional blood flow through the heart; provide one-way flow of blood into, out of, and within the heart.
   a. Vavular disease, damage to the heart valves, and/or valve stenosis (thickening of the valve walls) can result in regurgitation (backflow) and/or impaired blood flow to the heart and body.

Table 8-1

Heart Tissue and Impact of Damage

HEART TISSUE	FUNCTIONAL IMPLICATIONS AND RELATED CONDITIONS, IF DAMAGED
Pericardium: fibrous protective sac enclosing the heart.	Increases workload on the heart; dyspnea; angina; lower extremity edema; heart failure; pericardial effusion.
Epicardium: inner layer of pericardium.	Decreased ability to respond to injury to the heart; e.g.; following a myocardial infarction (MI).
Myocardium: heart muscle, the major portion of the heart.	Angina; dyspnea; related signs and symptoms of myocardial infarction (MI); myocarditis.
Endocardium: smooth lining of the inner surface and cavities of the heart.	Joint pain; angina during inhalation; dyspnea; fatigue; lower extremity edema; endocarditis; heart valve damage.

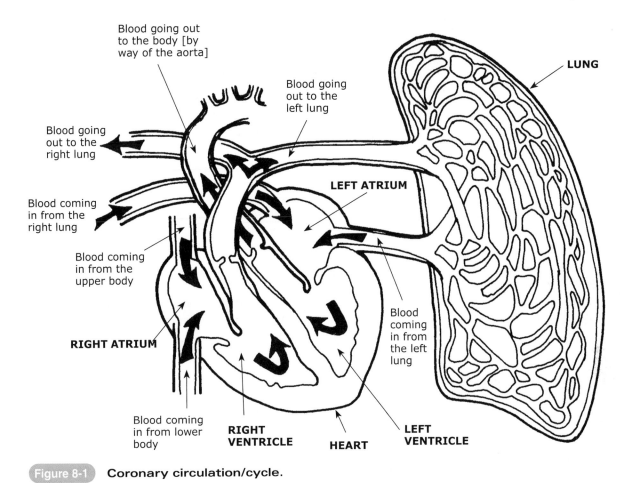

Blood going out
to the body [by
way of the aorta]

Blood going
out to the
left lung

LUNG

Blood going
out to the
right lung

Blood coming
in from the
right lung

LEFT ATRIUM

Blood coming
in from the
upper body

Blood
coming
in from
the left
lung

RIGHT ATRIUM

Blood coming
in from lower
body

RIGHT
VENTRICLE

HEART

LEFT
VENTRICLE

Figure 8-1   **Coronary circulation/cycle.**

Table 8-2

Heart Chambers and Chamber Mechanism
Right atrium (RA): receives blood from systemic circulation (from the superior and inferior cava); during systole (contraction), blood is sent into the right ventricle.
Right ventricle (RV): pumps blood via the pulmonary artery to the lungs for oxygenation; the low-pressure pulmonary pump.
Left atrium (LA): receives oxygenated blood from the lungs and the four pulmonary veins; during systole, blood is sent into the left ventricle.
Left ventricle (LV): pumps blood via the aorta throughout the entire systemic circulation; walls of the left ventricle are thicker and stronger than right ventricle and form most of the left side and apex of the heart; the high-pressure systemic pump.

4. Cardiac cycle and related conditions.
   a. The rhythmic pumping action of the heart.
   b. Systole: the period of ventricular contraction.
   c. Diastole: the period of ventricular relaxation and filling of blood.
   d. Atrial contraction occurs during the last third of diastole and completes ventricular filling.

5. Coronary circulation and related conditions.
   a. Right coronary artery (RCA): supplies the right atrium, most of the right ventricle, and in most individuals the inferior wall of the left ventricle, atrioventricular (AV) node.
   b. Left coronary artery (LCA): supplies most of the left ventricle, sinoatrial (SA) node.
   c. Veins: parallel arterial system.

6. Conduction: specialized tissue allows rapid transmission of electrical impulses in the myocardium; includes nodal tissue and Purkinje fibers.
   a. Sinoatrial (SA) node: the main pacemaker of the heart; controls the flow of blood through the heart and thereby the normal perfusion of the body's systems and structures.
      (1) SA node dysfunction results in irregular heart rhythm and atrial fibrillation, and increases the risk of stroke.
   b. Atrioventricular (AV) node: connects conduction and synchronizes contractions between the atria and the ventricles to support blood flow.
      (1) AV node damage can result in heart block.
   c. Purkinje tissue: the specialized conducting tissue of the ventricles.

Table 8-3

Possible Clinical Manifestations of Cardiac Failure

LEFT VENTRICULAR FAILURE	RIGHT VENTRICULAR FAILURE
Signs and symptoms of pulmonary congestion:	
Dyspnea, dry cough	Dependent edema
Orthopnea	Weight gain
Paroxysmal nocturnal dyspnea (PND)	Ascites
Pulmonary rales, wheezing	Liver engorgement (hepatomegaly)
Signs and symptoms of low cardiac output:	
Hypotension	Anorexia, nausea, bloating
Tachycardia	Cyanosis (nail beds)
Lightheadedness, dizziness	Right upper quadrant pain
Cerebral hypoxia: irritability, restlessness, confusion, impaired memory, sleep disturbances	Jugular vein distension
Fatigue, weakness	Right-sided S_3 heart sounds
Poor exercise tolerance	Murmurs of pulmonary or tricuspid insufficiency
Enlarged heart on chest x-ray	
S_3 heart sound, possibly S_4	
Murmurs of mitral or bicuspid regurgitation	

(1) Damage to the purkinje fibers can result in arrhythmia.

7. Myocardial fibers: striated muscle tissue/fibers that exhibit rhythmicity of contraction; sustained by continuous O_2 delivery from the coronary arteries.

    (1) Coronary artery disease (CAD) decreases O_2 delivery; damage to the myocardial fibers may result in arrhythmia.

8. Hemodynamics.

  a. Cardiac output: the amount of blood ejected from the heart per minute; dependent on heart rate and stroke volume.

  b. Stroke volume: the average amount of blood ejected per heartbeat.

Peripheral Circulation

1. Arteries.

  a. Transport oxygenated blood from areas of high pressure to lower pressures in the body tissues.

  b. Refer to Figure 8-2.

2. Capillaries.

  a. Function for the exchange of nutrients and fluids between blood and tissues.

3. Veins.

  a. Transport dark, unoxygenated blood from tissues back to the heart.

  b. Refer to Figure 8-3.

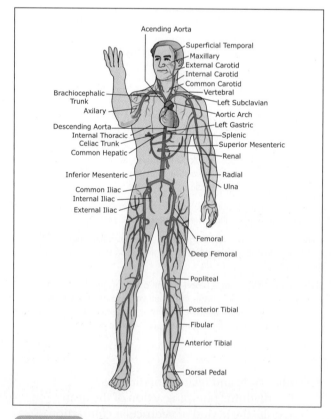

Figure 8-2   **Circulatory system: Arteries.**

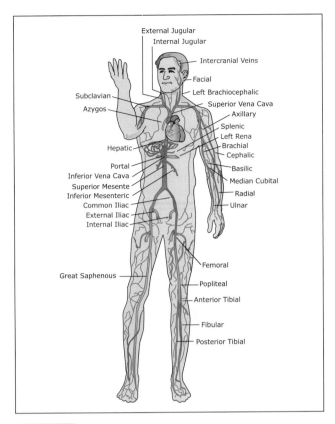

Figure 8-3   **Circulatory system: Veins.**

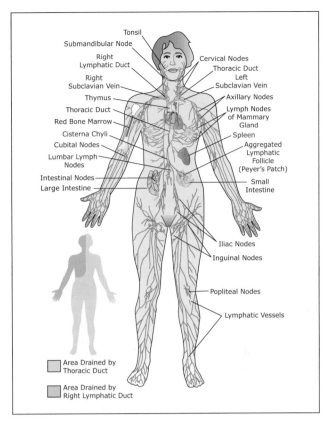

Figure 8-4   **Lymphatic system.**

4. Lymphatic system.
   a. Drains lymph from bodily tissues and returns it to venous circulation.
   b. Contributes to immune system function; lymph nodes collect cellular debris and bacteria; remove excess fluid, blood waste, and protein molecules; and produce antibodies.
   c. Refer to Figure 8-4.

Neurohumoral Influences

1. Neural control of heart rate and blood vessels.
2. Parasympathetic control (cholinergic): cardioinhibitory center; slows rate and force of myocardial contraction; decreases myocardial metabolism; causes coronary artery vasodilation.
   a. A gradual decrease in heart rate is expected during the recovery phase following engagement in exercise or activity.
      (1) Abnormal, consistent decrease in heart rate (i.e., bradycardia) decreases the supply of oxygen-rich blood to the body.
      (2) Syncope, shortness of breath, angina, confusion, and decreased endurance can result.

> CAUTION: Monitoring vital signs to track changes in heart rate during interventions is required to ensure safety.

3. Sympathetic control (adrenergic): cardioacceleratory center; causes an increase in the rate and force of myocardial contraction and myocardial metabolism; causes coronary artery vasoconstriction.
   a. A gradual increase in heart rate is expected during active engagement in exercise or other activities.
4. Additional control mechanisms.
   a. Baroreceptors: the main mechanism controlling heart rate; respond to changes in blood pressure.
      (1) A rapid decrease in blood pressure could result in syncope.
   b. Chemoreceptors: sensitive to changes in blood chemicals (i.e., O_2, CO_2, lactic acid).
   c. Body temperature: heart rate changes analogously to temperature.
   d. Ion concentrations: variations in ion concentrations can result in clinical conditions that impact function. Refer to Box 8-1.
   e. Peripheral resistance.
      (1) Increased peripheral resistance increases arterial blood volume and pressure.

Chapter 8

BOX 8-1 ▷ Conditions and Functional Implications Related to Variations in Ion Concentrations

- Hyperkalemia: increased potassium ions, decreases the rate and force of contraction, and produces EKG changes.
- Hypokalemia: decreased potassium ions, produces EKG changes; arrhythmias, may progress to ventricular fibrillation.
- Hypercalcemia: increased calcium concentration; increases heart rate.
- Hypocalcemia: decreased calcium concentration; depresses heart action.

(2) Decreased peripheral resistance decreases arterial blood volume and pressure.

(3) Influenced by arterial blood volume: viscosity of blood and diameter of arterioles and capillaries.

EXAM HINT: The NBCOT® OTR® exam content outline identifies knowledge of the "expected patterns, progressions, and prognoses associated with conditions that limit occupational performance . . . (including the) signs and symptoms of disease, stages of disease, (and) secondary complications" (NBCOT®, 2022, p. 3) as essential for competent and safe practice. The application of knowledge about the above and following conditions will be required to correctly answer NBCOT® exam items about working with clients with cardiovascular disorders.

Coronary Artery Disease (CAD)

Definition

1. Atherosclerotic disease process that narrows the lumen of coronary arteries resulting in ischemia to the myocardium.

EXAM HINT: Knowledge of the "precautions or contraindications associated with a client's condition or stage of recovery" is identified as essential for competent and safe practice (NBCOT®, 2022, p. 7). Therefore, you should be sure you know all risk factors and precautions for, and complications of, cardiovascular disorders and the effective response of an OT practitioner.

Atherosclerosis

1. Etiology.
   a. Disease of lipid-laden plaques (lesions) affecting moderate and large-size arteries.
   b. Characterized by thickening of the intimal layer of the blood vessel wall from the focal accumulation of lipids, platelets, monocytes, plaque, and other debris.
2. Onset: variable depending on the presence or absence of risk factors.
3. Prevalence: increases with age and the presence of risk factors.
4. Prognosis: good with early detection and treatment.
5. Multiple risk factors. Refer to Box 8-2.

CAUTION: Two or more of the risk factors described in Box 8-2 increase the risk of CAD.

BOX 8-2 ▷ Risk Factors for Atherosclerosis

- Nonmodifiable risk factors: age, sex, race, family history of CAD.
- Modifiable risk factors: cigarette smoking, high blood pressure, elevated cholesterol levels and low-density lipoprotein (LDL) levels, elevated blood homocystine, emotional stress.
- Contributory risk factors: diabetes, obesity, sedentary lifestyle, and elevated blood homocystine and fibrinogen levels.

Main Clinical Syndromes of CAD

1. Characteristics.
   a. Involves a spectrum of clinical entities ranging from angina to infarction to sudden cardiac death.
   b. An imbalance of myocardial oxygen supply and demand resulting in ischemic chest pain.
   c. Subacute occlusion may produce no symptoms.
   d. Symptoms present when lumen is at least 70% occluded.
2. Angina pectoris: the clinical manifestation of ischemia that is characterized by mild to moderate substernal chest pain/discomfort; most commonly felt as pressure or dull ache in the chest and left arm but may be felt anywhere in the upper body including the neck, jaw, back, arm, and epigastric area.
   a. Usually lasts less than 20 minutes due to transient ischemia.

b. Represents an imbalance in myocardial oxygen supply and demand that can be brought on by the following.
  (1) Increased demands on the heart: exertion/exercise, emotional upsets, smoking, extremes of temperature (especially cold), overeating, tachyarrhythmias.
  (2) Sasospasm: symptoms may be present at rest.
c. Types of angina.
  (1) Stable angina: classic exertional angina occurring during exercise or activity.
    (a) Relieved with rest and/or sublingual nitroglycerin.
  (2) Unstable angina (pre-infarction, crescendo angina): coronary insufficiency at rest without any precipitating factors or exertion.
    (a) Pain is difficult to control.

> **RED FLAG:** If chest pain (angina) increases in severity, frequency, and duration, there is an increased risk for myocardial infarction or sudden death (i.e., lethal arrhythmia).

  (3) Variant angina (Prinzmetal's angina): caused by vasospasm of coronary arteries in the absence of occlusive disease.
    (a) Responds well to nitroglycerin or a calcium channel blocker long term.

> **RED FLAG:** Angina is potentially a sign of an impending life-threatening situation. If a client complains of angina during an evaluation or intervention session the OT practitioner should IMMEDIATELY STOP the session and monitor vital signs. If it is documented in the medical record that the person is prescribed sublingual nitroglycerin for angina, the OT practitioner should have the client take their medicine to alleviate symptoms. They should monitor the client's symptoms and vital signs to see if the angina resolves. The OT practitioner should notify the client's physician. If the client is receiving services on an inpatient unit, they should be returned to their room.

3. Myocardial infarction (MI): prolonged ischemia, injury, and death of an area of the myocardium caused by occlusion of one or more of the coronary arteries; results in necrosis of heart tissue.
  a. Precipitating factors: atherosclerotic heart disease with thrombus formation, coronary vasospasm or embolism; drug toxicity.
  b. Presenting signs and symptoms. Refer to Box 8-3.
  c. Common infarction sites for coronary artery occlusion.
    (1) Inferior MI, right ventricle infarction, disturbances of upper conduction system: right coronary artery.
    (2) Lateral MI, ventricular ectopy: circumflex artery.
    (3) Anterior MI, disturbances of lower conduction system: left anterior descending artery.

BOX 8-3 ▷ Signs and Symptoms of CAD

- Severe substernal pain of more than 20 minutes' duration which may radiate to neck, jaw, arm, and/or epigastric area.

  > CAUTION: Pain may be misinterpreted as indigestion.

- Pain unrelieved by rest and/or sublingual nitroglycerin.
- Dyspnea, rapid respiration, shortness of breath.
- Indigestion, nausea, and vomiting.
- Women are more likely than men to experience the common symptoms of shortness of breath, nausea/vomiting, and back or jaw pain.

  > CAUTION: Presenting signs in women may vary and are often mistaken as something else (e.g., the flu or acid reflux) and not an MI.

- Symptoms that women may more typically present include:
  - Chest pain that is not severe or long-lasting but characterized by uncomfortable pressure, squeezing, fullness, or pain in the center of the chest that may persist for more than a few minutes or go away and come back.
  - Pain or discomfort in one or both arms, the back, neck, jaw, or stomach with or without chest pain.
  - Breaking out in a cold sweat and/or being light-headed.

---

d. Results and functional implications of impaired ventricular function.
  (1) Decreased stroke volume, cardiac output, and ejection fraction.
  (2) Increased end diastolic ventricular pressure.
e. Electrical instability and arrhythmias present in injured and ischemic areas.
4. Heart failure (HF).
  a. A clinical syndrome in which the heart is unable to maintain adequate circulation of the blood to meet the metabolic needs of the body.
  b. Etiology: may be caused by coronary artery disease, valvular disease, congenital heart disease, hypertension, infections.
  c. Physiological abnormalities: decreased cardiac output, elevated end diastolic pressures (preload); increased heart rate; impaired ventricular contractility.
  d. Types of heart failure and their clinical manifestation. Refer to Table 8-3.
  e. Associated symptoms: muscle wasting, myopathies, osteoporosis.
  f. Possible clinical manifestations of heart failure. Refer to Table 8-3.

Classification of Heart Failure

1. The New York Heart Association (NYHA) Functional Classification is the most commonly used classification system to assess the stage of heart failure.

Table 8-4

The New York Heart Association (NYHA) Functional Classification	
FUNCTIONAL CAPACITY CLASSES	**OBJECTIVE ASSESSMENT CLASSES**
Class I: persons with cardiac disease but resulting in no limitation of physical activity. • Ordinary physical activity does not cause undue fatigue, palpitation, dyspnea, or angina pain.	Class A: no objective evidence of cardiovascular disease. • No symptoms and no limitation in ordinary physical activity.
Class II: persons with cardiac disease resulting in slight limitation of physical activity. They are comfortable at rest. • Ordinary physical activity results in fatigue, palpitation, dyspnea, or angina pain.	Class B: objective evidence of minimal cardiovascular disease. • Mild symptoms and slight limitation during ordinary activity. Comfortable at rest.
Class III: persons with cardiac disease resulting in marked limitation of physical activity. They are comfortable at rest. • Less than ordinary activity causes fatigue, palpitation, dyspnea, or angina pain.	Class C: objective evidence of moderately severe cardiovascular disease. • Marked limitation in activity due to symptoms, even during less-than-ordinary activity. Comfortable only at rest.
Class IV: persons with cardiac disease resulting in inability to carry on any physical activity without discomfort. • Symptoms of heart failure or the angina syndrome may be present even at rest. If any physical activity is undertaken, discomfort increases.	Class D: objective evidence of severe cardiovascular disease. Severe limitations. • Symptoms are experienced even while at rest.

a. The NYHA places people in one of four classes based on an objective assessment that determines their functional capacity. Refer to Table 8-4.
  (1) Functional capacity is how a person with cardiac disease feels while engaged in physical activity.
  (2) Objective measurements include electrocardiograms, stress tests, x-rays, echocardiograms, and radiological images. Refer to Table 8-5.

> **EXAM HINT:** The NYHA classification relates symptoms to everyday activities and quality of life, and its categories describe functional limitations experienced during physical activity. The application of knowledge about the NYHA categories can be used to correctly answer NBCOT® exam items about the task of selecting and implementing "interventions for improving . . . physiological status, considering client condition and current stage of recovery, to support occupational performance" (NBCOT®, 2022, p. 10), which has been identified as a key task performed by occupational therapists in the NBCOT® OTR® exam content outline.

Medical and Surgical Management

1. A variety of medical and surgical diagnostic procedures are commonly used to support an accurate diagnosis and to guide intervention strategies for clients with cardiovascular and pulmonary disorders. Refer to Table 8-5.
2. Dietary and lifestyle interventions: healthy food choices, low-salt and low-cholesterol diets, physical activity, weight reduction, and smoking cessation.
3. Pharmaceutical interventions: medications designed to manage specific aspects of existing cardiovascular function or prevent or decrease the risk of cardiac events and the progression of related diseases; drugs aimed at reducing oxygen demand on the heart and increasing coronary blood flow; drugs may be prescribed alone or in combinations.

a. Types of medications. Refer to Table 8-6 for a description of medications that are typically used to treat and/or manage cardiac conditions, their actions, and functional implications.
  (1) Due to the psychosocial impact of cardiac conditions, anxiolytic and/or antidepressant medications may be prescribed to address a client's anxiety and/or depression.
    (a) Because the sympathetic effects of these medications (e.g., drowsiness, decreased blood pressure and heart and respiration rates, pose health and safety risks (particularly if they occur during intervention), all team members involved in the person's care must recognize and monitor these effects.

> **CAUTION:** All medications have potential side effects. The OT practitioner must be aware of the following potential negative impact(s) of medications on the client and respond accordingly.
> • Unusual symptoms during assessment or intervention may indicate an adverse drug reaction; the OT practitioner must alert the cardiologist or attending physician if these occur.
> • For clients taking anticoagulants, the OT practitioner should be aware of bruising or cuts; if a cut occurs, it may take longer to stop bleeding or require immediate medical attention.
> • Clients taking beta-blockers may not demonstrate the expected increase in heart rate or blood pressure during activity or exercise; therefore, the OT practitioner should adjust expected parameters accordingly and utilize rate of perceived exertion (RPE) scales as an indication of the effects of activity or exercise.

Table 8-5

Cardiopulmonary Diagnostic Procedures

DIAGNOSTIC PROCEDURE	PURPOSE
Chest x-ray	To evaluate evidence of congestion in the lungs, heart chamber hypertrophy, and structural abnormalities.
Electrocardiogram (ECG)	To identify cardiac arrhythmias, assess amount and location of damage to the myocardium, determine adequacy of oxygenation of the myocardium.
Holter monitor	To record ECG signals over a 24-hour period while the person engages in normal daily routine to determine heart function during various activities.
Echocardiogram (ultrasound)	To record size, structure, and motion of the heart and vessels; reveals valvular defects and structural abnormalities.
Cardiac stress test	To record cardiac activity during graded exercise; used to determine the extent to which cardiac disease affects functional capacity; provides guidelines related to the type and amount of physical activity that a person can engage in safely.
Cardiac catheterization (an invasive procedure)	To visualize coronary circulation to determine the degree of CAD, congenital heart defect, valvular disease, myocardial damage.
Pulmonary function test	To determine cause of dyspnea, degree of lung disease; provides information related to endurance potential for functional activities.

Table 8-6

Common Cardiac Medications, Their Actions, and Functional Implications

MEDICATION GROUP	COMMON MEDICATIONS	MEDICATION ACTIONS	FUNCTIONAL IMPLICATIONS
Nitrates/Vasodilators	Isordil, Minoxidil, Nitroglycerin	Relax blood vessels, increase blood flow and oxygen to heart, and reduce cardiac workload.	Eases angina.
Angiotensin-Converting Enzyme (ACE) Inhibitors	Capoten, Monopril, Vasotec	Decrease preload through peripheral vasodilation, reduce oxygen demand, and improve blood flow; an antihypertensive.	Decreases blood pressure.
Angiotensin II Receptor (ARB) Inhibitors	Cozaar, MIcardis	Block effects of angiotensin to prevent blood pressure from rising; antihypertensive.	Decreases blood pressure.
Beta-blockers	Atenolol, Corgard, Inderal, Metoprolol/Lopressor	Reduce myocardial demand by reducing heart rate and contractility, control arrhythmias, and relieves chest pain; antihypertensive.	Regulates heart rhythm, eases angina, and decreases blood pressure.
Calcium Channel Blockers	Cardizem, Norvasc, Procardia	Inhibit flow of calcium ions.	Decreases heart rate, decreases contractility, dilates coronary arteries, decreases blood pressure, controls arrhythmias; controls and eases angina; regulates heart rhythm; eases angina; decreases blood pressure.
Arrhythmias	Cardiac glycosides, Digoxin, Digitalis	Increase contractility and decrease heart rate.	Mainstay in the treatment of CHF (e.g. digoxin).
Diuretics	Esidrix, Lasix, Microzide	Decrease myocardial work (reduce preload and afterload); antihypertensive.	Decreases blood pressure.
Hypolipidemic Agents	Colestid, Mevacor, Zocor	Reduce serum lipid levels when diet and weight reduction are not effective.	Manages high cholesterol.
Anticoagulants	Eliquis, Coumadin	Prevent blood clot formation that may interfere with blood circulation or cause venous thrombosis.	Used to treat certain blood vessel, heart, and lung conditions; often prescribed to prevent first or recurrent strokes.
Antiplatelet agents	Aspirin, Plavix	Prevent platelets from forming clots.	Usually prescribed for unstable angina, after a MI or transient ischemic attack, or as a preventative measure in the early stages of coronary artery disease; dual antiplatelet therapy (DAPT) prescribes aspirin and another antiplatelet agent together.

RED FLAG: Combinations of medications can have an adverse effect on blood pressure during position changes (moving from supine to sit; sit to stand) and during activity; careful monitoring of vital signs during position changes is required.

4. Surgical interventions: surgical procedures often result in deconditioning and impact the client's occupational performance.
   a. Angioplasty (percutaneous transluminal coronary angioplasty [PTCA]): under fluoroscopy, surgical dilation of a blood vessel using a small balloon-tipped catheter inflated inside the lumen.
      (1) Relieves obstructed blood flow in acute angina or acute MI.
      (2) Results in improved coronary blood flow and left ventricular function and anginal relief.
   b. Intravascular stents: an endoprosthesis (pliable wire mesh) implanted postangioplasty to prevent restenosis and occlusion in coronary or peripheral arteries.
   c. Coronary artery bypass grafting [CABG]: surgical circumvention of an obstruction in a coronary artery using an anastomosing graft (saphenous vein, internal mammary artery).
      (1) Results in improved coronary blood flow and left ventricular function and anginal relief.

CAUTION: Surgery results in deconditioning that must be addressed.

   d. Transplantation: used in end-stage myocardial disease, e.g., cardiomyopathy, ischemic heart disease, valvular heart disease.
      (1) Major problems post-transplantation: rejection, infection, complications resulting from immunosuppressive therapy.
   e. Ventricular assistive devices (VADs).
      (1) Implanted device (accessory pump) that improves tissue perfusion and maintains cardiogenic circulation.
      (2) Used with severely involved patients (e.g., cardiogenic shock, unresponsive to medications, severe ventricular dysfunction; those awaiting heart transplant).
      (3) Often called the "bridge to transplantation."
5. Thrombolytic therapy for acute MI.
   a. Medications administered to activate the body's fibrinolytic system, dissolve clot, and restore coronary blood flow (e.g., streptokinase, tissue plasminogen [TPA], urokinase).

Peripheral Vascular Disease (PVD)

1. Arterial disease.
   a. Occlusive peripheral arterial disease (PAD). Refer to Table 8-7.
      (1) Chronic, occlusive arterial disease of medium and large-sized vessels.
      (2) Associated with hypertension and hyperlipidemia; patients may also have CAD, diabetes, cerebrovascular disease, metabolic syndrome, history of smoking.
      (3) Diminished blood supply to affected extremities with pulses decreased or absent.
      (4) Early stages: clients exhibit intermittent claudication. Pain is described as burning, searing, aching, tightness, or cramping. Occurs regularly and predictably with walking and is relieved by rest.
      (5) Late stages: clients exhibit rest pain, muscle atrophy, trophic changes (i.e., hair loss, skin, and nail changes).
      (6) Affects primarily lower extremities.
   b. Thromboangiitis obliterans (Buerger's disease): chronic inflammatory vascular occlusive disease of small arteries and also veins.
      (1) Begins distally and progresses proximally in both lower and upper extremities.
      (2) Symptoms include pain, paresthesias, cold extremities, diminished temperature sensation, and fatigue; there is a risk of ulceration and gangrene.
   c. Diabetic angiopathy: consistent and noncontrolled elevation of blood glucose levels and accelerated atherosclerosis; neuropathies are a major problem; ulcers and diabetic retinopathy are common outcomes.

CAUTION: Untreated ulcers can lead to gangrene and amputation. Refer to Chapter 9 for information on the prevention and management of ulcers. Unmanaged diabetic retinopathy can result in blindness. Refer to Chapter 5's section on age-related vision loss.

   d. Raynaud's phenomenon: episodic spasm of small arteries and arterioles; abnormal vasoconstriction reflex exacerbated by exposure to cold or emotional stress; tips of fingers develop pallor, cyanosis, numbness, and tingling; mostly affects females. Refer to Chapter 9.
2. Venous disease.
   a. Varicose veins: distended, swollen superficial veins; tortuous in appearance; may lead to varicose ulcers.
   b. Superficial vein thrombophlebitis: clot formation and acute inflammation in a superficial vein; localized pain usually in saphenous vein.
   c. Deep vein thrombosis (DVT): inflammation of a vein in association with the formation of a thrombus; usually occurs in lower extremities.
      (1) Associated with venous stasis (e.g., bed rest, lack of leg exercise), hyperactivity of blood coagulation, and vascular trauma.
      (2) Early mobility (i.e., out of bed activities) after surgery helps eliminate venous stasis.

Table 8-7

Differential Diagnosis: Peripheral Vascular Diseases

	CHRONIC ARTERIAL INSUFFICIENCY	CHRONIC VENOUS INSUFFICIENCY	CHRONIC LYMPHATIC INSUFFICIENCY
Etiology	Atherosclerosis Thrombosis Emboli Inflammatory process	Thrombophlebitis Trauma Vein obstruction (clot) Vein incompetence	Primary lymphedema Secondary lymphedema
Risk factors	Age: >60 years Smoking Diabetes mellitus Gender: slightly higher in men Dyslipidemia Hypertension Hyperhomocysteinemia Race (African American)	Venous hypertension Varicose veins Inherited trait Gender: female Age Increased BMI Sedentary lifestyle/prolonged sitting Ligamentous laxity	Lymphadenectomy Radiation treatment Inflammatory arthritis Obesity
SIGNS AND SYMPTOMS: DETERMINED BY LOCATION AND DEGREE OF VASCULAR INVOLVEMENT			
Pain	Severe muscle ischemia/intermittent claudication Worse with exercise, relieved by rest Rest pain indicates severe involvement Muscle fatigue, cramping, numbness Paresthesias over time	Minimal to moderate steady pain Aching pain in lower leg with prolonged standing or sitting (dependency) Superficial pain along course of vein	Heaviness, tightness, aching, or discomfort
Location of pain	Usually calf, lower leg, or dorsum of foot May occur in thigh, hip, or buttock	Muscle compartment tenderness	Edematous limb
Vascular	Decreased or absent pulses Pallor of forefoot on elevation Dependent rubor	Venous dilatation or varicosity Edema: moderate to severe, especially after prolonged dependency	Rare complications unless severe and untreated edema
Skin changes	Pale, shiny, dry skin Loss of hair Nail changes Coolness of extremity	Hemosiderin deposition: dark, cyanotic, thickened, brown skin Lipodermatosclerosis: fibrosing of the subcutaneous tissue May lead to stasis dermatitis, cellulitis	Cutaneous fibrosis May lead to cellulitis, lymphangitis
Acute	Acute arterial obstruction: distal pain, paresthetic, pale, pulseless, sudden onset	Acute thrombophlebitis (deep venous thrombosis, DVT): Calf pain, aching, edema, muscle tenderness, 50% asymptomatic	Rarely acute, usually progressive over time except with changes in pressure to limb altering flow (repeated blood pressure measurements, airplane flights)
Ulceration	May develop in toes, feet, or areas of trauma; pale or yellow to black eschar, gangrene may develop; regular in shape and may appear punched out	May develop at sides of ankles, especially medial malleolus along the course of veins; gangrene absent; painful, shallow, exudative and have granulation tissue in the base; irregular borders	Unusual

Adapted from Bickley, L., & Szilagyi, P. G. (2017). Bates' Guide to physical examination and history taking (11th ed.). Lippincott Williams & Wilkins.

(3) DVT may be a contributing factor to or a complication of cerebral vascular accident (CVA) or the result of prolonged bed rest during serious illness.

(4) Initially, the client may be asymptomatic.

(5) Signs and symptoms include progressive inflammation with tenderness to palpation; change in lower extremity temperature, color, circumference, appearance, or tenderness/pain.

> **RED FLAG:** DVT may be life threatening; thus, its symptoms require *immediate* medical attention.

d. Chronic venous insufficiency.
  (1) Characterized by chronic leg edema, skin pigmentation changes, scaly appearance, itchy.
  (2) Refer to Table 8-7.

3. Lymphedema.
  a. A chronic, progressive disorder with excessive accumulation of fluid due to obstruction of lymphatics.
  b. Causes swelling of the soft tissues in arms and legs.
  c. Results from mechanical insufficiency of the lymphatic system.
  d. Stages of lymphedema.
    (1) Refer to Table 8-8.

Table 8-8

Lymphedema Summary

ETIOLOGY	Primary lymphedema: congenital condition with abnormal lymph node or lymph vessel formation (hypoplasia or hyperplasia). Secondary lymphedema: occurs as a result of injury to lymphatic vessels (e.g., cancer surgery and/or radiation, chronic venous insufficiency) or parasitic infection (filariasis).
PROGRESSIVE OVER TIME	Without treatment, may develop into fibrosis, chronic infection (cellulitis, lymphangitis) or loss of limb function.
SYMPTOMS	Heaviness, tightness or pain; swelling and persistent edema; loss of ROM and function in an arm or leg.
SKIN CHANGES	Hardening and/or discoloration of skin.
DIAGNOSIS	History, visual inspection and palpation, girth measurements. Tests may include: MRI and CT scans; Doppler ultrasound, radionuclide imaging of the lymphatic system (lymphoscintigraphy).
STAGING	A four stage system. Stage 0, latent lymphedema: no visible changes in limb or upper body, may notice difference in feeling—mild tingling, unusual tiredness, or slight heaviness, may remain in this stage for months or years before obvious symptoms develop. Stage 1, spontaneously reversible lymphedema: limb is soft and pitting; swelling may increase overnight. Stage 2, spontaneously irreversible lymphedema: swelling with increase in fibrotic tissue; risk for infection. Stage 3, lymphostatic elephantiasis: extreme increase in swelling; skin changes (fibrosis, sclerosis, papillomas).
TREATMENT	Complete decongestive therapy (CDT): manual lymph drainage, short-stretch compression bandages, exercises, functional training, skin care, and lymphedema education.

Pulmonary System

Function

1. Respiration, delivers oxygen to cardiovascular system.
2. Removes carbon dioxide and other by-products from body.

Anatomy and Physiology

EXAM HINT: The NBCOT® OTR® exam content outline identifies knowledge of the "impact of body functions and body structures on occupational performance" (NBCOT®, 2022, p. 3) as essential for competent and safe practice. While the NBCOT® exam will likely not ask *direct* questions about the structure of the pulmonary system, knowing the major structures and functions of this system can help you correctly answer NBCOT® exam items about the *functional implications* of pulmonary dysfunction. For example, damage to the bronchioles and alveoli results in decreased gas exchange, compromised lung function, and signs and symptoms of chronic obstructive pulmonary disease (COPD).

1. Bony thorax: musculoskeletal structures support the ability of the lungs to fully inflate during inspiration and deflate during expiration.
2. Airways: integrity of the upper (nose, pharynx, larynx) and lower conducting airways (trachea to terminal bronchioles, respiratory bronchioles, alveolar ducts, alveolar sacs, and alveoli) support efficient inspiration and expiration.
3. Lungs and pleura.
4. Muscles of ventilation.
   a. Primary muscles of inspiration: diaphragm, intercostals.
   b. Accessory muscles of inspiration: used when a more rapid or deeper inhalation is required or in disease.
   c. Expiratory muscles.
      (1) Resting expiration: done by passive relaxation of inspiratory muscles and elastic recoil tendency of lungs.
      (2) Expiratory muscles used when quicker, fuller expiration is desired or in disease.
5. Mechanics of breathing: forces acting upon the rib cage include elastic recoil of the lungs, bony thorax, and muscles.

6. Ventilation and perfusion: the movement of gas in and out of the pulmonary system.
   a. Measurements include volumes, capacities, flow rates.
   b. Optimal respiration occurs when ventilation and perfusion (blood flow to lungs) are matched.
   c. Body position/gravity affects distribution of ventilation and perfusion. Breathing patterns and rate of respiration may change depending on the person's position.

 ## Pulmonary Diseases

> **EXAM HINT:** The NBCOT® OTR® exam content outline identifies knowledge of the "expected patterns, progressions, and prognoses associated with conditions that limit occupational performance . . . (including the) signs and symptoms of disease, stages of disease, (and) secondary complications" (NBCOT®, 2022, p. 3) as essential for competent and safe practice. The application of knowledge about the following clinical conditions will be required to correctly answer NBCOT® exam items about working with clients with pulmonary dysfunction.

Pneumonia

1. Bacterial pneumonia: an intra-alveolar bacterial infection.
   a. Gram-positive bacteria usually acquired in the community; pneumococcal pneumonia (streptococcal) is the most common type.
   b. Gram-negative bacteria usually develop in a host who has an underlying chronic condition, acute illness, recent antibiotic therapy; usually results in early tissue necrosis and abscess formation.
2. Viral pneumonia: an interstitial or interalveolar inflammatory process caused by viral agents (influenza, adenovirus, cytomegalovirus, herpes, parainfluenza, respiratory syncytial virus, measles).
3. Aspiration pneumonia: aspirated material causes an acute inflammatory reaction within the lungs; usually found in persons with impaired swallowing ability (dysphagia). Refer to Chapter 9.
4. Pneumocystis pneumonia (PCP): pulmonary infection caused by a fungus (*Pneumocystis carinii*) in immunocompromised hosts; most often found in patients following transplantation, neonates, and those infected with HIV.

Severe Acute Respiratory Syndrome

1. Severe acute respiratory syndrome (SARS).
   a. An atypical respiratory illness caused by a coronavirus.

2. Coronavirus disease (COVID).
   a. An airborne infection caused by a virus called SARS-CoV-2.
   b. Part of the coronavirus family that cause a variety of conditions (e.g., head/chest colds, SARS).
   c. Spreads quickly through droplets.
   d. Symptoms may appear 2–14 days after exposure to the virus.
   e. Possible symptoms include the following.
      (1) Fever or chills.
      (2) Cough.
      (3) Shortness of breath or difficulty breathing.
      (4) Fatigue.
      (5) Muscle or body aches.
      (6) Headache.
      (7) New loss of taste or smell.
      (8) Sore throat.
      (9) Congestion or runny nose.
      (10) Nausea or vomiting.
      (11) Diarrhea.
   f. Older adults and individuals with certain underlying medical conditions are at an increased risk of severe illness from COVID (e.g., cancer, end stage renal disease, chronic obstructive pulmonary disease, asthma, cystic fibrosis, cardiac conditions, HIV, tuberculosis, immunological disorders, substance abuse).

> **CAUTION:** Because SARS and COVID are passed in the form of droplets that can be inhaled, airborne precautions must be used in addition to standard precautions. A surgical mask is required when working with clients that are positive for the infection. Refer to Appendix 3A: Standard Precautions and Appendix 3B: Transmission-based Precautions in Chapter 3.

   g. Some individuals may exhibit long-term effects from the virus; i.e., post-COVID conditions (PCC) or long COVID.
      (1) Most commonly occurs in individuals who had a severe COVID illness.
      (2) COVID signs, symptoms, and conditions are present four weeks or more after the initial phase of infection.

(3) May be multisystemic.

(4) May present with a relapsing–remitting pattern and progression or worsening over time.

(5) Conditions can last weeks, months, or years

(6) Severe and life-threatening events may occur months or years after infection.

(7) Also called long-haul COVID, post-acute COVID-19, post-acute sequelae of SARS CoV-2 infection (PASC), long-term effects of COVID, and chronic COVID.

> **RED FLAG:** If an individual is showing any of the following symptoms, the OT practitioner should call for *immediate* medical attention. COVID emergency warning signs include the following.
> - Trouble breathing.
> - Persistent pain or pressure in the chest.
> - New confusion.
> - Inability to wake or stay awake.
> - Pale, gray, or blue-colored skin, lips, or nail beds, depending on skin tone.

Tuberculosis (TB)[1]

1. An airborne infection caused by a bacterium (*Mycobacterium tuberculosis*).
2. Transmission and risk factors.
   a. A person with TB of the throat or chest can pass the infection by sneezing or coughing.

> **CAUTION:** Because TB is passed in the form of droplets that can be inhaled, airborne precautions must be used in addition to standard precautions. A surgical mask is required when working with clients that are positive for the infection. Refer to Appendix 3A: Standard Precautions and Appendix 3B: Transmission-based Precautions in Chapter 3.

   b. People most at risk for infection are those who are in close contact with an infected individual on a daily/regular basis (e.g., family members, friends, co-workers, and health-care personnel).
   c. The risk for rapid onset of TB disease increases for persons with certain diseases and conditions (e.g., diabetes, HIV/AIDS, substance abuse, low body weight).
   d. People who have had a TB infection within two years of treatment are at high risk for reinfection.
3. Signs and symptoms of TB.
   a. A bad cough for more than two weeks.
   b. Chest pain.
   c. Blood-tinged sputum or phlegm.
   d. Weakness or fatigue.
   e. Weight loss.

f. Loss of appetite.
g. Chills/fever.
h. Night sweats.

4. Asymptomatic TB infection: the TB cells become inactive but remain alive in the body.
   a. Infected people do not feel ill and are not contagious. They:
      (1) Usually have a positive TB skin test.
      (2) Can develop full-blown TB later, if they do not get drug treatment for the TB infection.
5. Sequelae of TB: once the infection settles into a person's lungs, it can spread to other parts of the body and can result in other serious conditions. These can include the following.
   a. Joint damage (arthritis), meningitis, and liver or kidney problems.
   b. Spine: Rood's disease, a vertebral collapse caused by TB resulting in compression of the spinal cord, can occur.

Chronic Obstructive Diseases

1. Chronic obstructive pulmonary disease (COPD): a disorder characterized by poor expiratory flow rates.
   a. Peripheral airways disease: inflammation of the distal conducting airways; associated with smoking.
   b. Chronic bronchitis: chronic inflammation of the tracheobronchial tree with cough and sputum production lasting at least three months for two consecutive years.
   c. Emphysema: permanent abnormal enlargement and destruction of air spaces distal to terminal bronchioles; may result in destruction of acini, the functional units for gas exchange in the lungs.
      (1) Results in airway dilation, premature airway closure, air trapping, and increased residual air volume or hyperinflation.
      (2) Signs and symptoms: clients present with a mixture of clinical features. These include the following.
         (a) Primary complaint of dyspnea on exertion.
         (b) Diminished breath sounds, wheezing (typically associated with exertion).
         (c) Prolonged expiratory phase.
         (d) Pursed lip breathing.
         (e) Physical presentation may include enlarged anterior/posterior dimensions of the chest wall (barrel chest), hypertrophied accessory muscle from overuse, use of accessory muscles for breathing, forward leaning posture.
         (f) Presence of a chronic cough and sputum production will vary and depend on the infectious history of the person.
         (g) Disease advancement may result in the patient becoming cachectic (emaciated),

---

[1] This section was completed by Ann Burkhardt.

signs of right heart failure due to secondary pulmonary hypertension.

(3) Interventions.

(a) Smoking cessation.

(b) Short-acting and long-acting bronchodilators.

- Anticholinergic drugs to block bronchoconstriction (e.g., Atrovent, Ventolin, Proventil, Maxair), not the first line of medications.

> CAUTION: Clients that are prescribed these medications may experience symptoms during evaluation and/or intervention sessions. If a client demonstrates shortness of breath or difficulty breathing, the *FIRST* thing the OT practitioner should do is stop the activity and advise the client to use their inhaler. If symptoms do not resolve, this can be a medical emergency.

- Xanthine derivatives (e.g., theophylline) for bronchodilation, limitation of inflammatory response.
- Corticosteroids for anti-inflammatory effects.

(c) Preventive vaccination against influenza and pneumococcus.

(d) Oxygen therapy to:

- reduce level of dyspnea.
- improve/decrease maximal voluntary ventilation, polycythemia, by correcting hypoxemia.
- decrease pulmonary hypertension.
- improve quality and quantity of sleep.
- improve cognitive function and exercise tolerance.

(e) Surgeries may include bullectomy, volume reduction, lung transplantation.

(4) Prognosis: varies depending on degree of obstruction, presence of hypercapnia (increased levels of CO_2), recurrence of infections, and the development of right heart failure.

2. Asthma: an increased reactivity of the trachea and bronchi to various stimuli (allergens, exercise, cold); manifests by widespread narrowing of the airways due to inflammation, smooth muscle constriction, and increased secretions.

a. Factors associated with the development of asthma: maternal smoking, early infections, environmental factors, genetics.

b. Risk factors: childhood asthma, family history, maternal smoking, occupational exposures, environmental exposure, exposure to second-hand smoke.

c. Sign and symptoms: wheezing, dyspnea, chest pain, facial distress, nonproductive cough with acute exacerbation in which the airways may become obstructed with vicious, tenacious mucous (more severe in children than adults).

(1) Symptoms in adults may include paroxysmal nocturnal dyspnea, morning chest pain, and increased symptoms with exposure to cold.

d. Prevention and intervention.

(1) Smoking cessation and minimizing exposure to second-hand smoke.

(2) Annual flu shot.

(3) Avoidance of stimulants that precipitate asthmatic episode.

(4) Use of short- and long-acting bronchodilators.

(a) Common medications: albuterol (e.g., Ventolin, Proventil), Atrovent with albuterol, Combivent.

(5) Establishment of a routine exercise program.

e. Reversible in nature.

3. Cystic fibrosis. Refer to Pediatric Pulmonary Disorders section.

4. Hyaline membrane disease/respiratory distress syndrome. Refer to Pediatric Pulmonary Disorders section.

Chronic Restrictive Diseases

1. Etiology varies.

2. Diseases are all characterized by difficulty expanding the lungs causing a reduction in lung volumes.

3. Restrictive disease due to alteration in the chest wall: restricted motion of the bony thorax with diseases such as ankylosing spondylitis, arthritis, scoliosis, pectus excavatum, arthrogryposis, or the integumentary changes of the chest wall due to thoracic burns or scleroderma.

4. Restrictive disease due to alteration in the neuromuscular apparatus: decreased muscular strength results in an inability to expand the rib cage, seen in disease states such as multiple sclerosis, muscular dystrophy, Parkinson's disease, spinal cord injury (SCI), or cerebrovascular accident (CVA).

Carcinomas

1. Refer to Chapter 9.

Other Pulmonary Conditions

1. Refer to Table 8-9.

> CAUTION: Persons that have had surgery with anesthesia are at risk for atelectasis. To prevent atelectasis, they are given inspiration spirometers post-surgery. It is important for OT practitioners to observe when a client is having difficulty breathing at rest or during activity post-surgery. The use of an inspiration spirometer should be included in the person's ADL routine.

Chapter 8

Table 8-9

Other Pulmonary Conditions
Pulmonary edema: excessive seepage of fluid from the pulmonary vascular system into the interstitial space; may eventually cause alveolar edema. Pulmonary emboli: a thrombus from the peripheral venous circulation becomes embolic and lodges in the pulmonary circulation. • Small emboli do not necessarily cause infarction.
Pleural effusion: excessive fluid between the visceral and parietal pleura, caused mainly by: • increased pleural permeability to proteins from inflammatory diseases (e.g., pneumonia, rheumatoid arthritis, systemic lupus). • neoplastic disease (i.e., abnormal growth of cells; tumor). • increased hydrostatic pressure within pleural space (e.g., congestive heart failure). • decrease in osmotic pressure (i.e., hypoproteinemia). • peritoneal fluid within the pleural space (i.e., ascites in cirrhosis). • interference of pleural reabsorption from a tumor invading pleural lymphatics.
Atelectasis: collapsed or airless alveolar unit, caused by: • hypoventilation secondary to pain during the ventilator cycle (due to pleuritis, postoperative pain, rib fracture). • internal bronchial obstruction (e.g., aspiration, mucus plugging). • external bronchial compression (e.g., tumor or enlarged lymph nodes) • low tidal volumes (due to narcotic overdose, inappropriately low ventilator settings). • neurologic insult.

Occupational Therapy Cardiopulmonary Evaluation

EXAM HINT: In the NBCOT® OTR® exam content outline, Domain 1 Evaluation and Assessment comprises 23% of the exam and focuses on the ability to "acquire information regarding factors that influence occupational performance on an ongoing basis throughout the occupational therapy process" (NBCOT®, 2022, p. 3). The application of knowledge about the following assessment methods can help you correctly answer Domain 1 exam items about the evaluation of clients with cardiopulmonary disorders.

The Occupational Profile

1. The occupational profile obtains information from the client's medical record and interview to determine their medical and occupational history, activity patterns, roles, interests, values, priorities, needs, and desired outcomes to inform the OT process. Refer to Chapter 3.
   a. Medical record: review current medical status and past medical history to learn about the onset of a cardiac incident and/or cardiopulmonary condition, past and current diagnoses, chronic and/or co-occurring conditions, premorbid status, and current functional level.
      (1) Review diagnostic tests (refer to this Chapter's Medical and Surgical Management section) and results to determine implications for OT

intervention including activity restrictions, vital sign parameters, and prognosis.
   b. Client interview: obtain information about the client's social and occupational history, educational/learning, family configuration, social supports, and personal goals.
      (1) This information is used to establish a client-centered intervention and discharge plan.
      (2) Refer to Chapter 3 for interview guidelines and Box 3-2 for questions that can be used to effectively obtain a client's occupational profile.

Analysis of Occupational Performance

1. Identify the impact of presenting symptoms on occupational performance through the client interview and observation of performance.
   a. Refer to preceding interview section and interview and observation guidelines in Chapter 3.
2. Assess the impact of presenting symptoms on occupational performance through the completion of formal assessments.
   a. Pain/angina: note location, severity, and type. Refer to Table 8-10.
   b. Dyspnea (i.e., shortness of breath): note severity, position, and times at which discomfort is experienced. Refer to Table 8-11.

Table 8-10

Anginal Scale

0 No angina
1 Light, barely noticeable
2 Moderate, bothersome
3 Severe, very uncomfortable
4 Most pain ever experienced

Table 8-11

Modified Borg Dyspnea Scale (Borg, 1982)

0	Nothing at all
0.5	Very, very slight (just noticeable)
1	Very slight
2	Slight
3	Moderate
4	Somewhat severe
5	Severe
6	Severe
7	Very severe
8	Very severe
9	Very, very severe (almost maximal)
10	Maximal

c. Fatigue/perceived exertion: note severity, time of occurrence, and association with activities.
d. Palpitations: note the client's awareness of heart rhythm abnormalities including pounding, fluttering, racing heartbeat, skipped beats.
e. Dizziness: note time of occurrence and association with postural changes during activity.
f. Edema.
   (1) Fluid retention may be identified by swelling, especially in the lower extremities, or sudden weight gain.
   (2) Note location, measurements, time of day when edema is most prominent, and resolution with activity.
   (3) Refer to Chapter 11.

EXAM HINT: In the NBCOT® OTR® exam content outline, a key task of the occupational therapist is to "identify the influence of . . . body functions and body structures . . . on occupational performance" (NBCOT®, 2022, p. 3). Thus, the application of knowledge about the above presenting symptoms and the following assessment approaches will be required to correctly answer NBCOT® exam items about the evaluation of clients with cardiopulmonary disorders.

Vital Signs

1. Important and reliable indicator of activity tolerance and response to evaluation and treatment.
   a. Refer to Table 8-12 for normal vital sign values for infants and adults.
   b. Must be monitored before activity, during activity, and after activity to ensure compliance with parameters.

CAUTION: Possible side effects of medications must be reviewed and taken into account when monitoring vital signs.

2. Pulse/heart rate: rhythmical throbbing of arterial wall as a result of each heartbeat; influenced by force of contraction, volume and viscosity of blood, diameter and elasticity of vessels, emotions, exercise, blood temperature, and hormones.
   a. Assessment: done by palpation of peripheral pulses; with normal rhythm palpate 30 seconds; with irregular rhythm palpate one to two minutes.
      (1) Taken prior to activity, during activity, and after activity.
   b. Palpation sites.
      (1) Radial: most common monitoring site; radial artery, radial wrist at base of thumb.
      (2) Temporal: superior and lateral to eye.
      (3) Carotid: on either side of the anterior neck between the sternocleidomastoid muscle and trachea; best reflects cardiac function.
      (4) Brachial: the medial aspect of the antecubital fossa; used to monitor blood pressure.
      (5) Femoral.
      (6) Popliteal.
      (7) Pedal.
3. Pulse/heart rate (HR) parameters.
   a. Normal adult HR is 70 beats per minute (bpm); range 60–100 bpm.
      (1) As an individual ages, the normal resting heart rate range may increase up to 100 bpm.
   b. Pediatric: newborn is 120 bpm; range 70–170 bpm.

Table 8-12

Normal Values for Infants and Adults

PARAMETER	INFANT	ADULT
Heart Rate	120 bpm	60–100 bpm
Blood Pressure	75/50 mm Hg	<120/80 mm Hg
Respiratory Rate	40 br/min	12–20 br/min
PaO_2	75–80 mm Hg	80–100 mm Hg
$PaCO_2$	34–54 mm Hg	35–45 mm Hg
pH	7.26–7.41	7.35–7.45
Tidal Volume	20 mL	500 mL

Chapter 8

c. Tachycardia: greater than 100 bpm.

d. Bradycardia: less than 60 bpm.

e. Irregular: force and frequency vary; may be due to arrhythmia, myocarditis.

f. Weak, thready pulse.

g. Bounding, full pulse.

h. Bruit: abnormal sound or murmur; associated with atherosclerosis.

4. Auscultation of heart: done with a stethoscope to assess heart sounds.

a. Note the addition of extra, abnormal heart sounds.

5. Blood pressure (BP).

a. Monitor at rest, during evaluation/activity, post activity.

b. Normal adult BP is <120/80 mm Hg (systolic/diastolic); range between 110 and 140 systolic, 60 and 80 diastolic.

c. Pediatric: 1 month: 80 systolic, 45 diastolic; 6 years: 105–125 systolic, 60–80 diastolic.

d. Hypertension: BP above 120/80. Refer to Table 8-13.

e. Increased BP may be related to stress, pain, hypoxia, drugs, and disease.

f. Decreased BP may be related to bed rest, drugs, arrhythmias, blood loss/shock, and MI.

g. Orthostatic hypotension: a sudden drop in blood pressure that can occur with positional changes, especially from supine or sitting to standing.

(1) Also called postural hypotension, it can cause dizziness, weakness, nausea, blurred vision, and syncope (i.e., fainting).

(2) Orthostatic hypotension can occur after surgery, several days of bed rest, secondary to other conditions (e.g., Parkinson's disease, SCI), and as a side effect of medications.

> CAUTION: People at risk for orthostatic hypotension should be advised to move slowly when changing positions (e.g., standing up slowly after crouching to garden).

Table 8-13

2017 ACC/AHA Blood Pressure Guidelines*			
	BP, mmHg		
	SYSTOLIC		**DIASTOLIC**
Normal	<120		<80
Elevated	120–129	and	<80
Stage 1	130–139	or	80–89
Stage 2	at least 140	or	at least 90
Hypertensive crisis	>180	and/or	>120

*2017 ACC/AHA Guideline for the Prevention, Detection, Evaluation, and Management of High Blood Pressure in Adults. Journal of the American College of Cardiology, 71(19), May 2017.

6. Respiration.

a. Monitor at rest, during evaluation/activity, post activity.

b. Rate and depth of breathing: normal is 12–18 breaths per minute.

c. Auscultation of lungs/respiratory sounds.

(1) Normal: soft, rustling sound heard throughout all inspiration and start of expiration.

(2) Abnormal: crackles/rales.

(a) Rattling, bubbling sounds; may be due to secretions in the lungs.

(b) Wheezes, whistling sounds.

7. Oxygen saturation (SpO2).

a. SpO2 must be maintained at 90% or above for patients with cardiac conditions during activities and at 86% or above for patients with pulmonary conditions.

b. Monitor with pulse oximeter at rest, during an evaluation/activity, and post activity.

c. Energy conservation and work simplification techniques are effective intervention strategies. Refer to Chapter 11.

d. Nasal cannula O2 may be prescribed by the physician for participation in activities if SpO2 falls below 90%.

Condition of Extremities

1. Diaphoresis: excessive sweating associated with decreased cardiac output.

2. Pulses: decreased or absent pulses associated with peripheral vascular disease (PVD). Refer to Table 8-14.

3. Skin color and vascular status.

a. Cyanosis: bluish color related to decreased cardiac output or cold; especially lips, fingertips, nail beds.

b. Pallor: absence of rosy color in light skinned individuals, associated with decreased peripheral blood flow, PVD.

c. Rubor: dependent redness with PVD.

d. Temperature.

e. Skin changes: clubbing of fingernails; pale, shiny, dry, abnormal pigmentation; ulceration, dermatitis; gangrene.

Table 8-14

Grading Scale for Peripheral Pulses	
0	Absent pulse, not palpable
1+	Pulse diminished, barely perceptible
2+	Easily palpable, normal
3+	Full pulse, increased strength
4+	Bounding pulse

f. Intermittent claudication: pain, cramping, fatigue occurring during exercise that is relieved by rest; associated with PVD; pain is typically in calf.

g. Edema. Refer to Table 11-3.

Functional Mobility Assessment

1. Bed mobility.
2. Transfers.
3. Wheelchair mobility.
4. Ambulation status.
5. Refer to Chapter 16.

Cognition

1. Provides a baseline of the client's ability to understand, process, retain, and apply the information that is taught during intervention.
   a. Orientation.
   b. Memory.
   c. Concentration.
   d. Judgment.
2. Refer to Chapters 13 and 14.

Activities of Daily Living/ Instrumental Activities of Daily Living

1. Self-care.
2. Household management tasks.
3. Leisure activities.
4. Community activities.
5. Note level of function and type of assistance required.
6. Note level of dyspnea and angina reported during activities. Refer to Tables 8-10 and 8-11.
7. Refer to Chapter 15 for more information on evaluation of ADL and instrumental activities of daily living (IADL).

Activity Tolerance

1. Graded exercise test done by an exercise physiologist or a physical therapist (Six-Minute Walk Test, physical performance tests).
2. Observation of activities with monitoring of vital signs (heart rate, blood pressure, respiration rate, rate of perceived exertion, pulse oximetry).

3. Periodic monitoring of dyspnea, angina, and claudication pain. Refer to Tables 8-10 and 8-11.
4. Periodic monitoring of exertion.
   a. Borg Dyspnea Scale: a self-report of perceived exertion with a rating scale that ranges from no exertion at all (e.g., sitting or lying) to maximal exertion (e.g., hard work that is not advisable to engage in).
      (1) Refer to Table 8-11.
5. Metabolic equivalent levels (METs) are used to determine the energy expenditure required for activity performance. Refer to Table 8-15.
   a. Because the energy expended during an activity can vary due to personal differences in activity performance and variability in activity demands, Table 8-15 provides MET ranges for several activities.
      (1) For example, the amount of energy expended to paint a picture will depend on a person's painting style. vital capacity, and co-morbidities.

> **EXAM HINT:** When answering NBCOT® exam items about the use of METs during the assessment of a client's activity tolerance, remember that the client's current physical status and pattern of activities prior to the cardiac event must be considered to determine the correct answer. The use of activity analysis to assess activity demands and their relationship to MET levels can help you determine correct answers to exam items about MET levels.
>
> For example, the person's position (e.g., standing or sitting) will change the MET level of an activity and impact the client's ability to engage in occupations. If an exam item describes a client as physically improving, a correct answer will include the person transitioning to a higher MET level to engage in the same activity (e.g., grooming in standing after grooming in sitting).

> **EXAM HINT:** If you are not an excellent memorizer and are running out of study time, do not attempt to completely memorize Table 8-15; rather, pick a few activities representative of each level and memorize these. If an exam item contains a scenario about a specific MET level, you can recall these memorized activities. If your memorized activities are not an answer choice, you can use your activity analysis skills to reason which activity most closely matches the activities that you had memorized. For example, ironing in a standing position has similar activity demands to washing dishes in a standing position.

Chapter 8

Table 8-15

Metabolic Equivalent Levels for Common Activities

MET LEVELS	ACTIVITIES OF DAILY LIVING (MET LEVEL)	INSTRUMENTAL ACTIVITIES OF DAILY LIVING (MET LEVEL)	LEISURE AND WORK ACTIVITIES (MET LEVEL)
<1.5 METs Very light activities	Grooming done by another person (1.3) Passive sexual activity i.e., kissing, hugging (1.3)	Repairing clothing, sewing a button or a hem while seated (1.3) Wrapping a present while seated (1.3)	Keyboarding, writing, playing a low–key video game while seated (1.0) Reading (1.3) Knitting, crocheting (1.3)
1.5 to <3 METs Light activities	Eating, bathing while seated (1.5) Toileting, eliminating, seated or standing (1.8) Grooming, seated or standing (2.0) Showering, dressing/undressing, hair styling in standing (2.5) Active sexual activity; i.e., fondling. (2.8)	Light homemaking: washing dishes while standing, straightening a bed, preparing food (1.8–2.5) Loading/unloading washer and dryer, folding and hanging clothes (1.8–2.0) Ironing (1.8) Gardening, light (2.0) Putting away groceries (2.5) Mowing lawn with a rider mower (2.5)	Doing arts and crafts, seated (1.5–3.0), standing arts and crafts (2.5–3.0) Driving a car, motorcycle, golf power cart (1.5–3.0) Walking slowly around home, store, or office; up to 2.5 mph pace (2.0–2.8) Playing a musical instrument (2.0–2.5) Stretching (2.3) Physically active video gaming (2.3) Doing calisthenics (2.8) Playing pool, bowling (2.0–3.0)
3 to <6 METs Moderate activities	Active sexual activity; i.e., intercourse and orgasm (5–6)	Sweeping, vacuuming, mopping interior floors (3.0–3.5) Making a bed and changing its linens (3.3) Preparing meals and cooking (3.5) Heavy cleaning: washing windows or a car, cleaning a garage (3.0–4.0) Pushing a wheelbarrow (220 lb. load) (3.0–4.0) Doing moderate yard work; raking, pruning, sweeping (4.0) Digging a garden (3.5–5.0) Mowing lawn with a walking power mower (5.5)	Walking, 3.0 mph to 4.0 mph (3.0–6.0) Cycling, 6 mph to 10 mph (3.0–6.0) Playing recreational sports; basketball, tennis, volleyball, archery, golfing while pulling a bag cart, fly fishing (3.0–4.5) Brick laying (3.0–4.0) General carpentry (3.6) Calisthenics, moderate; resistance training, 8–15 repetitions (3.5) Endurance promoting video gaming (3.8) Upper body exercise (4.3) Water aerobics and water exercise (5.3) Ice or roller skating, 9 mph (5.0–6.0) Canoeing, kayaking, 4 mph (5.0–6.0)
≥6 to 10 METs Vigorous activities		Doing vigorous yard work (6.0) Scrubbing a bathroom (6.5) Carrying heavy loads (7.5) Carrying groceries up stairs (7.5) Shoveling, 10 min./22 lbs (6.0–7.0), 10 min./31 lbs (8.0–9.0) Carrying boxes or furniture up stairs (9.0)	Walking very briskly, 4.5 mph (6.3) Jogging, 5.0 mph, and running at <6.0 mph (8.0–10.0) Cycling, 11 mph to 13 mph (6.0–10.0) Calisthenics, vigorous (8.0) Stair climbing, fast pace (8.8) Walking/hiking, up to steep grades with a backpack (7.0–9.0) Bicycling on flat land, light effort (6.0), moderate (8.0), fast pace (10.0) Swimming, leisurely (6.0), moderately (8.0) Competitive sports, i.e., skiing, soccer, tennis singles, badminton (6.0–8.0) Manual lawn mowing (6.0–7.0) Ice hockey (7.0–8.0) Canoeing, kayaking 5 mph (7.0–8.0)
10+ METs Very vigorous activities		Shoveling, 10 min./35 lbs (6.0–7.0)	Cross country skiing, 5+ mph Running, 6 mph (10.0), 7 mph (11.5), 8 mph (13.5), 9 mph (15.0), 10 mph (17.0) Swimming, very vigorously (11.0)

References

American College of Sports Medicine. (2014). ACSM's guidelines for exercise testing and prescription (9th ed.). Lippincott Williams & Williams.

Causey–Upton, R., Hatch, B.C., & Benthall, D.H. (2019). Cardiopulmonary conditions and treatment. In A.J. Mahle & A.L. Ward (Eds.), Adult physical conditions: Intervention strategies for occupational therapy assistants (pp. 680–681). F.A. Davis.

Psychosocial Assessment

1. Overt signs and symptoms of depression, anxiety, and/or stress and the observed effects on the individual's ability to engage in and complete activities.
2. Stress management/coping styles and psychosocial, family/caregiver, and spiritual supports.
3. Refer to Chapter 10 and Chapter 14.

Environmental Assessment

1. Accessibility issues related to safety, risk for falls, and environmental barriers in the discharge environment.
2. Physical demands of the discharge environment (e.g., the presence of stairs and/or airborne irritants).
3. Refer to Chapter 16.

Role of the Occupational Therapy Assistant (OTA)/ Certified Occupational Therapy Assistant (COTA®)

1. The OTA/COTA® can contribute to the evaluation process in collaboration with the occupational therapist.
   a. Supervision by an occupational therapist is required.
   b. The level of supervision required will be determined by the OTA's/COTA®'s experience.
2. Service competency must be established.
3. The OTA/COTA® cannot independently evaluate or interpret evaluation results.

Occupational Therapy Cardiopulmonary Intervention

Overview and General Guidelines

1. Intervention must consider the systems and structures that are damaged, the resulting condition(s), and their functional implications. For example, implications for intervention with a client with an acute condition (e.g., MI) will differ from those of a client with a chronic condition (e.g., COPD).
   a. Refer to Tables 8-1, 8-2, and 8-3.
2. Identify the setting along the continuum of care (i.e., acute, sub-acute, long-term, homecare, outpatient/community-based programs) in which the client is receiving services.
3. Select a frame of reference/practice approach to inform clinical reasoning and guide interventions.
   a. Depending on the client's status and intervention goals, biomechanical, restorative, rehabilitative approaches, or compensatory and adaptive approaches may be used.
      (1) Refer to Box 8-4.
4. Safety precautions are always adhered to and the client's physical response(s) to interventions are closely monitored regardless of the frame of reference or approaches used.

CAUTION: Monitoring vital signs to track changes in heart rate, blood pressure, oxygen saturation, and respiration prior to, during, and following interventions is required. Reinforce cardiac and postsurgical precautions during routine activities and interventions.

> **BOX 8-4** ▷ Commonly Used Frames of Reference, Practice Approaches and Techniques Used in Cardiopulmonary Rehabilitation
>
> ---
>
> - Biomechanical/Restorative approaches focus on restoring the person to their prior level of function (Patnaude, 2022). Typical approaches and techniques include:
>   - graded exercises (range of motion, strengthening, activity tolerance).
>   - occupation-based activities adhering to prescribed MET levels.
>   - energy conservation and work simplification techniques
>   - refer to Chapter 11 for Biomechanical Approaches and Table 8-15 for MET Levels
> - Compensatory/Adaptive approaches focuses on occupational performance within the limitations of a chronic or progressive condition (Cole & Tufano, 2020; Patnaude, 2022). Typical approaches and techniques include:
>   - adaptation of activities to decrease activity demands.
>   - adaptive equipment and compensatory techniques.
>   - focus on occupation-based activities while adhering to prescribed MET levels. Refer to Table 8-15 for MET Levels.

   (1) Cessation of intervention and rest required.
   (2) Seek emergency medical assistance if symptoms do not resolve (Crawford, 2022).

CAUTION: During all stages of rehabilitation, the OT practitioner must observe for signs and symptoms of cardiac distress. Refer to Table 8-3 for signs and symptoms of cardiac failure.

5. Health literacy is supported by client education about self-monitoring of vital signs, rate of perceived exertion, level of fatigue, specific techniques for dyspnea, activity adaptations, and environmental modifications.
6. Review the outcomes of intervention and determine the setting to which the client is being discharged (e.g., a sub-acute rehabilitation facility, skilled nursing facility [SNF], home).
   a. Implement interventions that enable a successful transition to the discharge setting.

> **EXAM HINT:** In the NBCOT® OTR® exam content outline, Domain 3 Select and Manage Interventions comprises 38% of the exam. The application of knowledge about cardiopulmonary interventions can help you effectively determine the correct answers to Domain 3 exam items that address the selection and implementation of "interventions to promote healing and enhance engagement in occupation-based activities" (NBCOT®, 2022, p. 7). for clients with cardiopulmonary disorders.

Phase 1: Inpatient Rehabilitation/ Hospitalization Stage (Acute)

1. Begins when the patient is determined to be medically stable following the cardiac or pulmonary event (MI, CABG, angioplasty, valve repair/replacement, CHF, etc.).
   a. Typically, after 24 hours or until the patient is stable for 24 hours.
2. Program focus.
   a. Patient and family education regarding disease process and recovery.
      (1) Increase knowledge of energy conservation and work simplification principles and techniques. Refer to Chapter 11.
      (2) Increase knowledge of the approximate metabolic cost of activities. Refer to Table 8-15.
   b. Improve ability to carry out self-care and functional activities that require a low-level of energy expenditures.
   c. Decrease anxiety.
   d. Promote risk factor modification (i.e., support smoking cessation and dietary modification efforts if warranted).
   e. Discharge to home.
3. Evaluation and intervention.
   a. Initiated at bedside with a monitored, functional assessment of self-care and mobility.
   b. If the client is pain free, exhibits no arrhythmia, and has regular pulse of 100 or less, an activity program is initiated.

> **CAUTION:** Intense monitoring is required during activity, especially in the coronary care unit (CCU).

c. Beginning activities at a MET level = 1–2.
   (1) Bed mobility, static standing.
   (2) Transfer from bed to chair/bedside commode.
   (3) Bed bath, feeding, grooming at sink in sitting.
   (4) Active range of motion/warm-up exercises.
   (5) Wheelchair mobility/ambulation in room.
d. All activities use energy conservation techniques. Refer to Chapter 11 for the principles of energy conservation and work simplification.

> **EXAM HINT:** The NBCOT® OTR® exam content outline identifies knowledge of the "techniques for promoting improved . . . breathing patterns during functional tasks" (NBCOT®, 2022, p. 10) as essential for competent and safe practice. Thus, the application of knowledge about the following techniques will be required to correctly answer NBCOT® exam items about working with clients with cardiopulmonary disorders.

e. Breathing exercises. Refer to Table 8-16.
   (1) Techniques are done during all exercises and activities.
f. Vital signs and exertion scales are monitored prior to each activity, at the peak of each activity, immediately upon cessation of activity, and at four to five minutes post activity.

Table 8-16

Dyspnea Control and Management Techniques

Dyspnea Control Postures: positions to reduce breathlessness.
Technique:
- In sitting, the person bends forward at the waist to rest forearms on a flat surface (tabletop) or thighs.
- In standing, the person leans forward and props body on a surface (countertop) or ambulatory device (walker).

Pursed Lip Breathing: provides resistance to expiration, increases use of the diaphragm, and decreases recruitment of the accessory muscles.
Technique:
- With their mouth closed, the person first breathes in slowly through their nose for two counts (i.e., a normal breath).
- The person then puckers or 'purses' their lips as if they were going to whistle or slowly blow out the candles on a birthday cake.
- They breathe out through their pursed lips for four counts. Some resistance will be felt during expiration.
- Expiration should take twice as long as inspiration.

Diaphragmatic breathing: increases the use of the diaphragm and improves chest volume.
Technique:
- The person lies down (supine) on their back and places a small book on their abdomen.
- They inhale slowly through the nose to make the book rise.
- They then exhale through pursed lips to make the book fall.

References: Cleveland Clinic. (n.d.). Pursed Lip Breathing (clevelandclinic .org).

Crawford, E. J. (2022). Cardiac dysfunction and chronic obstructive pulmonary disease. In M. E. Patnaude (Ed.), Early's physical dysfunction practice skills for the occupational therapy assistant (4th ed., pp. 593–606). Elsevier.

g. Client education to ensure their competence in self-monitoring vital signs and consistency in their reporting of their level of perceived exertion.

   (1) Clear and accurate instructions must be provided for the meaning of exertion scale ratings (i.e., all ratings should reflect the client's perceptions of how the exercise is making them feel; how hard they are working to perform the exercise).

h. Adhere to activity guidelines and MET levels. Refer to Table 8-15.

   (1) As the client's activity tolerance improves, more strenuous, higher MET level activities are added in progression from basic ADL to IADL.

> **EXAM HINT:** In the NBCOT® OTR® exam content outline Domain 2 Analysis, Interpretation, and Planning comprises 23% of the exam. In this Domain, knowledge of "clinical decision-making for assessing and adapting the intervention plan and prioritizing goals based on client response to intervention . . . (including) physiological changes . . . (and) precautions or contraindications associated with a client's condition or stage of recovery" (NBCOT®, 2022, p. 7) is identified as essential for the competent management of the intervention plan. Thus, the application of knowledge about the following contraindications/precautions can help determine the correct answer to exam items about working with clients with cardiopulmonary disorders.

i. Adhere to any contraindications/precautions as per physician orders.

   (1) Observe/monitor for signs and symptoms of cardiac distress. Refer to Table 8-3.

   (2) Adhere to activity guidelines and MET levels. Refer to Table 8-15.

   (3) Observe for decrease in systolic BP greater than 20 mm Hg.

   (4) Observe facial expression; be alert to facial changes.

   (5) Monitor heart rate (use facility specific guidelines, if available).

      (a) Max HR 100 very light activity—very high risk.

      (b) Max HR 120 light activity—less than six weeks after MI or surgery.

      (c) Max HR 130 recent bypass surgery, cardiomyopathy, CHF.

      (d) Target HR 60%–80% person's max HR: treadmill test.

   (6) Monitor BP also for resting systolic BP <120 mm Hg; diastolic 80 mm Hg.

   (7) Monitor oxygen saturation (O_2 sat); below 86% for pulmonary patients, below 90% for cardiac patients.

   (8) Monitor ECG for signs and symptoms of myocardial ischemia.

   (9) Monitor exertion scales for signs and symptoms of distress during activity, speed of recovery. Refer to Tables 8-10 and 8-11.

> **CAUTION:** The following precautions should be followed:
> - Avoid isometric muscle work, straining, breath holding (Valsalva).
> - Avoid overhead exercises or holding UEs over head for extensive time periods.
> - Avoid lateral arm movements and exercises that stretch the chest and pull an incision.

> **RED FLAG:** There are clinical signs/symptoms and diagnoses for which therapy is contraindicated and should not be implemented. These include uncontrolled atrial/ventricular arrhythmias, recent embolism/thrombophlebitis, dissecting aneurysm, severe aortic stenosis, acute systemic illness, acute MI, digoxin toxicity, acute hypoglycemia or metabolic disorder, third-degree heart block, and unstable angina.

j. Patients are generally discharged to Phase 2 when they are able to carry out activities at MET level 3.5. Refer to Table 8-15.

   (1) MET levels should be used as a general reference to determine the approximate level of energy required to perform an activity.

   (2) MET levels are used to quantify the amount of energy required to perform an activity and to provide the OT practitioner with a guideline for grading activities used during intervention.

      (a) Selection of activities based on MET level must take into consideration the client's physical status and activity patterns prior to the cardiac or pulmonary event, as well as the client's subjective report of level of exertion during their activity performance.

k. Educate the individual about heart disease and the recovery process; provide emotional support.

4. Length of stay in the hospital is typically 5–14 days.

a. Three to five days is common for an uncomplicated MI (no post-MI angina, malignant arrhythmias, or heart failure).

b. Continued inpatient services may be required in a transitional setting for up to six weeks post cardiac event, surgery, or pulmonary disease exacerbation.

> **RED FLAG:** The contraindications (refer to Box 8-5) for inpatient cardiac rehabilitation and adverse responses to inpatient exercise leading to exercise termination must be considered. Refer to Table 8-3 for signs and symptoms of cardiac failure.

c. Box 8-6 identifies the possible outcomes of cardiac rehabilitation.

BOX 8-5 ▷ Contraindications for Inpatient and Outpatient Cardiac Rehabilitation

- **Absolute Contraindications**
  - Acute MI (within 2 days).
  - Unstable angina not previously stabilized by medical therapy.
  - Uncontrolled cardiac arrhythmias causing symptoms or hemodynamic compromise.
  - Acute PE or pulmonary infarction.
  - Acute myocarditis or pericarditis.
  - Acute aortic dissection.
- **Relative Contraindications**
  - Left main coronary stenosis.
  - Moderate stenotic valvular heart disease.
  - Electrolyte abnormalities.
  - Severe arterial hypertension.
  - Tachyarrhythmias or bradyarrhythmias.
  - Hypertrophic cardiomyopathy and other forms of outflow tract obstruction.
  - Mental or physical impairment leading to inability to exercise adequately.
  - High-degree atrioventricular block.

BOX 8-6 ▷ Possible Outcomes of Cardiac Rehabilitation

- Decreased HR at rest and during exercise; improved HR recovery after exercise.
- Increased stroke volume.
- Increased myocardial oxygen supply and myocardial contractility; myocardial hypertrophy.
- Improved respiratory capacity during exercise.
- Improved functional capacity of exercising muscles.
- Reduced body fat, increased lean body mass; successful weight reduction requires multifactorial interventions.
- Decreased serum lipoproteins (cholesterol, triglycerides).
- Improved glucose tolerance.
- Improved blood fibrinolytic activity and coagulability.
- Improvement in measures of psychological status and functioning: increased self-confidence and sense of well-being.
- Increased participation in exercise; improved outcomes with adherence to rehabilitation programming.
  - Decreased angina in patients with CAD: anginal threshold is raised secondary to decreased myocardial oxygen consumption.
  - Reduced total and cardiovascular mortality in patients following myocardial infarction.
  - Decreased symptoms of heart failure, improved functional capacity in patients with left ventricular systolic dysfunction.
  - Improved exercise tolerance and function in patients with cardiac transplantation.

EXAM HINT: In the NBCOT® OTR® exam content outline, knowledge of the "strategies for addressing and enhancing health literacy with a client and relevant others" (NBCOT®, 2022, p. 6) is identified as required for competent and safe practice. Thus, it is likely that the NBCOT® exam will include items about interventions that promote health literacy for clients with cardiopulmonary disorders in inpatient, outpatient, home, and community-based practice settings.

Phase 2: Outpatient Rehabilitation/Convalescence Stage (Subacute)

1. Begins as early as 24 hours after discharge from the hospital.
   a. Frequency of visits depends on the clinical needs of the client.
2. Program focus.
   a. Educate the client on the importance of continued exercise.

b. Build up activity tolerance.

c. Improve the client's ability to carry out IADL and community tasks.

d. Improve the client's ability to perform work activities.

e. Support the client's efforts in smoking cessation and lifestyle changes as needed.

3. Evaluation and intervention.

a. Home evaluation.

b. Consumer and family education.

c. Graded exercise program with slow and gradual increase of weight.

d. Begin with activities at MET level 4–5, gradually increasing as the client's tolerance improves. Refer to Table 8-15.

e. Practice of functional activities in the discharge environment.

f. Use of energy conservation techniques and compensatory techniques in daily tasks.

g. Community activities.

h. Work site evaluation, if applicable.

4. Length of outpatient program is dependent on several factors including the client's physical and mental status post event and/or surgery, progress through MET levels, activity tolerance, and prognosis.

5. The contraindications provided in Box 8-5 and the effects provided in Box 8-6 are applicable to outpatient cardiac rehabilitation.

Phase 3: Maintenance/Training Stage (Community Exercise Programs)

1. Clients generally attend maintenance/training sessions once a week following the completion of Phase 2.

2. Groups may be integrated into individual exercise programs.

3. Occupational therapy intervention is provided as necessary for IADL, leisure pursuits, and work.

4. Maintenance gym program.

a. Weight training to maintain upper and lower body strength.

b. Cardiovascular training to maintain cardiopulmonary health.

Rehabilitation Guidelines for Lymphatic Disease

1. Occupational therapy evaluation tools and foci.

a. Occupation-based assessments to determine impact on occupational performance.

b. Biomechanical assessments: upper extremity ROM and MMT, pain, activity tolerance, endurance, and edema.

(1) Measurement of lymphedema swelling: circumferential girth measurement.

(a) The volumeter is the best objective measurement tool.

(b) The time of day when measurements are taken should be recorded.

(2) Refer to Chapter 11 for more information about biomechanical assessments.

> **EXAM HINT:** In the NBCOT® OTR® exam content outline, Domain 1 Evaluation and Assessment including acquiring "information regarding factors that influence occupational performance on an ongoing basis throughout the occupational therapy process" (NBCOT®, 2022, p. 3) and Domain 3 Select and Manage Interventions including selecting and implementing "interventions to promote healing and enhance engagement in occupation-based activities" (NBCOT®, 2022, p. 7), respectively, comprise 23% and 38% of the exam. The application of knowledge about the preceding evaluation foci and tools and the following interventions can help you effectively determine the correct answers to exam items that address OT evaluation and interventions for clients with lymphatic disease.

2. Occupational therapy intervention.

a. Phase I interventions: management of edema secondary to lymphatic dysfunction.

(1) Short-stretch compression bandages, worn 24 hours/day.

(a) These provide slow resting pressure and high working pressure to enhance lymphatic return at rest, improve activity of lymphatic system, and facilitate return during muscle pumping activities.

(2) Manual lymph drainage (MLD) with complete decongestive therapy.

(a) Massage and passive range of motion (PROM) to assist lymphatic flow.

(b) Emphasis on decongesting proximal segments first (trunk quadrant), then extremities, directing flow distal to proximal.

(c) Compression using multi-layered padding and short-stretch bandages.

(3) Exercise; stretching and low-to-moderate intensity aerobic exercise combined with rest; tai chi, yoga, movement to support lymphatic drainage.

> **RED FLAG:** Strenuous activities, jogging, ballistic movements, and rotational motions are contraindicated, as they are likely to exacerbate lymphedema.

(4) Relaxation, deep-breathing, and energy conservation/work simplification techniques to address stress, pain, fatigue, and breathing.

(5) Custom compression garments; provided once limb reduction plateaus (four to six months).

(6) Referral to a certified lymphedema therapist.

b. Occupation-based interventions.

(1) Engagement in ADL, IADL, work, and leisure activities with adaptations, if needed.

(2) Energy conservation techniques to minimize exacerbation of swelling.

c. Client and family education.

(1) Skin care, donning and doffing compression garments, environmental modifications to improve mobility and function.

(2) Managing psychosocial issues including stress, distress, depression, and anxiety.

3. Phase II intervention: self-management and daily home program.

a. Skin care.

b. Compression bandages.

c. Exercise.

d. Lymphedema bandaging at night.

e. MLD as needed.

f. Compression pumps: use with caution; limited benefits.

> **RED FLAG:** Pressures >45 mm Hg are contraindicated.

4. Education.

a. Skin and nail care.

b. Self-bandaging, garment care.

c. Infection management.

d. Maintain exercise while preventing lymph overload.

e. Incorporation of home management program into daily routine.

Basic Life Support and Cardiopulmonary Resuscitation (CPR)

> **RED FLAG:** If a client appears to be experiencing cardiac arrest (as evident by a sudden loss of responsiveness and/or no normal breathing), this is a medical emergency. If in a medical setting, the OT practitioner must *immediately* activate the setting's emergency system (e.g., calling a code blue). If the practitioner is in a home or community-based setting, they must call 911 immediately. In all settings, the practitioner must implement and maintain CPR until emergency personnel arrive.

1. Current CPR guidelines. Refer to Table 8-17.

a. Refer to Figure 8-5 and Table 8-17.

Role of the OTA/COTA®

1. The OTA/COTA® implements intervention with supervision of the occupational therapist.

a. The level of supervision required depends upon the OTA's/COTA®'s experience and established service competence and the regulations from the licensure board in the state of practice.

2. During the implementation of intervention, the OTA/COTA® informs the supervising occupational therapist of any change in the individual's status and any other relevant information that may affect treatment.

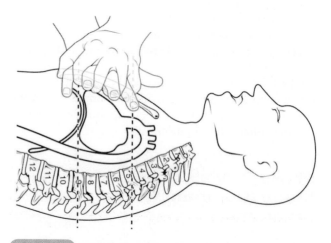

Figure 8-5 **CPR Technique.**

Table 8-17

Summary of Key Basic Life Support (BLS) Components for Adults, Children, and Infants

COMPONENT	RECOMMENDATIONS		
	ADULTS	CHILDREN	INFANTS
Recognition	Unresponsive (all ages) No breathing, not breathing normally (e.g., only gasping)	Same as for adults	Same as for adults
CPR Sequence	CAB	CAB	CAB (ABC for neonates)
Compression Rate	At least 100/minute	Same as for adults	Same as for adults

Compression Depth	At least 2 inches (5 cm)	At least ⅓ AP depth, about
		  2 inches (5 cm)
			At least ⅓ AP depth, about
			  1½ inches (4 cm)

Chest Wall Recall	Allow complete recoil between compressions, HCPs rotate compressors every 2 minutes	Same as for adults	Same as for adults

Compression Interruption	30:2 (1 or 2 rescuers)	30:2 single rescuer, 15:2
		  2 HCP rescuers
			30:2 single rescuer, 15:2
			  2 HCP rescuers

Airway	Head tilt-chin lift (HCP suspected trauma: jaw thrust)	Same as for adults	Same as for adults

Compression-to-Ventilation
  Ratio (until advanced
  airway placed)
	30:2 (1 or 2 rescuers)	30:2 single rescuer or 15:2
		  2 HCP rescuers
			30:2 single rescuer or 15:2
			  2 HCP rescuers

Ventilations: when rescuer
  untrained or trained and
  not proficient
	Compressions only	Compressions only	Compressions only

Ventilations with Advanced Airway (HCP)	One breath every 6–8 seconds (8–10 breaths/min) Asynchronous with chest compressions About 1 second per breath Visible chest rise	Same as for adults	Same as for adults

Defibrillation	Attach and use AED as soon as available. Minimize
	  interruptions in chest compressions before
	  and after shock, resume CPR, beginning with
	  compressions immediately after each shock
		Same as for adults	Same as for adults

Abbreviation Key: ABC, airway, breathing, compression; AED, automatic electronic defibrillator; AP, anteroposterior; CAB, compressions, airway, breathing; CPR, cardiopulmonary resuscitation; HCP, health-care provider.
From 2010 American Heart Association Guidelines for CPR and ECG. Downloaded from circ.ahajournals.org on July 5, 2011.

Pediatric Pulmonary Disorders[2]

EXAM HINT: Correct answers to NBCOT® exam items about an OT practitioner working with a child with a pulmonary disorder will recognize the need to consider child developmental issues during evaluation and intervention and the impact of prognosis on the family system and the child's intervention plan. Correct answers will also include collaboration with the family throughout the OT process and family education in the intervention and discharge plans.

---

[2] This section was revised by Cynthia H August and Rita P. Fleming-Castaldy. Marge E. Moffett Boyd and Jan G. Garbarini previously contributed to this section.

Cystic Fibrosis (CF)

1. Etiology.
   a. Inherited mutation(s) of the CTFR gene.
   b. Both parents must carry at least one mutated CTFR gene which they pass to their children.
      (1) Inheriting a mutated CTFR gene from both parents results in CF.
2. Prognosis.
   a. CF is a progressive condition which causes buildup of mucus in the lungs resulting in frequent infections and impairment of the ability to breathe.

b. With regular medical interventions to clear the airways and prevent and treat infections, individuals with CF can expect to live into their 30s and 40s, and in milder cases beyond their age 40s.
3. Diagnosis.
   a. Detectable in routine newborn screenings within the first month of life and before symptoms appear.
   b. Presence of thick, sticky mucus which plugs passageways in the lungs and pancreas.
   c. Salt concentration in the sweat.
   d. Recurring bouts of pancreatitis.
   e. Persistent cough with mucus.
   f. Activity intolerance.
   g. Repeated lung infections.
   h. Poor weight gain and slow growth rate.
   i. Frequent and greasy bulky stools and difficulty with bowel movements.
4. Complications can affect respiratory functions, the digestive system, and other organs.
   a. Reduced life expectancy.
      (1) The abnormal mucous clogs the lungs and leads to life-threatening lung infections and respiratory failure.
      (2) The mucous obstructs the pancreas and stops natural enzymes from helping the body break down and absorb food.
   b. Nutritional deficiency.
   c. Diabetes.
   d. Liver disease.
   e. Intestinal obstruction.
   f. Developmental delays.
5. Medical management/relevant pharmacology.
   a. Inhaled medications to open airways.
   b. Chest therapy to loosen secretions that block lung airways.
   c. Vitamin and mineral supplements, enzymes.
   d. Antibiotics.
6. Effect on function.
   a. Exercise and activity intolerance.
   b. Difficulty engaging with daily childhood occupations due to fatigue and medical complications.
   c. Social isolation while in medical care and to prevent infections.

Respiratory Distress Syndrome (RDS) or Hyaline Membrane Disease (HMD)

1. Etiology.
   a. Premature birth.
   b. Insufficient production of surfactant to keep alveoli (air pockets of the lungs) open.
2. Diagnosis.
   a. Lungs collapse after each breath.
   b. X-ray of lungs reveals "ground glass" appearance.

c. Collapsed alveoli are dense and appear white on the x-ray as opposed to the black appearance on an x-ray of air-filled alveoli.
3. Medical management/relevant pharmacology.
   a. Mild case.
      (1) Supplemental oxygen alone, or in combination with positive airways pressure (CPAP), which is a mixture of oxygen and air provided under pressure through short, two-pronged tubes placed in the nose.
      (2) Injection of surfactant to mitigate symptoms and promote exchange of oxygen and carbon dioxide in the alveoli.
   b. Severe case.
      (1) Intubation and a mixture of oxygen and air provided by a ventilator under positive end-expiratory pressure (PEEP).
      (2) Administration of exogenous surfactant to mitigate symptoms and promote exchange of oxygen and carbon dioxide in the alveoli.
   c. When infants are premature, a single dose of surfactant replacement may be given within six hours of developing RDS/HMD to reduce the severity of RDS/HMD and the risk of chronic lung disease.
4. Complications/secondary diagnosis.
   a. Risk of severe intracranial hemorrhage.
   b. Risk of bronchopulmonary dysplasia (BPD).
   c. Risk for developmental delay; severe developmental delay.

> CAUTION: The risk for these complications is far greater for infants who do not receive the aforementioned treatments.

5. Effect on function.
   a. The future intellectual development of the premature infant who had RDS/HMD and who received the latest treatments appears to be good.
   b. The functional effects for infants who develop BPD or who incur a severe intracranial hemorrhage may include motor, sensory, cognitive, and/or language impairments.
   c. For premature infants with RDS/HMD, functional effects may include visual defects, hypotonia, and other health issues that can impact development.

Bronchopulmonary Dysplasia (BPD)

1. Etiology.
   a. Respiratory disorder caused by damage associated with supplemental oxygen and/or mechanical ventilation.
      (1) More common with infants experiencing late onset sepsis, infection, and inflammation.
      (2) More common with infants with advanced intraventricular hemorrhage.

b. A complication of prematurity (infant born at less than 32 weeks gestation) and extremely low birth weight (less than two pounds).

2. Diagnosis.
   a. Labored breathing.
   b. Rapid rate of breathing.
   c. Bluish discoloration around mouth and lips.
   d. Chest x-ray shows collapsed lung, inflammation, or infection.
   e. Blood tests to determine oxygen levels and determine the presence of an infection.

3. Medical management/relevant pharmacology.
   a. Months or years of oxygen therapy and artificial ventilation.
   b. Bronchodilators and diuretics to keep the airways and lungs dry.
   c. Steroid therapy.
   d. Supplemental vitamin A.

4. Complications.
   a. Low tolerance for physical activity leading to increased risk for developmental delays.
   b. Feeding problems can lead to poor nutrition.
      (1) Malabsorption problems.
      (2) Fragile bones with an increased risk of fractures.

5. Effect on function.
   a. Poor exercise/activity tolerance due to illness and compromised respiration.
   b. Reduced ability to socialize due to long periods of poor health and the increased susceptibility to infection.

Occupational Therapy Evaluation Foci for Pediatric Pulmonary Disorders

1. Assess overall the child's developmental skills (e.g., motor, sensory, cognitive, social, language).
2. Assess the development of childhood occupations in multiple contexts (e.g., home, childcare, school, playground).
3. Assess the psychosocial status of the child and family/caregivers. Typical areas of concern include the following.
   a. Social isolation related to frequent hospitalizations, ongoing home treatment, and school absences.
   b. Physical and emotional fatigue related to the intense level of care that is required.
   c. Emotional stress related to complications (e.g., infections), related symptoms (e.g., pain), and prognosis (e.g., decreased life expectancy).
   d. Presence or absence of support systems available and accessible to the family and caregivers.
4. Assess the environment to determine needed modifications to conserve energy and enable occupational performance.
5. Assess positioning equipment needs and activity adaptations to enable occupational performance.

Occupational Therapy Intervention Foci for Pediatric Pulmonary Disorders

1. Monitor development and any changes in the medical status (e.g., breathing, neurological condition, response to medication).
2. Provide treatment to facilitate the child's cognitive, sensorimotor, and psychosocial development.
3. Provide treatment to improve the child's endurance, postural stability, and feeding.
4. Use positioning to promote postural drainage.
5. Provide environmental modifications and activity adaptations to enhance the child's occupational performance.
6. Train in energy conservation methods to enable the child's occupational performance.
7. Promote engagement in physical activity (especially play) within the child's capabilities.
8. Address psychosocial issues that arise.
9. Use coaching strategies to help parents/caregivers/teachers learn how to manage the child's daily medical and developmental needs including precautions for participation.
10. Develop and support the parents'/caregiver's advocacy skills to obtain respite and support services as needed and necessary modifications, equipment, and services for the child in the home and school.
11. Refer as necessary to other relevant service providers (e.g., support groups, respite programs).
12. Observe medical precautions during all OT sessions (i.e., respiratory/cardiac contraindications).

References

American Association of Cardiovascular and Pulmonary Rehabilitation (AACVPR). (2021). Guidelines for cardiac rehabilitation and secondary prevention programs (6th ed.). Human Kinetics.

American Heart Association. (2015). Heart attack symptoms in women. https://www.heart.org/en/health-topics/heart-attack/warning-signs-of-a-heart-attack/heart-attack-symptoms-in-women.

American Heart Association. (2020). Types of heart medications. https://www.heart.org/en/health-topics/heart-attack/treatment-of-a-heart-attack/cardiac-medications.

American Heart Association. (2021). The American Heart Association's diet and lifestyle recommendations. https://www.heart.org/en/healthy-living/healthy-eating/eat-smart/nutrition-basics/aha-diet-and-lifestyle-recommendations.

American Lung Association. (2020, March 3). Bronchopulmonary dysplasia. https://www.lung.org/lung-health-diseases/lung-disease-lookup/bronchopulmonary-dysplasia/learn-about-bpd

American Occupational Therapy Association. (2020). Occupational therapy practice framework: Domain and process (4th ed.). American Journal of Occupational Therapy, 74(2), 7412410010p1–7412410010p87

Batshaw, M. L., Roizen, N. J., & Lotrecchiano, G. R. (2013). Children with disabilities (7th ed.). Paul H. Brookes.

Centers for Disease Control and Prevention. (2022a). Cystic fibrosis. https://www.cdc.gov/genomics/disease/cystic_fibrosis.htm.

Centers for Disease Control and Prevention. (2022b). Symptoms of COVID-19. https://www.cdc.gov/coronavirus/2019-ncov/symptoms-testing/symptoms.html

Centers for Disease Control and Prevention. (2023a). About COVID-19. https://www.cdc.gov/coronavirus/2019-ncov/your-health/about-covid-19.html#:~:text=COVID%2D19%20spreads%20when%20an,eyes%2C%20nose%2C%20or%20mouth.

Centers for Disease Control and Prevention. (2023b, July 11). Infection control: Isolation precautions. https://www.cdc.gov/infectioncontrol/guidelines/isolation/index.html

Centers for Disease Control and Prevention. (2023c). Long COVID or post-COVID conditions. https://www.cdc.gov/coronavirus/2019-ncov/long-term-effects/index.html.

Centers for Disease Control and Prevention. (2023d). People with certain medical conditions. https://www.cdc.gov/coronavirus/2019-ncov/need-extra-precautions/people-with-medical-conditions.html

Ciccone, C. (2018). Medication. In W. DeTurk & L. Cahalin (Eds.), Cardiovascular and pulmonary physical therapy: An evidence-based approach (pp. 211–248). McGraw-Hill.

Cleveland Clinic. (n.d.). Pursed Lip Breathing. (clevelandclinic.org).

Collins, S., Morton, D., & Cocanour, B. (2018). Anatomy of the cardiopulmonary system. In W. DeTurk & L. Cahalin (Eds.), Cardiovascular and pulmonary physical therapy: An evidence-based approach (pp.85–104). McGraw-Hill.

Cole, M. B., & Tufano, R. (2020) Biomechanical and rehabilitative frames. In M. B. Cole & R. Tufano (Eds.), Applied theories in occupational therapy: A practical approach (2nd ed., pp. 227–237). Slack.

Crawford, E. J. (2022). Cardiac dysfunction and chronic obstructive pulmonary disease. In M. E. Patnaude (Ed.), Early's physical dysfunction practice skills for the occupational therapy assistant (4th ed., pp. 593–606). Elsevier.

Cystic Fibrosis Foundation. (n.d). About cystic fibrosis. https://www.cff.org/What-is-CF/About-Cystic-Fibrosis/

Department of Health and Human Services. (n.d.). What is long COVID? https://www.covid.gov/longcovid/definitions

Executive Committee. (2016). The diagnosis and treatment of peripheral lymphedema: 2016 Consensus Document of the International Society of Lymphology. Lymphology, 42, 170–184.

Johns Hopkins Cystic Fibrosis Center. (2018). Effects of CF. Retrieved from https://www.hopkinscf.org/what-is-cf/effects-of-cf/.

Lymph Notes. (2015). Lymphedema stages. http://www.lymphnotes.com/article.php/id/474/.

Matthews, M. (2018). Cardiac and pulmonary diseases. In H. Pendleton & W. Schultz-Krohn (Eds.), Pedretti's occupational therapy: Practice skills for physical dysfunction (8th ed., pp. 1117–1133). Elsevier Science/Mosby.

Mayo Clinic. (2021, November 23). Cystic fibrosis. https://www.mayoclinic.org/diseases-conditions/cystic-fibrosis/diagnosis-treatment/drc-20353706

Mayo Clinic. (2022a, June 25). Endocarditis. https://www.mayoclinic.org/diseasesconditions/endocarditis/symptoms-causes/syc-20352576

Mayo Clinic. (2022b, June 25). Tuberculosis. https://www.mayoclinic.org/diseases-conditions/tuberculosis/symptoms-causes/syc-20351250

McClure, M. K., McClure, R. J., Day, R., & Brufsky, A. M. (2010). Randomized controlled trial of the Breast Cancer Recovery Program for women with breast cancer–related lymphedema. American Journal of Occupational Therapy, 64, 59–72.

National Board for Certification in Occupational Therapy (NBCOT®). (2022). 2022 Occupational Therapist Registered (OTR®) Examination Content Outline. https://www.nbcot.org/-/media/PDFs/2022_OTR_Content_Outline.pdf

National Heart, Lung, and Blood Institute. (2022, March 24). Bronchopulmonary dysplasia. https://www.nhlbi.nih.gov/health/bronchopulmonary-dysplasia

Patnaude, M. E. (2022). Occupational therapy treatment in rehabilitation, disability, and participation. In M. E. Patnaude (Ed.), Early's physical dysfunction practice skills for the occupational therapy assistant (4th ed., pp. 10–12). Elsevier.

Rubio, K. (2018). Lymphedema self-management: Helping clients value home care programs. OT Practice, 23(1), 8–12.

Sandhu, S. (2009). AOTA comments on lymphedema for meeting of Medicare Evidence Development and Coverage Advisory Committee on November 18, 2009. https://www.aota.org/-/media/Corporate/Files/Advocacy/Reimb/News/Archives/Archived-Letters/Lymphedema%20letter%20to%20MedCAC.pdf.

Wells, C. (2018). Pulmonary pathology. In W. DeTurk & L. Cahalin (Eds.), Cardiovascular and pulmonary physical therapy: An evidence-based approach (3rd ed., pp. 163–210). McGraw-Hill.

Chapter 8

Review Questions

Following are seven questions about key content covered in this Chapter. These questions are not inclusive of the entirety of content related to cardiovascular and pulmonary system disorders that you must know for success on the NBCOT® exam. These questions are provided to help you "jump start" the thought processes you will need to apply your studying of content to the answering of exam items; hence, they are not in the NBCOT® exam format. Exam items in the NBCOT® format that cover the depth and breadth of content you will need to know to pass the NBCOT® exam are provided in the three online practice exams that accompany this text. The answers to the following questions are provided in Appendix 2.

1. An adult with a diagnosis of left ventricular failure congestive heart failure (CHF) has been referred to occupational therapy for Phase I cardiac rehabilitation during an acute hospitalization. What are the primary goals of inpatient cardiac rehabilitation? What symptoms of CHF does the occupational therapist need to be aware of that might manifest during therapeutic activities?

2. What are the clinical indications that may lead an occupational therapist to stop an activity during a cardiac rehabilitation intervention session? How does the occupational therapist monitor the patient during activity for signs/symptoms of distress?

3. An older adult status-post myocardial infarction (s/p MI) has been referred to occupational therapy for Phase II outpatient cardiac rehabilitation. The client is able to carry out all basic ADL independently and has fair tolerance for activities that require standing and overhead movements. The client lives with a spouse and identifies being a partner, home maintainer, and gardener as primary roles. The client would like to be able to resume role-related activities. The occupational therapy prescription calls for activities beginning at MET level 3 and increasing to MET level 5 according to the client's activity tolerance. Taking into consideration the therapy prescription, the client's current status, desired occupational roles, and activity preferences, which intervention approaches and activities should the occupational therapist include in the intervention plan?

4. You are completing a meal preparation assessment with a client who is living with chronic obstructive pulmonary disease (COPD). The client reports a score of 3/10 on the Modified Borg Dyspnea Scale. What does this tell you about the client's performance? What training approaches would you include in an intervention plan for the client?

(Continued)

Review Questions

5. You are working with a client who is recovering from a left total knee replacement. The medical record indicates that the client has a past medical history of severe COVID-19. The client begins to have trouble breathing and complains of pain and pressure in the chest. They suddenly appear to be confused. What should you do in response to your observations and the client's reported concerns?

▷

6. You have been asked to consult with a teacher to discuss precautions for a student who has a diagnosis of cystic fibrosis. What precautions should you discuss with the teacher? Provide a rationale for your recommendations.

▷

7. You are completing an occupational therapy evaluation on a 20-month-old toddler who was diagnosed with bronchopulmonary dysplasia (BPD) shortly after birth. What are the typical deficits resulting from BPD that the child may exhibit during the evaluation? Provide an explanation for your answers.

▷

Gastrointestinal, Renal-Genitourinary, Endocrine, Immunological, and Integumentary Systems Disorders

RITA P. FLEMING-CASTALDY, ANN BURKHARDT,
GERALDINE HEALY MARINI, and
CHRISTINA GAVALAS-VALDIVIA

Gastrointestinal System Disorders

Dysphagia and Swallowing Disorders

1. Structures involved and functions. Refer to Figure 9-1.
   a. Oral facial musculature.
      (1) Controls maintenance of the bolus in the oral cavity during mastication and swallowing.
   b. Pharyngeal and laryngeal structures.
      (1) The pharynx extends from the nares (nostrils) to the mouth and larynx; all a part of the alimentary canal.
         (a) Both air and food pass through the pharynx.
      (2) The larynx is also called the voice box.
         (a) It functions to protect the airway from the aspiration of food.
         (b) The larynx houses the vocal folds and manipulates the pitch and volume of someone's voice.
   c. Piriform sinuses.
      (1) A pear-shaped fossa located laterally to the laryngeal entrance that channels swallowed material just before it enters the esophagus.
   d. Vocal folds.
      (1) Tissue that opens when breathing or vibrating (e.g., when speaking or singing); also called the vocal cords.

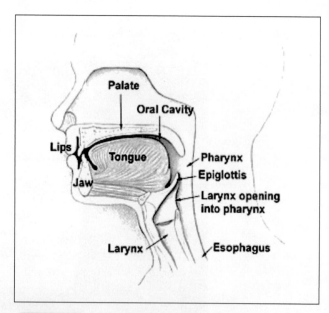

Figure 9-1 **Anatomy of Swallowing Structure.**

National Cancer Institute (n.d.). Head and neck cancer module. Retrieved from https://training.seer.cancer.gov/head-neck/anatomy/overview.html

(a) Controlled by the vagus nerve.
(b) The vocal cords protect the airway from choking and regulate the flow of air into the lungs.
(c) They are also important in producing sounds used for speech.
   e. Bronchioles/bronchi.
      (1) The major air passages of the lungs that diverge from the windpipe.
   f. Lungs.
      (1) In normal swallowing, the bolus does not enter the airway and the lungs.
      (2) A person who aspirates food or drink into their airway are at risk for pneumonia.
      (3) All people aspirate saliva in their sleep; however, for people with impaired immune systems, the risk for repeat pneumonia escalates.
   g. Esophagus.
      (1) Food or liquid normally enters the esophagus during a swallow.
      (2) The upper esophageal sphincter (UES) is a bundle of muscles at the top of the esophagus.
         (a) The muscles of the UES are consciously controlled and used when breathing, eating, belching, and vomiting.

> **EXAM HINT:** In the NBCOT® OTR® exam content outline, knowledge of the "impact of body functions and body structures on occupational performance" (NBCOT®, 2022, p. 3) is identified as essential for competent and safe practice. The application of knowledge about the major structures and functions of the gastrointestinal system described above and the conditions and impairments discussed in this Chapter can help you correctly answer NBCOT® exam items about the functional implications of damage to the gastrointestinal system.

2. Conditions and functional impairments.
   a. Facial paralysis.
      (1) Incomplete closure of the mouth.
      (2) Loss of the bolus out of the front of the oral cavity.
   b. Praxis/motor planning deficits.
      (1) Inability to effectively chew and coordinate tongue movements to propel the bolus toward the base of the tongue.
      (2) Residual food centrally located in the oral cavity.
      (3) Difficulty forming a bolus with smoother consistencies.
   c. Sensory impairment of the oral cavity.
      (1) Lack of awareness of residual food on the side of the mouth that has decreased sensation.

(2) Pocketing of food.

(3) Spillage of residual food into the airway at a time when the vocal cords are open; timing of the swallow sequence is off.

   d. Weakness of the tongue/base of tongue structures.

     (1) Inefficient propulsion of bolus into the pharyngeal cavity.

     (2) Lack of closure at the cricopharyngeal junction can result in the following.

       (a) Suboptimal propulsion of the bolus.

       (b) Interference with the normal timing of the swallow sequence.

       (c) Failure to trigger closure of the vocal folds during swallow; aspiration.

   e. Weakness of the elevation of the pharynx during swallow.

     (1) Incomplete triggering (diminished neural stimulation) of the pharyngeal phase of swallowing.

   f. Vocal cord paralysis.

     (1) Inefficient closure of the vocal folds during the pharyngeal phase of swallow.

       (a) Vocal cords are in paramedian position; swallow may be safe.

       (b) Vocal cords fail to meet/close to protect airway; aspiration may occur.

   g. Penetration of the bronchioles/bronchi by the bolus when aspiration occurs.

     (1) Food enters the lung; true aspiration occurs.

       (a) Bacteria can cause pneumonia (aspiration pneumonia). If the person's immune system is functioning well, they may not experience pneumonia.

   h. Clinical aspiration.

     (1) Food enters the airway.

       (a) Person can clear airway by coughing (reflex intact).

> **RED FLAG:** Silent aspiration occurs when the:
> - Bolus enters the lung and person does not react.
> - Bolus enters the lung and person experiences respiratory distress without a cough.
> - Person coughs too weakly to raise the bolus in order to expel it.

   i. Diminished esophageal motility.

     (1) Bolus sits in the esophagus and can slowly either move toward the stomach or upward toward the pharynx.

> **CAUTION:** Person may report feeling that food is stuck in the esophagus. Person aspirates when food propels upward and they cannot swallow it.

3. Functional observations.

   a. Staff report questioning swallowing dysfunction.

     (1) Person coughs during or after drinking water or other thin liquid.

(2) The person's face changes color during or after eating.

     (a) Flushed/reddened color, ashened appearance for persons with darker skin.

     (b) Blanches.

> **CAUTION:** The person gasps for breath, possibly indicating a partial or complete airway obstruction.

     (3) If an obstruction is visualized, it may be possible to remove the object and restore respiratory function.

> **RED FLAG:** Aspiration requires *immediate* action.
> - The Heimlich maneuver is used to clear the obstruction and raise the bolus that has been aspirated, as long as the person is awake and responsive. Refer to Figure 9-2.
> - If the person loses consciousness, basic life support procedures are used to continue to try to reestablish the airway. This includes abdominal thrusts, back blows, and periodically looking in the oral cavity to try to visualize the object.

4. Bedside swallowing evaluation.

   a. Assess level of alertness, ability to follow directions, level of awareness of impairment, orientation to activity.

   b. Assess sensory and motor components of swallowing.

   c. Assess ability to manage personal secretions via auscultation and clinical observation.

   d. Assess swallowing function using trial boluses.

     (1) Suggest diet modification, as indicated.

     (2) Recommend further testing if needed.

   e. Modified barium swallow (MBS).

     (1) Done with swallowing team and radiologist in a diagnostic radiology suite.

       (a) Person seated upright at edge of radiology table.

       (b) Person must have adequate sitting balance.

       (c) Person must be supervised at all times.

     (2) Person administered trial boluses of mixed food consistencies (e.g., purees, thick liquids, solids, thin liquids) laced with barium.

       (a) If the person aspirates, the test ceases.

     (3) Video records moving x-ray of swallow. Still x-ray shots are taken if aspiration is observed.

     (4) May be used to diagnose various swallowing disorders or gastrointestinal system dysfunction.

   f. Fiberoptic endoscopic esophageal swallow (FEES).

     (1) May be done at bedside or in an office setting.

     (2) Food consistencies are laced with green food coloring.

     (3) The person is given a variety of consistencies to swallow, and observation is made to determine

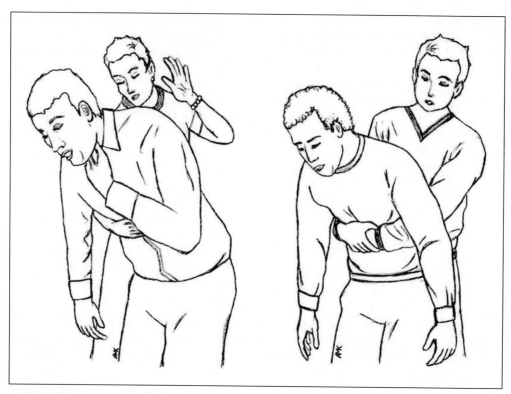

Figure 9-2 **The Heimlich Maneuver.**

Abdominal Thrust/Heimlich Maneuver. (2014). Retrieved January 10, 2018 from https://commons.wikimedia.org/wiki/Category:Abdominal_thrusts

whether the swallow is intact or impaired using a flexible endoscopic catheter containing a miniature video camera.

(4) Sensation for light touch in the pharyngeal cavity can be tested by forcing air through the endoscopic tube generating a light touch response.

(5) May be used to diagnose various swallowing disorders or gastrointestinal system dysfunction.

5. Relationship of swallowing dysfunction to occupation.

a. Disruption of the person's role relative to their family unit can result from decreased ability to comfortably eat at the dinner table.

(1) Modified diet could be infantilizing.

(2) Tube feeding may preempt person's ability to partake in a meal in a cultural/social context.

b. Disruption of swallowing ability may contribute to decreased comfort level for eating out in public.

(1) Person may choose not to dine in a public social context.

(2) If business lunches or dinners are part of a vocational role, the person may not be able to resume their vocation without modification of expectations regarding how participation in social meals relates to vocational performance.

c. Alteration of self-concept concerning life roles and appearance.

(1) If person is tube fed, how does that alter how they perceive self?

(a) Sex appeal can be questioned.

(b) Self-image as it impacts on life roles (e.g., a "foodie" or "fashionista") can be altered.

(2) If tube fed, how does that alter how others perceive them?

(a) Accepted, feared, or pitied by children, grandchildren, family, friends, and colleagues.

> **EXAM HINT:** The NBCOT® OTR® exam content outline identifies knowledge of "intervention strategies and techniques used to facilitate oral motor skills for drinking, eating, and swallowing" (NBCOT®, 2022, p. 9) as essential for competent and safe practice. The application of knowledge about the relationship of swallowing dysfunction to occupation described above and the intervention approaches described below can help you determine the correct answer for NBCOT® Domain 3 Intervention Management exam items about swallowing disorders.

6. Intervention.
   a. Provide family-centered intervention to determine an acceptable dinner table alternative for family interaction.
   b. Work with person toward developing new roles and occupations to transition from old role (i.e., head of table).
   c. Provide ongoing education and information to family regarding person's feeding/nutrition.
7. Refer to Chapter 12 for additional information about evaluation methods and intervention approaches for oral motor dysfunction; Chapter 14 for further information on psychosocial evaluations and interventions; and Chapter 15 for further information on evaluations and interventions for performance in areas of occupation.

> **EXAM HINT:** Correct answers to NBCOT® exam items about occupational therapy (OT) evaluation and intervention for persons with swallowing disorders should include collaboration with the person. Depending on the exam item, the scenario may also include collaboration with speech-language pathologists, dieticians, nurses, and/or family members.

Gastric Esophageal Reflux Disease (GERD)

1. Structures involved include the lower esophagus and gastric sphincter.
   a. Food enters the stomach and mixes with stomach acid/digestive juices.
   b. Lower esophageal sphincter inefficiently closes; stomach contraction propels acid/acidic bolus back into the esophagus.
2. Frequent complaints of people who have GERD (also known as chronic acid reflux).
   a. Heartburn/indigestion.
   b. Swallowing problems.
      (1) A sensation of feeling that something is getting 'stuck' in their throat.
      (2) Chest pressure/dull chest pain.
      (3) Regurgitation after swallowing.
      (4) Increased production of mucus; mimics postnasal drip symptoms.
3. Infants and children who experience GERD may present the symptoms of vomiting, crying, avoiding eating, and difficulties with sleeping and respiration.

> **EXAM HINT:** Although GERD will likely not be a diagnosis for which a person is referred to it is likely that an OT practitioner will work with people who are living with this condition. GERD is common (affecting 20% of the U.S. population) and its symptoms can have a significant impact on quality of life. The probability of having symptoms of GERD increase for persons who are over the age of 40, obese and/or pregnant, and for those who smoke or take certain medications (e.g., antibiotics, pain relievers) and dietary supplements (e.g., iron). There appears to be a 75% increase of GERD in people with asthma. Long term GERD may lead to more serious conditions, including esophageal cancer (Mayo Clinic, 2021a). Therefore, prevention, education, and health management are important intervention foci.

4. Intervention. OT practitioners can assist clients, parents, and caregivers by providing education to increase their health literacy about this condition, decrease and/or manage the symptoms of reflux, and improve quality of life.
   a. Medication management.
   b. Positional modifications.
      (1) Elevation of the head above the stomach, when the person is reclined, may discourage upward retropulsion of the bolus from the stomach (e.g., sleeping on an adjustable bed or with more than one pillow to elevate the head and discourage regurgitation associated with flat body posture).
   c. Diet modification and meal preparation.
      (1) Use and consume less spice.
      (2) Eat small meals on a more frequent basis.
   d. Mechanical stretching of the esophagus, when stricture plays a role in the condition.
   e. Stress management.
   f. Parent/caregiver education to identify and manage reflux in infants and children.
      (1) Like adults, medication management and postural modifications can help infants and children with GERD.
         (a) Hospitalization may be required if the infant or child is not gaining weight or losing weight, choking, exhibiting excessive irritability, vomiting, and/or showing skin discoloration and/or signs of dehydration.

Small Bowel Obstruction

1. Etiology.
   a. Secondary to scar tissue.
   b. Secondary to radiation of the abdomen; a long-term effect.
   c. Result of tumor obstruction.
2. Surgical treatment.
   a. Resection with open stoma (i.e., colostomy).
   b. Closed abdominal surgery.
3. Rehabilitation issues.
   a. Self-care aspects of stoma care must be addressed for persons with decreased fine motor skills (e.g., individuals with peripheral neuropathy secondary to chemotherapy treatment).
   b. Decreased mobility in gross movements (i.e., bending or stooping during daily tasks, including lower body dressing) can cause traction on the healing scar.
   c. Appetite may be altered in postoperative phase.

> CAUTION: Cognitive impairments may impede a person's ability to safely maintain stoma care (e.g., forgetting to properly clean and restore the collection bag can lead to the development of abscesses).

Neurogenic Bowel

1. Etiology: sympathetic nerve impairment, generally occurring in persons who have spinal cord injury above the (thoracic) T-6 level.
   a. Loss of control of anal sphincter.
   b. Sensory loss resulting in a lack of awareness of feces in the bowel.
   c. Motor loss resulting in decreased or lost ability to self-initiate/control bowel movements.
2. Flaccidity of muscles results in incontinence.
3. Autonomic dysreflexia, an extreme rise in blood pressure, can result.

> RED FLAG: Autonomic dysreflexia is a medical emergency if not reversed.

   a. Refer to Chapter 7's section on the complications of spinal cord injury for more information about the prevention and management of autonomic dysreflexia.

▶ Renal-Genitourinary System Disorders

Kidney Disease

1. Etiology: the kidneys become damaged and are not able to properly filter the blood resulting in increased toxins and extra fluid accumulation.
   a. Chronic kidney disease: kidney disease which occurs over time.
2. Risk factors for kidney disease include diabetes, uncontrolled or poorly controlled hypertension, and systematic lupus erythematosus.
   a. Diabetes.
      (1) Approximately 1 in 3 adults with diabetes have kidney failure.
      (2) 10%–40% of people with Type 2 diabetes develop severe kidney disease and end-stage renal disease (ESRD).
      (3) Diabetes can contribute to development of nephrotic syndrome.
   b. Hypertension (HTN).
      (1) Uncontrolled or poorly controlled hypertension is the primary diagnosis for 26% of all new cases of chronic kidney failure each year.

      (a) 65% of HTN in women and 78% of HTN in men can be directly attributed to obesity.
      (b) 60–65% of all persons with diabetes also have high blood pressure.
   c. Systematic lupus erythematosus.
      (1) Lupus can contribute to development of nephrotic syndrome.

> CAUTION: Personal lifestyle and habits can damage the kidneys. Refer to Box 9-1.

3. Stages of kidney disease.
   a. There are five stages of kidney disease, with progressive worsening of the glomerular filtration rate (GFR) which characterizes each stage of the disease.
   b. Focus of medical care and interventions.
      (1) Stage 1: prevention of progression of the kidney disease.
      (2) Stage 2: management of health conditions.
      (3) Stage 3: management of anemia and bone loss.
      (4) Stage 4: education for further management of kidney failure should be provided (i.e.,

---

BOX 9-1 ▷ Habits that can Cause Kidney Damage

- Insufficient water consumption: dehydration stresses renal function.
- Smoking: causes microvascular disease.
- Alcohol: over 8 oz. of alcohol daily can suppress function. Alcohol also causes release of water from the body and can lead to dehydration.
- Medications: if chemically based, may tax the organ's ability to filtrate out by-products.
- High-protein diet: too much protein in the diet taxes the metabolic capacity of the kidney.
- Physical inactivity: generates kidney stones.
- Sleeplessness: increases toxins that the kidney must filtrate.
- Overconsumption of salt and sugar.
- Delaying urine release: leads to urinary tract infection and absorption of bacteria into the bloodstream.
- Dietary deficiencies: the kidney needs vitamins and minerals. Most people lack adequate amounts of magnesium.
- Failing to medically treat viral and bacterial infections: many infections can be a signal of reduced kidney function brought on by a toxin buildup.
- Ignoring symptoms: changes in urine color, loss of breath, fatigue, bad breath, leg and waist pain, swelling, frequent feelings of coldness, dizziness, vomiting, and itchy skin.

BOX 9-2 ▷ Signs and Symptoms of Chronic Kidney Disease

- Vomiting.
- Loss of appetite.
- Fatigue and weakness.
- Sleep difficulties.
- Changes in urination output.
- Decreased mental sharpness.
- Muscle twitches and cramps.
- Swelling of feet and ankles.
- Persistent itching.
- Chest pain, if fluid builds up around the lining of the heart.
- Shortness of breath, if fluid builds up in the lungs.
- High blood pressure (hypertension) that is difficult to control.

Mayo Clinic. (2017). Patient care and health information. Diseases and conditions: Chronic kidney disease. https://www.mayoclinic.org/diseases-conditions/chronic-kidney-disease/symptoms-causes/dxc-20207466

---

hemodialysis versus peritoneal dialysis versus transplantation).

(5) Stage 5: for life to be sustained, the person must receive either dialysis or a kidney transplant.

RED FLAG: Chronic kidney disease can result in high blood pressure, heart disease, stroke, or death. Thus, the signs and symptoms of chronic kidney disease are critical to recognize. These are provided in Box 9-2.

4. Medical treatment of kidney disease and related conditions.
   a. Nephrotic syndrome treatment.
      (1) Treat with diuretics and drugs that prevent spillage of protein in the urine.
      (2) Drug control of fluid overload and/or spillage of protein into the urine (proteinuria).
      (3) Encourage compliance with drug therapy and dietary and exercise recommendations.
   b. Acute renal failure treatment.
      (1) Drug control of underlying medical contributory conditions.
      (2) Emergent, acute dialysis.
   c. End stage renal disease (ESRD) treatment.
      (1) Dialysis required to stay alive.
      (2) Hemodialysis requires presence of vascular access via a shunt or fistula.
         (a) Done through a machine called a "dialyzer." May be done at home.

(3) Peritoneal dialysis (PD): required catheter placed in abdomen. Can be done without a machine during the day 3–5 times.
   (a) Continuous cycling peritoneal dialysis (CCPD).
   (b) Nocturnal intermittent PD (NIPD).
(4) Kidney transplantation.
(5) Hypertension treatment: diet, medication, exercise, stress reduction, and smoking cessation. Refer to Chapter 8 for more information on hypertension treatment.
   d. Diabetes treatment. Refer to this Chapter's section on diabetes.
   e. Systematic lupus erythematosus treatment.
      (1) Control symptoms to prevent complications.
      (2) Treat with diuretics and drugs that prevent spillage of protein in the urine (angiotensin converting enzyme-ACE).
      (3) Refer to this Chapter's section on systematic lupus erythematosus treatment.
5. Impact on performance skills, client factors, and occupations.
   a. Motor skills can be affected by fatigue, muscle pain, edema, and weakness.
   b. Sensory skills can be affected by neuropathy (diabetes related, toxicity related, cyclosporin, antirejection drug related) and vision loss (diabetes related).
   c. Delusions due to sepsis or toxicity and neurocognitive disorders (i.e., multi-infarct or metabolic) can affect process skills.
   d. Neurocognitive disorders (i.e., multi-infarct or metabolic) can affect motor and process skills.

e. Perceptual (neurobehavioral) impairment can affect motor and process skills.

f. Psychological/emotional dysfunction can affect social interaction skills.

g. Impact on performance in activities of daily living (ADL).

(1) Bowel and bladder training and self-management.

(2) Practice meticulous sanitary technique with self-dialysis.

(3) Adhere to a disease-specific/highly restrictive diet.

(4) Cope with the impact of impotence on sexual participation and alterations in self-esteem and body image.

(5) Use adapted equipment to enable performance of self-care tasks.

(6) Pace oneself when fatigue limits performance.

h. Impact on instrumental activities of daily living (IADL).

(1) Home establishment and management.

(a) Accept impact of physical limitations (e.g., the need for lighter workload and housekeeping assistance).

(b) Cope with having an altered home maintainer role.

(2) Meal preparation.

(a) Adhere to changes in usual meal preparation habits to accommodate dietary limitations.

(3) Management of personal finances.

(a) Identify solutions and resources to cover the cost of care, which can be prohibitive if insurance does not provide adequate coverage.

(b) Plan and seek alternative participation means for coping with dialysis-related fatigue and its impact on community banking.

(4) Community mobility.

(a) Cope with the presence of fatigue and impaired functional mobility that limits community participation.

(b) Cope with altered functional mobility and to accept assistive technology solutions.

(c) Engage in additional planning that is needed for long distance travel.

i. Leisure/sports activities.

(1) Cope with the presence of fatigue and impaired functional mobility to participate in chosen activities.

(2) Adhere to participation precautions (e.g., the need to pace self and self-regulate to decrease fatigue) and engage in activities that minimize risk.

(3) Access leisure resources and sports facilities that provide adaptations that enable social participation and active engagement for persons whose condition and treatment (i.e., dialysis) tend to isolate them.

6. Impact on performance contexts.

a. Social context.

(1) How disease affects role in the family.

(2) How disease affects role in the workplace.

(3) How disease affects role in the community, including spiritual communities, social groups, and special interests.

b. Sociocultural context.

(1) How a cultural and/or religious group accepts or does not accept a condition and/or its treatment (e.g., resisting invasive interventions, such as dialysis).

(a) Explicit taboos on invasive treatments; some people will choose to end their lives by not starting dialysis based on cultural/religious beliefs.

(2) The individual's acceptance or nonacceptance of the impairment/disease (i.e., the personal meaning of having a machine perform a bodily function).

7. Occupational therapy evaluation and intervention.

a. Assess performance skills, client factors, occupations, performance patterns, and performance contexts to develop an individualized intervention plan. Chapters 11 to 16 provide information about specific evaluation tools.

b. Provide interventions to remediate deficits and compensate for limitations to enable occupational performance. Interventions can include the following.

(1) Education about activity and participation precautions to minimize risks (e.g., behaviors and habits that can cause strain to kidney function).

(2) Training in the safe and effective use of adaptive equipment (e.g., tub bench, built-up handled utensils, reachers, button hooks).

(3) Training in the safe and effective use of assistive mobility devices (e.g., ankle-foot orthoses, canes, walkers) and/or wheeled mobility.

(4) Energy conservation and work simplification techniques to compensate for fatigue during BADL, IADL, leisure, and/or work.

(5) Lifestyle redesign to change unhealthy habits and routines, develop new habits that support health and well-being, and implement new routines that include activities that support health and well-being.

(6) Health promotion and prevention to facilitate health management and maintenance.

(7) Education in community resources that enable participation (e.g., accessible public transportation).

(8) Referrals to obtain supportive counseling and social support, drug therapy, and complementary medicine, if indicated.

(9) Referrals to driving rehabilitation programs, if needed.

(10) Physical or cognitive assistance may be indicated for complex ADL and IADL.

c. Dialysis treatment-specific interventions.

(1) Manufacture devices to protect shunts postoperatively that are used for hemodialysis.

(2) Encourage movement and engage the person in activity participation during dialysis.

(a) When active, the body has a better ability to eliminate the lactic acid generated during dialysis.

(b) If the person remains inactive, fatigue and muscle soreness/stiffness will result from treatment.

(3) Teach the person to implement energy conservation and work simplification techniques when and if they experience chronic fatigue with dialysis treatment.

Neurogenic Bladder

1. Etiology: any condition interfering with sensory or motor pathways of the urinary system resulting in loss of bladder control.

a. These include central or peripheral nervous system disorders or both (e.g., CVA, trauma, infection, SCI).

2. Types of neurogenic bladder.

a. Flaccid (hypotonic): decreased contractions of the bladder; tends to cause overflow incompetence.

(1) Overflow incompetence is when urine is retained, but there is trickling of urine.

b. Spastic: involuntary contractions of the bladder.

(1) May have urinary frequency, nocturia, and loss of ability to completely empty bladder.

c. Mixed: both flaccid and spastic.

3. Complications include frequent infections, autonomic dysreflexia, urinary calculi.

4. Treatment includes catheterization, drugs, increased fluid intake, or surgery.

5. Management: diet, self-catheterization, medication, and bladder training.

Urinary Tract Infections (UTIs)

1. Due to bacteria or microorganisms entering the urethra or bladder.

2. Most common in women.

3. Can occur in any part of the urinary system.

a. When occurring in the bladder, it is known as cystitis.

(1) Cystitis is more common in older adults.

4. Symptoms: feeling need to urinate, frequent urination, pain upon urination, pain or discomfort in lower back or side. Fever may or may not be present.

> **CAUTION:** An older adult with a UTI may experience confusion, delirium, behavior changes, agitation, lethargy, decreased mobility, decreased appetite, urinary retention, and incontinence. Due to their age, the symptoms and behavioral changes that older adults may present with when they have a UTI mat be attributed to other conditions (e.g., a neurocognitive disorder). Consequently, they may be misdiagnosed and their UTI may be untreated.

> **RED FLAG:** If untreated, a UTI can develop into a kidney infection, which can then lead to kidney failure and septic shock.

Incontinence

1. Lack of bladder control.

2. Stress incontinence.

a. Etiology: local damage to bladder sphincter associated with the aftereffects of bearing children, morbid obesity, and weakening of accessory musculature associated with normal aging.

3. Urge incontinence: the immediate urge to urinate.

a. May be due to an overactive bladder, due to weak musculature, nerve damage, infection, or hormonal changes.

4. Overflow incontinence: occurs when the bladder is not completely empty after voiding.

a. Mostly occurs in people with multiple sclerosis, stokes, or diabetes.

5. Intervention.

a. Kegel exercises to strengthen pelvic floor.

> **RED FLAG:** Stopping and starting urine while emptying the bladder is not part of Kegel exercises and can be harmful; it can interfere with urinary reflexes and contribute to bladder infection.

b. Timed routines for emptying bladder before it is full enough to cause spillage.

c. Lifestyle adjustments to use incontinence supporting garments for a socially acceptable solution and to decrease public attention to the incontinence.

d. Medications may be used when the physician feels the person can tolerate the side effects of drug therapy support.

e. Electric stimulation may be used, if person fits the parameters of recovery for the condition.

f. Changes in diet.

Chapter 9

 Immunological System Disorders

Cancer[1]

1. Etiology: unknown for some cancers, strong link to risk factors for others.
2. Risk factors for cancer.
   a. Heredity.
      (1) Some tumors (i.e., breast, prostate, skin, and colon) seem to have high hereditary risk.
   b. Environmental.
      (1) Cluster patterns related to chemical pollution.
   c. Habit or lifestyle related.
      (1) Smoking, alcohol consumption, high-fat diets, and obesity may be linked to increased risk.
3. Prevention, early intervention, and control.
   a. Specific to type of cancer.
      (1) Recommended screening tests include mammograms and ultrasound, prostate and testicular exams, skin checks, colonoscopies, pap smears, blood tests, and abdominal ultrasound.
         (a) Cancer type and family history determine the screening method and its frequency.
   b. Recommended preventive measures.
      (1) Avoid environmental contributing factors (e.g., chemically contaminated land, lead paint).
      (2) Avoid and/or change contributory habits.
         (a) OT practitioners can provide wellness interventions for people who want to quit or change habits (e.g., cease smoking).
         (b) Wellness interventions.
            • Foster the use of self-regulatory behaviors.
            • Support person-directed actions to change habits.
            • Provide health-promoting, occupation-based alternatives to unhealthy habits.
            • Promote participation in programs that increase engagement in health-promoting behaviors (e.g., 12-step programs, support groups, individual treatment).

> **EXAM HINT:** The NBCOT® OTR® exam content outline identifies knowledge of "strategies used for addressing and enhancing health literacy with the client and relevant others . . . (including) informed decision-making" (NBCOT®, 2022, p. 6) as essential for competent practice. Based on this requirement, it is likely that the NBCOT® exam will include items about the occupational therapist's role in health promotion for persons with cancer and other conditions that can benefit from interventions focused on enabling personal wellness.

---

[1] Colleen Maher, OTD, OTR/L, CHT contributed to this section on cancer.

4. Diagnostic staging of cancer.
   a. Stage 1: tumor present, no perceived spread of disease.
      (1) Lesion operable.
      (2) Prognosis good (70%–90% mean survival at five years).
         (a) No spread of disease to the lymph nodes.
         (b) No metastatic lesions.
   b. Stage 2: localized spread of the tumor.
      (1) Lesion is operable and can be removed with margins.
      (2) Spread is limited and usually responds well to treatment (chemo/radiation/immuno-therapy).
      (3) Mean five-year survival rate is 45%–55%.
   c. Stage 3: extensive evidence of a primary tumor that has spread to other organs in the body.
      (1) Tumor can be surgically debulked, but some cells may remain behind.
      (2) There is deeper spread of the tumor cells in the lymphatics.
      (3) Widespread evidence of cancer throughout multiple organs of the body.
      (4) Mean five-year survival rate is 15%–25%.
   d. Stage 4: inoperable primary lesion.
      (1) Survival is dependent on the depth and extent of the tumor spread as well as the ability to have the tumor respond to therapy (mean five-year survival rate is less than 5%).
      (2) Multiple metastases.
5. Medical treatment.
   a. Surgery (i.e., lumpectomy, en bloc resection, reconstruction, and amputation).
      (1) Positioning postoperatively in the operating room.
      (2) Early movement postoperatively.
      (3) Client education for prevention of complications, such as lymphedema and loss of active range of motion (AROM), if the shoulder joint capsule tightens after surgery.
   b. Chemotherapy (i.e., intravenous, shunt, oral).
      (1) When people are receiving chemotherapy, they may experience the following.
         (a) Fatigue, referred to as cancer related fatigue (CRF).
         (b) Increased risk of excessive bleeding if cut or abraded (e.g., brushing teeth).
         (c) Acute onset of neuropathy resulting in difficulty using feeding utensils and ADL tools.
         (d) Loss of protective sensation.
         (e) Cancer related cognitive dysfunction (CRCD; often referred to "chemo brain".
   c. Radiation.
      (1) Radiation burns to skin and soft tissues in the line of radiation.

(a) The person may need to learn new skin care regimens that do not alter the pH of the skin to either intensify or lessen the impact of the radiation dose.

d. Immunotherapy.
  (1) Adherence to medication management, if part of the immunotherapy regime is important.

e. Hormonal therapy.
  (1) People receiving treatment may experience intensified signs and symptoms of estrogen withdrawal, such as musculoskeletal pain, hot flashes. Mood swings and behavioral changes can also occur.

f. Transplantation (i.e., bone marrow).
  (1) People who are undergoing bone marrow transplantation will be kept in physical isolation.

> **RED FLAG:** The risk for developing infections that can be life threatening is great.

  (a) Providing strategies to lessen the impact of anxiety, depression, and social isolation can be useful.

> **CAUTION:** Persons living with cancer and/or those receiving treatment often experience fatigue. Be sure to monitor vital signs and safety while performing activities. Watch for and report functional changes (e.g., strength and range of motion limitations and/or reports of pain which is often referred to as cancer related pain [CRP]).

6. Intervention.
  a. Preoperative.
    (1) Preoperative functional assessments and preparation of the client for postoperative phase and care.
    (2) Client and caregiver education concerning recovery and follow-up care/functional expectations and client engagement.
  b. Postoperative.
    (1) Intervention planning based on a client's medical status and blood value guidelines that can affect safety during activity (platelets, hemoglobin level).

> **CAUTION:** Postoperative precautions related to structural changes resulting from surgery must be followed. These will be dependent on the location of the tumor and the procedure done; for example, abdominal precautions when the tumor is in the abdominal cavity and regional precautions when there is an incision near a joint.

  c. Convalescence.
    (1) Intervention concerns of motor, sensory, cognitive, and/or neurobehavioral impairments.
      (a) Upper extremity ROM following breast cancer surgery and reconstruction. Follow physician's orders on any restrictions.

(b) Sensory re-education and precautions to address peripheral neuropathy.
(c) Education about fall risks and fall prevention. Refer to chapter 16.
(d) Cognitive training strategies and cognitive behavioral therapy (CBT)for CRCD.
(e) Activity tolerance and energy conservation techniques during daily activities to address CRF. (Radomski et al, 2021).
(f) Integrative medicine such as meditation, Yoga, and mindfulness can address fatigue and CRP.
(2) Psychological support to enhance coping ability during recovery from cancer treatment phase.
  (a) Liminality: self-recognition of vulnerability and self-sense of mortality.
  (b) Occupational role and body image adjustment.
  (c) Obtainment of social support.
(3) Lymphedema management: low stretch wraps, manual lymph drainage (requires specialized training), ROM, and compression garments. Refer to Chapter 8 for more information about lymphedema management.
(4) Development of health-supporting behaviors with follow-up support (e.g., diet, exercise, stress management, vocational skill support, or assistance to change job skills).

d. Palliative care.
  (1) Prevent and relieve suffering for persons with life-threatening illness through early identification, assessment, and treatment of pain.
  (2) Address physical, psychosocial, and spiritual needs.
  (3) Enhance quality of life by supporting clients' engagement in daily life occupations that they find meaningful and purposeful.
  (4) Consider environmental and contextual factors (e.g., accessibility of objects or places in the environment, social contacts available to prevent isolation) and client factors (e.g., decreased endurance, increased anxiety) that may limit a client's abilities and satisfaction when performing desired occupations.
  (5) Collaborate with the client and family members throughout the OT process to identify occupations that are meaningful, incorporate strategies that support occupational engagement, and provide caregiver training as needed.

e. End-of-life care (hospice).
  (1) Support quality of life as disease advances and functional status declines.
  (2) Provide the person with as much control as they can have and desire to have to their day-to-day life and lifestyle support.

(3) Be present, be accountable, listen, and counsel as needed concerning the progression of the disease and sense of liminality.

(4) Encourage planning for death, control over goodbyes, funeral arrangements, advanced directives, etc.

(5) Empower life celebration and life reflection (e.g., journaling, scrapbooks, phone call contact and recontact, letter writing).

(6) Refer for legal support, if needed and requested.

(7) Refer to Chapter 14 for additional information on psychosocial issues related to the end of life and adjustment to death and dying.

> **EXAM HINT:** When determining the correct answer to an exam item about an OT practitioner working with a person with cancer, be sure to consider the reported cancer stage. The correct answer to an exam item about a person recovering from the surgical removal of a Stage 2 breast tumor will likely include a rehabilitative approach; whereas, the correct answer to an exam item about a person with Stage 4 brain cancer that has reoccurred multiple times will likely include a palliative approach.

Scleroderma

1. An autoimmune disease of unknown origin causing overproduction of collagen fibers which harden and damage tissues and organs.
2. Three main components.
   a. Vascular (Raynaud's phenomenon, pulmonary hypertension, decreased esophageal motility).
   b. Fibrotic.
      (1) Scar tissue resulting from excess collagen (protein) causing thickness of skin and a burning sensation in the skin.
      (2) Fibrosis of the lungs causing restrictive lung disease.
   c. Autoimmunity.
3. Two basic types of the disease.
   a. Limited.
      (1) Skin involvement (with a good prognosis).
      (2) Linear scleroderma (bands of thicker skin, with a good prognosis).
   b. Systemic.
      (1) Systemic sclerosis of internal organs, which is life threatening.
      (2) CREST Syndrome (with a good prognosis).
         (a) Calcinosis, or calcium in the skin.
         (b) Raynaud's phenomenon.
         (c) Esophageal dysfunction.
         (d) Sclerodactyly of fingers and toes.
         (e) Telangiectasis or red spots covering the hands, feet, forearms, face, and hips.

(3) General morphea.
4. Risk factors: unknown, two main theories.
   a. Genetic.
   b. Environment.
5. Prevention.
   a. Control symptoms of Raynaud's phenomenon.
   b. Have screening echocardiograms to rule out pulmonary hypertension.
   c. Smoking cessation.
6. Intervention.
   a. Raynaud's phenomenon.
      (1) Keep fingers and toes warm.
      (2) Dress in layers.
      (3) Drug therapy: vasodilators.
      (4) Biofeedback.
   b. Pulmonary artery problems.
      (1) Drug therapy: Procardia SL, anticoagulation therapy.
      (2) Nasal canula oxygen.
   c. Gastrointestinal problems.
      (1) Drug therapy: antacids.
      (2) Dietary modifications: soft diet, avoidance of alcoholic beverages and spicy foods.
      (3) Treatment of infection.
   d. Fibrosis of the skin.
      (1) Protective gloves: cotton, insulated, mildly compressive.
      (2) Drug therapy.
   e. Myositis: inflammatory muscle disease.
      (1) Cessation of exercise.
      (2) Drug therapy: low dose of oral steroids.
   f. Fibrosis of the lungs.
      (1) Drug therapy.
7. Sequelae of scleroderma and recommendations.
   a. Poor circulation, as in Raynaud's phenomenon.
      (1) Use of dressing in layers of clothing and clothing style modifications for neutral warmth.
      (2) Biofeedback, guided imagery to concentrate on improving distal circulation.
      (3) Education to encourage skin inspection.
      (4) Activity modifications to prevent trauma to fingers and toes.
   b. Contractures.
      (1) Splinting at optimal resting length for hands/wrists to attempt to slow progressive development of contractures.
      (2) Use of silicone gel in the palms of the hands.
      (3) Use of electrical/mechanical vibration (muffled) to stimulate rapidly adapting-type A-nerve fibers and decrease burning sensation in hands.
   c. Facial disfigurement and alteration in body image and self-identity.
      (1) "Look good/feel better" programs.
      (2) Work with people to help them choose adaptations and new accessories to ease their adjustment to their changing appearance.
      (3) Support groups: in person and online.

d. Thoracic spinal lesions can result in paraparesis, neurogenic bowel/bladder, altered mobility, and altered occupational performance.
   (1) Neurorehabilitation and biomechanical approaches as indicated.
e. Space-occupying lesions in the brain produce stroke-like symptoms.
   (1) Intervention for functional deficits.

Acquired Immunodeficiency Syndrome (AIDS)

1. Etiology: infection by the human immunodeficiency virus (HIV).
2. Risk factors for infection.
   a. Unprotected sex.
   b. Contact with blood or body fluids.
3. Prevention.
   a. Avoid unprotected sex via abstinence or use of condoms.
   b. Avoid contact with body fluids.
   c. Practice standard precautions with all persons. Refer to Appendix 3-A and Appendix 3-B in Chapter 3.
4. Human immunodeficiency virus (HIV) infection.
   a. Retrovirus.
      (1) The virus can eclipse into the cell, remaining dormant until stimulated by the body.
   b. HIV attacks the lymphatic system, the system that protects the body's immunity to opportunistic infections.
      (1) The T-cells (also known as CD4+ cells) attack the cells of the body including central nervous system (CNS) cells, gastrointestinal tract cells, and uterine/cervical cells.
   c. Four stages of infection.
      (1) Primary infection (acute HIV): flu-like response to initial contact with the virus.
         (a) People are highly contagious during this time.
      (2) Clinical latent infection (chronic asymptomatic HIV): HIV replicates and affects the immune system, but no visible signs other than low white blood cell counts are detectable.
         (a) If a person is receiving highly active antiretroviral therapy (HAART), this stage can last for many years.
      (3) Symptomatic HIV infection: HIV continues to multiply and destroy immune cells.
         (a) The person may develop mild infections or chronic signs and symptoms.
         (b) If the person receives HAART, their infection will not progress to AIDS.
      (4) AIDS: untreated HIV infection causes severe damage to the person's immune system.

(a) The person is more likely to develop opportunistic infections or opportunistic cancers which are diseases that typically do not cause illness in a person with a healthy immune system.
   d. Presenting signs and sequalae of symptomatic HIV infection and AIDS.
      (1) Fatigue.
      (2) Weight loss, malabsorption of nutrients (wasting syndrome).
      (3) General malaise.
      (4) Fever.
      (5) Diarrhea.
      (6) Neurological impairments.
         (a) Myelopathy (spinal cord pathology).
         (b) Peripheral neuropathies.
         (c) Sensory and visual impairments (i.e., peripheral or central nervous system).
      (7) Neurocognitive impairments.
         (a) Cognitive impairment (i.e., safety issues, communication and expression impairments).
         (b) Affective changes (e.g., alteration of personality, decreased ability to engage as before in interpersonal relationships).
         (c) AIDS dementia complex (ADC).
      (8) All of the above symptoms and sequelae can contribute to decreased occupational performance and a diminished quality of life.
   e. Drug therapy: highly active antiretroviral therapy (HAART).
      (1) These medications may also be called antiretroviral drugs (ART), antiretrovirals (ARVs), or anti-HIV drugs.
         (a) The use of HAART has resulted in a dramatic change in the management, treatment, and survivability of persons with a diagnosis of HIV/AIDS.
   f. Complications of advanced disease occur with much less frequency in the current medical environment.
   g. Treatment advances using HAART and personal adherence to health maintenance regimens have resulted in transforming the outcome of AIDS from a fatal diagnosis to a long-term condition with which a person can live well.

Hepatitis

1. Etiology: a viral infection.
2. Risk factors.
   a. Type A.
      (1) Contaminated seafood.
      (2) Protective immunization possible.
   b. Types B, C, and other identified forms.

(1) Body and bloodborne exposure.

(2) Protective immunization possible for type B.

(3) Health-care workers are most susceptible to hepatitis B.

(4) It is estimated that many people in the U.S. population may have undetected hepatitis C infections that they can potentially (and unknowingly) communicate to others.

> **CAUTION:** Standard precautions must be used with all persons in all situations to prevent contact with blood or body fluids. Refer to Appendix 3-A in Chapter 3.

3. Sequelae.
   a. Fever.
   b. Fatigue.
   c. These contribute to decreased tolerance for activity participation and lack of energy.
   d. Hepatitis C infections can cause life-threatening cirrhosis over time and may contribute to chronic fatigue and disability.

Tuberculosis (TB)

1. Refer to Chapter 8.

Methicillin-Resistant Staphylococcus aureus (MRSA)

1. A highly contagious skin infection that resists treatment from antibiotics, even broad-spectrum antibiotics.
2. Etiology: caused by a bacterial infection (staphylococcus aureus) that is normally found on the skin.
   a. The infection can be locally confined or systemic.
3. Risk factors.
   a. Having a weakened immune system.
   b. Confinement in a hospital or other health-care institutions.
   c. Living in close quarters (e.g., military barracks, college dormitory).
   d. Direct skin contact with an infected body part of another person (e.g., contact sports).
   e. Secondary skin contact from something used by someone with an infection (e.g., shared towels during sports activities).
4. Signs and symptoms.
   a. Typically, presents as red bumps that look like pimples or spider bites which may be swollen, painful, and warm to the touch.
      (1) The bumps can quickly turn into deep, painful abscesses (boils) that require surgical draining.
   b. Rash and/or skin abscess (pus) in the affected area.
   c. Fever.

d. Shortness of breath and/or chest pain.
e. Cough.
f. Fatigue.
g. Muscle aches and/or headaches.

5. Testing.
   a. Cultures of blood, sputum, skin, or urine.
6. Prevention.
   a. Avoid high-risk situations that contribute to possible exposure.
      (1) Avoid sharing personal items (e.g., razors or towels).
      (2) Avoid communal bathing/swimming where infected persons may have been.
      (3) Assure facilities being used are clean.
   b. Wash hands with soap and water or use hand sanitizer.
   c. Keep any wounds and cuts covered.
7. Medical treatment for MRSA.
   a. Draining of a skin sore by a physician.
   b. Antibiotic treatment.
   c. Additional measures depending on the severity and location of infection.
      (1) Intravenous fluids.
      (2) Oxygen.
      (3) Dialysis (if kidney failure occurs).
8. Sequelae of MRSA.
   a. Because MRSA infections are resistant to many antibiotics, they can spread and cause potentially life-threatening infections in the bloodstream, bones, joints, surgical wounds, heart valves, and lungs.
   b. MRSA is a frequent cause of skin and soft-tissue infections; recurrent infections are common (9–18%).

> **EXAM HINT:** In the NBCOT® OTR® exam content outline, knowledge of "precautions or contraindications associated with a client condition or stage of recovery" (NBCOT®, 2022, p. 7), "infection control procedures and universal precautions for reducing transmission of contaminants (and) preventive measures for minimizing risk and promoting safety . . . (including) personal safety in the client's environment" (NBCOT®, 2022, p. 13) is identified as essential for effective and competent risk management. Due to the highly contagious nature of MRSA and its potentially deadly outcome, NBCOT® exam items about an OT practitioner working with persons with MRSA will likely focus on risk management. Therefore, correct answers to exam items will be consistent with the standard precautions that must be followed to protect service recipients and healthcare workers from infection and the spread of infection. Appendix 3A in Chapter 3 provides the complete CDC guidelines for all standard precautions.

Intervention for Immunological System Disorders

1. Overall goals and approaches can be preventive, restorative, supportive, and/or palliative depending on treatment setting, diagnosis, stage of illness, and expected outcomes.
2. Interventions to address impairment-level difficulties.
   a. Counsel people to be compliant with screening and treatment regimens.
   b. Set personal goals to invest behaviorally in one's health.
   c. Provide support to those dealing with immunological system disorders that are chronic illnesses (i.e., AIDS).
   d. Provide supportive counseling and social support for psychological disorders that can develop (e.g., anxiety disorder, depression, and/or adjustment disorders).
   e. Refer to physician for drug therapy and complementary medicine as indicated for accompanying physical and/or psychiatric disorders (e.g., kidney disease, depression).
3. Interventions to address activity-level limitations.
   a. Self-care.
      (1) Adaptations and training to complete self-care tasks with greatest ease while conserving energy. For example, for an individual with scleroderma may benefit from the following.
         (a) Alter grasp/pinch patterns and level of upper extremity demand.
         (b) Alter size of feeding utensils and toothbrushes to accommodate decreased ability to open mouth.
         (c) Prevent shearing forces on skin during specific personal ADL tasks.
   b. Work.
      (1) Work capacity evaluations.
      (2) Modifications to worksite to allow participation in component tasks and activities.
      (3) Counseling and intervention for transition to disability status when work is no longer possible.
   c. Leisure/sports.
      (1) Modify specific tasks and activities (e.g., to protect body parts involved by sclerodermic changes).
      (2) Determine interests and skills to introduce new leisure or sports activities of interest to the person to transition to less physically demanding tasks as a disease progresses.
   d. Rest and sleep.
      (1) Monitor and intervene to maximize the ability to be well positioned during rest and sleep.
      (2) Monitor rest and sleep habits and patterns and intervene when strategies are needed to relax and unwind or to schedule time and opportunity for relaxation.
      (3) Refer to Chapter 15 for more information on rest and sleep evaluation and intervention.
4. Interventions to address participation constraints.
   a. Needs assessment to determine individual issues the person has with physical, social, economic, or political access to their personal, home, or community environments.
   b. Identification and facilitation of procurement of system changes to allow the person to access and participate in their community as a contributing member of society.
5. Acute hospitalization phase.
   a. Early mobilization.
   b. Preservation of function.
   c. Positioning.
   d. Psychological/emotional support.
   e. Prevention of long-term disability.
6. Inpatient rehabilitation.
   a. Evaluation and restoration of functional abilities.
      (1) BADL.
      (2) IADL.
      (3) Energy conservation and work simplification.
      (4) Wellness, health literacy, and health management.
   b. Restoration of activity/exercise tolerance.
   c. Achievement and maintenance of quality of life.
   d. Role readjustment intervention.
   e. Planning to return to work and community participation.
7. Home care.
   a. Use of a collaborative assessment (e.g., Canadian Occupational Performance Measure [COPM]) to set client goals.
   b. Evaluation and restoration of functional abilities for occupational performance.
   c. Restoration of activity/exercise tolerance.
   d. Community mobility.
8. Community-based care.
   a. School related.
      (1) Transition from home schooling back to school for the returning child.
      (2) Transition of having a student return to class for their classmates.
   b. Work related.
      (1) Participation as per Americans with Disabilities Act (ADA). Refer to Chapters 4 and 15.
   c. Population-related intervention.
      (1) Coalition-related and grant-funded initiatives for prevention and outreach programs.

Endocrine System Disorders

Diabetes

1. A medical condition affecting the body's ability to properly use the hormone insulin.
   a. Insulin helps to remove glucose from the bloodstream into the cells for proper metabolism.
   b. Types.
      (1) Type 1 diabetes: insulin dependent; formerly known as juvenile diabetes.
      (2) Type 2 diabetes: non-insulin dependent.
2. Prognosis: diabetes remains the seventh leading cause of death in the U.S.
3. Etiology and risk factors.
   a. Type 1 diabetes.
      (1) Autoimmune.
      (2) Genetic.
      (3) Environmental factors.
   b. Type 2 diabetes.
      (1) Older age.
      (2) Obesity.
      (3) Family history.
      (4) Prior history of gestational diabetes.
      (5) Impaired glucose tolerance.
      (6) Physical inactivity.
      (7) Race/ethnicity.
   c. Gestational diabetes (2%–10% of all pregnancies; 50% may go on later to develop type 2 diabetes in later life).
      (1) Usually resolves after pregnancy.
      (2) Occurs at a greater frequency in race/ethnicity risk groups.
      (3) Obesity is another risk factor.
   d. Other types of diabetes (1%–2% of all cases of diabetes).
      (1) Genetic syndromes.
      (2) Surgery.
      (3) Drugs (e.g., steroids).
      (4) Malnutrition.
      (5) Infections (e.g., MRSA).
4. Signs and symptoms.
   a. Frequent urination.
   b. Excessive thirst.
   c. Unexplained weight loss.
   d. Extreme hunger.
   e. Visual changes.
   f. Sensory changes (tingling/numbness) in the hands or feet.
   g. Fatigue.
   h. Very dry skin.
   i. Slow-healing wounds.
   j. Increased rate of infections.
5. Prevention.
   a. Regular physical activity may reduce the risk of type 2 diabetes.
   b. Maintaining normal body weight may prevent type 2 diabetes.
6. Sequelae/complications.
   a. Fatigue/decreased activity tolerance.
   b. Urinary disturbance.
   c. Visual loss, low vision, blindness.
   d. Peripheral neuropathy.
      (1) Amputations.
   e. Propensity to develop wounds.
   f. Connective tissue disease associated with diabetes.
      (1) There is a significantly higher incidence of Dupuytren's disease, limited joint motion, carpal tunnel syndrome, and flexor tenosynovitis in the diabetic population.
      (2) Characterized by development of soft tissue thickening in the palms of the hands and soles of the feet.
   g. Poor general health/increased rate of infections disrupt life roles and activity participation.
   h. Hypoglycemia: occurs when a person's blood sugar is very low; i.e., 70 milligrams per deciliter (mg/dL).
      (1) Onset is rapid and can occur in minutes.
      (2) Refer to Box 9-3 for signs and symptoms of hypoglycemia.
      (3) If the person is conscious, immediately provide carbohydrates in the form of hard candy, fruit juice, or honey. Symptoms may not resolve for 10–15 minutes.

> **RED FLAG:** If a person's status deteriorates during that time or does not improve, emergency medical services (EMS) should be called.

> **RED FLAG:** If the person demonstrates severe hypoglycemia, is unconscious, exhibits seizures, or is unable to follow simple commands or swallow safely, it is a medical emergency. EMS must be called *immediately*. Too low blood sugar may cause shock or coma. Immediate medical treatment (i.e., glucagon injection or intravenous [IV] glucose) is required.

   i. Hyperglycemic crisis: occurs when a person's blood sugar is abnormally high; i.e., 300 mg/dL.
      (1) Onset is gradual and can occur over several days.
      (2) Refer to Box 9-4 for signs and symptoms of hyperglycemia.

BOX 9-3 ▷ Signs and Symptoms of Hypoglycemia

- Early Signs and Symptoms include the following.
  - Pallor
  - Shakiness/trembling
  - Sweating
  - Excessive hunger
  - Tachycardia and palpitations
  - Fainting or feeling faint
  - Dizziness
  - Fatigue and weakness
  - Poor coordination and unsteady gait
- Late Signs and Symptoms include the following.
  - Nervousness and irritability
  - Headache
  - Blurred or double vision
  - Slurred speech
  - Drowsiness
  - Inability to concentrate, confusion, delusions
  - Loss of consciousness

BOX 9-4 ▷ Signs and Symptoms of Hyperglycemia

- Signs and Symptoms include the following.
  - Weakness
  - Increased thirst
  - Dry mouth
  - Frequent, scant urination
  - Decreased appetite, nausea/vomiting, abdominal tenderness
  - Dulled senses, confusion, diminished reflexes, paresthesias
  - Flushed, signs of dehydration
  - Deep, rapid respirations
  - Pulse: rapid, weak
  - Fruity odor to the breath (acetone breath)
  - Hyperglycemic coma

RED FLAG: Hyperglycemia is a metabolic emergency and a medical crisis. EMS should be called *immediately* as IV fluids and insulin are required. If hyperglycemia is not treated, a stroke or ketoacidosis (diabetic coma), which can lead to death, can occur. Refer to Box 9-4 for signs and symptoms.

- Diabetic ketoacidosis (DKA) is caused by very high or low insulin levels. This may be due to illness or missing insulin injections. Signs include dehydration, rapid and weak pulse, and acetone breath.
- Hyperosmolar coma is a serious condition due to extremely high blood sugar. It usually occurs in persons with Type II diabetics and may be caused by infection or illness. Signs include stupor, thirst, polyuria, and neurologic abnormalities.

7. Intervention.
   a. Preventive exercise and diet.
   b. Education about the need for the medical management of diabetes and the outcomes of effective management versus poor management.
   c. Training in health management and self-advocacy skills.
   d. Psychological and emotional support for learning to live with diabetes.
   e. Lifestyle redesign, adaptive strategies, and adapted equipment to facilitate participation in desired occupations.
   f. Lifestyle re-adjustment to complications when and if they occur.

(1) Low vision.
(2) Safety assessment and intervention.
(3) Physical adaptations.
   g. Protective issues regarding peripheral neuropathy.
      (1) Safety assessment.
      (2) Education concerning risk associated with sensory loss.
      (3) Skin care.
      (4) Pain management.
   h. Early attention to wound management.
      (1) Teach skin care and inspection techniques.
      (2) Teach person to self-advocate quickly when changes are observed.
   i. Assistance in problem-solving and modifying occupations as changes occur in the medical status of the condition.
      (1) Problem-solve resources for specialized treatment.
      (2) Teach person to recognize changes in their functional status that warrant further attention and intervention.

EXAM HINT: The NBCOT® OTR® exam content outline identifies the task of collaborating "with the client, the client's relevant others, occupational therapy colleagues, and other professionals using a client-centered approach and therapeutic use of self to manage occupational therapy services" (NBCOT®, 2022, p. 5) as essential for competent practice and states that performance of this task requires knowledge of "strategies for addressing and enhancing health literacy (NBCOT®, 2022, p. 6). Based on this requirement, it is likely that the NBCOT® exam will include items that require the application of knowledge about the above intervention approaches that OT practitioners should use when working with a person with diabetes.

Obesity and Bariatric Issues[2]

1. Obesity is defined as a condition characterized by excess body fat.
2. Body mass index (BMI): a formula for determining obesity. BMI is calculated by dividing an individual's weight in kilograms by the square of the person's height in meters.
   a. World Health Organization Classification adopted by the National Institutes of Health.
      (1) Overweight defined as BMI ranging from 25 to 29.9.
      (2) Obesity defined as BMI >30.
      (3) Morbidly obese defined as BMI >40.
3. A national health problem.
   a. Health risks and resultant conditions associated with obesity: metabolic syndrome, hypertension, hyperlipidemia, type 2 diabetes, cardiovascular disease, stroke, glucose intolerance, sleep apnea, gallbladder disease, menstrual irregularities, infertility, cancer (endometrial, breast, prostate, and colon), and chronic low back pain.
   b. The result is premature death and an increased mortality rate.
   c. Waist circumference is used to determine distribution of body fat. Abdominal obesity (central accumulation of fat) is an independent predictor of morbidity and mortality.
   d. Childhood obesity: most prevalent nutritional disorder affecting children in the U.S.
4. Etiology: health disparity; result of complex social, behavioral, cultural, environmental, physiological, and genetic factors.
   a. Social.
      (1) Education and income level.
      (2) Occupation.
      (3) Family background.
   b. Behavioral.
      (1) Eating on the run/fast food.
      (2) Eating alone.
      (3) Eating for solace/"comfort foods."
      (4) Binge eating.
   c. Cultural.
      (1) "Food and love" cultures (food given as a sign of affection).
      (2) Larger body size is more highly valued in several cultures.
      (3) Post-depression-era eating (i.e., consuming more because there is money to buy).
      (4) "Restaurant cultures" (e.g., larger portions, greater food diversity, higher fat content).
   d. Environmental.

      (1) Lack of time to devote to meal planning and preparation.
      (2) Lack of time to develop and maintain a proper exercise routine (e.g., the "sandwich" generation who provides simultaneous caregiving for their parents and children resulting in a real or perceived lack of time for self).
      (3) Lack of access to resources.
         (a) No facilities in which to exercise.
         (b) No exercise coach/partners.
   e. Physiological.
      (1) A nutritionally related imbalance that occurs resulting in excess body fat.
         (a) Poor diet and nutrition.
         (b) Eating processed foods.
         (c) Excessive food consumption: excess calories are consumed that are not expended by work or exercise.
         (d) Activity level: lack of exercise; poor choice of exercise in proportion to what is consumed.
         (e) Compulsive overeating: psychiatric disorder.
      (2) Excess body fat that occurs from a metabolic imbalance.
         (a) Gestational diabetes (passively introduced to fetus: results in oversized infants at birth).
         (b) Adrenal disorders: cortisol and stress.
      (3) Side effects of the atypical second-generation antipsychotic (SGA) medications.
         (a) SGAs affect the metabolism process, alter resting metabolic rate, and increase cravings for carbohydrates.
         (b) The rate of metabolic syndrome is substantially higher for persons with mental illness as compared to the general population.
5. Prevention.
   a. Education.
      (1) Raising awareness of behavioral factors that contribute to obesity (e.g., sedentary lifestyle).
      (2) Promoting community-driven group intervention options focused on health promotion and wellness.
   b. Habit intervention with occupations and activities that contribute to obesity (e.g., choose this/not that approaches, not eating while stressed, mindful eating).
   c. Tertiary intervention when overcoming obesity is not the issue; the focus is on the occupational needs of the client.
6. Sequelae.
   a. Decreased ability in performance areas of occupations (ADL, IADL, mobility, social participation).
   b. Symptomatology related to larger body size: musculoskeletal pain, limited community mobility, lower activity tolerance.

---

[2] Susan O'Sullivan contributed to this section.

7. Intervention.
   a. Lifestyle redesign: combination of changes in daily habits, patterns, and routines to reduce body weight through nutritional changes (e.g., emphasis on fruits, vegetables, whole grains, and lean protein) and changes in activity time engagement combined with increased physical activity.
      (1) Personalized plan to change lifestyle habits that contribute to obesity risk.
      (2) Personalized activity-focused exercise program combining personal interests, desired participation, goals, and positive meaning (e.g., OT walks with National Alliance on Mental Illness [NAMI]) for persons with metabolic syndrome caused by SGAs).
      (3) Instruction in self-monitoring of exercise responses (i.e., heart rate, perceived exertion).
      (4) Supportive coaching/counseling to improve compliance and make long-term, life-altering change.
   b. Inpatient rehabilitation care.
      (1) Access devices and equipment to maximize client participation in daily activities of meaning (ADL, IADL, mobility, and community participation).
         (a) Bariatric equipment: wheeled mobility, assistive devices, lifters, seating adaptations, clothing adaptations. Refer to Chapters 15 and 16.
      (2) Activity participation to relearn lifestyle modifications and to offer practice in altering habits and patterns that require adjustment in order to maximize the individual's participation and meaningful engagement.

8. Comorbidities, risks, and complications.
   a. Cardiopulmonary compromise is typically exhibited (i.e., shortness of breath, elevated blood pressure, and angina).
   b. Altered biomechanics affect hips, knees, ankle/foot; back and joint pain are common.
      (1) Increased risk of orthopedic injury.
   c. Increased risk of pressure ulcers due to shear forces and immobility.
   d. Increased occurrence of lymphedema, cellulitis, skin fold dermatitis, and other skin infections.
   e. Increased heat intolerance, risk of hyperthermia, and heat exhaustion.
   f. Increased risk of practitioner injury when using poor body mechanics or inadequate assistance during transfers and lifts.

Lyme Disease

1. Lyme disease is a bacterial infection and the most common insect spreading disease in the U.S. If left untreated the infection may spread to other parts of the body, including the joints, heart, and nervous system.
2. Etiology.
   a. Lyme disease is transmitted through a blacklegged tick infected with the bacteria Borrelia burgdorferi.
3. Prevention.
   a. Walk on trails to avoid contact with grass and brush.
   b. Avoid tick-infested areas.
   c. Wear light-colored clothing, so ticks can be easily seen.
   d. Tuck in clothing and tape clothing seams (i.e., where pants meet socks) to prevent entry.
   e. Spray insect repellent containing DEET on clothes and exposed skin, excluding the face.
   f. After being outdoors, change clothes and inspect skin for the presence of ticks.
   g. Remove any ticks with tweezers, grasping the tick as close to the skin surface as possible and pulling straight back.
4. Sequelae and symptoms.
   a. Impairs the immune response and affects the neurological and orthopedic systems.
   b. Early symptoms (3–30 days).
      (1) Fatigue.
      (2) Headache.
      (3) Chills and fever.
      (4) Muscle and joint pain.
      (5) Swollen lymph nodes.
      (6) Rash, erythema migranes: a circular red patch.
         (a) The center of the rash may clear as it enlarges, resembling a bulls-eye.
   c. Symptoms, if left untreated (days to months after the tick bite).
      (1) Arthritis: brief bouts of pain and swelling in one or more of the large joints.
         (a) Knees are the most commonly affected joints.
      (2) Nervous system abnormalities.
         (a) Numbness.
         (b) Pain.
         (c) Bell's palsy.
         (d) Meningitis.
         (e) CNS involvement may contribute to neurocognitive disorders and balance impairments.
      (3) Heart rate irregularities (Lyme carditis).
      (4) Bowel and bladder control problems associated with the antibiotics used to treat Lyme disease.
   d. Post-Lyme disease syndrome (PLDS) or post-treatment Lyme disease syndrome.
      (1) Cause of PLDS is unknown; individuals are symptomatic in the absence of clinically detectable infection.
      (2) Symptoms linger for months or years after a treated acute infection (estimated 10% of cases).
      (3) Symptoms may include persistent musculoskeletal pain (arthralgia, myalgia), fatigue,

impaired cognitive function, difficulty sleeping, and unexplained numbness.

5. Medical treatment.
   a. Antibiotics, oral or intravenous.
   b. Management of joint-related symptoms from the accompanying arthritis.
6. Intervention.
   a. Treat joint pain and swelling.
      (1) Provide education regarding acute arthritic flares.
         (a) Rest.
         (b) Anti-inflammatory medicine compliance.
         (c) Splinting or wrapping to protect inflamed joints and prevent overstretching of enlarged joint.
         (d) Teach energy conservation and work simplification.
      (2) Following flare, in subacute phase, provide gradual reintroduction of normal performance of daily tasks and activities.
   b. Treat nervous system abnormalities.
      (1) Numbness.
         (a) Safety assessment and intervention to preserve safety and prevent injury.
         (b) Management of esthesias that are perceived as painful.
         (c) Occupation-based interventions to encourage and preserve function and to cope with chronic pain conditions.
      (2) Pain.
         (a) Use of physical agent modalities to reduce pain.
         (b) Use of stress management (complementary care) techniques to control the intensity of the pain and to increase coping ability.
         (c) Use of neutral warmth to decrease intensity of pain.
      (d) Use of adapted techniques to avoid triggering of movements that exacerbate pain during activity (e.g., sit on higher seat to decrease stress load in sit or stand).
   (3) Bell's palsy.
      (a) Make a facial splint to prevent long-term asymmetry of facial muscles. Clip or pincer mold of the inside and outer lip of the mouth on the involved side. Elastic attaching mouth mold to earpiece (similar to eyeglass ear rim).
      (b) Use electric stimulation to stimulate denervated muscles.
      (c) Teach person to use their fingers to assist buccal closure and prevent spillage of the bolus through the lips.
      (d) Provide counseling concerning alteration in body image, since the individual is coping with a facial deformity.
   (4) Meningitis.
      (a) Acute care: positioning, splinting, supportive care while hospitalized.
      (b) Rehabilitation if there is recovery-related sequelae (i.e., neurological, motor, sensory, cognitive, and/or ADL impairment).
   (5) Heart rate irregularities.
      (a) Telemetry during daily performance of tasks and activities that support role performance.
      (b) Pulse oximetry measurements, if oxygenation is poor during performance of daily tasks and activities.
      (c) Work simplification, adaptation, and modification to prevent further complications associated with arrhythmia.

Integumentary System Disorders

Wounds and Pressure/ Decubitus Ulcers

1. Types of wounds or impaired skin integrities.
   a. Abrasions: trauma to the skin resulting in a breakage in skin integrity, often caused by a fall, or sliding impact to the body part.
   b. Punctures: small holes in the skin, allowing air passage into the wound.
   c. Bites: insect, animals, human.
   d. Surgical wounds: incisions, resections, grafts, amputations.
      (1) Surgical infections were the largest prevalence category, followed by diabetic wound infections.
   e. Diabetic ulcers.
   f. Pressure injuries: prolonged exposure to pressures exceeding capillary pressure.
   g. Traumatic wounds: burns/thermal injuries, gunshot wounds, degloving injuries, compression and crash injuries.
   h. Venous stasis ulcers: poor lower extremity circulation, varicose veins.
   i. Arterial ulcers: result from damage to the arteries due to lack of blood flow to tissue.

j. Chronic: wounds that remain unhealed after a month.

2. Etiology and risks.

  a. Wounds are mostly caused by metabolic disorders, vascular disease, and persistent local pressure to an area.

    (1) Pressure that interrupts normal circulation resulting in localized areas of cellular necrosis.

    (2) Greatest risk is over bony prominences (e.g., ischial tuberosity).

    (3) Intensity and duration of the pressure determine the severity of the decubiti.

  b. Refer to Box 9-5 for factors that predispose the development of decubiti ulcers.

> **CAUTION:** Be aware that wounds can be a complication of any diagnosis that compromises the person's sensorimotor, cardiopulmonary, renal-genitourinary, immunological, and/or endocrine systems.

3. Stages and signs of pressure ulcers.

  a. The National Pressure Ulcer Advisory Panel has updated the definitions and stage classifications of pressure ulcers.

BOX 9-5 ▷ Factors that Predispose Formation of Decubitus Ulcers

- Immobility or altered mobility.
- Significant weight loss.
- Edema.
- Incontinence.
- Sensory deficiencies.
- Circulatory abnormalities.
- Dehydration.
- Inadequate nutrition.
- Obesity.
- Age-related skin changes.
- Multiple comorbidities.
- Certain pathological conditions, including spinal cord injury (SCI), cerebral palsy, diabetes, cancer, burns, and hand injuries.

---

    (1) This revision includes the original four stages and two additional stages of deep tissue injury and unstageable pressure ulcers.

  b. Suspected deep tissue injury.

    (1) Localized discoloration of intact skin (purple or maroon) or a blister filled with blood resulting from damage of underlying soft tissue.

    (2) Deep tissue injury may be difficult to detect in individuals with darkly pigmented skin.

    (3) This stage may further evolve and can rapidly expose additional layers of tissue.

  c. Stage I pressure ulcer.

    (1) Skin is intact with visible nonblanchable redness over a localized area, typically over a bony prominence. Refer to Figure 9-3.

    (2) Visible blanching may not be evident in darkly pigmented skin; the color may appear different from the surrounding area.

    (3) The area may be soft or firm and/or cooler or warmer when compared to adjacent skin.

    (4) The area may be painful or itchy.

> **CAUTION:** A Stage I pressure ulcer may indicate "at risk" persons, but its signs can be difficult to detect.

  d. Stage II pressure ulcer.

    (1) Involves the dermis with partial-thickness loss, which presents as a shallow open ulcer that can be shiny or dry. Refer to Figure 9-3.

    (2) A Stage II ulcer can also present as a blister that is intact or open/ruptured.

    (3) The wound bed is a red/pink color without slough or bruising.

  e. Stage III pressure ulcer.

    (1) Involves full-thickness tissue loss with subcutaneous fat possibly visible. Refer to Figure 9-3.

    (2) The depth of tissue loss is not obscured if slough (i.e., dead matter/necrotic tissue) is present.

    (3) Bone, tendon, or muscle are not exposed or directly palpable.

    (4) The depth of a Stage III pressure ulcer can vary according to anatomical location and can range from shallow in areas that do not have subcutaneous tissue (e.g., the nose, ear) to very deep in areas with significant fat (e.g., the buttocks).

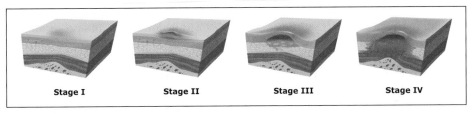

Stage I   Stage II   Stage III   Stage IV

Figure 9-3 **Stages of Pressure Ulcers.**

  f. Stage IV pressure ulcer.
   (1) Involves full-thickness tissue loss with bone, tendon, or muscle visible or directly palpable. Refer to Figure 9-3.
   (2) Similarly, the depth of a Stage IV pressure ulcer can vary according to anatomical location and can range from shallow in areas that do not have subcutaneous tissue (e.g., the nose, ear) to very deep in areas with significant fat (e.g., the buttocks).
   (3) Osteomyelitis is possible if Stage IV ulcers extend into muscle, fascia, tendon, and/or the joint capsule.
  g. Unstageable pressure ulcers.
   (1) Involves full-thickness tissue loss in which the wound bed has slough and/or eschar (i.e., a scab or dark crusted ulcer) which covers the base of the ulcer.
 4. Wound management including occlusive dressings, debridement, surgery, and/or grafting may be needed depending on the severity of the decubitus ulcer.
 5. Impact of wounds.
  a. Wounds and related conditions can negatively affect a person's ability to participate in their life roles, routines, and useful habits and can affect performance with self-care, work, educational activities, leisure activities, social participation, and rest and sleep.
  b. Wounds affect both the physical and psychological well-being of individuals.
  c. Wounds can adversely affect quality of life.
  d. Reduced social participation, self-efficacy, and reported quality of life due to discoloration of the skin, visible scars, contracting or hypertrophic scars, and conspicuous use of compression garments.
  e. Pain, depression, social isolation, and anxiety can result from the existence of wounds in the acute and chronic phases.
  f. Financial stability that can be affected by the inability to work due to a significant wound (AOTA, 2018).
 6. Evaluation.
  a. Early assessment is critical to prevent wounds from developing and/or progressing.
   (1) The skin integrity of all persons should be assessed.
   (2) The presence of risk factors for wounds should be assessed to determine the person's potential for developing a wound.
    (a) Refer to Box 9-5 for a list of risk factors for the development of decubiti ulcers.
  b. While nursing staff in medical model settings typically assume the responsibility for skin and risk assessments, OT practitioners can (and should) contribute to this process.
   (1) In nonmedical model settings (e.g., home care), the OT practitioner may need to take a more active role in the evaluation process.

   (2) Visually inspect the wound site and measure it using a disposable tape measure.
   (3) Rule out possible undermining and tunneling using a sterile cotton swab. Note the depth of the wound in centimeters.
   (4) Document observation of wound color and exudate.
   (5) Note any signs of infection.
   (6) Take circumferential measurements of a limb that has wounds just distal and proximal to the wound, when compared with the noninvolved side.
   (7) Administer an analog pain scale.
   (8) Administer the Canadian Occupational Performance Measure (COPM) to determine personal goals for treatment.
   (9) Change dressings daily and note progress of healing.
    (a) Caregivers should be trained by the occupational therapist to perform this assessment.
  c. Persons determined to be at a low risk for developing wounds should be re-evaluated whenever there is a change in their status.

> **RED FLAG:** Persons determined to be at a high risk for developing certain types of wounds (e.g., pressure ulcers) should be re-evaluated every 12 hours.

 7. Intervention.
  a. The need for assistance and/or accommodations for participation in activities and contexts specifically related to the wound should be addressed. Interventions include the following.
   (1) Management of the wound site, including applying wound care treatments and products to promote healing and manage drainage or odor.
   (2) Management of clothing and footwear that may no longer fit correctly or that may worsen the wound condition.
   (3) Education regarding donning/doffing, care of, and recommended wear schedule for pressure garments for scar management.
   (4) The promotion of restful sleep, despite the presence of pain.
   (5) Physical activity and functional mobility to prevent impairments in endurance, overall strength, cardiovascular status, pulmonary status, cognition, and to reduce pain at the wound site.
   (6) Bed mobility and positioning to relieve pressure on wounds, minimize pain, and prevent further skin breakdown from occurring.
   (7) Social participation opportunities to address potential self-efficacy and body image issues due to skin discoloration or scarring, and/or compression garment use.

b. Prevention is the most effective intervention for all wound types.
   (1) Use of wheelchair cushions, flotation pads, and pressure-relief bed aids to distribute pressure over a larger skin surface. The Centers for Medicare and Medicaid Services has divided pressure-reducing devices into three categories for reimbursement purposes.
       (a) Group 1: cushions or mattresses that use nonelectrical means (e.g., air, foam, gel, or water) to distribute pressure.
       (b) Group 2: dynamic, electric-powered devices (e.g., alternating and low air loss mattresses) for persons with full-thickness ulcers or those at moderate to high risk.
       (c) Group 3: dynamic, electric-powered devices (e.g., air-fluidized beds) for persons with nonhealing full-thickness ulcers.
   (2) Train the individual and/or caregivers in positioning and weight-shifting techniques and schedules.
       (a) Full push-ups, lateral leans, forward leans, or wheelchair tilt/recline options are common techniques used depending on the abilities of the individual.
       (b) Weight shifts should occur every 30 minutes for 30 seconds or every 60 minutes for 60 seconds.
       (c) Integrate weight-shifting into daily activities (e.g., lean forward to pick up the phone, lean sideways when reading the mail).

> CAUTION: The presence of substance abuse, cognitive deficits, and/or psychological impairments can jeopardize the individual's ability to understand and complete the required daily wound prevention regimen, increasing their risk for the development of wounds.

   (3) Train the individual and/or caregivers in proper skin care.
       (a) Keep skin free of excessive moisture, dryness, and heat.
       (b) Check skin at least two times per day for any evidence of breakdown. Most individuals perform this in bed in the morning before arising and in the evening before sleep.
       (c) Target for inspection of the scapula, elbows, ischia, sacrum/coccyx, trochanters, heels, ankles, and knees when checking for pressure sores.
   (4) Encourage adequate intake of fluids and food to maintain nutrition, promote healing, and achieve a recommended body weight.
c. Occupation-based interventions.
   (1) Encourage participation in meaningful and productive activities.
   (2) Individuals who pursue active lifestyles have fewer decubiti.

Whole-Body System Disorders

Heat Syndromes/Hyperthermia

1. Etiology and risk factors.
   a. Heat production increases with infection, exercise, and/or drugs.
   b. Heat loss decreases with high humidity and/or temperature, excess clothing, obesity, cardiovascular disease, dehydration, sweat gland dysfunction, lack of acclimatization, and/or drugs.
   c. When an individual's heat loss is not sufficient to offset their heat production, their body will retain heat, and a heat syndrome can develop.
   d. Older adults and individuals who are obese or taking drugs are at increased risk.
2. Prevention.
   a. In hot weather, wear lightweight, loose-fitting clothing.
   b. Avoid hot places; seek shade, use fans, and air conditioners.
   c. Rest frequently.
   d. Increase fluid intake.
3. Types, signs, and symptoms.
   a. Heat cramps are characterized by a normal body temperature, nausea, diaphoresis, muscle twitching or spasms, weakness, and/or severe muscle cramps.
   b. Heat exhaustion is characterized by a rapid pulse, decreased blood pressure, nausea, vomiting, cool, pallid skin, mental confusion, headache, and/or giddiness, but no fever.

> CAUTION: Heat exhaustion is a serious condition that if untreated can rapidly advance to heat stroke.

   c. Heat stroke is characterized by hot, dry red skin; a body temperature higher than 104°F; slow, deep respiration; tachycardia; dilated pupils; confusion; progressing to seizures and possibly loss of consciousness.

> **RED FLAG:** Heat cramps and heat exhaustion may turn into heat stroke if the body temperature increases to 103°F. This is a medical emergency and EMS must be called immediately.

> **RED FLAG:** Heat stroke requires emergency treatment. EMS should be immediately contacted. Hypothermia blankets, medications, and intravenous fluids are necessary. Do not try to force the person to drink fluids.

4. Intervention.
   a. Heat stroke: immediate cooling is necessary.
      (1) Move the person to a cooler area and remove as many clothes as possible to decrease the person's body temperature.
      (2) Immersing the person in cool water is the most effective intervention.
      (3) If cold water immersion is not possible, place ice packs on the person's arterial pressure points and spray their body with cool water.
   b. Heat cramps and heat exhaustion usually do not require hospitalization.
      (1) Loosen clothing and have the person lie in a cool place.
      (2) Replace fluid and electrolytes with fruit juice or a balanced electrolyte drink. If these are not available, give fluids and seek additional medical care.
      (3) Massage muscles if cramps are severe.
      (4) IV infusions and oxygen may be indicated if symptoms are severe.

References

American Cancer Society. (2021). Cancer facts and figures. https://www.cancer.org/content/dam/cancer-org/research/cancer-facts-and-statistics/annual-cancer-facts-and-figures/2019/cancer-facts-and-figures-2019.pdf

American Diabetes Association. (2021). Blood sugar testing and control. https://diabetes.org/healthy-living/medication-treatments/blood-glucose-testing-and-control/hypoglycemia

American Diabetes Association. (2019). Fast facts: Data and statistics about diabetes. https://professional.diabetes.org/sites/default/files/media/diabetes_fast_facts22322.pdf

American Occupational Therapy Association. (2011). The role of occupational therapy in end-of-life care. American Journal of Occupational Therapy, 65(Suppl.), S66–S75.

American Occupational Therapy Association. (2018). Position paper: The role of occupational therapy in wound management. American Journal of Occupational Therapy, 72(Suppl. 2), Article 212410057.

American Occupational Therapy Association. (2020). Occupational therapy practice framework: Domain and process (4th ed.). American Journal of Occupational Therapy, 74(2), Article 7412410010.

Armstrong, D. G., Boulton, A. J. M., & Bus, S. A. (2017). Diabetic foot ulcers and their recurrence. New England Journal of Medicine, 376, 2367–2375.

Balsara, Z., Ross, S. S., Dolber, P. C., Wiener, J. S., Tang, Y., & Seed, P. (2013). Enhanced susceptibility to urinary tract infection in the spinal cord-injured host with neurogenic bladder. Infection and Immunity, 81, 3018–3026.

Bergholdt, S. H., Søndergaard, J., Larsen, P. V., Holm, L. V., Kragstrup, J., & Hansen, D. G. (2013). A randomised controlled trial to improve general practitioners' services in cancer rehabilitation: Effects on general practitioners' pro-activity and on patients' participation in rehabilitation activities. Acta Oncologica, 52(2), 400–409.

Blanchard, S. A. (2009). Variables associated with obesity among African-American women in Omaha. American Journal of Occupational Therapy, 63, 58–68.

Braveman, B., & Hunter, E. G. (2017). Occupational therapy practice guidelines for cancer rehabilitation with adults. AOTA Press.

Braveman, B., Munoz, L.A., Hughes, J.K., & Nicholson, J. (2018). Cancer and oncology rehabilitation. In H. M. Pendleton & W. Schultz-Krohn (Eds.), Pedretti's occupational therapy: Practice skills for physical dysfunction (8th ed., pp. 1134–1141). Elsevier.

Burkhardt, A. (2006). Oncology. In W. Schultz-Krohn & H. Pendleton (Eds.), Occupational therapy: Practice skills for physical dysfunction (6th ed., pp. 1157–1168). Elsevier Science/Mosby.

Casale, R., Buounocore, M., & Matucci-Cerinic, M. (1997). Review article: Systemic sclerosis (scleroderma): An integrated challenge in rehabilitation. Archives of Physical Medicine and Rehabilitation, 78, 767–773.

Centers for Disease Control and Prevention. (2016). Healthcare-associated infections: MRSA in healthcare settings. https://www.cdc.gov/hai/organisms/mrsa-infection.html

Centers for Disease Control and Prevention. (2017a). Gestational diabetes. https://www.cdc.gov/diabetes/basics/gestational.html

Centers for Disease Control and Prevention. (2017b). HIV/AIDS: Surveillance overview. https://www.cdc.gov/hiv/statistics/surveillance/index.html

Centers for Disease Control and Prevention. (2020a). National Diabetes Statistics Report 2020. Estimates of diabetes and its burden in the United States. https://www.cdc.gov/diabetes/data/statistics-report/index.html

Centers for Disease Control and Prevention. (2020b). Prevalence of obesity and severe obesity among adults: United States, 2017–2018. https://www.cdc.gov/nchs/products/databriefs/db360.htm

Centers for Disease Control and Prevention. (2021a). About HIV. https://www.cdc.gov/hiv/basics/whatishiv.html

Centers for Disease Control and Prevention. (2021b). Chronic kidney disease initiative: CKD risk factor and prevention. https://www.cdc.gov/kidneydisease/publications-resources/annual-report/ckd-risk-prevention.html

Centers for Disease Control and Prevention. (2021c). Diabetes: What is type 1 diabetes? https://www.cdc.gov/diabetes/basics/what-is-type-1-diabetes.html

Centers for Disease Control and Prevention. (2021d). Infection control: Standard precautions for all patient care. https://www.cdc.gov/infectioncontrol/basics/standard-precautions.html

Centers for Disease Control and Prevention. (2021e). Lyme disease. https://www.cdc.gov/lyme/

Centers for Disease Control and Prevention. (2021f). Lyme disease statistics. https://www.cdc.gov/lyme/stats/humancases.html

Centers for Disease Control and Prevention. (2023). Chronic kidney disease initiative: Chronic kidney disease in the United States, 2023. https://www.cdc.gov/kidneydisease/publications-resources/ckd-national-facts.html

Clark, F. A., Blanchard, J., Sleight, A., Cogan, A., Floríndez, L., Gleason, S., & Vigen, C. (2015). Lifestyle redesign: The intervention tested in the USC Well Elderly Studies (2nd ed.). AOTA Press.

Cleveland Clinic. (2021a). GERD: Chronic acid reflux. https://my.clevelandclinic.org/health/diseases/17019-gerd-or-acid-reflux-or-heartburn-overview

Cleveland Clinic. (2021b). Urinary incontinence. https://my.clevelandclinic.org/health/diseases/17596-urinary-incontinence.

Cleveland Clinic. (2021c). Urinary tract infections. https://my.clevelandclinic.org/health/diseases/9135-urinary-tract-infections.

Curtin, R., Mapes, D., Schatell, D., & Burrows-Hudson, S. (2005). Self-management in patients with end stage renal disease: Exploring domains and dimensions. Nephrology Nursing Journal, 32, 389–395.

Dorsher, P. T., & McIntosh, P. M. (2012). Neurogenic bladder. Advances in Urology, Article 816274.

Ekberg, O., Hamdy, S., Woisard, V., Wuttge-Hannig, A., & Ortega, P. (2002). Social and psychological burden of dysphagia: Its impact on diagnosis and treatment. Dysphagia, 17(2), 139–146.

Farri, A., Accornero, A., & Burdese, C. (2007). Social importance of dysphagia: Its impact on diagnosis and therapy. ACTA Otorhinolaryngol Italia, 27, 83–86.

Forhan, M., Bhambhani, Y., Dyer, D., Ramos-Salas, X., Ferguson-Pell, M., & Sharma, A. (2010). Rehabilitation in bariatrics: Opportunities for practice and research. Disability and Rehabilitation, 32(11), 952–959.

Frolek Clark, G., Roberts, P., Cox, M. S., Holm, S., Kurfuerst, S. T., Lynch, A. K., & Schuberth, L. M. (2007). Specialized knowledge and skills in feeding, eating, and swallowing for occupational therapy practice. American Journal of Occupational Therapy, 61, 686–700.

Furusawa, K., Sugiyama, H., Ikeda, A., Tokohiro, A., Koyoshi, H., Takahashi, M., & Tajima, F. (2007). Autonomic dysreflexia during a bowel regimen program in patients with cervical spinal cord injury. Acta Medica Okayama, 61, 221–227.

George, B., & Malkenson, G. (2008). Pressure ulcers: A clinical review. Rehabilitation Management, 21(10), 16–19.

Jung, T.-D., & Park, S.-H. (2011). Intradialytic exercise programs for hemodialysis patients. Chonnam Medical Journal, 47(2), 61–65.

Karlsson, A. K. (1999). Scientific review: Autonomic dysreflexia. Spinal Cord, 37, 383–391.

Kest, H., & Kaushik, A. (2019). Vancomycin-resistant staphylococcus aureus: Formidable threat or silence before the storm? Journal of Infectious Disease and Epidemiology, 5(5), 93–101. doi.org/10.23937/2474-3658/1510093

Kimmel, P., & Rosenberg, M. (Eds.). (2015). Chronic renal disease. Elsevier Science.

King, J. M., & Ligman, K. (2011). Patient noncompliance with swallowing recommendations: Reports from speech-language pathologists. Contemporary Issues in Communication Science and Disorders, 38, 53–60.

Lin, Y. H., & Pan, P. J. (2012). The use of rehabilitation among patients with breast cancer: A retrospective longitudinal cohort study. BMC Health Services Research, 12(1), 282.

Mayo Clinic. (2018). Chronic kidney disease. https://www.mayoclinic.org/diseases-conditions/chronic-kidney-disease/symptoms-causes/syc-20354521

Mayo Clinic. (2021a). HIV/AIDS. https://www.mayoclinic.org/diseases-conditions/hiv-aids/symptoms-causes/syc-20373524

Mayo Clinic. (2021b). MRSA infection. https://www.mayoclinic.org/diseases-conditions/mrsa/symptoms-causes/syc-20375336

Mayo Clinic. (2021c). Type 1 diabetes. https://www.mayoclinic.org/diseases-conditions/type-1-diabetes/symptoms-causes/syc-20353011

Mewes, J. C., Steuten, L. M., Ijzerman, M. J., & van Harten, W. H. (2012). Effectiveness of multidimensional cancer survivor rehabilitation and cost-effectiveness of cancer rehabilitation in general: A systematic review. Oncologist, 17(12), 1581–1593.

National Board for Certification in Occupational Therapy (NBCOT®). (2022). 2022 Occupational Therapist Registered (OTR®) Examination Content Outline. https://www.nbcot.org/-/media/PDFs/2022_OTR_Content_Outline.pdf

National Cancer Institute. (2021, December 22). Cancer statistics. https://www.cancer.gov/about-cancer/understanding/statistics

National Institute of Diabetes and Digestive and Kidney Diseases. (n.d.). Peritoneal dialysis. https://www.niddk.nih.gov/health-information/kidney-disease/kidney-failure/hemodialysis

National Kidney Foundation. (2021). Nephrotic syndrome. http://www.kidney.org/atoz/content/nephrotic.cfm

National Pressure Injury Advisory Panel. (2017). NPIAP pressure injury stages. https://npiap.com/page/PressureInjuryStages

Nussbaum, S. R., Carter, M. J., Fife, C. E., DaVanzo, J., Haught, R., Nusgart, M., & Cartwright, D. (2018). An economic evaluation of the impact, cost, and Medicare policy implications of chronic nonhealing wounds. Value Health, 21, 27–32.

Pizzi, M., & Burkhardt, A. (2003). Adult immunological diseases. In E. Crepeau, B. Schell, & E. Cohn (Eds.), Willard and Spackman's occupational therapy (10th ed., pp. 821–834). Lippincott.

Pizzi, M., & Teaford, G. (2018). HIV infection and AIDS. In H. M. Pendleton & W. Schultz-Krohn (Eds.), Pedretti's occupational therapy: Practice skills for physical dysfunction (8th ed., pp. 1166–1183). Elsevier.

Poole, J. L. (2010). Musculoskeletal rehabilitation in the person with scleroderma. Current Opinions in Rheumatology, 22, 205–212.

Prieto, L., Thorsen, H., & Juul, K. (2005). Development and validation of a quality of life questionnaire for patients with colostomy or ileostomy. Health and Quality of Life Outcomes, 12, 62.

Radomski, M.V., Anheluk, M., Carroll, G., & Zolla, J. (2021). Cancer. In D.P. Direte & S.A. Gutman (Eds.), Occupational therapy for physical dysfunction (8th ed., pp. 979–993). Wolters Kluwer.

Reingold, F. S., & Jordan, K. (2013). Obesity and occupational therapy. American Journal of Occupational Therapy, 67(Suppl.), S39–S46.

Rosenbloom, A. L. (2004). Connective tissue disorders in diabetes. In R.A. DeFronzo, E. Feraninni, H. Keen, & P. Zimmet (Eds.), International Textbook of Diabetes Mellitus (3rd ed., pp. 1283–1309). John Wiley and Sons.

Saliman Reingold, F., & Salles-Jordan, K. (2013). Obesity and occupational therapy. American Journal of Occupational Therapy, 67(Suppl. 6), S39–S46. https://doi.org/10.5014/ajot.2013.67S39

Salyers, W. J., Mansour, A., El-Haddad, B., Golbeck, A. L., & Kallail, K. J. (2007). Lifestyle modification counseling in patients with gastroesophageal reflux disease. Gastroenterological Nursing, 30, 302–304.

Scleroderma Foundation. (2021, December 13). Scleroderma facts. https://scleroderma.org/wp-content/uploads/2021/12/Scleroderma-Overview-and-Causes-20211127.pdf

Sen, C.K. (2021). Human wound and its burden: Updated 2020 compendium of estimates. Advances in Wound Care, 10(5), 281-292. https://doi.org/10.1089/wound.2021.0026

Shen, X., & Shen, X. (2019). The role of occupational therapy in secondary prevention of diabetes. International Journal of Endocrinology, 2019, Article 3424727. https://doi.org/10.1155/2019/3424727

Shenot, P. J. (2023). Neurogenic bladder. Merck Manual professional version. https://www.merckmanuals.com/professional/genitourinary-disorders/voiding-disorders/neurogenic-bladder.

Siracusa, G., Sparacino, A., & Lentini, V. L. (2013). Neurogenic bladder and disc disease: A brief review. Current Medical Research and Opinion, 29(8), 1–19.

Smith, J. (2018). Eating and swallowing. In H. M. Pendleton & W. Schultz-Krohn (Eds.), Pedretti's occupational therapy: Practice skills for physical dysfunction (8th ed., pp. 669–700). Elsevier.

Takaya, Y., Kumasaka, R., Arakawa, T., Ohara, T., Nakanishi, M., Noguchi, T., & Goto, Y. (2014). Impact of cardiac rehabilitation on renal function in patients with and without chronic kidney disease after acute myocardial infarction. Circulation Journal, 78, 377–384.

Toalson, P., Ahmed, S., Hardy, T., & Kabinoff, G. (2004). The metabolic syndrome in patients with severe mental illnesses. Primary Care Companion to the Journal of Clinical Psychiatry, 6, 152–158.

Tubaro, A., Puccini, F., De Nunzio, C., Digesu, G. A., Elneil, S., Gobbi, C., & Khullar, V. (2012). The treatment of lower urinary tract symptoms in patients with multiple sclerosis: A systematic review. Current Urology Reports, 13, 335–342.

World Health Organization. (n.d.). Definition of palliative care. https://www.who.int/cancer/palliative/definition/en/

Review Questions

Gastrointestinal, Renal-Genitourinary, Endocrine, Immunological, and Integumentary Systems Disorders

Following are six questions about key content covered in this Chapter. These questions are not inclusive of the entirety of content related to disorders of the gastrointestinal, renal-genitourinary, endocrine, immunological, and integumentary systems that you must know for success on the NBCOT® exam. These questions are provided to help you "jump-start" the thought processes you will need to apply your studying of content to the answering of exam questions; hence, they are not in the NBCOT® exam format. Exam items in the NBCOT® format which cover the depth and breadth of content you will need to know to pass the NBCOT® exam are provided in the three online practice exams that accompany this text. The answers to the following questions are provided in Appendix 2.

1. You work with clients who have dysphagia and swallowing disorders to develop their feeding skills. What would you do if a client chokes and cannot clear their airway during the activity?

2. You are working with clients who have a colostomy or a stoma due to surgery to their bowel. Some clients do not have the intact fine motor functioning to learn to manage their stoma independently. What can you do to work with these clients to develop their ability to manage their stoma care independently?

3. Describe options that could be useful in providing intervention for someone who has bladder urgency with stress urinary incontinence and a diagnosis of non-insulin-dependent diabetes mellitus.

4. You are treating an adult client with a diagnosis of scleroderma and Stage IV colon cancer who was referred to occupational therapy because soft tissue/connective tissue changes are affecting hand function. Would it be appropriate to establish a goal with the client to address the evolving contractures? Describe your rationale.

(Continued)

Review Questions

5. You work in a community that has people living and working in it who have spinal cord injuries. A primary care doctor refers clients to you who have reddening of skin in their sacral regions. What could you work on with these clients to improve their skin integrity and prevent decubiti?

▶

6. You are working with a young adult who has a new diagnosis of diabetes. What areas should you assess during evaluation? When collaborating with the client to plan intervention, what are important considerations to discuss with them to inform their intervention plan?

▶

▶10

Psychiatric and Cognitive Disorders

WILLIAM L. LAMBERT, DONNA COSTA,
RITA P. FLEMING-CASTALDY, and
MACKENZIE THOMPSON[1]

[1] Janice Romeo contributed to prior editions of this chapter.

Signs and Symptoms of Psychiatric Illness and/or Cognitive Disorders

EXAM HINT: Understanding how the following signs and symptoms of psychiatric illnesses and cognitive disorders impact functional performance can help you correctly answer NBCOT® Domain 1 exam items. This Domain focuses on the therapist's responsibility for acquiring "information regarding factors that influence occupational performance on an ongoing basis throughout the occupational therapy process" (NBCOT®, 2022, p. 3) and identifies knowledge of the "signs and symptoms of disease, stages of disease, (and) secondary complications" (NBCOT®, 2022, p. 3) as essential for competent and safe practice. For example, addressing the impact of sundowning would be a priority for an occupational therapy (OT) practitioner who provides home-based services to a person with neurocognitive disorders.

Attention

1. The ability to remain focused on the various aspects of an activity or experience or the ability to concentrate.
2. Disturbances of attention.
   a. Distractibility is the inability to concentrate one's attention without attention being drawn to unimportant or irrelevant stimuli.
   b. Selective inattention is blocking out those activities, objects, or concepts that produce anxiety.
   c. Hypervigilance is excessive attention and alertness that guards against potential danger.

Consciousness

1. A state of awareness that responds to external stimuli.
2. Disturbances of consciousness.
   a. These disturbances are usually a result of brain pathology.
   b. Disorientation is a disturbance of orientation to person, place, or time. Situation is sometimes used as a fourth consideration.
   c. Delirium is an acute, reversible disorder that presents as a disoriented reaction with confusion, lability, and disturbances in behavior, e.g., aggression.
      (1) It may be associated with fear and hallucinations.
   d. Confusion involves inappropriate reactions to environmental stimuli, manifested by a disordered orientation in relation to person, place, and time.

   e. Sundowner syndrome occurs in the late afternoon and at night in older people, often seen in individuals with neurocognitive disorders.
      (1) Characterized by drowsiness, confusion, ataxia, falling, agitation, and sometimes aggression.
      (2) It is associated with sedation, neurocognitive disorders, and changes in orienting cues such as light, familiar people, and objects.

Emotion

1. A feeling state associated with affect and mood that consists of psychological and physical components (e.g., fear, anger, joy).
   a. Physiological disturbances associated with mood are frequently autonomic in nature.
2. Affect is the observable component of emotions.
   a. Appropriate affect is consistent/congruent with the accompanying idea, thought, or speech.
   b. Disturbances of affect.
      (1) Inappropriate affect is inconsistent/incongruent with the accompanying idea, thought, or speech.
      (2) Blunted affect is a severe lack of affect. As seen clinically, an affect that does not demonstrate the ability to change is observed.
      (3) Restricted or constricted affect is observed as reduced affect, but less so than blunted affect.
      (4) Flat affect is the absence of any affective signs of emotion.
      (5) Labile affect is rapid and abrupt changes in affect.
3. Mood is a pervasive and sustained emotion manifested by thoughts and actions (e.g., elation, anger, depression).
   a. Rapid changes in affect (lability) are usually accompanied by rapid changes in mood.
   b. These rapid changes are frequently referred to as "mood swings."
4. Other emotions.
   a. Anxiety is a feeling of apprehension or worry associated with anticipation of future danger.
      (1) Free-floating anxiety is a pervasive anxiety that does not have a specific focus.
   b. Fear is an anxiety that is focused on a real danger.

Memory

1. A process where what has been experienced or learned is registered and stored, can be retained to varying degrees, and can be recalled at will.

Table 10-1

Levels of Memory

Immediate Memory: the ability to recall material within seconds or minutes; also known as short-term memory.
Example: a person remembers and enters a code they have been provided to change a password to a website within the established time constraints.

Recent Memory: the ability to recall events of the past few days; also called working memory.
Example, a person returning home after a weekend trip remembers where they parked their car in the airport lot before their trip.

Recent Past Memory: the ability to recall events of the past few months.
Example: during a fall prevention screening, an older adult accurately reports how many times they have fallen in the past three months.

Remote Memory: the ability to recall events of the distant past, also known as long-term memory.
Example: a person enters a secure website and successfully verifies their identity by responding to a previously entered security question that asks them to name the high school they attended.

Procedural Memory: an automatic sequence of behavior such as a conditioned response.
Example: a person is able to effectively perform all tasks associated with their morning routine.

Declarative Memory: recall that is specific to consciously learned facts, such as school subjects.
Example: an OT student is able to correctly identify the twelve cranial nerves on an exam.

Semantic Memory: knowing the meaning of words and being able to classify information.
Example: upon completion of a course about electronic communications, a person understands the terms that are used for this communication mode (e.g., email, video conferencing, social media, smartphone applications [apps]).

Episodic Memory: knowledge of one's personal experiences.
Example: a person accurately responds to a question about where they celebrated their birthday last year.

Prospective Memory: the capacity to remember to carry out actions in the future. Prospective memory is clinically important, especially with regard to a person's ability to live safely and independently.
Example, a person remembers to turn off the stove before they leave the kitchen, pay bills by their due date, and that they have scheduled appointments that they need to keep.

2. Levels of memory. Refer to Table 10-1.
3. Disturbances of memory.
   a. Amnesia is an inability to recall past experiences or personal identity.
      (1) It may be caused by organic or emotional dysfunction.
      (2) Retrograde amnesia is the inability to remember events that occurred prior to the precipitating event.

Motor Behavior

1. Behavioral and motoric expressions of impulses, drives, wishes, motivations, and cravings.
2. Disturbances of motor behavior.
   a. Echopraxia is the meaningless imitation of another person's movements.
   b. Catatonia is characterized by immobility or rigidity.
   c. Stereotypy is "repetitive, abnormally frequent, non-goal-directed movements" (APA, 2022, p. 135).
   d. Psychomotor agitation is excessive motor and cognitive activity, usually nonproductive and in response to inner tension.
   e. Hyperactivity is restless, sometimes aggressive or destructive activity, often associated with brain pathology.

f. Psychomotor retardation is decreased or slowed motor and cognitive activity.
g. Aggression is forceful, angry, or destructive speech and/or behavior.
h. Acting out is the physical expression of thoughts and impulses.
i. Akathisia is the state of restlessness characterized by an urgent need for movement, usually as a side effect of medication.
j. Ataxia is the irregularity or failure of muscle coordination upon movement.

Perception

1. The process of interpreting sensory information received from the environment.
2. Disturbances of perception.
   a. Hallucinations are false sensory perceptions that are not in response to an external stimulus.
      (1) Often referred to clinically as "responding to internal stimuli."
   b. Illusions are misperceptions or misinterpretations of real sensory events.
   c. Disturbances associated with cognitive disorders.
      (1) Agnosia is the inability to understand and interpret the significance of sensory input.

(a) Visual agnosia is the inability to recognize people and objects.

(2) Astereognosis is the inability to identify objects through touch.

(3) Apraxia is the inability to carry out specific motor tasks in the absence of sensory or motor impairment.

(4) Adiadochokinesia is the inability to perform rapidly alternating movements.

(5) Refer to Chapter 13 for additional information about cognitive-perceptual deficits.

3. Disturbances associated with conversion and dissociative phenomena.

a. These disturbances are in response to repressed material and involve physical symptoms and distortions that are not under voluntary control or associated with a physical disorder.

b. Depersonalization is a subjective sensation of unreality about oneself or the environment.

c. Derealization is a subjective sense that the environment is unreal.

d. Fugue is a state of serious depersonalization, often involving travel or relocation, in which the individual takes on a new identity with amnesia for their old identity.

e. Dissociation involves the separation of a group of mental or behavioral processes from the rest of the person's psychic activity.

(1) It may involve separating an idea from its emotional tone.

Speech

1. The expression of ideas, thoughts, and feelings through language.

2. Disturbances in speech.

a. Pressured speech is rapid and increased in amount. It may be difficult to understand and/or interrupt.

b. Poverty of speech is limited in amount; i.e., one-word answers to questions.

c. Poverty of content in speech is speech that is adequate in amount but conveys little information due to vagueness, lack of specificity, and limited detail.

d. Nonspontaneous speech consists of responses that are given only when spoken to directly.

e. Stuttering consists of the repetition or prolongation of sounds or syllables.

f. Perseveration in speech is continued, persistent repetition of a word or phrase, often in response to different stimuli or different questions.

3. Disturbances in language output.

a. Expressive aphasia (i.e., Broca's) is a disturbance in which the individual knows what they want to say but cannot say it.

b. Receptive aphasia (i.e., Wernicke's) is an organic loss of the individual's ability to comprehend what has been said to them.

c. Nominal aphasia (also known as anomial or amnestic) is the inability to name objects.

d. Global aphasia involves all forms of aphasia.

Thought

1. Thinking is a goal-directed reasoned flow of ideas and associations.

a. When thinking follows a logical sequence, it is considered normal.

2. Disturbances in form of thought. Refer to Box 10-1.

3. Disturbances in content of thought. Refer to Box 10-2.

> **EXAM HINT:** The application of knowledge about the signs and symptoms of psychiatric illnesses and cognitive disorders described in this section can help you correctly answer NBCOT® Domain 3 exam items about selecting and managing interventions "to promote healing and enhance engagement in occupation-based activities" (NBCOT®, 2022, p. 7). For example, an effective intervention approach to enable the occupational performance of a distractible person would include the use of a structured activity in an environment with minimal auditory or visual stimulation.

BOX 10-1 ▷ **Disturbances in Form of Thought**

- **Circumstantiality:** speech that is delayed in reaching the point and contains excessive or irrelevant details.
- **Flight of ideas:** rapid shifts in thoughts from one idea to another.
- **Loosening of Associations:** a disorder of the logical progression of thoughts where seemingly unrelated and unconnected ideas shift from one subject to another.
- **Perseveration:** a persistent focus on a previous topic or behavior after a new topic or behavior has been introduced.
- **Tangentiality:** the abrupt change of focus to a loosely associated topic.
- **Thought blocking:** the interruption of a thought process before it is carried through to completion.

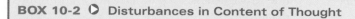

BOX 10-2 ▶ **Disturbances in Content of Thought**

- **Compulsions:** are a need to act on specific impulses to relieve associated anxiety.
- **Concrete Thinking:** characterized by actual things, events, and immediate experience; the inability to think abstractly.
- **Delusions:** are false beliefs about external reality without an appropriate stimulus that cannot be explained by the individual's cognitive level or cultural background.
- **Obsessions:** a persistent thought or feeling that cannot be eliminated by logical thought.

Diagnosis of Psychiatric Disorders

Determination of Diagnosis

1. The individual's psychiatric history and physical status is reviewed.
2. A clinical interview, which includes a mental status examination, is conducted.
3. Clinical observation of the individual. This includes:
   a. Appearance.
   b. Speech.
   c. Actions.
   d. Thoughts.

EXAM HINT: In the NBCOT® OTR® exam content outline, Domain 1 Evaluation and Assessment comprises 23% of the exam and knowledge of the "administration, purpose, indications, advantages, and limitations of standardized and nonstandardized screening and assessment tools" (NBCOT®, 2022, p. 4) is identified as essential for competent and safe practice. The application of knowledge about a mental status examination and the commonly used assessments described in the following section can help you correctly answer Domain 1 exam items about the evaluation of a person's mental status.

The Mental Status Examination

1. General description of the individual.
   a. Appearance.
   b. Behavior and psychomotor activity.
   c. Attitude toward examiner.
2. Mood and affect.
   a. Mood (pervasive, sustained emotion).
   b. Affect (observable expression of mood).
   c. Appropriateness of mood and affect.

3. Speech.
4. Perceptual disturbances.
5. Thought.
   a. Process or form of thought. Refer to Box 10-1 for form of thought disturbances that can occur when a person has a psychiatric illness or a cognitive disorder.
   b. Content of thought. Refer to Box 10-2 for content of thought disturbances that can occur when a person has a psychiatric illness or a cognitive disorder.
6. Sensorium and cognition.
   a. Alertness and level of consciousness.
   b. Orientation to person, place, time, and situation.
   c. Memory.
   d. Concentration and attention.
   e. Capacity to read and write.
   f. Abstract thinking.
   g. Fund of information and intelligence.
7. Impulse control.
8. Judgment and insight.
9. Reliability.

Commonly Used Short Assessments of Mental Status

1. OT practitioners often use the following shortened forms as screening tools to assess mental status and cognitive functioning.
   a. The Mini-Mental State Examination (also known as Folstein Mini-Mental).
   b. The Short Portable Mental.
   c. The Montreal Cognitive Assessment (MoCA).
   d. The Saint Louis University Mental Status (SLUMS).
2. Refer to Chapter 14 for specific information about the above mental status examinations.

Diagnostic Information According to Diagnostic and Statistical Manual of Mental Disorders, 5th edition Text Revision (DSM-5-TR™)

1. The DSM-5-TR™, published by the American Psychiatric Association (APA), provides a categorical guide to mental health diagnoses.
   a. DSM-5-TR™ delineates the specific symptoms of each diagnosis and enables a universal understanding of what constitutes psychiatric disorders.
      (1) DSM-5-TR™ helps mental health professionals (i.e., psychologists, social workers, nurses, OT practitioners, and others) assist the attending psychiatrist in formulating as accurate a diagnosis as possible.
      (2) DSM-5-TR™ is an essential guide that provides uniformity in how each mental health disorder may be viewed, discussed, and addressed by OT practitioners and other clinicians.
      (3) Using the standardized diagnostic language of the DSM-5-TR™ can help the treatment team formulate an effective interdisciplinary evaluation and intervention plan.

2. The following sections provide information about major mental disorders including DSM-5-TR™ diagnostic criteria, onset, prognosis, and diagnostic-specific considerations for OT.

> **EXAM HINT:** The NBCOT® OTR® exam content outline identifies knowledge of the "impact of typical development and aging on occupational performance, health, and wellness across the life span (and the) expected patterns, progressions, and prognoses associated with conditions that limit occupational performance" (NBCOT®, 2022, p. 3) as essential for competent and safe practice. Therefore, the application of knowledge about the typical onset age of psychiatric and cognitive disorders can help you determine a correct answer about working with a person with one of these diagnoses. Correct answers to exam items will be developmentally appropriate. For example, eating disorders often develop during adolescence; thus, issues of role identity and peer relationships would be important to consider when selecting the correct answer to an exam item about working with a person with an eating disorder.

Schizophrenia Spectrum and Other Psychotic Disorders[2]

Schizophrenia

1. Diagnostic criteria.
   a. Criterion A: the presence of two or more of the following symptoms, referred to clinically as positive symptoms. These include:
      (1) Delusions.
      (2) Hallucinations.
      (3) Disorganized speech.
      (4) Grossly disorganized or catatonic behavior.
      (5) Negative symptoms (see the following text).
   b. Criterion B: disturbance in one or more areas of function such as work, interpersonal relations, or self-care.
   c. Criterion C: ongoing signs of the illness for six months including at least one month of symptoms that meet criterion A.

   d. Positive symptoms are the excesses or distortions of normal function as found in criterion A.
   e. Negative symptoms represent a loss or absence of function.
      (1) Restricted emotion (i.e., affective flattening).
      (2) Difficulty in experiencing pleasure (i.e., anhedonia).
      (3) Decreased thought and speech (i.e., alogia).
      (4) Lack of energy (i.e., anergia) and initiative.

   > **CAUTION:** Anergia is often *incorrectly* interpreted as a lack of motivation.

      (5) Inability to relate to others.
2. Specifiers are provided for each diagnosis to further describe and clarify what the presenting individual is experiencing in terms of the disorder. These include:
   a. The identification of the frequency of the presenting condition (e.g., first episode or multiple episodes) and the current status of the presenting condition (e.g., acute episode, in partial remission, or in full remission).

---

[2] *Psychotic* is often used interchangeably with *thought disorder*. A *thought disorder* is any disturbance of thinking that affects language, communication, or thought content and is a predominate feature of schizophrenia.

b. Additional specifiers can include noting if the condition is continuous, unspecified, or with catatonia.

c. The current severity of the condition is also specified.

3. Onset and prognosis.

a. The onset of schizophrenia is usually between early adolescence and the early thirties.

b. Recovery is possible with effective intervention. Chapter 14 provides information about the recovery model and effective interventions for persons with psychiatric disorders.

(1) 50% of diagnosed cases have been found to sustain a good outcome of either a complete recovery or sufficient recovery to live an independent, satisfying life.

(2) 25% are able to lead satisfying lives with ongoing supports.

(3) The prognosis is poorer for the remaining 25% of individuals with schizophrenia who have repeated hospitalizations, periods of exacerbation, and episodes of major mood disorders.

Other Psychotic Disorders

1. Schizoaffective disorder.

a. Diagnostic criteria.

(1) The person has an uninterrupted period of illness during which, at some point, there is a major depressive or manic episode concurrent with positive or negative symptoms associated with schizophrenia (APA, 2022).

2. Schizophreniform disorder.

a. Diagnostic criteria.

(1) The individual meets the criteria for schizophrenia; however, the episode lasts more than one month but less than the six months required for a diagnosis of schizophrenia.

3. Delusional disorder.

a. Diagnostic criteria.

(1) The presence of one or more delusions for the duration of one month or longer and the criteria for schizophrenia has not been met.

4. Brief psychotic disorder.

a. Diagnostic criteria.

(1) Criterion A: presence of one or more sensory, behavioral, cognitive, or psychomotor symptoms, including delusions, hallucinations, disorganization of speech or behavior, and/or catatonia.

(2) Criterion B: symptoms range from one day to one month in duration, followed by complete resolution of symptoms and return to prior level of functioning (APA, 2022).

> **EXAM HINT:** The NBCOT® OTR® exam content outline identifies knowledge of the "expected patterns, progressions, and prognoses associated with conditions that limit occupational performance . . . (including the) signs and symptoms of disease, stages of disease, (and) secondary complications" (NBCOT®, 2022, p. 3) as essential for competent and safe practice. Therefore, the application of knowledge about the presenting symptoms of schizophrenia and other psychotic disorders described in this and prior sections and the following information about their functional impact can help you determine correct answers to exam items about the evaluation of persons with these disorders.

Impact on Function

1. Many individuals with psychotic disorders demonstrate deficits in cognitive-perceptual and social interaction skills that affect all areas of function.

a. The deficits in the processing of sensory information that are experienced by some individuals make interaction with the environment difficult and frightening.

b. Individuals who have difficulty with their own ego boundaries often exhibit behaviors that do not conform with established social norms (i.e., behaviors others view as inappropriate such as intrusiveness).

c. Some individuals have lost or failed to develop the social and communication skills necessary for effective and satisfying interpersonal interactions and relationships.

d. Cognitive deficits due to thought disorders and difficulty performing basic skills interfere with all areas of occupation including activities of daily living (ADL), instrumental activities of daily living (IADL), and leisure, social participation, education, and work activities.

e. It is important to assess and continue to monitor the degree of assistance and structure the person may need to support their recovery, attain their goals for occupational performance, and maintain optimum independence in their environments of choice.

2. The functional impact of psychotic disorders can be minimized and/or remediated with individualized interventions that focus on symptom management, skill development, and personal empowerment.

Symptom Management

1. Treatment consists primarily of the use of antipsychotic medications, the provision of a structured

supportive environment, and the implementation of an individualized intervention program to develop illness management skills and competencies to enable occupational performance.

2. Psychopharmacology.
   a. First generation antipsychotic medications.(or typical antipsychotic)
      (1) Thorazine, Prolixin, Haldol, Navane, Mellaril, Stelazine, and Trilafon. These are infrequently used but occasionally still prescribed.
      (2) Long-acting injections are available for Haldol (once a month) and Prolixin (once every two weeks).
         (a) Long-acting injections can support an individual's ability to effectively self-manage their medication regimen.
      (3) Side effects of first generation antipsychotic medications may include dry mouth, blurry vision, constipation, parkinsonism, dystonias (i.e., impaired tonicity), akathisia (i.e., restless, anxiety-provoking need for movement), and cardiovascular disorders.

> CAUTION: To address the side effect of photosensitivity, a person should be taught to take sunburn precautions whenever they are outdoors (e.g., use sunscreen, wear a hat and long-sleeved shirts and pants).

> CAUTION: The side effect of orthostatic/postural hypotension can increase the person's risk for falls.

         (a) Neuromuscular side effects may be treated by Cogentin, Artane, Benadryl, and Symmetrel.
      (4) Complications of first generation antipsychotic medications may include:
         (a) Neuroleptic malignant syndrome: an autonomic emergency leading to increased blood pressure, tachycardia, sweating, convulsions, and coma.
         (b) Tardive dyskinesia: a neurologic disorder resulting from long-term or high-dose use of antipsychotic medications characterized by abnormal, involuntary, irregular movements of the head, limbs, and trunk, often presenting as slow, rhythmic, automatic, stereotyped movements.
         (c) Neuroleptic-induced parkinsonism (pseudo-Parkinson's): a disorder that presents with muscle stiffness, cog-wheel rigidity, shuffling gait, stooped posture, and drooling. The pill-rolling tremor of idiopathic parkinsonism is rare, but regular, coarse tremors may be present, and tremors of the lips and mouth can also be seen with this disorder.

      (5) Second generation or atypical antipsychotics are not as problematic as the use of first generation medications such as Stelazine, Thorazine, and Mellaril.
   b. Second generation or atypical antipsychotics.
      (1) Clozaril, Risperdal, Zyprexa, Seroquel, Geodon, Saphris, Fanapt, Latuda, Symbyax, Invega, and Abilify.
         (a) Long-acting atypical injections are available for Risperdal Consta (once every two weeks) and Invega Sustenna (once every four weeks).
            • Long-acting injections can support an individual's ability to effectively self-manage their medication regimen.
      (2) Side effects vary with individual medications.

> CAUTION: Complications of Clozaril may include agranulocytosis, which is a decrease in certain white blood cells that is potentially fatal. A result of this potentiality necessitates weekly blood count monitoring initially, biweekly after six months, and monthly after a year of treatment. The resulting disruptions in lifestyle can be problematic for those on this medication, which can negatively impact adherence to medication regimen.

   c. Neuromuscular side effects may be treated by Cogentin, Artane, Benadryl, and Symmetrel.
      (1) Side effects include dry mouth, blurry vision, sedation, dizziness, hypotension, insomnia, and confusion.

> CAUTION: A complication that can occur with second generation antipsychotics is the development of metabolic syndrome. Metabolic syndrome is a cluster of conditions (i.e., high blood glucose, low levels of HDL [good cholesterol], high levels of triglycerides, large weight circumference, and high blood pressure) that are risk factors for heart disease and stroke. Refer to Chapter 9 for more information about metabolic syndrome and the conditions that comprise it.

Diagnostic-Specific Considerations for Occupational Therapy

1. When working with persons with psychotic disorders, the presence of disordered thinking requires the OT practitioner to communicate simply, clearly, and concretely.
2. External structure and consistency to organize the individual's thinking, environment, and daily activities are often required.

3. The provision of supports and tools to enable recovery is essential (e.g., a Wellness and Recovery Action Plan [WRAP]). Refer to Chapter 14 for more information about the recovery model and other psychosocial rehabilitation approaches.
4. Refer to this chapter's sections on OT mental health evaluation and OT mental health intervention for additional guidelines.
5. Chapter 14 provides further information on OT psychosocial evaluation and intervention approaches and describes specific interventions to manage psychotic behaviors (i.e., delusions and hallucinations).

> **EXAM HINT:** The medical management of psychiatric disorders includes the prescription of medications. Thus, OT practitioners should know the positive effects of medications that can enhance performance (e.g., decreasing hallucinations/delusions; alleviating anxiety/depression) and use this knowledge to support the effective use of medications. OT practitioners should also understand how medication side effects can diminish performance (e.g., blurring vision), present safety risks (e.g., orthostatic/postural hypotension, dizziness), and impact health (e.g., increasing blood pressure) to effectively address these effects.

Bipolar and Related Disorders

Overview

1. Bipolar and related disorders are diagnosed based on the incidence of manic, hypomanic, and/or major depressive episodes.
2. Mood episodes are not coded diagnoses in and of themselves.
3. Treatment addresses the symptoms of the episode experienced by the person.
   a. Interventions will vary with shifts in mood.

Diagnostic Criteria for Bipolar and Related Disorders

1. Bipolar I disorder.
   a. One or more manic episodes.
   b. May be combined with hypomanic or major depressive episodes.
2. Bipolar II disorder.
   a. One or more major depressive episodes.
   b. There must be at least one hypomanic episode.
   c. There is no history of a manic episode.
3. Other related disorders.
   a. Cyclothymic disorder is characterized by several periods of hypomanic and depressive symptoms, which do not meet the criteria for a manic, hypomanic, or major depressive episode, lasting for at least two years.

Onset and Prognosis

1. The median age of onset for bipolar disorder is 25 years, although the illness can start in early childhood or as late as the 40s and 50s.
2. While the prognosis for repeated recurrences of bipolar and related disorders is poor, recovery is possible.
   a. Early intervention is more effective than later intervention.
   b. The use of effective medications and interventions based on a recovery model have increased the number of individuals with bipolar and related disorders who are able to maintain satisfying lifestyles, resulting in a more favorable overall prognosis.
   c. Minimizing the frequency of episodes helps with recovery.

Manic Episode

1. Diagnostic criteria.
   a. At least three of the following symptoms must persist for the period of at least one week:
      (1) Mood is uncharacteristically and consistently elevated or irritable.
      (2) Increase in targeted, goal-directed behavior or restless, purposeless behaviors (psychomotor agitation).
      (3) Inflated self-esteem or thoughts of grandeur, potentially resulting in grandiose and/or impulsive behaviors.

(4) Decreased need for sleep.

(5) Pressured or quick speech, potentially related to feelings of rushed/racing thoughts.

(6) Increased engagement in subjectively pleasurable activities that may be high risk, painful, harmful, or have adverse consequences.

b. Symptoms of mood disturbance or psychotic features usually cause a marked impairment in daily function or require hospitalization to prevent harm, whether to self or to others (APA, 2022).

c. Behaviors often associated with a manic episode.

(1) Treatment resistance resulting from failure to recognize illness.

(2) Suggestive or flamboyant dress.

(3) Gambling, promiscuity, excessive spending, or giving things away.

(4) Irritable, assaultive, or suicidal behavior.

2. Impact on function.

a. The lack of inhibition experienced during a manic phase may lead to excessive spending, impulsive travel, flamboyant and promiscuous dress and/or behaviors.

b. Individuals may be euphoric in early phases, but may become labile, threatening, and assaultive.

c. Individuals may have high, often undirected, energy levels and require little sleep.

d. Poor judgment can lead to dangerous situations, poor self-care, problems in relationships, and decreased or irresponsible work performance.

e. The incidence of substance abuse is increased.

3. Symptom management.

a. Mood-stabilizing medications are typically the first line of psychopharmacologic treatment.

(1) Lithium: Eskalith, Lithobid, and time-released forms.

(a) Side effects include excessive thirst, tremors, excessive urination, weight gain, nausea, diarrhea, and cognitive impairment.

CAUTION: Blood levels must be monitored to maintain the narrow therapeutic window. High levels of lithium may cause nerve damage and death.

RED FLAG: Early symptoms of toxicity include motoric disturbances.

(2) Anticonvulsants.

(a) Depakote, Tegretol, Lamictal, Topamax, Neurontin, and Trileptal.

(b) Side effects include drowsiness, ataxia, weight gain, and sedation.

CAUTION: The side effect of dizziness can increase the person's risk for falls.

(3) Antipsychotic medications.

(a) Zyprexa, Seroquel, Risperdal, Geodon, and Abilify. Refer to the prior section on psychotic disorders.

EXAM HINT: The NBCOT® OTR® exam content outline identifies knowledge of the "internal and external factors influencing a client's engagement in occupation . . . (including) medication side effects and interactions" (NBCOT®, 2022, p. 4) and the "precautions or contraindications associated with a client condition or stage of recovery" (NBCOT®, 2022, p. 7) as essential for competent practice. The application of knowledge about the medications prescribed for each of the diagnoses included in this chapter can help determine the correct answer to exam items about medication precautions and activity contraindications during evaluation and intervention (e.g., addressing the side effect of photosensitivity before initiating a group that uses gardening as a therapeutic modality).

4. Diagnostic-specific considerations for OT.

a. Limit-setting to set and improve boundaries, reduce the individual's fears of losing control, increase participation in the intervention process, and promote safety.

b. Engagement in activities that provide structure and the opportunity for release of excess energy in a positive and therapeutic manner.

c. Periods between episodes should be used to educate the individual, the family, and significant others on symptom management.

d. Refer to this chapter's sections on OT mental health evaluation and OT mental health intervention for additional guidelines.

e. Chapter 14 provides additional information on OT psychosocial evaluation and intervention approaches and describes specific intervention approaches for managing manic or monopolizing behaviors.

Major Depressive Episode

1. Diagnostic criteria.

a. Five or more diagnostic symptoms must be present for at least two weeks:

(1) One of the five symptoms must include a depressed mood or a notable loss of interest/pleasure most of the day, nearly every day.

(2) Significant fluctuations in weight, potentially along with appetite changes.

(3) Difficulty falling or staying asleep (insomnia), or excessive sleeping throughout the day (hypersomnia).

(4) Changes in thinking or behavior, such as a slowing down of thinking and motor speed (psychomotor retardation) or restless, purpose-less movement patterns (psychomotor agitation).

(5) Fatigue or a loss of energy that impacts completion of daily activities.

(6) Changes in mood or self-perception, including feelings of worthlessness, inadequacy, or extreme guilt about thoughts/feelings.

(7) Decreased ability to concentrate on tasks, which may be an isolated symptom or related to difficulty sleeping, fatigue, and/or psychomotor changes.

(8) Recurrent suicidal thoughts, with or without a plan or attempt at suicide (APA, 2022).

b. Behaviors often associated with depressive episodes.

(1) Irritability, anxiety, phobias, and obsessive thinking.

(2) Difficulties in social interactions, relationships, and sexual functioning.

(3) Self-destructive behavior including suicide and substance abuse.

(4) May be manifested as somatic complaints.

(5) There may be an increased use of medical services.

c. Symptoms are significant enough to cause marked disruption in important areas of daily function, including social or occupational contexts (APA, 2022).

2. Impact on function.

a. Individuals are often tearful, brooding, and isolative.

b. Anxiety leads to excessive concerns about physical health, complaints of pain, and substance abuse.

c. Hopelessness, lack of energy, and slow thought processing lead to limited interest in activity and difficulty performing tasks in all areas of occupation, including personal and instrumental ADL, leisure, social participation, education, and work activities.

3. Symptom management.

a. Antidepressant medications.

(1) Selective serotonin reuptake inhibitors (SSRIs): Prozac, Zoloft, Paxil, Celexa, and Lexapro.

(a) Side effects include nausea, headache, sexual dysfunction, and insomnia.

> **CAUTION:** The side effects of disturbed balance, and orthostatic/postural hypotension can increase the person's risk for falls and fractures. Increased heart rate, dysrhythmias, and seizures can also result from antidepressant use.

(2) Tricyclics: Elavil, Tofranil, and Norpramin.

(a) These are now rarely used secondary to the efficacy of the SSRIs and selective norepinephrine or serotonin and norepinephrine inhibitors (SNRIs).

(b) Side effects include dry mouth, blurred vision, sedation, and other anticholinergic effects.

> **CAUTION:** The side effect of orthostatic/postural hypotension can increase the person's risk for falls.

(3) SNRIs: Effexor, Cymbalta.

(a) Side effects vary but may include hypertension, anxiety, dizziness, sedation, nervousness, weight gain, nausea, and sweating.

> **CAUTION:** The side effect of dizziness can increase the person's risk for falls.

(4) Atypical antidepressants: Wellbutrin and Remeron.

(a) Similar in effect to SSRIs and SNRIs.

(b) Wellbutrin has fewer sexual side effects.

(5) Monoamine oxidase inhibitors (MAOIs): Nardil and Parnate.

(a) Side effects include weight gain, hypotension, insomnia, and liver damage.

> **CAUTION:** Dietary restrictions for individuals taking MAOIs must be followed:
> - Ingesting foods or beverages that contain the amino acid tyramine can suddenly increase blood pressure and may lead to stroke or other serious cardiac reactions.
> - Foods and beverages with tyramine must be completely avoided. These include aged cheeses (e.g., cheddar), pickled foods (e.g., sauerkraut, herring), cured or smoked meats (e.g., salami, sausage, pepperoni, hot dogs), liver, yogurt, sour cream, fruits that must ripen to eat (e.g., avocados, bananas), fava beans, peapods, chocolate, beer and red wine (including nonalcoholic and alcohol-reduced), meat tenderizers, soy products (soy sauce, tofu), yeast extracts, and any product that has been improperly stored, over-ripened, not fresh, and/or past an expiration date.
> - Many over-the-counter drugs also contain ingredients that can cause a serious interaction with MAOIs. These include cold, sinus, and hay fever medications, nasal decongestants, asthma inhalants, "pep" pills, and appetite suppressants.

RED FLAG: Severe headaches or palpitations can be the first sign of a hypertensive crisis. The medication should be stopped immediately, and a physician consulted.

    (b) MAOIs that are administered via a skin (transdermal) patch (e.g., Selegiline [Emsam]) may have fewer side effects than MAOIs taken orally.
- Persons who take the lowest-dose patch may be advised by their physician that they do not need to follow the MAOI dietary restrictions.

CAUTION: A doctor's opinion should be sought before anyone taking a MAOI decides to not follow the MAOI food and over-the-counter medication restrictions.

EXAM HINT: The NBCOT® OTR® exam content outline identifies knowledge of the "internal and external factors influencing a client's engagement in occupation . . . (including) medication side effects and interactions" (NBCOT®, 2022, p. 4) and "precautions or contraindications associated with a client condition" (NBCOT®, 2022, p. 7) as essential for competent and safe practice. Knowing that a lack of adherence to MAOI dietary restrictions may seriously impact a person's health can assist with selecting the correct answer to a NBCOT® exam item. For example, the correct answer for an exam item that includes a participant in a meal preparation group who is taking a MAOI would include adherence to MAOI dietary restrictions.

  b. The most effective treatment involves antidepressant medication combined with psychotherapy.
  c. Cognitive approaches (i.e., cognitive behavioral therapy [CBT]) are helpful for those who demonstrate self-awareness, intact cognitive skills, and the ability to actively participate in the intervention process. Refer to Chapter 14 for more information about CBT.
  d. Electroconvulsive therapy (ECT) is very effective and the treatment of choice for those who have been unresponsive to trials on medications and other interventions.
    (1) How ECT works is not fully understood.
      (a) A limiting factor is that ECT often produces memory loss and confusion for the period surrounding treatment. Both are reversible, and evolution of ECT over the past decades has produced innovations that diminish cognitive effects while maintaining benefits.

4. Diagnostic-specific considerations for OT.
  a. The provision of a safe environment and the management of behaviors that threaten the safety and well-being of the individual are paramount.
    (1) Individuals must be closely monitored for self-destructive and/or suicidal behavior.

CAUTION: The most dangerous time for self-destructive and/or suicidal behaviors may be when the depression begins to lift and the person becomes mobilized. This includes the days after inpatient admission and just prior to discharge.

EXAM HINT: In the NBCOT® OTR® exam content outline, Domain 2 Analysis, Interpretation, and Planning comprises 23% of the exam. In this Domain, knowledge of "precautions or contraindications associated with a client condition or stage of recovery . . . (including) suicidal ideation" (NBCOT®, 2022, p. 7) is identified as essential for competent and safe practice. Thus, an awareness of conditions that can contribute to suicide risk can help you determine correct answers to exam items about planning intervention for a person with depression.

  b. Refer to this chapter's sections on OT mental health evaluation and OT mental health intervention for additional guidelines.
  c. Chapter 14 provides further information on OT psychosocial evaluation and intervention approaches and describes specific interventions to manage suicidal behaviors and other depressive symptoms.

Hypomanic Episode

1. Symptoms are the same as for a manic episode; however, they are not severe enough (i.e., they last for four days rather than one week) to cause marked impairment in social or occupational function or to require hospitalization.

EXAM HINT: The NBCOT® OTR® exam content outline identifies knowledge of the "expected patterns, progressions, and prognoses associated with conditions that limit occupational performance . . . (including the) signs and symptoms of disease, stages of disease, (and) secondary complications" (NBCOT®, 2022, p. 3) as essential for competent and safe practice. Thus, the application of knowledge about the presenting symptoms of bipolar and related disorders described above and in prior sections and the following information about depressive disorders can help you determine the correct answer to exam items about working with persons with these conditions.

Depressive Disorders

Overview

1. Depressive disorders share the common presentations of sad, sometimes irritable mood that along with changes in cognitive and physical health affect one's ability to function.
2. They are differentiated by length of time, number of episodes, and specific type and number of symptoms.

Diagnostic Criteria for Depressive Disorders

1. Major depressive disorder.
   a. The presence of one or more major depressive episodes.
2. Persistent depressive disorder (dysthymia).
   a. Characterized by at least two years of a depressed mood, most days, with depressive symptoms.
   b. Criteria for a major depressive disorder may be continuously present for two years.
3. Disruptive mood dysregulation disorder.
   a. Temper outbursts that are characterized as:
      (1) Severe and recurrent verbal or behavioral episodes.
      (2) Inconsistent with the expectations for the person's developmental level.
      (3) The outbursts are considered an over-reaction (either in intensity or duration of response) based on the stimuli (APA, 2022).
   b. Diagnosis is made between the ages of 6 and 18 based on observations from others such as parents, teachers, and/or peers.

4. Premenstrual dysphoric disorder.
   a. Symptoms include marked affective lability, irritability or anger, increased interpersonal conflicts, depressive symptoms, depressed mood, and/or marked anxiety.

Onset and Prognosis

1. While major depressive disorder can develop at any age, the median age at onset is 32.
2. The prognosis for major depressive disorder is better for persons with mild depressive episodes, those without psychotic symptoms, and those who follow treatment recommendations, have a strong support system, and good pre-morbid functioning.

Impact on Function

1. Major depressive disorder and persistent depressive disorder (dysthymia).
   a. Refer to prior section on major depressive episode.

Symptom Management

1. Refer to prior section on major depressive episode.

Diagnostic-Specific Considerations for Occupational Therapy

1. Refer to prior section on major depressive episode.

Substance-Related and Addictive Disorders

Overview

1. Substance-related disorders are diagnosed based on the taking of a drug of abuse (including alcohol and prescription medications), the side effects of medication(s), and/or exposure to toxins (e.g., inhalants, lead).
2. Substance-related disorders are categorized by the specific substance (i.e., alcohol or opioid).
   a. Each substance-related disorder is then classified according to the symptoms of the disorder. These include:

(1) Use: consumption that causes impairment that adversely affects daily functioning in occupational roles, fulfilling personal responsibilities, and interacting socially; it may cause personal harm (e.g., alcohol use disorder).
(2) Intoxication: use that causes problems both behaviorally and mentally and changes in the pupils followed by feeling drowsy, slurring words, and/or experiencing attention and memory problems (e.g., opioid intoxication disorder).

(3) Withdrawal: stopping significant consumption which causes physical symptoms (e.g., tremors, difficulty sleeping) as well as mental symptoms (e.g., hallucinations, anxiety).

3. Non-substance-related addictive disorders include gambling disorders that produce addictive behaviors that appear comparable to the behaviors of persons with substance use disorders.

Substance Use Disorders

1. Diagnostic criteria.
   a. Two of the following symptoms must be present within a 12-month period, due to problematic substance use resulting in significant impairment in occupational performance.
      (1) Substances are used in larger quantities than intended and/or effects last for longer than anticipated.
         (a) Over time, this may result in the development of tolerance to substances, in which larger quantities are intentionally used to obtain similar or desired effects.
      (2) A significant amount of time is dedicated to substance acquisition or use.
      (3) The desire to use substances is strong throughout the day and attempts to reduce substance use are unsuccessful despite efforts.
         (a) Behaviors continue despite the potential for physical harm due to recurrent substance use.
         (b) Attempts to cease and/or reduce substance use may result in withdrawal after prolonged, frequent substance use.

> CAUTION: Withdrawal signs and symptoms include sensory, motor, and psychological changes (including autonomic hyperactivity, insomnia, nausea, vomiting, hallucinations, psychomotor agitation, anxiety, or generalized tonic-clonic seizures).

      (4) Ongoing substance use causes marked disruption in social, occupational, vocational, educational, and/or recreational aspects of daily life. This may cause a reduction in engagement in valued activities or an inability to meet expectations associated with roles.
         (a) Substance use continues despite the individual's awareness of the impact on function (APA, 2022).

Onset and Prognosis

1. The onset of substance abuse is not specific to any age. For example, a person may begin abusing alcohol as a preadolescent, another may begin abusing prescribed pain medications (opioids) as an older adult.

2. The misuse and overuse of prescribed medications and opioids has increased dramatically in the United States, resulting in a national drug crisis.
   a. In the past 15 years there has been a dramatic increase in opioid overdoses in America.
      (1) The majority of overdose deaths are related to opioid use.

3. Prognosis varies depending on several factors, including the substance(s) used, their quantity, and length of time used; the person's level of engagement and investment in treatment for substance use; and the degree and type of support that is available to them.
   a. Various adverse effects of substance use may include brain and liver damage, heart disease, and fetal damage during pregnancy.

Impact on Function

1. The impact substance use has on the individual depends on the type of substance used and on whether the individual is abusing the substance or is dependent upon it.

2. Results of disorders of use.
   a. Disinterest and inability to care for self and others.
   b. Difficulty with and loss of personal relationships.
   c. Inability to be productive and/or maintain employment.
   d. Absence of leisure and/or social pursuits that do not involve substance use.
   e. Involvement with the legal system.

3. Prolonged use may lead to severe physical, cognitive, and psychiatric problems and can result in death.

Medical Management

1. Medications to help the individual refrain from substance use can be provided.

2. The timely administration of Naloxone to a person who has overdosed on an opioid (e.g., Fentanyl) can save their life.
   a. As per the Surgeon General's advisory, all health care providers should know how to administer Naloxone.

3. Methadone clinics and the use of methadone for detoxification and maintenance for opioid dependence is the most accepted approach for heroin addiction.

4. Medical management is typically supplemented with psychotherapy and support groups (e.g., Alcoholics Anonymous, Narcotics Anonymous).

Diagnostic-Specific Considerations for Occupational Therapy

1. Due to the presence of learned "survival skills," the individual's abilities and potential may be overestimated.

a. The occupational therapist apprises the team and the individual of the person's actual skills and deficits as evident during evaluation and intervention.

b. The occupational therapist assists the team and the person in identifying realistic expectations and discharge plans.

2. The individual's identification of the reasons for substance use is important to address during the evaluation process.

3. The development of the skills necessary to cope with life stressors without substance use is critical for a substance-free lifestyle. Skills needed include:

a. Communication and social skills to support substance-free social participation and advocate for access to needed services.

b. Skills to engage productively in work, education, and/or other productive activities (e.g., volunteering, home management).

c. Skills to use leisure time without using substances.

4. Societal stigma and lifelong patterns of denial, resistance, and other defensive behaviors can make treatment challenging and difficult.

5. Referrals to support groups, including Alcoholics Anonymous, Narcotics Anonymous, and specialized addiction providers can sustain recovery.

6. Refer to this chapter's sections on OT mental health evaluation and OT mental health intervention for additional guidelines.

7. Chapter 14 provides further information on OT psychosocial evaluation and intervention approaches.

Gambling Disorder

1. Diagnostic criteria.

a. Four or more of the following gambling behaviors must be true for at least 12 months:

(1) Thoughts of gambling occupy the mind most of the day.

(2) The individual has made multiple unsuccessful attempts to decrease gambling behaviors and is usually restless, irritable, unhappy, or preoccupied with gambling due to efforts to control behaviors.

(3) Gambling behaviors increase in the presence of stress.

(4) The individual is in serious financial trouble due to betting larger amounts of money to experience desired effects.

(a) The individual may ask for or rely on money from close friends or family members to relieve financial stress caused by gambling behavior.

(5) Excessive gambling behavior continues on subsequent days after losing money to attempt to break even or 'chase' losses.

(6) The individual lies to downplay the frequency or effects of gambling, which causes marked stress in vocational, educational, and personal/social areas of functioning.

(7) Gambling behavior must be problematic and recurrent, causing clinically significant impairment that is not better explained by mania (APA, 2022).

Anxiety Disorders

Overview

1. Anxiety disorders include a range of disorders that include episodic periods of intense anxiety to chronic periods of lower levels of anxiety.

2. Anxiety is an internal sense of apprehension and psychological distress. It may or may not have a specific focus.

Panic Attacks and Agoraphobia

1. Panic attacks are symptoms of anxiety.

a. They are not coded diagnoses.

2. Panic attacks are discrete periods of intense fear or discomfort, in which four or more symptoms develop abruptly and reach a peak within minutes.

a. Physical symptoms: heart palpitations, sweating, trembling/shaking, sensations of choking or feeling short of breath, chest pain, nausea/vomiting, feeling dizzy or faint, and chills or hot flashes.

b. Psychological symptoms: de-realization, feelings of loss of control, and fear of dying.

c. Neurologic symptoms: paresthesia (APA, 2022).

3. Agoraphobia associated with panic attacks.

a. Anxiety about being in places or situations from which escape may be difficult or embarrassing, or in which help may not be available if needed.

b. Situations are avoided or endured with anxiety about having a panic attack.

Specific Anxiety Disorders

1. Generalized anxiety disorder.
   a. Consists of six months of persistent and excessive unfocused anxiety and worry.
2. Panic disorder.
   a. Recurrent panic attacks followed at least once by concern for recurrence.
3. Selective mutism.
   a. Consistent inability to speak in social situations when it is expected (i.e., in school), despite being able to speak in other circumstances.
   b. This behavior must persist for at least one month and not be better explained by a communication disorder (APA, 2022).
4. Separation anxiety disorder.
   a. Individuals, typically young children, become excessively attached to another individual and experience severe anxiety when separated.
5. Social phobia.
   a. A clinically significant anxiety from certain types of social or performance situations leading to avoidance.
6. Specific phobia.
   a. A clinically significant anxiety from a specific object or situation leading to avoidant behavior.

Onset and Prognosis

1. Anxiety disorders often begin in childhood but may develop at any time.
2. Prognosis varies with the specific disorder.

Impact on Function

1. The degree of impact varies with the severity and type of anxiety disorder.
2. Reactions may vary from temporary discomfort to severely avoidant and paralyzing behavior.

Symptom Management

1. Psychotherapy to explore psychodynamic issues.
2. Cognitive-behavioral therapy to develop skills to manage symptoms.
3. Several types of medications may be helpful depending on the specific disorder.
   a. Anxiolytic medications include Xanax, Valium, Ativan, Klonopin, Serax, and BuSpar.
      (1) Side effects include drowsiness, ataxia, headache, nausea, depression, and dependence.
   b. Antidepressant medications are helpful in some cases.
      (1) Refer to mood disorder section for side-effect information.
   c. In some cases, hypnotic medications to induce sleep may be used briefly.
      (1) Hypnotic medications include Restoril, Dalmane, Ambien, and Benadryl.
      (2) Side effects are similar to those of the anxiolytics.

Diagnostic-Specific Considerations for Occupational Therapy

1. Skills training and using cognitive behavioral approaches may reduce anxiety and avoidant behavior.
2. Developing relaxation and stress management skills may decrease the incidence and severity of symptoms.
3. Providing graded activities designed to promote self-efficacy may increase self-confidence, motivation, and participation in intervention.
4. Using systematic desensitization, which involves incremental exposure in attempts to diminish anxiety related to specific fears through the use of imagery and relaxation, and then contact with the image or actual object.
   a. Used most often with phobic disorders and requires special training.
5. Refer to this chapter's sections on OT mental health evaluation and OT mental health intervention for additional guidelines.
6. Chapter 14 provides further information on OT psychosocial evaluation and intervention approaches.

> **EXAM HINT:** The NBCOT® OTR® exam content outline identifies knowledge of the "expected patterns, progressions, and prognoses associated with conditions that limit occupational performance . . . (including the) signs and symptoms of disease, stages of disease, (and) secondary complications" (NBCOT®, 2022, p. 3) as essential for competent and safe practice. Thus, the application of knowledge about the presenting symptoms of anxiety, substance use, and gambling disorders described above and in prior sections and the following information about personality disorders can help you determine the correct answer to exam items about working with persons with these conditions.

Personality Disorders

Diagnostic Criteria

1. Persistent patterns in cognition, affect, behavior, or interpersonal functioning are experienced or expressed despite being notably different from the expectations and norms of one's culture (APA, 2022).
   a. The pattern is stable, inflexible, and evident in wide-ranging social and personal situations.
   b. This long-lasting pattern typically begins in adolescence or early adulthood.

Specific Personality Disorders

1. Antisocial personality disorder.
   a. This disorder is characterized by continual antisocial or criminal acts, but it is not synonymous with criminality.
   b. It is an inability to conform to social norms that involves many aspects of the individual's adolescent and adult development.
   c. Persons with antisocial personality disorder have no regard for the safety or feelings of others, and they lack remorse.
   d. Individuals diagnosed with a conduct disorder that does not respond to treatment or is untreated can be a precursor to developing this disorder.
2. Avoidant personality disorder.
   a. Persons with this disorder show an extreme sensitivity to rejection, which may lead to a socially withdrawn life.
   b. These individuals are not, however, asocial. They show a great desire for companionship but consider themselves inept or unworthy.
   c. Individuals with avoidant personality disorder need unusually strong and repeated guarantees of uncritical acceptance.
   d. These persons are commonly referred to as having an inferiority complex.
3. Borderline personality disorder.
   a. Individuals with borderline personality disorder experience extraordinarily unstable affect, mood, behavior, relationships, and self-image.
   b. Fear of real or imagined abandonment leads to frantic efforts to avoid it.
   c. A pattern of unstable and intense interpersonal relationships with alternating extremes of idealization and devaluation (splitting).
   d. Recurrent self-destructive or self-mutilating behavior may be threatened or carried out. Refer to Chapter 14's section on self-injurious behavior.

   e. Chronic feelings of emptiness.
   f. A history of trauma (i.e., physical, sexual, emotional abuse) is more common in those with borderline personality disorder than in the general population (APA, 2022).
4. Dependent personality disorder.
   a. Persons with this disorder subordinate their own needs to those of others and need others to assume responsibility for major areas in their lives.
   b. Individuals with dependent personality disorder lack self-confidence.
   c. They may experience discomfort when alone for more than a brief period.
5. Histrionic personality disorder.
   a. This disorder is characterized by colorful, dramatic, extroverted behavior in excitable, emotional persons.
   b. An inability to maintain deep, long-lasting attachments with accompanying flamboyant presentation is often characteristic.
6. Narcissistic personality disorder.
   a. Persons with this disorder are characterized by a heightened sense of self-importance and a grandiose feeling that they are special in some way.
7. Obsessive-compulsive personality disorder.
   a. Characterized by emotional constriction, orderliness, perseverance, stubbornness, and indecisiveness.
   b. The essential feature is a pervasive pattern of perfectionism and inflexibility.
   c. It should not be confused with obsessive-compulsive disorder.
8. Paranoid personality disorder.
   a. Persons with this disorder are characterized by long-standing suspiciousness and mistrust of people in general.
   b. They can often appear hostile, irritable, and angry.
9. Schizoid personality disorder.
   a. This is frequently diagnosed in individuals who display a lifelong pattern of social withdrawal.
   b. Their discomfort with human interaction, their introversion, and their bland, constricted affect are noteworthy.
   c. Persons with schizoid personality disorder are often seen by others as eccentric, isolated, or lonely.
10. Schizotypal personality disorder.
    a. Persons with this disorder appear odd or strange in their thinking and behavior to those who come in contact with them.
    b. Magical thinking, peculiar ideas, ideas of reference, illusions, and derealization are part of this individual's everyday world.

Onset and Prognosis

1. Symptoms of personality disorders usually begin in childhood or early adolescence.
2. The prognosis for individuals with personality disorders varies, with the condition often remaining unchanged.
   a. There is an increased risk of the development of depressive disorders among persons with personality disorders.
   b. There is some evidence that the symptoms of avoidant, borderline, and antisocial personality disorders may decrease with age.

Impact on Function

1. The type and degree of impact on areas of occupation, personal relationships, and daily life depend on the severity and type of personality disorder.

Symptom Management

1. Psychotherapy and certain medications may reduce symptomatology for some persons.

2. Dialectical behavior therapy (DBT) has demonstrated success in the treatment of borderline personality disorder. Refer to Chapter 14 for more information on DBT.
3. Monitoring, supervision, and hospitalization may be required during periods of increased symptoms, and/or aggressive or self-destructive behavior.

Diagnostic-Specific Considerations for Occupational Therapy

1. Individualized assistance to help the person identify the previous diagnostic-specific issues may increase their commitment to treatment and the pursuit of behavioral change.
2. Cognitive behavioral approaches (including DBT) can increase functional and coping skills and may decrease symptomatic behavior.
3. Refer to this chapter's sections on OT mental health evaluation and OT mental health intervention for additional guidelines.
4. Chapter 14 provides further information on OT psychosocial evaluation and intervention approaches and describes CBT and DBT principles and methods.

▶ Obsessive-Compulsive and Related Disorders

Specific Disorders

1. Obsessive-compulsive disorder.
   a. Obsessions are persistent thoughts or feelings that are unwanted, intrusive, and inappropriate based on the stimulus or situations.
   b. Compulsions are irresistible urges that take the form of repetitive behaviors carried out in an attempt to reduce anxiety or anticipated negative consequences related to obsessions.
      (1) Behaviors are typically executed according to strict or specific rules that manifest as ritualistic (i.e., washing hands three times prior to eating, locking and unlocking a door four times before exiting the house).
   c. Obsessive thoughts and compulsive behaviors are time-consuming and intrusive, although the individuals realize they are not rational.
2. Body dysmorphic disorder.
   a. The person is preoccupied with perceived physical flaws (whether imagined or slight) that are imperceptible, acceptable, or insignificant to others.

   b. Concerns regarding appearance cause repetitive thoughts or behaviors as an attempt to conceal or improve perceived flaws.
   c. Recurring thoughts of imperfections cause clinically significant interruptions in social and occupational areas of functioning in daily life.
3. Hoarding disorder.
   a. There is a perceived need to save items and significant difficulty discarding possessions, regardless of value, need, or practicality.
   b. The thought of parting with items may result in marked distress and attempts to justify why the items are needed or will be needed in the future.
   c. Accumulation of items results in cramped, cluttered living conditions that may compromise cleanliness and safety within the home.
4. Trichotillomania.
   a. Compulsive, irresistible desire to pull out one's hair, typically of the scalp, eyelashes, or eyebrows although sites may vary over the body, resulting in hair loss.
   b. Hair-pulling often results in bald or patchy spots, potentially impacting social and occupational functioning.

5. Excoriation disorder.
   a. Repeated picking at one's own skin, resulting in skin lesions and causing significant disruption in daily occupations (APA, 2022).

Onset and Prognosis

1. Obsessive-compulsive and related disorders can develop in childhood but may develop at any time.
2. Prognoses vary with the specific disorder.

Impact on Function

1. The degree of impact varies with the severity and type of disorder.
2. Reactions may vary from temporary discomfort to severely avoidant and paralyzing behavior.

Symptom Management

1. Psychotherapy to explore psychodynamic issues.
2. Cognitive-behavioral therapy to develop skills to manage symptoms.
3. Several types of medications may be helpful depending on the specific disorder.
   a. Anxiolytic medications include Xanax, Valium, Librium, Ativan, Klonopin, and BuSpar.
      (1) Side effects include drowsiness, ataxia, headache, nausea, depression, and dependence.
   b. Antidepressant medications are helpful in some cases such as Anafranil, Paxil, Prozac, and Zoloft.
   c. Antiobsessional medications such as Luvox may be used.
      (1) Side effects are similar to that of the SSRIs.
   d. In some cases, hypnotic medications to induce sleep may be used briefly.
      (1) Hypnotic medications include Restoril, Dalmane, Ambien, and Benadryl.
      (2) Side effects are similar to those of the anxiolytics.

Diagnostic-Specific Considerations for Occupational Therapy

1. Skills training and using cognitive behavioral approaches may reduce obsessive thoughts and compulsive behaviors.
2. Developing relaxation and stress management skills may decrease the incidence and severity of symptoms.
3. Providing graded activities designed to promote self-efficacy may increase self-confidence, motivation, and participation in intervention.
4. Refer to this chapter's sections on OT mental health evaluation and OT mental health intervention for additional guidelines.
5. Chapter 14 provides further information on OT psychosocial evaluation and intervention approaches and describes CBT principles and methods.

Trauma- and Stressor-Related Disorders

EXAM HINT: The NBCOT® OTR® exam content outline identifies knowledge of the "influence of lived experiences and identity on occupational performance . . . (including a) history of trauma and adverse childhood events" (NBCOT®, 2022, p. 4) as essential for competent and safe practice. The application of knowledge about the following trauma- and stressor-related disorders can help you determine exam items about working with persons with these diagnoses.

Reactive Attachment Disorder (RAD) of Infancy or Early Childhood

1. Diagnostic criteria.
   a. Childhood is characterized by social neglect or instability/inconsistency of primary caregivers, leading to insufficient or frequently changing care that alters the nature of interactions with caregivers.
   b. Reactive attachment disorder is characterized by:
      (1) Persistent failure to initiate or respond in a developmentally appropriate fashion to most social interactions.
      (2) Interactions are excessively inhibited, hypervigilant, or highly ambivalent and contradictory in nature.
2. Etiology.
   a. Exact cause is unknown.
   b. Early poor experiences with initial caregivers and/or pathogenic care may contribute to the disorder.
      (1) Indicators of pathogenic care:
         (a) Persistent disregard of the child's basic emotional needs.
         (b) Persistent disregard of the child's basic physical needs.
         (c) Repeated changes of primary caregiver or a succession of caregivers prevents the establishment of stable, appropriate attachments.

3. Onset and prognosis.
   a. Onset begins before five years of age.
   b. There is a high risk of prevalence for toddlers and children in foster care and orphanages and for children with frequently changing caregivers.
   c. Prognosis: unknown.
4. Impact on function.
   a. Children with RAD exhibit challenging behaviors. These include the following.
      (1) A high need to be in control.
      (2) Frequent lying.
      (3) Affectionate and overly related with strangers.
      (4) Frequent episodes of hoarding or gorging on food without physical need.
      (5) Denial of responsibility.
      (6) Projecting blame for their actions on others.
   b. Due to these behaviors, children with RAD can be frustrating to work with and difficult to parent.
5. Symptom management.
   a. No one standard effective treatment for RAD is apparent in the literature.
6. Diagnostic-specific considerations for OT.
   a. Close and ongoing collaboration with the child's family and/or caregivers facilitates successful outcomes.
   b. Actively involve parents or caregivers in treatment.
   c. Assist children to form a more secure sense of self.
   d. Limit the child's exposure to multiple caregivers.
   e. Provide high levels of structure and consistency.
   f. Goals need to be specific, realistic, and attainable.
   g. Refer to this chapter's sections on OT mental health evaluation and OT mental health intervention for additional guidelines.
   h. Chapter 14 provides further information on OT psychosocial evaluation and intervention approaches and describes specific interventions to manage behaviors.

Disinhibited Social Engagement Disorder

1. Diagnostic criteria.
   a. A child initiates active interaction with unfamiliar adults, while displaying at least two of the following behaviors:
      (1) Little reservation when approaching unfamiliar adults.
      (2) Overly familiar use of words or actions despite novelty and unfamiliarity of relationship.
      (3) The child is willing to leave with an unfamiliar adult without much or any hesitation, consideration, or checking back with the primary caregiver.
   b. The child's upbringing is characterized by patterns of social neglect, deprivation, or constant changing of primary caregivers, resulting in insufficient care for forming stable relationships with adults and caregivers.
   c. The child has a minimum of a nine-month-old developmental age (APA, 2022).

Post-traumatic Stress Disorder

1. Diagnostic criteria.
   a. Exposure to threats or actual events which can result in sexual violence, bodily injury, or death, by:
      (1) Personally and directly experiencing the trauma.
      (2) First-hand witnessing of the traumatic event happening to another individual.
      (3) Learning about traumatic events experienced by close friends or family, after the fact.
      (4) Repeated or extreme exposure to visuals or explanations of aversive details associated with the traumatic events and negative consequences.
   b. Presence of intrusion symptoms (for more than one month):
      (1) Recurrent, unwanted, intrusive memories and/or dreams related to or depicting the traumatic event.
      (2) Physical or mental exposure to the traumatic event or related situations causes the individual to believe and/or act as if the traumatic event is reoccurring.
      (3) Experience of marked, prolonged physiological reactions and/or psychological distress associated with exposure to internal or external cues related to the traumatic event.
   c. Notable changes in patterns or behaviors as an attempt to avoid external stimuli or reminders associated with the traumatic event.
   d. Reminders of the traumatic event may have adverse reactions on cognition, focus, mood, sleep patterns, arousal, and reactivity or exaggerate vigilance, startle responses, and irritability (APA, 2022).

Acute Distress Disorder

1. Similar to post-traumatic stress disorder; however, it immediately follows the event. The symptoms do not persist beyond one month.

Adjustment Disorders

1. Diagnostic criteria.
   a. A clearly identifiable stressor causes onset of emotional and/or behavioral symptoms within three months of experiencing the stressor.
      (1) Symptoms resolve and disappear within six months of the stressor or its consequences being removed.
   b. Symptoms cause marked distress in important areas of function, including social and occupational, due to reactions that are disproportionate to the frequency or severity of the stressor.
   c. The symptoms are not better explained by another disorder, attributable to an exacerbation of symptoms from a pre-existing diagnosis, or warranted as part of a normal bereavement response.

> **EXAM HINT:** The NBCOT® OTR® exam content outline identifies knowledge of the "expected patterns, progressions, and prognoses associated with conditions that limit occupational performance . . . (including the) signs and symptoms of disease, stages of disease, (and) secondary complications" (NBCOT®, 2022, p. 3) as essential for competent and safe practice. Thus, the application of knowledge about the presenting symptoms of obsessive-compulsive and trauma- and stressor-related disorders described in this and prior sections and the following information about neurocognitive disorders can help you determine the correct answer to exam items about working with persons with these conditions.

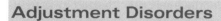

Neurocognitive Disorders³

Diagnostic Criteria

1. Conditions for which the primary symptoms are cognitive deficits. This may be from substance abuse, medical conditions, or other known or unknown causes.
2. Delirium.
   a. A disturbance of consciousness (awareness of environment) with a decreased ability to attend.
   b. There is a change from previous cognition and/or perception.
   c. It covers a short period of time (hours to days) and tends to fluctuate.
   d. There are many causes.
      (1) Brain dysfunction.
      (2) Medication.
      (3) Endocrine disorders.
      (4) Cardiac disorders.
      (5) Infections and inflammations.
      (6) Liver function disorders.
3. Major neurocognitive disorder.
   a. Clinical assessment reveals significant impairment in cognitive functioning that is a marked decline from a prior level of performance, as reported by the individual, clinician, or other knowledgeable source (APA, 2022).

³ Neurocognitive disorders were previously termed *dementia* in prior editions of the *DSM*™, and the term *dementia* is still typically used in clinical practice.

4. Mild neurocognitive disorder.
   a. Similar to major neurocognitive disorder, with the difference that the cognitive deficits do not interfere with independence in everyday activities.

Onset and Prognosis

1. Delirium occurs in approximately one in five hospitalized individuals, with greater prevalence reported for older patients.
   a. It may resolve quickly or take several days.
   b. It is more severe with advanced age.
   c. It may indicate a poor prognosis over time.
2. The prevalence and onset of neurocognitive disorder increases with age.
   a. There may be periods of plateauing with a gradual decline over time.

Impact on Function

1. The degree of impact varies according to the nature and severity of the symptoms.
2. The individual may require intervention varying from education in compensatory strategies to the need for total care.
3. Table 10-2 describes the progressive impact of neurocognitive disorders on functional abilities and occupational performance according to DSM-5 and the Global Deterioration Scale for Assessment of Primary

Table 10-2

Neurocognitive Disorders: Presenting Signs and Functional Impact

STAGE/LEVEL	PRESENTING SIGNS	FUNCTIONAL ABILITIES	FUNCTIONAL LIMITATIONS
Very Mild Cognitive Decline Reisberg Level 2	The person experiences typical age-related memory loss (e.g., the person forgets the location of their keys); changes are not noticed by others.	Independent in activities daily living (ADL), instrumental activities of daily (IADL), work, leisure, and social participation.	Participation in activities may require more concentration and time and/or the use of compensatory strategies (e.g., 'talking' pill bottles)
Mild Cognitive Impairment Reisburg Level 3	One or more cognitive domains is affected at a level that is noticeable to themselves and others and evident on mental status exams.	Activity adaptations and compensation strategies can be used to maintain independence in familiar, noncomplex ADL, IADL, work, leisure, and social participation activities. Challenging situations (e.g., a noisy environment) are recognized by the person and avoided to minimalize their deficits (e.g., distractibility)	Participation in activities requires more concentration and time and the use of compensatory strategies (e.g., written directions for a work task that was once intuitive). The difficulties experienced when completing complex occupational tasks can result in the person withdrawing from situations that will call attention to their deficits. Learning, remembering, and using new information (e.g., the names of new neighbors, following directions to a new restaurant) is difficult.
Moderate Neuro-cognitive Decline Reisburg Level 4	Moderate cognitive decline in one or more cognitive domains (e.g., the person is more forgetful, has difficulty finding words). The person and others express concern about the cognitive decline and modest impairments are evident on objective cognitive assessments.	Independent in simple, repetitive ADL (e.g., grooming) and following simple verbal cues and demonstration to complete other IADL, leisure, and social participation tasks (e.g., tearing lettuce to make a salad, setting the table for dinner) The person can live in their home with assistance.	The person cannot independently perform familiar, challenging activities or follow and sequence written cues (e.g., following the directions on a can of soup to cook the soup for lunch).
Major/Moderately Severe Neuro-cognitive Decline Reisburg Level 5	Significant cognitive decline in two or more cognitive domains. The person and others express concern about significant cognitive decline and substantial impairments are evident on objective cognitive assessments.	Able to perform ADL and very structured, repetitive, and highly familiar IADL, leisure, and social participation activities with encouragement, cues, and assistance (e.g., sweeping a floor, weeding a garden). The person can live in their home with substantial assistance.	The person is unable to use judgement to make decisions (e.g., what to wear based on the weather). The person cannot perform most IADL and cannot drive.
Severe Neurocognitive Decline Reisburg Level 6	Severe impairment in multiple cognitive domains documented by objective cognitive assessments.	Able to perform components of familiar ADL tasks (e.g., self-feeding) and follow demonstration and hand-over-hand cues (e.g., brushing teeth). Able to make emotional connections with people and respond to pleasant sensory input (e.g., swaying to music)	The person needs assistance to complete ADL, cannot speak in full sentences, and is incontinent. The person needs 24/7 care.
Very Severe Neuro-cognitive Decline Reisburg Level 7	Very severe impairment in multiple cognitive domains.		The person is dependent in all ADL, loses speech and motor abilities, and is nonresponsive to others The person requires 24/7 care.

References:

Hugo, J. & Ganguli, M. (2014). Dementia and cognitive impairment: Epidemiology, diagnosis, and treatment. Clinics in Geriatric Medicine, 30(3), 421–442. doi: 10.1016/j.cger.2014.04.001.

Reisberg, B., Ferris, S. H., de Leon, M. J., & Crook, T. (1982). The global deterioration scale for assessment of primary degenerative dementia. American Journal of Psychiatry, 139, 1136–1139.

Chapter 10

Degenerative Dementia (typically called the Reisberg levels).

a. The cognitive domains referred to in Table 10-2 are complex attention, executive function, learning and memory, language, perceptual-motor, and social cognition.

Symptom Management

1. Medical treatment involves resolution of the causes of the disorder, if possible.
2. There are a limited number of newer medications that appear to maintain or slow the decline of cognitive function (e.g., Aricept, Cognex).
3. If causes of the disorder are not treatable, attempts are made to mitigate symptoms where possible.

Diagnostic-Specific Considerations for Occupational Therapy

1. Maintenance of quality of life through activity adaptation and environmental modification. Refer to Chapters 15 and 16.
2. Family education to understand the nature of the person's disorder and improve the management of its symptoms and functional effects. Refer to Table 10-3.
3. Refer to this chapter's sections on OT mental health evaluation and OT mental health intervention for additional guidelines.

> **CAUTION:** The OT practitioner should be aware that some of the causes of cognitive decline and neurocognitive disorders can be reversed with treatment. Table 10-4 identifies reversible causes of mental confusion that should be considered before a diagnosis of a neurocognitive disorder is made. OT practitioners should screen for these causes and act accordingly.

> **EXAM HINT:** The NBCOT® OTR® exam content outline identifies knowledge of "strategies for addressing and enhancing health literacy with the client and relevant others . . . . (including) caregiver training (and) teaching-learning models, (and) methods for making health information accessible" (NBCOT, 2022, p. 6) as required for competent and safe practice. Therefore, if an NBCOT® exam item includes a scenario in which a person is confused due to a potentially reversible cause, a correct answer may include instructing caregivers on how to provide an environment that meets a person's sensory needs and/or cues that enable performance. Referring a client to an audiologist for a hearing evaluation, a primary care physician for an evaluation of polymedication, and/or a psychiatrist or nurse practitioner who specializes in working with older adults for an evaluation of depression could also be correct answers.

4. Chapter 14 provides further information on OT psychosocial evaluation and intervention approaches and describes specific interventions to manage neurocognitive disorders.

Table 10-3

Task Management Strategy Index Items Used by Caregivers of Persons Living with Neurocognitive Disorders
Keep things that the person likes to use, look at, or touch in easy reach.
Put items that are needed by the person in a place where they will notice them.
Show the person what to do by demonstrating the activity.
Put away items that are not needed for what the person is doing.
Use pictures to help the person remember what to do.
Use bright colors or signs to help the person notice an item.
Use clothing that is easy to put on or take off.
Have the person do simple, repetitive chores such as folding laundry, making beds, or drying dishes.
Try to ignore the person's mistakes.
Plan a routine for the person and try to stick to it.
Use intercom or other monitoring device to supervise the person when he/she is in another room.

Reference: Gitlin, L., Winter, L., Dennis, M. P., Corcoran, M., Schinfeld, S., & Hauck, W. W. (2002). Strategies used by families to simplify tasks for individuals with Alzheimer's disease and related disorders: Psychometric analysis of the Task Management Strategy Index (TMSI). Gerontologist, 42(1), 61–69.

Table 10-4

Reversible Causes of Mental Confusion

Sensory changes and problems

Age-related losses in hearing, vision, touch, etc.

Unavailable or inadequate prostheses such as hearing aids, glasses, dentures, etc.

Sensory overload; too much, too long, too fast.

Sensory deprivation; too little stimulation, isolation, restraints.

Loss of cues to aid orientation and memory such as clocks, magazines, calendars, and strict adherence to routines and rituals.

Depression

Drug use and misuse

Drug interactions, side effects, and buildup from longer absorption and elimination times.

Over-the-counter cold, sleeping, and pain remedies; often taken without the physician's knowledge and which react with prescribed drugs.

Infections/Inflammation

Viral or bacterial infections; may be accompanied by fever.

Urinary tract infections, pneumonia, etc.

Gallbladder disease.

Metabolic problems caused by

Liver or kidney disease.

Thyroid disorders (hyperthyroidism and hypothyroidism).

Dehydration from diuretics, low fluid intake, hot weather.

Poorly controlled diabetes.

Feeding and Eating Disorders

Anorexia Nervosa

1. Diagnostic criteria.
    a. Low body weight due to difficulty maintaining body weight within or above normal parameters for sex, age, and height or due to an inability to gain weight as expected during growth periods.
    b. Despite being underweight, there is a fear of gaining weight or becoming fat; the individual tends to perceive self as being heavier than in actuality.
    c. Alteration in self-perception of body weight or shape.
        (1) Physical body weight or shape is considered important in determination of self-evaluation or self-worth.
        (2) The individual may not realize, or may deny, the presence of low body weight and/or the seriousness of the effects despite being ill or hospitalized.
    d. Two types may be identified, either food restrictive type or binge eating/purging type (APA, 2022).

2. Onset and prognosis.
    a. Anorexia most commonly begins in the midteens.
    b. The long-term prognosis may not be good, with mortality rates of approximately 5.35%.
3. Behavioral characteristics.
    a. Individuals often exhibit obsessive/compulsive behavior, depression, anxiety, rigidity, perfectionism, and poor sexual adjustment.

Bulimia Nervosa

1. Diagnostic criteria.
    a. Ongoing binge eating of much larger portions than would be expected and feeling the inability to control consumption to avoid gaining weight.
    b. Attempts are made to avoid gaining weight through vomiting, using laxatives, fasting, and engaging in extreme amounts of exercise.
    c. Personal self-concept defined by body proportions and size.

d. Symptoms are not occurring as part of anorexia nervosa.
2. Onset and prognosis.
   a. The usual age of onset of bulimia is later than that of anorexia.
      (1) It begins in adolescence or in early adulthood.

> CAUTION: Adolescents with bulimia have reported higher rates of suicide ideation and suicide attempt than adolescents with anorexia.

3. Behavioral characteristics.
   a. Obsession with personal appearance and attractiveness to others.
   b. Individuals maintain a normative weight.

Binge-Eating Disorder

1. Diagnostic criteria.
   a. Inability to control binge-eating, recurrent periods of consuming an exorbitant amount of food in a discrete situation.
   b. Binge-eating episodes may include:
      (1) Eating until uncomfortably full or when not feeling physically hungry.
      (2) Eating more and at a faster pace than usual.
      (3) Experiencing feelings of guilt or depression after excessive eating.
      (4) Frequent solitary eating due to embarrassment over behaviors.
   c. Binge-eating behaviors result in clinically significant distress.
   d. The severity of binge-eating disorder is based on the frequency of episodes ranging from mild (1–3 episodes per week) to extreme (14 or more binge eating episodes per week) (APA, 2022).
      (1) Average frequency for a clinical diagnosis is a minimum of one time per week for at least three months (APA, 2022).

Other Feeding and Eating Disorders

1. Pica.
   a. Persistent eating of nonfood substances, which is inconsistent with cultural or developmental expectations.
   b. Recurrent patterns of behavior must be present for at least one month.
2. Rumination disorder.
   a. Repeated, unintentional regurgitation of undigested or partially digested food, followed by rechewing and either swallowing or spitting food out, for at least one month.

3. Avoidant/restrictive food intake disorder.
   a. Persistent failure to meet nutritional needs and expectations, resulting in any of the following symptoms:
      (1) Nutritional deficiency.
      (2) Significant weight loss.
      (3) Reliance on oral nutritional supplements or alternative feeding methods (i.e., enteral feeding via pump).
      (4) Clinical disturbance in psychological functioning (APA 2022).

Impact on Function

1. ADL such as self-care, eating, and feeding can be severely disrupted.
2. IADL such as shopping for clothing and food, meal preparation and clean-up, and health management and maintenance can be significantly affected.
3. Work skills can be intact unless food-restricting behaviors and/or medical problems interfere with work performance or prevocational/vocational skill development.
   a. Focus on weight control may interfere with pursuit of vocational goals and/or the development of prerequisite skills.
4. Leisure skills can be intact unless affected by food-restricting behaviors and/or medical complications.
   a. Activities may focus mainly on appearance, rather than on those that have meaning or purpose.
   b. Exercise activities previously done for fun (e.g., running, swimming, cycling) may now be done excessively without enjoyment to decrease weight.
5. Social participation (including family, community, and peer/friend) can be greatly impacted by the excessive use of food-restricting behaviors, the need to maintain secrecy about the behaviors, and feeling ashamed, guilty, embarrassed, and/or depressed about atypical and disturbed eating habits and patterns.

Symptom Management

1. Antidepressant medications may be used in anorexia nervosa, but they are more effective for individuals with bulimia.
   a. Antipsychotics can be used as well to improve distorted thinking and perceptions.
2. Treatment of any of the resulting medical complications such as cardiac disturbances (hypotension, slow heart rate), reduced thyroid metabolism, osteoporosis, seizures, severe dehydration, electrolyte imbalances, irregular bowel movements, pancreatitis, peptic ulcers, gastric and/or esophageal inflammation

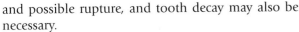

and possible rupture, and tooth decay may also be necessary.

3. Treatment most often takes place in outpatient or day care programs.

4. Hospitalization may be necessary if the individual has medical difficulties, is suicidal, cannot care for themself, or needs to be removed from their environment.

5. Behavioral programs designed around a privileging system are often used.
   a. Consistency among staff is crucial for program effectiveness.

6. Medical management also typically includes individual psychotherapy, family counseling, and behavioral and/or cognitive therapies.

Diagnostic-Specific Considerations for Occupational Therapy

1. The building of trust is essential to effective intervention due to the secrecy, guilt, anger, resistance, and ego fragility often associated with the disorder and its stages of recovery.

2. The OT practitioner must be honest, supportive, and gently confrontational when indicated.

3. Evaluation and intervention must include the identification of the socioemotional needs the eating disorder had fulfilled for the person so that health-promoting occupation-based alternatives can be explored and developed.
   a. Non-food-related areas of interest and meaningful purposeful activities should be pursued to promote a reality-based body image and foster improved coping.

4. Education about nutritional food management and the development of healthy leisure time (i.e., does not involve excessive exercise) are key.

5. Refer to this chapter's sections on OT mental health evaluation and OT mental health intervention for additional guidelines.

6. Chapter 14 provides further information on OT psychosocial evaluation and intervention approaches.

Disruptive, Impulse-Control, and Conduct Disorders

Specific Disorders

1. Oppositional defiant disorder.
   a. Negativistic, hostile, and defiant behaviors that result in functional impairment.

2. Conduct disorder.
   a. Disregard for the rights of others leading to aggression toward people and animals, destruction of property, deceitfulness, theft, or serious violation of rules.

3. Unspecified disruptive, impulse control, and conduct disorder.
   a. Children who do not meet the criteria for conduct disorder or oppositional defiant disorder; however, they display significant functional impairment and conduct and oppositional behaviors are present.

Onset and Prognosis

1. Oppositional defiant disorder.
   a. Oppositional, negative behavior begins in early childhood.
   b. The course and prognosis depend on the severity of behaviors, the presence of other disorders, and the intactness of the family.
   c. It is most likely to progress into a conduct disorder if aggression is prominent.

2. Conduct disorder.
   a. Typically emerges between middle childhood through middle adolescence ages but can occur during preschool ages (APA, 2022).
   b. Prognosis is related to the age of onset and the severity of symptoms and behavior.
      (1) Severe conduct disorder is often associated with the development of other disorders and substance abuse later in life.
   c. Assaultive behavior and parental criminality correlate highly with future incarceration.

Impact on Function

1. Children with these behavior disorders have difficulty at school and with the formation of healthy social and familial relationships.

2. Difficulties within the family affect not only the child but all family members, impacting on their role performance.

Symptom Management

1. Behavioral techniques are often the most effective forms of intervention with adolescents.
2. The identification and treatment of other disorders, (e.g., attention deficit hyperactivity disorder [ADHD], learning disorders, substance use, depression) is important.
3. The use of medications such as antipsychotics, antidepressants, anxiolytics, and mood stabilizers may be helpful.
4. A consistent approach from all team members is essential.

Diagnostic-Specific Considerations for Occupational Therapy

1. Contributing disorders (e.g., attention deficit hyperactivity disorder, mood disorders, learning disorders) and their effect on the performance skills and areas of occupation must be evaluated and addressed in intervention.
2. The child's goals, stressors, and family and social relationships should be considered.
3. Skill development may improve emotional adjustment.

4. Behavioral approaches must be consistent throughout all programming.
5. The OT practitioner should assist parents, other family members, teachers, and other school personnel to understand the nature of the child's condition and to develop strategies for behavior management.
6. Refer to this chapter's sections on OT mental health evaluation and OT mental health intervention for additional guidelines.
7. Chapter 14 provides further information on OT psychosocial evaluation and intervention approaches and describes specific interventions to manage offensive, intrusive, and escalating behaviors.

> **EXAM HINT:** The NBCOT® OTR® exam content outline identifies knowledge of the "expected patterns, progressions, and prognoses associated with conditions that limit occupational performance . . . (including the) signs and symptoms of disease, stages of disease, (and) secondary complications" (NBCOT®, 2022, p. 3) as essential for competent and safe practice. Thus, the application of knowledge about the presenting symptoms of feeding and eating disorders, disruptive, impulse control and conduct disorders described in this and prior sections and the following information about neurodevelopmental and intellectual disorders can help you determine the correct answer to exam items about working with persons with these conditions.

Neurodevelopmental Disorders

Autism Spectrum Disorder (ASD)

1. Etiology.
   a. Organic brain pathology.
   b. May or may not be seen with other disorders.
      (1) Rett's syndrome, if associated with ASD, is now specified as "Known Genetic Condition" (refer to subsequent section).
2. Onset and prognosis.
   a. May occur from birth up to three years of age.
   b. The prognosis for children with ASD is dependent upon the combined impact of the following three parameters:
      (1) Severity of ASD.
      (2) Level of general intelligence.
      (3) Change in symptom expression over time.

   c. Life expectancy is not affected, although a supervised living setting may be necessary.
3. Diagnostic characteristics.
   a. Presence of at least two core symptom domains:
      (1) Impaired social communication and social interaction.
      (2) Restricted, repetitive patterns of behavior, interests, or activities.
   b. Behavioral characteristics.
      (1) Impaired nonverbal behaviors (e.g., infrequent/ poor eye contact, impaired attachment behavior, anxiety with changes in typical routines).
      (2) Difficulty relating to others and forming relationships at an age-appropriate level.
      (3) Lack of spontaneous social-seeking behavioral interactions with others and lack of awareness of

others who are seeking interactions (e.g., sharing a snack, pointing at an object of interest).

(4) Lack of social reciprocation due to decreased ability to infer feelings and intentions of others (e.g., the child does not understand that sharing is expected; the child does not point at an object to have the parents name the object or point to pictures in a book and look to the reader for a response).

(5) Difficulty with communication.

    (a) Lack of initiation, reflection, and/or development of spoken language or alternative means for communication.

    (b) If speech is developed, difficulty in initiating or engaging in conversation and lack of appropriate context.

    (c) Stereotyped echolalia and/or use of indiscernible language.

(6) Lack of spontaneous pretend, imitative, or exploratory play.

(7) Repetitive and stereotyped behaviors and movements in one or more of the following:

    (a) Ritualistic nonfunctional routines, preoccupation.

    (b) Rigid observance of nonfunctional routines or behavioral patterns.

    (c) Repetitive motor action (e.g., flapping and wiggling of fingers, head banging, rocking of the head or body).

    (d) Restrictive fixation on parts of a whole object (e.g., wheel of a toy car).

c. Delay or impairment in social interaction, language, and/or play (symbolic or imaginative) is present before three years of age.

d. Not better described as Rett's syndrome or childhood disintegrative disorder.

e. Difficulty with sensory processing and perception of various sensory stimuli; difficulty in modulation of stimuli at various levels of the continuum, e.g., hyper- or hyporesponsiveness.

f. Common associated behaviors may include unanticipated mood swings, temper tantrums, lack of ability to focus, insomnia, and enuresis.

4. Symptom management.

a. Medications prescribed will depend on the presenting symptoms.

(1) Seizure medications.

(2) Medication for muscle deterioration and/or complications due to abnormal tone.

(3) Medications to increase alertness.

(4) Medications to modulate behaviors.

5. Diagnostic specific considerations for OT.

a. Evaluate developmental and functional levels. Refer to Chapter 5.

b. Develop sensorimotor, social interaction, vocational readiness, and community participation skills relevant to the child's level. Refer to Chapter 5 and Chapter 15.

c. Provide sensory integrative intervention, if indicated. Refer to relevant sections in Chapter 5 and Chapter 12.

d. Collaborate with the speech-language pathologist to obtain and train in technologically based augmentative communication. Refer to Chapter 16.

e. Provide adaptive and positioning equipment to facilitate function (e.g., the stereotypical movements of licking, biting, and slapping of the hands in a child with Rett's syndrome may require adaptations to maintain the integrity of the skin, such as dynamic elbow orthoses that inhibit a hand-to-mouth pattern by limiting full elbow flexion).

f. Table 10-5 outlines specific strategies that OT practitioners can use when working with children with ASD.

g. Collaborate with the family and interdisciplinary team to promote occupational performance and social participation.

h. Refer to this chapter's sections on OT mental health evaluation and OT mental health intervention for additional guidelines.

i. Chapter 14 provides further information on OT psychosocial evaluation and intervention approaches and describes specific interventions to manage challenging behaviors.

Chapter 10

Specific Strategies for Occupational Therapy Sessions when Working with Children with Autism Spectrum Disorder

Improve Engagement and Interaction, Reduce Fear or Anxiety

- Imitate the child and wait for the child to initiate interaction via eye contact, touch, or moving into closer physical proximity.
- Alter your proximity to the child.
- Reduce the use of direct eye contact.
- Alter the therapist's motor and verbal pace.
- Alter the therapist's voice volume or intonation.
- Use musical or sing-song vocalizations that the child finds humorous.
- Use preferred objects, colors, or movements within therapy tasks to elicit desired gross or fine motor skills. This should be a fun game.
- Interact playfully, make work into play.
- Create fun problems to solve (e.g., "Oh no, the pig (stuffed toy) is trapped in the mud, you have to help get him out. How can we save him?").
- Sing familiar songs and leave out the last word, to encourage the child to vocalize to fill in where you have omitted the word.

Improve Motor Skills/Praxis

- Create fun obstacles/challenges that encourage therapeutically desired movements while engaging the child in a preferred activity of his/her choice.
- Climb, walk, or crawl on raised surfaces to increase attention to motion. For example, climb across a wide balance beam or a horizontal ladder at two to three feet off the ground (while maintaining safety).
- Gradually increase motoric sequences that are completed before a desired event or object is provided (e.g., placing a favorite toy in an increasing number of layers to open prior to placing it up a ramp or ladder).
- Alternate preferred sensory activities with more challenging motor tasks.
- Sing about the motor activity you are doing using a familiar tune (e.g., use the tune of "Row, Row, Row Your Boat," to sing "push, push, push that cart gently down the hall").

Improve Comfort, Reduce Fear and Anxiety

- Carefully grade the introduction of novelty into a session.
- Attend to the sensory environment and the child's response (i.e., nonverbal responses, facial expression) to the sensory environment.
- Alter lighting, noise, smells.
- Provide opportunities for deep pressure and proprioception through active play.

Improve Behavior and Task Completion, Reduce Fear or Anxiety

- Use objects, visual cues, or schedules to help the child predict what will come next, what will happen, or how many times a particular action/behavior is expected.
- Use prompts that are familiar to the child.
- Know and use the child's preferred reinforcers throughout the OT "work."
- Provide clear boundaries regarding areas of the intervention space so that it is clear which type of activity occurs in each area.
- Provide choices or choice boards, visual schedules, or other visual materials to aid in understanding what is to be done.
- Provide written instructions if a child can read.

Improve Play and Ideational Praxis

- Use realistic prompts to introduce role play (e.g., fireman's hat, realistic dress-up clothing).
- Use movie characters and stories to begin to introduce pretend play.
- Promote imagination in your sessions.
- Have the child help you create a game out of unusual materials.
- Have the child help you build an obstacle course or sensorimotor activity.
- Discuss the different ways you can use certain objects based on their properties (affordances).
- Try to add to current ideas with prompting (e.g., "can you think of another way to do that?").
- Take turns between imitating the child and having the child attempt to imitate you.
- Use silly motions, vocalizations, and sequences to be playful.

Adapted from Miller-Kuhaneck, H. (2016). Autism spectrum disorder. In J. Case-Smith & J. C. O'Brien (Eds.). Occupational therapy for children and adolescence (7th ed., p. 777). Elsevier. Reprinted with permission.

Attention Deficit Hyperactivity Disorders

Overview

1. Attention deficit hyperactivity disorders (ADHD) are listed in the DSM-5-TR™ in a new category of neurodevelopmental disorders.
2. The etiology of ADHD is unknown; however, there are suggested contributing factors. These include the following.
   a. Genetic factors include higher occurrence in monozygotic twins than in dizygotic twins, and twice the occurrence in siblings of hyperactive children.
   b. Neurologic factors include the possibility of minimal or subtle brain damage due to circulatory, toxic, metabolic, or mechanical effects during fetal or perinatal periods; and infection, inflammation, and/or trauma during early childhood.
   c. Neurochemical dysfunction related to neurotransmitters in the adrenergic and the dopaminergic systems.
   d. Psychosocial factors include stress, anxiety, or predisposing factors such as temperament.
3. Subtypes of ADHD specify whether the disorder has one of the following presentations.
   a. Combined presentation.
   b. Predominantly inattentive presentation.
   c. Predominantly hyperactive/impulsive presentation.

Diagnostic Criteria

1. Children.
   a. The presence of six or more symptoms in the inattention domain, the hyperactivity-impulsivity domain, or both.
   b. Symptoms in the inattention domain or hyperactivity-impulsivity domain that interfere with occupational activities are present for at least six months or more. Refer to Box 10-3.
   c. Visual-perceptual, auditory-perceptual, language, and/or cognitive problems may be present.
   d. Some of the symptoms that result in impairment were evident before seven years of age.
   e. Symptoms that result in impairment are present in two settings, such as school, home, and/or work.
2. Adolescents/adults.
   a. Adolescents and adults (aged ≥17) are required to present with a minimum of five (rather than six) symptoms.
   b. Symptoms should have been present before age 12 (not before age seven).
   c. Motor symptoms of hyperactivity may appear less in adolescence and adulthood; however, restlessness, inattention, poor planning, and impulsivity may persist.
   d. Impairments tend to be present into adulthood.
3. A diagnosis of ASD may accompany a diagnosis of ADHD.

BOX 10-3 ◗ ADHD Diagnostic Criteria

- **Inattention Domain Symptoms:**
  - Lack of attention to detail.
  - Poor listening.
  - Limited follow-through of tasks.
  - Difficulty with organization.
  - Avoidance of tasks that require sustained attention.
  - Tendency to lose things.
  - Distractibility.
  - Forgetfulness.
- **Hyperactivity Domain Symptoms:**
  - Fidgeting
  - Inability to remain seated.
  - Inappropriate activity level for a given situation.
  - Difficulty with quiet sedentary activities.
  - Frequent movement.
  - Excessive talking.
- **Impulsivity Domain Symptoms:**
  - Answering questions before they are fully stated.
  - Difficulty with turn taking.
  - Interrupting the conversations or activities of others.

Onset and Prognosis

1. Symptoms are often noted during the toddler/early childhood years.
   a. The impact of symptoms on function typically become more evident when a child begins school; thus, most persons with ADHD are diagnosed during their elementary school years when behavior interferes with their adjustment to school.
      (1) Caution is advised to not make a diagnosis in early childhood years.
2. The prognosis for a person with ADHD can vary.
   a. The symptoms of ADHD can improve with age and effective medical and behavioral interventions.
   b. The development of depression, sleep, anxiety, personality, and substance use disorders can impact the prognosis of persons with ADHD.

Impact on Function

1. Infants are over-active, difficult to soothe when crying, and demonstrate poor sleeping habits.
2. Defensiveness to environmental stimuli, frequent irritability, aggressive behavior, emotional lability, and fluctuating and unpredictable performance.
3. Difficulty with delayed gratification in the school and home.
4. Deficits in perceptual motor tasks with disorders in reading, mathematics, written expression, and general coordination resulting.
5. Disorders of memory, thinking, speech, and hearing.
6. Depression secondary to frustration and difficulty with learning.
   a. This often leads to low self-esteem and conduct disorders.

Symptom Management

1. The medications prescribed will depend on the presenting symptoms.
   a. Stimulants.
      (1) Most commonly used; they include dextroamphetamine (e.g., Dexedrine, Focalin) for children three years and older, and methylphenidate (e.g., Concerta, Ritalin, Adderall, Metadate) for children six years and older.
         (a) Side effects include loss of appetite, weight loss, disturbed sleep patterns, and slow growth.
   b. Antidepressants.
      (1) Imipramine.
      (2) Used when stimulants are unable to be used.

> **CAUTION:** Careful monitoring of cardiac functioning is required.

   c. Anxiolytics.
      (1) Clonidine (Catapres) and Guanfacine (Tenex).

> **CAUTION:** Require careful dosing and competent adults for administration. Medications cannot be stopped suddenly because this could medically compromise the child.

2. Monitoring of medication and its impact on cognitive and psychosocial function (e.g., learning and self-esteem).
3. Psychotherapy, behavior modification, parent and individual counselling may be indicated.

Diagnostic-specific Considerations for Occupational Therapy

1. The impact of the person's behavior on school, home, play/leisure, and social participation must be considered.
2. Environmental modifications and activity adaptations to structure the client's home environment can enhance function.
3. Environmental modifications and activity adaptations to structure the child's environment at school and the adult's environment at work can support more successful outcomes (e.g., the elimination of sensory distracters, the use of lists, datebooks, and/or texted reminders).

4. Training in social skills and self-management (i.e., the use of humor, personally initiated time-outs) can improve adaptive behaviors.
5. Interventions to promote sensory modulation are emphasized. Refer to Chapter 12.
6. Consultation is provided to parents, family members, teachers, and employees regarding strategies for the provision of structure and expectations in a manner that fosters the person's psychosocial adaptation.
7. In school-based practice, ongoing collaboration with individualized education planning team members and parents is vital.
8. Refer to this chapter's sections on OT mental health evaluation and OT mental health intervention for additional guidelines.
9. Chapter 14 provides further information on OT psychosocial evaluation and intervention approaches and describes specific interventions to manage challenging behaviors.

> **EXAM HINT:** The NBCOT® OTR® exam content outline identifies knowledge of the "expected patterns, progressions, and prognoses associated with conditions that limit occupational performance . . . (including the) signs and symptoms of disease, stages of disease, (and) secondary complications" (NBCOT®, 2022, p. 3) as essential for competent and safe practice. Thus, the application of knowledge about the presenting symptoms of ADHD described in this section and the following information about intellectual disorders can help you determine the correct answer to exam items about working with persons with these conditions.

Intellectual Developmental Disorders

Overview

1. Etiology.
   a. Genetic conditions such as chromosomal abnormalities (e.g., Down syndrome, fragile X syndrome, Prader-Willi syndrome, and Klinefelter's syndrome).
   b. Metabolic conditions such as phenylketonuria, hypothyroidism, and Tay-Sachs disease.
   c. Prenatal infections such as rubella, toxoplasmosis, and AIDS.
   d. Maternal substance abuse.
   e. Perinatal factors such as trauma and prematurity.
   f. Acquired conditions, including infections such as encephalitis and meningitis.
   g. Head trauma sustained in motor vehicle accidents, falls, child abuse, etc.
2. Onset and prognosis.
   a. Onset of deficits begins in the developmental period for genetic and prenatal causes.
   b. Likely lifelong disorders with treatment focused on rehabilitation, management of symptoms, and adaptive strategies.

Diagnostic Classification and Functional Implications

1. The essential features include:
   a. Criterion A: deficits in general mental abilities.

b. Criterion B: impairment in everyday adaptive functioning, in comparison to an individual's age-, gender-, and socioculturally matched peers.

c. Criterion C: onset is during the developmental period.

2. The diagnosis of intellectual disability is determined by clinical assessment and standardized testing of intellectual and adaptive functioning.

3. Deficits in adaptive functioning impact everyday life activities (occupations) and are a central focus of OT intervention.

4. The American Association on Intellectual and Developmental Disabilities has categorized adaptive functioning into three domains. Refer to Box 10-4.

a. Diagnosis is based on the measurement of intelligence or IQ tests; however, it should be noted that IQ scores do not provide a full profile of an individual's capabilities.

(1) Individuals who score more than two standard deviations below the norm, or below an IQ of 70, are considered to have an intellectual disability.

b. The severity of an intellectual disability is classified as mild, moderate, severe, and profound.

(1) Mild intellectual disability.

(a) The individual can acquire the ADL, IADL, social, and vocational skills to function independently in desired occupational roles.

(b) Minimal support is required.

(c) Additional intermittent support may be required in special circumstances (e.g., when moving, beginning a new job).

(2) Moderate intellectual disability.

(a) The individual can acquire independence in routine daily skills and the skills needed to function in desired occupational roles when provided with supports and structure (e.g., work in a vocational rehabilitation [sheltered] workshop).

(b) Moderate support and assistance may be required to perform specific occupations (e.g., meal preparation, use of public transportation).

(c) Supervised living is required.

(3) Severe intellectual disability.

(a) The individual can acquire communication skills and some basic health habits (e.g., brushing teeth).

(b) Significant impairments in motor functioning and physical development are typical.

(c) Assistance is required for performance of most tasks in all areas of occupation on a daily basis.

(d) Supervised living is required.

(4) Profound intellectual disability.

(a) Significant impairments in motor functioning and physical development are typical.

(b) Extensive support and 24-hour assistance and supervision are required for ADL and safety.

(c) Supervised living is required.

c. Multiple disabilities such as hearing and other sensory impairments, seizures, and other neurologic abnormalities may be associated with various syndromes (e.g., fetal alcohol syndrome).

5. Impact on development.

a. The developmental impact of intellectual disability can vary greatly.

(1) The impact is greatest in children with severe and profound intellectual disability.

b. Cognitive development.

(1) Slower learning ability.

(2) Shorter attention span.

(3) Difficulty with problem-solving and critical thinking.

(4) Difficulty generalizing information and mastering abstract thinking.

(5) Increased distractibility.

c. Motor development.

(1) Slower development with the attainment of physical milestones occurring at a later age than typical.

(2) Uncoordinated appearance and movements.

(3) Low muscle tone.

d. Sensory development.

(1) Diminished sensory modulation abilities.

(2) Hypersensitivity or hyposensitivity to all sensory stimuli.

e. Language development.

(1) Decreased ability in recalling and retrieving words secondary to cognitive deficits (e.g., inattention and impaired memory).

BOX 10-4 ▷ Adaptive Functioning Domains for Intellectual and Developmental Disabilities

- **Conceptual Skills:** language and literacy; money, time, and number concepts; and self-direction.

- **Social Skills:** interpersonal skills, social responsibility, self-esteem, gullibility, naïveté, wariness, social problem-solving, and the ability to follow rules/obey laws and to avoid being victimized.

- **Practical Skills:** activities of daily living (personal care), occupational skills, health care, travel/transportation, schedules/routines, safety, use of money, use of the telephone.

(2) Difficulty grasping and expressing concepts secondary to cognitive deficits (e.g., impaired abstract thinking).

(3) Difficulty with the motor aspects of creating language secondary to motor deficits (e.g., low tone).

    f. Psychosocial development.

(1) Impaired ability to respond to social cues can result in a number of behavioral outcomes. These can include excessive shyness and aggressiveness.

(2) Hyperactivity and distractibility can also impede psychosocial development.

6. Symptom management.

    a. Dependent upon presenting symptoms and complications.

    b. Psychological, audiological, and speech evaluations and interventions may be indicated.

    c. Intermittent support may be required in special circumstances.

Diagnostic-specific Considerations for Occupational Therapy

1. Self-determination and person-centered planning within the person's capabilities should be a priority.
2. Support and assistance may be required to address performance skills and patterns in areas of occupation.
3. Development of community and social participation skills are a major focus.
4. Interdisciplinary team and family collaboration is helpful to support the development of the person's functional and social skills and to promote participation in desired occupations.
5. If the person is of school age, collaboration with the educational team is needed to develop an individualized educational program. Refer to Chapter 4.

Occupational Therapy Mental Health Evaluation

Evaluation Foci

EXAM HINT: In the NBCOT® OTR® exam content outline for the occupational therapist, "Domain 1 Evaluation and Assessment: Acquire information regarding factors that influence occupational performance on an ongoing basis throughout the occupational therapy process" (NBCOT®, 2022, p. 3) comprises 23% of the exam. The application of knowledge about the evaluation foci described below and the evaluation tools described in Chapter 14 can help you effectively determine the correct answers to exam items about OT evaluation and assessment for persons with psychiatric conditions and cognitive disorders.

1. Determination of values, interests, desired occupational roles, and self-determined goals.
2. Identification of cognitive, perceptual, and psychosocial strengths and skills, and their ability to facilitate recovery.
3. Identification of cognitive, perceptual, and psychosocial deficits and limitations and their impact on function and lifestyle.
4. Determination of functional problems associated with psychiatric symptoms (e.g., safety awareness and judgment).
5. Treatment history and ability and interest to engage in recovery (i.e., readiness for change).
6. Identification of coping skills, stressors, and environmental and social supports.

7. Refer to Chapter 14 for additional information about psychosocial evaluation methods and specific assessment tools.

Role of the Occupational Therapy Assistant (OTA)/ Certified Occupational Therapy Assistant (COTA®)

1. The OTA/COTA® can contribute to the evaluation process in collaboration with the occupational therapist.
   a. Supervision by an occupational therapist is required.
   b. The level of supervision required will be determined by the OTA's/COTA®'s experience established service competence, state laws, and other regulatory and payer requirements.
2. The OTA/COTA® can collect evaluation data and administer assessments of occupations, client factors, performance skills, patterns, and contexts and report assessment results to the supervising occupational therapist.
3. The supervising occupational therapist is responsible for determining which assessment(s) will attain information essential for setting goals and planning intervention and the interpretation of the information reported by the OTA/COTA®.
   a. While the OTA/COTA® cannot independently interpret evaluation results, they can contribute to this process.
4. All evaluation activities completed by an OTA/COTA® must comply with federal and state laws and other regulatory and payer requirements (AOTA, 2021).

Occupational Therapy Mental Health Intervention

Intervention Foci

1. The foci of intervention during periods of acute hospitalization include the following.
   a. Management of all behaviors that threaten the safety and well-being of the individual as well as that of others on the unit.
   b. Stabilization of behavior to enable engagement in intervention.
   c. Engagement in activities that are "do-able" (e.g., brief and structured) to enable success and promote reality-based thinking.
      (1) Graded activities are designed to promote self-efficacy, which can increase self-confidence, motivation, and participation in treatment.
   d. Engagement of the person in the treatment process.
   e. Development of relaxation and stress management skills to help decrease the incidence and severity of symptoms and facilitate recovery.
   f. Development of the skills needed to pursue desired occupational roles and attain self-determined goals.
   g. Engagement in activities to improve communication skills and self-expression.
   h. The gathering and sharing of ongoing assessment information with the treatment team.
      (1) The person's status typically changes drastically during the course of an acute hospitalization due to the stabilizing effects of psychotropic medications.
         (a) The input of OT practitioners about a patient's observed symptoms and functional behaviors is critical in assisting with the effective titration of psychotropic medications.
   i. Assistance with discharge planning to support recovery and a healthy lifestyle.
2. The foci of intervention during periods of long-term hospitalization include the following.
   a. Development and implementation of a plan for self-determined goal achievement.
   b. Provision of a normalizing environment that enables participation in meaningful and desired occupational roles.
   c. Engagement of the person in the treatment process.
   d. Provision of graded activities to develop the skills needed for competence in ADL, IADL, social participation, leisure, school, and/or work.
   e. Development of relaxation and stress management skills to help decrease the incidence and severity of symptoms and facilitate recovery.
   f. Continuation of assessment to determine realistic and meaningful discharge goals.
   g. Development of the skills and external supports needed to pursue desired post-discharge occupational

roles, participate in the anticipated discharge environment, and attain self-determined discharge goals.
3. The foci of intervention in community settings include the following.
   a. Provision of services that facilitate recovery and assist in the maintenance of existing skills.
   b. Assistance with the continued development of skills needed for community living, social participation, and the pursuit of valued occupational roles.
   c. Development of skills and supports to enable ongoing recovery (e.g., WRAP, NAMI [National Alliance for the Mentally Ill]).
   d. Development of skills and the provision of assistance, if needed, to obtain concrete practical resources to support community living (e.g., supplemental security income [SSI], affordable housing, and food stamps).
   e. Monitoring of the individual for changing clinical, personal, and social needs.
4. Refer to Chapter 14 for additional information about psychosocial intervention approaches and treatment methods.

> **EXAM HINT:** In the NBCOT® OTR® exam outline for the occupational therapist, "Domain 3 Select and Manage Interventions: Select and implement interventions to promote healing and enhance engagement in occupation-based activities" (NBCOT®, 2022, p. 7) comprises 38% of the exam. The application of knowledge about the general intervention foci described above, the diagnostic-specific interventions described throughout this chapter, and the intervention methods and approaches described in Chapter 14 can help you effectively determine the correct answers to exam items about OT interventions for persons with psychiatric and cognitive disorders.

Role of the OTA/COTA®

1. The OTA/COTA® implements intervention with supervision of the occupational therapist.
   a. The level of supervision required depends upon the OTA's/COTA®'s experience and established service competence and the regulations from the licensure board in the state of practice.
2. During the implementation of intervention, the OTA/COTA® informs the supervising occupational therapist of any change in the individual's status and any other relevant information that may affect treatment.
3. All intervention activities completed by an OTA/COTA® must comply with federal and state laws and other regulatory and payer requirements (AOTA, 2021).

Chapter 10

▶ References

American Academy of Child and Adolescent Psychiatry. (2019). Facts for families: Children with oppositional defiant disorder. https://www.aacap.org/AACAP/Families _and_Youth/Facts_for_Families/FFF-Guide/Children -With-Oppositional-Defiant-Disorder-072.aspx.

American Association on Intellectual and Developmental Disabilities. (2013). Defining criteria for intellectual disability. http://aaidd.org/intellectual-disability/definition.

American Occupational Therapy Association. (2020). Occupational therapy practice framework: Domain and process (4th ed.). American Journal of Occupational Therapy, 74(Supplement 2): 7412410010. https://doi.org/10.5014/ ajot.2020.74S2001.

American Psychiatric Association. (2022). Diagnostic and statistical manual of mental disorders (5th ed.) Text Revision (TR)™. Author.

Anxiety and Depression Association of America. (2022). Anxiety disorders facts and statistics. https://adaa.org/ understanding-anxiety/facts-statistics.

Autism Speaks. (n.d.). What is autism? https://www.autism speaks.org/what-autism.

Ayd, F. J. (2000). Lexicon of psychiatry, neurology, and the neurosciences (2nd ed.). William and Wilkins.

Bains, N., & Abdijadid, S. (2022). Major depressive episode. In StatPearls. https://www.ncbi.nlm.nih.gov/books/NBK559078.

Batshaw, M. L., Roizen, N. J., & Pellegrino, L. (2019). Children with disabilities (8th ed.). Paul H. Brookes.

Boland, R., & Verduin, M. (2022). Kaplan and Sadock's concise textbook of clinical psychiatry (5th ed.). Lippincott Williams & Wilkins.

Bonder, B. (2022). Psychopathology and function (6th ed.). Slack.

Centers for Disease Control and Development. (2023a). Autism and Developmental Disabilities Monitoring (ADDM) Network. https://www.cdc.gov/ncbddd/autism/addm.html.

Centers for Disease Control and Prevention. (2023b). Attention-deficit hyperactivity disorder (ADHD). https://www .cdc.gov/ncbddd/adhd/.

Cleveland Clinic. (2018). Oppositional defiant disorder. https://my.clevelandclinic.org/health/diseases/9905 -oppositional-defiant-disorder.

Cornell, C., & Hamrin, V. (2008). Clinical interventions for children with attachment problems. Journal of Child and Adolescent Psychiatric Nursing, 21(1), 35–47.

Costa, D. (2009, June 29). Eating disorders: Occupational therapy's role. OT Practice, 13–16.

Crnic, K., Neece, C., McIntyre L., Blacher, J., & Baker, B. (2017). Intellectual disability and developmental risk: Promoting intervention to improve child and family well-being. Child Development, 88, 436–445.

Cutler, J. L. (2014). Psychiatry (4th ed.). Oxford University Press.

Erskine, H., Ferrari, A., Nelson, P., Polanczyk, G., Flaxman, A., Vos, T., . . . Scott, J. (2013). Epidemiological modelling of attention-deficit/hyperactivity disorder and conduct disorder for the Global Burden of Disease Study 2010. Journal of Child Psychology and Psychiatry, 54(12), 1263–1274.

Fichter, M., & Quadflieg N. (2016). Mortality in eating disorders: Results of a large prospective clinical longitudinal study. International Journal of Eating Disorders, 49(4), 391–401.

Fleming-Castaldy, R. (2014). Activities, occupations, and empowerment. In J. Hinojosa & M. L. Blount (Eds.), The texture of life: Purposeful activities in the context of occupation (4th ed., pp. 393–415). AOTA Press.

Genetic and Rare Diseases Information Center. (2023). Rett syndrome. https://rarediseases.info.nih.gov/diseases/5696/ rett-syndrome#ref_11332.

Girolamo, G. D., Dagani, J., Purcell, R., Cocchi, A., & Mcgorry, P. D. (2011). Age of onset of mental disorders and use of mental health services: Needs, opportunities and obstacles. Epidemiology and Psychiatric Sciences, 21(1), 47–57.

Glanzman, M. M., & Sell, N. (2019). Attention-deficit/ hyperactivity disorder. In M. L. Batshaw, N. J. Roizen, & L. Pellegrino (Eds.), Children with disabilities (8th ed., pp. 347–373). Paul H. Brookes.

Hardy, L. (2007). Attachment theory and reactive attachment disorder: Theoretical perspectives and treatment implications. Journal of Child and Adolescent Psychiatric Nursing, 20(1), 27–39.

Hay, P., & Mitchison, D. (2014). The epidemiology of eating disorders: Genetic, environmental, and societal factors. Clinical Epidemiology, 6, 89–97.

Hilton, C. L., & Kramer, J. (2019). Assessment and intervention of social participation and social skills. In J. C. O'Brien & H. Kuhanek (Eds.), Case-Smith's occupational therapy for children and adolescence (8th ed., pp. 328–373). Elsevier.

Kuhaneck, H. (2019). Autism spectrum disorder. In O'Brien, J., & Kuhanek, H. (Eds.), Case Smith's occupational therapy for children and adolescence (8th ed., pp.786–813). Elsevier.

Lenzenweger, M., Lane, M. Loranger, A., & Kessler, R. (2007). DSM-IV personality disorders in the National Comorbidity Survey Replication. Biological Psychiatry, 62, 553–564.

Livneh, H., & Antonak, R. F. (1997). Psychosocial adaptation to chronic illness and disability. Aspen.

MacRae, A. (2019). Cara and Macrae's psychosocial occupational therapy: An evolving practice (4th ed.). Delmar Cengage Learning.

McKenzie, K., Milton, M., Smith, G., & Ouellette-Kuntz, H. (2016). Systematic review of the prevalence and incidence of intellectual disabilities: Current trends and issues. Current Developmental Disorders Reports, 3, 104–115.

Merikangas, K., He, J., Burstein, M., Swanson, S., Avenevoli, S., Cui, L., . . . Swendsen, J. (2010). Lifetime prevalence of mental disorders in U.S. adolescents: Results from the National Comorbidity Survey Replication-Adolescent Supplement (NCS-A). Journal of the American Academy of Child and Adolescent Psychiatry, 49(10), 980–989.

Miller, L. J. (2014). Sensational kids: Hope and help for children with sensory processing disorder (SPD) (Revised ed.). G. P. Putnam & Sons.

Moreira, A., Van Meter, A., Genzlinger, J., & Youngstrom, E. (2017). Review and meta-analysis of epidemiologic studies of adult bipolar disorder. Journal of Clinical Psychiatry, 78, 1259–1269.

Nasreddine, Z. S., Phillips, N. A., Bédirian, V., Charbonneau, S., Whitehead, V., Collin, I., . . . Chertkow, H. (2005). The Montreal Cognitive Assessment, MoCA: A brief screening tool for mild cognitive impairment. Journal of the American Geriatrics Society, 53, 695–699.

National Alliance on Mental Illness. (2017). Bipolar disorder. https://www.nami.org/About-Mental-Illness/Mental-Health-Conditions/Bipolar-Disorder.

National Board for Certification in Occupational Therapy (NBCOT®). (2022). 2022 Occupational Therapist Registered (OTR®) Examination Content Outline. https://www.nbcot.org/-/media/PDFs/2022_OTR_Content_Outline.pdf.

National Eating Disorders Association. (2022). Statistics and research on eating disorders. https://www.nationaleatingdisorders.org/statistics-research-eating-disorders.

National Institute on Drug Abuse. (2020). Sex and gender differences in substance use. https://www.drugabuse.gov/publications/research-reports/substance-use-in-women/sex-gender-differences-in-substance-use.

National Institute of Mental Health. (2022a). Depression. https://www.nimh.nih.gov/health/topics/depression.

National Institute of Mental Health. (2022b). Schizophrenia. https://www.nimh.nih.gov/health/topics/schizophrenia.

National Institute of Mental Health. (2023). Bipolar disorder. https://www.nimh.nih.gov/health/topics/bipolar-disorder.

O'Brien, J. C., & Kuhanek, H. (2019). Case-Smith's occupational therapy for children and adolescents (8th ed.). Mosby Elsevier.

PDR Staff. (2016). Physician's desk reference (71st ed.). PDR Network.

Potvin, D., & Ratto, A. (2019). Autism spectrum disorders. In M. L., Batshaw, N. J. Roizen, & L. Pellegrino (Eds.), Children with disabilities (8th ed., pp. 317–346). Paul H. Brookes.

Pritchett, R., Pritchett, J., Marshall, E., Davidson, C., & Minnis, H. (2013). Reactive attachment disorder in the general population: A hidden ESSENCE disorder. Scientific World Journal, 1–6.

Ryan, D. J., Oregan, N. A., Caoimh, R. Ó., Clare, J., O'Connor, M., Leonard, M., . . . & Timmons, S. (2013). Delirium in an adult acute hospital population: Predictors, prevalence and detection. BMJ Open, 3(1), 1–9.

Shapiro, B. K., & Batshaw, M. L. (2019). Intellectual disability. In M. L. Batshaw, N. J. Roizen, & L. Pellegrino (Eds.), Children with disabilities (8th ed., pp. 249–264). Paul H. Brookes.

Sheperis, C., Renfro-Michel, E., & Doggett, R. (2003). In-home treatment of reactive attachment disorder in a therapeutic foster care system: A case example. Journal of Mental Health Counseling, 25, 76–88.

Smink, F. R., Hoeken, D. V., & Hoek, H. W. (2012). Epidemiology of eating disorders: Incidence, prevalence and mortality rates. Current Psychiatry Reports, 14, 406–414.

Substance Abuse and Mental Health Services. (2023). Alcohol, tobacco, and other drugs. https://www.samhsa.gov/find-help/atod.

Swanson, S., Crow, S., Le Grange, D., Swendsen, J., & Merikangas, K. (2011). Prevalence and correlates of eating disorders in adolescents: Results from the national comorbidity survey replication adolescent supplement. Archives of General Psychiatry, 68, 714–723.

Tariq, S. H., Tumosa, N., Chibnall, J. T., Perry, M. H., & Morley, J. E. (2006). Comparison of the Saint Louis University Mental Status examination and the Mini-Mental State Examination for detecting dementia and mild neurocognitive disorder: A pilot study. American Journal of Geriatric Psychiatry, 14, 900–910.

United States Surgeon General. (2018). Surgeon general releases advisory on naloxone, an opioid overdose-reversing drug. https://www.hhs.gov/about/news/2018/04/05/surgeon-general-releases-advisory-on-naloxone-an-opioid-overdose-reversing-drug.html

Volkert, J., Gablonski, T., & Rabung, S. (2018). Prevalence of personality disorders in the general adult population in Western countries: Systematic review and meta-analysis. British Journal of Psychiatry, 213, 709–715.

Review Questions

Psychiatric and Cognitive Disorders

Below are five questions about key content covered in this chapter. These questions are not inclusive of the entirety of content related to psychiatric and cognitive disorders that you must know for success on the NBCOT® exam. These questions are provided to help you "jump start" the thought processes you will need to apply your studying of content to the answering of exam questions; hence they are not in the NBCOT® exam format. Exam items in the NBCOT® format which cover the depth and breadth of content you will need to know to pass the NBCOT® exam are provided in the three online practice exams that accompany this text. The answers to the below questions are provided in Appendix 2.

1. You are asked to provide consultation services for an individual who lives in a group home. The resident has become dehydrated and inconsistent in taking oral medications. You interview the resident about their daily habits and routines and learn that the resident will not drink the tap water in the group home. The resident states, "The water is poisoned. They are trying to poison me. If I drink the water I will die." Identify the psychiatric symptom that is preventing this person from drinking the water. Describe an intervention approach you would use to help the resident hydrate and take prescribed medications. Explain the importance of this person staying hydrated and taking prescribed medications.

2. Upon evaluation of an adolescent you find that the teen has great difficulty reading the various nonverbal behaviors of others (e.g., eye contact, facial expression, gestures and body language) that are needed to regulate social interactions. The adolescent has not been able to develop relationships with a peer group. They are is preoccupied with and intensely interested in World War II, its history, battles, and generals and talks about nothing else. The teen's bedroom is filled with World War II memorabilia and books about the war. Their cognitive, language and communication skills, and ADL development have been age-appropriate; however, they have not developed age-appropriate social interaction skills. Based on this information, what diagnosis is most reflective of this teen's functional status? What intervention goals would be helpful to work on with this adolescent?

3. You are conducting an evaluation of a 16-month-old toddler. The parent reports that the toddler has frequent tantrums with no clear precipitant. The parent thinks these behaviors may be the result of the toddler's frustration due to language delays. When unable to reach a toy, the toddler pulled the parent's hand toward the toy without pointing. The toddler also did not point to pictures in books. When playing with blocks or cars, the toddler lined them up, but did not spontaneously manipulate or move them. The toddler exhibited a rigid and limited repertoire of play and interaction skills. What diagnosis is most consistent with the toddler's presenting behaviors? Explain your rationale.

(Continued)

Review Questions

4. You are a home health therapist providing services to a client who is an older adult. The client's caregiver reports that the client is having trouble remembering things, sustaining attention, and making decisions. The caregiver reports the client seems mentally confused and asks whether the symptoms are indicative of dementia. As a therapist, you know that there are possible reversible causes of mental confusion. What are the reversible causes of mental confusion that you should consider during your intervention and inform the caregiver to consider for further evaluation?

5. You observe that a very thin client in your outpatient partial hospital program has been losing weight. The individual has no medical problems. The physician supervising the program states the client is well below the normal weight for age and height. The client participates in cooking groups with peers but will not eat whatever is prepared other than salad without dressing. When encouraged to try other foods, the client says, "I don't want to get fat, and I already need to lose a few pounds." You are concerned that the individual has anorexia nervosa. What signs of this eating disorder are being exhibited? What additional symptoms would you expect to see that would indicate this diagnosis?

Biomechanical Approaches: Evaluation and Intervention

COLLEEN MAHER and RITA P. FLEMING-CASTALDY

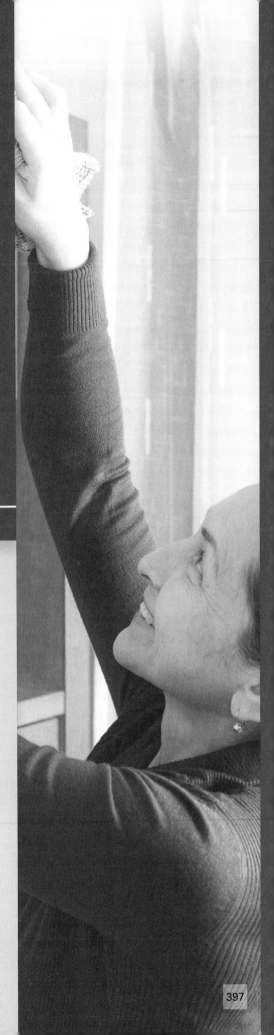

Biomechanical Approach

Overview

EXAM HINT: The NBCOT® OTR® exam content outline identifies the task of assessing "a client's functional skills, roles, prioritized needs and wants, and performance context to evaluate their occupational performance" (NBCOT®, 2022, p. 4) as essential to competent and safe entry-level practice and states that performance of this task requires knowledge of "resources and considerations for acquiring information about the client's current condition and occupational performance . . . (including) theoretical approach and frame of reference" (NBCOT®, 2022, p. 4). Thus, the application of knowledge about the biomechanical frame of reference will be required to correctly answer NBCOT® exam items about working with persons with musculoskeletal disorders.

1. The biomechanical approach focuses on the range of motion, strength, and endurance required to perform an occupation.
2. It is most commonly used to treat persons with lower motor neuron deficits and orthopedic problems.
3. The biomechanical approach should *not* be used in isolation.
   a. This approach is most effective when used in combination with other occupational therapy (OT) theoretical approaches, models of practice, and frames of reference that focus on the person's engagement in meaningful occupations and desired purposeful activities. Refer to Chapter 14.
4. Settings that most commonly use the biomechanical approach.
   a. Hand clinics.
   b. Work programs.
   c. Physical medicine and rehabilitation (PM&R) departments.
   d. Ergonomic programs.

Evaluation

EXAM HINT: In the NBCOT® OTR® exam content outline, Domain 1 Evaluation and Assessment comprises 23% of the exam and knowledge of the "administration, purpose, indications, advantages, and limitations of standardized and nonstandardized screening and assessment tools" (NBCOT®, 2022, p. 4) is identified as essential for competent and safe practice. Thus, the application of knowledge about the following biomechanical assessment tools and procedures can help you correctly answer Domain 1 exam items about the evaluation of persons with musculoskeletal disorders.

Range of Motion (ROM)

1. Measurement tool: goniometer consisting of an axis, stationary and movable arms.
2. Prior to assessing ROM, check prescription and chart for specific ROM orders and ROM restrictions.
3. Always begin with a ROM screen to determine which movements need to be tested.
4. Begin in the anatomical position.
   a. There are exceptions such as the forearm for which it begins with the elbow flexed to 90° and the forearm in neutral.

5. Types of ROM.
   a. Functional ROM: ROM needed to perform functional movements (e.g., reach to top of head, small of back).
   b. AROM: active ROM - movement produced by one's own muscle.
   c. PROM: passive ROM - movement produced by an external force.
   d. AAROM: active assistive ROM, movement produced by one's own muscles and assisted by an external force.
   e. Finger ROM: total active motion (TAM) and total passive motion (TPM).
      (1) Measures tendon excursion.
      (2) Add extension deficits and subtract from flexion measurement, e.g., for digit 2 (index finger) measurements of MCP 10°–50°, PIP 15°–75°, and DIP 0°–10°; the TAM is 110°.
      (3) An alternative method to measure finger ROM is to measure flexion of the digits to the distal palmar crease (DPC) in centimeters (cm) (Adam, Grenne, & Toppzian, 1992; Rowe & Zeiner, 2021).
6. There are precautions and contraindications to performing joint measurements.

CAUTION: The therapist should maintain close communication with the physician to determine the conditions in which ROM measurements should be restricted or are contraindicated.

a. The following are examples of conditions that should prompt the therapist to consult with the physician prior to proceeding with ROM measurements.
   (1) Bone metastasis.
   (2) Unhealed fracture or recent dislocation.
   (3) Infection.
   (4) Postsurgery.
   (5) Unstable joints.
   (6) Joint inflammation
   (7) Skin grafts.
   (8) Others as identified by the physician (Shurtleff & Kaskutas, 2018).
7. Recording measurements.
   a. Neutral zero method: anatomical position is 0.
   b. Starting position/ending position (e.g., 0°–15°).
   c. Do not use negatives (Rowe & Zeiner, 2021; Shurtleff & Kaskutas, 2018).
   d. Within functional limits (WFL): ROM is functional.
   e. Within normal limits (WNL): ROM achieves normal ranges (e.g., shoulder flexion 0°–180°).
8. Review bony landmarks and normal ranges. Refer to Table 11-1 for the average normal joint ROM measurements.

EXAM HINT: The application of the above ROM information will be required to correctly answer NBCOT® exam items. For example, a NBCOT® OTR® exam item scenario may include ROM measurements for a person's upper extremity. Based on these measurements, you will need to determine if the person's ROM is within functional limits or if there are limitations that will inhibit activity performance. Based on this analysis, you will need to select the best activity for an intervention session focused on improving the person's occupational performance.

Muscle Strength

1. Begin by performing a MMT screen to determine which muscles need to be tested.
2. Types of manual muscle tests (MMTs) (Kaskutas, 2018; Rowe & Zeiner, 2021).
   a. Break test is the most common MMT.
      (1) Test position: gravity eliminated (lessened) or against gravity.
      (2) Stabilization: usually proximal to the joint the muscle crosses over. Do not hold over the muscle belly being tested.

(3) Resistance: applied in opposite direction of movement; should be gradual.
(4) Muscle grades: refer to Table 11-2.

Grip Strength

1. Measurement tool: dynamometer.
2. Position of upper extremity: shoulder adducted to side, elbow flexed to 90°, and forearm in neutral.
3. Types of grip strength tests.
   a. Dynamometer handle placed on position #2. The mean of three trials of each hand is compared to the norms (Rowe & Zeiner, 2021).
   b. One trial in all five positions for each hand. A bell curve is observed if the individual is applying maximal effort.
   c. Sphygmomanometer cuff, vigorimeter, or handheld bulb dynamometer should be used to evaluate the grip strength of a person with arthritis or an older adult. The bulb dynamometer has become a more popular alternative to the Jamar dynamometer.

Pinch Strength

1. Measurement tool: pinchmeter.
2. Position of upper extremity: shoulder adducted to side, elbow flexed to 90°, and forearm in neutral.
3. Types of pinch strength test.
   a. Key or lateral pinch: thumb pulp to the lateral aspect of the index middle phalanx.
   b. Three jaw chuck (palmar pinch): pulp of thumb to pulps of index and middle fingers.
   c. Tip to tip: thumb pulp to pulp of index finger.
4. Three trials on each hand are obtained for all pinch strengths. The mean of three trials on each hand is compared to the norms (Rowe & Zeiner, 2021).

Endurance/Activity Tolerance

1. Two types: muscular endurance and cardiorespiratory endurance.
2. Muscular endurance.
   a. Count number of repetitions per unit of time.
   b. Measure time until fatigue while holding isometric contraction.
3. Cardiorespiratory endurance.
   a. Use metabolic equivalent (MET) levels (Sahu, 2017).
   b. Measure frequency, intensity, and time to complete activity (Adam et al., 1992; Rowe & Zeiner, 2021).
4. Refer to Chapter 8.

Chapter 11

Table 11-1

Joint ROM Measurements

	ROM
Spine	
Cervical Spine	
Flexion	0–45
Extension	0–45
Lateral flexion	0–45
Rotation	0–60
Thoracic and Lumbar Spine	
Flexion	0–80
Extension	0–30
Lateral flexion	0–40
Rotation	0–45
Shoulder	
Flexion	0–170
Extension	0–60
Abduction	0–170
Horizontal abduction	0–40
Horizontal adduction	0–130
Internal rotation	0–70
External rotation	0–90
Elbow and Forearm	
Flexion	0–135–150
Supination	0–80–90
Pronation	0–80–90
Wrist	
Flexion	0–80
Extension	0–70
Ulnar deviation	0–30
Radial deviation	0–20
Thumb	
MP flexion	0–50
IP flexion	0–80–90
Adduction	0–50
Fingers	
MP flexion	0–90
MP hyperextension	0–15–45
PIP flexion	0–110
DIP flexion	0–80
Abduction	0–25

(Continued)

Table 11-1

Joint ROM Measurements (*Continued*)

	ROM
Hip	
Flexion	0–120
Extension	0–30
Abduction	0–40
Adduction	0–35
Internal rotation	0–45
External rotation	0–45
Knee	
Flexion	0–135
Ankle and Foot	
Plantar flexion	0–50
Dorsiflexion	0–15
Inversion	0–35
Eversion	0–20

Reprinted from Shurtleff, T., & Kaskutas, V. (2018). Joint range of motion. In H. M. Pendleton & W. Schultz-Krohn (Eds.), Pedretti's occupational therapy: Practice skills for physical dysfunction (8th ed. p. 484). Elsevier. Copyright 2018 by Elsevier Inc. Reprinted with permission.

Edema

1. The body's initial response to injury.
   a. It is the transfer of exudate in which the fluid from the bloodstream moves to the interstitial tissue.
   b. Edema can be localized or diffuse.
2. Types.
   a. Pitting - acute: finger makes an indentation.
   b. Brawny (nonpitting) - chronic: firm to touch.
3. Evaluation of circumference.
   a. Measurement tool: tape measure, recorded in centimeters.
   b. Compare extremities, document landmarks.
   c. To measure the entire hand, use the figure-of-eight method; this is the most reliable method.
4. Evaluation of hand and arm mass.
   a. Measurement tool: volumeter, recorded in milliliters (mL).
   b. Significant change in edema would be more than 10 mL (Olvera-Dyckes, 2020; Rowe & Zeiner, 2021).
5. Edema scale.
   a. Refer to Table 11-3.

Table 11-2

Muscle Testing Grading System

GRADE	DEFINITION	DESCRIPTION
5	Normal	The part moves through full ROM against gravity and takes maximal resistance.
4	Good	The part moves through full ROM against gravity and takes moderate resistance.
4–	Good minus	The part moves through full ROM against gravity and takes less than moderate resistance.
3+	Fair plus	The part moves through full ROM against gravity and takes minimal resistance before it breaks.
3	Fair	The part moves through full ROM against gravity and is unable to take any added resistance.
3–	Fair minus	The part moves less than full range of motion against gravity.
2+	Poor plus	The part moves through full ROM in a gravity-eliminated plane, takes minimal resistance, and then breaks.
2	Poor	The part moves through full range of motion in a gravity-eliminated plane, no resistance.
2–	Poor minus	The part moves less than full ROM in a gravity-eliminated plane, no resistance.
1	Trace	Tension is palpated in the muscle or tendon, but no motion occurs at the joint.
0	Zero	No tension is palpated in the muscle or tendon.

Rowe, V., & Zeiner, T.L. (2021). Motor function assessment: Range of motion, strength, and endurance. In D.P. Dirette & S.A. Gutman (Eds.), Occupational therapy for physical dysfunction (8th ed., p. 227). Wolters Kluwer. Reprinted with permission.

Sensation

1. Demonstrate sensory test with vision; then occlude vision for actual testing.
2. Test uninvolved side first. Apply stimulus to volar and dorsal surfaces (exceptions will be noted).

CAUTION: Standard application procedures for the progressive application of sensory testing stimuli must be followed to ensure assessment validity. These standards are based on diagnoses.
- Spinal cord injuries are tested proximal to distal following dermatome pattern (ASIA scale; refer to Chapter 7).
- Neurologic disorders are tested for dermatome pattern.
- Peripheral nerve injuries are tested distal to proximal following peripheral nerves.

Table 11-3

Edema Scale

SCORE	CLINICAL SIGNS
0	• No edema
+1	• Barely discernable pit; immediate rebound • Normal foot and leg contours
+2	• Deeper pit (<5 mm); a few seconds to rebound • Fairly normal foot and leg contours
+3	• Deep pit (5–10 mm); 10–12 seconds to rebound • Foot and leg swelling
+4	• Even deeper pit (>1 cm); >20 seconds to rebound • Severe foot and leg swelling

Shotwell, M. P., Robinson Johnson, K., & Miranda-Flecha, I. (2017). Evaluation of acute care patients. In H. Smith-Gabai and S.E. Holm (Eds.), Occupational therapy in acute care (2nd ed., p. 53). AOTA Press. Reprinted with permission.

3. Peripheral nerve injuries assess for peripheral nerve involvement. Order of return: pain, moving touch, static light touch, and touch localization.
4. Types of sensory testing.
   a. Light touch: cotton swab or cotton ball. Person responds "yes" or "touched" when touched. Scoring: + (intact), – (impaired), or 0 (absent).
   b. Localization: cotton swab. Person responds "yes" when touched and then with vision points to area touched. Scoring +, –, 0.
   c. Pain (protective sensation): opened paper clip. Person responds "sharp" or "dull." Scoring: correct response indicates "intact" pain sensation, incorrect responses indicate "impaired" pain sensation. No sense of either sharp or dull is "absent."
      (1) Note: a response of sharp to the dull stimulus may indicate hypersensitivity (Abrams & Ivy, 2018).
   d. Temperature sensation: test tubes or thermal kit. Person responds "hot" or "cold." Scoring: +, –, 0.
      (1) Prior to using physical agent modalities with extreme temperatures, it is recommended to test temperature sensation from a safety standpoint to avoid burns (Abrams & Ivy, 2018).
   e. Stereognosis: recognition by touch of common objects. Scoring: number of correct objects.
      (1) A second set of identical common objects should be used for individuals with expressive aphasia.
   f. Moving two-point discrimination: Disk-Criminator, Boley Guage, or paper clip.
      (1) Testing begins with points 5–8 mm apart.
      (2) Applied proximal to distal on fingertips in a longitudinal orientation following the digital nerve.
      (3) Person responds to the number of points they feel, "one" or "two."

(4) Seven out of ten responses must be correct before decreasing the distance of the two points.
(5) Scoring: normal = 2 mm (Dellon, 1978; Klein, 2020; Stone, 1992).
g. Static two-point discrimination: Disk-Criminator, Boley Guage, or paper clip.
   (1) Test begins at 5 mm.
   (2) Applied to fingertips in a longitudinal orientation.
   (3) Person states "one" or "two" in response to the number of points they feel.
   (4) Distance between points is increased until seven out of ten responses are correct.
   (5) Test is stopped at 15 mm.
   (6) Scoring.
      (a) Normal = 5 mm.
      (b) Fair = 6–10 mm.
      (c) Poor = 11–15 mm.
      (d) Protective = one point perceived.
      (e) Anesthetic = no points perceived (Bell Krotoski, 2011; Dellon, 1987; Klein, 2020; Stone, 1992).
h. Touch/Pressure Test: determines light touch and deep pressure by using monofilaments (Semmes Weinstein); the most reliable sensory assessment.
   (1) Monofilaments are applied perpendicular to the skin.
   (2) Scoring: normal is 2.83; diminished light touch is 3.61; diminished protective sensation is 4.31; loss of protective sensation is 6.65, and untestable is > than 6.65 (Stone, 1992).
i. Proprioception: position sense.
   (1) The OT practitioner positions involved extremity.
   (2) Person duplicates position with contralateral extremity.
j. Kinesthesia: movement sense.
   (1) The OT practitioner moves segment.
   (2) Person responds up or down.
5. Refer to Figure 6 in Chapter 6 and Table 11-4 for dermatome distribution.

Coordination/Dexterity/Functional Assessments

1. The evaluations included in this chapter are based on the author's review of NBCOT® self-assessment tools, major OT textbooks, and feedback obtained from OT practitioners regarding measures used in practice.
   a. As of the publication of this text, NBCOT® has not made public the names of the specific evaluation tools that may be on the exam.
2. Types of coordination and dexterity assessments.

EXAM HINT: The NBCOT® OTR® exam may include the names of specific evaluation tools; therefore, a review of major commercially available coordination assessments is important for NBCOT® exam preparation. This can increase understanding and knowledge of common approaches in the evaluation of coordination and further strengthen the clinical reasoning skills needed to answer exam items that address the evaluation of coordination.

a. Purdue Pegboard.
   (1) Test of fingertip dexterity and assembly job simulation.
   (2) Subtests.
      (a) Thirty-second test: right hand, left hand, both hands, R+, L+, both.
      (b) One-minute test: assembly.
   (3) Scoring: thirty second test is the number of pins placed in the board in 30 seconds. Assembly is the number of parts assembled during one minute.
b. Minnesota Manual Dexterity Test.
   (1) Test of gross hand and arm movements.
   (2) Subtests.
      (a) Placing test: measures rate of hand movement (one hand only).
      (b) Turning test: measures rate of finger manipulation (bilateral).
   (3) Scoring: time to complete board. One practice trial and four scored trials.
c. O'Connor Tweezer Test.
   (1) Test of eye-hand coordination using tweezers.
   (2) Scoring: the number of seconds to place all pins in board using tweezers.
d. Crawford Small Parts Dexterity Test.
   (1) Test of fine motor dexterity using small tools (tweezers and screwdriver).
   (2) Scoring: time to complete assembly.
e. Nine Hole Peg Test.
   (1) Measures finger dexterity.
   (2) Scoring: time for each hand to place nine pegs in a square board and remove them.
   (3) The Purdue Pegboard is preferred over the Nine Hole Peg Test because it is unilateral and bilateral. It is also more reliable.
f. Jebson-Taylor Hand Function Test.
   (1) Test of hand function.
   (2) Seven subtests.
      (a) Writing.
      (b) Simulated page turning.
      (c) Picking up common objects.
      (d) Simulated feeding.
      (e) Stacking.
      (f) Picking up large light objects.
      (g) Picking up large heavy objects.
   (3) Scoring: time to complete each subject.

Table 11-4

Dermatomes

SPINAL SEGMENT	DERMATOME LOCATION	MUSCLES FACILITATED	FUNCTION
CN V	Anterior facial region	Mastication	Ingestion
C3	Neck region	Sternocleidomastoid, upper trapezius	Head control
C4	Upper shoulder region	Trapezius (diaphragm)	Head control
C5	Lateral aspect of shoulder	Deltoid, biceps, rhomboid major and minor	Elbow flexion
C6	Thumb and radial forearm	Extensor carpi radialis, biceps	Shoulder abduction, wrist extension
C7	Middle finger	Triceps, extensors of wrist and fingers	Wrist flexion, finger extension
C8	Little finger, ulnar forearm	Flexor of wrist and fingers	C8 finger flexion
T1	Axilla and proximal medial arm	Hand intrinsics	Abduction and adduction of fingers
T2–T12	Thorax	Intercostals	Respiration
T4–T6	Nipple line	Intercostals	Respiration
T11	Midchest region, lower rib	Abdominal wall, abdominal muscles	T5–T7 superficial abdominal reflex
T10	Umbilicus	Psoas, iliacus	Leg flexion
L1–L2	Inside of thigh	Cremasteric reflex, accessory muscles	Elevation of scrotum
L2	Proximal anterior thigh	Iliopsoas, adductors of thigh	Reflex voiding
L3–L4	Anterior knee	Quadriceps, tibialis anterior, detrusor urinae	Hip flexion, extensors of knee, abductors of thigh
L5	Great toe	Lateral hamstrings	Flexion at knee, toe extension
L5–S1	Foot region	Gastrocnemius, soleus, extensor digitorum longus	Flexor withdrawal, urinary retention
S2	Narrow band of posterior thigh	Small muscles of foot (flexor digitorum, flexor hallucis)	Bladder retention

McCormack, G. (1996). The Rood approach to treatment of neuromuscular dysfunction. In L. W. Pedretti (Ed.), Occupational therapy: Practice skills for physical dysfunction (4th ed., p. 383). Elsevier/Mosby. Reprinted with permission.

3. The OT practitioner should determine which assessment is best based on the individual's occupational profile.

> **EXAM HINT:** When answering exam items about the best evaluation tool to use with a person, pay careful attention to information that is provided in the exam item scenario about the person's roles and related activities. For example, the best assessment to use with a person who is identified as having the role of a jeweler is the O'Connor tweezer test. This assessment requires fine manipulation of small pins using a tweezer, which is a tool used by jewelers. For an exam item that states the person works as a machinist who assembles small parts, the best assessment would be the Purdue Pegboard assembly test.

4. Informal assessment of coordination should include the following.
   a. Fine motor: observation of routine task performance.
      (1) Handwriting, manipulation of various-sized objects, handling money, cutting food, and buttoning are examples of daily tasks that should be observed to assess fine motor coordination.
   b. Gross motor: observation of activities that include gross motor movements.
      (1) Tossing a ball, reaching into cabinets for specific items, and dressing are examples of activities that should be observed to assess gross motor coordination.

Role of the Occupational Therapy Assistant (OTA)/ Certified Occupational Therapy Assistant (COTA®)

1. The OTA/COTA® can contribute to the evaluation process in collaboration with the occupational therapist.
   a. Supervision by an occupational therapist is required.
   b. The level of supervision required will be determined by the OTA's/COTA®'s experience.
2. Service competency must be established.
3. The OTA/COTA® cannot independently evaluate or interpret evaluation results.

Intervention

Increasing Range of Motion

1. Passive ROM and passive stretching.
   a. PROM is moving the joint to the desired range using an external force.
      (1) PROM can be performed by the OT practitioner gently moving the extremity to the desired range or when resistance is felt.
   b. Passive stretching is PROM with overpressure.

> **CAUTION:** A careful review of the physician's orders is paramount to distinguish the type of passive exercise being requested.

   c. Heat or other thermal agents prior to stretch increases extensibility.
   d. Joint mobilization requires special training. It is more effective when performed before passive ROM.
   e. Manual stretching within the individual's tolerance.
      (1) Contract/relax and hold/relax increase ROM.
   f. Codman's exercise (pendulum exercise): common form of PROM used for postsurgical shoulder patients.
      (1) Refer to Figure 11-1.
   g. Instruction in home exercises. Stress the importance of home exercises to facilitate change in tissue length.
   h. Orthoses: dynamic mobilization (acute joint stiffness), static progressive, and serial casting (chronic joint stiffness) (Hock & DeMott, 2021).
   i. Exercise equipment: continuous passive movement (CPM), pulleys.
2. Active ROM.
   a. Should be performed when PROM is greater than AROM.
   b. Differential tendon gliding exercises: differentiates tendon movement and increases tendon excursion.
      (1) Refer to Figure 11-2.

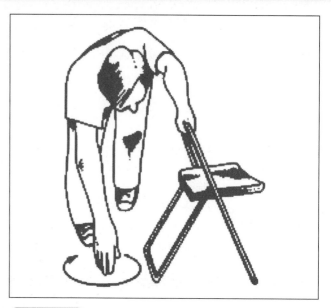

Figure 11-1 Codman's exercise.

Hawkins, R. J., Bell, R. H., & Lippitt, S. B. (1996). Atlas of shoulder surgery. St. Louis, MO: Mosby. Reprinted with permission.

   c. Blocking exercises: used to isolate individual joint motion.
   d. Emphasize functional use; encourage use for ADL and role activities.
   e. Additional ROM interventions to support occupations: wall walking, AROM, cane exercises.
   f. Purposeful and occupation-based activities: ADL, IADL, and work activities. Incorporate the individual's leisure interests (e.g., crafts, games, sports).

> **CAUTION:** Heterotopic ossification may result from overstretching (especially noted in elbow flexors).

Increasing Strength

1. High resistance, low repetitions.
2. Type of contractions.
   a. Isometrics: contraction without movement.
      (1) Sometimes can produce more forceful contraction.

> **RED FLAG:** Isometrics are contraindicated for persons with hypertension and cardiovascular problems. They can increase blood pressure (BP) and heart rate (HR), so they should be avoided.

   b. Isotonic: contraction with movement.
      (1) Eccentric = lengthening.
      (2) Concentric = shortening.

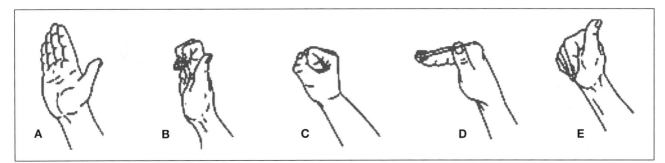

Figure 11-2 **Tendon gliding exercises.**
The five positions: A. Straight. B. Hook. C. Fist. D. Tabletop. E. Straight fist. Adapted with permission from Rozmaryn, L. M., Dovelle, S., Rothman, E. R., Gorman, K., Olvey, K. M., & Bartko, J. J. (1998). Nerve and tendon gliding exercises and the conservative management of carpal tunnel syndrome. Journal of Hand Therapy, 11, 171–179. Reprinted with permission.

c. How to distinguish the type of contraction during a functional activity.
   (1) Anytime a person moves against gravity or away from the earth they are performing a concentric contraction. Also, when a person moves in a horizontal plane it is always a concentric contraction. Examples include the following.
      (a) Reaching into a cabinet above shoulder level would be a concentric contraction of the shoulder flexor (anterior deltoid).
      (b) Reaching over to wash the opposite axilla would be a concentric contraction of the shoulder adductor (pectoralis major).
   (2) Anytime a person moves with gravity or toward the earth it can be a concentric or an eccentric contraction. Examples include the following.
      (a) When the arm is used to remove a glass from an overhead cabinet and the person slowly lowers the glass to the counter (the movement is toward extension) that is an eccentric contraction of the anterior deltoid (the muscle is acting as a brake to slowly lower the arm down).
      (b) When a person lowers their arm with force, such as slamming a book down on a desk, this is a concentric contraction of the shoulder and elbow extensors.
   (3) The performance of tasks requires a combination of different types of muscle contractions. For example, lifting groceries from the trunk of a car to chest level (concentric), carrying the groceries from the car into the kitchen (isometric), and then slowly lowering the groceries onto the table (eccentric).

Increasing Endurance

1. Work at 50% of maximal resistance or less.
2. Increase repetitions and duration, not resistance.
3. Use energy conservation methods.

Edema Reduction Techniques

EXAM HINT: The NBCOT® OTR® exam content outline identifies knowledge of the "techniques for . . . edema reduction . . . (including) manual edema mobilization (NBCOT®, 2022, p. 10) as required for competent and safe practice. The application of knowledge about the following edema reduction techniques can help you determine the correct answer for NBCOT® exam items involving working with clients who have edema.

1. Elevation: extremity should be placed above the heart.

CAUTION: Avoid extreme positions of elevation for individuals with right-sided heart weakness; this can cause the fluid to empty into the heart too fast.

2. AROM: assists with fluid drainage.
3. Manual edema mobilization (MEM): hands-on technique that activates the lymphatic system to remove edema.
   a. This technique requires specialized training. The efficacy of MEM is supported by evidence (Artzberger, 2014).

RED FLAG: MEM is contraindicated with CHF, cardiac or pulmonary problems, renal problems, liver disease, active cancer, blood clot, and active infection (Borst, 2021).

4. Retrograde massage assists with the return of blood and lymphatic fluids to the venous system.
   a. Although this type of massage is still being used, it has limited evidence to support its efficacy; thus, it is slowly being replaced by MEM.
   b. Instructions.
      (1) Gentle stroking is applied in centripetal direction.

(2) Massage should be performed with the extremity elevated.

> **RED FLAG:** Retrograde massage is contraindicated when cardiac edema is present.

5. Compression garments prevent reaccumulation of fluids following massage. Garments should not be too tight.
   a. Common types.
      (1) Compression glove.
      (2) Stockinet with elastic (Tubigrip™): watch rolling.
      (3) Ace wraps.
      (4) Custom-made compression garments.
      (5) Coban™ wrap (digit is wrapped distal to proximal).
         (a) Effective for decreasing edema in a digit.
         (b) Avoid too much tension.
         (c) The individual can exercise and use their hand for ADL and role activities while wearing Coban™.
6. Cold packs: most effective when combined with elevation.
   a. Monitor vascular status.

> **RED FLAG:** Contraindications include impaired sensation, nerve regeneration, impaired circulation, DVT, thrombophlebitis, and chronic wounds (Olvera-Dyckes, 2020, p. 103).

7. Contrast bath.
   a. Technique of immersing the hand in warm (temperature of bath water) and cold water.
      (1) Evidence is conflicting as to its effectiveness in reducing hand edema.
8. Other edema techniques: elastic bandage wraps and intermittent compression pump.
   a. These techniques are not as common.

> **CAUTION:** Heat is commonly contraindicated. However, if the use of heat is warranted in a mild case of edema, it could be cautiously used and combined with elevation.

> **RED FLAG:** MEM and other edema interventions are contraindicated for many conditions.
> • Do **NOT** use with people with infection, grafts, or wounds; vascular/circulation damage; blood clots; unstable fractures; active cancer; uncontrolled hypertension; congestive heart failure (CHF) or cardiac edema; kidney problems; active TB; liver disease; and severe pulmonary problems (Borst, 2021; Olvera-Dyckes, 2020).

Scar Management

1. ROM: early mobilization programs are most effective.
2. Massage (circles and friction).
3. Compression: Coban™ for digits, compression glove for the hand, and compression sleeve for the upper extremity.
4. Scar pad with compression. Scar pads can be purchased at health supply stores.
5. Orthotics: to prevent contractures resulting from scar.
6. Edema control: especially in acute phase.

Sensory Training

1. Desensitization for hypersensitivity.
   a. If postsurgery, begin in periphery of the scar and as tolerated work over the scar.
   b. Massage.
   c. Textures (graded materials and contact particles); 10–15 minutes, 3–4 times daily.
   d. Vibration.
   e. Desensitization kits (commercial and homemade).
   f. Fluidotherapy.
   g. Desensitization program: should be performed several times daily.

> **EXAM HINT:** The NBCOT® OTR® exam content outline states the task of selecting and implementing "interventions for improving sensory . . . status, considering client condition and current stage of recovery, to support occupational performance" (NBCOT®, 2022, p. 10) is essential to entry-level practice and that performance of this task requires knowledge of the "techniques for sensory . . . reeducation" (NBCOT®, 2022, p. 10). The application of knowledge about the above desensitization methods and the following sensory reeducation approaches can help you determine the correct answer for NBCOT® exam items about working with clients who are hypersensitive or have impaired sensation.

2. Sensory reeducation.
   a. Same as b through e in number 1 above.
      (1) For textures: apply textures (five different types) for one minute with the person's eyes open and then one minute with eyes closed.
   b. Mirror therapy: use textures in both hands to stimulate sensory receptors-cortical reorganization. Refer to Chapter 12.
   c. Review safety precautions.

d. Loss of protective sensation: the person is at high risk for injury.

> CAUTION: For a person with impaired or no protective sensation, the OT practitioner must emphasize safety precautions and teach the person to avoid use of hands where vision is occluded.

e. Impaired discriminative sensation: the person has protective sensation, but they have difficulty discriminating objects from one another or identifying an object when vision is occluded. Examples of activities include identifying objects (discriminative training) with eyes closed and picking objects out of a rice bowl (Abrams & Ivy, 2018).

Improving Coordination

1. Begin with gross motor activities and gradually grade up to fine motor activities.
2. Select activities in which the ROM required is within the person's reach and yet challenging.
3. Focus on accuracy and speed.
    a. Begin with slow gross movements and gradually progress to faster precise movements.

Energy Conservation and Work Simplification Principles and Methods

1. Plan short rest periods (5–10 minutes) during daily routine.
2. Schedule tasks for the day, week, and month to alternate and balance heavy and light work tasks.
3. Organize tasks; gather all necessary items and equipment before beginning task.
4. Avoid multiple trips to obtain items by using a utility cart, a bucket, walker bag, and/or backpack to carry all items needed in one trip.
5. Eliminate tasks that are nonessential.
6. Delegate tasks that are beyond one's capacity.
7. Combine tasks to eliminate extraneous work.
8. Sit to work at a table or use a high stool for countertop work.
9. Organize cabinets so that items are easy to reach and in convenient locations.
10. Use adaptive equipment (e.g., reachers) to avoid bending and stooping.
11. Use electrical appliances (e.g., mixers) to decrease personal effort.
12. Slide rather than lift heavy items.
13. Use lightweight equipment, tools, and utensils.

14. Rest before fatigue sets in; intermittent rest during an activity is more effective than resting after exhaustion has occurred.

> CAUTION: An activity should not be started, if it cannot be immediately stopped when fatigued.

> EXAM HINT: In the NBCOT® OTR® exam content outline, knowledge of the "methods for grading an activity, task, or technique based on . . . client status, response to intervention, and client needs" (NBCOT®, 2022, pp. 8–9) is identified as essential for competent and safe practice. The application of knowledge about the above energy conservation and work simplification principles and methods and the following joint protection principles and methods can help you determine the correct answer to NBCOT® exam items about the implementation of adaptive interventions that enable occupational performance.

Joint Protection Principles and Methods

1. Maintain joint ROM by using maximal ROM during daily activities.
2. Maintain muscle strength by using maximal strength during daily activities.
3. Use the strongest and largest joint that is possible for task completion.
    a. Use knees and hips for lifting, not the back.
    b. Push large items that need to be moved with a full body rather than pulling.
    c. Lift objects with both hands, palms pointed upward.
    d. Carry purses, bags on the forearm rather than wrist; most preferred is use of an ergonomically designed backpack.
4. Use each joint in its most stable and functional position.
    a. Stand directly in front of item to be reached for, opened or closed, rather than to the side.
    b. Keep wrists and fingers in proper alignment.
5. Avoid holding joints in one position or sustaining muscle contractions for extended periods of time.
    a. Use adaptive equipment to hold items for long periods of time (e.g., a book holder).
    b. Take breaks from extended activities.
6. Avoid positions of deformity and activities in the direction of deformity (e.g., ulnar drift).
    a. Perform movements in the direction opposite the potential deformity (e.g., opening a door with the left hand and closing it with the right hand to prevent ulnar drift).

b. Use adaptive equipment that is ergonomically designed (e.g., tools and utensils with angled handles that eliminate deviations at the wrist).

7. Do not start an activity that cannot be immediately stopped if it requires capacities beyond existing capabilities.

> **CAUTION:** Recognize that some discomfort may be a reality of activity performance, but pain is a warning sign that indicates an activity should be modified or stopped (Hammond, 2014).

Body Mechanics Principles and Methods

> **EXAM HINT:** The NBCOT® OTR® exam content outline identifies knowledge of the "techniques for promoting . . . body mechanics . . . during functional tasks" (NBCOT®, 2022, p. 10) and "preventive measures for minimizing risk and promoting safety . . . (including) proper body mechanics" (NBCOT®, 2022, p. 13) as required for competent and safe practice. The application of knowledge about the following body mechanics principles and methods can help you determine the correct answer to NBCOT® exam items about the use of these to enable occupational performance.

1. Do not move items that are too heavy; ask for assistance.
2. Slide or push an object along the surface rather than lift it, if possible.
3. Directly face the object about to be lifted. Do not face the direction in which the item is going to move.
4. Keep object close to the body during lifting and carrying.
5. Hold object centered at waist level.
6. Feet should be kept flat on the floor; balancing on toes should be avoided.
7. Maintain a firm and broad base of support. Maintain the body balanced over a wide stance.
8. Bend at the knees and hips, not at the waist.
9. Keep the back as straight as possible.
10. Breathe while lifting.
11. Lift by straightening legs; do not pull upward with arms and back.
12. Move smoothly; do not jerk.
13. Do not rotate or twist the trunk. Pick up the object completely and then pivot the entire body.
14. Lower the body to the level of work (Maher, 2014).
15. Refer to Chapter 15.

> **EXAM HINT:** Recognize that the principles, methods, and techniques of energy conservation, work simplification, joint protection, and body mechanics are not just applicable to persons with musculoskeletal disorders. Thus, the integration of these principles and techniques with knowledge of diagnostic information will likely be required to correctly answer exam items. For example, exam item scenarios that include individuals with progressive conditions such as Friedreich's ataxia, ALS, MS, COPD, and Duchenne muscular dystrophy will often have a correct answer that includes activity modifications that employ energy conservation and work simplification principles to prevent fatigue and maximize function.
>
> Similarly, the integration of these principles and techniques with knowledge of activity demands and the principles of activity analysis will likely be required to correctly answer exam items. For example, the correct answer to an exam item about a person doing a task that places them at risk for a repetitive stress disorder or a work injury will likely require you to apply your knowledge of joint protection and body mechanics principles and techniques, regardless of the person's diagnosis.

Orthotics

1. Orthoses, also referred to as splints, are used to manage many conditions.
   a. While the term "splint" is commonly used in practice, for the purpose of reimbursement the terms "orthotic" or "orthosis" must be used.

> **EXAM HINT:** In the NBCOT® OTR® exam content outline, knowledge of the "types and functions of immobilization, mobilization, and restriction orthoses for managing specific conditions and congenital anomalies across the life span" (NBCOT®, 2022, p. 10) is identified as essential for competent and safe practice; thus, knowledge of the following information will help you determine the correct answer to NBCOT® items about working with people who need orthoses.

2. Types of orthotics.
   a. Static: has no moving parts and immobilizes a joint or part.
   b. Dynamic: includes a resilient component (elastic, rubber band, or spring) that the individual moves.
      (1) Designed to increase PROM or to augment AROM.
   c. Serial static orthosis: a static orthosis or the use of casting material that is remolded to address changes in joint motion.

(1) Designed to increase PROM by lengthening tissue.

d. Static progressive orthosis: includes a static adjustment part (e.g., turnbuckle or strap) that allows the person or OT practitioner to make changes in the tension or angle to increase motion without remodeling the orthosis (Hock & DeMott, 2021).

3. Purposes of orthotics.
   a. Rest.
   b. Prevent deformities and contractures.
   c. Increase joint ROM.
   d. Protect bone, joint, and soft tissue.
   e. Increase functional use.
   f. Decrease pain.
   g. Restrict ROM.

4. Hand orthotic design standards.
   a. Maintain arches of the hand.
      (1) Proximal transverse arch.
      (2) Distal transverse arch.
      (3) Longitudinal arch.
   b. Do not impinge upon creases of the hand.
      (1) Distal and proximal palmar creases.
      (2) Distal and proximal wrist creases.
      (3) Thenar crease.

> **EXAM HINT:** Correct answers to NBCOT® exam items will adhere to the above orthotic design standards and the following mechanical principles of orthotics.

5. Mechanical principles of orthotic fabrication.
   a. Decrease pressure: wide, long orthotic base is the most desirable. Round edges are needed.
   b. Use sling applied with a 90° angle of pull.
   c. Use low load to increase duration.
   d. Maintain three-point pressure versus circumference.
   e. Avoid the position of deformity.
      (1) Wrist flexion.
      (2) MCP hyperextension.
      (3) IP joints flexed.
      (4) Thumb adducted.
   f. Select the appropriate orthotic position.[1]
      (1) Resting hand orthosis: used to rest structures or protect structures of the hand.
         (a) Wrist 0°–20° extension.
         (b) MCPs 20°–30° flexion.
         (c) IPs 10°–30 flexion (may be referred to as slight flexion).

---

[1] There are slight variations reported in OT and splinting textbooks in regard to the exact degrees for resting hand (functional) orthotics and safe (antideformity) orthotics. Thus, it is unlikely that the NBCOT® exam will include items that have two possible correct answers that include these subtle variations. To determine the correct answer to an exam item, you should consider the position(s) in which the joints are placed and not focus so much on the specific degrees.

(d) Thumb in slight extension and abducted (Hock & DeMott, 2021).
(2) Safe position orthosis: used to prevent deformity position in dorsal hand burns and maintain the length of the collateral ligaments; may be referred to as intrinsic-plus or antideformity orthosis.
   (a) Wrist 15°–30° extension.
   (b) MCPs 50°–70° flexion
   (c) IPs in full extension.
   (d) Thumb palmar abduction (Hock & DeMott, 2021).

> **CAUTION:** Check the individual's skin condition before and after making any orthosis.

6. Education.

> **EXAM HINT:** In the NBCOT® OTR® exam content outline, knowledge of "client-centered education and training methods for the safe and effective use of orthotic . . . devices" (NBCOT®, 2022, p. 11) is identified as essential for competent and safe practice. Thus, knowing the following education approaches can help you correctly answer NBCOT® exam items about the occupational therapists' role in orthotic device training.

   a. Instruct orthotic wearer in procedures for orthotic maintenance and routine skin inspection and care.
      (1) Check skin when donning and doffing.
      (2) Provide wear and care form and instruct the person in its use and importance.
   b. Ensure the individual accepts and understands the purpose(s), function(s), and limitation(s) of the orthotic.
   c. Teach proper technique for donning and doffing orthosis. If the person is unable to don and doff the orthosis teach them how to self-direct their care with a family member, caregiver, and/or personal care assistant.
   d. Provide functional training in the use of orthotics in role activities (e.g., use of tenodesis orthosis to do schoolwork).
   e. Reevaluate the individual's use of the orthosis at periodic intervals.

7. Occupational therapist/OTA roles.
   a. The occupational therapist/OTA team must carefully assess for the most appropriate orthosis.
   b. The occupational therapist must set the orthotic goals.
   c. Experienced OTAs can fabricate static orthotics and assist with dynamic orthoses.

8. Orthotics for common diagnoses.

EXAM HINT: In the NBCOT® OTR® exam content outline, knowledge of the "types and functions of . . . orthoses for managing specific conditions" (NBCOT®, 2022, p. 10) is identified as essential for competent and safe practice; thus, knowing the following diagnostic-specific orthoses and their purposes will help you determine the correct answer to NBCOT® items about the best orthoses for people who have these conditions.

a. Brachial plexus injury: flail arm orthosis.
   (1) This orthosis is used for positioning.
b. Radial nerve injury: Colditz orthosis or radial nerve orthosis to assist with partial wrist motion and finger extension (Colditz, 1987).
   (1) This orthosis is used for function. It assists the digits with extension to release an object.
      (a) Some OT practitioners will provide a resting hand orthosis for night use to prevent any flexion contractures.
c. Median nerve injury: opponens orthosis and web spacer orthosis.
   (1) The opponens orthosis is used to hold the thumb in opposition to use during functional activities.
   (2) Thenar webspacer is used to prevent thumb adduction contracture.
d. Ulnar nerve injury: anticlaw orthosis or called lumbrical bar orthosis to position MCPs in flexion.
   (1) This orthosis is used to prevent clawing of the fourth and fifth digits.
e. Combined median ulnar: figure-of-eight or lumbrical bar orthosis to position MCPs in flexion for digits 2–5. Refer to Figure 11-3.
   (1) These orthoses are used to prevent the hand from assuming the intrinsic minus position.
f. Spinal cord (C6–C7): a wrist-driven wrist-hand orthosis; also called a flexor hinge orthosis, or tenodesis orthosis is a device "that transfers power from the extended wrist to the radial fingers, allowing a stronger pinch" (Budash, 2021, p. 832).
   (1) This orthosis is used to facilitate grasp and release using tenodesis and enable sustained tenodesis grasp against resistance (e.g., during meal preparation when peeling and/or chopping vegetables).
g. Carpal tunnel syndrome: wrist orthosis positioned in neutral. Refer to Figure 11-4.
   (1) This orthosis is used to decrease carpal canal pressure (especially at night).
h. Cubital tunnel syndrome: elbow orthosis positions at 30° of flexion.
   (1) This orthosis is used to prevent elbow flexion at night, which will decrease ulnar nerve symptoms.
i. de Quervain's: forearm base thumb spica orthosis includes wrist, IP joint free; also called a long opponens orthosis.

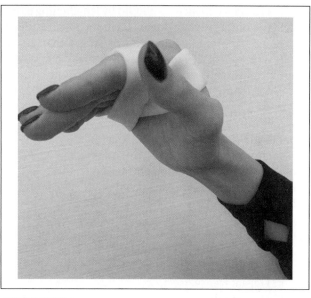

Figure 11-3   Figure-of-eight or lumbrical bar orthosis.

Photo courtesy of Kylie Tomlinson.

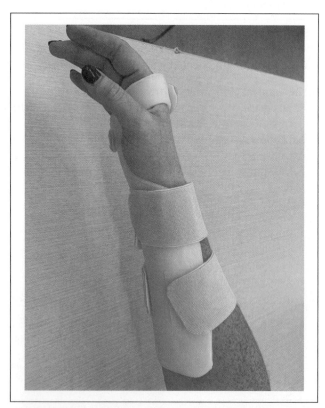

Figure 11-4   Carpal tunnel syndrome wrist orthosis.

Photo courtesy of Megan Deiling.

   (1) This orthosis is used to place the first dorsal compartment (APL and EPB) at rest.
j. Skier's thumb: ulnar collateral ligament (UCL) hand-based thumb CMC orthosis, also called a short opponens orthosis. Refer to Figure 6-8.

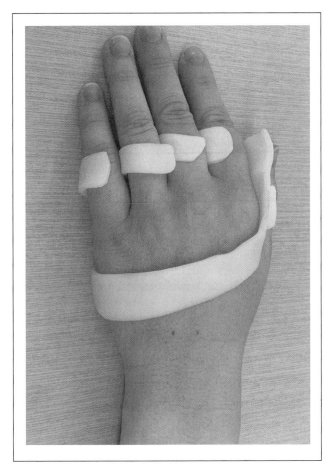

Figure 11-5   **Ulnar drift orthosis.**

Photo courtesy of William Tarelton.

(1) This orthosis is used to protect the ulnar collateral ligament of the MCP joint of the thumb until it heals.

k. CMC arthritis: hand-based thumb CMC orthosis or short opponens.
   (1) This orthosis is used to place the CMC joint of the thumb at rest until inflammation decreases.
      (a) A commercial brand is the Comfort Cool Thumb™ CMC orthosis.

l. Ulnar drift: ulnar drift orthosis. Refer to Figure 11-5.
   (1) This orthosis is used to decrease pain, provide stability, and realign the MCP joints of digits 2–5 for a person with arthritic changes.
      (a) Commercial brand is a neoprene anti-ulnar deviation orthosis.

m. Flexor tendon injury: dorsal blocking orthosis.
   (1) This orthosis is used to protect the repair site and to allow for early controlled mobilization while wearing the orthosis.

n. Swan neck: silver rings, 3-point oval 8™ orthosis or digital dorsal orthosis in slight PIP flexion.
   (1) These orthoses are used to place the PIP joint in slight flexion to prevent further development of the swan neck deformity.

o. Boutonniere: silver rings, 3-point oval 8™ orthosis, or PIP extension orthosis.
   (1) These orthoses are used to place the PIP joint in extension to allow for the lateral bands to move dorsal to the PIP axis.
      (a) This is often combined with DIP flexion exercises while wearing the orthosis.

p. Arthritis/RA flare up: resting hand orthosis.
   (1) This orthosis is used to place the joints at rest until inflammation decreases.

q. Flaccidity: resting/functional hand orthosis.
   (1) This orthosis is used to prevent joint contractures and hold the hand in a position of function until muscle return occurs.
      (a) Common wearing schedule is at night and on and off throughout the day.
   (2) Chapter 12 provides additional information about orthoses that are prescribed for persons with neurological conditions.

r. Spasticity: spasticity orthosis or cone orthosis.
   (1) These orthoses are used to prevent joint contracture.
   (2) Chapter 12 provides additional information about orthoses that are prescribed for persons with neurological conditions.

s. Muscle weakness (amyotrophic lateral sclerosis, spinal cord injury, Guillain-Barré): mobile arm support (MAS) or deltoid sling/suspension sling.
   (1) These orthoses/slings are used to support the proximal upper extremity to allow for use of distal extremity during activities such as eating.
   (2) Mounts to wheelchair.
   (3) Prevents loss of shoulder motions.
   (4) Refer to Figure 12-6.

t. Dorsal hand burns: wrist 15°–30° extension, MCP 50°–70° flexion, and IPs in full extension.
   (1) This orthosis is used to maintain soft tissue structures in a safe position and prevent deformity (Hock & DeMott, 2021).

Physical Agent Modalities (PAMs)

1. PAMs can be used as interventions to support occupations for purposeful and occupation-based activities.
   a. PAMs are *not* an appropriate OT intervention *if* they are used in isolation of purposeful or occupation-based activities.
   b. PAMs *are* an appropriate OT intervention *if* they precede, support, and/or enable the individual's ability to perform purposeful activities and meaningful occupations.
   c. PAMs are, therefore, interventions to support occupations for they add to and complement the primary OT intervention methods of purposeful activity and meaningful occupation.

d. Many states require specialized training to use PAMs as an OT intervention.

> **EXAM HINT:** In the NBCOT® OTR® exam content outline, knowledge of the "indications, contraindications, precautions, and clinical application of superficial thermal agents. . . . (and of) deep thermal, mechanical, and electrotherapeutic physical agent modalities" (NBCOT®, 2022, p. 8) is identified as essential for safe and competent and safe practice. Some superficial thermal PAM examples include "dry whirlpool, hot packs, (and) cryotherapy" (NBCOT®, 2022, p. 8). Deep thermal, mechanical, and electrotherapeutic PAM examples include "transcutaneous and neuromuscular electrical stimulation (and) biofeedback" (NBCOT®, 2022, p. 8). Thus, knowing the following information about PAMs will help you correctly answer NBCOT® exam items about their safe, effective, and ethical use in OT practice.

2. Common types of PAMs used by entry-level occupational therapists.
   a. Thermotherapy: a superficial thermal agent.
      (1) Paraffin.
      (2) Hot packs.
      (3) Fluidotherapy.
      (4) Whirlpool.
   b. Cryotherapy: a superficial thermal agent.
      (1) Cold packs.
      (2) Ice massage.
   c. Mechanotherapy.
      (1) Ultrasound.
   d. Electrical stimulation.
      (1) Neuromuscular electrical stimulation (NMES).
      (2) Transcutaneous electrical nerve stimulator (TENS).
      (3) High-voltage galvanic stimulation (HVGS).
      (4) Iontophoresis.
3. Superficial thermal.
   a. Types of heat transfer.
      (1) Conduction (hot packs and paraffin). Direct contact of PAM and body part. Heats superficial structures up to 1–2 centimeters.
      (2) Convection (fluidotherapy or whirlpool). Circulation of air, liquid or other medium transfers thermal energy to the body part.
      (3) Conversion (ultrasound). Mechanical energy changes to heat. Heats deeper structures up to 4–5 cm (Bracciano, 2021; Hunter, 2020).
   b. Benefits of thermotherapy (heat).
      (1) Relieves pain.
      (2) Increases tissue extensibility (increases ROM).
      (3) Assists with tissue healing (increased blood flow).
      (4) Decreases muscle spasms.

> **RED FLAG:** Heat is contraindicated for many conditions.
> • Do **NOT** use with people with postsurgical repairs/wounds/staples, infection, infectious disease with fever, acute injuries, impaired sensation, acute flareup (e.g., RA), edema, impaired vascular supply, tumors or active cancer, multiple sclerosis, lymphedema, or deep vein thrombosis (DVT) (Bracciano, 2021).

c. Application of superficial thermal heat modalities.
   (1) Hot packs.

> **CAUTION:** Check skin prior to and after application.

   (a) Check temperature of hydrocollator; 165°F is the standard.
   (b) Place hot pack in cover and add four layers of a folded towel (one towel) in between the person's skin and the hot pack cover. For fragile skin, an additional towel should be considered.
   (c) Check skin after five minutes to assess for burn or any other skin issues.
   (d) Hot pack is removed after a total of 15-20 minutes.

   (2) Paraffin.

> **CAUTION:** Check skin prior to and after application.

   (a) Check temperature of paraffin; 113°F–130°F is the standard.
   (b) After washing and thoroughly drying the hand, dip the hand into paraffin and quickly pull out. Repeat this process 8–10 times, forming a glove of paraffin over the hand.
   (c) Following the dip method, the hand should be wrapped with cellophane and then covered with a towel for 15–30 minutes (Walter & Winston, 2018).

   (3) Fluidotherapy.
   (a) In addition to the heating benefits listed above, fluidotherapy is effective in decreasing hypersensitivity.
   (b) Preheat the fluidotherapy machine (temperature can range between 102°F and 118°F).
   (c) Adjust the blowers according to the person's sensitivity (if the person is hypersensitive, begin with turning the blowers down).
   (d) Place the person's hand in the fluidotherapy via a sleeve on the machine for 20 minutes. During this time the person can exercise their hand and wrist.

(e) Treatment is for 20 minutes. The person's hand is slowly removed from the machine making certain no particles of ground cornhusk spill out (Bracciano, 2021; Walter & Winston, 2018).

(4) Whirlpool.[2]

    (a) To clean and debride wounds:

- Fill tank with water at 100°F–108°F if treating burns, water should be set at body temperature.
- Maintain sterile technique.
- Adjust turbine and turn it on. Low agitation is recommended. Check temperature again.
- Slowly lower the extremity into the whirlpool.

    (b) Treatment will be for 10–20 minutes.

4. Cryotherapy.

  a. Benefits of cryotherapy.

    (1) Relieves pain.

    (2) Controls edema.

    (3) Decreases abnormal tone.

    (4) Facilitates muscle tone.

    (5) Commonly used to treat acute injuries and postsurgical repairs.

> **RED FLAG:** Cryotherapy is contraindicated for several conditions.
> - Do **NOT** use with persons with "impaired sensation, nerve regeneration, impaired circulation, DVT, thrombophlebitis and chronic wounds" (Olvera-Dyckes, 2020, p.103).

  b. Application of cryotherapy.

    (1) Ice pack.

      (a) Apply a dry or wet towel between the client's skin and the cold pack.

      (b) Cold pack remains cold for up to 10–15 minutes.

> **CAUTION:** Check skin prior to, three to five minutes after application, and after application has ended.

    (2) Another commonly used type of cryotherapy includes ice massage (used for smaller areas; applied in circular motion directly to the skin for 4–5 minutes) (Bracciano, 2021; Walter & Winston, 2018).

5. Electrical stimulation.

  a. Benefits of electrical stimulation.

    (1) Controls pain.

    (2) Decreases swelling.

    (3) Stimulates and strengthens muscles.

    (4) Muscle re-education.

    (5) Stimulates denervated muscle.

> **RED FLAG:** Electrical stimulation is contraindicated for many conditions.
> - Do not use with people with a cardiac pacemaker, any implanted electrical stimulation, pregnancy, cancer, active TB, active hemorrhage, presence of thrombosis or thrombophlebitis or over the carotid sinus (Olvera-Dyckes, 2020).

  b. Common types used in OT.

    (1) Transcutaneous electrical stimulation (TENS): decreases pain (based on gate control theory).

    (2) Neuromuscular stimulation (NMES): increases muscle contraction and strength.

    (3) Both of the above can be used as part of a home program with proper education and understanding of the client.

6. Ultrasound.

  a. Types: continuous (thermal effects) and pulsed (nonthermal effects).

  b. Benefits of continuous ultrasound.

    (1) Increases tissue extensibility (increases ROM, decreases joint stiffness).

    (2) Reduces pain.

    (3) Increases blood flow and tissue permeability.

    (4) Reduces muscle spasms.

    (5) Reaches deeper tissues (up to 5 cm).

  c. Benefits of pulsed ultrasound.

    (1) Decreases inflammation.

    (2) Heals tissue.

> **RED FLAG:** Ultrasound is contraindicated for many conditions.
> - Do not use with people who are pregnant, hemorrhagic conditions, or have an active malignant tumor. Some joint replacements (cemented or plastic), thrombophlebitis, fractures, bony prominences or infections, electronic stimulators or over the spinal cord.
> - Do not apply to the area near a pacemaker, growth plates, healing fractures, and/or breast implants.

> **CAUTION:** Prior to using with persons with soft tissue repairs (e.g., tendons and/or ligaments), acute inflammation, healing fracture, or breast implants the occupational therapist should consult with the surgeon (Bracciano, 2021; Walter & Winston, 2018).

---

[2] Whirlpool (WP) is not as commonly used as in the past; now it is used on a case-by-case basis. WP has been replaced by more advanced wound management interventions. WP requires strict cleaning and disinfecting procedures; refer to Centers for Disease Control and Prevention for recommendations.

7. Guidelines for competent and ethical use of PAMs by OT practitioners.
   a. PAMs should be used when they can benefit the individual's intervention program.
   b. PAMs should not be used when they will not benefit the individual's intervention program.
   c. Indications, contraindications, and precautions for use of PAMs must be adhered to strictly.

> **RED FLAG:** In general, PAMs are contraindicated for many conditions.
> - Do not use if a person is pregnant or has cancer, a pacemaker, cognitive impairment, sensory impairment, vascular impairment, or deep vein thrombosis, thrombophlebitis, and hemorrhagic conditions.
> - Prior to using PAMs with an individual, diagnostic and age considerations must be carefully reviewed. For example, ultrasound is never used over a growth plate.

   d. Practitioner competence must be established for any and all PAMs used in OT intervention.
   e. Refer to the American Occupational Therapy Association Position Paper of Physical Agent Modalities.
   f. The use of physical agent modalities in OT is determined by state practice act and the institutional standards.
      (1) Because the NBCOT® exam is a national exam, it will not include exam items with questions about state- or facility-specific standards.

Role of the OTA/COTA®

1. The OTA/COTA® implements intervention with supervision of the occupational therapist.
   a. The level of supervision required depends upon the OTA's/COTA®'s experience and established service competence and the regulations from the licensure board in the state of practice.
2. During the implementation of intervention, the OTA/COTA® informs the supervising occupational therapist of any change in the individual's status and any other relevant information that may affect treatment.

References

Abrams, M. R., & Ivy, C. C. (2018). Evaluation of sensation and intervention for sensory dysfunction. In H. M. Pendelton & W. Schultz-Krohn (Eds.), Pedretti's occupational therapy: Practice skills for physical dysfunction (8th ed., pp. 580–593). Elsevier.

Adams, L. S., Grenne, L. W., & Toppzian, E. (1992). Range of motion. In American Association of Hand Therapists (Ed.), Clinical assessment recommendations (2nd ed., pp. 55–70).

American Occupational Therapy Association. (2012). Physical agent modalities. American Journal of Occupational Therapy, 66(Suppl. 6), S78–80.

American Society of Hand Therapists. (1992). Clinical assessment recommendations (2nd ed.).

Artzberger, S. (2014). Edema reduction techniques: A biologic rationale for selection. In C. Cooper (Ed.), Fundamentals of hand therapy: Clinical reasoning and treatment guidelines for common diagnoses of the upper extremity (2nd ed., pp. 35–50). Elsevier.

Bell Krotoski, J. (2011). Sensibility testing: History, instrumentation, and clinical procedures. In T.M. Skirven, A.L. Osterman, & J.M. Fedorczyk (Eds.), Rehabilitation of the hand and upper extremity (pp. 894–921). Elsevier Mosby.

Borst, M.J. (2021) Motor function interventions. In D.P. Dirette & S.A. Gutman (Eds.), Occupational therapy for physical dysfunction (8th ed., pp. 268–288). Wolters Kluwer.

Bracciano, A.G. (2021). Physical agent modalities and biofeedback. In D.P. Dirette & S.A. Gutman (Eds.), Occupational therapy for physical dysfunction (8th ed., pp. 487–507). Wolters Kluwer.

Budash, D. E. (2021). Spinal cord injury. In D.P. Dirette & S.A. Gutman (Eds.), Occupational therapy for physical dysfunction (8th ed., pp. 812–856). Wolters Kluwer.

Colditz, J. (1987). Splinting for radial nerve palsy. Journal of Hand Therapy, 1, 18–23.

Dellon, A.L. (1978). The moving two-point discrimination test: Clinical evaluation of the quickly adapting fiber/receptor system. Journal of Hand Surgery, 3(5), 474–481.

Dellon, A.L., Mckinnon S.E., & Crosby, P.M. (1987). Reliability of two-point discrimination measurements. Journal of Hand Surgery, 12(5, Part 1), 693–696.

Greene, D., & Roberts, S. (2016). Kinesiology movement in the context of activity (3rd ed.). Mosby.

Hock, N.S., & DeMott, L. (2021). Upper extremity orthoses. In D.P. Dirette & S.A. Gutman (Eds.), Occupational therapy for physical dysfunction (8th ed., pp. 431–465). Wolters Kluwer.

Hunter, K.B. (2020). Physical agent modalities in the hand clinic. In C. M. Wietlisbach (Ed.), Cooper's fundamentals of occupational therapy (3rd ed., pp. 104–113). Elsevier.

Jebsen, R. H., Taylor, N., Trieschmann, R. B., Trotter, M. J., & Howard, L. A. (1969). An objective and standardized test of hand function. Archives of Physical Medicine and Rehabilitation, 50, 311–319.

Kaskutas, V. (2018). Evaluation of muscle strength. In H. M. Pendelton & W. Schultz-Krohn (Eds.), Pedretti's Occupational therapy: Practice skills for physical dysfunction (8th ed., pp. 512–579). Elsevier.

Klein, L. J. (2020). Evaluation of the hand and upper extremity. In C. M. Wietlisbach (Ed.), Cooper's fundamentals of occupational therapy (3rd ed., pp. 46–65). Elsevier.

Knight, K. L., & Draper, D. O. (2013). Therapeutic modalities: The art and science. Lippincott Williams & Wilkins.

Lafayette Instrument. (1969). Minnesota Manual Dexterity Test.

Lafayette Instrument. (1986). O'Connor Tweezer Dexterity Test.

Lafayette Instrument. (2015). Purdue Pegboard Procedure Manual.

National Board for Certification in Occupational Therapy (NBCOT®). (2022). 2022 Occupational Therapist Registered (OTR®) Examination Content Outline. https://www .nbcot.org/-/media/PDFs/2022_OTR_Content_Outline.pdf.

Neer, C. (1990). Shoulder reconstruction. W.B. Saunders.

Olvera-Dyckes, A.E. (2020). In C. M. Wietlisbach (Ed.), Cooper's fundamentals of occupational therapy (3rd ed., pp. 100–103). Elsevier.

Rowe, V.T., & Zeiner, T. L. (2021). Motor function assessment: Range of motion, strength, and endurance. In D.P. Dirette & S.A. Gutman (Eds.), Occupational therapy for physical dysfunction (8th ed., pp. 197–267). Wolters & Kluwer.

Sahu, K. (2017). Energy conservation and work simplification strategies. In H. Smith-Gabai & S.E. Holm (Eds.), Occupational therapy in acute care (2nd ed., pp. 587–693). AOTA Press.

Shurtleff, T., & Kaskutas, V. (2018). Joint range of motion. In H. M. Pendelton & W. Schultz-Krohn (Eds.), Pedretti's Occupational therapy: Practice skills for physical dysfunction (8th ed., pp. 477–511). Elsevier.

Stone, J.H. (1992). Sensibility. In American Association of Hand Therapists (Ed.), Clinical assessment recommendations (2nd ed., pp. 71–84).

Walter, J.R., & Winston, K. (2018). Therapeutic occupations and modalities. In H. M. Pendelton & W. Schultz-Krohn (Eds.), Pedretti's Occupational therapy: Practice skills for physical dysfunction (8th ed., pp. 710–727). Elsevier.

Wietlisbach, C. M., & Branham, F. D. B. (2014). Physical agent modalities and biofeedback. In M. V. Radomski & C. A. Trombly Latham (Eds.), Occupational therapy for physical dysfunction (7th ed., pp. 558–588). Lippincott Williams & Wilkins.

Review Questions

Biomechanical Approaches: Evaluation and Intervention

Following are six questions about key content covered in this chapter. These questions are not inclusive of the entirety of content related to biomechanical approaches that you must know for success on the NBCOT® exam. These questions are provided to help you "jump-start" the thought processes you will need to apply your studying of content to the answering of exam questions; hence, they are not in the NBCOT® exam format. Exam items in the NBCOT® format which cover the depth and breadth of content you will need to know to pass the NBCOT® exam are provided in the three online practice exams that accompany this text. The answers to the following questions are provided in Appendix 2.

1. You work in a practice setting that serves many clients with musculoskeletal disorders. The majority of clients have decreased ROM. What are the different types of ROM you should consider during assessment? How should you document your evaluation and its results?

2. A new client is admitted into an intensive care unit with a diagnosis of a spinal cord injury. The physician requests an evaluation to help in determining the level of injury. How would you perform a light touch sensory test? How does this method of testing differ from the procedures used during sensory testing for other major diagnostic categories?

3. An adult client is having difficulty performing daily activities due to decreased ROM and pain in both shoulders. You decide to treat the client with preparatory interventions followed by an occupation-based intervention. What interventions can you use to increase ROM and decrease pain?

4. You provide consultation services to a Center for Independent Living that serves persons with a diversity of disabilities. You are scheduled to conduct an educational session on energy conservation and work simplification. What key principles and methods should you be sure to include in your presentation?

5. Your client is diagnosed with rotator cuff tendonitis and is experiencing severe pain. The physician has ordered the use of transcutaneous electrical nerve stimulation (TENS), gentle ROM, and below shoulder level ADL. During your evaluation, you review the client's past medical history. You learn that the person has a history of cardiac issues that required the implantation of a pacemaker. Which of the prescribed interventions will you use with this client? What are additional interventions you can use with this client to decrease pain and prepare the person for occupation-based interventions?

6. Your client is status post a below knee amputation. You assess the strength of the client's triceps in preparation for transfer training. The results of the MMT reveal that the client can take moderate resistance and then break. What muscle grade would you document the client possesses?

Neurological Approaches: Evaluation and Intervention

DANIEL GELLER AND GLEN GILLEN

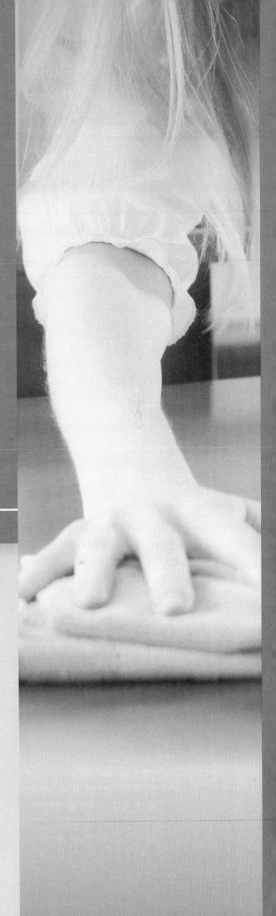

Neurological Frames of Reference Related to Motor Performance

EXAM HINT: The NBCOT® OTR® exam content outline identifies knowledge of "resources and considerations for acquiring information about the client's current condition and occupational performance . . . some examples include . . . . theoretical approach and frame of reference" (NBCOT®, 2022, p. 4) as essential for competent and safe practice. The application of knowledge about the following neurological frames of reference can help you determine correct answers to exam items about working with persons with neurological disorders.

Contemporary Task-Oriented Approaches to Motor Control Training

1. General principles/assumptions.
   a. Contemporary approaches to motor control training are based on current research and knowledge of motor behavior.
   b. Approaches reject assumptions of the reflex-hierarchical model of motor control and of the traditional neurophysiologic therapies.
   c. Remediation of client factors and environmental modifications to improve task performance is included.
   d. Based on a systems model of motor control.
      (1) Proposes that motor control is determined by interactive systems (motor, cultural, environmental, etc.), behavioral tasks, and adaptive/anticipatory mechanisms.
   e. Movement is controlled by the integration and interaction of multiple systems including environmental influences, sensorimotor factors, musculoskeletal factors, regulatory functions, and behavioral/emotional goals.
   f. The role of the structures responsible for motor control is to tune and prepare the motor system to respond to changing environmental and task demands.
   g. Interventions are also guided by therapist's understanding of motor learning principles.
   h. Control is not simply over muscle actions, but over the interactions of kinematic variables.
   i. Movement dysfunction following central nervous system (CNS) damage reflects the system's best effort to accomplish task goals.
2. Principles of the Contemporary Task-Oriented Approach.

   a. Occupational performance emerges from the interaction of multiple systems including personal and performance contexts.
   b. Personal and environmental systems, including the CNS, are heterarchically organized.
   c. An individual's behavioral changes reflect their attempts to compensate and to achieve functional goals.
   d. Individuals must practice with varied strategies to find optimal solutions for motor problems and develop skill in performance.
   e. Functional tasks help organize motor behavior.
   f. The therapist must determine which control parameters or systems (personal, environmental, etc.) have positive or negative influences on motor behavior.
   g. Practice opportunities are provided which are appropriate to the person's stage of learning.
   h. The therapist conducts the evaluation using a top-down approach.
   i. Evaluation efforts initially focus on role performance and occupational performance tasks because they are the goals of motor behavior.
   j. After a person has identified the most important role and occupational performance limitations, the therapist uses task analysis to identify which subsystem(s) of the person and/or environmental factor(s) are limiting functional performance.
   k. Interventions are focused on the following.
      (1) Helping individuals adjust to role and task performance limitations.
      (2) Creating an environment that utilizes the common challenges of everyday life.
      (3) Practicing functional tasks or close simulations to find effective and efficient strategies for performance.
      (4) Providing opportunities for practice outside of therapy time.
      (5) Remediating client factors and/or performance skills to support occupations.
      (6) Minimizing inefficient or ineffective movement patterns.
      (7) Adapting the environment.
      (8) Modifying the task.
      (9) Using assistive technology.
3. Principles of Carr and Shepherd's Motor Relearning Program (MRP).
   a. The person is an active participant whose goal is to relearn effective strategies for performing functional movement.
   b. Postural adjustments and limb movements are linked together in the learning process.

c. Successful task relearning has occurred when activities are performed automatically and efficiently.

d. The learning of skills does not follow a developmental sequence.

e. Continued practice of compensatory strategies limits functional recovery.

f. Intervention is not focused on learning specific movements but instead on learning general strategies for solving motor problems.

g. Obstacles to efficient movement include loss of soft tissue extensibility, balance loss, fixation patterns due to postural insecurity, and muscle weakness.

h. Abnormal movement patterns are attributed to the repeated practice of compensatory movement strategies that become overlearned.

4. Principles of motor learning.

a. Contemporary approaches to treating motor dysfunction incorporate principles of motor learning during interventions focused on remediating motor control in persons with CNS dysfunction. Refer to Table 12-1.

b. The ultimate goal of utilizing motor learning theory is the acquisition of functional skills that can be generalized to multiple situations and environments.

c. Stages of motor learning.

(1) Skill acquisition stage (cognitive stage) occurs during initial instruction and practice of a skill.

(2) Skill retention stage (associative stage) involves "carryover," as individuals are asked to demonstrate their newly acquired skill after initial practice.

(3) Skill transfer stage (autonomous stage) involves the individual demonstrating the skill in a new context.

(4) Refer to Table 12-2 for further description of these stages.

d. Practice.

(1) Blocked (constant) practice involves repeated performance of the same motor skill (e.g., practice bed mobility several times in a row, then practice sit to stand several times in a row).

(2) Random (or variable) practice involves practice of several tasks that are presented in a random order, encouraging reformulation of the solution to the presented motor problem (e.g., practice transfer to multiple surfaces in one session, such as couch, toilet, bench, chair, car).

(a) Variable conditions involve practice of skills in various contexts to improve transfer of learning and retention of skills.

(3) Practice of the whole task (e.g., practice putting on a shirt).

(4) Practice of parts of the task (e.g., practice only buttoning the shirt).

(5) Massed practice: practice schedule in which the amount of rest between practice is very small (e.g., constraint induced movement therapy [CIMT]).

(6) Distributed practice: practice schedule in which the rest periods between sessions are relatively long (e.g., practice sessions of a tub transfer are spaced to include rest).

(7) Mental practice involves cognitive rehearsal of a skill without actually moving.

(8) Action observation involves observing a healthy person performing a skill or functional task either through video or live performance. This intervention is based on evidence that similar cortical motor areas are activated by either performance or observance of a skill or task (Rao, 2021).

(9) Mirror therapy involves placing a mirror in the midsagittal plane of the person between their extremities. The impaired arm/hand is placed behind the mirror, while the unimpaired arm is in front of the mirror. The person moves the unimpaired arm/hand while watching the mirror reflection, giving the visual illusion of normal movement of the impaired arm (Rao, 2021).

(a) Refer to Figure 12-1.

e. Intrinsic feedback.

(1) Information (tactile, vestibular, visual, auditory) received by the learner as a result of performing the task (e.g., when closing a container, a person receives visual task-intrinsic feedback from seeing if the container is fully closed. In addition, the person receives tactile task-intrinsic feedback from their hands while closing the container).

f. Extrinsic feedback (also known as augmented feedback).

(1) Feedback provided from an outside source (e.g., the therapist or a mechanical device).

(2) Concurrent versus terminal feedback.

(a) Concurrent feedback: given during task performance (e.g., while the person is standing and reaching for an object the therapist says, "Stand up straight").

(b) Terminal feedback: given after task performance (e.g., after the person completes dressing, the therapist says, "You didn't line up the buttonholes and buttons correctly").

(3) Immediate versus delayed feedback.

(a) Immediate feedback: given immediately after performance (e.g., right after the person locks the wheelchair before a transfer, the therapist says, "Glad you locked your brakes first").

(b) Delayed feedback: feedback delayed by some amount of time (e.g., the therapist says, "You did better this morning about locking your brakes. Please keep checking your wheelchair brakes").

Chapter 12

Table 12-1

Summary of Motor Learning Principles/Considerations

PRINCIPLES/CONSIDERATIONS	EXAMPLES
Classification of tasks to be learned: Learning is contingent on the type of task that is being learned.	
– Discrete tasks: Tasks with a recognizable beginning and end.	Kick a ball, push a button.
– Continuous tasks: There is no recognizable beginning and end. Tasks are performed until they are arbitrarily stopped.	Jogging, driving, swimming.
– Serial tasks: Comprised a series of movements linked together to make a "whole."	Play an instrument, dressing, light a fireplace.
– Closed tasks: Performed in a predictable and stable environment. Movements can be planned in advance.	Oral care, signing a check, bowling.
– Open tasks: Performed in a constantly changing environment that may be unpredictable.	Driving in traffic, catching an insect, soccer.
– Variable motionless tasks: Involve interacting with a stable and predictable environment, but specific features of the environment are likely to vary between performance trials.	Performance of activities of daily living outside of the usual home environment.
– Consistent motion tasks: An individual must deal with environmental conditions that are in motion during activity performance; the motion is consistent and predictable between trials.	Stepping onto an escalator, assembly line work, retrieving luggage from an airport baggage carousel.
Practice conditions: The law of practice refers to performance changing linearly with the amount of time spent in practice.	
– Massed practice: Rest time is much less than practice time.	Constraint-induced movement therapy.
– Distributed practice: Practice time is equal to or less than rest time.	Practice sessions of a tub transfer are spaced to include rest breaks.
– Blocked practice: Repetitive practice of the same task, uninterrupted by practice of other tasks.	Practicing moving from sit to stand multiple times in a row. Practice sequence of tasks "A," "B," and "C": AAAAABBBBBBBCCCCC.
– Random or variable practice: Tasks being practiced are ordered randomly. Attempt multiple tasks or variations of a task before mastering any one of the tasks.	Practice transferring to multiple surfaces (couch, toilet, bench, chair, stool, car) in one occupational therapy session. Practice sequence of tasks "A," "B," and "C": ACBACABCCBACABCACABBACCACB.
– Whole practice: The task is practiced in its entirety and not broken into parts.	Practicing dressing.
– Part practice: The task is broken down into its parts for separate practice.	Don/doff shirt.
Feedback: A key feature of practice is the information the learners receive about their attempts to learn a skill.	
– Inherent (intrinsic) feedback: Feedback normally received while performing a task.	Knowing you made an error as you spill water when trying to pour from a pitcher to a cup.
– Augmented feedback: Information about task performance that is supplemental to inherent feedback.	A therapist provides feedback related to task performance. "You need to lock your wheelchair brakes."
– Concurrent feedback: Given during task performance.	While practicing reaching, the therapist says, "Don't hike your shoulder."
– Terminal feedback: Given after task performance.	After practice of reaching, the therapist says, "You didn't open your hand wide enough."
– Immediate feedback: Given immediately after performance.	Right after an attempt at a tub transfer, the therapist says, "That was perfect."
– Delayed feedback: Feedback is delayed by some amount of time.	The occupational therapist says, "You did better this morning but keep checking your brakes."
– Knowledge of results (KR): Feedback given after task performance about the outcome.	The occupational therapist says, "Your shirt is on backwards" or "You dropped the cup."
– Knowledge of performance (KP): Feedback given after task about the nature of performance.	The occupational therapist says, "Next time, dress your right arm first" or "Your elbow was bent."

Gillen, G. & Nilsen, D.M. (2019). Motor function and occupational performance. In B. A. B. Schell & G. Gillen (Eds.), Willard and Spackman's occupational therapy (13th ed., pp. 870–900). Wolters Kluwer. Reprinted with permission.

Table 12-2

Motor Learning Stages and Training Strategies

COGNITIVE STAGE CHARACTERISTICS

- The learner develops an understanding of task; cognitive mapping assesses abilities, task demands; identifies stimuli, contacts memory; selects response; performs initial approximations of task; structures motor program; modifies initial responses.

- "What to do" decision.

Training Strategies

- Highlight purpose of task in functionally relevant terms.

- Demonstrate ideal performance of task to establish a reference of correctness.

- Have patients verbalize task components and requirements.

- Point out similarities to other learned tasks.

- Direct attention to critical task elements.

- Select appropriate feedback.

  – Emphasize intact sensory systems, intrinsic feedback systems.

  – Carefully pair extrinsic feedback with intrinsic feedback.

  – High dependence on vision: have patient watch movement.

  – Knowledge of Performance (KP): focus on errors as they become consistent; do not cue on large number of random errors.

  – Knowledge of Results (KR): focus on success of movement outcome.

- Ask learner to evaluate performance, outcomes; identify problems, solutions.

- Use reinforcements (praise) for correct performance, continuing motivation.

- Organize feedback schedule.

  – Feedback after every trial improves performance during early treatment.

  – Variable feedback (summed, fading, bandwidth designs) increases depth of cognitive processing, improves retention; may decrease performance initially.

- Organize initial practice.

  – Stress controlled movement to minimize errors.

  – Provide adequate rest periods (distributed practice) if task is complex, long, or energy costly or if learner fatigues easily, has short attention, poor concentration.

  – Use manual guidance to assist as appropriate.

  – Break complex tasks down into component parts, teach both parts as integrated whole.

  – Utilize bilateral transfer as appropriate.

  – Use blocked (repeated) practice of same task to improve performance.

  – Use variable practice (serial or random practice order) of related skills to increase depth of cognitive processing and retention; may decrease performance initially.

  – Use mental practice to improve performance and learning, reduce anxiety.

- Assess, modify arousal levels as appropriate.

  – High or low arousal impairs performance and learning.

  – Avoid stressors, mental fatigue.

- Structure environment.

  – Reduce extraneous environmental stimuli and distracters to ensure attention and concentration.

  – Emphasize closed skills initially, gradually progressing to open skills.

(Continued)

Chapter 12

Chapter 12

Table 12-2

Motor Learning Stages and Training Strategies (*Continued*)

ASSOCIATIVE STAGE CHARACTERISTICS

- The learner practices movements, refines motor programs: spatial and temporal organization; decreases errors and extraneous movements.
- Dependence on visual feedback decreases, increases for use of proprioceptive feedback; cognitive monitoring decreases.
- "How to do" decisions.

Training Strategies

- Select appropriate feedback.
  - Continue to provide KP, intervene when errors become consistent.
  - Emphasize proprioceptive feedback, "feel of movement" to assist in establishing an internal reference of correctness.
  - Continue to provide KR; stress relevance of functional outcomes.
  - Assist learner to improve self-evaluation, decision-making skills.
  - Facilitation techniques, guided movements may be counterproductive during this stage of learning.
- Organize feedback schedule.
  - Continue to provide feedback for continuing motivation; encourage patient to self-assess achievements.
  - Avoid excessive augmented feedback.
  - Focus on use of variable feedback (summed, fading, bandwidth) designs to improve retention.
- Organize practice.
  - Encourage consistency of performance.
  - Focus on variable practice order (serial or random) of related skills to improve retention.
- Structure environment.
  - Progress toward open, changing environment.
  - Prepare the learner for home, community, work environments.

AUTONOMOUS STAGE CHARACTERISTICS

- The learner practices movements, continues to refine motor responses, spatial and temporal highly organized, movements are largely error-free, minimal level of cognitive monitoring.
- "How to succeed" decision.

Training Strategies

- Assesses need for conscious attention, automaticity of movements.
- Select appropriate feedback.
  - Learner demonstrates appropriate self-evaluation, decision-making skills.
  - Provide occasional feedback (KP, KR) when errors evident.
- Organize practice.
  - Stress consistency of performance in variable environments, variations of tasks (open skills).
  - High levels of practice (massed practice) are appropriate.
- Structure environment.
  - Vary environments to challenge learner.
  - Ready the learner for home, community, work environments.
- Focus on competitive aspects of skills as appropriate, e.g., wheelchair sports.

O'Sullivan, S., & Schmitz, T. (2007). Physical rehabilitation (5th ed.). F.A. Davis Company. Reprinted with permission.

Figure 12-1   Mirror Therapy.
Picture by Daniel Geller. Reprinted with permission.

   (4) Knowledge of performance (KP), which is verbal feedback about the process or performance itself (e.g., the therapist says, "Next time lean forward more when trying to stand up").

   (5) Knowledge of results (KR), which is the feedback about the outcome or end product or results of the motor action (e.g., the therapist says, "You were able to retrieve the cup from the cabinet 3 out of 5 times, you stood 2 minutes longer today than yesterday").

g. Factors/conditions that promote generalization of motor learning.
   (1) Capacity to generate intrinsic feedback.
   (2) High feedback regarding knowledge of performance.
   (3) Low extrinsic feedback regarding knowledge of results.
   (4) Practice conditions that are variable, random.
   (5) Whole task performance as opposed to breaking activities into contrived parts.
   (6) High contextual interference utilizes environmental conditions that increase the difficulty of learning such as noise distractions, crowded environments, and random practice.
   (7) Practice in naturalistic settings.
      (a) The setting in which the skill being taught will be utilized or an environment that closely resembles the one in which the skill will be performed.

h. Performance, learning, and generalization.
   (1) Definitions.
      (a) Performance: the behavioral act of executing a skill or task at a specific time and situation.
      (b) Learning: change in the capability of a person to perform a task or skill as a result of practice.
   (2) The initial task is the first activity performed by the client.
   (3) Retention: the ability to perform the same task following an interval of practice (Magill, 2021).
   (4) Near transfer is an alternate form of the initial task. Very similar to initial task but has minimal number of changes in task parameters.
   (5) Intermediate transfer has a moderate number of changes in task parameters but still has some similarities to the initial task.
   (6) Far transfer introduces an activity that is conceptually the same as, but physically different from, the initial task.
   (7) Very far transfer requires spontaneous use of the new strategy in daily functional activities.

i. Task categories.
   (1) Specificity of where action begins and ends.
      (a) Discrete tasks: specific beginning and end of a single movement (e.g., flipping a switch, hitting a piano key, hitting one key on the computer, pushing a button).
      (b) Serial tasks: continuous discrete motor skills to make a "whole" activity (e.g., typing a letter, playing the piano, shifting gears in a standard car).
      (c) Continuous tasks: arbitrary beginning and end of the action, repetitive movements (e.g., walking, swimming).
   (2) Stability of the environment.
      (a) Closed tasks: the environment is stable and predictable and methods of performance are consistent over time (e.g., picking up a cup, buttoning a shirt, walking alone down a hallway, hitting a ball off a tee, performing oral hygiene).
      (b) Variable motionless tasks: also involve interacting with a stable and predictable environment, but specific features of the environment are likely to vary between performance trials (e.g., performance of ADL outside of the usual home environment, such getting on and off the toilet in a public bathroom).
      (c) Open tasks: require people to make adaptive decisions about unpredictable events because objects within the environment are in random motion during task (e.g., walking in a park, catching a thrown ball, walking in the home with moving pets).

(d) Consistent motion tasks: require an individual to deal with environmental conditions that are in motion during activity performance; the motion is consistent and predictable between trials (e.g., stepping onto an escalator).

j. Refer to Table 12-2 for training strategies appropriate for each stage of motor learning.

> **EXAM HINT:** The NBCOT® OTR® exam content outline identifies knowledge of the "techniques for . . . motor reeducation" (NBCOT®, 2022, p. 10) as essential for competent and safe practice. The application of knowledge about the contemporary task-oriented approaches to motor learning presented in this section, the motor learning principles/considerations provided in Table 12-1, and the strategies provided in Table 12-2 can help you determine correct answers for NBCOT® Domain 3 exam items about selecting and managing interventions for motor reeducation.

Review of Neurophysiologic Frames of Reference

1. Also known as sensorimotor approaches.
   a. They include the neurodevelopmental treatment approach (NDT), proprioceptive neuromuscular facilitation (PNF), Brunnstrom's approach, and Margaret Rood's approach.
   b. Refer to Table 12-3 for a summary and comparison of these traditional approaches.
2. Utilized for persons with CNS dysfunction.
3. Approaches developed in the 1940s and 1950s that were based on the understanding of nervous system pathology at that time.
   a. They are outlined in this Chapter only because this information is included in key occupational therapy textbooks that the NBCOT® identifies as the references for the composition of NBCOT® exam items.

Table 12-3

Comparison of Key Treatment Strategies Used in the Traditional Sensorimotor Approaches

KEY TREATMENT STRATEGIES	ROOD APPROACH	BRUNNSTROM APPROACH (MOVEMENT THERAPY)	PROPRIOCEPTIVE NEUROMUSCULAR APPROACH	NEURODEVELOPMENTAL TREATMENT
Sensory stimulation used to evoke a motor response	YES (Uses direct application of sensory stimuli to muscles and joints)	YES (Movement occurs in response to sensory stimuli)	YES (Tactile, auditory, visual sensory stimuli promote motor responses)	YES (Abnormal muscle tone occurs, in part, because of abnormal sensory experiences)
Reflexive movement used as a precursor for volitional movement	YES (Reflexive movement achieved initially through the application of sensory stimuli)	YES (Move patient along a continuum of reflexive to volitional movement patterns)	YES (Volitional movements can be assisted by reflexive supported postures)	NO
Treatment directed toward influencing muscle tone	YES (Sensory stimuli used to inhibit or facilitate tone)	YES (Postures, sensory stimuli used to inhibit or facilitate tone)	YES (Movement patterns used to normalize tone)	YES (Handling techniques and postures can inhibit or facilitate muscle tone)
Developmental patterns/ sequences used for the development of motor skills	YES (Ontogenic motor patterns used to develop motor skills)	YES (Flexion and extension synergies; proximal to distal return)	YES (Patterns used to facilitate proximal to distal motor control)	YES
Conscious attention is directed toward movement	NO	YES	YES	YES
Treatment directly emphasizes development of skilled movements for task performance	NO	NO	NO	YES

Schultz-Krohn, W., & Mc Laughlin-Gray, J. (2018). Traditional sensorimotor approaches to intervention. In H. Pendelton & W. Schultz-Krohn (Eds.), Pedretti's Occupational Therapy: Practice skills for physical dysfunction (8th ed., 766–797). Elsevier. Reprinted with permission.

(1) Consequently, some NBCOT® exam items may reflect these traditional perspectives.
4. General assumptions/principles/treatment foundations.
   a. Controlled movement is preceded by stereotypic reflex responses.
   b. Sensory input regulates motor output and sensation is necessary for movement to take place.
   c. Normal movements are governed by hierarchical centralized motor programs that determine muscle activation patterns.
     (1) The cerebral cortex controls the middle levels (basal ganglia, brain stem, etc.) which in turn control the spinal cord.
   d. Damage to higher control centers release lower-level or primitive reflexes and movement patterns from inhibition.
   e. When basic movements and postures are normalized, skilled movement would occur automatically.
   f. "Integration" of lower-level spinal and brain stem reflexes occurs by eliciting higher-level righting and equilibrium responses.
   g. Controlled sensory input applied by the therapist can influence motor responses (i.e., a reflex model of control).
   h. The use of "facilitation" and "inhibition" techniques can improve motor performance.

Neurodevelopmental Treatment (NDT)/The Bobath Technique

1. Principles/assumptions.
   a. Normalization of postural and limb tone is prerequisite to normal movement.
     (1) Tone abnormalities include flaccidity (low tone) or spasticity (high tone).
   b. Avoidance of movements and activities that increase tone.
   c. Inhibition of primitive reflexes and abnormal postural and limb movements.
   d. Development of normal patterns of posture and movement.
   e. Improvement of the quality of movement and performance of the involved side.
   f. Associated reactions (nonfunctional and involuntary changes in the uninvolved limb position and tone) should be avoided.
   g. Postural reactions are considered the basis for control of movement.
     (1) These reactions include righting, equilibrium, and protective responses.

h. Loss of postural control results in overuse of the sound side and limits functional movements.
i. The stereotypical patterns of the trunk and limbs observed in persons with CNS dysfunction are viewed as abnormal patterns of motor coordination.
j. Focus is on improving the quality of movement.
   (1) Normalization of movement patterns.
   (2) Integration of both sides of the body/reestablishment of symmetry of the sides of the body to increase functional use.
   (3) Establishment of the ability to weight bear and weight shift through the limbs.
   (4) Establishment of normal righting and equilibrium patterns.
k. "Handling" is the primary intervention to promote normal movement.

> **EXAM HINT:** Understanding the principles and approaches of each neurological frame of reference can help you effectively determine the correct answer to NBCOT® exam items about working with persons with neurological disorders according to a specific practice model. For example, a correct answer for an exam item about the use of a contemporary task-oriented approach to motor control training would include client engagement in a functional task (e.g., dressing, meal preparation) to help organize motor behavior. A correct answer for an exam item about the use of the NDT approach with a child with hypertonia would include the therapist using handling to promote normal movement and avoiding movements and activities that increase tone.

Proprioceptive Neuromuscular Facilitation (PNF)

1. Principles/assumptions.
   a. The response of the neuromuscular mechanisms can be hastened through stimulation of the proprioceptors.
     (1) Utilized for neurologic and orthopedic populations throughout the lifespan.
   b. Techniques are superimposed on patterns of movement (diagonals) and posture, focusing on sensory stimulation from manual contacts, visual cues, and verbal commands.
   c. Normal motor development proceeds in a cervicocaudal and proximodistal direction.
   d. Early motor behavior is dominated by reflex activity.

(1) Mature motor behavior is supported or reinforced by postural reflexes that are integrated throughout the lifespan.

e. Early motor behavior is characterized by spontaneous movement, which oscillates between extremes of flexion and extension.

(1) These movements are rhythmic and reversing in character.

f. Developing motor behavior is expressed in an orderly sequence of total patterns of movement and posture.

g. In development, there are shifts between flexor and extensor dominance.

h. Locomotion depends on reciprocal contraction of flexors and extensors.

i. The maintenance of posture requires continual adjustment for nuances of imbalance.

j. Frequency of stimulation and repetitive activity are used to promote and retain motor learning, and to develop strength and endurance.

k. Goal-directed activities coupled with techniques of facilitation are used to hasten learning of total patterns of walking and self-care activities.

l. Goal-directed activity is made up of reversing movements.

m. Diagonal patterns or mass movement patterns are utilized during functional activities.

(1) All patterns cross midline and encourage rotary components to movement.

(2) Upper extremity patterns are identified as D1 or D2, flexion or extension. Refer to Figure 12-2 and Figure 12-3.

(a) D1 flexion.
• Scapula: abducted and upwardly rotated.
• Shoulder: flexed, adducted, externally rotated.

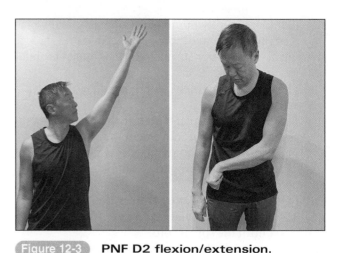

Figure 12-3   **PNF D2 flexion/extension.**

Photos by Daniel Geller. Reprinted with permission.

• Elbow: slightly flexed.
• Forearm: supinated.
• Wrist: flexed toward radial side.
• Fingers: flexed, adducted.
• Thumb: flexed, adducted.
• Functional examples: combing the left side of the head with the right arm, reaching for a cup in an upper right cabinet with the left arm.

(b) D1 extension.
• Scapula: adducted, downwardly rotated.
• Shoulder: extended, abducted, internally rotated.
• Elbow: extended.
• Forearm: pronated.
• Wrist: extended toward ulnar side.
• Fingers: extended, abducted.
• Thumb: extended, abducted.
• Functional examples: reaching for the arm rests in chair to push while standing, placing a cup into a dishwasher, reaching back with the right arm to wash the right buttock and back in standing.

(c) D2 flexion.
• Scapula: adducted and upwardly rotated.
• Shoulder: flexed, abducted, externally rotated.
• Elbow: extended.
• Forearm: supinated.
• Wrist: extended toward radial side.
• Fingers: extended, abducted.
• Thumb: extended, abducted.
• Functional examples: raising arm in class to ask a question, reaching for a cup in an upper right cabinet with the right arm, reaching for a cup in an upper left cabinet with the left arm.

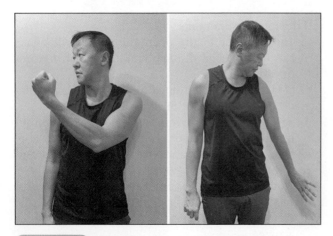

Figure 12-2   **PNF D1 flexion/extension.**

Photos by Daniel Geller. Reprinted with permission.

(d) D2 extension.
- Scapula: abducted and downwardly rotated.
- Shoulder: extended, adducted, internally rotated.
- Elbow: toward flexion.
- Forearm: pronated.
- Wrist: flexed toward ulnar side.
- Fingers: flexed, adducted.
- Thumb: flexed, abducted, opposed.
- Functional examples: washing the left thigh with the right arm, putting on a seatbelt, donning a belt.

Brunnstrom's Movement Therapy

1. Principles/assumptions.
   a. Brunnstrom's approach focused on facilitating recovery through a specific sequence.
   b. Treatment is focused on the promotion of movement from reflexive to volitional.
      (1) Seven stages of motor recovery following the onset of hemiplegia that the individual progresses through in a stereotypical fashion were identified by Brunnstrom. Refer to Table 12-4.
      (2) This recovery pattern includes the identification of developing synergies.

Margaret Rood's Approach

1. Principles/assumptions.
   a. Sensorimotor control is developmentally based.
      (1) Treatment must begin at the person's current level and progress sequentially.
   b. Rood proposed four sequential phases of motor control.

   (1) Reciprocal inhibition/innervation.
      (a) An early mobility pattern that is primarily a reflex governed by spinal and supraspinal centers (e.g., protective reflex, stepping reflex).
   (2) Co-contraction.
      (a) Defined as a simultaneous contraction of the agonist and antagonist that provides stability in a static pattern.
      (b) Utilized to hold a position or object for a long duration (e.g., standing at a concert, using arm as a prop to stand).
   (3) Heavy work.
      (a) Also termed "mobility superimposed on stability."
      (b) In these patterns, proximal muscles contract and move and the distal segments are fixed (e.g., downward dog to upward dog positions in yoga, stance phase in gait).
   (4) Skill.
      (a) Considered the highest level of control and combines stability and mobility.
      (b) These patterns consist of a stabilized proximal segment while the distal segments move in space (e.g., changing a lightbulb, writing on chalk board, kicking a ball).
   c. Muscular responses of the agonists, antagonists, and synergists are believed to be reflexively programmed according to a purpose or plan.
   d. Rood described a sequence of motor development termed "ontogenic motor patterns" that includes eight different patterns in sequence (i.e., supine withdrawal, rollover, prone extension, neck co-contraction, prone on elbows, quadruped, standing, and walking).
   e. Rood proposed that the motor response that is achieved is dependent on the type of sensory stimulation that the therapist applies.

Table 12-4

Brunnstrom's Stages of Motor Recovery

STAGE	DESCRIPTION
I	Flaccid, no voluntary movement
II	Synergies and spasticity are developing
III	Increase in spasticity and beginning of voluntary movement in synergy
IV	Decrease in spasticity and voluntary movement beginning to move out of synergy
V	Spasticity continues to decrease, and voluntary movement become more complex without synergistic patterns
VI	Spasticity almost gone and isolated voluntary movement
VII	Normal movement (Gellert & Pulaski, 2021)

Evaluation of Motor Control Dysfunction

EXAM HINT: In the NBCOT® OTR® exam content outline, Domain 1 Evaluation and Assessment comprises 23% of the exam and knowledge of the "administration, purpose, indications, advantages, and limitations of standardized and nonstandardized screening and assessment tools . . . (including) criterion-referenced tests, norm-referenced tests, client and caregiver interviews, (and) observation" (NBCOT®, 2022, p. 4) is identified as essential for competent and safe practice. The application of knowledge about the following assessments can help you determine the correct answer to Domain 1 exam items about the evaluation of motor control.

Assessment for Components of Motor Control

1. Spasticity is evaluated by the elicitation of velocity-dependent stretch reflexes.
   a. The limb is quickly stretched in a direction opposite the pull of the muscle group being tested.
      (1) Objectively measured by the five-point Ashworth Scale (0 = no increase in tone and 4 = limb rigid in flexion or extension) (Ashworth, 1964) or the six-point Modified Ashworth Scale (MAS) which has an additional level to indicate resistance through less than half the movement (Bohannon & Smith, 1987).
         (a) The MAS is the more widely used measure. Refer to Box 12-1.
      (2) Quick stretch is applied in a direction opposite the pull of the muscle group being tested and graded utilizing a "minimal/moderate/severe" rating scale depending on which point in the

range elicits a stretch reflex (minimal if "catch" is felt at end of range, moderate if "catch" is felt at mid-range, and severe if "catch" is felt at the beginning of the range).

2. Reflex testing.
   a. Utilized to evaluate involuntary stereotyped responses to a particular stimulus.
   b. Responses develop during fetal life and persist through early infancy.
   c. Reflexes may be released after brain injury or not integrated during early development secondary to CNS pathology.
   d. Intensity and quality of the response is monitored.
   e. A response to stimulus is termed "positive," and no response to stimulus is "negative."
   f. The therapist notes the highest level of reflex control achieved.
   g. Examples of reflexes that are tested. Refer to Table 12-5.
   h. The therapist must be aware of the age range that is considered normal for each reflex. (Refer to Chapter 5.)
   i. Treatment is planned to progress individual to an age-appropriate level of reflex hierarchy.

3. Qualitative descriptions of motor control.
   a. Evaluation of motor control should include observations of the quality of movement during performance of functional tasks.

EXAM HINT: Understanding how the following qualitative motor control issues can impact function can help you correctly answer NBCOT® exam items about the best approach to use to enable occupational performance for persons with impaired movement. For example, it may be helpful to teach a person with dysdiadochokinesia to move slower during daily living tasks.

   b. Examples of motor control issues resulting in observable poor quality of movement.
      (1) Intention tremor is the worsening of action tremor as the limb approaches a target in space.
      (2) Dysmetria is the undershooting (hypometria) or overshooting (hypermetria) of a target.
      (3) Dyssynergia is a breakdown in movement resulting in joints being moved separately to reach a desired target as opposed to moving in a smooth trajectory; decomposition of movement.
      (4) Dysdiadochokinesia is impaired ability to perform rapid alternating movements.
      (5) Ataxia is loss of motor control including tremors, dysdiadochokinesia, dyssynergia, and visual nystagmus.

BOX 12-1 ▸ Modified Ashworth Scale (MAS)

- 0 = no increase in muscle tone.
- 1 = slight increase in muscle tone with catch and release or minimal resistance at the end of the ROM in flexion or extension.
- 1+ = slight increase in muscle tone with a catch followed by minimal resistance through the remainder (less than half) of the ROM.
- 2 = marked increase in muscle tone through most of the ROM, but affected parts are easily moved.
- 3 = considerable increase in tone, passive movement is difficult.
- 4 = the affected part is rigid in flexion or extension.

Table 12-5

Testing of Major Reflexes

REFLEX	STIMULUS	RESPONSE
Grasp	Pressure to palm of hand.	Finger flexion that resists object removal.
Flexor Withdrawal	Stimuli to sole of foot.	Flexion of stimulated leg.
Crossed Extension	Passively flex extended leg while opposite leg is flexed.	Extension of opposite leg with adduction and internal rotation.
Asymmetrical Tonic Neck Reflex (ATNR)	Rotate head 90°.	Limb extension on face side, flexion dominated on skull side.
Symmetrical Tonic Neck Reflex (STNR)	Flexion of the head followed by head extension.	Flexion of head results in flexion of arms/extension of legs. Extension of head results in extension of arms/flexion of legs.
Tonic Labyrinthine	Prone position followed by supine position.	Prone results in flexor posturing of arms/legs. Supine results in extensor posturing of arms/legs.
Positive Supporting Reaction	Contact to ball of foot in upright position.	Extension of the legs.
Associated Reactions	Resisted voluntary movements of the less involved limb.	Involuntary movement of the contralateral resting limb (i.e., "overflow").
Neck Righting acting on the Body	Head rotation to one side.	Body rotates to align with head.
Body Righting acting on the Body	Limb* (usually lower) rotation to one side.	Segmental rotation of the trunk.
Optical Righting	Alter body position in all directions.	Head orients to vertical with mouth horizontal.
Protective Extension	Displace center of gravity outside the base of support.	Arms and legs respond to protect against falling.
Equilibrium Reactions	Displace center of gravity by tipping support surface.	Righting of head/trunk/limbs.
Babinski Reflex	Stimulation on plantar aspect of foot on the lateral side from heel to metatarsals then medial towards the big toe with blunt end of reflex hammer.	Flexion of the toes (pathology: extension of the toes).
Hoffman's Sign	Stabilize the DIP of third digit and flick the fingernail.	No movement of the thumb and index finger (pathology: adduction of the thumb and flexion of index finger).

* Note: some sources also identify head rotation to one side as a stimulus for the body acting on body reflex.
Reference: Nilsen, D.M., & Gillen, G. (2021). Motor control assessment. In D.P. Dirette & S.A. Gutman (Eds.), Occupational therapy for physical dysfunction (8th ed., pp. 309–326). Wolters Kluwer.

(6) Resting tremor is an involuntary tremor noted in resting postures.

(7) Rigidity is an increased resistance to passive movement throughout the range; may be "cogwheel" (alternative contraction/relaxation of muscles being stretched) or "lead pipe" (consistent contraction throughout range).

(8) Bradykinesia is an overall slowing of movement patterns.

(9) Akinesia is the inability to initiate movements.

> **EXAM HINT:** Points 6 to 9 are cardinal signs for Parkinson's disease. Refer to Chapter 7.

(10) Athetosis is a dyskinetic condition that includes inadequate timing, force, and accuracy of movements in the trunk/limbs; movements are writhing and worm-like.

(11) Dystonia is an involuntary sustained distorted movement or posture involving contraction of groups of muscles.

(12) Chorea consists of involuntary movements of the face and extremities which are spasmodic and of short duration.

    (a) Chorea is the hallmark symptom of Huntington's disease.

(13) Hemiballismus is a unilateral chorea characterized by violent, forceful movements of the proximal muscles.

4. Assessment for glenohumeral joint inferior subluxation.

a. Allow the person's arm to dangle into gravity.

b. Palpate the space underneath the acromion process with your index finger.

c. Compare to the intact side and document the width of the space in terms of finger breadths (e.g., right shoulder inferior subluxation of one finger breadth).

Chapter 12

Role of the OTA/COTA® in Evaluation

1. The OTA/COTA® contributes to the evaluation process in collaboration with the supervising occupational therapist.
   a. The level of supervision an OTA/COTA® will require depends upon their experience, established service competence, state laws, and other regulatory and payer requirements.
2. The OTA/COTA® can collect evaluation data and administer assessments of occupations, client factors, performance skills, patterns, and contexts and report assessment results to the supervising occupational therapist.
3. The supervising occupational therapist is responsible for determining which assessment(s) will attain information essential for setting goals and planning intervention and the interpretation of the information reported by the OTA/COTA®.
   a. While the OTA/COTA® cannot independently interpret evaluation results, they can contribute to this process.
4. All evaluation activities completed by an OTA/COTA® must comply with federal and state laws and other regulatory and payer requirements (AOTA, 2021).

Orthotic Interventions for Neuromotor Dysfunction

EXAM HINT: The NBCOT® OTR® exam outline identifies knowledge of the "types and functions of immobilization, mobilization, and restriction orthoses for managing specific conditions" (NBCOT®, 2022, p. 10) as essential for competent and safe practice. The application of knowledge about the purposes and types of orthoses used to address neuromuscular dysfunction can help you determine correct answer for NBCOT® exam items about orthotic interventions for persons with neuromotor dysfunction.

Purposes of Orthoses

1. Orthoses may be utilized in the population with neuromuscular dysfunction to meet the following goals.
   a. Prevent/correct deformity via prolonged stretch and proper alignment.
   b. Control spasticity by aligning joints and providing prolonged stretch to spastic muscles.
   c. Prevent/decrease/accommodate contractures of the joint or soft tissue.
   d. Correct biomechanical malalignment by external force.
   e. Position the hand in a functional posture to promote engagement in activities (e.g., hand-based spica [opponens] orthosis to position thumb in opposition for grasp).
   f. Compensate for weakness to allow intact muscle groups to function.
   g. Provide proximal support.
   h. Support a painful joint.
   i. Promote distal mobility.
   j. Enhance a specific activity (e.g., fabrication of a typing or writing orthosis or utilization of a cock-up orthosis for feeding).
   k. Immobilize joints and soft tissues to promote healing.
   l. Prevent or reduce scarring via prolonged pressure and appropriate stretch.

Types of Orthoses

1. Orthosis classification.
   a. Static (no moving parts) orthoses are utilized for external support, prevention of motion, stretching of contractures, aligning joints for healing, resting joints, or reducing pain.
   b. Dynamic (moving parts are included) orthoses have a resilient component (elastic bands or spring) and are utilized to increase passive motion, assist weak motions, or substitute for lost motion.
   c. Serial orthoses are utilized to achieve a slow, progressive increase in motion by progressive remolding.
2. Hand-/wrist-based orthoses may be dorsal or volar.
   a. Cock-up orthosis.
      (1) Supports the wrist in 10°–20° of extension to prevent contracture.
      (2) Allows the digits to function (e.g., to support flaccid wrist).
   b. Resting hand orthosis.
      (1) Utilized for persons who need to have their wrist, digits, and thumb supported in a functional position for prolonged periods (i.e., when developing contracture of the long flexors).

c. Opponens orthosis.
   (1) May be short (hand-based and does not support wrist) or long (forearm-based and supports wrist).
   (2) Designed to support the thumb in a position of abduction and opposition.
   (3) Utilized during functional activities to compensate for weakness patterns.
3. Types of inhibitory/tone normalizing orthoses.
   a. Based on the neurophysiologic frames of reference.
   b. Bobath finger spreader (abduction orthosis).
      (1) This soft orthosis positions the digits and thumb in abduction to reduce tone.
   c. Rood cone.
      (1) Based on Rood's inhibitory principles of sustained deep pressure.
      (2) This cone-shaped orthosis is utilized to reduce flexor spasticity in the hand.
   d. Orthokinetic orthoses.
      (1) This type of orthosis utilizes tactile input (e.g., via elastic bandages) to facilitate and/or inhibit appropriate muscle groups.
   e. Spasticity reduction orthosis.
      (1) This orthosis places the spastic distal extremity on submaximal stretch to reduce spasticity.

> CAUTION: Any static orthosis that is used to decrease tone in the neurological hand may cause hand deformity.
>
> This risk increases if the person has moderate to severe hand spasticity. For example, when a person with spasticity coughs or exerts themselves (e.g., when transferring, walking), the tone in their hand increases.
>
> - The static orthosis is not malleable; thus, the increased tone forces the fingers/wrist into irregular positions. If the hand is in these irregular positions for long periods of time, it will become contracted into these positions.

4. The benefits versus the risk of using a static orthosis must be carefully weighed.
   a. If using a static orthosis, the therapist should carefully and routinely monitor the orthosis and the person's response to the orthosis.
   b. Orthosis options to decrease risk should be considered.
      (1) Fabricating orthoses for the wrist separately from the fingers and having the person alternate wearing the wrist and finger orthoses will not put the long flexors in a severe stretch that could increase tone.
      (2) The SaeboStretch can be an option for a person who has minimal to moderate tone. This orthosis is malleable and will allow for an increase in tone during exertion. Refer to Figure 12-4.
5. Types of supportive orthoses.
   a. Overhead suspension sling.

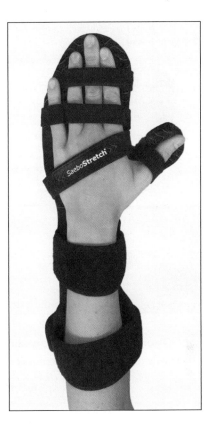

Figure 12-4   **SaeboStretch (dynamic resting hand orthosis).**

Photo by Christina Gavalas-Valdivia. Reprinted with permission.

   (1) This orthotic device incorporates an arm support that is supported by a sling and suspended by an overhead rod.
   (2) Can be used for exercise or to engage in functional tasks.
   (3) Persons presenting with proximal weakness (amyotrophic lateral sclerosis, Guillain-Barré syndrome, muscular dystrophy) with muscle grades in the 1/5 to 3/5 range are appropriate candidates.
   (4) Refer to Figure 12-5.
   b. Balanced forearm orthoses (mobile arm supports or ball-bearing forearm orthoses).
      (1) Consists of an arm trough, proximal and distal arms, and a support bracket that can be placed on wheelchair or table.
      (2) Allows a person with weak proximal musculature to utilize available control of the trunk and shoulder to engage in functional tasks or for exercise.
      (3) Refer to Figure 12-6.
   c. Shoulder slings.
      (1) Utilized to support a flaccid arm after neurologic insult for short and controlled periods of time.
      (2) One sling may not meet the needs of every person, so it's important to be familiar with a variety of slings.

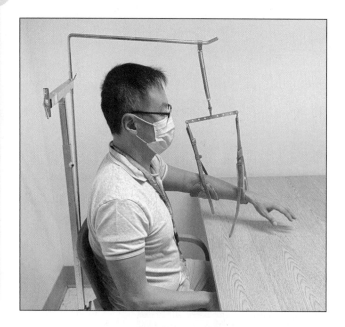

Figure 12-5   **Overhead suspension sling.**

Photo by Daniel Geller. Reprinted with permission.

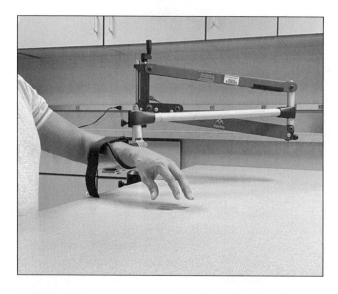

Figure 12-6   **SaeboMAS (Mobile Arm Support).**

Photo by Daniel Geller. Reprinted with permission.

CAUTION: Long-term use may be detrimental in terms of soft-tissue contracture, edema, and the development of pain syndromes.

(3) Types of slings. Table 12-6 describes the functions, precautions, and limitations of different slings.

(4) Refer to Figures 12-7 to 12-9.

d. Supports may be utilized on a wheelchair to position a flaccid arm (e.g., lapboards, arm troughs, etc.).

Table 12-6

Shoulder Sling Descriptions

Arm Pouch sling
Function: supports the weight of the affected arm. Refer to Figure 12-7.
Limitations and Precautions: because this orthosis holds the arm in flexor pattern (i.e., shoulder internal rotation, elbow flexion), it should only be used for short periods of time. This sling also impedes elbow flexion/extension and functional use of the distal extremity.

Shoulder saddle sling
Function: this sling supports distal weight of the affected arm with a forearm cuff and can be worn under clothing. This sling permits elbow flexion/extension and functional use of the arm (if the person is able) and does not hold the arm in a flexor pattern.
Limitations and Precautions: the forearm cuff may cause skin sheering and irritation.

Hemi shoulder sling
Function: similar to the shoulder saddle sling; however, the arm is supported with a humeral cuff instead of forearm cuff. This sling permits elbow flexion/extension and distal function (if the person is able) and does not hold the arm in a flexor pattern. Refer to Figure 12-8.
Limitations and Precautions: the humeral cuff may cause skin sheering and irritation and may not support the weight of the entire arm as well as other slings.

GivMohr Sling:
Function: this sling supports the distal weight of the affected arm, permits elbow flexion/extension, and does not hold the arm in a flexor pattern. Refer to Figure 12-9.
Limitations and Precautions: the handpiece that supports the weight of the arm may impede distal function.

Reference: Gillen, G., & Nilsen, D.M. (Eds.). (2021). Stroke rehabilitation: A function-based approach (5th ed.). Elsevier.

RED FLAGS:
• Avoid traction injuries to a flaccid shoulder during upright activities; lack of adequate support (e.g., shoulder sling, manual support) can cause development of a painful shoulder.
• Only use an arm pouch sling during functional mobility and transfers as prolonged use can lead to contractures and shoulder pain.
  • A shoulder saddle sling and a GivMohr sling may be better options.
• Avoid the use of overhead pulleys in persons with poor shoulder alignment and poor shoulder function. These can cause the development of a painful shoulder.

Orthotic Implementation and Training

1. Fabrication material must be chosen based on its characteristics (e.g., resistance to stretch, memory, conformability/drape, rigidity/flexibility, and self-adherence).
2. Wearing schedules must be prescribed to enhance the function of the orthosis.
   a. Orthoses that are utilized to decrease spasticity or reverse contractures require longer wearing times.

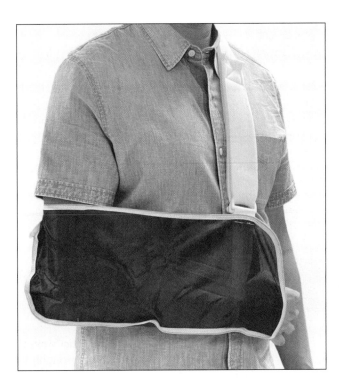

Figure 12-7 Arm pouch sling.
Photo by Daniel Geller. Reprinted with permission.

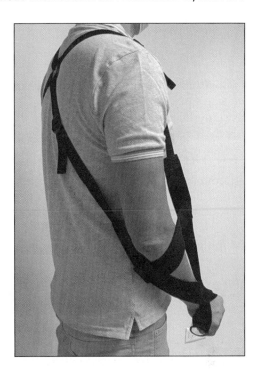

Figure 12-9 GivMohr sling.
Photo by Daniel Geller. Reprinted with permission.

3. Orthoses must be monitored for pressure over bony prominences.
4. Instruct the person in procedures for routine skin inspection and care.

> **RED FLAG:** The ability of persons to effectively self-monitor the use of their orthoses can be hindered by diminished sensation (e.g., hypoesthesia), impaired cognitive-perceptual skills (e.g., unilateral neglect), and/or impaired neurovascular status (e.g., diabetic neuropathy). Consequently, caregiver education about the orthosis wearing schedule, application, and management is required.

5. Train the individual and/or caregivers in donning/doffing of the orthosis and routine maintenance procedures (e.g., washing the orthosis with soap and water).
6. Instruct the person and and/or caregivers about the purposes, functions, and limitations of the orthosis to ensure acceptance of the orthosis and enhance its effective use during functional activities.
7. Reassess the fit, function, and construction of the orthosis at periodic intervals.
8. Assess the person's habitual use of the orthosis and address any issues that hinder use.
9. All orthotic training should be documented.
10. Refer to Chapter 11 for additional information about education and training methods for the safe and effective use of orthotic devices.

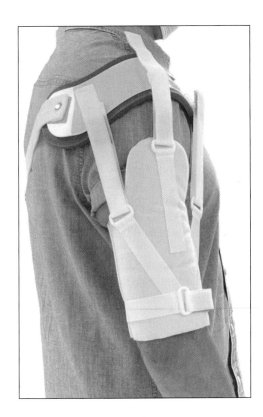

Figure 12-8 Hemi shoulder sling.
Photo by Daniel Geller. Reprinted with permission.

EXAM HINT: The NBCOT® OTR® exam content outline identifies the task of providing "training in the use of orthotic . . . devices to support functional outcomes" (NBCOT®, 2022, p. 10) as essential to entry-level practice and states that performance of this task requires knowledge of "client-centered education and training methods for the safe and effective use of orthotic . . . devices" (NBCOT®, 2022, p. 11) for competent and safe practice. Therefore, it is likely that the NBCOT® exam will test your knowledge of orthotic education and training for clients and/or caregivers.

Role of the OTA/COTA® in Intervention

1. The occupational therapist and OTA/COTA® team must carefully assess for most appropriate orthosis.
2. The occupational therapist must set orthotic goals.
3. Experienced OTAs/COTA®s can fabricate static orthoses and assist with dynamic orthoses upon establishment of service competency.

 ## Oral Motor Dysfunction

Presenting Characteristics

1. May result in speech impairments (i.e., dysarthria), swallowing impairments (i.e., dysphagia), or psychosocial stresses related to facial asymmetry and/or drooling.

Evaluation

1. Range of motion, strength, and tone of the lips, cheeks, and tongue.
2. Extra- and intra-oral sensation.
3. Dentition (e.g., integrity of teeth, denture fit, etc.).
4. Pre-oral stage.
   a. Person engages in food set-up.
   b. Person has visual and olfactory awareness of the food.
   c. Person brings food to mouth (e.g., use of utensils, cup, etc.).
5. Oral-preparatory stage.
   a. Person demonstrates the ability to open mouth.
   b. Muscles of mastication are used to prepare food (if solid) into a bolus.
   c. The bolus is contained in the oral cavity.
   d. A cohesive bolus is formed.
   e. At this stage, the soft palate rests on the tongue to prevent fluid or the bolus from moving into the pharynx (Avery, 2021).
6. Oral stage.
   a. Oral stage of swallow: the lips, buccal muscles, and tongue propel the bolus posteriorly into the pharynx.
7. Pharyngeal stage.
   a. The presence of a swallow reflex.
      (1) Laryngeal elevation: when the larynx rises to approximate the epiglottis and protect the airway.
      (2) Soft-palate elevation: when the soft palate rises to close off the nasopharynx to prevent food/liquid from entering the nasal cavity.

   (3) Pharyngeal peristalsis: when peristaltic "waves" of muscle contraction propel food through the pharynx.
8. Esophageal stage.
   a. The propulsion of the bolus through the esophagus.
   b. Relaxation of the lower esophageal sphincter, allowing the bolus to move into the stomach (Avery, 2021).
9. Airway protection via the following mechanisms.
   a. Gag reflex that expels a bolus that is too large from entering the pharynx.
   b. Volitional and spontaneous cough is utilized to clear the pharynx of residual material.
   c. Vocal fold adduction closes off the airway and prevents food from entering the larynx.
   d. Reflexive inhibition of respiration which prevents inhalation of food into the airway.
10. Primitive reflexes. Refer to Table 12-7.
11. Cranial nerve testing. Refer to Table 12-8.
12. Objective testing; i.e., modified barium swallow/videofluoroscopy, fiberoptic endoscopic evaluation of swallowing (FEES) may be required depending on consistency of bedside evaluation and/or departmental procedures.
    a. Refer to Chapter 9 for additional information about the evaluation of swallowing.

EXAM HINT: The NBCOT® OTR® exam content outline identifies knowledge of the "intervention strategies and techniques used to facilitate oral motor skills for drinking, eating, and swallowing" (NBCOT®, 2022, p. 9) as essential for competent and safe practice. The application of knowledge about the following direct and indirect interventions for oral motor dysfunction can help you determine the correct answer for NBCOT® exam items about oral motor dysfunction.

Table 12-7[1]

Testing of Primitive Reflexes in Persons with Neurological Disorders

REFLEX	STIMULUS	IMPACT ON ORAL-MOTOR DEVELOPMENT AND FUNCTION	PATHOLOGICAL RESPONSE IF PRESENT BEYOND TYPICAL AGE OF INTEGRATION*
Rooting Reflex	Light stroking from the corner of the mouth along the cheek in a direction toward the ear.	This reflex allows the child to seek food as in mother's breast brushing across cheek.	Head turning and tongue protrusion toward the direction of the stimulus.
Jaw Jerk (Phasic Bite Reflex)	Center of the mandible is firmly tapped one to two times.	This reflex allows for jaw movements needed in feeding; i.e., up and down motion of jaw.	Reflexive jaw closure/opening response.
Bite Reflex (Tonic Bite Reflex)	Tongue depressor is placed lightly between the upper and lower teeth.	When this reflex is present, the person is unable to chew foods. The use of utensils for feeding is difficult for they can trigger a bite reflex.	Strong closure of the mouth, difficulty releasing objects placed in the mouth.
ATNR	Rotate head 90°.	This reflex is responsible for eye–hand coordination. When this reflex is present it may prevent hand to mouth and symmetrical behaviors.	Limb extension on face side, flexion dominated on skull side.
STNR	Flexion of the head followed by head extension.	This reflex's separate arm and leg movement allows for balance and trunk control for posture development needed in feeding.	Flexion of head results in flexion of arms/extension of legs. Extension of head results in extension of arms/flexion of legs.

*Refer to Table 5-4: Reflexes that Integrate During Typical Development in Chapter 5.
Reference: Mandich, M. (2016). The newborn. In A. Cronin & M. Mandich (Eds.), Human development and performance throughout the lifespan (2nd ed., pp. 172–199). Cengage Learning.

Table 12-8

Cranial Nerves

NUMBER/NAME	FUNCTION	TESTING PROCEDURE
I. Olfactory	Sensory: Carries impulse for sense of smell.	Person is asked to sniff various aromatic substances.
II. Optic	Sensory: Carries impulses for vision.	Eye-chart testing, visual field testing.
III. Oculomotor	Motor: Fibers to the superior, inferior, and medial rectus muscles of the eye and to the smooth muscle controlling lens shape. Medial and vertical eye movements. Sensory: Proprioception of the eye.	Pupil sizes are compared for shape and equality, pupillary reflex is tested; visual tracking is tested.
IV. Trochlear	Proprioceptor and motor fibers for superior oblique muscle of the eye. Downward and inward eye movements.	Tested with cranial nerve III relative to following moving objects.
V. Trigeminal	Motor and sensory for face, conducts sensory impulses from mouth, nose, eyes; motor fibers for muscles of mastication. Control of jaw movements.	Pain, touch, and temperature are tested with proper stimulus; corneal reflex tested with a wisp of cotton; person is asked to move jaw through full ranges of motion.
VI. Abducens	Motor and proprioceptor fibers to/from lateral rectus muscle. Lateral eye movements.	Tested in conjunction with cranial nerve III relative to moving eye laterally.
VII. Facial	Mixed (sensory and motor): sensory fibers to taste buds and anterior two-thirds tongue; motor fibers to muscles of facial expression and to salivary glands.	Check: symmetry of face, ask person to attempt various facial expressions; sweet, salty, sour, and bitter substances are applied to tongue to test tasting ability.

(Continued)

[1] Rita P. Fleming-Castaldy and Geraldine Healy Marini developed and contributed to this table.

Table 12-8

Cranial Nerves (*Continued*)

NUMBER/NAME	FUNCTION	TESTING PROCEDURE
VIII. Vestibulocochlear	Sensory: Transmits impulses for senses of equilibrium and hearing.	Hearing is checked with a tuning fork.
IX. Glossopharyngeal	Motor fibers for pharynx and salivary glands; sensory fibers for pharynx and posterior tongue. Taste sensation for sweet, bitter, and sour.	Gag and swallow reflexes are checked; posterior one-third of tongue is tested for taste.
X. Vagus	Sensory/motor impulses for larynx and pharynx; parasympathetic motor fibers supply smooth muscles of abdominal organs; sensory impulses from viscera.	Tested in conjunction with cranial nerve IX.
XI. Spinal Accessory	Sensory/motor fibers for sternocleidomastoid, trapezius muscles, muscles of soft palate, pharynx, and larynx. Movement of neck and shoulders.	Sternocleidomastoid and trapezius muscle testing.
XII. Hypoglossal	Motor/sensory fibers to/from tongue. Movement of tongue.	Ask person to stick out tongue, positional abnormalities are noted.

Intervention

1. Direct therapy involves techniques that utilize a bolus.
   a. Modification of consistency, amount, and pacing of solids and liquids.
   b. Utilizing postural interventions to increase swallowing efficiency during meals.
      (1) Chin tuck.
      (2) Forward head tilt/chin tuck.
      (3) Head turn.
   c. Utilizing specific swallowing adaptations.
      (1) Supraglottic swallow technique to voluntarily close/protect the airway during food intake.
      (2) Mendelsohn's maneuver (voluntarily prolonging the rise of the larynx by prolonging tongue contraction).
2. Indirect therapy involves procedures that do not include use of a bolus.
   a. Thermal (cold) stimulation provides sensory input to the swallowing receptors via a chilled dental examination mirror to elicit a swallow reflex.
   b. Reflex facilitation.
   c. Strengthening, facilitation, and coordination of oral movements.
   d. Airway adduction procedures.
   e. Positioning to maintain the trunk/head/neck in correct postures.
3. Refer to Chapter 9 for further information on dysphagia and swallowing disorders.

Role of the OTA/COTA® in Evaluation and Intervention

1. The OTA/COTA® contributes to the evaluation and intervention process in collaboration with the supervising occupational therapist. The level of supervision an OTA/COTA® will require depends upon their experience, established service competence, state laws, and other regulatory and payer requirements.
2. The OTA/COTA® implements the intervention plan and provides direct services to attain intervention goals in collaboration with the supervising occupational therapist.
3. During the implementation of intervention, the OTA/COTA® informs the supervising therapist of any change in the individual's status and any other relevant information that may affect treatment.
4. All evaluation and intervention activities completed by an OTA/COTA® must comply with federal and state laws and other regulatory and payer requirements (AOTA, 2021).

Limb and Postural Control Impairments

Overview of Constraint Induced Movement Therapy (CIMT)

1. CIMT is a task-oriented approach that can be used with persons with neurological conditions who present with control of the wrist and digits.
2. Current and past protocols have used the following motor control inclusion criteria for the more affected side.
   a. 20° of extension of the wrist and 10° of extension of each finger, or
   b. 10° extension of the wrist, 10° abduction of the thumb, and 10° extension of any two other digits, or
   c. Able to lift a washrag off a tabletop using any type of prehension and then release it.

> **EXAM HINT:** The NBCOT® OTR® exam content outline identifies knowledge of motor reeducation techniques including constraint-induced movement and "techniques for promoting improved postural stability . . . during functional tasks" (NBCOT®, 2022, p. 10) as essential for competent and safe practice. The application of knowledge about previously described contemporary task-oriented approaches to motor control training and the following CIMT intervention guidelines can help you determine the correct answer for NBCOT® Domain 3 exam items about selecting and managing interventions for persons with limb and postural control impairments.

Constraint Induced Movement Therapy (CIMT) Intervention Guidelines

1. CIMT has three major components (Rao, 2021).
   a. Massed practice and shaping of the affected limb during repetitive functional activities is the focus of therapeutic intervention.
      (1) Massed practice: practice schedule with very short rest periods (3 to 6 hours per day).
      (2) Shaping: supervised activities to be graded for increased challenge.
   b. Restraint of the less affected upper extremity with a orthosis or glove to remind the person to use the affected limb during therapy and at home, thus "forced use" of the affected arm.
   c. "Transfer Package": adherence enhancing behavioral methods designed to promote transfer of training to ADL (e.g., contracts, adherence logs).
2. An environment that utilizes the common challenges of everyday life is created by the therapist (shaping).
   a. In this environment, the practicing of functional tasks or close simulations that have been identified as important by participants is used to find effective and efficient strategies for performance.
3. Opportunities for practice outside of therapy time (e.g., homework assignments, circuit training, etc.) are provided.
4. Adaptations to the environment, task modifications, assistive technology, and/or a reduction in the effects of gravity are used to enhance occupational performance.
5. Contemporary motor learning principles are used to train or retrain skills. These include the following approaches.
   a. Using random and variable practice within natural contexts in treatment.
   b. Providing decreasing amounts of physical and verbal guidance.
   c. Helping the client develop problem-solving skills so that they can find their own solutions to occupational performance problems.
6. For persons with poor control of movement (e.g., incoordination, tremor, ataxia, dysmetria, etc.), the degrees of freedom are constrained to enhance performance.

Ayres Sensory Integration® and Sensory Processing Approaches[2]

Overview

1. Ayres Sensory Integration® is based on the theoretical premise that inherent neural organization of sensory information creates pathways for increasingly mature and effective adaptive responses.
2. The Ayres Sensory Integration® approach was initially developed by Dr. A. Jean Ayres in the 1950s.
   a. Since the seminal work of Dr. Ayres, numerous occupational therapists have contributed to sensory integration and sensory processing scholarship which has further defined theory, concept development, and intervention approaches.
3. To protect the integrity of Dr. Ayres' work and assure fidelity in research to theory, principles, and interventions, the Baker/Ayres Trust trademarked the term Ayres Sensory Integration® in 2007.
   a. This trademark process distinguishes differences between interventions aimed to address sensory processing issues from those aimed to impact the neurological mechanisms associated with sensory integrative dysfunction.

Principles/Assumptions of Ayres Sensory Integration® Approach

1. Plasticity of the CNS creates opportunities to facilitate optimal development through highly structured, sensory rich activities.
2. A therapeutic environment of planned 'just-right' challenges leverages sensory and motor learning experiences that allow for active problem-solving and increasingly mature adaptive responses.
   a. Mature adaptive responses can include an increased ability to filter sensory distractions while attending to cognitive tasks, the ability to develop precise fine and visual motor skills as seen in writing, and the development of complex motor planning as observed in the gross motor skills that are used to play games and on playgrounds.
3. Sensory integration occurs in a developmentally sequential manner.

---

[2] Cynthia H. August, Jan G. Garbarini, and Marge E. Moffett Boyd contributed this section on Ayres Sensory Integration® approach.

4. Higher cortical processing functions are dependent on adequate processing and organization of sensory stimuli by lower brain centers.
5. Adequate modulation of facilitatory and inhibitory sensory stimuli must occur for an adaptive response to occur.
6. Adaptive responses support the progressive development of motor, praxis, and attentional skills and social behaviors.
7. Ayres Sensory Integration® interventions require advanced training, specialized and suspended equipment, and a child-driven playful context.
8. Ayres Sensory Integration® is designed to have a long-lasting neurophysiological impact on child performance and is provided consistent with the principles of sensory integration theory.
9. Ayres Sensory Integration® is an individualized intervention that is family and child centered.

Principles of a Sensory Processing Approach

1. Sensory processing interventions aim to modify a regulatory state without having a lasting neurophysiological impact.
2. Tailored sensory experiences and tools are used to support function.
   a. Examples include the use of a therapy ball as a classroom seating option and the use of a weighted vest during instructional times. Both options have the intended impact of supporting modulation of sensory experiences for improved performance.
3. Experiences of sensory tools may be passive or active.
   a. Examples of passive sensory experiences include rolling a ball over a child's body as they lie in a prone position and listen to soft music; having the child wear a weighted blanket or vest during class time.
   b. Examples of active sensory experiences include the use of a stability ball for seating, fidget toys, and/or gum or other chewing objects to promote increased attention during instructional time.
4. Sensory tools are used in natural environments without disruption to routines.
5. Interventions may or may not be playful.
6. Interventions may be group based or can be individualized.
7. Specialized equipment is minimal and advanced training is not required.

Evaluation for Sensory Integration and Sensory Processing Disorders

> **EXAM HINT:** The NBCOT® exam may include the names of specific evaluation tools; therefore, knowing the following assessments can help you determine the correct answer for NBCOT® exam items that address the evaluation of sensory processing disorders.

1. Sensory Integration and Praxis Tests (SIPT).
   a. Measure sensory integration skills that are associated with learning disabilities, emotional disorders, and minimal brain dysfunction.
   b. Standardized tests for children 4–8.11 years of age.
      (1) Seventeen tests primarily address the relationship among tactile processing, vestibular-proprioceptive processing, visual perception, and practicability.
      (2) Test scoring requires either computerized scoring by the publishing company or use of a software program purchased from the publisher.
   c. Categorized into four overlapping groups.
      (1) Measures of tactile and vestibular-proprioceptive sensory processing.
      (2) Tests of form and space perception and visual motor coordination.
      (3) Tests of practicability.
      (4) Measures of bilateral integration and sequencing.
   d. The purchase, administration, and interpretation of the SIPT *requires* certification.
2. DeGangi-Berk Test of Sensory Integration (TSI).
   a. A standardized test for children three to five years of age.
   b. Measures sensory integrative function with focus on the vestibular system.
   c. Categorized into three areas: bilateral motor coordination, postural control, and reflex integration.
3. Test of Sensory Functions in Infants.
   a. A standardized test for children 1–18 months of age.
   b. Assesses the level of an infant's sensory responsiveness to a variety of sensory stimuli.
4. Sensory Processing Measure (SPM).
   a. A test for elementary school–age children.
   b. Measures sensory processing, praxis, and social participation across different environments.
   c. Assesses visual, auditory, tactile, olfactory-gustatory, proprioceptive, and vestibular behaviors.
   d. The Home Form is completed by the primary caregiver, the Main Classroom Form is completed by the primary classroom teacher, and the School Environments Form is completed by other school personnel involved with the child in other settings (e.g., art/music/physical education class, bus, cafeteria, playground).
5. Sensory profile-2.
   a. Refer to Chapter 5.
6. Additional tests assess sensorimotor components indicative of sensory processing deficits.
   a. Informal assessment and observation.
      (1) Consider the context of standardized tests along with informal observations.
      (2) Clinical observations, although unpublished and nonstandardized, are commonly used.
      (3) Classroom, playground, home observations.
   b. Assess certain reflexes, crossing body midline, bilateral coordination, and muscle tone.
   c. Interview parents and teachers.

> **EXAM HINT:** In the NBCOT® OTR® exam content outline, knowledge of "interventions to support . . . sensory arousal (which include) sensory modulation" (NBCOT®, 2022, p. 9) is identified as essential for competent and safe practice. Thus, the application of the following general sensory integration and deficit-specific intervention principles can help you determine the correct answer for NBCOT® Domain 3 exam items about selecting and managing interventions for persons with sensory integration and sensory processing disorders.

Intervention

1. General application principles for Ayres Sensory Integration® Approach. During intervention, the occupational therapist completes the following.
   a. Controls sensory input that is child driven and play based to improve sensory processing, facilitate sensory integration, and elicit an adaptive response.
   b. Creates an environment to facilitate active participation for the "just right challenge."
   c. Ensures registration of meaningful sensory input to obtain an adaptive response.
   d. Balances structure and freedom, tapping into the child's inner drive to obtain neural organization.
   e. Gradually introduces activities requiring more mature and complex patterns of behaviors.
   f. Promotes organized adaptive responses to enhance a child's general behavioral organization, including socialization.
2. Specific intervention principles for sensory integration and sensory modulation deficits.
   a. The occupational therapist generally grades for the appropriate combination of the type of movement, rate of movement, and amount of proprioceptive resistance.
      (1) Firm pressure and resistance are less threatening than light touch; refer to subsequent proprioceptive section.

(2) Linear movement is less threatening than angular; refer to subsequent vestibular section.

(3) Slow movement is less threatening than rapid movement; refer to subsequent vestibular section.

b. A combination of stimuli must be used to elicit an adaptive response and for effective intervention.

(1) This combination is a starting point for children with severe processing deficits.

c. The therapist closely observes child's responses and adheres to all precautions.

d. Intervention for tactile deficits.

(1) Tactile modulation for tactile defensiveness, hypersensitivity/overresponsivity, hyposensitivity/underresponsivity, and sensory seeking.

(a) Self-applied stimuli are more tolerable than passive application of tactile stimuli.

(b) Provide firm pressure making sure that the child can see the source of the stimuli that is being applied. Firm pressure tends to be calming, while light touch can be perceived aversive. The face, abdomen, and palmar surfaces of the extremities are particularly sensitive to light touch.

(c) Provide controlled sensory activities that simultaneously provide tactile and vestibular-proprioceptive information.

(d) Begin with slow linear movements and deep touch-pressure.

(e) Apply tactile stimuli in the direction of hair growth which is less aversive.

(f) Follow tactile stimuli with joint compression.

(g) Monitor and adjust stimuli that seem to influence modulation of stimuli (e.g., lighting, sound, etc.).

> CAUTION: Be alert and assess the child's behavioral responses up to a few hours following treatment when negative impacts may still be demonstrated.

(h) Tactile defensiveness and sensory seeking can be reduced if the treatment approach is effective.

(2) Tactile discrimination.

(a) Provide deep-touch pressure to the hands as well as the body.

(b) Deficits in tactile discrimination are rarely seen in isolation, and somatodyspraxia is typically seen; therefore, treatment for tactile discrimination is usually performed simultaneously when providing treatment for deficits in motor planning.

(c) Provide graded activities requiring tactile discrimination using a mixture of textures and items.

e. Intervention for proprioception deficits.

(1) Deficits in modulation demonstrated by overresponsivity, underresponsivity, and sensory seeking.

(a) Provide firm touch, pressure, joint compression, or traction.

(b) Provide resistance to active movement to help the child learn the appropriate amount of force to perform tasks.

(c) Provide activities in various body positions combining vestibular proprioceptive information (e.g., yoga).

(d) Provide slow linear movement, resistance, and deep pressure.

(e) Use adaptive techniques (e.g., weighted vests).

(2) Discrimination deficits.

(a) Provide treatment as noted previously.

(b) Provide activities requiring the child to demonstrate the ability to grade the force or efforts of movement.

f. Intervention for vestibular deficits.

(1) Deficits in modulation of vestibular input include overresponsivity, underresponsivity, hypersensitivity (aversion response), sensory seeking, and gravitational insecurity (fear response).

(a) Grade for type and rate of movement and for the amount of resistance.

• Precautions must be observed.

(b) Slowly introduce linear movement with touch pressure in prone and provide resistance to active movements, especially for gravitational insecurity.

(c) Use linear vestibular stimuli to increase awareness of spatial orientation (otolith organ).

(d) Provide rapid rotary and angular movements with frequent starts/stops and acceleration/deceleration to increase ability to distinguish the pace of movement (semcircular canals).

3. Knowledge of the effects of various sensory stimuli is required for competent and safe practice.

> CAUTION: A therapist must be very aware of intervention precautions because their impact may not be apparent for several hours.
>
> • The therapist should continually ask the child how they are feeling and observe for signs of reactions that involve the autonomic nervous system (e.g., pupil dilation, sweaty palms, and changes in the rate of respiration).

4. Provide interventions to develop compensatory skills (e.g., environmental adaptations, handwriting supports).

5. Reduce environmental barriers and identify facilitators of occupational performance.
   a. Provide a safe physical and emotionally supportive environment for the child.
6. Use group treatment to develop the social interaction skills needed for improved occupational performance in a classroom, with peer groups, and/or in after-school programs.
7. Consult with and/or educate teachers and parents.
8. Share strategies to promote the child's occupational performance in the home, school, and community.

 # References

Anzalone, M. E., & Lane, S. J. (2012). Sensory processing disorder. In S. J. Lane & A. C. Bundy (Eds.), Kids can be kids: A childhood occupations approach (pp. 437–459). F.A. Davis.

Asher, I. E. (Ed.). (2014). Occupational therapy assessment tools: An annotated index (4th ed.). AOTA Press.

Ashworth, B. (1964). Preliminary trial of carisoprodol in multiple sclerosis. Practitioner, 192, 540–542.

Avery, W. (2021). Dysphagia management. In G. Gillen & D.M. Nilsen (Eds.), Stroke rehabilitation: A function-based approach (5th ed., pp. 670–689). Elsevier.

Bohannon, R. W., & Smith, M. B. (1987). Interrater reliability of a modified Ashworth scale of muscle spasticity. Physical Therapist, 67, 206–207.

Bundy, A. C., & Murray, E. A. (2002). Sensory integration: A. Jean Ayres' theory revisited. In A. C. Bundy, S. J. Lane, & E. A. Murray (Eds.), Sensory integration: Theory and practice (2nd ed., pp. 3–33). F.A. Davis.

Dirette, D.P., & Gutman, S. (Eds.). (2021). Occupational therapy for physical dysfunction (8th ed.). Wolters Kluwer.

Gellert, K.M., & Pulaski, K.H. (2021). Functional uses of neurological approaches: Rood, Brunnstrom, proprioceptive neuromuscular facilitation, neuro-developmental treatment. In D.P. Dirette & S.A. Gutman (Eds.), Occupational therapy for physical dysfunction (8th ed., pp. 717–734). Wolters Kluwer.

Gillen, G. (2009). Cognitive and perceptual rehabilitation: Optimizing function. Elsevier/Mosby.

Gillen, G., & Nilsen, D.M. (Eds.). (2021). Stroke rehabilitation: A function-based approach (5th ed.). Elsevier.

Gillen, G., & Nilsen, D.M. (2021). Upper extremity function and management. In G. Gillen & D.M. Nilsen (Eds.), Stroke rehabiliation: A function-based approach (5th ed., pp. 413–474). Elsevier.

Gutman, S. A., & Schonfeld, A. B. (2019). Screening adult neurologic populations: A step-by-step instruction manual (3rd ed.). AOTA Press.

Haynes, C. J., & Anderson, M. (2014). Sensory assessments. In I. E. Asher (Ed.), Occupational therapy assessment tools: An annotated index (4th ed., pp. 363–441). AOTA Press.

Just Trademarks. (n.d.). Ayres Sensory Integration: Trademark details. https://trademarks.justia.com/786/43/ayres-sensory-78643634.html

Katz, N., & Toglia, J. (2018). Cognition, occupation, and participation across the lifespan: Neuroscience, neurorehabilitation, and models of intervention in occupational therapy (4th ed.). AOTA Press.

Lane, S. J. (2020a). Sensory modulation functions and disorders. In A. C. Bundy, S. J. Lane, & E. A. Murray (Eds.), Sensory integration: Theory and practice (3rd ed., pp. 151–180). F.A. Davis.

Lane, S. J. (2020b). Structure and function of the sensory systems. In A. C. Bundy, S. J. Lane, & E. A. Murray (Eds.), Sensory integration: Theory and practice (3rd ed., pp. 58–114). F.A. Davis.

Lane, S. J., Smith Roley, S., & Champagne, T. (2014). Sensory integration and processing: Theories and applications to occupational performance. In B. Schell, G. Gillen, & M. E. Scaffa (Eds.), Willard and Spackman's occupational therapy (12th ed., pp. 816–868). Lippincott, Williams & Wilkins.

Magill, R., & Anderson, D. (2021). Motor learning and control concepts and applications (12th ed.). McGraw Hill.

Miller, L. J. (2014). Sensational kids hope and help for children with sensory processing disorders (SPD). Penguin Group.

National Board for Certification in Occupational Therapy (NBCOT®). (2022). 2022 Occupational Therapist Registered (OTR®) Examination Content Outline. https://www.nbcot.org/-/media/PDFs/2022_OTR_Content_Outline.pdf

Nilsen, D.M., & Gillen, G. (2021). Motor control assessment. In D.P. Dirette & S.A. Gutman (Eds.), Occupational therapy for physical dysfunction (8th ed., pp. 309–326). Wolters Kluwer.

Parham, L. D., & Mailloux, Z. (2020). Sensory integration. In J. C. O'Brien & H.M. Kuhaneck (Eds.), Case Smith's occupational therapy for children and adolescents (8th ed., pp. 516–549). Elsevier.

Pearson Education Limited. (2021). Sensory Integration and Praxis Test (SIPT). https://www.pearsonclinical.co.uk/store/ukassessments/en/Store/Professional-Assessments/Motor-Sensory/Sensory/Sensory-Integration-and-Praxis-Test/p/P100009228.html.

Rao, A.K. (2021). Approaches to motor control dysfunction. In G. Gillen & D.M. Nilsen (Eds.), Stroke rehabilitation: A function-based approach (5th ed., pp. 332–348). Elsevier.

Schmidt, R. A., Lee, T. D., Winstein, C.J., Wulf, G., & Zelaznik, H.N. (2019). Motor control and learning: A behavioral emphasis (6th ed.). Human Kinetics.

Schultz-Krohn, W., & Pendleton, H. (Eds.). (2018). Pedretti's occupational therapy: Practice skills for physical dysfunction (8th ed.). Elsevier Science/Mosby.

Shumway-Cook, A., & Woollacott, M. H. (2017). Motor control: Translating research into clinical practice (5th ed.). Lippincott Williams and Wilkins.

Smith Roley, S., Mailloux, Z., Miller-Kuhaneck, H., & Glennon, T. (2007). Understanding Ayres Sensory Integration®. OT Practice, 12(17), CE1–CE8.

Watling, R., & Clark, G.F. (2011). Using sensory integration and sensory-based occupational therapy interventions across pediatric practice settings. OT Practice, 16(17), CE1–CE8.

Chapter 12

Review Questions

Following are eight questions about key content covered in this chapter. These questions are not inclusive of the entirety of content about occupational therapy evaluation and intervention approaches for neurological disorders that you must know for success on the NBCOT® exam. These questions are provided to help you "jump-start" the thought processes you will need to apply your studying of content to the answering of exam questions; hence, they are not in the NBCOT® exam format. Exam items in the NBCOT® format that cover the depth and breadth of content you will need to know to pass the NBCOT® exam are provided in the three online practice exams that accompany this text. The answers to the following questions are provided in Appendix 2.

1. What level of motor control must be present for a person to be a candidate for CIMT?

2. What is the correct procedure to evaluate the severity of spasticity in a muscle or group of muscles?

3. What is the purpose of applying a static orthosis to an affected body part?

4. You are working with a client with hemiplegia after a brain tumor resection. They are learning to transfer using a tub bench for the first time. The person is at the cognitive stage of learning. According to principles of motor learning, what types of interventions would be appropriate to teach this transfer skill at this stage of learning?

5. You are working with a person with a swallowing disorder. You have determined that direct interventions using a bolus are indicated. Which approaches would you use?

(Continued)

6. You receive a referral for occupational therapy services for a toddler. The parents report that the toddler dislikes changes to daily routines, meeting strangers, and being touched. During your evaluation, you observe that the toddler does not like to move or explore unfamiliar objects and toys. Upon analysis of evaluation results, you determine that the toddler is overresponsive to sensory stimuli and avoids all sensory experiences. According to the principles of Ayres Sensory Integration® approach, what types of sensory stimuli should you introduce during interventions with this toddler and how should you structure your initial intervention sessions? Explain your rationale.

7. You are working with a client with a flaccid arm post-stroke. Name three practice interventions you could implement that aid in upper extremity (UE) skill learning/re-learning and describe them.

8. You are working with a client to perform a sit <-> stand transfer onto a raised toilet seat with arm rests, for the first time, in the client's hospital room. The client requires a great deal of feedback and practice. The next day, you have the client perform the same toilet transfer as they did the day before with minimal feedback. The client is at which stage of motor learning on the second day? Explain your reasoning. Three days later, you ask your client to transfer onto a commode without arm rests in the clinic bathroom and they are able to perform with no cues. The client is at which stage of motor learning three days later? Explain your reasoning.

Cognitive-Perceptual Approaches: Evaluation and Intervention

DANIEL GELLER and GLEN GILLEN

Overview of Cognitive-Perceptual Terminology/Symptoms

Perception

1. The integration/interpretation of sensory impressions received from the environment into psychologically meaningful information.

Cognition

1. The ability of the brain to process, store, retrieve, and manipulate information. It involves the skills of understanding and knowing, the ability to judge and make decisions, and an overall environmental awareness.

Cognitive-Perceptual Deficits

1. Occur as a result of multiple pathologies including CVA, TBI, neoplasms, acquired diseases, psychiatric disorders, and/or developmental disabilities.

> **EXAM HINT:** In the NBCOT® OTR® exam content outline Domain 1 Evaluation and Assessment comprises 23% of the exam and focuses on the ability of the therapist to "acquire information regarding factors that influence occupational performance on an ongoing basis throughout the occupational therapy process" (NBCOT®, 2022, p. 3). Thus, the application of knowledge about the following functional impairments can help you correctly answer Domain 1 exam items about the evaluation of persons with cognitive and/or perceptual deficits.

Functional Impairments

1. Acalculia.
   a. The inability to perform calculations.
   b. Example: the person is unable to calculate change at a grocery store.
2. Agraphia.
   a. The inability to write.
   b. Example: the person cannot sign their name despite previously knowing how to write.
3. Impaired alertness or arousal.
   a. The person has a decreased response to environmental stimuli.
   b. Example: the person needs tactile or verbal cues to stay awake during an evaluation.

4. Alexia.
   a. The inability to read.
   b. Example: the person cannot read a menu despite being literate.
5. Anomia.
   a. Loss of the ability to name objects or retrieve names of people.
   b. Example: the person is not able to name an apple but knows what it is and what to do with it.
6. Anosognosia.
   a. An unawareness of a motor deficit.
   b. May be related to a lack of insight regarding disabilities.
   c. Example: the person is not aware that they have hemiplegia.
7. Aphasia.
   a. Broca's (expressive) aphasia: loss of expressive language indicated by a loss of speech production.
      (1) Example: the person presents with non-fluent speech.
   b. Wernicke's (receptive) aphasia: a deficit in auditory comprehension that affects semantic speech performance, manifested in paraphasia or nonsensical syllables.
      (1) Example: the person is not able to comprehend verbal directions for using an adaptive device; they cannot follow verbal commands.
   c. Global aphasia: a severe loss of the ability to comprehend and express.
8. Apraxia.
   a. Ideational apraxia: a breakdown in the knowledge of what is to be done or how to perform; a loss of the concept or idea required to perform the task; a lack of knowledge regarding object use.
      (1) The neuronal model about the concept of how to perform is lost, although the sensorimotor system may be intact.
      (2) Daily life errors that result can include tool misuse, poor initiation, poor organization and sequencing, perseveration, and performance latency.
         (a) Examples: using a comb to brush teeth; placing butter into a cup of juice; using a finger as a tool, such as brushing one's teeth or stirring a drink with a finger.
   b. Motor apraxia/ideomotor apraxia: loss of access to kinesthetic memory so that purposeful movement cannot be achieved because of ineffective motor planning or sequencing, even though the idea or concept of the task is intact.

(1) Other deficits such as comprehension, sensory, or motor impairments must be ruled out.

(2) The person is unable to perform a task upon request but may perform the task spontaneously.

(3) Daily life errors that can result include clumsiness, slowness, poor hand shaping of objects, timing errors, and poor gesture production (e.g., salute, peace sign, pointing).

(4) Examples: awkward grasp patterns on toothbrush making oral care ineffective; difficulty manipulating coins from the hand into a vending machine coin slot.

9. Astereognosis, also known as tactile agnosia.
   a. The inability to recognize objects, forms, shapes, and sizes by touch alone.
   b. A failure of tactile recognition although sensations (i.e., tactile and proprioception) are intact.
   c. Example: the person cannot recognize that the object in their hand is a quarter without looking at it; the person cannot use their sense of touch to locate the remote on a nightstand in the dark and must turn the lights on to find it; the person will not be able to differentiate objects in their pocket, such as keys and coins, until looking at them.
10. Impaired attention.
   a. An inability to attend to or focus on specific stimuli.
   b. May result in distraction by irrelevant stimuli.
   c. Includes difficulty with sustained attention and selective attention in addition to dividing and alternating/switching attention.
   d. Example: background noise (e.g., a television) distracts the person from the task at hand; the person cannot attend to more than one task at a time.
11. Body scheme disorders.
   a. Loss of awareness of body parts, as well as the relationship of the body parts to each other and objects; includes the following.
   (1) Right-left indiscrimination: the inability to discriminate between the right and left sides of the body or to apply the concepts of right and left to the environment.
      (a) Examples: the person cannot determine which is their left arm; the person is not able to successfully use the cue "the bathroom is on the right"; the person places a shoe on the wrong foot.
   (2) Somatoagnosia: a body scheme disorder that results in diminished awareness of body structure and a failure to recognize body parts as one's own.
      (a) Examples: the person denies ownership of a body part; the person attempts to dress the therapist's arm as if it was their own arm; the person places shaving cream on the mirror as if on their own face.
   (3) Unilateral body neglect: failure to respond to or report unilateral stimulus presented to the body side contralateral to the lesion.
      (a) Examples: the person spends 75% of the time brushing the right side of their hair and 25% on the left; the person only applies shaving cream to the right side of the face; while donning an overhead shirt, the person does not completely pull down the shirt on left side of trunk.
12. Disorientation.
   a. Lack of knowledge of person, place, and time.
   b. Example:
   (1) Person: the person is unable to state their name; the person is unable to correctly choose their name when given choices.
   (2) Place: the person is unable to state that they are in the hospital; the person is unable to correctly choose where they are when given choices.
   (3) Time: the person states that it is March 8 despite it being March 25.
13. Figure/ground dysfunction.
   a. An inability to distinguish foreground from background.
   b. Example: the person has difficulty locating a white bar of soap on a white sink; the person has difficulty finding a key in a cluttered drawer.
14. Memory loss.
   a. Long-term memory loss.
   (1) Lack of storage, consolidation, and retention of information that has passed through working memory.
   (2) Includes the inability to retrieve this information.
   (3) Example: the person is unable to remember their phone number, address, or place of birth.
   b. Short-term memory loss.
   (1) Lack of registration and temporary storing of information received by various sensory modalities.
   (2) Includes the loss of working memory.
   (3) Examples: the person is not able to remember the instructions given for a self-care routine; the person is not able to remember the therapist's name in the middle of an evaluation.
   c. Refer to Chapter 10 for further information about the different types and levels of memory.
15. Impaired organization and sequencing.
   a. The inability to organize thoughts with activity steps properly sequenced.
   b. While impaired organization and sequencing may occur due to ideational apraxia, it can occur on its own.

c. Examples: the person dons their shoes and socks before pants; the person pours laundry detergent into a washing machine after the rinse cycle.

16. Perseveration.
   a. The continuation or repetition of a motor act (premotor perseveration) or task (prefrontal perseveration).
   b. While perseveration may occur due to ideational apraxia, it can occur on its own.
   c. Examples:
      (1) Premotor: the person continues to pull up a sock even though it is already covering the foot; the person washes the same part of the face or brushes the same teeth, combs the same part of hair.
      (2) Prefrontal: the person washes their face completely, then repeats and repeats.

17. Impaired problem solving.
   a. The inability to manipulate a fund of knowledge and apply this information to new or unfamiliar situations.
   b. Example: the person is not able to figure out why their wheelchair keeps moving on an incline and attempts to stand; the person cannot figure out why a drain is clogged and how to stop a sink from overflowing with water.

18. Spatial relations impairment.
   a. Difficulty relating objects to each other or to the self, secondary to a loss of spatial concepts (e.g., up/down, front/back, under/over, etc.).
   b. Example: the person has difficulty orienting clothing to the body correctly such as putting a shirt on backwards; the person has difficulty aligning fitted sheets to the bed.

19. Topographical disorientation.
   a. Difficulty finding one's way in space secondary to memory dysfunction or an inability to interpret sensory stimuli.
   b. Example: the person is not able to find their hospital room after completing an OT session; after completing an errand, the person tends to wander and not find their way back home.

20. Unilateral spatial neglect.
   a. Inattention to, or neglect of, stimuli presented in the extra-personal space contralateral to the lesion. This can include near extra-personal space (i.e., in arm's reach) and/or far extra-personal space (i.e., outside of arm's reach).
   b. May occur independently of visual deficits.
   c. Examples.
      (1) Far extra-personal space: the person with left side neglect is not able to locate a clock on the left wall of a room; the person with right side neglect bumps into objects on the right side while walking.
      (2) Near extra-personal space: the person with left side neglect asks for silverware which is already placed on the left side of the plate; the person with right side neglect eats food only from left side of plate; the person with left side neglect is unable to find clothing on the left side of bed while dressing.

> **EXAM HINT:** The NBCOT® OTR® exam content outline identifies knowledge of the "impact of body functions and body structures on occupational performance (including) cognitive impairments" (NBCOT®, 2022, p. 3) as essential for competent and safe practice. Understanding how cognitive-perceptual deficits can impact function can help you correctly answer NBCOT® exam items about the best approach to use. to enable occupational performance for persons with cognitive-perceptual impairments. For example, it may be helpful to train a person with left-side unilateral spatial neglect to utilize visual scanning strategies to increase attention to the left environment.

Visual Foundation Skills

1. These skills must be evaluated to differentiate perceptual dysfunction and visual system deficits. For example, one cannot accurately assess figure-ground if a person's visual acuity is poor and not compensated (Gillen & Hreha, 2021).
   a. Visual acuity.
      (1) The clarity of vision both near and far with glasses, as needed.
      (2) Normal visual acuity is 20/20.
      (3) Functional implications if impaired: vision is blurred.
         (a) Near acuity problem examples: difficulty reading, difficulty typing on a computer/tablet.
         (b) Far acuity problem examples: difficulty reading traffic signs, difficulty reading a whiteboard/blackboard from the back of a room.
      (4) Corrective lenses can remediate acuity deficits; a referral to an optometrist or ophthalmologist is required.
      (5) Visual acuity testing: refer to Table 13-1.

> **EXAM HINT:** While occupational therapists can evaluate visual foundation skills, they cannot diagnose visual disorders or prescribe corrective lenses. Therefore, if an exam item scenario includes a therapist determining that a person has poor visual acuity, the correct answer would include a referral to an optometrist or ophthalmologist.

   b. Visual fields.
      (1) The available vision to the right, left, superior (upward), and inferior (downward) when eyes are positioned straight ahead.
      (2) Visual fields extend approximately 65 degrees upward, 75 degrees downward, 95 degrees

Table 13-1

Evaluation of Visual Foundation Skills

SKILL	TESTING METHOD
Visual acuity	Visual acuity testing: • Near visual acuity: the therapist sits across from the person who has one eye occluded* and Snellen chart is held 16 inches away from the person at eye level. The therapist asks the person to read the letters on the chart. • Far visual acuity: the Snellen chart is placed on a wall 20 feet away from the person who has one eye occluded.* The therapist asks the person to read the letters on the chart. Both eyes are tested individually and together.
Visual Fields	Confrontation testing, the therapist: • sits across from the person who has one eye occluded* and asks them to look directly at the therapist's nose. • assesses if the person is moving their eye. • reaches their arm to the extreme periphery of the person's field of vision and tells the person that when they see a "wiggling" finger in their peripheral vision, they should point or say yes. All visual fields should be tested with each eye and together.
Pursuits	The therapist: • sits across from the person with one eye occluded* and asks the person to follow a pen, which is approximately 12 inches away. • moves the pen in the pattern of X, H, O. • assesses for smooth eye movements, range of motion, and head compensation as a compensatory strategy. Both eyes are tested individually and together.
Saccades	The therapist: • sits across from the person with one eye occluded.* • presents two different colored targets (e.g., one green and one red)16 inches from the person's face at eye level and about 4 inches from midline. • asks the person to look at the red and green targets when asked (i.e., the person's eye will move from one target to the other on command). • assesses for smooth eye movements, range of motion, and head compensation as a compensatory strategy. Both eyes are tested individually and together.
Scanning	Letter cancellation assessment, the therapist: • tapes the assessment at midline of the person sitting and asks them to cancel out certain letters. • observes for missing letters, skipping lines, and disorganized scanning.
Strabismus	The therapist: • looks at the person's eye and observes deviation. Can be deviated in any direction.
Convergence and Divergence	The therapist: • sits across from the person and uses a pen tip (held vertically) as the object for the person to fixate on, which is held at eye level 12 inches away at the bridge of their nose. • tells the person to keep looking at the tip of the pen while the therapist moves the pen closer toward the bridge of their nose (testing for convergence) and then back to starting position (testing for divergence). • should watch both eyes carefully to observe if one eye drifts off; thus, the eyes are not working as a team.

* Vision can be occluded by a patch, the person's hand or an occlude.

outward, and 60 degrees inward for each eye (Scheiman, 2011).

(3) Functional implications if impaired: the inability to see objects in an affected visual field.

(a) For example in right homonymous hemianopsia the right temporal field and left nasal field are affected; thus, the person cannot to see objects on the right side. Refer to Figure 13-1.

(4) Confrontation testing: refer to Table 13-1.

c. Oculomotor mobility.

(1) Control of eye movements.

(2) Pursuits: the ability to accurately follow a moving object with the eyes in a smooth fashion (e.g., watching a baby crawl on the floor).

Figure 13-1   Right homonymous hemianopsia.

Retrieved from Hemianopsia (2012) http://en.wikipedia.org /wiki/File:Lhvf.png

(a) Functional implications if impaired: difficulty with driving, playing sports, and completing writing tasks.

(3) Saccades: the ability to look from one object quickly and accurately to the other (e.g., the ability to read, write, and drive).

(a) Functional implications if impaired: poor concentration and attention when reading and writing.

(4) Pursuits and saccades testing: refer to Table 13-1.

d. Scanning.

(1) Ability to systematically observe and locate items in the environment.

(2) Functional implications if impaired: difficulty with finding items in kitchen cabinets and the refrigerator, difficulty reading and writing.

(3) Scanning testing: refer to Table 13-1.

e. Strabismus.

(1) Deviation of one eye or one eye at a time while looking at a target.

(2) Functional implications if present: double vision near and/or far. However, the person may not report double vision if the eye that is deviated is suppressed.

(3) Strabismus testing: refer to Table 13-1.

f. Convergence and divergence.

(1) Convergence: the ability for both eyes to work as a team and both turn inward to maintain single vision close up.

(2) Divergence: the ability for both eyes to work as a team and both move outward and maintain single vision far away.

(3) Functional implications if impaired: near or far double vision. However, a person may not complain of double vision due to suppression of the eye that drifts during testing.

(4) Convergence and divergence testing: refer to Table 13-1.

2. For additional information about the evaluation of vision and intervention for visual deficits, refer to the section on low vision in Chapter 16.

> **EXAM HINT:** While occupational therapists can evaluate visual foundation skills, they cannot diagnose visual disorders or prescribe corrective lenses. Therefore, if an exam item scenario includes a therapist determining that a person has poor visual acuity, the correct answer would include a referral to an optometrist or ophthalmologist.

Cognitive-Perceptual Evaluation

Overview

> **EXAM HINT:** The NBCOT® OTR® exam may include a description of evaluation methods and/or the names of specific assessment tools; therefore, a review of the following nonstandardized screening methods and major cognitive-perceptual assessments is important for effective NBCOT® exam preparation. An increased understanding and knowledge of common approaches used to evaluate cognition and perception can strengthen the clinical reasoning skills you will need to correctly answer NBCOT® Domain 1 Evaluation and Assessment exam items about the evaluation of persons with cognitive and perceptual impairments.

1. As of the publication of this text, NBCOT® has not made public the names of the specific assessments that may be on the exam.

a. The assessments included in this Chapter are based on the authors' review of NBCOT® self-assessment tools, major OT textbooks, and feedback obtained from OT practitioners regarding measures used in practice.

Nonstandardized Screening Methods for Cognitive and Perceptual Impairments during Daily Activities

1. The observation of a person performing routine tasks can provide multiple opportunities to screen for cognitive-perceptual deficits.

2. Non–standardized observations during daily routine include:

a. Alertness or arousal: when impaired, the person requires sensory cues to maintain arousal such as a loud voice, tactile stimulation, and/or vestibular input (e.g., the person appears lethargic or may fall asleep during activities of daily living (ADL) performance).

b. Anosognosia: when evident, the person is unaware of motor deficits, which may be related to lack of insight regarding their disability (e.g., trying to get out of bed when both left and right arm are paralyzed).

> **CAUTION:** This is a safety concern as a person with anosognosia may be a fall risk due to their lack of awareness of their deficits.

c. Attention: attentional deficits can be observed according to the multiple components of attention.
   (1) Sustained attention: when impaired, the person is not able to attend to long conversations, instructions, class lessons, television shows, or movies.
   (2) Selective attention: when impaired, the person has difficulty processing and filtering relevant information in the presence of irrelevant stimuli (e.g., studying outside with the noise of traffic and children playing).
   (3) Divided attention: when impaired, the person is unable to do two tasks at the same time (e.g., make toast and tea simultaneously).
   (4) Attentional switching: when impaired, the person has difficulty switching attention from one task to another (e.g., going from typing a paper to answering the phone and then back to typing).
d. Body neglect: when evident, the person does not attend to one side of the body (e.g., the person dresses one side of the body or shaves one side of the face [usually the left]).
   (1) The person does not incorporate the involved limbs into activities such as bed mobility or sandwich making.
e. Ideational apraxia: when evident, the person uses objects incorrectly (e.g., using a hairbrush as a toothbrush), cannot sequence the steps of an activity (e.g., preparing a meal), and/or may not engage in a task.
f. Motor/ideomotor apraxia: when evident, the person appears 'clumsy,' has difficulties crossing midline and with manipulation activities (e.g., manipulating coins), uses awkward grasp patterns (e.g., when answering the phone), has difficulty with bilateral activities (e.g., folding a sheet).
g. Perseveration: when evident, the person repeats the same motor act such as continuing to wash one arm or continuing to pull up a sock that already covers the foot, has difficulty terminating a hand to mouth pattern when the plate or bowl is empty, repeats the same task (e.g., dress, undress, dress, undress).
h. Sequencing and organization: when impaired, steps of the task are not in a logical order (e.g., putting on shoes and socks before pants) or steps of the activity are left out (e.g., washing dishes without soap).
i. Somatagnosia: when impaired, the person attempts to dress the therapist's arm; they may attempt to brush the teeth of their mirror image.
j. Spatial neglect: when evident, the person cannot find food on one side of the plate or the phone on one side of the desk (usually the left side) or cannot balance a checking account (e.g., the number $1,550.00 may be perceived as 50.00).

   (1) The person gets lost easily during ambulation or wheelchair mobility due to only responding to only one side of the environment.

> **CAUTION:** This is a safety concern as a person with spatial neglect who is ambulating or using a wheelchair may bump into objects or people on the affected side; this is a fall hazard for them and a safety hazard for others.

k. Spatial relations dysfunction: when evident, the person has difficulty with dressing (e.g., orienting a shirt to the body; thus, the shirt is put on backwards or upside down) and/or aligning/moving their body in space during a transfer.
   (1) The person is observed undershooting or overshooting when reaching for glasses and/or spilling milk when pouring into a glass.
l. Visual agnosia: when evident, the person cannot recognize objects (e.g., a glass in a sink).
   (1) Other senses such as touch are required to recognize objects.

> **EXAM HINT:** In the NBCOT® OTR® exam content outline, Domain 1 Evaluation and Assessment comprises 23% of the exam and knowledge of the "administration, purpose, indications, advantages, and limitations of standardized and nonstandardized screening and assessment tools (including) criterion-referenced tests, norm-referenced tests, client and caregiver interviews, (and) observation" (NBCOT®, 2022, p. 4) is identified as essential for competent and safe practice. Thus, the application of knowledge about the above nonstandardized screening methods and the following standardized measures can help you correctly answer Domain 1 exam items about the evaluation of persons with cognitive and/or perceptual deficits.

Allen Cognitive Level Test

1. Utilized for populations with psychiatric disorders, acquired brain injury, and or dementia.
2. Used as a screening tool to estimate an individual's cognitive level.
3. The person performs three leather lacing stitches progressing in complexity.
   a. The task demands for each stitch are proposed to require the use of abilities associated with Allen's levels of cognition.
4. Allen has developed a six-level scale of cognitive function: Level 1 = automatic actions to Level 6 = planned actions (Erez & Katz, 2018).
   a. Refer to Chapter 14.
5. Usually 20 minutes to administer.

Arnadottir Occupational Therapy Neurobehavioral Evaluation (A-ONE)

1. Utilized in the adult population presenting with cognitive/perceptual (neurobehavioral) deficits by evaluators *who have completed A-ONE training.*
2. Structured observations of ADL and mobility skills are performed to detect underlying neurobehavioral dysfunction.
3. A system of error analysis is utilized to document the underlying performance components (e.g., neglect, spatial dysfunction, body scheme disorder, apraxia) that have a direct impact on daily living tasks.
4. Scoring.
   a. Functional Independence Scale with 0 = unable to perform to 4 = independent.
   b. Neurobehavioral Specific Impairment Scale with 0 = no neurobehavioral impairment is observed to 4 = unable to perform secondary to neurobehavioral dysfunction (Árnadóttir et al., 2008).
5. Usually 25 minutes to administer.

> **EXAM HINT:** It is important to remember that the NBCOT® exam tests entry-level knowledge. Therefore, evaluations that require a practitioner to complete training *prior to* using them (e.g., A-ONE, MoCA) should only be considered as a potential correct answer *if* the therapist's completion of this training is described in the exam item scenario.

Assessment of Motor and Process Skills (AMPS)

1. Refer to Chapter 15.

Behavioral Inattention Test

1. Utilized with adults post acquired brain injury with suspected unilateral spatial neglect.
2. Examines the presence of neglect and its impact on functional task performance.
3. Includes nine activity-based subtests including picture scanning, menu reading, map navigation, address and sentence copying, card sorting, article reading, telephone dialing, coin sorting, and telling/setting the time.
4. Includes six pen/paper subtests including line crossing, star cancellation, letter cancellation, figure and shape copying, and line bisection (Wilson et al., 1987).
5. Usually 30–40 minutes to administer.

Catherine Bergego Scale (CBS)

1. A standardized checklist to detect presence and degree of unilateral neglect during observation of everyday life situations.
2. A functional scale consisting of ten items related to neglect in everyday life (i.e., gaze orientation, limb awareness, auditory attention, personal belongings, dressing, grooming, navigation, collisions, meals, and cleaning after meal).
3. Scoring.
   a. For each item: 0= no neglect, 1= mild neglect, 2 = moderate neglect, 3= severe neglect.
   b. Neglect severity (total score): Absent (0); mild (1–10), moderate (11–20); severe (21–30).
4. Usually takes 30 minutes to administer (Azouvi et al., 2003).
5. Kessler Foundation Neglect Assessment Process (KF-NAP).
   a. Modified the CBS to better convey the purpose of the observation.
   b. Includes right-sided neglect symptoms.
   c. Provides a manual with detailed instructions on administration and scoring (Chen et al., 2015).

Cognistat Cognitive Assessment/Neurobehavioral Cognitive Status Examination

1. The Cognistat is a screening and assessment tool for rapid testing of people with cognitive dysfunction.
   a. Utilized in populations with stroke, TBI, dementia, delirium, major psychiatric disorders, substance abuse, neurocognitive disorders, and mild cognitive impairments (MCI).
   b. Includes testing in three general areas (i.e., consciousness, orientation, simple attention) and five major domains (i.e., language, constructional ability, memory, calculation skills, and executive skills).
   c. Can be used with adolescents, adults, and older adults.
2. Usually less than 30 minutes to administer (Cognistat, 2021).

Executive Function Performance Test (EFPT)

1. A standardized objective performance test that assesses executive function (EF) deficits during the performance of real-world tasks.
   a. Tasks include cooking oatmeal, making a phone call, managing medications, and paying a bill.

2. A structured cueing and scoring system is used to assess EF in regard to initiation, organization, sequencing, judgment and safety, and task completion.
   a. Each EF area is given a score depending on the level of cueing necessary to support task performance (0 = independent [no cues required], 1 = verbal guidance, 2 = gestural guidance, 3 = verbal direct instruction, 4 = physical assistance, 5 = do for participant).
      (1) The score reflects the participant's capacity for EF during performance of everyday tasks.
   b. Higher scores reflect a need for greater cueing and indicate more severe EF deficits (Erez & Katz, 2018).
3. Usually 30–45 minutes to administer.
4. The precursor to the EFPT is the Kitchen Task Assessment (KTA). Refer to Chapter 15.

Kettle Test (KT)

1. For adults who are post-stroke, have mild dementia, or healthy older adults.
2. Performance based test during which the person assemble an electric kettle and prepares two different hot beverages.
   a. Task selection is designed to tap into basic cognitive processes (i.e., attention, memory), as well as higher level cognitive processes (i.e., executive functioning). Safety and awareness are also assessed.
3. Scoring is based on the 13 steps of the task.
   a. Each step is scored on a 0–4 scale which depends on the level of cueing (0 = intact performance, 1 = slow and/or trial & error, or questionable performance but independent, 2 = received general cues, 3 = received specific cues, 4 = received demonstration or physical assist.
   b. Total score is 52.
      (1) Higher scores reflect more difficulty with task performance (Erez & Katz, 2018; Hartman-Maeir et al., 2005; Hartman-Maeir et al., 2009).
4. Administration time ranges from 5–30 minutes.

Lowenstein Occupational Therapy Cognitive Assessment (LOTCA)

1. Utilized for persons who have experienced a stroke, TBI, or brain tumor.
2. Measures basic cognitive functions that are prerequisite for managing everyday tasks.
3. Consists of 20 subtests in five areas: orientation, visual, spatial perception, visual motor organization, and thinking operations.
4. Abilities are scored from 1 = low ability to 4 = high ability (Katz et al., 1989).

5. Usually 45 minutes to administer, reported administration times ranges from 30–90 minutes.

Mini-Mental State Examination (MMSE) or Folstein Test

1. A screening tool for cognitive impairment; most commonly used to screen for neurocognitive disorders.
2. Consists of 11 questions in five different cognitive areas: orientation, registration, attention and calculation, recall, and language.
3. The maximum total score is 30.
   a. A score lower than 23 indicates cognitive impairment (Folstein et al., 1975).
4. Usually 5–10 minutes to administer.
5. Refer to Chapter 14 for more information.

Montreal Cognitive Assessment (MoCA)

1. A screening instrument for mild cognitive dysfunction that is administered by evaluators who have *completed the one-hour MoCA training and certification module.*
2. Requires certification to administer.
3. The MoCA assesses eight cognitive domains: attention and concentration, executive functions, memory, language, visuoconstruction skills, conceptual thinking calculations, and orientation.
4. It takes approximately 10 minutes to administer.
5. The total possible score is 30 points; a score of 26 or above is considered normal; less than 10 = severe cognitive impairment, 10-17 = moderate impairment, 18-25 = mild impairment (Nasreddine, 2021).

Multiple Errands Test (MET)

1. Utilized for adults who have experienced an acquired brain injury.
2. Measures the impact of executive functioning deficits on the performance of multiple everyday tasks in a real-life environment.
3. Has several versions: MET-R (revised), MET-HV (hospital version), MET-SV (simplified version), VMET (virtual).
4. In all versions, the tasks are divided into errands (e.g., purchasing an item, mailing a letter), obtaining information (e.g., the closing time of a library, the price of candy bar), meeting the assessor at a particular place and time, and informing the assessor when all tasks are completed.

5. While performing the tasks, the person must adhere to specific rules (e.g., adhering to spending limits, only purchasing a certain number of items, not visiting the same area twice).
6. Score is based on the total number of errors recorded by the therapist and the time it took to complete the tasks (Alderman et al., 2003; Morrison et al., 2013).
7. Approximately 60 minutes to administer.

Rivermead Behavioral Memory Test-Third Edition (RBMT-3)

1. Designed to identify memory deficits through everyday activities.
2. Assesses visual and auditory memory, immediate and delayed recall, and recognition.
3. Contains 14 subtests such as immediate and delayed recall of a story (therapist reads a story), immediate and delayed recall of a route (therapist demonstrates a route to walk in the room), immediate and delayed recall of a novel task (therapist demonstrates the use of different colored pieces to make a shape), questions about orientation, and delayed recall of a picture.
4. Takes around 30 minutes to administer (Wilson et al., 2008).

Rivermead Perceptual Assessment Battery

1. For individuals 16 years and older who are experiencing visual-perceptual deficits after head injury or stroke.
2. Consists of 16 performance tests that assess form and color constancy, object completion, figure-ground, body image, inattention, and spatial awareness.
3. Utilizes deficit-specific tasks in isolation from ADL tasks.
4. Scoring is based on accuracy of task completion and the time taken to complete each task (Whiting et al., 1986).
5. Usually 30 minutes to administer.

Weekly Calendar Planning Activity (WCPA)

1. For adolescents to older adults with suspected executive function deficits with acquired brain injury.

2. Designed to examine how subtle executive functioning difficulties affect performance in multi-step activities in daily life.
3. The person is asked to organize 10–18 appointments or errands (10 for short form, 17 for adults, 18 for youth) into a weekly schedule while adhering to rules, avoiding conflicting appointments, and monitoring time.
4. The test has three levels of difficulty based on the person's age and cognitive functioning.
   a. Level 1: lower functioning adults (20–25 minutes to administer).
   b. Level 2: moderate functioning adults (20–25 minutes to administer).
      (1) This level test is the one that is most often used.
   c. Level 3: higher functioning adults (30–40 minutes to administer).
5. The WCPA also has a short form (only for adults) with 10 items instead of 17 (10–15 minutes to administer).
   a. This version was designed to be used by therapists in an inpatient setting who work with people who are lower functioning and for therapists who have a limited amount of time to complete an evaluation.
6. Scoring is based on 1) appointments as entered or missing, 2) appointments in correct day/time, 3) appointments labeled correctly, and 4) awareness of errors (AbilityLab, 2021; MultiContext, 2017; Toglia, 2015).

Role of the Occupational Therapy Assistant (OTA)/ Certified Occupational Therapy Assistant (COTA®)

1. The OTA/COTA® can contribute to the evaluation process in collaboration with the occupational therapist.
   a. Supervision by an occupational therapist is required.
   b. The level of supervision required will be determined by the OTA's/COTA®'s experience.
2. Service competency must be established.
3. The OTA/COTA® cannot independently evaluate or interpret evaluation results.

Cognitive-Perceptual Intervention

EXAM HINT: In the NBCOT® OTR® exam content outline, Domain 3 comprises 38% of the NBCOT® exam. This domain is defined as the selection and management of "interventions to promote healing and enhance engagement in occupation-based activities" (NBCOT®, 2022, p. 7). Thus, the application of knowledge about the following cognitive-perceptual intervention approaches can help you correctly answer NBCOT® Domain 3 exam items about intervention management for persons with cognitive and/or perceptual deficits.

Remedial/Restorative/Transfer of Training Approach

1. Focuses on the remediation of impairments to increase function.
2. Uses deficit specific cognitive and perceptual retraining activities to address identified impairment.
3. Targets the cause of symptoms.
4. Emphasizes client factors and performance skills.
5. Assumes improvements in client factors and performance skills will result in increased occupational performance.
6. Assumes the cerebral cortex is malleable and can reorganize.
7. Utilizes tabletop and computer activities such as memory drills, block designs, parquetry, pegboard copying design, sequencing cards, picture matching.

Compensatory/Adaptive/ Functional Approach

1. Focuses on decreasing activity and participation restrictions.
2. Involves repetitive practice of functional tasks.
3. Emphasizes modification (e.g., modifying clothing closures by using Velcro to replace buttons and/or zippers for those with motor apraxia).
4. Activity choices are driven by tasks the person needs or wants to perform.
5. Treats symptoms, not their cause.
6. Utilizes techniques of environmental adaptation (e.g., placing a list of morning care activities on the bathroom mirror for those with memory loss or sequencing deficits) and compensatory strategies (e.g., taping lectures in school for those with poor sustained attention).

a. The use of compensatory cognitive strategies requires a level of awareness of deficits.
7. Uses environmental modifications.
   a. These do not require insight or learning of the person and may be caregiver driven (i.e., the caregiver will make the environmental modification for the person to be successful).
8. Treatment is task specific.
9. Utilizes functional tasks (e.g., ADL, IADL, work, and leisure tasks) that the individual desires or is required to perform at discharge as the basis of treatment.

Information Processing Approach

1. Provides information on how the individual approaches the task.
2. Investigates how performance changes with cueing.
3. Standardized cues are given to determine their effect on performance. For example, "Try re-reading the recipe" or "Try speaking the steps out loud."
4. Cues or feedback are utilized to draw attention to relevant features of the task.
5. Investigative questions (e.g., "Why do you think it took so long to get dressed?" or "Do you know why I had to help you balance the checking account?") are used to provide insight to the underlying deficits.

Dynamic Interactional Approach

1. Emphasizes transfer of information from one situation to the next.
2. Utilizes varying treatment environments.
3. Practice of a targeted strategy with varied tasks and in diverse situations (e.g., multi-contextual) is emphasized.
4. Emphasizes metacognitive skills (i.e., self-awareness of strengths and deficits) as the basis of learning and generalization of learning.
5. Transfer of learning must be taught from one situation to the next and does not occur automatically.
6. Transfer of learning occurs through a graded series of tasks that decrease in similarity (e.g., training a person with visual neglect to use scanning strategies to find items in a refrigerator and then use these strategies for a less similar task such as scanning to cross the street).
7. The person's processing abilities and self-monitoring techniques are used to facilitate learning for different tasks or environments.

8. The therapist utilizes awareness questioning (e.g., "How do you know this is right?") to help the individual detect errors, estimate task difficulty, and predict outcomes.

The Quadraphonic Approach

1. Based on remediation.
2. Based on information processing theory and teaching/learning theory.
3. Micro-perspective includes evaluation and management of client factors and performance skills such as attention, memory, perception, higher level cognition (e.g., judgement, executive functions, problem solving), sequencing, and initiation.
4. Macro-perspective evaluation includes the use of narratives, interview, real-life occupations (e.g., shopping, cooking, other IADL).
5. Makes use of several theories.
   a. Information processing.
      (1) For example, for those that are minimally responsive after head injury, the type of sensory stimulus the person responds to (e.g., a loud voice, painful tactile stimulus, various aromas) is determined.
   b. Teaching/learning evaluation.
      (1) For example, the person's stage of learning, which environment is most appropriate for treatment (i.e., quiet bedside vs. stimulating OT clinic), and/or which cues are most effective (e.g., using more visual/gestural cues for those with aphasia) are determined.
   c. Neurodevelopmental evaluation.
      (1) For example, the person's level of postural control, symmetry of movement, mobility, and stability are assessed.
   d. Biomechanical evaluation.
      (1) For example, the person's AROM, endurance, strength, coordination are assessed.

Neurofunctional Approach

1. Based on learning theory.
2. Specifically used for individuals with acquired neurological impairments (e.g., TBI, CVA).
3. Focuses on retraining real world skills rather than cognitive-perceptual processes.
4. Utilizes an overall adaptive approach but incorporates some remediation components.
5. Treatment is focused on training specific functional skills in true contexts.

Cognitive Disabilities Model

1. Originally developed for use with individuals who have psychosocial dysfunction, currently also being utilized with persons with neurologic dysfunction and neurocognitive disorders.
2. Describes cognitive function on a continuum from level 1 (profoundly impaired) to level 6 (normal).
3. Each level describes the extent of a person's disability and difficulty in performing occupations.
4. After the person's level has been established, routine tasks are presented that the person can perform or that have been adapted so that they can perform them.
5. Focus is placed on adaptive approaches and strengthening residual abilities.
6. Refer to Chapter 14.

General Intervention Strategies for Specific Deficits

1. Impaired alertness or arousal.
   a. Increase environmental stimuli.
   b. Use gross motor activities.
   c. Increase sensory stimuli.
2. Impaired awareness.
   a. Prediction method: the goal is to have the person predict how well they will perform a task of interest and then have them compare their prediction to their actual performance through a discussion with the therapist.
      (1) For example, have the person predict the following: 1) how difficult it will be to make a sandwich (e.g., very easy, easy, moderately hard, hard, very hard), 2) how long it will take to complete making the sandwich, 3) how many errors they will make, and 4) how much assistance they will require (e.g., minimal, moderate, maximal) prior to performing the task and then compare afterwards.
   b. Provide feedback about the person's performance.
   c. Role reversal (i.e., the therapist performs the task just as the person performed it and then the person tries to detect the errors).
   d. Video tape the person performing an activity/completing a task, have the person observe the recording, and discuss their performance.
   e. Group treatments and peer feedback (Gillen, 2009).
3. Aphasia: a communication disorder due to brain damage that is characterized by impaired language modalities such as speaking, listening, reading, and writing.
   a. Expressive aphasia.

(1) Speech and language symptoms: short simple utterances, halting and hesitant speech, awkward effortful articulation, poor sentence structure and grammar.
(2) Intervention guidelines.
    (a) Give the person time to speak.
    (b) Encourage participation in conversation and use of alternative means of communication (i.e., gestures, drawing).
    (c) Use visual supports.
    (d) Highlight key words.
    (e) Use concise sentences and simplify grammatical structures.
    (f) Pay attention to facial gestures and body language.
    (g) Train in the use of augmentative communication devices, such as smart phones, electronic tablets, laptops (Stewart and Riedel, 2021).

b. Receptive aphasia.
(1) Speech and language symptoms: fluent uninterrupted string of words (i.e., increased flow of unfocused and incomprehensible speech), use of jargon, verbal paraphasia (i.e., when an entire word is replaced with the intended word such as saying "drive" instead of "car") and neologisms (i.e., made up words).
(2) Intervention guidelines.
    (a) Stop strategy: use cues (i.e., gestures) to stop the flow of incomprehensible speech.
    (b) During an increased flow of speech, refocus the person to change topics.
    (c) Simplify written material.
    (d) Speak slowly, clearly, and with normal loudness; simplify spoken material.
    (e) Use common words and simple sentence structure.
    (f) Give the person time to comprehend and respond (Stewart and Riedel, 2021).

4. Apraxia.
  a. Motor/ideomotor apraxia.
    (1) Strategy training: teaching a person to compensate for apraxia by instruction, assistance, or feedback.
    (2) Decrease manipulation demands (e.g., the use of an electric razor and/or electric toothbrush).
    (3) Decrease the degrees of freedom (i.e., the number of joints) to perform the task (e.g., when applying make-up place the elbow on a table).
    (4) Provide hand over hand tactile-kinesthetic input.
    (5) Educate the person to move their arm along a supported surface to give maximal tactile feedback (e.g., have the person slide their hand down their leg as they reach for a shoe near their feet).
    (6) Utilize visual cues.

(7) Demonstrate the task while sitting parallel to the person.
(8) Demonstrate the required action/movement and ask person to copy afterwards (Gillen, 2009, 2021).

b. Ideational apraxia.
(1) Provide step by step instructions.
(2) Use hand over hand guiding techniques.
(3) Provide opportunities for motor planning and motor execution.
(4) Use tactile exploration of tools and functional objects to enhance performance (e.g., the tines on the fork).
(5) Grade the number of objects/tools during the task (e.g., only place the toothbrush on the sink when grooming and add more grooming tools such as a razor and comb when the person improves) (Gillen, 2009, 2021).

5. Body neglect.
  a. Awareness training.
    (1) Discuss task performance.
    (2) Provide feedback about observed difficulties.
    (3) Provide video feedback with discussion (Gillen, 2009).
  b. Provide bilateral activities.
  c. Guide the affected side through the activity.
  d. Increase sensory stimulation to the affected side (e.g., vibration, PROM or AROM).
  e. Teach the use of mental imagery: imagine the affected limb moving (Gillen, 2009).

6. Memory loss.
  a. Use rehearsal strategies.
  b. 'Chunk' information (e.g., for recalling a phone number, the person could chunk the digits into three groups: first, the area code (such as 123), then a three-digit chunk (456), and, last, a four-digit chunk (7890).
  c. Utilize memory aids (e.g., smart phones, alarm watches, timers, daily planners).
  d. Utilize 'temporal tags', focusing on when the event to be remembered occurred.

7. Perseveration.
  a. Bring perseveration to a conscious level and train the person to inhibit the behavior.
  b. Redirect attention.
  c. Engage the individual in tasks that require repetitive action (e.g., washing face, brushing teeth) that have a concrete outcome (e.g., a clean face, clean teeth) to promote successful participation and effective task termination.
  d. Assist the person in the initiation of a new movement or task (Gillen, 2021).

8. Sequencing and organization deficits.
  a. Use external cues (e.g., written directions, daily planners).

b. Grade tasks that are increasingly complex in terms of the number of steps required.

c. Maps and diagrams may be helpful.

d. Repetitive practice and getting person into a routine helps (Gillen, 2021).

9. Spatial neglect.

a. Awareness training.

b. Provide graded scanning activities.

c. Grade activities from simple to complex.

d. Use anchoring techniques to compensate (e.g., a strip of red tape placed on the left side of the sink to draw attention to the left hemi-field; placing the left arm on the table while eating).

e. Utilize manipulative tasks in conjunction with scanning activities.

f. Use external cues (e.g., colored markers and written directions).

g. Modify the environment.

(1) If the person is unaware of neglect, place items in the non-neglected area (e.g., for a person with left neglect and no awareness of deficit, place all grooming items on the right side of the sink so person can find objects for grooming).

(2) If person is aware of the neglect, place items on the neglected side to force scanning into that area (e.g., for a person with left neglect and aware of this deficit, place grooming items midline to left to force scanning to the left) (Gillen, 2009).

10. Spatial relations dysfunction.

a. Utilize activities that challenge underlying spatial skills (e.g., orienting clothing to the body during dressing, wrapping a gift, making a bed).

b. Utilize tasks that require discrimination of right/left (e.g., use cues such as "dress your left arm first" or "the plates are in the right lower cabinets").

EXAM HINT: The NBCOT® OTR® exam content outline identifies knowledge of "interventions to support cognitive, visual-motor, visual, and perceptual processing (and) compensatory and remedial strategies for managing cognitive and perceptual deficits" as essential for competent practice (NBCOT®, 2022, p. 9). Knowing the intervention strategies described in this section can help you determine the correct answer to NBCOT® Domain 3 exam items about intervention management for persons with cognitive-perceptual deficits.

Role of the OTA/COTA®

1. The OTA/COTA® implements the intervention plan and provides direct services to attain intervention goals in collaboration with the supervising occupational therapist.

a. The level of supervision required depends upon the OTA's/COTA®'s experience and established service competence and the regulations from the licensure board in the state of practice.

2. During the implementation of intervention, the OTA/COTA® informs the supervising occupational therapist of any change in the individual's status and any other relevant information that may affect treatment.

3. All intervention activities completed by an OTA/COTA® must comply with federal and state laws and other regulatory and payer requirements (AOTA, 2021).

References

Abilitylab. (2020, August 12). Weekly calendar planning activity. https://www.sralab.org/rehabilitation-measures/weekly-calendar-planning-activity.

Alderman, N., Burgess, P. W., Knight, C., & Henman, C. (2003). Ecological validity of a simplified version of the multiple errands shopping test. Journal of the International Neuropsychological Society, 9, 31–44.

American Occupational Therapy Association. (2013). Cognition, cognitive rehabilitation, and occupational performance. American Journal of Occupational Therapy, 67, S9–S31. doi:10.5014/ajot.2013.67S9.

Árnadóttir, G. (2021). Impact of neurobehavioral deficits on activities of daily living. In G. Gillen & D. M. Nilsen (Eds.), Stroke rehabilitation: A function-based approach (5th ed., pp. 556–592). Elsevier.

Árnadóttir, G., & Fisher, A. G. (2008). Rasch analysis of the ADL scale of the A-ONE. American Journal of Occupational Therapy, 62, 51–60.

Azouvi, P., Oliver, S., de Montety, G., Samuel, C., Louis-Dreyfus, A., & Tesio, L. (2003). Behavioral assessment of unilateral neglect: Study of the psychometric properties of the Catherine Bergego Scale. Archives of Physical Medicine and Rehabilitation, 84, 51–57.

Below, C. P., & Lewis, K. (2021). Visual function intervention. In D.P. Dirette & S. A. Gutman (Eds.), Occupational therapy for physical dysfunction (8th ed., pp. 100–116). Wolters Kluwer.

Chen, P., Chen, C. C., Hreha, K., Goedert, K. M., & Barrett, A. M. (2015). Kessler Foundation Neglect Assessment Process uniquely measures spatial neglect during activities of daily living. Archives of Physical Medicine and Rehabilitation, 96, 869–876.

Christy, K., & Huffine, N. (2021). Visual perceptual assessment and intervention. In D. P. Dirette & S. A. Gutman (Eds.), Occupational therapy for physical dysfunction (8th ed., pp. 117–142). Wolters Kluwer.

Cognistat. (2021). The cognitive test for screening and assessment. https://www.cognistat.com/.

Dirette, D. P., & Fortuna, J. (2021). Visual function assessment. In D. P. Dirette & S. A. Gutman (Eds.), Occupational therapy for physical dysfunction (8th ed., pp. 781–799). Wolters Kluwer.

Dirette, D. P., & Gutman, S. (Eds). (2021). Occupational therapy for physical dysfunction (8th ed.). Wolters Kluwer.

Dirette, D. P., & McCormack, G. L. (2021). Cognitive assessment. In D. P. Dirette & S. A. Gutman (Eds.), Occupational therapy for physical dysfunction (8th ed., pp. 143–160). Wolters Kluwer.

Erez, A. B., & Katz, N. (2018). Cognitive Functional Evaluation. In N. Katz & J. Toglia (Eds.), Cognition, occupation and participation across the lifespan: Neuroscience, neurorehabilitation, and models for intervention in occupational therapy (4th ed., pp. 69–85). AOTA Press.

Fisher, A. G. (1999). Assessment of Motor and Process Skills. (3rd ed.). Three Star Press.

Fisher, A. G., & Griswold, L. A. (2019). Performance skills: Implementing performance analyses to evaluate quality of occupational performance. In B. A. B. Schell & G. Gillen (Eds.), Willard and Spackman's occupational therapy (13th ed., pp. 335–350). Wolters Kluwer.

Folstein, M.F., Folstein, S. E., & McHugh, P. R. (1975). "Mini-mental state": A practical method for grading cognitive state of patients for the clinician. Journal of Psychiatric Research, 12, 189–198. https://doi.org/10.1016/0022-3956(75)90026-6.

Gillen, G. (2009). Cognitive and perceptual rehabilitation: Optimizing function. Elsevier/Mosby.

Gillen, G. (2021). Treatment of cognitive-perceptual deficits: A function-based approach. In G. Gillen & D. M. Nilsen (Eds.), Stroke rehabilitation: A function-based approach (5th ed., pp. 593–626). Elsevier.

Gillen, G., & Hreha, K. (2021). Managing visual and visuospatial impairments to optimize function. In G. Gillen & D. M. Nilsen (Eds.), Stroke rehabilitation: A function-based approach (5th ed., pp. 537–555). Elsevier.

Gillen, G., & Nilsen D.M. (Eds.). (2021). Stroke rehabilitation: A function-based approach (5th ed.). Elsevier.

Gutman, S. A., & Schonfeld, A. B. (2019). Screening adult neurologic populations: A step-by-step instruction manual (3rd ed.). AOTA Press.

Hartman-Maeir, A., Armon, N., & Katz, N. (2005). The Kettle test: A cognitive functional screening test protocol. (Available from School of Occupational Therapy, Hebrew University of Jeruselem & Hadassah).

Hartman-Maeir, A., Harel, H., & Katz, N. (2009). Kettle test - A brief measure of cognitive functional performance: Reliability and validity in stroke rehabilitation. American Journal of Occupational Therapy, 592–599.

Katz, N., Itzkovich, M., Averbuch, S., & Elazar, B. (1989). Loewenstein Occupational Therapy Cognitive Assessment (LOTCA) battery for brain-injured patients: Reliability and validity. American Journal of Occupational Therapy, 43, 184–192.

Katz, N., & Toglia, J. (Eds.). (2018). Cognition, occupation and participation across the lifespan: Neuroscience, neurorehabilitation, and models for intervention in occupational therapy (4th ed.). AOTA Press.

Morrison, M. T., Giles, G. M., Ryan, J. D., Baum, C. M., Dromerick, A. W., Polatajko, H. J., & Edwards, D. F. (2013). Multiple errands test-revised (MET-R): A performance based measure of executive function in people with mild cerebrovascular accident. American Journal of Occupational Therapy, 67, 460–468.

Multicontext. (2017). Weekly calendar planning activity (WCPA). https://multicontext.net/weekly-calendar-planning-activity.

Nasreddine, Z. S. (2021). MoCA Cognitive Assessment. https://www.mocatest.org/

National Board for Certification in Occupational Therapy (NBCOT®). (2022). 2022 Occupational Therapist Registered (OTR®) Examination Content Outline. https://www.nbcot.org/-/media/PDFs/2022_OTR_Content_Outline.pdf.

Radomski, M. V., & Giles, G. M. (2021). Cognitive intervention. In D. P. Dirette & S. A. Gutman (Eds.), Occupational therapy for physical dysfunction (8th ed., pp. 161–175). Wolters Kluwer.

Scheiman, M. (Ed.). (2011). Understanding and managing vision deficits: A guide for occupational therapists (3rd ed.). Slack.

Schultz-Krohn, W., & Pendleton, H. (Eds.). (2018). Pedretti's occupational therapy: Practice skills for physical dysfunction (8th ed.). Elsevier Science/Mosby.

Stewart, C., & Riedel, K. (2021). Managing speech and language deficits after stroke. In G. Gillen & D. M. Nilsen (Eds.), Stroke rehabilitation: A function-based approach (5th ed., pp. 653–669). Elsevier.

Toglia, J. P. (2015). Weekly Calendar Planning Activity: A performance test of executive function. AOTA Press.

Whiting, S., Lincoln, N. B., Bhavnani, G., & Cockburn, J. (1986). Rivermead perceptual assessment battery. Occupational Therapy in Health Care, 3(3–4), 209–210.

Wilson, B. A., Cockburn, J., & Halligan, P. (1987). Development of a behavioral test of visuospatial neglect. Archives of Physical Medicine and Rehabilitation, 68, 98–102.

Wilson, B. A., Greenfield, E., Clare, L., Baddeley, A., Cockburn, J., Watson, P., Tate, R., Sopena, S., Nannery, R., & Crawford, J. (2008). Rivermead Behavioural Memory Test- RBMT-3. (3rd ed.). Pearsons Assessment.

Review Questions

Cognitive-Perceptual Approaches: Evaluation and Intervention

Below are six questions about key content covered in this chapter. These questions are not inclusive of the entirety of content about cognitive-perceptual evaluation and intervention approaches that you must know for success on the NBCOT® exam. These questions are provided to help you "jump start" the thought processes you will need to apply your studying of content to the answering of exam questions; hence, they are not in the NBCOT® exam format. Exam items in the NBCOT® format which cover the depth and breadth of content you will need to know to pass the NBCOT® exam are provided in the three online practice exams that accompany this text. The answers to the below questions are provided in Appendix 2.

1. You are observing a person with apraxia eat breakfast. What behaviors would you most likely observe?

2. Your client presents with right-sided unilateral spatial neglect and poor awareness. The client has a supportive partner. What environmental modifications will be useful for their partner to implement in their home to maximize performance and safety indoors?

3. What are examples of activities you can use to evaluate components of attention?

4. Your client has left-sided body neglect. Describe the behaviors would you expect to see during the person's morning self-care routine.

5. You are working in acute care with a person with low arousal after a head trauma. Describe approaches and activities that would be useful to include during interventions with this person.

6. You are working in the outpatient setting with a person who had stroke. The person complains of blurry vision/double vision while reading. What should you evaluate to determine the person's visual status? Identify the assessments that would be best to use with this person and describe how you would perform them.

14

Psychosocial Approaches: Evaluation and Intervention

RITA P. FLEMING-CASTALDY, WILLIAM L. LAMBERT, and DONNA COSTA[1]

[1] Janice Romeo contributed to this chapter in earlier editions of this text.

Psychosocial Frames of Reference and Models of Practice

Overview

1. Psychosocial models of practice and frames of reference are used to address the psychosocial needs of *all* persons in *all* practice settings.
   a. Their effective use requires clinical reasoning to select assessments, identify factors that enable or limit occupational performance, develop client-centered, occupation-based intervention goals, and implement interventions.

EXAM HINT: The NBCOT® OTR® exam content outline identifies knowledge of the "resources and considerations for acquiring information about the client's current condition and occupational performance . . . (including) theoretical approach and frame of reference" (NBCOT®, 2022, p. 4) as essential for competent practice. The application of knowledge about the following occupational therapy (OT) frames of reference can help you determine the correct answer to NBCOT® exam items about psychosocial OT practice.

Occupational Therapy Models of Practice and Frames of Reference

EXAM HINT: All occupational therapy models presented in this section, except for the Cognitive Disability model, are applicable to all people across the life span, including children and adolescents.

Model of Human Occupation (MOHO)

1. Principles.
   a. "Occupation is dynamic and context-dependent" (Kielhofner, 2004, p. 151).
   b. Personal occupational choices and engagement in occupation shape the individual.
   c. Three elements are inherent to humans.
      (1) Volition includes thoughts and feelings that motivate people to act and is composed of personal causation, values, and interests.
      (2) Habituation includes organized, recurring patterns of behavior and is composed of roles and habits.
      (3) Performance capacity includes the physical and mental skills needed for performance and the subjective experience of engaging in occupation.
   d. The environment impacts the individual through the opportunities, demands, resources, and constraints it provides.
      (1) The environment is divided into physical and social components.
      (2) Each component is influenced by the culture(s) in which it takes place.

2. Evaluation.
   a. Focuses on exploring the individual's occupational history, goals, volition, habits, and occupational performance.
   b. Many tools have been designed specifically for use with the MOHO (e.g., OCAIRS, OSA); however, any procedure or instrument that provides pertinent information about the environment and the person may be used.

3. Intervention.
   a. Focuses on occupational engagement and includes activities that are purposeful, relevant, and meaningful to people and their social context.

Person-Environment-Occupation (PEO) Model

1. Principles.
   a. Occupational performance is dynamic in nature.
   b. Occupational performance is considered the outcome of the transactional relationship between people, their occupations, and the environment.
   c. Occupational performance necessarily changes across the life span.

2. Evaluation.
   a. Addresses the occupational performance issues that the client identifies.
   b. Emphasizes the environment of the individual to include where they live, work, and play.
   c. Evaluation is client centered and flexible as there are no model-specfic evaluations.

3. Intervention.
   a. Considers the transactional relationships of occupations with people and their environment to address occupational performance issues and goals.
   b. Recognizes the temporal nature of occupational performance as the person, their environment, and occupations are constantly changing.
   c. Offers many avenues for change, as practitioners can be flexible in their choice of intervention strategies.

Life-Style Performance Model

1. Principles.
   a. The Life-Style Performance Model seeks to identify and describe the nature and critical "doing" elements of an environment that support and foster achievement of a satisfying, productive lifestyle.
   b. It proposes a method for looking at the match between that environment and the individual's needs.
   c. Four hypotheses are proposed.
      (1) "Mastery and competence in those activities that are valued and given priority in one's society or social group have greater meaning in defining one's social efficacy than competence in activities that carry less social significance.
      (2) "A total activity and each of its elements have symbolic as well as reality-based meanings that notably affect individual experiences and motivation.
      (3) "Mastery and competence are more readily achieved, and the sense of personal pleasure and intrinsic gratification is more intense, in those activities that are most closely matched to one's neurobiology and psychological structure.
      (4) "Competence and achievement are most readily seen and verified in the end-product or outcome of an activity; thus, the ability to do, to overcome, and to achieve becomes obvious to self and others" (Fidler, 1996, pp. 115–116).
   d. Performance and quality of life can be enhanced by an environment that provides for 10 fundamental human needs.
      (1) Autonomy: self-determination.
      (2) Individuality: self-differentiation.
      (3) Affiliation: evidence of belonging.
      (4) Volition: having alternatives.
      (5) Consensual validation: acknowledgment of achievement and verification of perspectives.
      (6) Predictability: discernment and evaluation of cause and effect.
      (7) Self-efficacy: evidence of competence.
      (8) Adventure: exploration of the new and unknown.
      (9) Accommodation: freedom from physical or mental harm and compensation for limitations.
      (10) Reflection: contemplation of events and the meaning of things.
   e. Performance is measured in the quality of functioning in four domains.
      (1) Self-care and maintenance.
      (2) Intrinsic gratification.
      (3) Societal contribution.
      (4) Reciprocal relationships.
2. Evaluation.
   a. Focuses on obtaining an activity history and a life-style performance profile related to the four skill domains.
   b. Environmental factors are explored.
3. Intervention.
   a. Addresses five main questions that identify the focus of intervention.
      (1) What does the person need to be able to do?
      (2) What is the person able to do?
      (3) What is the person unable to do?
      (4) What interventions are needed, and in what order?
      (5) What are the characteristics and patterns of activity and of the environment that will enhance the person's quality of life?
   b. Any interventions or activities that promote performance in the four domains are acceptable.

Ecology of Human Performance (EHP) Model

1. Principles.
   a. The EHP model emphasizes the role of an individual's context (i.e., a person's cultural, physical, and social environments) and how the environment impacts a person and their task performance.
   b. The four main constructs of this model include the person, tasks, context, and personal-context-task transaction.
   c. There are 11 assumptions of this model.
      (1) Ecology refers to the interaction between a person and their environment.
      (2) A person's performance is understood by looking at the relationship between the person, context, and task.
      (3) Performance occurs when a person acts to engage in tasks within a context.
      (4) Each person is a unique individual with sensorimotor, cognitive, and psychosocial skills and abilities.
      (5) The range of a person's performance is based on the transaction between the person and the context.

Chapter 14

(6) Skills that a person possesses can be increased or decreased due to illness and/or stress; a person's interests and life experiences lead to continually changing variables.

(7) Contexts are dynamic rather than static; there is a reciprocal relationship between a person and their context where one influences the other.

(8) The roles that a person has in life are made up of tasks; the transactional relationship between the person, task, and context makes up occupations and roles.

(9) There is a difference between a person's performance in their natural contexts and simulated experiences.

(10) In the OT process, people are empowered by increasing their self-determination.

(11) This model defines independence as using the supports in a person's context to meet their needs and wants.

2. Evaluation.
   a. Utilizes checklists that were designed along with this model. These include checklists for the person, the environment, task analysis, and personal priorities.
   b. The Sensory Profile. Refer to this chapter's assessment section.

3. Intervention.
   a. Five specific strategies designed to help the person, context, task. These include the following.
      (1) Establish and restore: enhancing a person's abilities by teaching skills lost due to illness or disability or never learned.
      (2) Alter: assessing a person's contexts to determine which is the best match for the person's abilities.
      (3) Adapt/modify: changing the context or task in some way so that it leads the person to successful performance.
      (4) Prevent: minimizing risks that might develop so that problems in performance do not develop.
      (5) Create: assisting the person by promoting enriching and complex performances in the person's context.

Occupational Adaptation

1. Principles.
   a. Occupational adaptation is concerned with the processes that the individual goes through to adapt to their environment.
   b. It consists of three elements: the person, the occupational environment, and the interaction between the two.
      (1) The person element consists of the sensorimotor, cognitive, and psychosocial components of the individual.

(2) The occupation environment is viewed as the physical, social, and cultural systems within which work, play/leisure, and self-maintenance take place.

(3) The outcome of the interaction between the person and the environment is referred to as the occupational response.

c. The occupational adaptation model makes two basic assumptions.
   (1) "Occupation provides the means by which humans adapt to changing needs and conditions, and the desire to participate in occupation is the intrinsic motivational force leading to adaptation.
   (2) "Occupational adaptation is a normative process that is most pronounced during periods of transition, both large and small. The greater the adaptive transitional needs, the greater the importance of the occupational adaptation process, and the greater the likelihood that the process will be disrupted" (Schkade & Shultz, 1992, pp. 829–830).

2. Evaluation.
   a. Focuses on occupational environment, role expectation, and the individual's potential for adaptation and the best means for adaptation to occur.

3. Intervention.
   a. Focuses on increasing the skills needed for occupational adaptation.
   b. Addresses both the individual and the environment.

Role Acquisition Frame of Reference

1. Principles.
   a. The individual employs task and social skills to meet the demands of personally desired and necessary roles.
   b. Performance is addressed through function/dysfunction continuums in seven categories.
      (1) Task skills.
      (2) Interpersonal skills.
      (3) Family interaction.
      (4) Activities of daily living.
      (5) School.
      (6) Work.
      (7) Play/leisure/recreation.
   c. Temporal adaptation addresses the individual's temporal orientation and ability to organize their use of time in a need-satisfying manner.

2. Evaluation.
   a. Focuses on gathering data indicative of function/dysfunction in the above categories.

3. Intervention.
   a. Focused on the acquisition of the specific skills people need to function in their environment.

b. The principles of learning are used to promote skill development. Refer to Chapter 3's section on education and training.

c. General postulates for change are provided to guide the intervention process.

  (1) Long-term goals are set based on the person's expected environment.

  (2) Initially, tasks and interpersonal skills can be taught separately, or they can be taught within the context of the learning of social roles.

  (3) An adequate repertoire of behavior is acquired through activities that elicit the desired behavior, are interesting to the client, include socializing, and apply the principles of learning. Refer to Chapter 3.

  (4) Intrapsychic content is shared matter-of-factly with the client and reality testing is provided.

  (5) The OT practitioner must know specifically what kind of behavior they wish to promote or enhance.

d. Specific postulates are provided for each of the continuums.

e. Any treatment activities or strategies that employ the teaching-learning principles are acceptable.

> **EXAM HINT:** To the best of our knowledge, the NBCOT® exam does not ask direct questions about the above frames of reference (FsOR) or models of practice (e.g., what are the hypotheses of Fidler's Lifestyle Performance Model?; what are the three main elements of the MOHO?). However, exam items may mention a particular theoretical model or frame of reference in the item's scenario. Determining the correct answer to these items will require you to apply your knowledge about how different FsOR or models of practice can be used to guide evaluation and intervention. Correct answers to an exam item will be consistent with the principles of the FOR or model of practice identified in the item stem. Incorrect answers will be inconsistent with these.

Cognitive Disability Frame of Reference

1. Principles.

  a. Based on the stages of cognitive development as described by Piaget and knowledge of the neurobiological sciences at the time of the model's development.

  b. Cognitive ability is determined by biological factors, and the potential for improvement is dictated by those factors.

  c. Functional behavior is based on cognition.

d. If the person's cognitive level cannot change, adapting the activity or task provides opportunities for the individual to succeed.

e. Once the maximum level has been achieved, compensations must be made biologically, psychologically, or environmentally.

f. Cognitive performance is placed on a continuum divided into six levels that are further divided into modes as outlined in Box 14-1.

> **EXAM HINT:** While these six levels are expanded into 54 modes in the Cognitive Disability's FOR, to the best of our knowledge the NBCOT® exam will likely only test the six main levels that are outlined in Box 14-1.

BOX 14-1 ▷ Cognitive Levels

- **Automatic Actions, Level I:** characterized by automatic motor responses and changes in the autonomic nervous system.
  - Conscious response to the external environment is minimal.
- **Postural Actions, Level II:** characterized by movement that is associated with comfort.
  - There is some awareness of large objects in the environment, and the individual may assist the caregiver with simple tasks.
- **Manual Actions, Level III:** characterized by beginning to use hands to manipulate objects.
  - The individual may be able to perform a limited number of tasks with long-term repetitive training.
- **Goal Directed Actions, Level IV:** characterized by the ability to perform simple tasks through to completion.
  - The individual relies heavily on visual cues.
  - They may be able to perform established routines but cannot cope with unexpected events.
- **Exploratory Actions, Level V:** characterized by overt trial-and-error problem solving.
  - New learning occurs.
  - This may be the typical level of functioning for 20% of the population.
- **Planned Actions, Level VI:** characterized by the absence of disability.
  - The person can think of hypothetical situations and do mental trial-and-error problem solving.

> **EXAM HINT:** Be aware that the NBCOT® exam will likely include items that require specific knowledge of the Cognitive Disability FOR (e.g., the functional abilities of a person who achieves a particular score on the ACLS-5). The rationale for this inclusion is that this FOR provides a classification system for persons with cognitive disorders.

2. Evaluation.
   a. Focus is on identifying the individual's current cognitive abilities and their implications for performance, independence, and the need for assistance.
      (1) The potential for improvement is also considered.
   b. Observation during functional tasks is emphasized.
   c. Several evaluation tools have been developed to assist with the identification of the individual's cognitive level.
      (1) The Allen Cognitive Level Screen-5 (ACLS-5) is a structured task that allows the evaluator to observe the individual performing three increasingly complex leather lacing stitches and make determinations about that person's cognitive skill level.
         (a) The Allen Diagnostic Module provides craft projects that can be used for evaluation as well as treatment that can also be used to determine the individual's level of skills according to the first five levels listed above. (Refer to this chapter's evaluation section.)
      (2) The Routine Task Inventory gathers data about the individual's activities of daily living (ADL) performance from an informed caregiver. Refer to Chapter 15.
      (3) The Cognitive Performance Test assesses the functional performance of individuals with Alzheimer's disease. The focus is on the identification of the effects that particular deficits have on the performance of ADL.

> **EXAM HINT:** In the NBCOT® OTR® exam content outline, knowledge of the "administration, purpose, indications, advantages, and limitations of standardized and nonstandardized screening and assessment tools" (NBCOT®, 2022, p. 4) is identified as an essential task for competent practice. The application of knowledge about the above evaluation principles and tools can help you correctly answer Domain 1 exam items about the evaluation of persons with cognitive disorders.

3. Intervention.
   a. Activities are selected based on the individual's highest cognitive level.
   b. Therapy focuses on maintaining the individual's highest level of function.
   c. Environmental changes and activity adaptations are made to compensate for deficits and allow the greatest degree of independence.
   d. The OT practitioner works with the team to develop an appropriate discharge plan.

   e. The OT practitioner should meet with the family or other caregivers to develop understanding of the individual's abilities, limitations, and care needs.
      (1) Refer to Table 10-2 for additional information about the impact of neurocognitive disorders on functional abilities and occupational performance.

> **EXAM HINT:** The NBCOT® OTR® exam content outline identifies knowledge of "interventions to support cognitive . . . processing (and) . . . compensatory and remedial strategies for managing cognitive and perceptual deficits" (NBCOT®, 2022, p. 9) as essential for competent practice. The application of knowledge about the above intervention methods will help you correctly answer NBCOT® Domain 3 exam items about working with persons with cognitive disabilities.

Sensory Models

1. This approach in mental health is known by several different terms, including sensory integration, sensory processing, sensory motor model, sensory defensiveness, sensory modulation, and sensory-based treatment.
2. The use of sensory-based models to inform evaluation and intervention is widespread in psychosocial practice across the developmental continuum.
3. Sensory-based models are used to address mental health needs in numerous practice settings including early intervention and preschool programs, schools, residential programs (e.g., group homes, skilled nursing facilities), and acute, long-term and community-based psychiatric setting.
   a. They can be effectively used to de-escalate agitated behaviors and decrease the need for physical restraints.

> **EXAM HINT:** Because the use of sensory models and sensory modulation approaches by OT practitioners in mental health practice is widely recognized as effective, it is likely that there will be items on the NBCOT® exam about the application of this model.

4. The model of Sensory Processing looks at how sensory input is processed and then responded to in one of four patterns of neurological thresholds.
   a. Sensory seeking.
   b. Sensory avoiding.
   c. Sensory sensitivity.
   d. Poor registration.

e. Refer to Chapter 12 for comprehensive information about this model.

5. Sensory Modulation approach for adults.
   a. Sensory modulation approaches are used by OT practitioners to help prepare, enhance, and/or maintain the person's ability to engage actively in valued life roles and meaningful activities.
      (1) Approaches include the use of sensory-related assessment tools, sensorimotor activities, sensory modalities, environmental modifications, and education and training in how to self-regulate and self-organize.
   b. The implementation of a Sensory Modulation Program requires the use of a strengths-based, person-centered, and relationship-centered model of care.
      (1) It is essential to assist each individual in recognizing not only their symptom(s) and challenges but also their unique assets and strengths that can be used to explore, practice, and integrate sensory modulation approaches into their daily life.

6. Evaluation.
   a. Assessments used in sensory models include the Adolescent/Adult Sensory Profile and the Allen Cognitive Level Screen. Refer to this chapter's assessment section.

> **EXAM HINT:** The NBCOT® OTR® exam content outline identifies knowledge of "interventions to support . . . sensory arousal . . . (including) sensory modulation" (NBCOT®, 2022, p. 9) as essential for competent practice. The application of knowledge about the following sensory-based intervention methods will help you correctly answer NBCOT® Domain 3 exam items about intervention management for persons with sensory processing disorders.

7. Intervention.
   a. Education to increase an individual's knowledge about their personal responses to sensory input and how these affect their social interactions and emotional regulation.
   b. Training in self-regulation/self-modulation/self-soothing approaches. These can include the use of the following.
      (1) Sensory diets comprised of alerting/calming stimuli and heavy work patterns.
      (2) Multisensory environments, 'Snoezelen" rooms and/or "Comfort Rooms" that have alerting and calming features.
      (3) Therapeutic weighted blankets, dolls, and stuffed animals.

▶ Interdisciplinary Mental Health Practice Models

> **EXAM HINT:** The NBCOT® OTR® exam content outline identifies knowledge of the "resources and considerations for acquiring information about the client's current condition and occupational performance . . . (including) . . . theoretical approach and frame of reference" (NBCOT®, 2022, p. 4) as essential for competent practice. The application of knowledge about the following interdisciplinary mental health practice models can help you determine the correct answer to NBCOT® exam items about psychosocial OT practice.

Cognitive Behavioral Frame of Reference/Cognitive Behavioral Therapy (CBT)

1. Relevance to OT practice.
   a. CBT is widely used in practice today with children, adolescents, and adults.
      (1) Many of the suggested interventions in this frame of reference fall within the scope of OT practitioners' professional preparation and OT's domain of practice.
   b. Research has supported CBT as an effective approach for a diversity of populations.
      (1) CBT has been shown to be especially effective in the treatment of individuals with depression.
         (a) Individuals with depression tend to distort reality through dysfunctional thought processes.
         (b) CBT works to alter these individuals' negative thoughts about themselves, the world, and the future by correcting misinterpretations of life events.
      (2) CBT is also used with individuals with schizophrenia, anxiety, bipolar, panic, obsessive-compulsive, personality, somatoform, and eating disorders.

2. Principles.
   a. CBT combines principles of cognitive therapy and behavioral therapy.
      (1) Cognitive therapy looks at a person's thoughts and beliefs, while behavioral therapy looks at a

person's actions and attempts to change maladaptive/ineffective patterns of behavior.

b. Cognitive restructuring is the foundational process of CBT that seeks to alter negative thoughts and beliefs (i.e., cognitive distortions) by questioning, challenging, and modifying them to be more accurate and positive and to facilitate adaptive emotional behavioral changes.

c. The three components of cognitive therapy are didactic aspects, cognitive techniques, and behavioral techniques.

   (1) Didactic aspects involve the practitioner explaining the basic concepts and principles of CBT to the client.

   (2) Cognitive techniques involve "eliciting automatic thoughts, testing automatic thoughts, identifying maladaptive underlying assumptions, and testing the validity of maladaptive assumptions" (Sadock & Sadock, 2008, p. 462).

   (3) Behavioral techniques are used with cognitive techniques to test and challenge maladaptive and inaccurate cognitions.

d. A pattern of negative thinking termed the *cognitive triad* is identified.

   (1) This triad is composed of negative self-evaluation, a pessimistic world view, and a sense of hopelessness regarding the future.

   (2) This triad particularly underlies depression and is evident in other disorders.

e. Three basic principles of cognitive therapy can help individuals with depression. These include:

   (1) All moods are created by a person's thoughts and the way they look at and interpret situations and events.

   (2) When people are depressed, their thoughts are pervasively negative.

   (3) Research has indicated that negative thoughts that cause emotional distress usually contain distortions.

f. The development of insight is necessary for growth and change.

   (1) Thinking influences behavior.

   (2) Changing the way a person thinks reduces symptoms.

   (3) Thinking can be self-regulated.

   (4) Change occurs through individuals' involvement in learning and developing skills.

3. Evaluation.

a. The Beck Depression Inventory (BDI-II) is the primary initial evaluation tool.

   (1) The BDI-II is a self-completed questionnaire that assesses level of depression.

   (2) No special training is required to administer this client-completed evaluation.

   (3) Interpretation of the results of the BDI-II must be completed by a mental health professional who has completed required training and acquired adequate knowledge about the BDI-II and CBT.

   (4) Refer to this chapter's assessment section for more information about this scale.

b. The evaluation of cognition is frequently completed by OT practitioners.

c. A variety of cognitive assessments are available for use by OT practitioners that are consistent with a CBT approach. Refer to this chapter's section on assessments and Chapter 13.

> **EXAM HINT:** The NBCOT® OTR® exam content outline identifies knowledge of "interventions to support cognitive . . . processing . . . (and) compensatory and remedial strategies for managing cognitive . . . deficits" (NBCOT®, 2022, p. 9) and "strategies for promoting wellness and mental health" (NBCOT®, 2022, p. 10) as essential for competent practice. The application of knowledge about the following intervention methods will help you correctly answer NBCOT® Domain 3 exam items about intervention management using CBT.

4. Intervention.

a. General postulates for change are used to guide the intervention process.

   (1) Dysfunctional cognitive processes produce psychological disorders.

   (2) Altering a person's cognition can improve their psychological health.

   (3) Cognitions are the prime cause of psychopathology, and therefore, are the focus of intervention.

      (a) Automatic thoughts cause psychological disorder and through cognitive restructuring these thoughts are brought to awareness to be confronted and facilitate change.

b. Approaches using CBT emphasize the following.

   (1) Assisting the person in the identification of current problems and potential solutions.

   (2) Using active and collaborative therapist-client interaction as an essential part of the therapeutic process.

   (3) Helping the individual learn how to identify distorted or unhelpful thinking patterns, recognize and change inaccurate beliefs, and relate to others in more positive ways.

   (4) Gaining insight and acquiring skills that "maximize client functioning and quality of life through the development of coping skills and meaningful healthy occupational patterns" (Hemphill-Pearson, 2008, p. 68).

   (5) Facilitating the individual's active role in the therapeutic process by frequently providing homework and structured assignments as part of the intervention process.

(a) Intervention goals are designed to help the client monitor and refute negative thoughts about themselves.

(6) Scheduling activities.

   (a) Increasing mastery and pleasure.

   (b) Grading tasks to enable success.

(7) Cognitive rehearsal.

(8) Self-reliance training.

   (a) Self-reliance can be facilitated by performing ADL (e.g., making one's bed, doing personal shopping, and preparing one's own meals).

(9) Role playing.

(10) Diversion techniques and visual imagery.

(11) Engaging in physical, work, leisure/play, and/or social participation activities.

  c. Research in the area of cognitive functioning supports the importance of providing clients with meaningful tasks and therapeutic activities.

(1) OT practitioner's focus on meaningful occupation and purposeful activities is inherently congruent with CBT.

(2) Many of the life skills workbook activities used by OT practitioners apply CBT principles.

   (a) Activity gradation, an area of specialization for OT practitioners, is particularly useful in providing effective treatment using the CBT frame of reference.

5. Dialectical behavior therapy (DBT).

  a. A form of CBT.

(1) The evaluation and intervention foci of DBT and its emphasis on skills training are consistent with OT practitioners' professional preparation and OT's scope of practice.

  b. Focus of DBT.

(1) Addresses suicidal thoughts and actions and self-injurious behaviors.

(2) Commonly used with individuals with borderline personality disorder since a feature of this diagnosis is suicidal thinking and self-injurious behavior.

(3) Also used to treat individuals who have depression, substance abuse issues, and/or eating disorders.

  c. Evaluation.

(1) Often begins with an accurate DSM-5™ diagnosis received from a psychiatrist.

(2) Evaluation tools are not trait or diagnostically based.

(3) A variety of psychological evaluations may be used, including those that address personality.

(4) OT assessments that focus on functioning in performance areas and performance contexts can provide relevant information for intervention planning.

  d. Intervention.

(1) Skills training is used to help "individuals change behavioral, emotional, thinking, and interpersonal patterns associated with problems in living" (Linehan, 2015. p, 3).

(2) Skills training using DBT approaches teaches the four core skills of emotional regulation, interpersonal effectiveness, mindfulness, and distress tolerance.

(3) DBT groups address how the acquisition of skills affects occupational performance and provide opportunities to practice new skills.

(4) A strong therapist-client relationship is essential.

   (a) Rapport is used for validation as well as confrontation.

Recovery Model[2]

1. Relevance to OT practice.

  a. Recovery principles and approaches are highly congruent with those of OT.

  b. The active use of the recovery model throughout the OT process can help practitioners empower people by fostering the person's intrinsic motivation to establish a sense of hope for the future.

  c. The primary focus of the recovery process is to improve quality of life and the ability to attain desired life goals through self-advocacy.

2. Principles.

  a. Conceptualizes recovery from illness as a journey of healing and transformation that enables individuals with mental illness to live a meaningful life in a community of their choice.

  b. Individuals with mental illness can meet their potential and find meaning and purpose in their lives.

  c. Major concepts which guide recovery.

(1) Self-direction: consumers identify their own goals and their own personal track to recovery.

(2) Individualized and person-centered: recovery is unique as dictated by each individual's personal strengths, needs, past experiences, cultural background, and desires.

(3) Empowerment: people take control over their lives by making educated decisions that impact on their recovery.

(4) Holistic: recovery signifies the interrelatedness of the mind, body, spirit, and community.

(5) Nonlinear: recovery can include episodes that disrupt the track to recovery, but individuals can learn from setbacks and proceed in a manner that supports continued recovery.

---

[2] Patricia Wisniewski, EdD, OTR/L, CPRP contributed to this section.

Chapter 14

Chapter 14

(6) Strengths-based: recovery builds on and exercises an individual's strengths.
(7) Peer support: reciprocal relationships with others who have lived experience in supporting recovery principles are formed.
(8) Respect: recovery is based on the premise of social acceptance of self and by others, including society, one's community, and service providers.
(9) Responsibility: personal commitment to self in working toward personal goals, including taking care of oneself to promote overall health and wellness.
(10) Hope: being a change agent in recovery enables the person to embrace an optimistic future.
(11) Family: members play an essential role in a person's recovery. They remain committed to supporting an individual's potential and personal strengths, despite potential setbacks.
(12) Community: supports inclusion and remains steadfast in eliminating barriers to recovery.
3. Evaluation.
  a. Interdisciplinary assessments used in the recovery model include quality of life questionnaires and empowerment scales.
  b. Occupational therapy assessments that are consistent with the recovery model include the following.
    (1) Canadian Occupational Profile Measure (refer to Chapter 15).

(2) Role Checklist (refer to this chapter's evaluation section).
(3) Assessment of Motor and Process Skills (refer to Chapter 13).
(4) Barth Time Construction (refer to this chapter's evaluation section).
(5) Worker Role Interview (refer to Chapter 15).
4. Intervention.
  a. The development and implementation of a Wellness Recovery Action Plan (WRAP®) is an essential part of the recovery process. To create a WRAP®, the person does the following.
    (1) Develops a 'wellness toolbox' that identifies their skills and strategies they can use to maintain daily wellness, deal with symptom triggers, manage early warning signs of relapse, and address worsening symptoms.
    (2) Formulates a desired action plan to be implemented if a crisis impedes their ability to be safe, self-manage, and/or make decisions.
  b. Storytelling is a means of decreasing stigma and supporting others by sharing experiential life experiences.
  c. Advocacy through the dissemination of knowledge, skill development in activism, and forming support groups to prevent discrimination and improve acceptance in society.
  d. Table 14-1 describes representative actions OT practitioners can take to implement the Recovery Model.

Table 14-1

Implementation of the Recovery Model by Occupational Therapy Practitioners

RECOVERY COMPONENT	REPRESENTATIVE OCCUPATIONAL THERAPY PRACTITIONER ACTIONS
Individualized and Person-centered	Intervention plans are based on collaboration with service recipients, address the individual's unique concerns, and enable engagement in self-identified personally desired occupational roles.
Self-direction	The person's voice is actively solicited to establish self-determined goals and design interventions which reflect the person's priorities and support their autonomy, control, and choice.
Hope	Hope for recovery is raised by increasing occupational performance skills, expanding social resources, improving self-efficacy, promoting health and well-being, and improving quality of life.
Responsibility	Interventions which integrate personal choice, expect active participation, respect risk-taking, and facilitate external support foster the individual's ownership of illness management and recovery.
Empowerment	Practitioners empower people with SMI by teaching them self-advocacy skills to confront the socio-political contexts that limit occupational engagement and social participation.
Respect	Services which support and accept people with SMI, value and protect their civil liberties, and are designed *with* a person and not provided *to* a person convey respect.
Peer Support	Peer support and a sense of belonging and community are fostered when opportunities for sharing encouragement, knowledge, occupational engagement, and participation are provided.
Strengths-based	The occupational profile and occupation-based assessments provide information about a person's roles, abilities, aspirations, and resources to support the construction of a strengths-based intervention plan.
Non-linear	A continuous, dynamic, transactional relationship is established that recognizes progress can include setbacks; learning to make meaning from them can foster personal growth and positive change.
Holistic	Occupation-based practice models describe the interrelationships between people's aspirations, capabilities, roles, and contexts to address the multidimensional and complex dimensions of occupational engagement.

Adapted from Clay, P. (2013) Shared principles: The recovery model and occupational therapy. Mental Health Special Interest Section Quarterly, 36(4), 1–3.

Psychiatric Rehabilitation

1. Relevance to OT practice.
   a. Psychiatric rehabilitation and the profession of OT both share the common goal of eliminating barriers and promoting health and wellness.
   b. Both believe recovery from physical, mental, emotional, and cognitive disabilities is possible.
      (1) Recovery is not a linear process, rather individuals will experience challenging periods when progress may lapse.
      (2) Recovery is person specific.
   c. The goal of psychiatric rehabilitation is to help individuals develop the skills necessary to compensate for, adapt to, and/or control the influence symptoms have on function, including any disability caused by social or environmental barriers.

2. Principles.
   a. Individualization: any service provided to an individual is structured to support each person's unique needs.
   b. Client involvement: individuals control their recovery.
   c. Partnership with service providers: a mutual rapport between all persons involved nurtures a commitment based on respect and trust for everyone.
   d. Community-based services: all services are provided where the individual lives, works, and socializes.
   e. Strengths-focused: build on a person's strengths rather than focusing on their weaknesses.
   f. Situational assessments: the focus is on collecting data while observing the individual in the environment where challenges are experienced.
   g. Holistic approach: treatment and rehabilitation services are viewed as equal and mutually dependent methods that support recovery.
   h. Continued, accessible, coordinated services: services are always available for any given period of time.
   i. Vocational focus: work is healing; a psychiatric rehabilitation professional partners with individuals (regardless of their abilities) to develop work skills, habits, and resources needed to become successful.
   j. Skills training: includes all actions or behaviors necessary to accomplish a task.
      (1) For example, writing an email to a friend includes not only knowing how to organize your thoughts, but also knowing how to use proper grammar and punctuation, operate a computer, practice computer etiquette, and acknowledge a reply.
   k. Environmental modification: changing the environment so it supports function.
   l. Partnership with family: family is viewed as a consistent source of support; thus, family education is provided to nurture healthy relationships.
   m. Evaluation of outcomes: service providers are expected to monitor the services they provide for effectiveness to ensure compatibility with the individuals being served.

3. Evaluation.
   a. Assessments are based on real-life situations that will provide accurate data specific to an individual, environment, and activity at a moment in time.
   b. Evaluation of readiness for change is an essential component of the evaluation process.
      (1) Foremost, individuals with a mental illness have to make a conscious effort to address the effects of their illness on their lives.
      (2) The effort includes acknowledging one has a mental illness and overcoming stigma or other barriers that may hinder recovery.

> **EXAM HINT:** In the NBCOT® OTR® exam content outline, the task of implementing "occupation-based strategies to support participation in activities of daily living (ADL), instrumental activities of daily living (IADL), health management, rest and sleep, education, work, play, leisure, and social participation across the life span" (NBCOT®, 2022, p. 8) and knowledge of "strategies for promoting wellness and mental health" (NBCOT®, 2022, p. 10) is identified as essential for competent practice. The application of knowledge about the intervention approaches described in the prior section on the recovery model and the psychiatric rehabilitation intervention foci and programs described in the following will help you correctly answer NBCOT® Domain 3 exam items about working with persons with psychiatric disorders.

4. Intervention.
   a. Intervention is designed to help persons with psychiatric disorders acquire the physical, emotional, social, and intellectual skills they need to live and work in the community at their highest functional level with the least amount of professional support as the individual deems necessary.
   b. Assertive community treatment (ACT) uses a variety of interdisciplinary interventions aimed at restoring function and role performance in the community.
   c. Interventions take place where a person chooses to live, work, and socialize.
   d. Day programs that embed psychiatric rehabilitation principles include clubhouses where the goal is to improve quality of life by instilling self-worth and determination in its members.
      (1) Clubhouse members include individuals who have a psychiatric disability and staff who share all responsibilities in managing the clubhouse.
         (a) Common modules that support the work-ordered day at a clubhouse include outreach, transitional employment, education, meal preparation, and advocacy.
      (2) Refer to Chapter 4 for more information about psychiatric day programs and clubhouses.
   e. Case management services strive to ensure continuity accessibility, accountability, and efficiency of care.

(1) Refer to Chapter 4 for more information about the case management programs.

f. Vocational programs view work as a natural activity and provide services and supports to enable the assumption or resumption of the role of a worker based on the belief that all individuals are capable of achieving success.

(1) Refer to Chapters 4 and 15 for more information about vocational, work, and supported employment programs.

g. Supported education programs provide structure, enable self-determination, foster hope, and promote empowerment in secondary and/or post-secondary education settings.

(1) Refer to Chapters 4 and 15 for more information about supported education programs.

Psychosocial Evaluation

EXAM HINT: In the NBCOT® OTR® exam content outline, the task of assessing "a client's functional skills, roles, prioritized needs and wants, and performance context to evaluate their occupational performance" and knowledge of the "administration, purpose, indications, advantages, and limitations of standardized and non-standardized screening and assessment tools (including) criterion-referenced tests, norm-referenced tests, client and caregiver interviews (and) observation" (NBCOT®, 2022, p. 4) are identified as essential for competent practice. The application of knowledge about the following assessment methods and the evaluation tools mentioned in the prior frames of reference/models of practice section can help you correctly answer Domain 1 exam items about the evaluation of persons with psychosocial needs and disorders.

Evaluation Foci

1. Current and desired occupational performance and roles.
2. Personal interests, values, attitudes, concerns, and goals.
3. Performance skills (i.e., process, cognitive, perceptual, psychological, motor, and social interaction) that enable and/or hinder occupational performance.
4. Social, cultural, spiritual, and physical contexts that enable and/or hinder occupational performance.
5. Client factors and/or medical conditions that impact occupational performance.
6. Precautions and safety issues related to self-injurious, suicidal, and/or aggressive behaviors.
7. Social supports (e.g., family, caregiver, significant others, community).
8. Desired outcomes.
   a. If the person is hospitalized, discharge planning begins on day one of hospitalization.
9. Probable (and possible) living environments of choice.
10. Refer to Chapter 3 for comprehensive information about the evaluation process including the

obtainment of the client's occupational profile and an analysis of their occupational performance.

Assessment Methods

1. Interviews—structured and unstructured.
   a. Occupational profile.
2. Standardized tests.
3. Clinical observation.
4. Rating scales.
5. Questionnaires.
6. Self-report inventories.

Role of the OTA/COTA® in Evaluation

1. The OTA/COTA® can contribute to the evaluation process in collaboration with the supervising occupational therapist.
   a. The level of supervision required will be determined by the OTA's/COTA®'s experience, established service competence, state laws, and other regulatory and payer requirements.
2. The OTA/COTA® can collect evaluation data and administer assessments of occupations, client factors, performance skills, patterns, and contexts and report assessment results to the supervising occupational therapist.
3. The supervising occupational therapist is responsible for determining which assessment(s) will attain information essential for setting goals and planning intervention and the interpretation of the information reported by the OTA/COTA®.
   a. While the OTA/COTA® cannot independently interpret evaluation results, they can contribute to this process.
4. All screening and evaluation activities completed by an COTA/OTA® must comply with federal and state laws and other regulatory and payer requirements (AOTA, 2021).

Major Psychosocial Assessments

EXAM HINT: The evaluations included in this chapter are based on the authors' review of NBCOT® self-assessment tools, major OT textbooks, and feedback obtained from OT practitioners regarding measures used in practice. The NBCOT® exam may include the names of specific evaluation tools; therefore, a review of the following major psychosocial assessments is important for exam preparation. This can increase your understanding and knowledge of the evaluation approaches commonly used in practice and further strengthen the clinical reasoning skills you will need to answer NBCOT® Domain 1 Evaluation and Assessment exam items.

General Assessments of Mental Status

1. Mini-Mental State Examination (also known as the Folstein Mini-Mental).
   a. Focus: a widely used, quick screening test of cognitive functioning.
   b. Method.
      (1) Structured tasks are presented in an interview format.
      (2) Part one requires verbal responses to assess orientation, memory, and attention.
      (3) Part two assesses the ability to write a sentence, name objects, follow verbal and written directions, and copy a complex polygon design.
   c. Scoring and interpretation.
      (1) Point value of each item ranges from 1 to 5.
      (2) The maximum score is 30 and a score of 24 or below indicates cognitive impairment.
   d. Population: individuals with cognitive or psychiatric dysfunction.
2. Short Portable Mental Status Questionnaire.
   a. Focus: intellectual function.
   b. Method.
      (1) A short questionnaire asks nine questions such as "What day of the week is it?" and "Who is the president of the United States now?"
      (2) A subtraction task requests, "Subtract 3 from 20 and keep subtracting 3 from each new result."
   c. Scoring and interpretation.
      (1) Each item receives one point if response is inaccurate.
      (2) One point is added for education beyond high school, and one point is subtracted if education does not go beyond grade school.

(3) The number of errors is totaled with a potential error score of 10.
   (a) A score of 0–2 indicates intact intellectual function.
   (b) A score of 3–4 indicates mild intellectual impairment.
   (c) A score of 5–7 indicates moderate intellectual impairment.
   (d) A score of 8–10 indicates severe intellectual impairment.
d. Population: individuals with cognitive or psychiatric dysfunction.

Assessments of Cognition, Affect, and/or Sensory Processing

1. Adult/Adolescent Sensory Profile.
   a. Focus: allows clients to identify their personal behavioral responses to daily sensory experiences and develop strategies for enhanced participation.
      (1) There are four quadrants (i.e., sensory sensitivity, sensation avoiding, poor registration, sensation seeking) that cover the sensory processing categories of taste/smell, movement, visual, touch, activity level, and auditory.
   b. Method.
      (1) Requires the completion of a 60-item questionnaire about an individual's reactions to daily sensory experiences via the person's self-report.
   c. Scoring and interpretation.
      (1) Cut-off scores indicate typical performance and probable, definite, and significant differences.
         (a) Differences indicate which sensory system is hindering performance.
         (b) Can be used for intervention planning.
   d. Population: 11–65 years.
2. Allen Cognitive Level Screen-5 (ACLS-5).
   a. Focus: assesses the cognitive level of the individual according to the Allen cognitive levels. Refer to this chapter's prior section on the Cognitive Disabilities model.
   b. Method.
      (1) Requires the performance of several leather lacing stitches following instruction and/or demonstration.
      (2) Comparable tasks may be substituted.
      (3) Administration time varies.

c. Materials: kit contains a leather purse, lacing strip, needle, and manual for wording for standardized instructions and scoring.
   (1) The Large Allen Cognitive Level Screen-5 (LACLS-5) is available to enable this tool to be used by persons who have impairments in hand function and/or vision that may impact their task performance.
d. Scoring and interpretation.
   (1) The task demands for each stitch are proposed to require the use of abilities associated with Allen's cognitive levels.
      (a) Level 3: running stitch.
      (b) Level 4: whipstitch.
      (c) Level 5: cordovan stitch.
   (2) The ACLS-5 manual provides detailed scoring tables that list specific behaviors that may be observed during task completion and their corresponding level and mode of performance.
      (a) Scores range from 3.0 to 5.8 and correspond to their respective mode on the Allen scale.
   (3) Identification of Allen cognitive level yields information about the individual's abilities and limitations.
e. The Allen Diagnostic Module (ADM) can be used to assess an individual's cognitive level.
   (1) Consists of 24 craft projects.
   (2) Provides Allen cognitive level ratings from 3.0 to 5.8.
   (3) Activities are delineated according to the ACL scale.
   (4) Provides observation criteria for each activity.
f. Population: adults with psychiatric or cognitive dysfunction.

> **EXAM HINT:** Know the ACL test, its method, scoring, and interpretation. This is *must know* information because this evaluation can be considered a classification system for persons with disabilities similar to the Rancho scale for persons with traumatic brain injury.

3. Beck Depression Inventory.
   a. Focus: measurement of the presence and depth of depression.
   b. Method.
      (1) Administered by an interviewer to persons who have language or comprehension difficulties or completed as a questionnaire by the individual.
      (2) The individual rates their feelings relative to 21 characteristics associated with depression (i.e., mood, pessimism, sense of failure, lack of satisfaction, guilt, sense of punishment, self-dislike, self-accusations, suicidal wishes, crying spells, irritability, social withdrawal, indecisiveness, distortion of body image, work inhibition, sleep disturbance, fatigability, loss of appetite, weight loss, somatic preoccupation, loss of libido).

c. Scoring and interpretation.
   (1) Items are scored as 0–3, with 3 being the most severe.
   (2) The 21 item ratings are totaled with higher scores indicating higher levels of depression.
d. Population: adolescent and adult.
4. Elder Depression Scale.
   a. Focus: assesses depression in older adults.
   b. Method: completion of a 30-item checklist that looks at the presence of characteristics associated with depression (somatic concerns, affect, cognitive impairment, feelings of discrimination, impaired motivation, lack of future orientation, lack of self-esteem).
   c. Scoring and interpretation.
      (1) Items are scored yes or no.
      (2) A score of 10–11 is the threshold most often used to indicate depression.
   d. Population: older adults.
5. Hamilton Depression Rating Scale.
   a. Focus: measures the severity of illness and changes over time in individuals diagnosed with a depressive illness.
   b. Method.
      (1) Information is gathered through interview and consultation with family, staff, and other informed individuals.
      (2) The evaluator rates the information obtained relative to 17 symptoms and characteristics (i.e., depressed mood, guilt, suicide, initial insomnia, middle insomnia, delayed insomnia, work and interest, retardation, agitation, psychic anxiety, somatic anxiety, gastrointestinal somatic symptoms, general somatic symptoms, genital symptoms, hypochondriasis, insight, weight loss).
      (3) Also rated are diurnal variation, depersonalization, paranoid symptoms, and obsessional symptoms.
   c. Scoring and interpretation.
      (1) Items are rated 0–2 (0 = absent, 1 = trivial, 2 = present) or 0–4 (0 = absent, 1 = trivial, 2 = mild, 3 = moderate, 4 = severe).
      (2) The scores for items 1–17 are totaled for a final score.
      (3) The significance of the total score is not made. Subsequent changes are noted to determine changes in the individual's status.
   d. Population: individuals with a diagnosis of mood disorder.

Assessments of Task Performance

1. Bay Area Functional Performance Evaluation (BaFPE).
   a. Focus: assesses the cognitive, affective, performance, and social interaction skills required to perform ADL.

b. Method.
  (1) Brief interview prior to assessment to collect basic demographic and clinical information and to familiarize the individual with the evaluation.
  (2) The Task Oriented Assessment (TOA).
    (a) Measures cognition, performance, affect, qualitative signs, and referral indicators through the completion of five standardized, timed tasks (i.e., sorting shells, bank deposit slip, house floor plan, block design, draw-a-person).
    (b) Evaluator observes and rates task performance but does not provide guidance for task completion.
  (3) The Social Interaction Scale (SIS).
    (a) Assesses general ability to relate appropriately to other people within the environment through observations of the individual in five situations (i.e., one to one, mealtime, unstructured group, structured activity group, structured verbal group).
  (4) Optional self-report social interaction questionnaire.
  (5) Perceptual motor screening.
c. Scoring and interpretation of TOA.
  (1) Scoring consists of 3 component, 12 parameter, and 5 task scores.
  (2) Ten functional components of the five tasks are rated (i.e., paraphrase, productive decision-making, motivation, organization of time and materials, mastery and self-esteem, frustration tolerance, attention span, ability to abstract, verbal or behavioral evidence of thought or mood disorder, ability to follow instructions leading to correct task completion).
  (3) Norms are presented for comparison with specific adult psychiatric populations.
d. Scoring and interpretation of SIS.
  (1) Scoring consists of seven situation and five parameter scores as well as one total SIS score.
  (2) Seven categories are rated (i.e., response to authority figures, verbal communication, psychomotor behavior, independence/dependence, socially appropriate behavior, ability to work with peers, participation in group/program activities).
e. The TOA and SIS scores are not combined for a total BAFPE score.
  (1) The results of the TOA and SIS are used as indicators of overall functional performance, and provide information about the person's cognitive, affective, social, and perceptual motor skills.
f. Population: adults with psychiatric, neurological, or developmental diagnoses.

2. Comprehensive Occupational Therapy Evaluation Scale (COTE Scale).
  a. Focus: a structured method for observing and rating behaviors and behavioral changes in the areas of general, interpersonal, and task skills.
    (1) Seven items address general behavior such as appearance, punctuality, and activity level.
    (2) Six items address interpersonal behavior such as cooperation, sociability, and attention-getting behavior.
    (3) Twelve items address task behavior such as concentration, following directions, and problem-solving.
    (4) It may be used for initial assessment and to record progress.
  b. Method.
    (1) The individual's behavior is observed during a therapeutic session as the individual completes a task.
    (2) Behavior is rated by the therapist according to specific criteria presented for each item.
    (3) The tasks used are selected/designed by the therapist.
  c. Scoring and interpretation.
    (1) Each item is rated on a scale of 0 (normal) to 4 (severe).
    (2) Results may be used to plan treatment and assist with discharge planning.
  d. Population: adults with psychiatric diagnoses.
3. The Kohlman Evaluation of Living Skills (KELS).
  a. Refer to Chapter 15's section on the evaluation of ADL and IADL.
4. The Milwaukee Evaluation of Daily Living Skills (MEDLS).
  a. Refer to Chapter 15's section on the evaluation of ADL and IADL.
5. Test of Grocery Shopping.
  a. Refer to Chapter 15's section on the evaluation of ADL and IADL.

Assessments of Occupational Performance and Occupational Roles

1. Activity Card Sort (ACS).
  a. Focus: the identification of a person's level and amount of involvement in instrumental, leisure, and social activities.
  b. Method.
    (1) The individual is presented with a set of 89 cards that each pictorially represent real people engaging in an activity and asked to manually sort the cards according to level and amount of involvement (i.e., never done, gave up doing,

do less than in the past, do the same, do more than in the past).

(2) The real-life activities presented for sorting include 20 instrumental activities, 35 low-physical-demand leisure activities, 17 high-physical-demand leisure activities, and 17 social activities.

c. Scoring and interpretation.

(1) Total scores (current, previous, and percentage retained) for each of the activity categories (i.e., instrumental, low-physical-demand leisure, high-physical-demand leisure, and social activities) are obtained.

(2) Categorical scores are compiled into Global Scores for Current Activity, Previous Activity, and Percent Retained.

(a) These scores can be used to monitor changes in activity participation over time by comparing previous to current activity participation.

(3) The ACS can be used for initial assessment, goal-setting, and intervention planning.

(a) Only activities that a person identifies as part of their daily routine are included in the scoring.

(b) The information acquired can help the therapist assist clients in building (or rebuilding) routines composed of meaningful and healthy activities.

(4) The person's responses can contribute to the development of an occupational history.

(a) The pictorial representations of the activities often trigger memories and/or associations that when shared by the person can enhance the therapist's understanding of the person's activity engagement and motivation.

d. Population: originally developed for older adults with neurocognitive disorders; it is now being used in a broader context.

(1) Three versions are currently available to address the unique needs of adults and older adults residing in institutional settings, living in the community, or recovering from an incurred illness, injury, or disability.

2. Activities Health Assessment.

a. Focus: time usage, patterns, and configurations of activities, roles, and underlying skills and habits.

b. Method.

(1) The person completes an Idiosyncratic Activities Configuration Schedule by constructing a color-coded chart that depicts the way their time is spent during a typical week.

(a) Activities configuration is a term used to denote a measure that asks a person to record their daily activities for a week and describe the needs the activities satisfy, whether the person wants to or has to do each activity, how well the person does the activity, and how the person feels while engaging in the activity.

(2) The person completes the Idiosyncratic Activities Configuration Questionnaire.

(3) Therapist interviews person using interview guidelines.

c. Administration time.

(1) Time is dependent on whether schedule is completed retrospectively during a 60-minute session or over the course of a week (7 days).

(2) Questionnaire time is 60 minutes to 2 hours.

(3) Interview time is 45–60 minutes.

d. Scoring and interpretation.

(1) Not scored. Activities classified by type and then subgrouped according to questionnaire and interview guidelines.

(2) A determination of the person's activities health is made by the person and the therapist based on the completed schedule, questionnaire, and interview.

(3) Significance is placed on the person's interpretation of the level of balance, satisfaction, and comfort to which each activity contributes.

e. Population: adults through older adults.

3. Adolescent Role Assessment.

a. Refer to Chapter 5.

4. Barth Time Construction (BTC).

a. Focus: time usage, roles and underlying skills and habits.

b. Method.

(1) The person constructs a color-coded chart, individually or in a group format, which depicts the way their time is spent during a typical week.

(2) A COTE scale may also be completed by the therapist based on observations made during the session.

c. Scoring and interpretation.

(1) Not scored. Percentages of time are calculated according to main groupings.

(2) Significance of information is based on the client's reported use of time and a discussion with the individual about their satisfaction with their time use and its efficacy.

d. Population: adolescents through older adults.

5. Canadian Occupational Performance Measure (COPM).

a. Refer to Chapter 15's section on the evaluation of ADL and IADL.

6. Goal Attainment Scaling (GAS).

a. Focus: facilitates active participation in the goal-setting process by having the individual and/or caregivers identify desired intervention outcomes for the client that are personally relevant to them.

   (1) Used postintervention, the GAS assesses the individual's attainment of their goals and relevant changes in occupational performance.

b. Method: a personal interview is used during goal-setting and post-treatment sessions.

c. Scoring and interpretation: as a goal setting and program evaluation tool, the GAS does not have a scoring protocol.

   (1) In writing the goals, the practitioner seeks to accurately predict the level of performance the person is expected to achieve after a specified duration of intervention and identify equal increments above and below the expected level of performance.

   (2) For example, a five-point scale is used for scaling goals with 0 (zero) being used to represent the predicted expected level of performance and –2 to +2 being used to respectfully indicate performance below or above expectations.

d. Population: older children, adolescents, adults, and caregivers of younger children and/or adults who are unable to participate in an interview.

7. Model of Human Occupation Screening Tool (MOHOST).

a. Focus: this screening tool provides ratings on the person's volition, habituation, communication and interaction skills, motor skills, process skills, and the environment to provide an overview of their occupational functioning.

b. Method: the therapist reviews the person's chart, conducts an interview with them, and directly observes the person.

   (1) The interview focuses on a discussion of the person's roles, routines, interests, and motivators.

   (2) Observations can be conducted informally in open settings and/or formally in group settings or on a 1:1 basis.

   (3) The therapist discusses what they have learned about the person with them, the interdisciplinary team, and their carers (with the person's permission).

c. Scoring and interpretation.

   (1) There are four categories on the rating scale.
      (a) F = facilitates occupational performance.
      (b) A = allows occupational performance.
      (c) I = inhibits occupational performance.
      (d) R = restricts occupational performance.

   (2) As a screening tool, the MOHOST can help identify the need for a formal evaluation of the person.

d. Population: adolescents, adults, older adults.

EXAM HINT: Because the MOHOST is a screening tool, correct answers to exam items about what an OT practitioner should do after administering the MOHOST would include the completion of a formal evaluation. Any answer choice that includes goal-setting, intervention planning, and/or implementing/managing intervention would be an incorrect answer for an exam item. Goals cannot be established and treatment cannot be implemented or managed until after an evaluation is completed.

8. Occupational Circumstances Assessment Interview Rating Scale (OCAIRS), version 4.

a. Focus.
   (1) The nature and extent of an individual's occupational adaptation.
   (2) Based on the Model of Human Occupation (MOHO), this interview obtains, analyzes, and reports information relevant to intervention and discharge planning.
   (3) Twelve areas of occupational adaptation are explored; these include personal causation, self-perception of past circumstances and experiences, social environment, physical environment, values, interests, roles, habits, skills, readiness for change, and long- and short-term goals.

b. Method.
   (1) Information is gathered using a semi structured interview format composed of guided questions in 12 delineated areas.
   (2) Questions may be adapted to meet the needs and abilities of the individual.

c. Scoring and interpretation.
   (1) Following the interview, the therapist rates each item on a scale of 1–4 (4 being the highest) according to item-specific guidelines.
   (2) The person's self-report and perceptions provide qualitative data to explain the rationales for the quantitative ratings.
   (3) A case analysis method is used to interpret the data according to the MOHO to obtain a profile of the person's strengths and weaknesses.

d. Population: originally designed for adult through older adults with psychiatric diagnoses; it is now being used in a broader context.
   (1) Three interview formats are currently available to address population-specific issues; these are physical disabilities, mental health, and forensic mental health.

9. Occupational Performance History Interview-II (OPHI-II).

a. Focus: gathers information about an individual's life history, past and present occupational performance, and the impact of the incidence of disability, illness, or other traumatic event in the person's life.

b. Method.
 (1) Information is gathered using a semi structured interview format.
 (2) Interview questions cover five content areas
  addressing daily routines, occupational
  roles, occupation/activity choices, critical life
  choices, and occupational behavior settings.
c. Scoring and interpretation.
 (1) Following the interview, the therapist rates the
  person's occupational identity and competence and the impact of the person's occupational behavior settings on a scale of 1–4 with
  1 equaling extreme occupational dysfunction
  and 4 equaling exceptional occupational competence.
 (2) Ratings are used to identify the individual's life
  history pattern.
 (3) A narrative of the individual's life history pattern is written based on their self-report.
d. Population: adolescents to older adults who are
 able to participate in a comprehensive interview.
 (1) The OPHI is not recommended to be used
  with children less than 12 years old.
10. Occupational Self-Assessment (OSA).
 a. Focus: an individual's perceptions of their efficacy
  in areas of occupational performance and their
  importance.
 b. Method: two-part self-report. Clients are given a
  list of 21 everyday activities.
 c. Scoring and interpretation: clients use a four-
  point scale to rate how well they do each activity
  to assess occupational competence and then complete a four-point scale to report how important
  the activity is to assess the value of the occupation.
 d. Population: adults 18 years and older.
11. Pediatric Activity Card Sort.
 a. Refer to Chapter 5.
12. Role Checklist (RC).
 a. Focus: assesses self-reported role participation
  and the value of specific roles to the individual.
 b. Method.
  (1) A checklist is completed by the individual
   alone or with the therapist.
   (a) Part I Time asks the person to identify the
    major roles that have been part of their life
    in the past, present roles, and anticipated
    future roles; these roles include student,
    worker, volunteer, caregiver, home main-
    tainer, friend, family member, religious
    participant, hobbyist/amateur, participant
    in organizations, other (this last category
    enables the person to identify a role that
    is not listed).
   (b) Part II Value asks the person to identify the
    degree to which they value each role.

c. Scoring and interpretation.
 (1) The person's responses are totaled to identify
  roles that have been continuous in the person's life, roles that have been disrupted or
  changed, present roles, roles that are desired
  for the future, and valuable, somewhat valuable, and very valuable roles.
 (2) The data collected can be further discussed
  with the individual to gain additional information about their participation. Interview
  questions can be used to prompt the person to
  describe what they actually did within each of
  the roles and their level of satisfaction.
  (a) This information can be used to identify
   goals, plan intervention, implement role-
   focused interventions and plan discharge.
d. The Role Checklist Version 3: Satisfaction and
 Performance (RCv3) has revised the original Role
 Checklist in the following ways.
 (1) The identification of past role participation
  has been eliminated.
 (2) The criterion that required participation being
  "within one week" for six of the 10 roles was
  removed and the criterion of "on a regular
  basis" was added.
 (3) The value ratings of roles were removed and
  replaced by satisfaction ratings ranging from
  "very dissatisfied" to "very satisfied" for roles
  in which the person is currently engaged.
 (4) For roles that are not identified as currently
  being performed, the person's interest in
  future engagement in these roles are rated as
  "I would like to do this now," "I would like to
  do this in the future," or "I am not interested
  in this doing this."
 (5) All responses are also explored further via an
  interview with the person after the completion
  of the assessment tool.
e. Population: adolescents through older adults with
 physical or psychosocial dysfunction.

> **EXAM HINT:** Although the Role Checklist was published
> over 40 years ago, it is still commonly used in practice.
> Thus, the NBCOT® exam may have the original version
> or the revised RCv3 as an answer option for an exam
> item. In determining whether either of these assessment
> tools are the correct answer to an exam item, remem-
> ber that both can provide helpful information from
> the individual's perspective about their roles in a client-
> centered, holistic manner which can be used to develop
> rapport, initiate meaningful discussions, and establish
> intervention priorities.

13. Refer to Chapter 15 for additional information
 about evaluation tools for the occupational performance areas of ADL, IADL, leisure, and work.

Psychosocial Intervention

General Intervention Considerations

1. The environmental context in which the intervention will be implemented will influence intervention goals and activities.
   a. A setting's primary focus (e.g., transition to post-secondary life versus vocational rehabilitation) will determine the focus of intervention.
      (1) Refer to Chapter 4 for more information about mental health practice settings and their intervention foci.
   b. A setting's length of stay (LOS) (e.g., 2–5 days for an acute care unit, 2–4 weeks for a partial hospitalization program, unlimited for a clubhouse) and its characteristics (e.g., institutional versus community-based) will determine the type of intervention activities that can be used to attain goals.
      (1) Refer to Chapter 4 for more information about the LOS and characteristics of mental health practice settings.
   c. In school-based settings, psychosocial OT is provided according to the Individuals with Disabilities Education Improvement Act (IDEA) of 2004.
      (1) OT interventions are included in an individualized education program (IEP) or as a component of response to intervention (RtI) services.
      (2) Refer to Chapter 4 for more information about school-based practice, mandated IEP services, and the multi-tiered approach used in RtI.

> **EXAM HINT:** The NBCOT® OTR® exam content outline identifies knowledge of the "factors for determining and managing context and activities to meet individual and group intervention goals and objectives. . . . (including) client needs and priorities (and) response to intervention" (NBCOT®, 2022, p. 7) as essential for competent practice. The application of knowledge about the above contextual factors that can influence intervention and the following indicators for one-to-one and group interventions can help you determine the correct answer for NBCOT® exam items about psychosocial interventions.

2. One-to-one versus group intervention.
   a. Box 14-2 describes indicators for one-to-one intervention.
      (1) On inpatient psychiatric units, one-to-one interventions are indicated for patients who are on suicide precautions or are a danger to self or others.

BOX 14-2 ▷ Indicators for One-to-One Intervention

- The issues that must be addressed are only specific to the individual person or they require privacy.
- A need for greater control over the context and environment than can be afforded in a group.
- An inability to tolerate and/or participate in group interactions.
- The presence of behaviors that would be disruptive to the attainment of group goals.
- The difficulty or complexity of activity demands relative to the person's performance skills and performance patterns.
- Refusal to attend groups.

   b. Benefits of group intervention.
      (1) More cost effective.
      (2) Effective at assisting members to learn to live in social environments.
      (3) Takes advantage of group dynamics and the therapeutic milieu.
         (a) Refer to Chapter 3 for a comprehensive review of group dynamics and therapeutic groups.
         (b) Groups that are facilitated in a therapeutic manner by an OT practitioner are inherently curative.
         (c) Box 3-4 in Chapter 3 outlines the 11 curative factors described by Yalom that can be present in group interventions.

3. Factors that influence the effectiveness of intervention.
   a. Skillful therapeutic use of self.
   b. Exploration of the needs and wants of the individual.
   c. The establishment of meaningful and attainable goals.
   d. Engagement of the person throughout the intervention process in a collaborative manner.
      (1) The impact of symptoms, client factors, and performance skills on the individual's ability to engage in this process must be considered. Refer to this chapter's subsequent section on the management of challenging behaviors.
   e. Prioritization of the most meaningful and goal-directed use of the person's time.
   f. Practitioner's skill with activity analysis, adaptation, and gradation and environmental modification.
   g. Understanding the impact of environmental and personal contextual factors on the intervention process and addressing these in a proactive manner.

EXAM HINT: Correct answers for NBCOT® exam items about psychosocial interventions will employ the above factors that positively influence the effectiveness of intervention and will apply the following principles for the design and progression of treatment activities to achieve desired goals (e.g., the skilled use of activity analysis to select interventions that match the person's capabilities to attain client-centered goals).

4. The relationship of intervention activities to desired goals and the person's status.
   a. Intervention should follow a "top-down" approach to first address the client's occupational performance goals, rather than a "bottom-up" approach that addresses client factors and performance limitations.
      (1) In certain practice settings (e.g., acute care with a one-to-three-day length of stay) and in certain clinical situations (e.g., there are major concerns for a client's safety), initial intervention may need to first focus on the client factors and performance limitations that are preventing desired occupational performance.
   b. Intervention activities should be individualized, client-centered, and focus on developing the skills the client needs to engage in desired occupations, meaningful activities, and valued roles.
      (1) Activities that require the actual desired skills or behaviors, in their natural environment, are often the most effective (e.g., assisting the client to use a checking account to pay bills).
      (2) Activities that simulate desired behaviors in a clinical setting may be less effective (e.g., using kits that simulate checking materials).
      (3) Activities that utilize the performance skills of desired behaviors and rely on generalization may be the least effective (e.g., practicing basic arithmetic calculations).
      (4) Refer to Chapter 3 for comprehensive information about intervention planning and implementation.

Role of the OTA/COTA® in Intervention

1. The OTA/COTA® contributes to the intervention plan in collaboration with the client and the supervising occupational therapist.
2. The OTA /COTA® implements the intervention plan and provides direct services to attain intervention goals in collaboration with the supervising occupational therapist.
   a. The level of supervision an OTA/COTA® will require depends upon their experience, established service

competence, state laws, and other regulatory and payer requirements.
3. All intervention activities completed by an OTA/COTA® must comply with federal and state laws and other regulatory and payer requirements (AOTA, 2021).

General Considerations for Group Intervention

1. The taxonomy of groups described by Anne Mosey provides a useful framework for designing OT intervention groups.
   a. Evaluation groups.
      (1) Designed to gather information about the individual's task and group interaction skills that can be used to establish goals and plan intervention.
         (a) Although their primary purpose is evaluation, these groups are often therapeutic through their process and/or content and can help establish rapport.
      (2) Refer to Chapter 3 for more information about the purposes and assumptions, member criteria, the leader's role, and suitable activities for evaluation groups.
   b. Task-oriented groups.
      (1) The purpose is to assist the members in becoming aware of their needs, values, ideas, and feelings through the performance of a shared task.
         (a) Refer to Chapter 3 for more information about the purposes and assumptions, member criteria, the leader's role, and suitable activities for task-oriented groups.
   c. Developmental groups.
      (1) The purpose is to assist the members to acquire and develop group interaction skills.
         (a) Table 3-13 in Chapter 3 describes the purposes and foci of the five levels of developmental groups.
         (b) Table 3-14 in Chapter 3 describes the activities that are used in the five levels of developmental groups to attain individual and group goals.
      (2) Developmental groups offer five levels of interaction. Box 14-3 describes the different levels of interaction for each group type.
      (3) The OT practitioner's directive leadership role decreases and their facilitative/advisory leadership role increases as a group progresses from parallel groups to mature groups.
         (a) Box 3-7 in Chapter 3 describes the role of the leader in the five levels of developmental groups in more detail.
   d. Thematic groups are designed to help members acquire specific skills by teaching them how to complete skill-based activities during group sessions.

> **BOX 14-3 ◗ Interaction Levels for Developmental Groups**
>
> - **Parallel:** members in these groups complete individual tasks; minimal interaction is required for task completion.
> - **Project/Associative:** members of these groups complete common, short-term activities that require some interaction and rudimentary cooperation.
> - **Egocentric Cooperative/Basic Cooperative:** members of these groups complete long-term tasks that require joint interaction to complete; however, completion of the task is not the group's primary focus. The main purpose is for members to begin to express their needs and address those of others.
> - **Cooperative/Supportive Cooperative:** members of these groups are not focused on the completion of a specific task, rather their aim is to learn to work together cooperatively, enjoy each other's company, and meet each other's emotional needs.
> - **Mature:** members of these groups are responsive to all members' needs and each member can carry out a variety of tasks and roles. They have a good balance between completing a task and meeting the needs of the members.

    (1) Refer to Chapter 3 for more information about the purposes and assumptions, member criteria, the leader's role, and suitable activities for thematic groups.

  e. Topical groups focus on the discussion of activities and issues outside of the group that are current or anticipated.

    (1) Refer to Chapter 3 for more information about the purposes and assumptions, member criteria, the leader's role, and suitable activities for topical groups.

  f. Instrumental groups are concerned with meeting health needs and maintaining function.

    (1) Refer to Chapter 3 for more information about the purposes and assumptions, member criteria, the leader's role, and suitable activities for instrumental groups.

2. The curative factors of groups described by Irving Yalom support the inherent value of OT interventions that use a group format.

  a. Groups and group activities that are designed to facilitate these curative factors are most effective.

    (1) Box 3-4 in Chapter 3 describes the 11 curative factors described by Yalom that can be present in group interventions.

3. Considerations in group planning.

  a. Member demographics including gender, age, culture, and ethnicity.

  b. Individual characteristics of members.

    (1) Cognitive level.

    (2) Functional skills.

    (3) Individual goals.

    (4) Contraindications and safety issues.

  c. Logistical considerations.

    (1) Number of people in the group.

    (2) Length of sessions.

    (3) Number of sessions.

    (4) Space availability.

    (5) Environmental characteristics.

    (6) Budget and materials required.

    (7) Number of leaders.

    (8) Open group versus closed group.

  d. Frame of reference.

4. Elements of a group protocol.

  a. Title/name: reflect the purpose or goal of the group (e.g., Communication Skills Group), not the media used (e.g., Crafts Group).

  b. Purpose: a brief statement of what the group hopes to accomplish (e.g., to improve the members' ability to effectively and appropriately communicate to others their needs and feelings and to enter into satisfying interpersonal relationships).

  c. Rationale: explains the value of this group to the members, and why it is important to offer this service to this population.

  d. Theoretical base/frame of reference: explains in brief and readily understandable terms the theory on which this intervention is based and the rationale for its use.

  e. Criteria for membership: explains who should/should not be included in the group, and what will indicate when the member will no longer benefit from participation.

  f. Goals/anticipated outcomes: the expectations of what the members will be able to do as a result of having attended this group.

    (1) A list of "individual/member/patient/client will . . ." statements, (e.g., individual/member/patient/client will be able to initiate and sustain social interactions with peers).

  g. Method/format: explains how the group will be carried out.

    (1) Includes the format, scheduling, activities, materials, procedures, and other pertinent logistics.

    (2) Includes the information another practitioner would need to lead this group.

  h. Role of the OT practitioner: the tasks of the practitioner in preparing for and leading the group.

    (1) Includes such things as supplying materials, designing activities, facilitating interaction, providing a safe environment, etc.

    (2) Refer to Chapter 3 for further information about leadership roles and styles.

  i. Quality assurance: explains how the need for this intervention and its effectiveness will be monitored.

  j. Outcome measures: determine whether the identified goals were met.

  k. The actual format used to write protocols varies from setting to setting.

5. Procedure for developing a group.
   a. Conduct a needs assessment to identify intervention needs. Refer to Chapter 4 for needs assessment procedures.
   b. Develop the protocol.
   c. Present the protocol to the treatment team or program administrators.
   d. Select potential members who would benefit from the group.
   e. Meet with each potential member to explain the purpose and circumstances of the group.
   f. Hold introductory sessions of the group and revise the protocol as needed.
6. Group member leadership roles (Refer to Chapter 3).
7. Considerations in activity selection.
   a. Degree and type of structure (inherent or imposed).
   b. Type(s) and degree of instruction provided.
   c. Degree of new learning required.
   d. Complexity of the activity.
   e. Length of time for completion.
   f. Nature and degree of skill required for engagement and completion.
   g. Degree of challenge to the members' skills.

Intervention Group Types

> **EXAM HINT:** Group interventions are commonly used in psychosocial settings across the continuum of care; thus, knowing the following group types and their purposes can help you determine the correct answer for NBCOT® exam items about group interventions.

1. ADL/IADL groups.
   a. Focus on the development of ADL skills (e.g., personal hygiene, dressing, sexual activity) and IADL skills (e.g., meal preparation, financial management, community mobility) to enable independent living.
   b. May be conducted in a modular and/or psychoeducational format.
2. Basic task skills groups.
   a. Include intervention activities designed to develop the basic cognitive skills (e.g., attention, ability to follow multistep directions, problem-solving) necessary for the completion of simple tasks.
      (1) This group uses a skill acquisition approach that differs from the psychodynamic approach used in the task-oriented group described by Fidler and Mosey.
3. Community participation/reintegration groups.
   a. Focus on the identification and use of community resources (e.g., leisure facilities) and the development of skills (e.g., the use of public transportation) to enable full community participation.
   b. May be conducted in a modular and/or psychoeducational format.
4. Coping skills groups.

   a. Focus on identifying and implementing the problem-solving and stress-management techniques needed to cope with life stressors.
5. Directive groups.
   a. These are highly structured groups designed to assist persons with limited abilities in developing basic task and social skills.
   b. Each session is divided into five parts followed by a 15-minute review of the session by the leaders.
      (1) Part I consists of an orientation to the purpose and goals of the group (maximum of five minutes).
      (2) Part II involves a review of everyone's name and the introduction of new members (5–10 minutes).
      (3) Part III consists of warm-up activities to help members be comfortable and engage them in the group (5–10 minutes).
      (4) Part IV involves one or more activities designed to address the goals of the group and the needs of its members (10–20 minutes).
      (5) Part V includes activities designed to give meaning to the activities and closure to the group (10 minutes).
6. Discharge planning groups.
   a. Focus on activities to problem-solve potential obstacles and identify resources for successful post discharge community reintegration.
7. Goal-setting groups.
   a. Consist of activities designed to identify personal objectives and treatment goals and the steps needed for their achievement.
8. Leisure groups.
   a. May include the identification of interests, development of activity specific skills, identification of resources, and recognition of the importance of healthy use of unstructured time for personal well-being.
9. Modular groups.
   a. The focus of each session is rotated in a way that allows an individual to join the group at any time and still cover each topic (e.g., an independent living skills group that addresses meal preparation the first session, financial management the second, community mobility the third, etc., and then begins the cycle again with a session on meal preparation).
10. Play groups.
    a. Frequently used in pediatric settings for observation, assessment, and to teach and develop skills.
    b. Play groups provide opportunities to develop play, task, and social skills at the child's developmental level and provide a developmentally appropriate outlet for children to express thoughts and feelings.
11. Pre-vocational groups.
    a. Focus on the identification of personal skills, limitations, and interests, and the development of work habits and behaviors.

b. The desired outcome is the development of the knowledge and skills that are prerequisite for participation in vocational training, vocational rehabilitation, or for the acquisition of competitive employment.

12. Psychoeducational groups.
    a. An intervention approach that uses a classroom format and the principles of learning to provide information to members and to teach skills.
    b. A teacher/student relationship exists.
    c. The use of homework assignments is encouraged to facilitate skill development and generalization of learning.

13. Reminiscence groups.
    a. Activities are designed to review past life experiences to promote the use of cognitive abilities and foster a sense of personal worth.
    b. Current memory is not necessary, nor is it facilitated.

14. Self-awareness groups.
    a. Include such activities as values clarification, awareness of personal assets, limitations, and adaptive/maladaptive behaviors, and the individual's impact on others.

15. Sensory awareness groups.
    a. Include activities to promote sensory functions and environmental awareness.

16. Sensorimotor groups.
    a. Incorporate gross motor challenges and sensory-rich activities to improve body awareness, sensory processing and modulation, and developmentally appropriate play.

17. Social interaction groups.
    a. Include interventions to develop communication skills, socially acceptable behaviors, and interpersonal relationship skills.
    b. May be conducted in a modular and/or psychoeducational format.

Managing Challenging Behaviors

EXAM HINT: The NBCOT® OTR® exam content outline identifies knowledge of "adaptive and preventive strategies for supporting optimal engagement in occupation" (NBCOT®, 2022, p. 9), "precautions or contraindications associated with a client's condition or stage of recovery," (NBCOT®, 2022, p. 7) and "preventive measures for minimizing risk and promoting safety" (NBCOT®, 2022, p. 13) as essential for competent and safe practice. The application of knowledge about the following methods for managing behaviors that can hinder occupational performance and/or place the client or others at risk will help you correctly answer NBCOT® Domain 3 Intervention Management exam items and Domain 4 Competency and Practice Management exam items.

1. Hallucinations.
   a. Create an environment that is not over-stimulating and free of stimuli that can trigger hallucinations and interfere with reality-based activity (e.g., if a person experiences auditory hallucinations, do not play background music during a group).
   b. Use highly structured, simple, concrete, and tangible activities that hold the individual's attention.
   c. When the person appears to be focusing on a hallucinatory experience, attempt to redirect them to reality-based thinking and concrete actions.

2. Delusions.
   a. Do not attempt to refute the delusion.
   b. Redirect the individual's thoughts to reality-based thinking and concrete actions.
   c. Avoid discussions and other experiences that focus on and validate or reinforce delusional material.

3. Akathisia.
   a. Allow the person to move around as needed if it can be done without causing disruption to others.
   b. Keep in mind that participation on many levels and in many forms can be beneficial to the individual.
   c. Whenever possible, select gross motor and active tasks over fine motor or sedentary ones.

4. Offensive physical and/or verbal behavior.
   a. Set limits and immediately address the behavior during a session.
   b. The reasons the behavior is not acceptable should be clearly presented in a manner that is not confrontational or judgmental.
   c. The consequences of continued offensive behavior should be clearly communicated.
   d. It is required that staff protects all clients from the threat of harm or abuse by another person.

> **CAUTION:** The needs and safety of the entire unit, program, and/or group must be considered when addressing offensive behaviors.

5. Manic or monopolizing behavior.
   a. Select or design highly structured activities that hold the individual's attention and require a shift of focus from person to person.
   b. Thank the individual for their participation and redirect attention to another group member/program participant.
   c. Refer to limit-setting discussed above.

6. Escalating behavior.
   a. Avoid what can be perceived as challenging behavior (e.g., eye contact, standing directly in front of the person).
   b. Maintain a comfortable distance.

> **CAUTION:** Avoid positions where either you or the person feels trapped.

   c. Actively listen.
   d. Use a calm, but not patronizing, tone.

(1) Speaking in a softer or lower tone than the individual is often effective in decreasing the volume and intensity of the escalating individual's speech.

e. Speak simply, clearly, and directly. Avoid miscommunication.

f. Do not make or communicate value judgments about the individual's thoughts, feelings, or behaviors.

g. Clearly present what you would like the person to do.

h. Individuals most often calm in response to the above interventions. If an individual continues to escalate and is nonresponsive to interventions, additional steps are needed to ensure safety.

(1) Remove other persons from the area.

(2) Get or send for other staff.

7. Disruptive behavior in children.

a. Disruptive behavior violates social norms and can range in its severity (e.g., repeatedly stating that an activity is "dumb" versus aggressively throwing the activity's materials).

(1) Recognize that disruptive behavior is a child's ineffective way of expressing their thoughts and feelings; it is *not* "acting out"; rather it is behavior exhibited by children with impulse-control, disruptive, and/or conduct disorders.

b. Use the ABC model to understand and respond to disruptive behaviors. Refer to Table 14-2.

c. Identify ways that antecedents to disruptive behaviors can be eliminated, avoided, and/or modified and implement these.

d. Discuss the consequences of behavior with the child and their implications.

e. Identify personally meaningful reinforcers and use these to increase the frequency of adaptive behaviors that result in positive outcomes and decrease the frequency of maladaptive behaviors that result in negative outcomes.

Table 14-2

The ABC Model for Understanding Behavior

A = Antecedent: the event that precedes a behavior; the stimulus that triggers the behavior.
Examples: a child playing a board game is not doing well and a peer calls them a "loser"; a student standing in a school cafeteria line is bumped by another student.

B = Behavior: the measurable and observable actions in response to the event or stimulus.
Examples: a child ignores the rules of the game in an attempt to win the game and their peers state these rules must be followed, in response, the child swears at them and calls them "stupid"; a student responds to being bumped by forcibly pushing the other student to the ground.

C = Consequence: the responses and actions that occur after the behavior occurs.
Examples: the peers playing the game with the child say they do not want to play with them anymore and the game ends; the student is removed from the lunchroom for a time-out and is unable to participate in the recess sensorimotor activities that they enjoy.

---

f. Depending on the nature of the disruptive behavior, the following therapeutic approaches can be used.

(1) Interpretation: a therapeutic technique in which the OT practitioner puts words to the observed behavior, enabling the child to effectively express the feelings they are experiencing.

(2) Redirection: a verbal tactic that refocuses the child on the assigned or current activity and provides concrete cues to enable effective participation.

(3) Limit setting: inform the child of what is permissible and what is unacceptable.

(4) Time-out: remove the child from a problematic situation to a specific area that is safe, quiet, and calm to for a brief amount of time (2–5 minutes, no more than 1 minute per age of the child).

(5) A behavioral or contingency contract: a mutually determined agreement between the OT practitioner and the child that clearly outlines specific attainable behavioral expectations, concrete plans for meeting these expectations, the consequences that will result if goals are not attained, and the benefits of goal attainment.

8. The effects of neurocognitive disorders (e.g., dementia).

a. Make eye contact and show that you are interested in the person.

b. Value and validate what is said by the person (e.g., if an older adult states that they need to pick up their child at day-care, respond by acknowledging the importance of their child in their life and asking them to tell you about their child).

c. Maintain a positive and friendly facial expression and tone of voice during all communications.

(1) Do not give orders.

(2) Use short, simple words and sentences.

(3) Do not argue or criticize.

d. Do not speak about the individual as if they were not there.

e. Use nonverbal communication.

f. Create a routine that uses familiar and enjoyable activities.

(1) Use activities that demonstrate and promote personal interests and independence.

(2) Do not introduce infantilizing activities.

(3) Analyze and grade activities carefully.

(4) Do not rush activities.

(a) It is the process of engaging in an activity that is important; task completion is not needed.

g. Note the effects of the time of day on behavior and activity performance.

h. Attend to safety issues at all times.

9. Lack of initiation/participation.

a. Together with the individual, identify the reasons for lack of participation (e.g., disinterest,

irrelevance of the activity, lack of skill, attention deficits, embarrassment, depression).
- b. Motivational hints.
  - (1) Individuals are more likely to participate in activities that address issues that are of interest or concern to them.
  - (2) The more ownership people have of the activity, the more they will participate.
  - (3) Success is motivating.
  - (4) Fun is motivating.
  - (5) Positive feedback and rewards are motivating.
  - (6) Everyone has their own motivators. It is important to identify what they are.
  - (7) Curiosity can be used to motivate.
  - (8) Food is often motivating (as per Maslow's hierarchy of needs). Refer to Chapter 5.
    - (a) Using secondary reinforcers such as praise is usually preferable to using primary reinforcers such as food.
  - (9) Offer choices.
  - (10) Encourage the individual to remain in the group and participate when/if they are ready.

Special Considerations in Psychosocial Evaluation and Intervention

Domestic Abuse/Intimate Partner Violence (IPV)

1. Facts and figures.
   - a. In the United States, domestic abuse/IPV is a major social justice crisis and critical health-care concern.
   - b. Domestic abuse/IPV knows no boundaries. It occurs regardless of socioeconomic factors, race, culture, ethnicity, religion, or age.
   - c. For more information, Refer to Fast Facts: https://www.cdc.gov/violenceprevention/intimatepartnerviolence/fastfact.html.
2. Definition and types.
   - a. Definitions vary greatly from state to state.
   - b. Definitions involve violence or abuse that is used to control another member of the household.
   - c. Domestic abuse/IPV can take one or more forms. Refer to Box 14-4.
   - d. Patterns of abuse.
     - (1) Impulsive abuse, during which the abuser has sudden attacks of rage, which may be regular or random.
     - (2) Premeditated abuse, during which the abuser is calm and calculating.
3. Signs of physical abuse.
   - a. Bruises at different stages of healing or in unusual places.
   - b. Burns suggestive of specific objects.
   - c. Lacerations to the face or genitals.
   - d. Orthopedic injuries that are inconsistent with the explanations.
   - e. Internal injuries of the head and organs.
   - f. Head and facial injuries suggestive of hitting, shaking, or pulling.
   - g. Reluctance to talk about injuries.

BOX 14-4 ◖ **Types of Domestic Abuse/Intimate Partner Violence**

- **Physical abuse:** hitting, kicking, punching, slapping, choking, and/or burning a person.
- **Emotional abuse:** criticizing, shaming, humiliating, playing mind games, abusing or killing pets, withholding affection, isolating, and/or dominating a person.
- **Economic abuse:** making a person ask for money, giving them a rigid allowance, and/or preventing a person from taking a job.
- **Intimidation and coercion:** making a person afraid, breaking things, displaying weapons, threatening to leave them, publicly sharing embarrassing and/or confidential information about them, falsely reporting them for something illegal, and/or making them do something illegal.
- **Using children:** making a parent feel guilty about their children, using their children to relay messages, using visitation to harass a parent, and/or threatening to take their children away from them.
- **Stalking:** following a person, having them followed, invading their home(s) and/or privacy, and/or creating fear of immediate harm.
- **Sexual abuse:** performing and/or requiring a person to perform unwanted sexual activities through force, threats, or intimidation.

- h. Abuser not wanting to leave the person they are abusing alone with others.
4. Reasons for failure to report or leave an abusive/violent relationship.
   - a. Economic pressure.
   - b. Religious beliefs.
   - c. Feeling of love for the abuser.
   - d. Believing the abuse is deserved.
   - e. Viewing abuse as normal due to exposure to abuse/violence as a child.

f. Fear of increasing abuse/violence.
g. Fear of retaliation.
h. Belief things will change.
i. Concern for children.
j. Nowhere to go.
k. Lack of support systems.
5. Role of the OT practitioner.
   a. Actively use therapeutic use of self to develop trust.
   b. Use the RADAR approach to screen for and respond to domestic abuse/IPV. Refer to Table14-3.

> **EXAM HINT:** Applying the RADAR approach and the assessment and intervention approaches described below can help you correctly answer NBCOT® exam items about the most effective ways an OT practitioner can screen for and respond to domestic abuse/IPV.

   c. Areas to address with the person who has been/is being abused.
      (1) The impact of stress, fear, and abuse on their occupational performance, social participation, and quality of life, and if a parent, the impact on their children.
      (2) Their available support network(s) (e.g., family, friends, neighbors, co-workers, employers, and/or religious leaders).
      (3) The need for escape and emergency plans.
      (4) National crisis hotlines and local crisis centers and resources that can provide support and concrete assistance to help ensure safety and enable a violence-free life (e.g., a shelter that provides a place to live, basic necessities, and counselling).
         (a) National Domestic Violence Hotline: 1-800-799-7233 (SAFE).
         (b) National Sexual Assault Hotline: 1-800-656-4673 (HOPE).
      (c) National Teen Dating Abuse Hotline: 1-866-331-9474.
   d. Intervention foci for working with a person who has been/is being abused.
      (1) Direct treatment of the person's physical and emotional injuries.
      (2) Development of the following to help the individual live a safe, empowered, and self-determined life.
         (a) Self-efficacy and assertiveness skills to help the person leave the relationship and/or not return to the relationship.
         (b) Task and social skills, as needed, to effectively engage in meaningful occupations and desired roles (e.g., home maintainer, worker, parent).
         (c) Self-advocacy skills to obtain treatment and concrete supports for independent living (e.g., Section 8 housing, Supplemental Nutrition Assistance Program [SNAP]).
   e. Inform supervisor as required by setting's policy and/or other professional staff as needed.
      (1) To maintain trust, the permission of the person should be sought prior to the disclosure of their situation to other team members.

> **CAUTION:** If a person refuses to give their permission, and there are serious concerns for their safety, the practitioner needs to carefully weigh the ramifications of potentially violating the person's trust versus those of not reporting. Sometimes maintaining trust to keep the person engaged in the relationship is best; other times, obtaining additional supports to ensure their safety is best. Because these situations are complex and any decision made must be tailored to the unique person's needs, this type of practice scenario will likely not be on the NBCOT® exam.

   f. Report abuse to authorities, if required by state law.
      (1) Less than 10 states have mandated reporting laws. Refer to Which States Have Mandatory Domestic Violence Reporting? (mandatedreportertraining.com).

> **CAUTION:** Reporting abuse to authorities can place the person (and if a parent, their children) at risk for retaliation. Violence typically escalates when survivors seek help to separate from their abusers. To address this reality, the coordination of multiple services and the provision of adequate services are required to keep survivors safe.

Table 14-3

The RADAR Approach for Domestic Abuse/IPV Screening and Response

R = Routinely ask. Inquiring about potential abuse when interviewing all clients can be the first step in intervention; this acknowledges that abuse is not an acceptable secret.

A = Affirm and ask. Acknowledge and support the person who discloses abuse. Ask direct questions of all clients to determine risk (e.g., Do you feel safe with your partner?).

D = Document. Formally record objective findings (e.g., the client has multiple bruises) and record the person's statements in quotes.

A = Assess. Ask targeted questions to assess the client's safety and if a parent, that of their children (i.e., has the abuse become more violent? are there weapons in the home?).

R = Review options and Refer. Discuss available resources and supports that can help keep the survivor safe. Refer the client to domestic violence/IPV hotlines, domestic violence/IPV shelters, and/or safe houses that have staff trained in family violence and safety planning.

Child Abuse

1. Refer to Chapter 5.

Elder Abuse

1. Refer to Chapter 5.

Patient/Client Abuse

1. Refer to Chapter 4.

Psychological Reaction to Disability

> **EXAM HINT:** The following information about the psychological reactions and psychosocial adjustment to disability apply to all persons with disabilities and the parents of children with disabilities. Correct answers to NBCOT® exam items will be respectful of a person's or family's stage of adjustment and include intervention approaches that foster adaptation to disability.

1. Several factors influence the individual's reaction to disability.
   a. Permanency of the disability.
   b. Sudden versus chronic onset.
   c. Appraisal of life experiences.
   d. Spiritual beliefs.
   e. Available resources and support systems.
   f. Cultural factors.
2. Adjustment.
   a. Active participation in social, vocational/educational, and play/leisure pursuits.
   b. Successful negotiation of the physical environment.
   c. Awareness of remaining strengths and assets as well as functional limitations.
3. Phases of adjustment.
   a. Shock.
      (1) Initial reaction to a sudden physical or psychological trauma.
      (2) Characterized by emotional numbness, depersonalization, and reduced speech and mobility.
   b. Anxiety.
      (1) A panic-stricken reaction to awareness of the seriousness of the situation.
      (2) Characterized by restlessness, confusion, racing thoughts, and psychological symptoms associated with anxiety.
   c. Denial.
      (1) Retreat from the realization of the seriousness and implications of the situation.
      (2) Characterized by minimalism, negation, aloofness, and unrealistic expectations.
   d. Depression.
      (1) Bereavement for the associated losses as the realities of those losses is identified.
      (2) Characterized by hopelessness, helplessness, isolation, and decreased self-esteem.
   e. Internalized anger.
      (1) Resentment and bitterness directed toward self.
      (2) Characterized by blaming of self for the event, the extent of the loss, or the failure to recover.
   f. Externalized anger.
      (1) An attempt to retaliate for imposed losses; directed against those associated with the onset of disability and/or the response to the situation, including service providers.
      (2) Characterized by aggression, antagonism, demanding and critical attitudes, and passive-aggressive behavior.
   g. Acknowledgment.
      (1) The first step toward acceptance of the situation.
      (2) Characterized by acceptance of a new self-concept and the identification of values and goals.
   h. Adjustment.
      (1) An emotional acceptance of the situation and reintegration into identified roles.
      (2) Characterized by a positive sense of self and potentialities, and achievement of meaningful goals.
4. OT intervention.
   a. Acknowledgment of the person's losses.
   b. Identification of what the individual is able to do with emphasis on their personal accomplishments and control.
   c. Assistance to the individual in their assumption of an active role in shaping their life.
   d. The use of person-centered approaches based on empowerment theory.
   e. Reduction of limitations through changes in the physical and social environment.
   f. Development of the skills necessary to participate in valued roles and meaningful occupations.
      (1) Stress management and coping skills.
      (2) Cognitive reframing/restructuring: the process of altering cognitions and cognitive processes (usually maladaptive thoughts and thinking) to facilitate changes in emotions and behavior. Refer to this Chapter's prior section on CBT.
   g. Acquisition of concrete resources and supports to enable full social participation.
   h. Development of peer supports.

Suicide

1. Facts.
   a. Suicide knows no boundaries. It occurs regardless of socioeconomic factors, race, culture, ethnicity, religion, or age.

b. In the United States, suicide is a leading cause of death, a major social-justice crisis, and a critical health-care concern.

c. For more information, Refer to Facts About Suicide | Suicide | CDC.

2. Identification of risk.

a. A member of the treatment team (usually a physician) will ask the individual about suicidal thinking.

b. It is important to identify the degree of risk.

(1) The person is asked if they were trying to hurt themselves how they would they do it.

(a) The degree of detail that is given indicates the seriousness of intent.

(b) The potential for the plan to succeed also indicates the degree of risk.

c. For more information, Refer to Risk and Protective Factors | Suicide | CDC.

EXAM HINT: Because suicide risk is present in all populations, OT practitioners have an ethical responsibility to be knowledgeable about the above methods for identifying suicide risk and the following factors that can increase this risk. Thus, you should be prepared to answer NBCOT® exam items about the need for an OT practitioner to take a proactive stance to prevent suicide in *all* practice settings (not just psychiatric ones) and with *all* populations (not just adults).

RED FLAG: The observance or knowledge of any of the following risk factors associated with suicide requires immediate action by OT practitioners to prevent suicide.

d. Risk factors for suicide.

(1) Previous attempt or fantasized suicide.

(2) Anxiety, depression, exhaustion, pervasive pessimism, or hopelessness.

(3) Availability of means of suicide (e.g., firearms in the home).

(4) Concern for effect of suicide on family members.

(5) Verbalized suicidal ideation, plan, or intent.

(6) Preparation of a will.

(7) Resignation after agitated depression.

(8) Proximal life crisis (e.g., the death of a family member/significant other, divorce, impending surgery, job loss, disciplinary or legal problems).

(9) Family history of suicide; exposure to suicide of others.

(10) Family violence, including physical or sexual abuse.

(11) Clinically diagnosed depression or other mental disorder.

(12) Co-occurring mental health and/or substance abuse disorders.

(13) Incarceration.

(14) Impulsive, self-injurious, and/or aggressive tendencies.

EXAM HINT: The NBCOT® OTR® exam content outline identifies knowledge of "precautions . . . associated with a client's condition or stage of recovery" (NBCOT®, 2022, p. 7) and "preventive measures for minimizing risk . . . in the intervention environment" (NBCOT®, 2022, p. 13) as essential for competent and safe practice. The application of knowledge about the following interventions will help you correctly answer NBCOT® exam items about the OT practitioner's response to suicide risk and intent.

3. OT intervention.

a. Identification of the motivation behind the suicidal intent and the identification of alternatives.

(1) Development of a contract for safety (also called an emergency or contingency plan) that specifies what the individual should do if they are experiencing suicidal ideation, plan, or intent.

(a) A contract for safety asks the individual to contract or commit to telling a designated person/persons if they are having thoughts of suicide.

b. Discussion of personally meaningful activities that are future-oriented (e.g., going to college, starting a new career, babysitting a grandchild, participating in family traditions with friends and/or family over the holidays).

c. Development of meaningful goals and identification of interests to increase participation in recovery.

d. Identification of positive personal attributes and support systems to increase hopefulness.

(1) This may be facilitated by a review of past accomplishments.

(2) This can be difficult to facilitate in individuals with depression

e. Development of problem-solving skills and stress management techniques to increase the individual's resilience and ability to manage life stressors.

f. Activities that produce successful outcomes (especially those with a visible end-product) and promote positive thinking.

g. Activities designed for the expression and validation of feelings.

h. Moderate physical activity elevates mood.

i. Development of skills that increase occupational performance.

j. Consumer/patient/client and family education that addresses the following.

(1) Management of relapse or set-backs in recovery with a plan in place for dealing with active suicidal ideations.

(2) Strategies for dealing with disappointment with progress and/or hopelessness.

(3) Methods for reinforcing and supporting engagement in treatment.

(4) Medication management.

(5) Support and advocacy groups and resources (e.g., the National Alliance on Mental Illness).

k. For more information, refer to Prevention Strategies | Suicide | CDC.

l. Contact the National Suicide Hotline 988 if needed.

Self-Harm/Self-Mutilation

1. Definition.
   a. "Deliberate destruction or alteration of one's body tissue without conscious suicidal intent" (Favazza, 1996, pp. xviii–xix).
   b. Also known as self-injurious behavior, parasuicide, self-wounding, and "cutting."
2. A maladaptive coping skill for dealing with uncomfortable feelings.
3. Occupational therapy intervention foci and approaches.
   a. Improve self-management by teaching stress, anger, and emotional regulation skills.
   b. Instruct clients in the use of alternative, less destructive coping strategies (e.g., snapping a rubber band worn on the wrist instead of cutting).
   c. Implement interventions using CBT principles. Refer to this chapter's prior section on CBT.
   d. Use DBT techniques, if appropriate to the client. Refer to this chapter's prior section on DBT.
   e. Provide instruction in the use of sensory approaches (tactile stimulation, massage, self-soothing) to manage the feelings that lead to self-harm.
   f. Develop problem-solving skills.
   g. Improve communication skills.

Life-Threatening Illness and Dying

1. The acquisition of an illness that threatens life and the progression of a condition to a terminal stage substantially impacts occupational performance and participation.
   a. The functional decline resulting from the condition or illness and/or the interventions used to manage and/or treat them can lead to disruptions in daily routines, a loss of life roles, social isolation, and decreased occupational engagement.
2. Stages of the individual's response to life-threatening illness and dying may include the following.
   a. Denial.
      (1) A coping strategy that allows the individual to refuse to accept or address the reality of their illness (e.g., "There must have been a mistake with the x-rays").

      (2) Denial may lead the individual to see many health professionals, hoping to find the one who will give a different prognosis.
      (3) Denial may be a response to the denial or discomfort experienced by others.
      (4) Denial will end when the individual is psychologically prepared to face the reality of the situation.
      (5) OT practitioners should allow the person to ask questions and discuss the situation at their own pace.
   b. Anger.
      (1) The individual becomes angry as they accept the reality of a life-threatening illness and/or impending death (e.g., "Get out of here. You don't know what it's like").
      (2) This anger may be projected onto anyone who is seen as healthy or in a better position.
      (3) Rages, outbursts, and hurtful behavior must be recognized for the purposes they serve.
      (4) OT practitioners should allow the individual to vent anger while identifying its source and developing more effective coping strategies.
   c. Bargaining.
      (1) In an attempt to gain control, the individual may bargain with doctors, caretakers, or a higher being (e.g., "Just let me go to my child's graduation and then I'll be okay with this").
      (2) Bargains are an attempt to buy time.
      (3) Bargains are often associated with guilt related to things not done or promises not kept.
      (4) The individual should not be expected to keep to these bargains.
      (5) OT practitioners should respond honestly to the person's questions.
   d. Depression.
      (1) As the individual acknowledges the reality of a life-threatening illness and/or impending death, they begin to identify the feelings of loss and become depressed.
      (2) The tendency is to say goodbye to all but a few and isolate oneself as thoughts and feelings turn inward.
      (3) OT practitioners can provide physical and psychological comfort for both the individual and their loved ones.
   e. Acceptance.
      (1) As the individual recognizes the reality of their life-threatening illness and impending death, they begin to make plans and think about the future for self and family.
      (2) It can be a time of peace without fear or despair.
      (3) OT practitioners can provide ongoing support to the individual and family to maintain quality of life, promote well-being, and maintain engagement in personally meaningful activities and valued relationships.

> **EXAM HINT:** Understanding the above stages of adjustment to life-threatening illness and dying, recognizing how these may be manifested behaviorally, and knowing the most effective OT intervention for each stage of adjustment can help you determine the correct answer for NBCOT® exam items about working with persons with these conditions and their families.

3. General considerations for working with persons with life-threatening illnesses and terminal conditions.
   a. Not all people go through these stages of adjustment during this major life transition.
   b. People who do go through these stages of adjustment can vary in their progression through each stage or they may stop at a stage (e.g., some may stay in denial as their preferred coping strategy).
   c. The needs of loved ones must be considered as they are likely going through stages similar to the dying individual.
   d. OT practitioners should assist the individual in coping with each stage without pushing for progression into the next stage.
4. OT intervention for persons who have life-threatening and terminal illnesses.
   a. Actively listen and respond to questions and expressed concerns in an honest and supportive manner that is respectful of the person's level of adjustment.

   b. Empower the individual to maintain as much control and independence as possible by self-directing their care and self-determining what they want to do each day.
   c. Adapt activities and modify the environment to help the individual pursue their interests, participate in meaningful occupations, and maintain their valued roles.
   d. Teach the individual effective self-management strategies to develop coping skills.
   e. Facilitate positive life review (i.e., that one's life had meaning and purpose) and support legacy transmission (i.e., conveying one's personal values and sense of self to others). This can be accomplished via the following approaches.
      (1) Engagement in structured life review/legacy interviews and facilitated life review/legacy discussions.
      (2) Completion of life review/legacy activities (e.g., creating photo albums, composing written, audio, and/or video life narratives).
      (3) Making and/or selecting gifts and mementos to give to significant others.
   f. Incorporate family and friends in the intervention process.
   g. While being realistic, the OT practitioner should not deprive the individual of hope.
   h. Refer to Chapter 4 for additional information about palliative and hospice care.

References

Allen, C., Austin, S., David, S., Earhart, C., McCraith, C., Riska-Williams, L. (2007). Manual for the Allen Cognitive Level Screen-5 (ACLS-5) and Large Allen Cognitive Level Screen-5 (LACLS-5). ACLS and LACLS Committee.

Allen, C. K., Earhart, C. A., & Blue, T. (1992). Occupational therapy treatment goals for the physically and cognitively disabled. American Occupational Therapy Association.

American Occupational Therapy Association. (2020). Occupational therapy practice framework: Domain and process (4th ed.). American Journal of Occupational Therapy, 74(Suppl. 2), 7412410010. https://doi.org/10.5014/ajot.2020.74S2001.

American Psychiatric Association. (2013). DSM-5: Diagnostic and statistical manual of mental disorders (5th ed.).

Asher, I. (2014). Occupational therapy assessment tools: An annotated index (4th ed.). AOTA Press.

Aslaksen, A., Scott, P., Haglund, L., Ellingham, B., & Bonsaksen, T. (2014). Using the Role Checklist Version 2: Quality of performance. [Occupational therapy process in a psychiatric hospital]. Ergoterapeuten, 4, 38–45.

Barbic, S., & Krupa, T. (2019). Recovery model. In B. Schell & G. Gillen (Eds.), Willard & Spackman's occupational therapy (13th ed., pp. 662–674). Wolters-Kluwer.

Bazyk, S. (2019). Occupational therapy's role in school mental health. In C. Brown, V. Stoffel, & J. Munoz (Eds.), Occupational therapy in mental health: A vision for participation (2nd ed., pp. 809–837). F.A. Davis.

Bonder, B. (2022). Psychopathology and function (6th ed.). Slack.

Boyt Schell, B. A., & Gillen, G. (Eds.). (2018). Willard and Spackman's occupational therapy (13th ed.). Lippincott Williams & Wilkins.

Brown, C. (2019). Cognition. In C. Brown, V. Stoffel, & J. Munoz (Eds.), Occupational therapy in mental health: A vision for participation (2nd ed., pp. 281–300). F.A. Davis.

Brown, C., Steffen-Sanchez, P., & Nicholson, R. (2019). Sensory processing. In C. Brown, V. Stoffel, & J. Munoz (Eds.), Occupational therapy in mental health: A vision for participation (2nd ed., pp. 323–341). F.A. Davis.

Bruce, M., & Borg, B. (2022). Psychosocial frames of reference: Core for occupation-based practice (6th ed.). Slack.

Cahill, S. (2022, January). Research brief: Occupational therapy and palliative care. OT Practice, 31–32.

Cara, E., & MacRae, A. (Eds.). (2019). Psychosocial occupational therapy: An evolving practice (4th ed.). Slack.

Centers for Disease Control and Prevention (CDC). (2022a, October 11). Fast facts: Preventing intimate partner violence. https://www.cdc.gov/violenceprevention/intimate partnerviolence/fastfact.html.

Centers for Disease Control and Prevention (CDC). (2022b, October 11). Prevention strategies. https://www.cdc.gov/suicide/prevention/index.html.

Centers for Disease Control and Prevention (CDC). (2022c, November 2). Risk and protective factors. https://www.cdc .gov/suicide/factors/index.html.

Centers for Disease Control and Prevention (CDC). (2023, May 8). Facts about suicide. https://www.cdc.gov/suicide/facts/index.html.

Centers for Disease Control and Prevention (CDC). (2023, May 9). Disparities in suicide. https://www.cdc.gov/suicide/facts/disparities-in-suicide.html.

Cole, M. B. (2017). Group dynamics in occupational therapy: The theoretical basis and practice application of group dynamics (5th ed.). Slack.

Cole, M., & Tufano, R. (2019). Applied theories in occupational therapy: A practical approach (2nd ed.). Slack.

Crabtree, L. (2017). Mental health practices with children and youth. In A. Wagenfeld, J. Kaldenberg, & D. Honaker (Eds.), Foundations of pediatric practice for the occupational therapy assistant (2nd ed., pp. 359–384). Slack.

Dean, E., Little, L., Wallisch, A., & Dunn, W. (2019). Sensory processing in everyday life. In B. Schell & G. Gillen (Eds.), Willard and Spackman's occupational therapy (13th ed., pp. 942–964). Lippincott Williams & Wilkins.

Drench, M., Noonan, A., Sharby, N., & Ventura, S. (2012). Psychosocial aspects of health care (3rd ed.). Pearson.

Early, M. (2017). Mental health concepts and techniques for the occupational therapy assistant (5th ed.). Lippincott Williams and Wilkins.

Fidler, G. S. (1996). Life-style performance: From profile to conceptual model. In R. P. Cottrell (Ed.), Perspectives on purposeful activity: Foundation and future of occupational therapy (pp. 113–121). American Occupational Therapy Association.

Fleming-Castaldy, R. (2014). Activities, occupations, and empowerment. In J. Hinojosa & M. L. Blount (Eds.), The texture of life: Purposeful activities in the context of occupation (4th ed., pp. 393–415). AOTA Press.

Fleming-Castaldy, R. (2020). Community mental health programs. In M. Scaffa & A. Reitz (Eds.), Occupational therapy in community-based practice settings (2nd ed., pp. 351–379). F.A. Davis.

Getty, S.M. (2015). Implementing a mental health program using the recovery model. OT Practice, 20(3), CE-1–CE-8.

Helfrich, C. A. (2000). Domestic violence: Implications and guidelines for occupational therapy practitioners. In R. P. Cottrell (Ed.), Proactive approaches in psychosocial occupational therapy (pp. 309–316). Slack.

Hemphill, B. J. (Ed.). (1988). Mental health assessment in occupational therapy. Slack.

Hemphill-Pearson, B. J. (Ed.). (2021). Assessments in occupational therapy mental health: An integrative approach (4th ed.). Slack.

Jacobs, K., & MacRae, N. (2017). Occupational therapy essentials for clinical competence (3rd ed.). Slack.

Kaplan, J. I., & Sadock, B. J. (2021). Synopsis of psychiatry (12th ed.). Lippincott Williams & Wilkins.

Kielhofner, G. (2009). Conceptual foundations of occupational therapy (4th ed.). F.A. Davis.

Kirby, A. V., Henderson, J., Schwartz, A., Kramer, J., Whitaker, B. N., & Terrill, A. L. (2020). Youth suicide prevention and occupational therapy: What can we do? SIS Quarterly Practice Connections, 5(3), 6–8.

Kurian, S., Kramer, J., O'Rourke, B., Rocco, C., & Newman, R. (2022, January). Making meaning while living with life threatening illness. OT Practice, 15–18.

Linehan, M. (2015). DBT skills training manual (2nd ed.). Guilford.

Mosey, A. C. (1996). Psychosocial components of occupational therapy (pp. 662–674). Raven Press.

National Alliance to End Homelessness. (2019). Domestic violence and homelessness. https://endhomelessness .org/homelessness-in-america/what-causes-homelessness/domestic-violence/.

National Board for Certification in Occupational Therapy (NBCOT®). (2022). 2022 occupational therapist registered (OTR®) examination content outline. https://www.nbcot .org/-/media/PDFs/2022_OTR_Content_Outline.pdf.

National Institute of Mental Health (NIMH). (2018). Suicide. https://www.nimh.nih.gov/health/statistics/suicide.

O'Brien, J. (2017). Introduction to occupational therapy (5th ed.). Elsevier Mosby.

Pratt, C. W., Gill, K. J., Barrett, N. M., & Roberts, M. M. (2016). Psychiatric rehabilitation (3rd ed.). Elsevier/Academic Press.

Reid, H., & Stoffel, V. (2019). Recovery. In C. Brown, V. Stoffel, & J. Munoz (Eds.), Occupational therapy in mental health: A vision for participation (2nd ed., pp. 3–13). F.A. Davis.

Schkade, J. K., & Schultz, S. (1992). Occupational adaptation: Toward a holistic approach for contemporary practice, part 1. American Journal of Occupational Therapy, 46, 829–837.

Schkade, J. K., & Schultz, S. (1992). Occupational adaptation: Toward a holistic approach for contemporary practice, part 2. American Journal of Occupational Therapy, 46, 917–925.

Scott, P. (2019). Role Checklist Version 3: Participation and Satisfaction. The Model of Human Occupation Clearinghouse.

Scott, P.J., McKinney, K.G., Perron, J.M., Ruff, E.G., & Smiley J.L. (2019). The Revised Role Checklist: Improved utility, feasibility, and reliability. OTJR: Occupation, Participation and Health, 39(1), 56–63.

Substance Abuse and Mental Health Services Administration. (2012). SAMHSA's working definition of recovery: 10 guiding principles of recovery. https://store.samhsa.gov/sites/default/files/d7/priv/pep12-recdef.pdf.

Review Questions

Following are eight questions about key content covered in this chapter. These questions are not inclusive of the entirety of content related to psychosocial occupational therapy (OT) approaches that you must know for success on the NBCOT® exam. These questions are provided to help you "jump start" the thought processes you will need to apply your studying of content to the answering of exam questions; hence, they are not in the NBCOT® exam format. Exam items in the NBCOT® format that cover the depth and breadth of content you will need to know to pass the NBCOT® exam are provided in the three online practice exams that accompany this text. The answers to the following questions are provided in Appendix 2.

1. What are key general postulates for change that are used in cognitive behavioral therapy (CBT) to guide the intervention process? How can these be applied throughout the OT process?

2. Identify three evaluation tools that can be used to assess an individual's cognitive level according to the Cognitive Disabilities model. Describe a practice situation in which each evaluation would be most effectively used.

3. Identify current intervention approaches that use sensory models to guide treatment and describe how they can be effectively applied in OT practice.

4. Describe three interventions that can effectively help individuals experiencing hallucinations and/or delusions manage their symptoms during an OT group.

5. A school-based occupational therapist receives numerous complaints from teachers and other school personnel about students "acting out" during class, lunch, recess, and transitions. Several report that sending students to the principal's office for disciplinary actions has not decreased these behaviors and they are concerned about the impact of these actions on the students. In response to these expressed concerns the therapist develops an education and training program based on the ABC model to help teachers and other school personnel understand and address students' disruptive behaviors in a more effective manner. Describe the main concepts and principles of this model. Provide an example as to how they can be effectively used by teachers and other school personnel to decrease the frequency of maladaptive behaviors that result in negative outcomes and increase the frequency of students' adaptive behaviors that result in positive outcomes.

(Continued)

Review Questions

6. The RADAR approach is used to screen for and respond to domestic abuse. How would an occupational therapist apply this approach?

▷

7. Your roommate with whom you share an eighth-floor apartment has been very sad and withdrawn for several weeks. This week, they cancelled their weekly therapy appointment and stopped attending classes and social activities that they previously had enjoyed. You ask them if everything is alright, and the reply is "no, not really." "I'm thinking of killing myself, I just can't take it anymore." "How do you think you would do it?" you ask. "I'm not quite sure, I think I have a couple of options here, belts, knives, I'm not sure which way I want to go, but I have to do it soon, maybe by the end of the week. Yes, definitely by the end of the week. All things considered, I think I'll jump out the window. I'm pretty sure the fall would kill me." What risk factors for suicide are you observing in your roommate, what levels of suicide lethality are present, and what should be your first intervention?

▷

8. You are conducting a group for individuals with recently acquired spinal cord injuries that resulted in paraplegia and the need to use a wheelchair for mobility. Adjusting to this abrupt change in their lives has been difficult for most group members. While participating in a group, one of the members says to you "you really have no idea what it's like to have to face using a wheelchair for the rest of your life, when just a month ago I ran my sixth marathon. Running has been my whole life. It was the way I relieved stress and stayed in shape. I guess that's all over now." What type of therapeutic approach should you take? What types of individual and group interventions might benefit this individual?

▷

Review>Practice>Motivate>Analyze>Apply

Occupational Engagement and Performance: Evaluation and Intervention

RITA P. FLEMING-CASTALDY and STEPHANIE J. BEISBIER

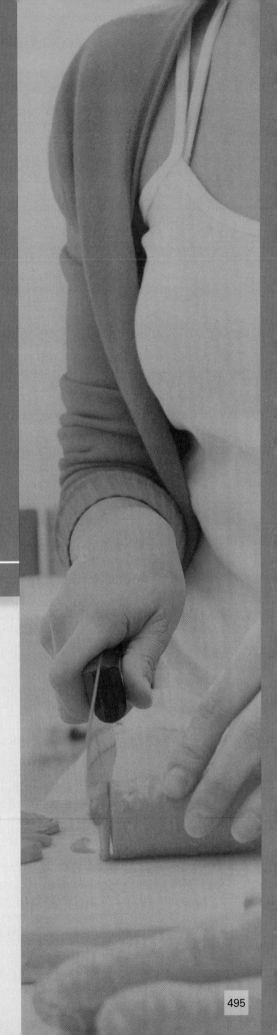

Occupations

Occupations Defined

1. "The everyday activities that people do as individuals, in families, and with communities to occupy time and bring meaning and purpose to life" (AOTA, 2020. p. 7). They include the following.
   a. Activities of daily living (ADL) are activities that people routinely perform (e.g., self-care).
      (1) They also termed "basic" activities of daily living (BADL) and "personal" activities of daily living (PADL).
      (2) ADL include functional mobility, sexual activity, and self-care tasks such as grooming and personal hygiene, bathing and showering, toileting and toilet hygiene, dressing, eating and swallowing, and feeding.
   b. Instrumental activities of daily living (IADL) support home and community living and are more complex than ADL.
      (1) IADL include home establishment and management, safety and emergency maintenance, meal preparation and clean-up, shopping, financial management, care of others, care of pets and animals, child rearing, communication management, religious and spiritual expression, driving, and community mobility.
   c. Work involves engaging in competitive employment for pay and other productive activities that make a societal contribution.
      (1) Work includes identifying and selecting employment interests and pursuits, seeking and acquiring employment, performing and maintaining a job, preparing for and adjusting to retirement, and exploring and participating in unpaid volunteer work.
   d. Education involves engaging in activities that are needed to participate in a learning environment and fulfill the role of student.
      (1) Education includes participation in formal academic education and non-academic extracurricular activities, exploration of informal personal educational needs or interests, and participation in informal education (e.g., a pottery class at a community center).
   e. Health management involves engaging in activities that support the development, management, and maintenance of health and wellness routines.
      (1) Health management includes communication with the health care system, social and emotional health promotion and maintenance, physical activity, and management of symptom(s), condition(s), medication(s), nutrition, and personal care device(s).
   f. Leisure involves engaging in intrinsically motivated discretionary activities done for personal pleasure, relaxation, diversion, entertainment, and/or self-fulfillment.
      (1) Leisure includes exploring personal interests, skills, and opportunities for leisure and planning and participating in leisure activities.
   g. Play involves engaging in intrinsically motivated, internally controlled, and freely chosen activities for fun.
      (1) Play includes exploring and participating in pretend, fantasy, symbolic, exploratory, practice, and constructive play activities and games with rules and obtaining, using, and maintaining play supplies, equipment, and toys.
   h. Social participation involves engaging in activities that foster and/or require social interactions with others and support social interdependence.
      (1) Social participation includes community, family, and peer group participation, friendships, and intimate partner relationships.
   i. Rest and sleep involves engaging in restorative activities that support health and occupational engagement.
      (1) Rest and sleep include identifying the need for rest, preparing for sleep, and participating in sleep (AOTA, 2020).

Overall Guidelines for the Evaluation of Occupations

EXAM HINT: In the NBCOT® OTR® exam content outline, Domain 1 Evaluation and Assessment comprises 23% of the exam. Domain 1 exam items focus on the therapist's ability to "acquire information regarding factors that influence occupational performance on an ongoing basis throughout the occupational therapy process" (NBCOT®, 2022, p. 3). The application of knowledge about the following guidelines can help you effectively determine the correct answer for NBCOT® exam items about the evaluation of occupational performance.

1. The focus of occupational therapy (OT) evaluation is the individual's ability to perform meaningful occupations that are needed and desired by the person.
2. Assessments should follow a "top-down" progression of considering the person's areas of occupation first, rather than a "bottom-up" approach, which focuses on performance skills.
   a. The evaluation process is "focused on finding out what the client wants and needs to do; determining what the client can do and has done; and identifying supports and barriers to health, well-being, and participation" (AOTA, 2020, p. 21).
   b. The desired outcome of evaluation is the identification of the person's occupational performance abilities, concerns, and difficulties and the establishment of the individual's priorities for performance in areas of occupation.
   c. In the AOTA Practice Framework, 4th edition (OTPF-4), this determination is called the occupational profile. Refer to Chapter 3 and Table 3-1.
3. After the completion of a person's occupational profile, their client factors, performance skills, patterns, and contexts, and activity demands are assessed to identify specific strengths and limitations that impact desired and needed occupational performance.
   a. All of the factors that may influence performance in areas of occupation are considered during screening.
      (1) Based on the results of screening, aspects that are determined to warrant further evaluation are specifically assessed.
   b. In certain practice settings (e.g., acute care with a three-day length of stay) and in certain clinical situations (e.g., there are major concerns for a client's safety) this determination of underlying problems may take precedence over the determination of an occupational profile (Gutman, Mortera, Hinojosa, & Kramer, 2007).
   c. To determine these capabilities, the evaluation process should include observation of the person's actual performance of an activity in context.
      (1) If it is pragmatically not possible during the evaluation process for the person to perform the activity in its natural context, an environment that closely simulates the natural one should be provided for the assessment (e.g., an ADL apartment on a rehabilitation unit to simulate the person's home).
   d. In the OTPF-4, this part of the evaluation process is called an analysis of occupational performance. Refer to Chapter 3 and Table 3-1.
4. Occupational performance assessment tools include interviews, checklists, task performance, rating scales, and standardized instruments.

   a. Subsequent sections in this Chapter outline the major assessment methods and published instruments used for the evaluation of performance in areas of occupation.

   > **EXAM HINT:** While reliability and validity studies have been conducted on a number of occupational performance assessments, there is great variability in the quality and availability of these studies; therefore, the NBCOT® exam is unlikely to test this information. Consequently, this information is not included in this Chapter. Readers seeking this information should consult specific assessment manuals.

   b. Assessment tools that primarily use an interview format to comprehensively evaluate an individual's occupational functioning (e.g., Model of Human Occupation Screening Tool [MOHOST]) and measures that evaluate performance in social participation (e.g., the Occupational Circumstances Assessment Interview Rating Scale [OCAIRS]) and the interaction/communication skills needed for socialization (e.g., the Bay Area Functional Performance Evaluation [BAFPE]) are described in Chapter 14.

   > **CAUTION:** Interpretation of occupational performance assessments that are used to determine a person's ability to live independently must be made cautiously due to the self-report and/or simulated nature of certain items and the limited number of items tested in many evaluation tools.

   c. Assessments that evaluate functional communication, functional mobility, and community mobility are provided in Chapter 16.
5. Many assessments used to measure occupational performance provide a determination of the person's level of functional performance along a level of assistance continuum that range from independent to dependent or dependent to independent.
   a. In 2019, the Centers for Medicare and Medicaid Services (CMS) removed the Functional Independence Measure (FIM) from the Inpatient Rehabilitation Facility Patient Assessment Instrument (IRF-PAI).
      (1) CMS now uses Section GG to measure a person's need for assistance with self-care and mobility and document the person's level of function according to a six-level independence scale (6 = most independent, 1 = most dependent) and a coding scale for activities not attempted. Refer to Table 15-1.

Table 15-1

The 6-Point Scale and Activity Not Attempted Codes

Coding: If helper assistance is required because patient's/resident's performance is unsafe or of poor quality, score according to amount of assistance provided. Activities may be completed with or without assistive devices.

6-Independent – Patient/resident safely completes the activity by him/herself with no assistance from a helper.

5-Setup or clean-up assistance – Helper sets up or cleans up; patient/resident completes activity. Helper assists only prior to or following the activity.

4-Supervision or touching assistance – Helper provides verbal cues and/or touching/steadying and/or contact guard assistance as patient/resident completes activity. Assistance may be provided throughout the activity or intermittently.

3-Partial/moderate assistance – Helper does LESS THAN HALF the effort. Helper lifts, holds, or supports trunk or limbs, but provides less than half the effort.

2-Substantial/maximal assistance – Helper does MORE THAN HALF the effort. Helper lifts or holds trunk or limbs and provides more than half the effort.

1-Dependent – Helper does ALL of the effort. Patient/resident does none of the effort to complete the activity. Or, the assistance of 2 or more helpers is required for the patient/resident to complete the activity.

If activity was not attempted, code reason:
07: Patient/resident refused.
09: Not applicable; not attempted and the patient/resident did not perform this activity prior to the current illness, exacerbation, or injury.
10: Not attempted due to environmental limitations (e.g., lack of equipment, weather constraints).
88: Not attempted due to medical condition or safety concerns.

Reference: Coding Section GG Self-Care & Mobility Activities Included on the Post-Acute Care Item Sets: Key Questions to Consider When Coding (cms.gov).

(2) Some payers may continue to use the FIM, but a phase out is likely.
    (a) CMS classifications often become the practice norm across practice settings as other payers adopt the language and measures used by CMS.

EXAM HINT: Although the FIM and its descriptive language (minimal, moderate, maximal) are no longer used by the CMS, these changes are rather recent (i.e., 2019). Therefore, the FIM scales may continue to be used in some settings with non-CMS payer sources. However, the NBCOT® exam will likely reflect current CMS documentation standards and require knowledge of the language and levels that are outlined in Table 15-1.

Evaluation Methods and the NBCOT® Exam

1. While some institutions and practitioners may develop their own occupational performance assessments to use in practice, the NBCOT® exam is a national exam, so it will only ask questions about published evaluation tools.
2. As of the publication of this text, NBCOT® has not made public the names of all specific assessments that may be on the NBCOT® exam.
    a. The assessments in this Chapter are based on a review of NBCOT® self-assessment tools, major OT textbooks, and feedback obtained from OT practitioners.

EXAM HINT: The NBCOT® OTR® exam content outline identifies knowledge of the "administration, purpose, indications, advantages, and limitations of standardized and nonstandardized screening and assessment tools (NBCOT®, 2022, p. 4) as essential for competent and safe practice. As a result, the exam will likely include a description of evaluation methods and/or the names of specific published assessment tools. Therefore, a review of the major occupational performance assessments is important for exam preparation. This review can also increase understanding and knowledge of major principles and common approaches in the evaluation of occupational performance assets and deficits. This can further strengthen the clinical reasoning skills needed to answer NBCOT® Domain 1 exam items that address the evaluation process.

General Occupation-based Intervention Guidelines

EXAM HINT: In the NBCOT® OTR® exam content outline, Domain 2 Analysis, Interpretation, and Planning comprises 23% of the exam and Domain 3 Select and Manage Interventions comprises 38% of the exam. Domain 2 exam items focus on the therapist's ability to "formulate conclusions regarding client needs and priorities to develop and monitor an intervention plan throughout the occupational therapy process" (NBCOT®, 2022, p. 5) and Domain 3 exam items focus on the therapist's ability to "select and implement interventions to promote healing and enhance engagement in occupation-based activities" (NBCOT®, 2022, p. 7). The application of knowledge about the following intervention guidelines can help you effectively determine the correct answers to Domain 2 and Domain 3 exam items.

1. Intervention should follow a "top-down" progression of considering the person's areas of occupation first rather than a "bottom-up" approach that focuses initially and/or solely on performance skills and client factors.
   a. The impact of performance skill deficits and client factors on occupational performance is considered after establishing the individual's desired occupational outcome(s).
   b. Specific interventions to remediate, alleviate, and/or compensate for the effects of performance skill deficits and client factors on occupational performance are often required.
   c. The focus of remediation interventions for performance skill deficits and client factors must be related to the individual's ability to perform meaningful occupations that are needed and desired by the person.

2. The entire therapy process should focus on client-centered care with an emphasis on respect for and partnership with each person.
3. Interventions for deficits or limitations that cannot be remediated should include recommendations for adaptive strategies and/or adaptive equipment that can compensate for these by enabling performance.
   a. Strategies that can be generalized to different situations are particularly helpful (e.g., the principles of energy conservation).
   b. Multiple factors should be considered when recommending adaptive strategies and/or equipment and engaging the client in the adaptation process. Refer to Table 15-2.

Table 15-2

Factors to Consider When Recommending Adaptations and Engaging the Person in the Adaptation Process

Prior to recommending adaptive strategies and/or equipment for engagement in occupations, activities, and/or tasks, the following should be determined.
The activity demands of the occupation, activity, or task including the following.
- Relevance and importance of the occupation, activity, or task to the individual.
- Objects to be used during occupation, activity, or task performance and their properties.
- Physical environment requirements of the occupation, activity, or task (i.e., space demands).
- Temporal requirements of the occupation, activity, or task (i.e., sequencing and timing demands).
- Required body functions and structures that are required to perform the occupation, activity, or task.
- Required actions and performance skills that are inherent to the occupation, activity, or task.

The person's performance skills, client factors, and/or contexts that prevent independent occupation, activity, or task performance.
The compatibility of the adaptive strategy and/or equipment with the person's personal and environmental contexts.
The capability for the adaptive strategy and/or equipment to enhance the individual's sense of personal control.

The impact of the use of the adaptive strategy and/or equipment on:
- the amount of effort needed to perform the occupation, activity, or task; adaptations should minimize effort.
- social opportunities or self-image; adaptations should not interfere with desired socialization or diminish the presentation or view of self.
- the temporal demands of a person's life; adaptations should be realistic given the time demand of a person's roles and contexts.
- the person's safety; adaptations must be safe.

When engaging the person in the adaptation process, the following should be employed.
- Principles of compensation and activity analysis, adaptation, and gradation should be creatively applied to effectively address the person's limitations and performance problems.
  - Refer to Chapter 3 for additional information on activity analysis, adaptation, and gradation.
- Adaptive strategies and equipment that are recommended to the person should be tested out on a trial basis to ensure that they help the person attain their desired goals for occupation, activity, and/or task performance.
- Principles of the teaching-learning process should be applied while educating the person and/or care givers about the effective and safe use of adaptive strategies and equipment.
  - Refer to Chapter 3 for additional information on the teaching-learning process.
- Training in adaptive strategies and/or equipment use must consider the person's privacy and dignity.
  - This is especially critical in interventions for the performance of personal care.
- Multiple opportunities to practice the use of adaptive strategies and equipment in the person's environment should be provided.

Evaluation of Activities of Daily Living and Instrumental Activities of Daily Living

EXAM HINT: The NBCOT® OTR® exam content outline identifies knowledge of the "administration, purpose, indications, advantages, and limitations of standardized and nonstandardized screening and assessment tools" (NBCOT®, 2022, p. 4) as essential for competent and safe practice. The application of knowledge about the following standardized assessments can help you correctly answer exam items about the evaluation of a person's ability to perform ADL and IADL.

Assessment of Motor and Process Skills (AMPS)

1. Focus: the analysis of an individual's performance and assessment of the effectiveness, efficiency, or safety of their task performance, including ADL, IADL, and some leisure activities.
   a. Performance analysis is what the therapist observes when the client is performing a task, while focusing on the quality of their performance skills (e.g., aligns, reaches, attends, looks) (Fisher & Griswold, 2019).[1]
2. Standardized versus non-standardized AMPS.
   a. The AMPS was a standardized assessment that included standardized tasks, a five-day certification course, and rater calibration.
   b. At the time of this text's publication, the AMPS training course and online materials were placed on an indefinite hold; thus, there is no further training of the standardized AMPS. Fisher and Griswold published a non-standardized administration method for the AMPS in 2019.
3. Method (non-standardized).
   a. Observe the client performing a chosen and prioritized daily task, that they deemed challenging, in their usual manner.
      (1) This task should be decided upon after the client interview and determined in a collaborative manner.

(2) If the AMPS is not being administered in the client's home, their home environment should be simulated, as best as possible. for the chosen task.
   b. The evaluator takes notes of observed occupational performance errors during the task.
4. Materials.
   a. The client should use their own materials, if available.
   b. If the client's personal materials are not available, the therapist can provide the materials needed to complete the task.
5. Scoring and interpretation.
   a. The client's level of performance skills (i.e., motor, process, social interaction skills) are rated based on observations of their task performance.
      (1) Each performance skill is rated on ease (i.e., physical effort and clumsiness), efficiency (i.e., time and space organization), and safety (i.e., risk of harm to self or objects), independence, and appropriateness for social interaction.
         (a) A non-standardized qualitative scale of no problem, mild problem, moderate problem, and severe problem is used for each performance skill.
   b. Interpretation and use of ratings.
      (1) From a list of all ineffective performance skills that were observed, the therapist selects up to 10 motor, process, and/or social skills that best capture the client's decreased ability to perform the task. The therapist uses the same process to identify the client's performance skill strengths that enable task performance.
      (2) The therapist summarizes and documents the quality of the client's occupational performance.
         (a) This information is used to collaborate with the client to determine occupation-based goals to address their decreased occupational performance.
6. Population: the non-standardized AMPS can be used with any population aged two years or older.
   a. It is not suitable for individuals who are unwilling to participate in a daily life task.

---

[1] Task analysis is different than activity analysis. Task analysis focuses on identifying the reasons the observed behaviors occurred (e.g., due to client factors, performance skill limitations, task demands, cultural influences). Activity analysis focuses on identifying the components of an activity that can be addressed via interventions. Refer to Chapter 3 for more information about activity analysis.

Barthel Index

1. Focus: measurement of a person's independence in ADL and functional mobility before and after intervention and the level of personal care assistance needed by the individual.

2. It includes 10 items.
   a. Feeding.
   b. Transferring.
   c. Personal grooming.
   d. Toileting.
   e. Control of bowel.
   f. Control of bladder.
   g. Bathing.
   h. Dressing.
   i. Walking on level ground.
   j. Negotiating/climbing stairs.
3. Method: direct observation of task performance, interview of individual and/or caregivers, and/or review of medical records.
4. Materials: score sheet, pencil, and everyday materials for task performance.
5. Scoring and interpretation.
   a. Items are scored according to a weighted system that reflects assisted performance (e.g., the individual receives minimal assistance during toilet transfer).
   b. The maximum score is 100 and reflects an individual's ability to do all 10 tasks independently.

> CAUTION: Because the Barthel's 10 tasks are limited to basic self-care, a high score on a Barthel does not equate with the ability to live independently and may be less sensitive at higher levels of functioning.

   c. Scores on the Barthel can be used to determine the need for personal assistance (e.g., a home health aide [HHA], a personal care assistant [PCA]) to perform basic ADL.
6. Population: adults and older adults with physical disabilities and/or chronic illnesses; typically used in medical model settings.

Canadian Occupational Performance Measure 5th edition (COPM)

1. Focus: identifies the individual's perception of satisfaction with performance and changes over time in the areas of self-care, productivity, and leisure.
2. Method.
   a. A semistructured interview identifies the individual's perception of their occupational performance in the following.
      (1) Self-care (i.e., personal care, functional mobility, community management).
      (2) Productivity (i.e., paid/unpaid work, household management, play/school).
      (3) Leisure (i.e., quiet recreation, active recreation, socialization).
   b. Caregivers of children and/or adults who are unable to participate in an interview may answer the COPM questions for their care recipient.
   c. Occupational performance problem areas are identified.
   d. The identified problems are rated for importance (1–10).
   e. The five most important self-identified problems are rated by the individual as to performance and satisfaction.
   f. Reassessment takes place at appropriate intervals.
3. Materials: the COPM manual and rating scale.
4. Scoring and interpretation.
   a. Items are rated on a scale of 1–10, with 10 being the highest.
   b. Total scores for performance and satisfaction are used to identify intervention foci, treatment outcomes, and individual satisfaction.
5. Population: individuals over the age of seven or the parents/caregivers of small children.

Cognitive Performance Test (CPT)

1. Focus: the assessment of six functional ADL and IADL tasks that require cognitive processing skills based on Allen's Cognitive Disabilities Model.
   a. Dressing.
   b. Shopping.
   c. Making toast.
   d. Making a phone call.
   e. Washing.
   f. Traveling.
2. Method.
   a. Standardized administration procedures are followed for each task.
   b. The evaluator asks the individual to do each task, providing demonstration, reassurance, cueing, more directions, and/or the addition or elimination of sensory cues, if needed, to facilitate task performance.
3. Materials: specific common items are delineated for each task.
4. Scoring and interpretation.
   a. Scoring guidelines according to Allen's levels are provided for each task.
   b. Level 1 represents the lowest functional level and Level 6 represents the highest.
   c. Total test scores range from 6 to 36.
   d. Average task performance score can be determined by dividing the total test score by six.
   e. CPT scores are used along with Allen's Cognitive Disabilities Model to determine a person's

capabilities and needs in other ADL tasks and their ability to live independently. Refer to Chapter 14 for more information about this model.

5. Population: adults and older adults with psychiatric and/or cognitive dysfunction.

Katz Index of ADL

1. Focus: assessment of level of independent functioning and type of assistance required in six areas of ADL.
   a. Bathing.
   b. Dressing.
   c. Toileting.
   d. Transferring.
   e. Continence.
   f. Feeding.
2. Method: the evaluator observes activity performance or interviews the individual about performance.
3. Materials: rating scale, pencil, and common task objects if activity is actually performed.
4. Scoring and interpretation.
   a. The evaluator rates each of the six activities as independent, some assistance required, or dependent.
   b. Specific criteria for each rating are provided for each activity.
   c. The individual ratings for the six activities are converted into a global letter score.
      (1) A = independent in all six activities.
      (2) B = independent in any five activities.
      (3) C = independent in all but bathing and one other activity.
      (4) D = independent in all but bathing, dressing, and one other activity.
      (5) E = independent in all but bathing, dressing, toileting, and one other activity.
      (6) F = independent in all but bathing, dressing, toileting, transfers, and one other activity.
      (7) G = dependent in all activities.
      (8) Other = the individual's functional performance cannot be classified in A–G categories.
   d. Scores can be used to evaluate intervention outcomes and prognosis in a broad, general manner.
5. Population: adults and older adults with chronic illness.

Kitchen Task Assessment (KTA)

1. Focus: measurement of the judgment, planning, and organizational skills used to perform a simple cooking task.
2. Method.
   a. A pre-test of washing hands is used to determine baseline abilities.

b. The evaluator instructs and observes the individual making cooked pudding from a mix.
   c. Large print task instructions are provided for the individual to review if needed.
   d. The evaluator can provide assistance, if needed, to facilitate successful task performance.
3. Materials: large-print task instructions, pudding mix, milk, pan, utensils, dishes, soap, water, and paper towels.
4. Scoring and interpretation.
   a. Scores of 0 = independent, 1 = verbal assistance, 2 = physical assistance, and 3 = totally incapable are rated for six categories of task skills.
      (1) Initiation.
      (2) Organization.
      (3) Performing all steps.
      (4) Proper sequence.
      (5) Judgment and safety.
      (6) Completion of task.
   b. Final scores can range from 0 to 18 with higher scores indicating increased impairment.
   c. Information on performance in each task can be used to develop interventions for the individual and adaptative strategies for their caregivers.
5. Population: originally developed for adults and older adults with neurocognitive disorders[2] but the KTA's use has expanded to other populations that have cognitive dysfunction.

Klein-Bell Activities of Daily Living Scale (K-B Scale)

1. Focus: assessment of independent functioning in ADL as evidenced by achievement of 170 items in six areas.
   a. Dressing.
   b. Elimination.
   c. Mobility.
   d. Bathing/hygiene.
   e. Eating.
   f. Emergency telephone communication.
2. Method.
   a. The evaluator observes and scores the individual's performance of each item and the behavioral components of each task.
   b. The use of assistive devices to perform activities is allowed.
3. Materials: manual, ADL scale, score sheet, pencil, everyday items for task performance.
4. Scoring and interpretation.
   a. All 170 items are rated as "achieved" or "failed."

---

[2] At the time of the KTA's publication, a neurocognitive disorder was called senile dementia of the Alzheimer's type (SDAT).

b. A rating of "achieved" is given if the individual is able to perform the task independently, with or without adaptive equipment.

c. A rating of "failed" is given if the person requires physical or verbal assistance to perform the task.

d. Use of this scale can increase caregivers' understanding of the individual's need for assistance.

e. The detailed behavioral component information is useful for intervention planning and evaluation of intervention outcomes.

   (1) As a result, this measure is often used in research studies.

5. Population: individuals from six months to older adults with any diagnosis (i.e., physical, psychosocial, cognitive, and/or developmental).

Kohlman Evaluation of Living Skills (KELS)

1. Focus: determination of an individual's knowledge and/or performance of 13 basic living skills needed to live independently in five main areas.

a. Self-care.

b. Safety and health.

c. Money management.

d. Community mobility and telephone.

e. Employment and leisure participation.

2. Method.

a. The evaluator provides standard instructions for the individual to complete some tasks (e.g., money management).

b. The evaluator uses standard questions to obtain the individual's self-report regarding performance of other tasks (e.g., leisure pursuits).

c. The evaluator does not provide additional instructions or feedback during the evaluation.

3. Materials: KELS manual which contains standard test forms, safety pictures, an equipment list for additional common materials, and score sheets.

4. Scoring and interpretation.

a. A score of "independent" or "needs assistance" is given according to standard scoring criteria established for each of the 13 items.

b. A "not applicable" score is used if warranted (e.g., a person has no need to do monthly bills).

c. A "see note" section is provided to record information about the person's unique circumstances and/or provide further information about their abilities or need for assistance.

d. There is no total score.

   (1) A checklist summarizes the individual's performance on the KELS.

   (2) The OT practitioner uses clinical reasoning to make recommendations about a person's ability to live independently or with assistance.

e. KELS scores can provide a general overview of a person's functional level and give a baseline for further evaluation and intervention.

5. Population: originally designed for adolescents and adults in acute psychiatric hospitals but its use has expanded to older adults and those with a diversity of diagnoses in a variety of settings.

Milwaukee Evaluation of Daily Living Skills (MEDLS)

1. Focus: the assessment of actual or simulated performance of basic living skills needed to function in the individual's expected environment.

a. Basic communication.

b. Personal care and hygiene (e.g., toileting, brushing teeth).

c. Medication management.

d. Personal health care (e.g., eyeglass care).

e. Time awareness.

f. Eating.

g. Dressing.

h. Safety in the home.

i. Safety in the community.

j. Use of telephone.

k. Transportation.

l. Maintenance of clothing.

m. Use of money.

2. Method.

a. A screening form is used to determine which of the MEDLS subtests are relevant to the individual and their expected environment (e.g., eyeglass care is only relevant to a person who wears eyeglasses; a person who is moving to a group home does not need to do household bills).

b. Items screened as needing evaluation are then administered according to standardized procedures.

c. All items have standard instructions and a time limit for task completion.

d. It is recommended that the evaluator schedule the administration of test items during the person's normal routine as relevant (e.g., assess personal care, hygiene, and dressing in the morning).

3. Materials: MEDLS manual with screening and reporting test procedures, forms, clothing and safety pictures, and an extensive equipment list of common everyday items.

a. It is recommended that the individual's own supplies be used.

4. Scoring and interpretation.

a. All items are scored according to standard criteria established for each subtest.

b. Results from MEDLS can provide comprehensive data on a number of performance-based ADL tasks that are useful for intervention and discharge planning.

5. Population: originally developed for adults (18 or older) who had at least a two-year history of mental illness and who had resided, for at least six months, in a psychiatric hospital, halfway house, group home, or skilled nursing facility (SNF), or who had participated for at least two years in an outpatient day treatment program, but its use has expanded to other populations with ADL deficits.

Performance Assessment of Self-Care Skills (PASS)

1. Focus: the measurement of occupational performance of daily life tasks.
2. The PASS has two versions (i.e., home and clinic) and consists of 26 tasks.
   a. Five functional mobility tasks (i.e., bed mobility, stair use, toilet mobility and management, bathtub and shower mobility, and indoor walking).
   b. Three personal self-care/ADL tasks (i.e., oral hygiene, trimming toenails, dressing).
   c. Fourteen IADL tasks with a cognitive emphasis (i.e., shopping, bill paying, check book balancing, mailing bills, telephone use, medication management, obtaining critical information from auditory and visual media, flashlight repair, home safety, playing bingo, oven use, stove top use, and the use of sharp utensils).
   d. Four instrumental IADL tasks with a physical emphasis (i.e., taking out the garbage, changing bed linens, sweeping, and clean up after meal preparation).
3. Method.
   a. The evaluator observes and scores the individual's task performance.
   b. The assessment may be given in total or selected items may be used alone or in combination.
   c. Each of the 26 tasks is broken down into subtasks.
      (1) If a task cannot be performed independently, the evaluator provides the minimal type and amount of assistance that is needed for the individual to be able to complete a subtask.
4. Materials: the manual includes administration and scoring guidelines, a materials list (most items are common everyday items or printable), administration and scoring videos, and documentation forms.
5. Scoring and interpretation.
   a. The scoring system is identical for each task and yields three types of scores: independence, safety, and task adequacy (i.e., process and quality) for each subtask.
      (1) The type and amount of assistance (e.g., number of prompts) are recorded by the evaluator.
      (2) The independence scores (0 - 3) for each subtask are derived from the frequency and level of assistance on a 9-point hierarchy scale of independence.
         (a) The independence scores for all subtasks are then averaged to obtain an independence mean score/summary score ranging between 0–3.
      (3) A single safety score (0–3) is obtained for the entire task based on the observed level of safe practices; each subtask does not receive a safety score.
      (4) The task adequacy scores (0–3) is also a single summary score that reflects the combined quality and process data.
6. Population: adult populations with various conditions and the healthy older adult population.

Routine Task Inventory (RTI)

1. Focus: measurement of an individual's level of impairment in ADL according to Allen's model of cognitive disabilities.
   a. Six physical scales in the areas of grooming, dressing, bathing, walking, feeding, and toileting.
   b. Eight instrumental scales in the areas of housekeeping, preparing food, spending money, taking medication, doing laundry, shopping, telephoning, and traveling.
2. Method: three different methods can be used.
   a. Observation of the individual's performance and completion of the rating scale for each item by the evaluator.
   b. Self-report by the individual if cognitively able to complete RTI questionnaire.
   c. Report of a caregiver familiar with the individual's functional performance through completion of the RTI questionnaire.
3. Materials: RTI questionnaire and a pencil.
4. Scoring and interpretation.
   a. Each item is rated according to behavioral criteria based upon Allen's cognitive levels of one through six.
   b. The comparisons between scores obtained when more than one evaluation method is used can be helpful in determining similarities and/or discrepancies between the individual's self-awareness of abilities, the caregiver's view of performance, and/or the evaluator's observance of performance.
   c. Interpretation of evaluation results can be used to design intervention based on Allen's Cognitive Disabilities Model. Refer to Chapter 14 for more information about this model.
5. Population: adults and older adults with cognitive impairments.

Test of Grocery Shopping Skills (TOGSS)

1. Focus: determination of a person's ability to shop for groceries in a grocery store using a grocery list.
   a. Because there are two grocery lists provided in the TOGSS, it can be used as an intervention pre-test/post-test to measure a person's skill acquisition.
   b. A companion tool called the Knowledge of Grocery Shopping Skills (KOGSS) can be used to assess a person's knowledge of grocery shopping.
2. Method.
   a. The evaluation is completed in the person's natural environment at a community grocery store.
   b. The individual is provided with a grocery list of 10 items of specific sizes and asked to locate and select the items at the lowest price.
   c. The OT practitioner observes the person during the performance of this task in the grocery store.
   d. The KOGSS is completed as a self-report.
3. Materials: grocery lists, self-assessment, and score forms.
4. Scoring and interpretation.
   a. A score is obtained based on the person's ability to efficiently and accurately find the correct items at the lowest price. There are three subscale scores.
      (1) Accuracy: the person's ability to find the correct item at the required size and lowest price.
      (2) Time: how long it took the person to find the items.
      (3) Redundancy: the number of aisles the person entered to look for items and how many times a person returned to the same aisle.
      (4) The OT practitioner also uses observation to assess the strategies the person uses to shop (e.g., scanning overhead signs, asking for help, scanning shelves, checking prices).
      (5) The KOGSS is scored to indicate a person's knowledge about grocery shopping; higher scores indicate greater knowledge.
5. Population: originally developed for persons with serious mental illness.
   a. Because the TOGSS assesses a person's executive functioning in the community, it can be used with persons who have cognitive impairments due to other diagnoses (e.g., traumatic brain injury, intellectual disability, neurocognitive disorders) which interfere with community living skills.

Developmental Evaluations Inclusive of ADL/IADL

1. Several developmental assessments include the performance of ADL/IADL in their administration method. Refer to Chapter 5 for information about the following assessments.

   a. Goal-Oriented Assessment of Lifeskills (GOAL).
   b. Pediatric Evaluation of Disability Inventory (PEDI).
   c. Pediatric Evaluation of Disability Inventory- Computer Adaptive Test (PEDI-CAT).

Evaluation of Sexual Expression and Activities

1. Sexual expression and sexuality are broad concepts that include sexual activity, gender roles and identity, sexual orientation, eroticism, and intimacy.
2. Sexual activity is defined in the OTPF-4 as "engaging in the broad possibilities for sexual expression and experiences with self or others (e.g., hugging, kissing, foreplay, masturbation, oral sex, intercourse)" (AOTA, 2020, p. 30).
3. Intimate partner relationships are defined in the OTPF-4 as "engaging in activities to initiate and maintain a close relationship, including giving and receiving affection and interacting in desired roles; intimate partners may or may not engage in sexual activity" (AOTA, 2020, p. 34).
4. The ADL of sexual activity is typically not included on commonly used ADL assessments.
5. Despite this gap, OT practitioners should assess this ADL during routine screenings and interviews, as appropriate.
6. Prior to screening or evaluation, the OT practitioner should actively reflect on their personal, familial, social, cultural, and/or religious values and beliefs about sexuality and their personal lived experiences.
      (1) Recognizing that perspectives on sexual expression and activities vary greatly and respecting these differences is an ethical responsibility for all OT practitioners.
         (a) Not doing so is a violation of the AOTA's Code of Ethics. Refer to Chapter 4 to review this code and Table 4-1 to review how the ethical principles of beneficence, nonmaleficence, autonomy, justice, and fidelity are applied in practice.
      (2) If upon self-reflection, an OT practitioner determines that their personal views are not compatible with a client's, the OT practitioner should actively use supervision and professional development activities to acquire the skills they need to effectively work with diverse clients.
         (a) Because this process will take time, the OT practitioner should honestly inform the client about their personal discomfort, acknowledge that this reality does not diminish the need for or relevance of an assessment of the person's sexual expression and activities, and refer the client to another practitioner who can complete this evaluation in a client-centered manner.

7. Evaluation foci.
   a. Determine if sexual activity and expression are valued.
   b. Identify potential obstacles for the attainment and maintenance of safe, satisfying sexual activity and expression. Obstacles can include the following.
      (1) Pathophysiological changes related to disease, disability, and/or the aging process.
      (2) Psychological and/or cognitive changes related to disease, disability, and/or the aging process.
         (a) Judgment, impulse control, and decision-making skills must be assessed to ensure safety.
      (3) A history of sexual trauma or abuse.
      (4) Anxiety and/or fear about expressing a nonmajority sexual orientation or gender identity.
      (5) Limited partner availability due to social demographics and/or sociocultural attitudes.
   c. Determine if a person's knowledge of their sexuality is adequate and appropriate for their age, developmental level, expected roles, and environmental contexts.

8. If an individual is reticent about discussing their sexual activity and expression during the OT evaluation, the OT practitioner must respect and accept this preference.
   a. Sexual concerns that are unexpressed during initial OT sessions are often brought forth during later sessions as a therapeutic relationship develops between the individual and the OT practitioner.
   b. Sessions focused on intimate self-care issues frequently precipitate questions regarding sexuality.
   c. An atmosphere of continuing permission to discuss sexual activity and expression should be maintained throughout the person's engagement in OT.

> **CAUTION:** The potential realities of sexual abuse, assault, and exploitation must be considered during the evaluation of all individuals regardless of age. OT practitioners are required by practice acts, protective legislation, and our professional Code of Ethics to report any suspected incidents of child, adult, or elder abuse or assault to the appropriate agency and/or local law enforcement.

Activities of Daily Living and Instrumental Activities of Daily Living Intervention

> **EXAM HINT:** According to the OTPF-4, independence does not require direct physical interaction with the environment or objects within the environment. People can be considered "independent whether they perform the specific occupations by themselves, in an adapted or modified environment, with the use of various devices or alternative strategies, or while overseeing (the) activity" (AOTA, 2020, p. 9). Thus, if an NBCOT® exam item includes a scenario about a person with significant motor impairments seeking to be independent in ADL/IADL, correct answers for NBCOT® exam items would include interventions to develop the person's skills to use adaptive equipment and/or assistive technology (AT), and/or their ability to self-direct the performance of desired activities.

ADL Intervention

1. Determine whether the ADL should be modified to enable individual performance, performance with external assistance, or eliminated.
   a. Activities that are valued, meaningful, and enjoyable to the person and related to desired role performance should be modified for individual performance, with appropriate equipment and/or supports provided as needed (e.g., brushing one's hair using an adapted brush to maintain one's appearance at school/work, using a smartphone application [app] to manage medications).
   b. Activities that are difficult to perform and/or are not enjoyable should be eliminated or performed with the assistance of others (e.g., if dressing independently requires a great deal of exertion that exhausts an individual, they may prefer to self-direct a PCA to complete dressing so that they have the energy they need to engage in the activities for which they are getting dressed).

> **EXAM HINT:** In the NBCOT® OTR® exam content outline, knowledge of "adaptive and preventive strategies for optimal engagement in occupation" (NBCOT®, 2022, p. 9) is identified as essential for competent and safe practice. The application of knowledge about the intervention principles, adaptive strategies, and adaptive equipment described in this section can help you effectively determine the correct answer to NBCOT® exam items about interventions to enable self-care performance.

2. Recommend adaptive strategies and equipment for ADL task performance.
   a. Table 15-2 describes factors that should be considered prior to recommending adaptative strategies and/or equipment to a person and strategies that should be used to engage the person in the adaptation process.
3. Provide adaptive equipment to compensate for functional impairments during ADL performance.
   a. Table 15-3 outlines the some of the adaptive equipment that can be used to enable the independent performance of ADL.

Table 15-3

Adaptive Equipment to Enable ADL

Toileting and Toilet Hygiene
  Personal urinal or catheter.
  Bedside (three-in-one) commode or raised toilet seat.
  Grab bars and/or toilet safety frame.
  Toilet lift.
  Bowel training device, bladder control devices.
  Skin inspection mirror.
  Toilet paper holder.

Grooming/Oral Hygiene
  Universal cuff to hold toothbrush, razor, comb, and/or brush.
  Built-up, angled, or long-handled brushes and/or razors.
  Adapted blow-dryer, nail clippers, and/or nail polish holders.
  Faucet turners, motion activated faucets.
  Electric toothbrush, floss holders, water flosser.

Bathing/Showering
  Grab bars and nonskid mat.
  Tub transfer bench/shower bench.
  Shower commode chair.
  Handheld shower.
  Antiscald valves and/or faucets.
  Built-up, angled, and/or long-handled bath sponge.
  Bath mitt.
  Soap on a rope, soap dish with suction cup.
  Storage units.

Dressing
  Reachers, dressing sticks, and pants dressing poles.
  Built-up, angled, or long-handled shoe horn.
  Pull-on clothing.
  Velcro™-type closures, and/or front opening closures.
  Button hook, zipper pull, and zipper loop or ring.
  Sock/stocking aid.
  Elastic shoelaces, slip-on shoes.

Feeding/Eating
  Adapted nipples and bottles for infants.
  Scoop dish or plate guards.
  Nonslip placemat or Dycem.
  Built-up, angled, weighted, long-handled, or swivel utensils.
  Rocker knife and/or spork.
  Sandwich holder.
  Electronic feeder.
  Adapted cups and long or angled straws.

Medication Management
  Easy-open, non-child-proof medication bottles.
  Pill organizers and medication reminders.
  Smartphone apps.
  Automated pill dispensers.

EXAM HINT: Understand that the type of adaptive equipment a person may need to use to independently complete desired activities and how long they will need to use the equipment will depend on the nature of their condition. For example, a person with a condition for which full recovery usually occurs (e.g., a hip fracture, rotator cuff tear) will typically only use adaptive equipment during their recovery. Conversely, persons with progressive disorders (e.g., muscular dystrophy, hereditary ataxia) will often use equipment to maintain the ability to perform tasks. However, as their condition progresses and independent task completion becomes difficult or impossible, persons with progressive disorders often decrease their equipment use and increase their self-direction of care. For persons with non-progressive conditions that result in residual deficits (e.g., amputation, stroke), a person's use of adaptive equipment will likely become integrated into their daily routine.

Therefore, NBCOT® exam items about the use of adaptive equipment should include information about a person's condition, their stage of recovery, and the type of activity they need/want to perform. To determine if answer options that include adaptive equipment are correct, you will need to apply your diagnostic knowledge *and* your activity analysis and adaptation skills.

   b. Table 15-4 describes the ADL abilities of persons with different levels of spinal cord injury (SCI) and the adaptive equipment that may be used to enable ADL performance at each level.

EXAM HINT: To determine the correct answer to a question about the type of adaptive equipment a person with a complete C7 SCI should use, you should carefully consider the information that is provided in the exam item scenario about the stage of the person's recovery and the activity demands of the specific task to be performed. A person with a complete C7 SCI has active wrist extension that can be used for a functional tenodesis grasp. However, in the early stages of recovery and while the person is acquiring the abilities needed to use a tenodesis grasp, the person may initially be taught to use a universal cuff to hold items that are needed to perform specific tasks (e.g., to hold a toothbrush to independently brush their teeth, to hold a spork to self-feed). Because continued use of a universal cuff can weaken a tenodesis grasp due to disuse, the use of a universal cuff is discontinued when the person develops a functional tenodesis grasp. While many tasks can be completed with a tenodesis grasp, the use of a tenodesis orthosis can enable independent performance in ADL and IADL tasks that require sustained grasp against resistance (e.g., shaving, peeling vegetables).

Chapter 15

Table 15-4

SCI Levels and Ability to Engage in Activities of Daily Living

SCI LEVEL	ACTIVITIES OF DAILY LIVING
C1–C3	Toileting and Bowel and Bladder Management, Bathing/Showering, Grooming, Dressing, and Feeding: Totally dependent. Can chew and swallow. Can self-direct and instruct others in preferences for care. • Equipment used as needed by caregiver to ease activity engagement can include a padded reclining shower/commode chair and handheld shower.
C4	Toileting and Bowel and Bladder Management, Bathing/Showering, Grooming, and Dressing: Same as C-1–3. Feeding: Can drink from a glass with a long straw and may be able to eat using a sandwich holder on a gooseneck feeder.
C5	Toileting and Bowel and Bladder Management: Total assistance is required with equipment used as needed. Equipment used may include: • padded rolling shower/commode chair. • electric leg bag emptier. Bathing/Showering: Moderate to total assistance is required with equipment used as needed. Equipment used may include: • roll-in padded shower/commode chair or padded transfer tub bench. • handheld shower head. • wash mitt or adapted loofah. Grooming: Assistance required for setup. Can be independent after set-up with equipment used as needed for activity engagement. Equipment used may include: • dorsal wrist orthosis and universal cuff for brushing teeth and combing hair. • wash mitt for washing the face. • electric razor that fits around the hand for shaving or a dorsal wrist orthosis and universal cuff to hold a manual safety razor. Dressing: Minimal to moderate assistance is required for upper body dressing with wrist/hand orthoses used as needed. Dependent with lower body dressing. Feeding: Total assistance required for setup, then independent with equipment. Equipment used may include: • suspension sling or mobile arm support. • dorsal wrist orthosis with universal cuff. • dycem to prevent slippage of plate. • scoop dish or plate guard. • angled utensils.
C6	Toileting and Bowel and Bladder Management: Maximal to total assistance is required using equipment as needed. May be independent with emptying a leg bag. Equipment used may include: • catheterization and bowel stimulation equipment. • padded shower/commode chair. • drop-arm commode. • tub bench with cutout. Bathing/Showering: Independent with the upper body; the lower body requires moderate to total assistance using equipment as needed. Equipment used may include: • a long handle sponge with universal cuff. • adapted loofah. • handheld shower. • tub bench or padded shower chair. Grooming: May require minimal to moderate assistance, but can be independent using equipment as needed. Equipment that may be used is the same as C5. Dressing: Independent with upper body dressing using equipment as needed. Moderate to total assistance for lower body dressing, including socks and shoes, using equipment as needed. Equipment used may include: • button hook, zipper pull, Velcro™ fasteners. • dressing stick, dressing hook orthosis. • thigh straps, leg lifter. • specialized accessible clothing. Feeding: Independent with or without equipment, except for cutting food which requires total assistance. Equipment used may include: • universal cuff or tenodesis orthosis. • adapted utensils. • scoop dish or plate guard. • cup with large handles.

(Continued)

Table 15-4

SCI Levels and Ability to Engage in Activities of Daily Living (Continued)

SCI LEVEL	ACTIVITIES OF DAILY LIVING
C7–C8	Toileting and Bowel and Bladder Management: Can be independent with bladder management, including emptying a leg bag, with equipment as needed although minimal assistance may be required. Minimal to total assistance for bowel management with equipment as needed. Equipment that may be used is the same as C6. Bathing/Showering: Can be independent with equipment used as needed; may require minimal to moderate assistance with the lower body. Equipment that may be used is the same as C6. Grooming: Independent using a tenodesis grasp or tenodesis orthosis if preferred, with equipment used as needed. Equipment that may be used is the same as C5. Dressing: Can be independent, with equipment used as needed. May require minimal assistance for lower body dressing with equipment used as needed. Equipment that may be used is the same as C6. Feeding: Independent with use of a tenodesis grasp or tenodesis orthosis if preferred, with equipment as needed. Equipment that may be used is the same as C6.
T1–T9	Independent in all self-care with equipment as needed; e.g., elevated padded toilet seat, tub bench, handheld shower, long handle sponge, thigh straps, reacher, dressing stick, and sock aide.
T10–S5	Independent in all self-care; uses a tub bench, handheld shower, and standard or raised padded toilet seat.

Note: The level of assistance and equipment required for ADL performance may vary within each SCI level, based on severity of injury (i.e., complete vs. incomplete), control of potentially innervated muscles (i.e., functional control of UE movement in cervical level SCIs, control of trunk muscles in thoracic level SCIs), and ability to adapt/compensate. Expected functional performance levels and suggested equipment outlined in this table are most common for individuals with a complete injury at the listed level of SCI.

Adapted from:

Model Systems Knowledge Translation Center (MSKTC). (2020, August). Resources offered by the MSKTC to support individuals living with spinal cord injury (6th ed.). National Institute on Disability, Independent Living, and Rehabilitation Research (NIDILRR grant number 90DP0082). https://msktc.org/sites/default/files/SCIFactsheetBookletEnglish2020.pdf.

Paralyzed Veterans of America (PVA). Consortium for spinal cord medicine (1999). Outcomes following traumatic spinal cord injury: Clinical practice guidelines for health-care professionals. https://pva.org/wp-content/uploads/2021/09/cpg_outcomes-following-traumatic-sci.pdf.

c. Prior to recommending adaptive equipment, the multiple dimensions of a person with a disability and the complexities of many disorders should be considered. For example, Friedrich's ataxia is characterized by tremors that may indicate the need for weighted utensils, but muscle strength is also limited so these utensils may be too heavy for functional use.

4. Train in the safe and effective use of adaptive equipment and AT.

5. Practice to attain proficiency in activity performance at relevant times and in real environments (e.g., brush teeth in the bathroom in the morning; self-feed during mealtimes).

6. Provide cues and assistance as needed. These can include the following.
   a. Verbal reminders and prompts.
   b. Nonverbal gestures, written directions, physical prompts to initiate.
   c. Hand-over-hand assistance through the complete activity movement.
   d. Visual supervision to ensure safety with minimal or no verbal or nonverbal cues.

7. Use thematic and topical groups to develop needed skills (e.g., grooming, medication management).

8. Teach principles and methods of energy conservation, work simplification, joint protection, and proper body mechanics. Refer to Chapter 11.

9. Educate and train caregivers to provide needed cues, physical assistance, and/or supervision.
   a. Teach organizational strategies (e.g., place clothing in the proper sequence for dressing).
   b. Teach activity analysis, gradation, simplification, and adaptation skills (e.g., for a person with a moderate to severe neurocognitive disorder, provide multiple small meals to decrease the amount of attention required to eat).
   c. Refer to Chapter 10 and Table 10-3 for additional information about strategies caregivers can use to improve the management of the symptoms and functional effects of neurocognitive disorders.

10. Educate the person and caregivers about environmental modifications and adaptive equipment and strategies that can be used during ADL to prevent falls.
    a. Refer to Chapter 16 for additional information about fall prevention.
       (1) Box 16-2 outlines extrinsic fall risk factors in the home and Box 16-3 describes strategies and modifications to prevent falls in the home.

11. Modify the environment to maximize performance and ensure safety. Refer to Chapter 16.
12. Educate the individual on PCA options (e.g., consumer-directed programs, agency-delivered services).
13. Train the person in self-advocacy and personnel management to develop the skills needed to direct others to assist with and/or perform ADL.
    a. Teach and practice methods for directing others to assist with ADL in the personally desired and acceptable manner.
    b. Provide assertiveness and personal advocacy training.

> **EXAM HINT:** The NBCOT® OTR® exam content outline identifies knowledge of "strategies for addressing and enhancing health literacy with the client and relevant others . . . (including) caregiver training, teaching-learning models . . . (and) informed decision-making" (NBCOT®, 2022, p. 6) as essential for competent practice. The application of knowledge about the education and training methods described in the preceding ADL intervention section can help you determine the correct answer for NBCOT® Domain 3 exam items about addressing and enhancing the health literacy of clients who have established goals for ADL performance and their significant others.

Sexual Expression and Activities Intervention

1. OT intervention is provided to enable satisfying, safe sexual expression and activities regardless of disability, disease, or advanced age.
2. Myths about the sexuality of the older adults and individuals with disability or disease processes must be confronted and debunked. Myths can include the following.
    a. They are asexual and have less interest in sexual expression than younger and/or healthier persons.
    b. They are physically unattractive and not desirable as a sexual partner and will be a burden to their partners.
    c. They inherently have poor judgment and cannot make appropriate decisions about their sexuality.
    d. Intercourse with mutual orgasm is the desired and primary means to express oneself sexually.
        (1) Intimate behaviors, such as mutual stimulation, cuddling, oral sex, and/or caressing are not adequate sexual activity.
        (2) Self-stimulation/masturbation is not an appropriate means of sexual expression.
    e. Individuals who live in shared residential settings such as nursing homes, group homes, and assisted living facilities are asexual.
        (1) They should be segregated according to gender.
        (2) Privacy for the individual is not essential and does not need to be respected.
    f. Individuals with disabilities and/or older adults who desire and/or engage in sexual activity are oversexed and inappropriate.
3. If the above myths are allowed to prevail, they can become internalized by the person and negatively impact their wellness and life satisfaction.
4. The PLISSIT model should be used by OT practitioners to guide their interventions related to sexual expression and activities and ensure that the person is provided opportunities to enhance their performance and engagement in this ADL, if they so desire.
    a. Table 15-5 describes the components of the PLISSIT model.

> **EXAM HINT:** If an NBCOT® exam item provides evaluation results that include a person identifying sexual expression as a desired occupation, a correct answer would include interventions that use the PLISSIT model described in Table 15-5. Because the myths about sexuality as previously described are pervasive in some practice settings, a correct answer could also include the OT practitioner debunking these myths and advocating for the person's right to sexual expression/activities.

5. Methods of intervention can include the one-on-one counseling sessions, therapeutic groups, the dissemination of printed materials, and/or self-advocacy training.
    a. In the OTPF-4, personal device management is identified as a component of health management and is inclusive of sexual devices.
        (1) To help a person manage a sexual device, an OT practitioner may adapt or modify the device to enable the person to use it in the desired manner (e.g., constructing an orthosis to hold a vibrator).
6. Interventions for individuals with cognitive impairments (e.g., poor impulse control, limited judgment) are essential to ensure their safety and protect them from sexual abuse, assault, and/or exploitation.
    a. Assertiveness training to increase understanding of the right to set limits on others and develop the ability to maintain these limits.
    b. Education about actions that can be taken if boundaries are violated.
    c. Training and practice in physical self-protection techniques.
    d. Role playing to simulate potential scenarios that can challenge the individual's sexual judgment.

The PLISSIT Model for Interventions Related to Sexual Expression and Activities

P = Permission: requires the OT practitioner to create an atmosphere that gives the individual permission to raise concerns about their sexuality and sexual activity(ies).

Incorporating sexuality into the OT initial and ongoing evaluation in a matter-of-fact manner is an effective method.

A practitioner who is not comfortable with creating a permissive atmosphere for the discussion of sexuality due to personal, social, cultural, and/or religious reasons must honestly acknowledge this fact to the client and refer them immediately to a team member who is comfortable with addressing the individual's concerns.

It is the team's responsibility to ensure that at least one team member is comfortable with evaluating and intervening with individuals with sexual expression concerns.

Supervision and continuing professional development activities should be pursued by all to develop this needed comfort.

LI = Limited Information: provided by the OT practitioner to ensure that the individual has accurate knowledge about their sexual abilities and potentials.

Facts are shared (e.g., there is sex after disability; older adults are sexually active), and myths are dispelled.

If an OT practitioner is uncertain about specifics related to the person's concerns, the practitioner should obtain the information they need to effectively address them.

SS = Specific Suggestions: provided by the OT practitioner to facilitate the individual's pursuit of satisfying sexual expression, either alone or with a partner.

The individual's (and partner's, if relevant) goals for sexual expression and activity are identified and strategies for achieving goals are explored.

Principles of activity analysis, gradation, modification, and simplification are used to facilitate goal attainment.

Nonmedical methods to manage pain, stiffness, and discomfort (e.g., warm baths, lubricants) are provided.

Positioning alternatives and adaptive equipment to facilitate desired sexual expression and activity are suggested.

Energy conservation methods (e.g., timing sex for when one has the most energy and use of sexual positions that require less energy expenditures) are suggested to those with limited endurance.

Catheter care, hygiene concerns, and skin care are addressed.

Referrals to a physician for medical management of pain, impotence or other sexual dysfunctions, and hormonal treatment.

IT = Intensive Therapy: indicated when the person requires intervention for long-standing relationship problems and/or enduring sexual problems.

These problems are often due to difficulties beyond the onset or presence of a disability.

Specialized training is required to provide intensive therapy, so a referral to the appropriate professional (e.g., marriage/relationship counselor, sex therapist) is indicated.

OT practitioners can become specialists in this area upon completion of an appropriate professional training program.

Chapter 15

e. Sex education (e.g., menstrual cycle information, prevention of sexually transmitted diseases).

f. Caregiver and family education.
   (1) Socially inappropriate sexual activity is often difficult for families to understand (e.g., an older adult with a neurocognitive disorder begins to disrobe in the living room).
      (a) Recognizing that this behavior is indicative of an underlying disorder or disease process is important.
      (b) Providing strategies for effectively managing undesirable behaviors is a main intervention focus (e.g., eliminate clothing fasteners in the front, divert the person's attention to an activity of interest).

IADL Intervention

1. Determine the expectations and demands of the individual's current and expected environment.
   a. Supportive living environments can range in expectations from requiring that a resident only clean their room (e.g., in a group home) to the complete management of a home with minimal supervision (e.g., a supported apartment).
   b. Independent living environments can also have a range of expectations and demands (e.g., one spouse/partner always does the budget, the other spouse/partner always cooks).

2. Determine whether the IADL activity should be modified to enable independent performance, self-directed performance with external assistance, or eliminated.
   a. Activities that are valued, meaningful, and enjoyable to the person and related to desired role performance should be modified for individual performance, with appropriate equipment and/or supports provided as needed (e.g., preparing after-school snacks for children).
   b. Activities that are difficult to perform and/or are not enjoyable should be eliminated or performed with the assistance of others (e.g., cleaning a refrigerator can be delegated to another person, a self-cleaning oven can eliminate this task).

> **EXAM HINT:** In the NBCOT® OTR® exam content outline, Domain 3 Select and Manage Interventions comprises 38% of the NBCOT® exam and knowledge of "adaptive and preventive strategies for optimal engagement in occupation" (NBCOT®, 2022, p. 9) is identified as essential for competent and safe practice. The application of knowledge about the preceding general intervention principles and the following adaptive strategies can help you effectively determine the correct answers for NBCOT® exam items about interventions to enable home management performance.

3. Recommend adaptive strategies and equipment for IADL task performance. Refer to Table 15-2 for factors that should be considered prior to recommending adaptative strategies and/or equipment to a person and strategies that should be used to engage the person in the adaptation process.
4. Provide adaptive equipment to compensate for functional impairments during IADL performance.
   a. Box 15-1 lists adaptive equipment that can be used to enable participation in household cleaning tasks.
   b. Box 15-2 lists adaptive equipment that can be used to enable participation in meal preparation and cleanup tasks.
   c. Table 15-6 describes the IADL abilities of persons with different levels of SCI and the adaptive equipment that may be used to enable IADL performance.
5. Train in the safe use of adaptive equipment and AT.
6. Teach principles and methods of energy conservation, work simplification, joint protection, and proper body mechanics. Refer to Chapter 11 for more information about these approaches.
7. Provide cues and assistance as needed. These can include the following.
   a. Verbal reminders and prompts.
   b. Nonverbal gestures, written directions, physical prompts to initiate.
   c. Hand-over-hand assistance through complete activity movement.
   d. Visual supervision to ensure safety with minimal or no verbal or nonverbal cues.
8. Practice to attain proficiency in activity performance at relevant times and in real environments (e.g., making a bed in the morning, cooking a meal in a kitchen at dinner time).
9. Recognize and respect personal, sociocultural, and socioeconomic differences (e.g., standards of cleanliness, dietary restrictions, and preferences).
   a. Use equipment that is socioeconomically appropriate (e.g., do not use an oven to teach meal preparation if someone only owns a microwave).
10. Use thematic and topical groups to develop needed skills (e.g., meal preparation group, financial management group).
11. Educate the person and their caregivers about environmental modifications and adaptive equipment and strategies that can be used during IADL to prevent falls.
   a. Refer to Chapter 16 for additional information about fall prevention.
      (1) Box 16-2 outlines extrinsic fall risk factors in the home and Box 16-3 describes strategies and modifications to prevent falls in the home.
12. Modify the environment to maximize performance and ensure safety. Refer to Chapter 16.
13. Educate and train caregivers to provide needed cues, physical assistance, and/or supervision.
14. Educate the individual on PCA options (e.g., consumer-directed programs, agency-delivered services).
15. Train the person in self-advocacy and personnel management to develop the skills needed to direct others to assist with and/or perform IADL.

BOX 15-1 ▷ Adaptive Equipment to Enable Participation in Cleaning Tasks

- Suction bottom bottle and glass brushes.
- Reachers.
- Aerosol can holders.
- Built up, angled, and/or long handled sponges, dusters, or dustpans.
- Angled and/or built up handled brooms and mops.
- Front-loading washers and dryers.
- Electronic dishwasher, self-cleaning oven.
- Automatic defrosting refrigerator.

BOX 15-2 ▷ Adaptive Equipment to Enable Participation in Meal Preparation and Cleanup Tasks

- Touch faucets.
- Antiscald faucets and/or valves.
- Jar openers, bowl holders, and pot/pan stabilizers.
- Nonskid pad, placemat, or Dycem.
- Cutting board with a stabilizing nail and built-up edges.
- Built-up, angled, and/or long handled utensils.
- Rocker knives.
- Adapted timers.
- Electric can opener.
- Lightweight pots, pans, and dishware.
- Automatic hot water dispenser and/or hotpots.
- Strap loops to open refrigerator, cabinets, and oven doors.
- Reachers and step stools.
- Utility cart.
- High kitchen stool.
- Microwave.
- Induction stovetop.

Table 15-6

SCI Levels and Ability to Engage in Instrumental Activities of Daily Living

SCI LEVEL	INSTRUMENTAL ACTIVITIES OF DAILY LIVING
C1–C4	**Communication Management:** Varies from independent to total assistance depending on equipment availability (i.e., mouth stick, head pointer, high tech computer accessibility options such as voice control, environmental control unit, communication board) for written and/or oral communication. **Home Management, Meal Preparation/Cleanup:** May be able to operate household lights and appliances using an environmental control unit. Totally dependent in all other activities. **Community Mobility:** Totally dependent with the use of accessible vans and/or public transportation with wheelchair lifts and tie-downs.
C5	**Communication Management:** Can be independent using hand orthosis and adaptive devices for page turning, writing, and button pushing, but may require some assistance. **Home Management, Meal Preparation/Cleanup:** Same as C1–C4. **Community Mobility:** Can be independent in driving with highly specialized equipment (i.e., specialized hand controls in a modified van with a wheelchair lift and an automatic wheelchair docking and locking feature). Requires assistance to transfer to standard vehicles (e.g., taxis, drive-share cars) and to use public transportation; the level of assistance needed will depend on the accessibility of the mode of transportation.
C6	**Communication Management:** Independent with or without equipment (i.e., tenodesis orthosis; writing orthosis for keyboard use, button pushing, page turning, and object manipulation). **Home Management:** Total assistance. **Meal Preparation/Cleanup:** Some assistance with simple meal preparation (e.g., making a sandwich); total assistance for complex meal preparation (e.g., cooking a complete hot meal). **Community Mobility:** Independent in driving while seated in a power or manual wheelchair using a modified van with a wheelchair lift, specialized hand controls, and wheelchair tie-downs. Non-driving aspects of community mobility (including transferring to standard vehicles and use of public transportation) require assistance, although it will vary based on the accessibility of the mode of transportation; may be able to secure wheelchair using tie-downs on public transportation.
C7–C8	**Communication Management:** Independent with adaptive devices as needed. **Home Management:** Independent with simple homemaking (e.g., dusting) using equipment as needed; some to total assistance for complex homemaking (e.g., laundry). **Meal Preparation/Cleanup:** Independent with simple meal preparation using equipment as needed; some to total assistance for complex meal preparation. **Community Mobility:** Can be independent with driving using hand controls after transferring from a wheelchair to a stand-alone driver's seat (e.g., a 'Captain's' seat), if able to load/unload a wheelchair and use a transfer/sliding board into the driver's seat without assistance. If assistance is required to load/unload a wheelchair into the vehicle and/or transfer into the driver's seat, driving can be independent from a modified van that is the same as C6. The assistance required for non-driving aspects of community mobility will vary based on the ability to transfer into a seat using a transfer/sliding board and the ability to manage a wheelchair for standard vehicles. Can be independent using accessible public transportation with a wheelchair lift.
T1–S5	**Communication Management:** Independent. **Home Management:** Independent with simple homemaking; some to total assistance for complex homemaking. **Meal Preparation/Cleanup:** Independent with all meal preparation and cleanup. **Community Mobility:** Independent in driving a car with hand controls, including loading/unloading a wheelchair. Can independently transfer into a standard vehicle with or without a transfer/sliding board and load/unload a wheelchair. Independent with accessible public transportation with a wheelchair lift.

Adapted from:

Model Systems Knowledge Translation Center (MSKTC). (2020, August). Resources offered by the MSKTC to support individuals living with spinal cord injury (6th ed.). National Institute on Disability, Independent Living, and Rehabilitation Research (NIDILRR grant number 90DP0082). https://msktc.org/sites/default/files/SCIFactsheetBookletEnglish2020.pdf.

Paralyzed Veterans of America (PVA). Consortium for spinal cord medicine (1999). Outcomes following traumatic spinal cord injury: Clinical practice guidelines for health-care professionals. https://pva.org/wp-content/uploads/2021/09/cpg_outcomes-following-traumatic-sci.pdf.

a. Teach and practice methods for directing others to assist with IADL in the personally desired and acceptable manner.

b. Provide assertiveness and personal advocacy training.

> **EXAM HINT:** The NBCOT® OTR® exam content outline identifies knowledge of "strategies for addressing and enhancing health literacy with the client and relevant others . . . (including) caregiver training, teaching-learning models . . . (and) informed decision-making" (NBCOT®, 2022, p. 6) as essential for competent practice. The application of knowledge about the education and training methods described in the preceding IADL intervention section can help you determine the correct answer for NBCOT® Domain 3 exam items about addressing and enhancing the health literacy of clients who have established goals for IADL performance and their significant others.

16. Refer to relevant social service programs (e.g., Supplemental Nutrition Assistance Program [SNAP], Home Energy Assistance Program [HEAP]).

17. Refer to the appropriate supportive living environment if independent living is not attainable (e.g., group home, halfway house, supported apartment). Refer to Chapter 4 for more information about residential settings.

18. Information about the evaluation of and intervention for the IADL of child rearing is provided in this Chapter's section on family participation.

19. Information about the evaluation of and intervention for the IADL of driving, and community mobility is provided in Chapter 16.

Health Management

Health Management Evaluation

1. The OT practitioner should assess the occupation of health management during the construction of an occupational profile.

2. Several evaluation tools described in the prior ADL/IADL evaluation section also include a health management component (e.g., the PASS, KELS, MEDLS).

Health Management Intervention

1. Incorporate the individual's personal preferences, circumstances, contexts, and needs into a customized healthy living regimen that takes into account any pre-existing medical conditions (AOTA, 2020).

2. Educate the person on how to build habits (including engagement in health-promoting activities) that allow them to attain and maintain targeted changes that support healthy living choices within the complex dynamic of their everyday lives.

3. Promote health literacy by facilitating the person's ability to understand and translate health instructions and recommendations to their performance of specific tasks and engagement in desired roles.

   a. Chapter 3 provides information about client and caregiver/family education to develop health literacy.

4. Train caregivers in strategies and techniques to support the person's participation in health management including medication management and other healthy practices.

5. Chapters 6–10 provide diagnostic-specific information that the OT practitioner can use to help a person develop and maintain health and wellness routines and manage their condition(s).

Evaluation of Family Participation

Overview

1. In the OTPF-4 family participation is defined as "engaging in activities that result in interaction in specific required and/or desired familial roles" (AOTA, 2020, p. 34).
2. The OT practitioner should assess the occupation of family participation during routine screenings and interviews to inform the development of an occupational profile. The aims of this process include the following.
   a. Determine past, current, and anticipated roles, responsibilities, and expectations of family members.
   b. Determine the family's routines, rituals, occupations, and co-occupations.
   c. Identify potential obstacles for the attainment and maintenance of satisfying family participation.
3. Some commonly used assessments include family participation (e.g., the Role Checklist).

> CAUTION: If the family and the OT practitioner do not share a common language, interpreters must be used to ensure the validity of information obtained.

4. The sociocultural background, values, and dynamics of the family must be considered during the evaluation process.
5. Individuals who live in shared residential settings such as nursing homes, group homes, and assisted living facilities and their families should receive intervention to assist with role transitions.
   a. Fellow residents and staff in these settings often assume the roles of surrogate family members.

Evaluation of Parenting and Childcare

1. While parent is a role that many assume in a family, the primary responsibilities associated with parenting and childcare may be assumed by others (e.g., a grandparent may assume the parenting role for their grandchild/grandchildren when their child cannot).
   a. In the OTPF-4, parenting and childcare are a component of the occupation of care of others.
2. In this Chapter section, the focus is on the evaluation of the parenting and childcare capabilities of a person with a disability.
   a. General information about providing family-centered services to evaluate a child with a developmental delay, disability, or medical condition is provided in Chapters 3 and 5.
      (1) Diagnostic specific information about evaluating a child with a disability or a medical condition is provided in Chapters 6–10.
3. To evaluate a person's ability to parent and care for a child/children, the OT practitioner should assess the following.
   a. The ability to care for the child's/children's physical and health needs.
   b. The ability to care for the child's/children's social and emotional needs.
   c. Knowledge of the child's/children's developmental level and its corresponding play and communication level.
   d. Available support networks (e.g., extended family, neighbors, religious congregation, community organizations).
   e. Problem-solving, coping strategies, and self-advocacy skills.

Family Participation Intervention

General Intervention Guidelines

1. Collaborate with the family on identifying desired goals.
   a. Provide interpreters, if necessary.

2. Determine whether the family activity should be modified to enable independent performance, self-directed performance with external assistance, or eliminated.
   a. Activities that are valued, meaningful, and enjoyable to family members and related to their desired

role performance should be modified for individual performance, with appropriate equipment and/or supports provided as needed (e.g., preparing the family's dinner using adaptive equipment, mowing the lawn using a rider mower).

b. Activities that are difficult to perform and/or are not safe should be eliminated or performed with the assistance of others (e.g., shopping for the family's weekly groceries, paying the bills).

3. Methods of intervention can include therapeutic groups, one-on-one teaching/training/coaching sessions, dissemination of printed materials, and/or advocacy training.

4. Design interventions using activities that are meaningful to the individual's role within the family.

5. Use topical and thematic groups to develop effective family participation skills.

a. Role-play to simulate potential scenarios that can challenge the individual's family skills (e.g., assertiveness training, anger management).

b. Teach and practice effective family communication.

c. Teach principles and methods of energy conservation, work simplification, joint protection, and proper body mechanics for family activities. Refer to Chapter 11 for more information about these approaches.

d. Develop parenting and childcare skills, if needed. Refer to the following section.

Intervention for Parenting and Childcare Activities

EXAM HINT: In the NBCOT® OTR® exam content outline, Domain 3 Select and Manage Interventions comprises 38% of the NBCOT® exam and knowledge of "adaptive and preventive strategies for supporting optimal engagement in occupation" (NBCOT®, 2022, p. 9) is identified as essential for competent and safe practice. The application of knowledge about the intervention principles and the adaptive equipment described in this section can help you effectively determine the correct answer to NBCOT® exam items about interventions to enable effective parenting and childcare.

1. In this Chapter section, the focus is on intervention that can enable effective parenting and childcare by a person with a disability.

2. General information about providing family-centered interventions for a child with a developmental delay, disability, or medical condition is provided in Chapters 3 and 5.

a. Diagnostic-specific information about interventions for a child with a disability or medical condition is provided in Chapters 6–10.

3. Activities that are valued, meaningful, and enjoyable to the person and related to desired role performance

should be modified for individual performance, with adaptive equipment and strategies and/or supports provided as needed (e.g., reading a bedtime story to children using an electronic page turner).

4. Activities that are difficult to perform and/or are not safe should be eliminated or performed with the assistance of others (e.g., bathing a toddler).

5. Teach the parent/caregiver how to care for the child's/children's physical needs and physically practice childcare tasks (e.g., placing the child into a front pack using proper body mechanics).

6. Instruct the parent/caregiver about typical developmental roles and tasks to ensure their expectations of their child/children are realistic.

7. Use coaching, modelling, and skills training.

8. Help the parent design a childcare routine that is do-able and supports goal attainment.

9. Recommend adaptive strategies and equipment for home management task performance that are related to parenting and childcare (e.g., preparing their child's/children's bag lunch for school in the evening to decrease the activity demands of the family's morning routine). Refer to Table 15-2.

10. Provide adaptive equipment and train in its use to compensate for functional impairments during parenting tasks.

a. Box 15-3 lists adaptive equipment that can be used by parents with disabilities to perform childcare tasks.

> **CAUTION:** Prior to making recommendations, the OT practitioner should consider the family's socioeconomic status and the cost of recommendations (e.g., premeasured formula and disposable diapers are convenient and energy saving, *but* they are expensive options).

BOX 15-3 ▷ Adaptive Equipment to Enable Participation in Childcare Tasks

- Adapted drop-side crib, raised and/or adjustable height crib mattress.
- Child-resistant one-handed crib wall release mechanism.
- Foam rubber bathing pads for sink, portable plastic tub, and/or reclining infant seat placed in tub.
- Changing tables at accessible height with safety straps and touch fasteners.
- Pillow to support breastfeeding, which for many mothers is physically the easiest method for feeding their infant.
- Lightweight and/or angled bottles.
- One-handed swing away release tray on high chair with safety strap.
- Food warmer tray.
- Pullover clothes.
- Velcro™ fasteners for bibs, diaper covers, and clothing.
- Infant carriers.

11. Baby furniture and equipment should be tested and used on a trial basis to ensure it matches the parent's/caregiver's capabilities.
12. Recognize and respect the personal, sociocultural, and socioeconomic differences within families.
13. Teach the child/children of a parent with a disability self-reliance at a young age.
    a. Arrange tasks so they are accessible to a child (e.g., storage for dishes and glasses next to the dishwasher, not in a high cabinet).
    b. Delegate tasks that are achievable for child's/children's developmental level (e.g., even a young child can move clothes from a front-loading washer to a front-loading dryer).

14. Modify the environment to maximize childcare task performance and ensure safety of the parent/caregiver and child/children. Refer to Chapter 16.
15. Refer family members/caregivers to support groups, local, and national organizations, and community and government resources.
16. Provide family/caregiver education in verbal and written formats in their language of choice.
17. Be aware of signs of child neglect or abuse.
    a. OT practitioners are required by the federal Child Abuse Prevention and Treatment Act (CAPTA), state practice acts, and our professional code of ethics to report any suspected incidents of child abuse, assault, or exploitation, to the appropriate agency and local law enforcement.

Play/Leisure Evaluation

Overview

1. Play and leisure are areas of occupation that are found in global assessment tools (e.g., the Role Checklist, Activity Card Sort, Occupational Performance History Interview-II) and in tools specific to play and leisure participation and performance. Refer to subsequent section.

> **CAUTION:** Standardized play assessments can have the limitation of altering or inhibiting a child's natural play when they use standardized settings, activities, and/or toys.

2. The completion of a focused activity analysis of a child's naturally occurring play activities provides an opportunity for the OT practitioner to assess the child's typical play performance, interests, and routine patterns.

> **EXAM HINT:** In the NBCOT® OTR® exam content exam, Domain 1 Evaluation and Assessment comprises 23% of the exam, and knowledge of the "administration, purpose, indications, advantages, and limitations of standardized and nonstandardized screening and assessment tools" (NBCOT®, 2022, p. 4) is identified as essential for competent and safe practice. The application of knowledge about the following measures can help you effectively determine the correct answer for NBCOT® exam items about the evaluation of a person's ability to engage in play/leisure.

Activity Index

1. Focus: determination of the individual's perception of the meaning of leisure and the extent the individual participates in leisure activities.
2. Method.
    a. Evaluator provides the individual with the Activity Index Questionnaire.
    b. Instructions are given to indicate the individual's level of participation in each of the 23 listed activities.
    c. The individual is instructed to fill in additional leisure activities of interest in the space provided, if appropriate.
3. Materials: questionnaire and a pencil.
4. Scoring and interpretation.
    a. The individual checks their level of interest and participation in each activity along a four-point scale.
        (1) Don't do/not interested.
        (2) Don't do/would like to do.
        (3) Do at least once a week.
        (4) Do at least three times a week.
    b. Interpretation of self-report results can be used to design interventions using activities that are meaningful to the individual and to promote their pursuit of preferred activities.
5. Population: developed for older adults, aged 65 and over, but has been used with other populations.

Interest Checklist

1. Focus: assessment of a person's level of interest in 80 leisure activities, additional leisure interests, and their perspective on how leisure interests and involvement has evolved over time.
   a. A modified Interest Checklist has fewer activities.
2. Method.
   a. The evaluator provides the individual with the 80-item or modified checklist.
   b. Instructions direct the individual to check their level of interest in each activity.
   c. Additional interests can be listed by the individual at the end of the checklist.
   d. Evaluator interviews the individual about their life history of leisure interests and pursuits.
3. Materials: checklist and a pencil.
4. Scoring and interpretation.
   a. The individual's level of interest is rated as strong, casual, or no interest.
   b. These scores do not indicate if the person actually pursues the activity.
   c. The interview is not rated; questions can be asked to obtain information about activity engagement.
   d. The checklist scores and qualitative data can provide guidance for planning interventions that use meaningful activities and promote the person's active pursuit of activities of interest.
5. Population: originally developed for adults, but it has been used with adolescents to older adults.

Leisure Diagnostic Battery (LDB)

1. Focus: measurement of an individual's leisure experience, and motivational and situational issues that influence leisure (e.g., perceived barriers to leisure and knowledge of leisure opportunities).
2. Method.
   a. The evaluator provides the individual with the LDB questionnaire and asks the individual to indicate their responses on the LDB's response sheet.
3. Materials: LDB questionnaire, response sheet, and pencil.
4. Scoring and interpretation.
   a. A one to three rating scale indicating agreement with statements.
   b. Information can be used to identify the individual's knowledge of leisure opportunities, environmental resources and barriers, and leisure characteristics that are motivating and interesting to the person.
5. Population: adults for the original LDB. Adapted scales have been developed for children aged 9–14 with no cognitive deficits and for children aged 9–14 with a diagnosis of intellectual disabilities.

Leisure Satisfaction Measure

1. Focus: measurement of an individual's perception that leisure pursuits are meeting personal needs in six needs categories.
   a. Psychological (i.e., enjoyable activities).
   b. Educational (i.e., intellectually stimulating activities).
   c. Social (i.e., activities that foster positive relationships with others).
   d. Relaxation (i.e., stress relieving activities).
   e. Physiological (i.e., activities that foster fitness, health, and wellness).
   f. Aesthetic (i.e., beautiful and well-designed activities).
2. Method: the evaluator gives the individual the questionnaire and asks them to respond to each question on a five-point scale.
3. Materials: questionnaire and a pencil.
4. Scoring and interpretation.
   a. Responses for each question are rated on a five-point scale with 1 = almost never true and 5 = almost always true.
   b. Information can be used to examine a person's use of leisure time, to discuss needs satisfied by leisure pursuits, and to identify ways leisure can be modified to better meet individual needs.
5. Population: adults and older adults with moderate to no cognitive disability.

Meaningfulness of Activity Scale

1. Focus: the measurement of the individual's level of enjoyment, motivational source, perception of competence, and participation in leisure.
2. Method: the evaluator provides the individual with a questionnaire and asks the individual to mark their responses on the form's rating scale.
3. Materials: questionnaire and a pencil.
4. Scoring and interpretation.
   a. Likert-type scales are used for three subscales.
      (1) Level of activity enjoyment.
      (2) Reason for doing the activity.
      (3) Perception of activity competence.
   b. The three subscale scores are totaled to obtain an overall meaningfulness of activity score.
   c. Information can be used to reinforce the pursuit of meaningful leisure and to plan intervention to promote adaptive leisure functioning.
5. Population: adults and older adults.

Minnesota Leisure Time Physical Activity Questionnaire

1. Focus: measurement of the energy expended by a person during engagement in leisure activities.
2. Method: the evaluator interviews the person using a list of 63 physical activities (excluding work) to determine which activities the individual has performed in the past 12 months.
3. Scoring.
   a. For each activity performed the individual specifies the level of participation for each month.
   b. The evaluator determines whether an activity is light, medium, or heavy according to evaluation standards.
   c. A total activity metabolic index and an estimate of average daily caloric expenditures are obtained.
   d. Information can be used to assess premorbid physical activity levels and examine their relationship with general health, disease, cardiovascular fitness, and weight control.
   e. Intervention plans can be made to increase physical activity to enhance health and fitness and reduce stress.
4. Population: adults.

Play Assessments

1. Refer to Chapter 5 for information about the following play assessments.
   a. Play History.
   b. Revised Knox Preschool Play Scale (RKPPS).
   c. Test of Playfulness (ToP) Revised Version 3.5.
   d. Transdisciplinary Play-Based Assessment (TPBA).

Additional Assessments Inclusive of Play/Leisure Activities

1. Activity and temporal adaptation assessments. Refer to Chapter 14 for information about the following assessments.
   a. Activity Card Sort (ACS).
   b. Activities Health Assessment.
   c. Barth Time Construction (BTC).
2. Occupational role and occupational performance interviews. Refer to Chapter 14 for information about the following assessments.
   a. Model of Human Occupation Screening Tool (MOHOST).
   b. Occupational Circumstances Assessment Interview Rating Scale (OCAIRS), version 4.
   c. Occupational Performance History Interview-II (OPHI-II).
   d. Occupational Self-Assessment.
   e. Role Checklist.
3. The Miller Function and Participation Scales (M-FUN) uses games to assess a child's visual-motor, fine motor, and gross motor skills. Refer to Chapter 5.

 ## Play/Leisure Intervention

General Intervention Guidelines

1. Recognize that play is a primary occupation of children, an age-appropriate occupation-based intervention modality, and a relevant outcome for intervention.
   a. Children with congenital conditions or those who acquired a disability at or before birth may have limited opportunities and experiences to engage in play and develop play skills.
2. Interventions to enable play should include the child's parents/caregivers. These can include the following.
   a. Education to help the parents/caregivers understand the importance of play for their child.
   b. Modeling of play behavior and encouragement to facilitate parents'/caregivers' play engagement with their child.
   c. Strategies to help families incorporate play into their daily routine (e.g., water play during bath time).
   d. Education about resources that support the parents/caregivers efforts to provide the child with typical childhood experiences (e.g., adapted toys, accessible playgrounds, sensory-friendly movie theatres).
3. Recognize that the acquisition of a disability often results in increased leisure time due to the loss of roles (e.g., worker).
   a. Provide support for losses, refer to support and/or disability advocacy groups.

b. Renew or adapt old interests.

c. Explore and develop new interests.

4. Play/leisure activities that are valued, meaningful, and enjoyable to the child/person should be adapted, modified, and/or simplified to facilitate satisfying engagement.

5. Provide adaptive equipment and AT to compensate for functional impairments during play/leisure activity performance.

a. Box 15-4 lists adaptive equipment that can be used to enable participation in play/leisure activities.

b. Table 15-7 describes the abilities of persons with different levels of SCI levels and the adaptive equipment that may be used to enable participation in play/leisure activities at each level.

6. Use thematic and topical groups to develop needed skills (e.g., a parenting play group for children with disabilities, a retirement planning group).

7. Teach principles and methods of energy conservation, work simplification, joint protection, and proper body mechanics. Refer to Chapter 11 for more information about these approaches.

8. Refer to relevant community and national resources (e.g., community centers, public libraries, free concerts, accessible playgrounds, Compeer, Special Olympics).

9. Explore and present internet and web-based opportunities for play and leisure participation (e.g., social networking, chat rooms, gaming sites).

BOX 15-4 ▷ Adaptive Equipment to Enable Participation in Play/Leisure Activities

- Universal cuff.
- Card holders.
- Book holders and electronic page turners.
- Writing orthosis, typing aids, weighted pens.
- Headsticks, mouthsticks.
- Electronic aids for daily living (EADL) to activate electronic equipment (e.g., TVs, lights). Refer to Chapter 16.
- Accessible gaming controls and programming.
- Adapted computer, keyboard guards, and voice-activated computer. Refer to Chapter 16.
- Smartphone applications.
- Speaker phones.
- Switches to activate toys that a child cannot operate by conventional means.
- Adapted play scooters, bicycle, and tricycles, battery-operated play vehicles. Refer to Chapter 16.
- Mobility equipment designed for sports participation. Refer to Chapter 16.

Table 15-7

SCI Levels and Ability to Engage in Play/Leisure Activities

SCI LEVEL	PLAY/LEISURE ACTIVITIES
C1–C4	Can play computer games, access the Internet and e-mail, and control radios, TVs, and other electronic devices using a mouthstick, head pointer, voice activation, or an EADL/environmental control unit. Can read using a mouthstick, head pointer, or electronic page turner to turn pages. Can paint with a mouthstick or head pointer.
C5	Can independently play computer and board games, do some crafts, turn pages for reading, use electronic devices, and access the Internet using a dorsal wrist orthosis, typing orthosis, and/or adaptive devices as needed (e.g., universal cuff and page turner).
C6 and C7	Can hold a phone, typing stick, and pen using a tenodesis grasp or tenodesis orthosis. Can independently play computer and board games, do some crafts, turn pages for reading, use electronic devices, and access the Internet using adaptive devices as needed (i.e., tenodesis orthosis, writing orthosis for keyboard use, typing stick, devices for page turning and object manipulation). If the person's tenodesis grasp is weak, a universal cuff may be used. Can play some wheelchair sports.
C8–T1	Can complete most leisure activities due to good functional use of both upper extremities.

References:

Model Systems Knowledge Translation Center (MSKTC). (2020, August). Resources offered by the MSKTC to support individuals living with spinal cord injury (6th ed.). National Institute on Disability, Independent Living, and Rehabilitation Research (NIDILRR grant number 90DP0082). https://msktc.org/sites/default/files/SCIFactsheetBookletEnglish2020.pdf.

Paralyzed Veterans of America (PVA). Consortium for spinal cord medicine (1999). Outcomes following traumatic spinal cord injury: Clinical practice guidelines for health-care professionals. https://pva.org/wp-content/uploads/2021/09/cpg_outcomes-following-traumatic-sci.pdf.

EXAM HINT: The NBCOT® OTR® exam content outline identifies the task of implementing "occupation-based strategies to support participation in . . . play, leisure, and social participation across the life span" (NBCOT®, 2022, p. 8) as essential to entry-level practice and knowledge of "interventions for supporting leisure and play" (NBCOT®, 2022, p. 8) as essential for competent and safe practice. The application of knowledge about the intervention principles, adaptive strategies, and adaptive equipment described in the above section and the developmental considerations provided in the following can help you effectively determine the correct answer for NBCOT® exam items about interventions to enable people's engagement in leisure and children's engagement in play.

Developmental Considerations for Play Interventions

1. Plan play interventions that consider the child's developmental level.
   a. Facilitate active participation in cause-and-effect learning.
2. Provide opportunities for culturally relevant solitary play and environmental mastery.

3. Facilitate active participation in cause-and-effect learning.
4. Provide opportunities for play with siblings and/or peers.
5. Provide toys that are safe, durable, and colorful.
6. Provide toys and activities that are visually and auditory stimulating.
7. Plan play spaces that are engaging, safe, and offer flexibility.

Education Evaluation

Overview and General Guidelines

1. The role of the student can occur across the lifespan from childhood to older adulthood in academic, nonacademic, extracurricular, and prevocational or vocational contexts.
2. The evaluation process must consider the person's developmental stage and their educational goals (e.g., an adolescent transitioning to post-secondary education, a retiree seeking to learn a new skill).
3. The OT practitioner can assess the occupation of education during the construction of an occupational profile. Refer to Chapter 3.
4. Screening focuses on the assessment of the person's performance skills, client factors, and/or contexts to determine the need for further evaluation. Refer to Chapter 3.
5. Based on the results of the screening, assessment tools are used to evaluate the developmental, motor, cognitive, perceptual, and process skills that are prerequisite to or related to learning. Refer to Chapters 5 and 11–14 for information about specific evaluation tools.
   a. The student's clinical condition(s) and approach(es) used with this/these conditions should be considered when determining assessment choice.
      (1) Refer to Chapters 6–10 for information about specific clinical conditions.
6. Performance skills and client factors that can impact educational performance (e.g., executive functioning, functional mobility) and specific education-related activities (e.g., keyboarding, group participation) should be formally evaluated.
7. Barriers and supports to education planning and engagement should be identified.

8. The adaptive equipment, AT, environmental modifications, and reasonable accommodations that can enable participation in education should be determined.
9. Some commonly used assessments include the role of students and the occupation of education (e.g., the Role Checklist, the COPM). Refer to Chapter 14 for information about these assessments.
10. Evaluation requirements for public school students are provided in the Individuals with Disabilities Education Act (IDEA) and the IDEA Improvement Act of 2004 (IDEA; Pub. L. 108-446).
    a. Refer to Chapter 4 for more specific information about school-based practice and the IDEA.

The School Function Assessment (SFA)

1. The School Function Assessment (SFA) is a measure that is commonly used to assess students in elementary school.
2. The SFA is a criterion referenced assessment specifically developed to measure a student's performance on functional school related academic and social tasks; it does not measure academic performance.
   a. The SFA is used in elementary school settings with students from kindergarten through grade six.
3. The SFA is completed by one or more school professionals that know the student well and have knowledge of their typical performance throughout the school environment.
4. The SFA is a questionnaire with three parts.
   a. Part I - Participation: assesses the student's level of participation in the classroom, playground, transportation, bathroom, transitions, and mealtime tasks.

b. Part II - Task Supports: assesses the level of assistance and adaptations the student is using for specific school related tasks.

c. Part III - Activity Performance: assesses student's performance of school tasks and identifies components of tasks, with a focus on the physical requirements of tasks and cognitive/behavioral requirements.

5. The SFA measures the extent of change over time with regards to the student's performance on all three parts of the assessment.

6. Scoring is based on a rating scale for each of the three parts.

   a. Part 1 is rated 1–6 ranging from extremely limited to full participation.

b. Part 2 is rated 1–4 ranging from extensive assistance and or adaptations to no assistance or no adaptations.

c. Part 3 is rated from 1–4 ranging from does not perform to consistent performance.

d. Raw scores are totaled for each section and converted to criterion scores which are plotted on a functional profile for interpretation of patterns of participation, support needs, and performance of school tasks.

   (1) Basic level of criterion cutoff scores, scores that fall below the cutoff point indicate a performance that does not meet expectations.

   (2) Advanced level scores that range from 0 to 100 indicate appropriate grade-level functioning.

Education Intervention

Overview and General Guidelines

1. Provide client-centered interventions to develop the performance skills, habits, and routines that are prerequisite to or required for learning.

2. Address client factors and contexts that impact the person's ability to engage in the role of student.

3. Educate and train in the use of AT and adaptive strategies and equipment to enable participation in educational activities.

4. Use universal design for learning principles to accommodate the person's needs regardless of age or ability. Refer to Table 16-1.

   a. Refer to Chapter 3 for more information about the teaching learning process, teaching methods, and education and training approaches.

5. Educate the person and/or parents/caregivers about the rights afforded to them by federal legislation that supports accessible education (e.g., the Americans with Disabilities Act [ADA], the IDEA).

   (1) Refer to Chapter 4 for more information about these laws.

6. Recommend environmental modifications and reasonable accommodations that can enable participation in educational settings.

   (1) Refer to Chapter 16 for information about environmental modifications and this Chapter's section on work for information about specific reasonable accommodations that are applicable to learning activities.

7. Develop the person's and/or parents'/caregivers' self-advocacy skills.

8. Inform the person and/or parents/caregivers about government and community resources and supports that can be used to attain education goals (e.g., federal grants for post-secondary education, free literacy programs at public libraries).

9. For adults with mental illness, use supported education models to enable their ability to develop and accomplish higher education goals in a client-centered and occupation-based manner. Refer to Chapter 4 for more information about supported education programs.

School-based Intervention for Children and Youth

1. In all schools (i.e., private and public) intervention should be provided in the least restrictive environment and integrated whenever possible into the student's school routine to attain educational and functional performance goals.

2. The student and parent(s)/caregiver(s) should be active partners in the establishment of goals and implementation of intervention to increase self-efficacy and engagement.

3. In public schools, interventions must be consistent with the requirements put forth in the IDEA, the IDEA Improvement Act of 2004 (IDEA; Pub. L. 108-446) and the Every Student Succeeds Act (ESSA).

a. The OT practitioner collaborates with school staff, the student, and their parent(s)/caregiver(s) to construct and implement the Individualized Education Program (IEP).

b. When the student is in secondary school, collaborate with school staff, the student, and their parent(s)/caregiver(s) to construct and implement a transition plan for post-secondary life.

c. Apply tiered services to meet the individual needs of students and help them attain academic, behavior, and social participation goals.

(1) Tier 1: early identification, screening, prevention, and instruction; provided to all students to support optimal learning outcomes.

(2) Tier 2: targeted interventions to develop a specific skill (e.g., social skills groups, self-management); typically provided in a small group format within a limited time frame.

(3) Tier 3: intensive individual intervention to remediate a student's skill deficits; provided for a longer duration of time.

4. Chapter 4 provides comprehensive information about federal education legislation and school-based OT practice.

a. Table 4-5 in Chapter 4 describes the three intervention tiers of Response to Intervention (RtI) and provides an intervention example for each tier.

Work Evaluation

Prevocational Assessment Process

1. A prevocational assessment is indicated for persons who have not acquired the skills and/or developed the habits that are prerequisite to work (e.g., persons who never worked) and those who lost these skills and habits due to the impact of a disorder (e.g., a traumatic brain injury) on their functional abilities.

2. Screen to identify client factors, contexts, performance skills, and/or performance patterns that could impact future work potential.

3. Determine if the individual is interested in a prevocational assessment.

4. Gather educational, work, social, and medical history information.

a. This can be obtained via the completion of an occupational profile.

5. Identify potential future work interests through the use of interest inventories and/or structured interviews.

6. Assess current level of skills that are pre-requisite to work.

a. Conduct structured observations of an individual performing work tasks in a prevocational group, rehabilitation workshop (formerly called sheltered workshop), or during a job simulation.

(1) Use rating scales or checklists to record observations of prevocational skills and behaviors.

(2) Table 15-8 outlines the essential work behavior skills that should be assessed.

b. Administer standardized assessments.

(1) Aptitude tests to determine individual's strengths and weaknesses in a variety of areas such as verbal and numerical abilities.

(2) Behavioral and personality tests to determine personality characteristics, attitudes, motivators, and intra- and interpersonal strengths.

(3) Manual dexterity tests to determine motor coordination skills such as speed and accuracy in performing motor tasks. Refer to Chapter 11.

7. Determine if the individual has the prerequisite skills for competitive employment or if a referral to a vocational program (e.g., a transitional employment program, state office for vocational rehabilitation) is indicated.

a. Identify existing abilities and supports.

b. Identify existing limitations and barriers.

c. Identify needed reasonable accommodations to perform essential job tasks.

8. Determine if prevocational and/or vocational training is indicated.

> **EXAM HINT:** In the NBCOT® OTR® exam content outline, Domain 1 Evaluation and Assessment comprises 23% of the exam. Domain 1 exam items focus on the ability of the therapist to "acquire information regarding factors that influence occupational performance on an ongoing basis throughout the occupational therapy process" (NBCOT®, 2022, p. 3). The application of knowledge about the prevocational assessment process described above and the work assessment guidelines provided in the following can help you effectively determine the correct answer for NBCOT® exam items about the evaluation of prevocational and vocational capabilities and work performance.

Table 15-8

Work Behavior Skills

PHYSICAL TOLERANCE AND DEMANDS	SENSORY/ PERCEPTION	MOTOR

• Work pace/ rhythm
• Standing tolerance
• Sitting tolerance
• Endurance
• Performance with repetition
• Muscle strength
• Walking
• Lifting
• Carrying
• Pushing
• Pulling
• Climbing
	• Color discrimination
	• Form perception
	• Size discrimination
	• Spatial relationship
	• Ability to follow visual instruction
	• Texture discrimination
	• Digital discrimination
	• Figure-ground
	• Form constancy
	• Visual closure
	• Parts-to-whole
	• Shape discrimination
	• Kinesthesia
		• Finger dexterity
		• Manual dexterity
		• Coordination:
		  – eye-hand
		  – eye-hand-foot
		  – fine motor
		  – gross motor
		  – bimanual
		  – bilateral
		• Use of hand tools
		• ROM:
		  – stooping
		  – kneeling
		  – crouching
		  – crawling
		  – reaching
		• Balancing

DAILY LIVING SKILLS	COGNITION	AFFECTIVE

• Self-care:
  – personal hygiene
  – grooming
  – dressing
  – eating/feeding
  – object manipulation
• Mobility:
  – transfers
  – travel (mode of)
  – transportation
• Communication:
  – with peers
  – with supervisor
  – writing
  – dialing phone
  – talking on phone
  – typing
	• Numerical ability
	• Measuring ability
	• Safety consciousness
	• Care in handling work and tools
	• Work quality
	• Accuracy
	• Neatness
	• Attention span
	• Planning/ organization
	• Ability to follow:
	  – verbal instruction
	  – written instruction
	• Retention of instruction
	• Work judgment
	• Ability to learn new tasks
	• Orientation
		• Attendance
		• Punctuality
		• Response to:
		  – praise
		  – criticism
		  – assistance
		  – frustrating situation
		• Relationship with:
		  – evaluator
		  – co-worker
		• Work flexibility
		• Attitude toward work
		• Behavior in structured setting
		• Ability to work independently
		• Initiative (in psychiatry you would also observe for additional pathological behavior)

Reprinted with permission from the Occupational Therapy Assistant Program, Wayne County Community College. 1001 West Fort St., Detroit, Michigan.

Work Assessment[3]

1. Initial screening and prevocational assessment as described previously.
2. Job site analysis: used to evaluate the work site and the activity demands of work tasks to determine if the individual can perform essential job functions. Steps include the following.
   a. Meeting and discussing job requirements with the employer (i.e., the essential and marginal functions of the job).
      (1) Refer to Chapter 4 for the definitions, criteria, and examples of essential and marginal job functions as per the Americans with Disabilities Act (ADA).
   b. Observing the actual work site (the environment and equipment/materials) and the work tasks required for return to work.
      (1) Refer to Figure 15-1 for illustrations of ergonomic risk factors for specific job tasks.
      (2) Refer to Table 15-9 for assessment guidelines for determining the general ergonomic risks of work tasks.
      (3) Refer to Table 15-10 for assessment guidelines for determining the ergonomic risks of computer work.
   c. Completing a detailed report for the referring physician and the insurance company that is paying for the evaluation.
3. Functional capacity evaluation (FCE) used to assess an individual's capabilities to participate in work. The FCE has two parts.
   a. The assessment of the physical and cognitive requirements for return to work.
      (1) The physical demands of a job (often termed a physical capacity evaluation) are assessed according to the descriptions provided in the O*NET, the Occupational Information Network, which has replaced the Dictionary of Occupational Titles (DOT).[4]
      (2) Cognitive abilities (i.e., ability to follow directions, safety, judgement, and memory) are assessed through observation.
   b. The assessment of specific job task performance.
      (1) Real or simulated work activities are used to assess an individual's ability to return to work (e.g., Valpar Work Samples or BTE).

> **EXAM HINT:** In the NBCOT® OTR® exam content outline, Domain 1 Evaluation and Assessment comprises 23% of the exam and knowledge of the "administration, purpose, indications, advantages, and limitations of standardized and nonstandardized screening and assessment tools" (NBCOT®, 2022, p. 4) is identified as essential for competent and safe practice. The application of knowledge about the non-standardized screening and assessment methods previously described and the standardized measures described in the following can help you can help you effectively determine the correct answer for NBCOT® exam items about the evaluation of work.

---

[3] Colleen Maher, OTD, OTR/L, CHT contributed to this section on work assessment.

[4] Note: in some sources and practice settings the DOT may still be referenced.

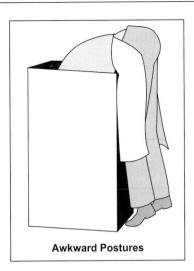

Awkward Postures

Overhead Work

Twisting and Carrying Loads

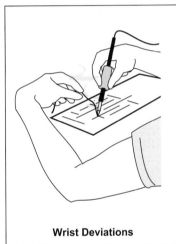

Wrist Deviations

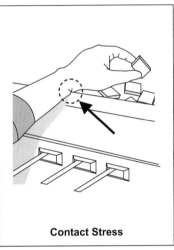

Contact Stress

Poor Shoulder/Wrist Position

Lifting Bulky Loads

Hand-Arm Vibration

Whole Body Vibration

Figure 15-1   **Ergonomic Risk Factors**

Illustrations of selected risk factor conditions. (Illustrations adapted from UAW-GM Center for Health & Safety [1990]; Putz-Anderson V [1988]; Grant et al. [1995]; Canadian Center of Occupational Safety and Health [1988]; American Meat Institute and Ergo Tech, Inc. [1990]). Published in Cohen, A. L., Gjessing, C. C., Fine, L. J., Bernard, B. P., & McGlothlin, J. D. (1997). Elements of ergonomics programs: A primer based on workplace evaluations of musculoskeletal disorders (p. 21). US Government Printing Office.

Table 15-9

General Ergonomic Risk Analysis Checklist

Check the box if your answer is "yes" to the question. A "yes" response indicates that an ergonomic risk factor that requires further analysis may be present.

MANUAL MATERIAL HANDLING

☐ Is there lifting of loads, tools, or parts?
☐ Is there lowering of loads, tools, or parts?
☐ Is there overhead reaching for loads, tools, or parts?
☐ Is there bending at the waist to handle loads, tools, or parts?
☐ Is there twisting at the waist to handle loads, tools, or parts?

PHYSICAL ENERGY DEMANDS

☐ Do tools and parts weigh more than 10 pounds?
☐ Is reaching greater than 20 inches?
☐ Is bending, stooping, or squatting a primary task activity?
☐ Is lifting or lowering loads a primary task activity?
☐ Is walking or carrying loads a primary task activity?
☐ Is stair or ladder climbing with loads a primary task activity?
☐ Is pushing or pulling loads a primary task activity?
☐ Is reaching overhead a primary task activity?
☐ Do any of the above tasks require five or more complete work cycles to be done within a minute?
☐ Do workers complain that rest breaks and fatigue allowances are insufficient?

OTHER MUSCULOSKELETAL DEMANDS

☐ Do manual jobs require frequent, repetitive motions?
☐ Do work postures require frequent bending of the neck, shoulder, elbow, wrist, or finger joints?
☐ For seated work, do reaches for tools and materials exceed 15 inches from the worker's position?
☐ Is the worker unable to change his or her position often?
☐ Does the work involve forceful, quick, or sudden motions?
☐ Does the work involve shock or rapid buildup of forces?
☐ Is finger-pinch gripping used?
☐ Do job postures involve sustained muscle contraction of any limb?

COMPUTER WORKSTATION

☐ Do operators use computer workstations for more than four hours a day?
☐ Are there complaints of discomfort from those working at these stations?
☐ Is the chair or desk nonadjustable?
☐ Is the display monitor, keyboard, or document holder nonadjustable?
☐ Does lighting cause glare or make the monitor screen hard to read?
☐ Is the room temperature too hot or too cold?
☐ Is there irritating vibration or noise?

Table 15-9

General Ergonomic Risk Analysis Checklist (Continued)

ENVIRONMENT

☐ Is the temperature too hot or too cold?
☐ Are the worker's hands exposed to temperatures less than 70°F?
☐ Is the workplace poorly lit?
☐ Is there glare?
☐ Is there excessive noise that is annoying, distracting, or producing hearing loss?
☐ Is there upper extremity or whole body vibration?
☐ Is air circulation too high or too low?

GENERAL WORKPLACE

☐ Are walkways uneven, slippery, or obstructed?
☐ Is housekeeping poor?
☐ Is there inadequate clearance or accessibility for performing tasks?
☐ Are stairs cluttered or lacking railings?
☐ Is proper footwear worn?

TOOLS

☐ Is the handle too small or too large?
☐ Does the handle shape cause the operator to bend the wrist in order to use the tool?
☐ Is the tool hard to access?
☐ Does the tool weigh more than nine pounds?
☐ Does the tool vibrate excessively?
☐ Does the tool cause excessive kickback to the operator?
☐ Does the tool become too hot or too cold?

GLOVES

☐ Do the gloves require the worker to use more force when performing job tasks?
☐ Do the gloves provide inadequate protection?
☐ Do the gloves present a hazard of catch points on the tool or in the workplace?

ADMINISTRATION

☐ Is there little worker control over the work process?
☐ Is the task highly repetitive and monotonous?
☐ Does the job involve critical tasks with high accountability and little or no tolerance for error?
☐ Are work hours and breaks poorly organized?

General ergonomic risk analysis checklist. (From Cohen, A. L., Gjessing, C. C., Fine, L. J., Bernard, B. P., & McGlothlin, J. D. (1997). Elements of ergonomics programs: A primer based on workplace evaluations of musculoskeletal disorders. US Government Printing Office.)

(Continued)

Table 15-10

Risk Analysis Checklist for Computer-User Workstations

"No" responses indicate potential problem areas that should receive further investigation.

1. Does the workstation ensure proper worker posture, such as			
• horizontal thighs?	☐ Yes	☐ No	
• vertical lower legs?	☐ Yes	☐ No	
• feet flat on floor or footrest?	☐ Yes	☐ No	
• neutral wrists?	☐ Yes	☐ No	
2. Does the chair			
• adjust easily?	☐ Yes	☐ No	
• have a padded seat with a rounded front?	☐ Yes	☐ No	
• have an adjustable backrest?	☐ Yes	☐ No	
• provide lumbar support?	☐ Yes	☐ No	
• have casters?	☐ Yes	☐ No	
3. Are the height and tilt of the work surface on which the keyboard is located adjustable?	☐ Yes	☐ No	
4. Is the keyboard detachable?	☐ Yes	☐ No	
5. Do keying actions require minimal force?	☐ Yes	☐ No	
6. Is there an adjustable document holder?	☐ Yes	☐ No	
7. Are arm rests provided where needed?	☐ Yes	☐ No	
8. Are glare and reflections avoided?	☐ Yes	☐ No	
9. Does the monitor have brightness and contrast controls?	☐ Yes	☐ No	
10. Do the operators judge the distance between eyes and work to be satisfactory for their viewing needs?	☐ Yes	☐ No	
11. Is there sufficient space for knees and feet?	☐ Yes	☐ No	
12. Can the workstation be used for either right- or left-handed activity?	☐ Yes	☐ No	
13. Are adequate rest breaks provided for task demands?	☐ Yes	☐ No	
14. Are high stroke rates avoided by			
• job rotation?	☐ Yes	☐ No	
• self-pacing?	☐ Yes	☐ No	
• adjusting the job to the skill of the worker?	☐ Yes	☐ No	
15. Are employees trained in			
• proper postures?	☐ Yes	☐ No	
• proper work methods?	☐ Yes	☐ No	
• when and how to adjust their workstations?	☐ Yes	☐ No	
• how to seek assistance for their concerns?	☐ Yes	☐ No	

Risk analysis checklist for computer-user workstations. (From Cohen, A. L., Gjessing, C. C., Fine, L. J., Bernard, B. P., & McGlothlin, J. D. (1997). Elements of ergonomics programs: A primer based on workplace evaluations of musculoskeletal disorders. US Government Printing Office.)

Specific Work Assessments

1. EPIC Functional Evaluation System.
   a. Focus: determination of the individual's capacity for lifting, carrying, climbing, industrial pulling and pushing, balance while walking, motor coordination, standing, whole-body range of motion, and finger and hand dexterity.
   b. Method: use of the commercially available standardized EPIC six modules.
   c. Materials: materials to simulate work for each of the six modules.
   d. Scoring and interpretation: formal training and certification are required for evaluators.
   e. Population: adults.
2. Jacob's Prevocational Assessment (JPVA).
   a. Focus: assessment of work-related skills in 14 major areas (e.g., cognitive-perceptual skills, motor skills).
   b. Method: the individual completes 15 brief tasks (e.g., money management, filing).
   c. Materials: JPVA manual and profile sheet; common items and readily available materials are identified for use.
   d. Scoring and interpretation: the evaluator checks off areas that were observed to present difficulty to the individual during task performance on a Profile Sheet. Time for task completion and comments about behavior are also recorded.
   e. Population: adolescents and preadolescents with learning disabilities.
3. McCarron-Dial Systems (MDS).
   a. Focus: assessment of the prevocational, vocational, and educational abilities of individuals with disabilities and/or sociocultural disadvantages in five main areas.
      (1) Cognitive, verbal, and spatial.
      (2) Sensory.
      (3) Motor.
      (4) Emotional.
      (5) Coping, integrative, and adaptive behaviors.
   b. Method.
      (1) A pre-screening interview is conducted and referral information is reviewed.
      (2) Work samples for each of the previous five main areas are administered in a structured test setting.
      (3) Systematic observation of the individual in a work or classroom setting is conducted.
   c. Materials.
      (1) The MDS is composed of three large briefcase-sized kits which include work samples, answer sheets, observation of behavior forms, and reporting forms.
      (2) Six established and published assessment tools (e.g., the Peabody and Wechsler tests) are used along with the work samples and behavioral observations.
      (3) A computer program to assist with computation and interpretation of data and report documentation is available.
   d. Scoring and interpretation.
      (1) Each of the six published instruments is scored according to their individual scoring protocol.
      (2) Work samples and behavioral observations are scored according to the quantity and quality of performance.
      (3) Completion of a minimum three-day workshop to develop administration, scoring, and interpretation skills is required of all purchasers of the MDS.

> **EXAM HINT:** If the MDS is an answer option in an NBCOT® exam item, the MDS can be a potentially correct answer *only if* the scenario indicates that the evaluation is being administered by a therapist who completed the MDS workshop. If this information is not provided, the MDS would be an incorrect answer.

   e. Population: individuals who are aged 16 years or older and who have a neurophysiological and/or neuropsychological impairment.
4. Reading-Free Vocational Interest Inventory.
   a. Focus: identification of vocational areas of interest and/or patterns of interest in a number of vocational areas (e.g., animal care, automotive, housekeeping, clerical work).
   b. Method.
      (1) The evaluator presents a group of three pictures representing unskilled, semi-skilled, and skilled job tasks, and requests that the individual select the picture that represents the job task most preferred.
      (2) This process continues for 55 sets of pictures.
      (3) Literacy is not required as the method uses entirely visual illustrations.
   c. Materials: a manual containing 165 pictures and a scoring profile sheet.
   d. Scoring and interpretation: the individual's selections are converted into a numerical score that represents their level of interest (i.e., low, average, high) in the 11 interest areas.
   e. Population: adolescents and adults with learning or developmental disabilities.
5. Smith Physical Capacity Evaluation.
   a. Focus: the individual's performance on 154 items.
   b. Method: performance of real or simulated work tasks based on person's interests.

c. Materials: equipment and supplies as needed to perform each specific work task.

d. Population: adults.

6. Testing, Orientation, and Work Evaluation in Rehabilitation (TOWER).

a. Focus: assessment of the individual's ability to complete specific work samples.

(1) The TOWER system focuses on 14 job training areas through the provision of 110 work samples.

(2) Clerical, assembly, and manufacturing jobs are the main focus.

b. Method.

(1) The evaluator selects preassembled work samples for the individual to complete that are appropriate to the individual's area(s) of interest for job training.

(2) Work samples progress from simple to complex.

c. Materials.

(1) All equipment and items needed to complete each work sample.

(2) Materials are not standardized but specific guidelines are provided for assembly of work samples.

d. Scoring and interpretation.

(1) Individual's performance can be compared to TOWER norms that were obtained for persons with disabilities.

(2) Interpretation of results of work sample performance can be applied to jobs that relate directly to the work samples.

e. Population: adults with physical and/or psychiatric disorders.

7. Valpar Component Work Sample (VCWS).

a. Focus: assessment of groups of skills that are required for specific employment tasks (e.g., clerical) and basic functional capabilities (e.g., upper extremity function, dexterity, visual coordination).

b. Method: completion of up to 23 work samples that are administered individually except for the cooperative assembly task. Samples can be completed repeatedly as part of an intervention program to improve functional performance.

c. Materials: each work sample has standardized equipment (e.g., pegboard, tape recorder). Specialized large equipment is required for certain work samples. A manual includes a materials list, administration guidelines, and scoring directions. A separate kit for administration to the visually impaired includes tactile or verbal modifications.

d. Scoring and interpretation: quality of and time for task performance are scored and converted to a Methods-Time Measurement (MTM) which is an industrial standard with normative data for comparisons. Seventeen worker behavior characteristics (e.g., ability to work with others/alone) are rated on a five-point scale.

e. Population: adults with disabilities and adults without disabilities. There is an adapted VCWS for the visually impaired.

8. Vocational Interest Inventory–Revised (VII-R).

a. Focus: measurement of student interest in eight employment areas for adolescents who are unclear about their vocational interests.

b. Method: completion of a questionnaire with 112 forced choice statements related to familiar job activities and job titles.

c. Materials: manual, pencil, and computer-scored test report.

d. Scoring and interpretation: the individual's occupational interests are compared to established norms and a list of interest-compatible college majors are obtained. Information is used for educational and vocational guidance.

e. Population: high school students.

9. Vocational Interest, Temperament, and Aptitude System (VITAS).

a. Focus: assessment of vocational interests, temperament, and aptitudes to assist with career guidance and vocational placement.

b. Method: completion of up to 22 work samples and a vocational interest interview. A sixth-grade reading level is needed to complete the VITAS.

c. Materials: work samples, tools, manual.

d. Scoring and interpretation: time and quality of performance are scored based upon the evaluator's observations and compared to established norms.

e. Population: adolescents aged 14+ years and adults.

10. Worker Role Interview (WRI).

a. Focus: determination of psychosocial and environmental factors related to an individual's past work experience, job setting, and ability to return to work.

b. Method: completion of a structured interview.

c. Materials: manual, rating forms, and a pencil.

d. Scoring and interpretation: the client's responses are scored on a one to four rating scale with one indicating problems related to a return to work and four indicating supports for a return to work.

Work Intervention

General Intervention Guidelines

> **EXAM HINT:** The NBCOT® OTR® exam content outline identifies knowledge of "principles of ergonomics and universal design for identifying, recommending, and implementing features and reasonable accommodations in the workplace . . . (and) processes and procedures for identifying, recommending, and implementing modifications in the workplace" (NBCOT®, 2022, p. 12) as essential for competent and safe practice. The application of knowledge about the following intervention guidelines and approaches can help you effectively determine the correct answer for NBCOT® exam items about OT services that enable work.

1. If the evaluation determines that a person does not have the prerequisite skills and habits needed for work, prevocational interventions should be provided to develop these before interventions are provided to develop the vocational skills needed for a specific job.
2. Use thematic work simulation and topical work habit and work adjustment groups to develop prerequisite work skills and job-specific skills. Refer to Chapter 3 for more information about thematic and topical groups.
   a. Task skills to enable successful completion of work tasks.
   b. Social skills to facilitate effective interactions with coworker(s) and employer(s).
   c. Work behaviors and habits to ensure a successful work experience.
   d. Refer to Table 15-8.
3. Educate and train in the use of adaptive strategies and equipment to compensate for functional limitations during work activity performance.
   a. Typing aids.
   b. Universal cuff, tenodesis orthosis, and other orthotics.
   c. Review Table 15-2.
4. Educate and train in the use of AT to compensate for functional limitations during work activity performance.
   a. Smartphone applications.
   b. Adapted computers.
   c. Refer to Chapter 16 for more information about computer adaptations and AT options.
5. Teach principles and methods of energy conservation and work simplification. Refer to Chapter 11 for more information about these approaches.

6. Modify and adapt work activities and provide instruction and practice in activity performance. Refer to Chapter 3 for more information about activity adaptation and gradation.
   a. Refer to Figure 15-2 for illustrations of adapting activities to control for specific ergonomic risk factor conditions.
7. Provide conditioning exercises and activities.
8. Educate about work safety and injury prevention.
   a. Teach principles and methods of joint protection and proper body mechanics. Refer to Chapter 11.
      (1) Refer to Figure 15-2 for illustrations of the use of proper body mechanics and joint protection techniques during the performance of specific work tasks.
      (2) Refer to Figure 15-3 for an illustration of a recommended seated workstation.
9. Educate employer(s) about reasonable accommodations to enable performance of essential job functions. Refer to Table 15-11 and Chapter 4.
10. Collaborate with employee assistance programs to obtain additional needed services (e.g., substance abuse counseling).
11. Refer clients to employee assistance programs (EAPs) for additional needed services (e.g., substance abuse counseling) to help them maintain employment.
12. Educate family members and significant others about the person's work capacities and limitations, with their permission.
13. Explore alternatives to competitive work if it is not an attainable goal (e.g., volunteer work).
14. Provide pre-retirement planning to ease the transition from competitive employment.
15. Provide follow-up referrals, as needed (e.g., vocational counselor, work support group, psychosocial clubhouse).
16. Refer to state offices for vocational and educational services for individuals with disabilities for further education and/or vocational training.

Interventions for Common Work-Related Difficulties

1. Cumulative trauma such as carpal tunnel syndrome and low back pain.
   a. Avoid static positions, repetition, awkward postures, forceful exertions, and vibration. Refer to Figure 15-1.

 Raise and tilt the container for easier access and to reduce bending and lifting burdens.

 Extend and support tool to reduce stress on arm and shoulder.

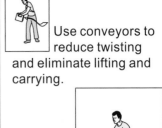 Use conveyors to reduce twisting and eliminate lifting and carrying.

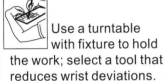 Use a turntable with fixture to hold the work; select a tool that reduces wrist deviations.

 Round or pad edges of guards, containers, or work tables.

 Raise worker with platform and use in-line tool to reduce wrist bending.

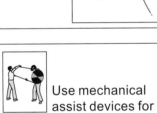 Use mechanical assist devices for less stressful handling.

Select power tools with anti-vibration properties. Use handle coatings that suppress vibrations; increase coefficient of friction to reduce force requirements.

 Use balancers, isolators and damping materials to reduce vibrations at the source or along trans-mission path. Make driving surface smooth.

Figure 15-2   **Examples of Activity Adaptations to Control for Specific Ergonomic Risk Factor Conditions**

Illustrations of some basic ways for controlling selected risk factor conditions. (Illustrations adapted from UAW-GM Center for Health & Safety [1990]; Putz-Anderson V [1988]; Grant et al. [1995]; Canadian Center of Occupational Safety and Health [1988]; American Meat Institute and Ergo Tech, Inc. [1990].) Published in Cohen, A. L., Gjessing, C. C., Fine, L. J., Bernard, B. P., & McGlothlin, J. D. (1997). Elements of ergonomics programs: A primer based on workplace evaluations of musculoskeletal disorders (p. 33). US Government Printing Office.

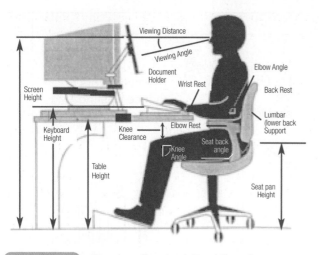

Figure 15-3 **Proper Seated Position for Computer User**

From Occupational Safety and Health Administration. (1997). Working safely with video display terminals. US Government Printing Office.

b. Design work tasks, workplace and workstation to be ergonomically correct to prevent further trauma. Refer to Figures 15-2 and 15-3.
2. Psychosocial and cognitive deficits.
   a. Engage the person in a program that matches their functional abilities and enables them to attain their work aspirations (e.g., vocational rehabilitation workshop, transitional employment program [TEP], supported employment).
   b. For competitively employed persons and persons in work programs, identify the reasonable accommodations that are needed to enable the completion of the essential functions of their job.
      (1) Educate the person about their ADA rights and provide interventions to develop self-advocacy skills, if needed.
      (2) Refer to Table 15-11 for specific accommodations to support psychosocial and cognitive abilities and address limitations that can impact work performance.

> **EXAM HINT:** The NBCOT® OTR® exam content outline identifies the task of implementing "occupation-based strategies to support participation in . . . work" (NBCOT®, 2022, p. 8) and knowledge of "prevocational (and) vocational . . . services, options, and resources for supporting strengths, interests, employment, and lifestyle goals across the life span" (NBCOT®, 2022, p. 9) as essential for competent and safe practice. The application of knowledge about the above general intervention guidelines and the following specific work programs can help you effectively determine the correct answer for NBCOT® exam items about prevocational and vocational services.

Table 15-11

Reasonable Accommodations to Enable Effective Work Performance	
WORK HABIT AND SKILL	**REASONABLE ACCOMMODATIONS**
Personal Self-Efficacy	• Reinforce effective work habits and skills as they occur. • Objectively assess job skills during performance of on-the-job tasks. • Provide a position in which there is a role model to follow and emulate. • Provide coaching and mentorship to develop effective work habits and skills. • Provide reasonable accommodations that enable success. • Teach self-advocacy skills. • Use positive feedback. • Initially provide close supervision and then cut back slowly as skills are maintained. • Maintain similarity and consistency in work tasks to support mastery. • Encourage positive self-talk and eliminate negative self-talk.
Duration of Concentration	• Put each work request in writing and leave in "to-do" box to avoid interruptions. • Provide good working conditions, such as adequate light, smoke-free environment, and reduced noise. • Provide clear directive commands on a regular basis. • Train in the use of stress management techniques (e.g., mindfulness to deal with stressors) that can impact concentration.
Screening Out Environmental Stimuli	• Work in a separate office or in a space that has minimal stimuli (e.g., a workstation in a back corner versus one at the entrance to the workspace). • Provide opaque room dividers between workstations. • Eliminate or decrease background noise. • Provide workers with headphones with microphones to use for telephone calls and video conferencing. • Allow a person to work after hours, when others are not around, or remotely.

(Continued)

Table 15-11

Reasonable Accommodations to Enable Effective Work Performance (*Continued*)

WORK HABIT AND SKILL	REASONABLE ACCOMMODATIONS
Maintaining Stamina Throughout the Workday	• Provide additional breaks or shortened workday. • Allow flexibility in the work schedule (e.g., rather than take an hour for lunch, take a half hour and use the remaining 30 minutes to take three 10-minute breaks; allow an extended workday to accommodate additional breaks or rest periods). • Avoid working during breaks and lunch; use this time to do a pleasurable activity (e.g., walking). • Distribute tasks throughout the day according to energy level. • Job-share with another employee. • Develop work simplification techniques, such as collecting all copying to be done at one time or using a wheeled cart to move supplies. • Provide a liberal leave policy, flexible hours, and back-up coverage that allow employees to take time off to address health concerns. • Individualize work assignments so they match the employee's ability to sustain effort and complete a task. • Provide training in on-the-job relaxation and stress-reduction techniques (e.g., mindfulness) and facilitate the use of these techniques throughout the workday.
Managing Time Pressure and Deadlines	• Maintain structure and monitor progress by using a daily time log and task schedule with specific deadlines. • Prioritize tasks and delegate tasks that can be performed by others. • Provide positive reinforcement when tasks are completed within the expected time. • Arrange a separate work area to reduce noise and interruptions. • Screen out unnecessary distractions.
Initiating and Maintaining Positive Interpersonal Work Relationships	• Provide 'meet and greet' orientation sessions for new employees to be introduced to co-workers, managers/supervisors, and support staff. • Allow sufficient time to make non-pressured, unhurried contacts. • Provide opportunities for co-workers to work together and connect during breaks and lunch at their comfort level. • Respect personal preferences for social interactions. • Respect personal space boundaries (e.g., stand at a 90° angle to another person instead of directly facing them). • Model and encourage direct, honest, and supportive communication. • Have an advocate or job coach to advise and support employees and provide guidance to managers/supervisors. • Provide supervision at mutually convenient times on a consistent basis. • Develop tolerance for and respond in an empathetic and helpful manner to unusual behaviors. • Provide awareness and advocacy training for all workers about diverse social communication needs, capabilities, and styles.
Focusing on Multiple Tasks Simultaneously	• Establish priorities for task completion to decrease the number of tasks that need to be completed within a specific time period. • Delegate tasks that can be performed by others. • Redistribute tasks among employees with the same skillset and responsibilities so each can effectively complete more of one type of task rather than having each employee complete multiple different tasks. • Arrange for all work tasks to be put in writing with clear expectations, due dates, and times. • Ensure that the workstation facilities the organization and implementation of multiple tasks.
Responding to Negative Feedback	• Establish clear work expectations and provide timely and consistent feedback. • Have the employee prepare their own work appraisal to compare with their supervisor's evaluation. • Have the supervisor collaborate with the employee to identify and implement strategies to change ineffective behaviors and/or those that are perceived negatively by others. • Provide positive reinforcement for observed behavioral change and effective and adaptive behaviors. • Provide on-site or remote access to crisis intervention and counseling services.
Symptoms Secondary to Prescribed Medications	• Provide release time for appointments with the prescribing professional (e.g., physician, psychiatrist, nurse practitioner). • Support the employee's efforts to work with their provider to establish a medication administration schedule that enables the fulfillment of work responsibilities (e.g., adjust medications to decrease drowsiness during the day). • Provide release time or changes in job tasks to accommodate medication side effects and match the person's capabilities.

References: Accommodations for Employees with Mental Health Conditions | U.S. Department of Labor (dol.gov).

Crist, P., & Stoffel, V. (1996). The Americans with Disabilities Act of 1990 and employees with mental impairments: Personal efficacy and the environment. In R. P. Cottrell (Ed.), Perspectives on purposeful activity: Foundation and future of occupational therapy (pp. 227–228). American Occupational Therapy Association.

Chapter 15

Table 15-12

Characteristics of Work Conditioning and Work Hardening Programs

PROGRAM	SERVICE PROVIDERS	TYPE OF ACTIVITIES	STAGE OF INTERVENTION	FOCUS OF INTERVENTION	ACCREDITATION REQUIREMENTS
Work Conditioning	One single discipline	Real and/or simulated work; conditioning and physical exercise.	Transition between acute care and return to work.	Physical and cognitive functions to improve work performance.	Not required, but can be obtained.
Work Hardening	Multi-disciplinary	Real or simulated work inclusive of physical, psychosocial, and cognitive components.	Transition between acute care and return to work.	Productivity, safety, physical tolerance, and worker behaviors to improve work performance.	CARF accreditation is required.

Specific Work Programs

1. Work-hardening program characteristics.
   a. Organized like the individual's job; the person must arrive on time, take structured breaks, focus on productivity, and communicate with supervisors and other program participants.
   b. Hours of work are similar to the person's previous job.
   c. Refer to Table 15-12.
2. Work conditioning program characteristics.
   a. Provided in a clinical manner to address performance skills and client factors.
   b. Hours of attendance may be one to eight hours.
   c. Refer to Table 15-12.
3. Ergonomic program characteristics.
   a. Prevention is the main focus to fit the workplace to the human body.
   b. Types of programs.
      (1) Ergonomic survey. Refer to Tables 15-9 and 15-10.
      (2) Specific job site analysis.
      (3) Manager and employee training.
      (4) Educational seminars.
      (5) Exercise and stretching programs.
4. Vocational rehabilitation (sheltered) workshop, TEP, and supported employment program characteristics.

   a. A multidisciplinary or interdisciplinary approach is used.
   b. Real work activities are used.
   c. Participants are considered as employees with supports provided as needed.
   d. Job coaches are used.
   e. Reasonable accommodations are provided. Refer to Table 15-11.
   f. A transition between program participation and competitive employment is provided according to participant's functional level.
   g. Vocational rehabilitation workshops and supported employment can be the final and permanent employment goal for an individual.
   h. Accreditation is not a requirement.
      (1) Vocational rehabilitation workshops, TEPs, and supported employment programs are usually part of an accredited hospital system or a major agency (e.g., The ARC).
   i. Refer to Chapter 4 for more information about the characteristics of these different programs.
5. Discharge criteria from work programs.
   a. The individual has met program goals.
   b. The individual has returned to work.
   c. The individual has not benefitted from the program.
   d. The individual declines services.

Rest and Sleep

Rest and Sleep Evaluation

1. Given the substantial evidence supporting the importance of rest and sleep to health and occupational performance and the inclusion of rest and sleep in the OTPF-4, this area of occupation is becoming more integrated into OT evaluation and intervention.
   a. Despite this increased focus, rest and sleep are typically not included in commonly used published assessments of occupational performance.

2. The OT practitioner can assess this area of occupation during routine screenings and interviews and during the construction of an occupational profile.
   a. Asking a person if they feel drowsy during the day is a quick and easy way to screen for problems with rest and sleep.
3. A more in-depth evaluation of rest and sleep for those who report drowsiness should focus on the identification of the following.
   a. The person's ability to identify the need for restorative rest and sleep.
   b. Typical rest and sleep patterns and routines, intermittent or chronic insomnia.
      (1) The use of OT assessments that focus on time use and temporal adaptation (e.g., the Barth Time Construction, an Activities Configuration) can provide helpful information about a person's typical rest and sleep patterns. Refer to Chapter 14 for more information about these evaluations.
   c. Obstacles to the attainment and maintenance of satisfying rest and sleep.
      (1) Personal issues (e.g., worrying about a loved one [e.g., a child's/friend's illness] and/or work stressors [e.g., fear of being laid off]; being a "light" sleeper who awakens easily).
      (2) Pathophysiological changes related to disease, disability, and/or the aging process (e.g., spasticity, chronic pain, unrelenting fatigue).
      (3) Post-traumatic stress disorder resulting in hypervigilance.
      (4) Sociocultural barriers (e.g., working a night shift job requires sleeping during daytime hours, which is not the norm for most persons, resulting in limited engagement with one's social network).
      (5) Setting constraints (e.g., having no control of one's sleep environment due to being a patient in a hospital or a resident in a SNF or other communal living setting).
4. Sleep checklists and sleep diaries can be used to obtain detailed information.
5. Persons with chronic and unrelenting insomnia should be referred to a sleep clinic/laboratory for an extensive overnight evaluation.

> **RED FLAG:** People with parasomnias (e.g., narcolepsy, restless leg syndrome, sleepwalking), those with (or at risk for) obstructive sleep apnea syndrome (OSAS), and persons with the pathophysiological changes as previously noted should be referred to a physician for a comprehensive medical evaluation to ensure that a comprehensive intervention plan is formulated to effectively address the person's primary condition(s). Because OSAS is deadly, physician referrals for persons with (or at risk for) OSAS must be completed *immediately*.

Rest and Sleep Intervention

1. Intervention must be client-centered, and focused on behavioral and environmental modifications to enable restorative rest and sleep.
2. Based on the person's concerns about and goals for sleep and rest, the OT practitioner can provide interventions that help them acquire the skills needed to do the following.
   a. Develop a daily pattern of relaxation activities (e.g., meditation, prayers, progressive muscle relaxation, visualization) and pre-sleep routines (e.g., turning off electronic devices, saying goodnight).
      (1) Pre-sleep meals should be consumed at least two hours before sleep is initiated.
      (2) Pre-sleep use of stimulants (e.g., caffeine, nicotine, alcohol) should be avoided.
   b. Establish healthy and restorative sleep-wake patterns (e.g., going to bed at a consistent time each evening).
   c. Alleviate symptoms that hinder rest and sleep (e.g., using energy conservation techniques, effective pain management).
   d. Modify the rest and sleep environment (e.g., playing soothing music to relax, using room-darkening shades if daytime sleep is needed due to night shift work, using earplugs/earbuds and/or "white noise" machines to block sound).
      (1) Dark, cool, quiet environments are most conducive to sleep.
   e. Implement sleep restriction training.
      (1) Wake up at the same time every day (i.e., no "sleeping in" on weekends).
      (2) Avoid naps until nighttime sleeping improves.
      (3) Limit the bedroom to sleep and sexual activities (i.e., not watching TV, text messaging, or cruising the Internet).
      (4) When sleepy, go to sleep.
      (5) If sleep is not attained, get up and do an activity that is boring until sleepy again.
      (6) Allow time for sleep restriction training to work.
         (a) It typically takes two to three weeks for the body to adjust to a new sleep routine.
   f. Employ cognitive-behavioral therapy (CBT) strategies to address thought processes that cause anxiety and hinder sleep (e.g., make a list of concerns to address upon awakening and leave them outside the bedroom door). Refer to Chapter 14.
3. In settings in which persons cannot control the environment (e.g., hospitals, SNFs, group homes), the OT practitioner should advocate for the implementation of practices and environmental modifications that support restorative sleep and rest.
   a. Practices can include only waking a patient if medically necessary, allowing flexibility in scheduling to respect residents' diverse circadian rhythms,

Chapter 15

providing earplugs/earbuds to patients and residents upon request, asking night and morning staff to maintain a quiet environment (e.g., speak softly when having conversations).

b. Environmental modifications can include lowering the volume of alarms, shutting off or dimming lights while patients and residents are sleeping, and adjusting a room's temperature to be cooler during sleep.

 # References

Ainsworth, E., & DeJonge, D. (2019). Measuring the person and the home environment. In E. Ainsworth & D. DeJonge (Eds.), An occupational therapist's guide to home modification practice (pp. 145–174). Slack.

Allen, C. K., Earhart, C. A., & Blue, T. (1992). Occupational therapy treatment goals for the physically and cognitively disabled. American Occupational Therapy Association.

American Occupational Therapy Association. (2017). Occupational therapy's role in medication management. American Journal of Occupational Therapy, 71(Suppl. 2), 7112410025p1–7112410025p20. https://doi.org/10.5014/ajot.2017.716S02

American Occupational Therapy Association. (2020). Occupational therapy practice framework: Domain and process—Fourth edition. American Journal of Occupational Therapy, 74(Suppl. 2), 7412410010p1–7412410010p87. https://doi.org/10.5014/ajot.2020.74S2001

American Occupational Therapy Association. (2021). Standards of practice for occupational therapy. American Journal of Occupational Therapy, 75(Suppl. 3), 7513410030. https://doi.org/10.5014/ajot.2021.75S3004

Asher, I. E. (2014). An annotated index of occupational therapy evaluation tools (4th ed.). AOTA Press.

Asrael, W. (1993). The PLISSIT model of sexuality counseling and education. In R. P. Cottrell (Ed.), Psychosocial occupational therapy: Proactive approaches (pp. 451–452). American Occupational Therapy Association.

Bhakta, T., & MacRae, N. (2022, December). Effects of occupational therapy and sleep hygiene in the hospital. OT Practice, 27–29.

Budash, D.E. (2021). Spinal cord injury. In D.P. Dirette & S.A. Gutman (Eds.), Occupational therapy for physical dysfunction (8th ed., pp. 812–838). Wolters Kluwer.

Brown, C., Rempfer, M., & Hamera, E. (2009). The Test of Grocery Shopping Skills (TOGSS). AOTA Press.

Brown, C., Stoffel, V., & Munoz, J. (Eds.). (2019). Occupational therapy in mental health: A vision for participation (2nd ed.). F.A. Davis.

Burns, S. P., & Hammond, M. C. (2009). Yes, you can!: Guide to self-care for persons with spinal cord injury-facing disability.

Clifton, D. (2004, December). Workers' Comp: A plethora of opportunities. Rehab Management, 32, 34–36.

Cohen, A. L., Gjessing, C. C., Fine, L. J., Bernard, B. P., & McGlothlin, J. D. (1997). Elements of ergonomics programs: A primer based on workplace evaluations of musculoskeletal disorders (DHHS [NIOSH] Publication No. 97–117). National Institute for Occupational Safety and Health.

Crist, P. A., & Stoffel, V. C. (2005). The Americans with Disabilities Act of 1990 and employees with mental impairments: Personal efficacy and the environment. In R. P. Cottrell (Ed.), Perspectives for occupation-based practice: Foundation and future of occupational therapy (pp. 289–299). American Occupational Therapy Association.

Dirette, D., & Gutman, S. (2019). Occupational therapy for physical dysfunction (8th ed.). Lippincott Williams & Wilkins.

Ellis, K. (2020). Sexuality. In J. O'Brien & H. Kuhaneck (Eds.), Case-Smith's occupational therapy for children and adolescents (8th ed., pp. 395–404). Elsevier.

Fisher, A. G., & Griswold, L. A. (2019). Performance skills: Implementing performance analyses to evaluate quality of occupational performance. In B. A. B. Schell & G. Gillen (Eds.), Willard and Spackman's occupational therapy (13th ed., pp. 335–350). Wolters Kluwer.

Gentry, T., & Loveland, J. (2013, January 21). Sleep: Essential to living life to its fullest. OT Practice, 18, 9–14.

Gutman, S., Mortera, M., Hinojosa, J., & Kramer, P. (2007). The issue is: Revision of the occupational therapy Practice Framework. American Journal of Occupational Therapy, 61, 119–126.

Hildebrand, M.W. (2021) Restoring home, work, and recreational roles. In. S. A. Gutman & D. Powers Dirette (Eds.), Occupational therapy for physical dysfunction (8th ed., pp. 617–640). Wolters Kluwer Health.

Hinojosa, J., Kramer, P., & Crist, P. (Eds.). (2005). Evaluation: Obtaining and interpreting data (2nd ed.). AOTA Press.

Kohlman Thomson, L. (2016). KELS: Kohlman Evaluation of Living Skills (4th ed.). AOTA Press.

Larson, K., Stevens-Ratchford, R. G., Pedretti, L., & Crabtree, J. (1996). ROTE: The role of occupational therapy with the elderly (2nd ed.). American Occupational Therapy Association.

Leonardelli, C. (1988). The Milwaukee Evaluation of Daily Living Skills. Slack.

Matuska, K.M. (Ed.). (2020). Ways of living: Intervention strategies to enable participation (5th ed.). AOTA Press.

Mosey, A. (1996). Psychosocial components of occupational therapy. Lippincott-Raven.

Moyers, P., & Dale, L. (2007). The guide to occupational therapy practice. AOTA Press.

Murphy, L., & Bowman, P. (2020). Community ergonomics and prevention of work-related injuries. In M. Scaffa & A. Reitz (Eds.), Occupational therapy in community-based practice settings (2nd ed., pp. 279–302). F.A. Davis.

National Board for Certification in Occupational Therapy (NBCOT®). (2022). 2022 Occupational Therapist Registered (OTR®) examination content outline. https://www.nbcot.org/-/media/PDFs/2022_OTR_Content_Outline.pdf

O'Brien, J. C. (2017). Introduction to occupational therapy (5th ed.). Elsevier Health Sciences.

O'Brien, J. & Kuhaneck, H. (Eds). (2020). Case-Smith's occupational therapy for children and adolescents (8th ed.). Elsevier.

Paralyzed Veterans of America (PVA). (1999). Consortium for spinal cord medicine. Outcomes following traumatic spinal cord injury: Clinical practice guidelines for health-care professionals. https://pva.org/wp-content/uploads/2021/09/cpg_outcomes-following-traumatic-sci.pdf

Pendleton, H. M., & Schultz-Krohn, W. (Eds.). (2017). Pedretti's Occupational therapy: Practice skills for physical dysfunction (8th ed.). Elsevier Health Sciences.

Rodgers, S., Ziviani, J., & Lim, S.M. (2015). Occupations of childhood and adolescence. In C. Christiansen, C. Baum, & J.M. Bass (Eds.), Occupational therapy performance, participation and wellbeing (pp. 129–155). Slack.

Schell, B., & Gillen, G. (2018). Willard and Spackman's occupational therapy (13th ed.). Wolters Kluwer Health.

Review Questions

Occupational Engagement and Performance: Evaluation and Intervention

Following are seven questions about key content covered in this Chapter. These questions are not inclusive of the entirety of content related to evaluation and intervention for performance in areas of occupation that you must know for success on the NBCOT® exam. These questions are provided to help you "jump-start" the thought processes you will need to apply your studying of content to the answering of exam questions; hence they are not in the NBCOT® exam format. Exam items in the NBCOT® format that cover the depth and breadth of content you will need to know to pass the NBCOT® exam are provided in the three online practice exams that accompany this text. The answers to the following questions are provided in Appendix 2.

1. An OT supervisor is orienting a new inpatient rehabilitation employee to the assessments the OT department uses to measure occupational performance. Many clients in the facility are covered by Medicare. The new employee is returning to an acute physical rehabilitation setting after fifteen years of school-based practice. At the onset of the orientation, the new employee states, "I had an exceptional course in assessment in my OT program, so I am familiar with Medicare's measurement of occupational performance. It is based on the Functional Independence Measure (FIM)." How should the OT supervisor respond?

2. The occupational therapy department in a skilled nursing facility (SNF) provides services to persons with physical disabilities, chronic illnesses, cognitive impairments, and neuro-cognitive disorders. What core ADL assessments can the SNF's occupational therapists use to evaluate clients with diverse conditions? What ADL assessments have been developed for specific client populations that would be helpful for the therapists to include in their "toolbox" to assess clients with physical disabilities and chronic illnesses and those with cognitive impairments and neurocognitive disorders?

3. An occupational therapist provides services to a client who recently incurred a complete C6 spinal cord injury (SCI). One focus of the interprofessional comprehensive intervention program is teaching clients toileting and bowel and bladder management. The therapist collaborates with nursing to enable the client to achieve this goal. What level of independence is expected to be achieved by this client? What adaptive equipment and strategies should the therapist teach the client to use to enable the client's independence?

4. A person with a C-7 SCI sets a goal to return to work as an accountant. The person expresses concern about the ability to complete a morning self-care routine and job tasks. What will be realistic for the person to expect to be able to do after receiving occupational therapy services to develop self-care and work skills?

(Continued)

Review Questions

5. An occupational therapist seeks to ensure that the ADL of sexual activity is addressed throughout the OT process. Which model can help the therapist achieve this aim? Describe the key points of this model.

6. An occupational therapist provides consultation to a local business that employs people with cognitive limitations due to psychiatric, physical, and intellectual disabilities. What strategies should the therapist share with employers to increase their employees' ability to concentrate, manage time, and focus on multiple tasks at the same time during the workday?

7. During an occupational therapy screening, a client reports feeling tired all of the time. What should the occupational therapist address during evaluation?

16

Mastery of the Environment: Evaluation and Intervention

RITA P. FLEMING-CASTALDY, MARLENE MORGAN,
CHRISTINA M. GAVALAS-VALDIVIA, and
ROCHELLE J. MENDONCA[1]

[1] Colleen McCaul DeRitis contributed to this chapter in prior editions of this text.

▶ General Environmental Considerations

Definition and Major Concepts

1. The environment includes "the physical, social, and attitudinal surroundings in which people live and conduct their lives" (American Occupational Therapy Association [AOTA], 2020, pp. 9–10).
2. The environment in which a person lives, and their exposure to various settings, influences their development and adaptation.
   a. Positive aspects of an environment (e.g., resourceful, supportive, accessible) can facilitate growth because it allows for adaptation and problem-solving strategies to be developed.
   b. Negative aspects of an environment (e.g., impoverished, hostile, or inaccessible) can hinder development and adaptation.
   c. A person cannot be fully understood without considerations of their current and expected environment.

> **EXAM HINT:** The environmental considerations described in this chapter are important for determining correct answers to NBCOT® exam items. For example, the correct answer for an exam item about an OT practitioner planning discharge with an older adult and family caregivers would consider the person's multiple contexts. These would include their physical (e.g., architectural barriers), sensory (e.g., home lighting), social (e.g., available social network), cultural (e.g., norms related to the care of older family members), personal (e.g., socioeconomic status and ability to pay for services and equipment not covered by Medicare), temporal (e.g., the person's and family's daily routine) and virtual (e.g., access to and ability to use assistive technology [AT]) contexts.

3. The natural/physical environment.
   a. Everything that is natural (e.g., animals, trees, mountains, sand dunes) or built (e.g., tools, devices, buildings, transportation systems).
   b. Includes the sensory qualities of the environment.
      (1) Visual: lighting, colors, clutter (e.g., dim lighting, pictures covering a wall).
      (2) Auditory: sound quality and volume (e.g., loudspeaker distortion, background noise).
      (3) Tactile: room temperature, seating textures.
      (4) Olfactory: pleasant or offensive odors.
      (5) Gustatory: pleasant or offensive tastes.
4. The human/social environment.
   a. Relationships with persons, groups, or populations with whom people have contact.

   b. Social aspects: social roles (e.g., a student, parent, or worker) and networks (i.e., groups of individuals who share interests and values).
   c. Cultural aspects: the values, norms, rituals, and expectations shared by a group of people.
5. Psychological aspects: characteristics that can affect mood and stress level (e.g., a calming, comfortable, cheerful environment versus a chaotic, uncomfortable, bare setting).

Legislation Related to the Environment

> **EXAM HINT:** The NBCOT® OTR® exam content outline identifies the task of recommending "environmental modifications, while considering accessibility guidelines, standards, and legislation, to support participation in occupation consistent with client needs and status, task demands, and context" (NBCOT®, 2022, p. 12) as essential for competent practice. The application of knowledge about the following laws can help you determine the correct answer for NBCOT® Domain 3 exam items about selecting and managing environmental modifications that are mandated by legislation.

1. Americans with Disabilities Act (ADA) of 1990: a civil rights law with mandates to enable full participation in society for people with disabilities.
   a. Several sections mandate accessible environments for persons with disabilities.
   b. Includes policies dealing with public service, employment, transportation, and public accommodations.
2. Omnibus Budget Reconciliation Act (OBRA) of 1990: mandates that restraints cannot be used without proper justification, agreement, and documentation.
3. Individuals with Disabilities Education Act (IDEA) of 1990 and IDEA Reauthorization Acts of 1997 and 2004: mandate that children with disabilities receive education in the least restrictive and most natural environment.
   a. Inclusive models are to be used to enable the child to be taught in a general education classroom.
   b. Student-directed Individualized Education Program (IEP) goals must be developed and implemented to prepare a student for independent living, employment, and social participation.
   c. Accommodations must be provided as needed to measure the functional performance and academic achievement of all students with disabilities.

4. Assistive Technology (AT) Act of 2004: focuses on improving access to and acquisition of AT by funding direct services to support individuals with all types of disabilities and all ages, in all environments including school, work, home, and leisure.

5. Fair Housing Amendments Act of 1988: requires that all multi-family housing with an elevator and all ground-floor units of buildings without an elevator meet seven accessibility requirements. These include the following.
   a. Accessible building entrance on an accessible route.
   b. Accessible public and common use areas.
   c. Sufficiently wide, usable doors for persons using wheelchairs.
   d. Accessible routes into and through the dwelling unit.
   e. Light switches, electrical outlets, thermostats, and other environmental controls in accessible locations.
   f. Reinforced walls in bathrooms to allow installation of grab bars.
   g. Usable kitchens and bathrooms to allow a wheelchair to maneuver in the space.

6. Section 504 of the Rehabilitation Act of 1973: requires that all programs receiving federal aid make reasonable accommodations for all qualified individuals with disabilities including accessible new constructions or alterations in physical spaces.

7. The role of the OT practitioner in environmental assessment and modification has increased with the implementation of the previously mentioned laws.

8. Refer to Chapter 4 for additional information about the above laws and other federal legislation that enables participation in a person's chosen environments.

The Role of the Occupational Therapy Practitioners

1. OT practitioners should be familiar with all aspects of a person's environment (i.e., living, vocational, and leisure) whether service delivery takes place in a hospital, nursing home, school, or home environment.

2. OT practitioners can provide direct services to enable environmental mastery and full community participation.

3. OT practitioners can advocate for compliance with the ADA, OBRA, IDEA, and other federal laws to enable independent living and community participation in environments of choice.

4. OT practitioners can advocate for and design home, school, work, and community environments that use principles of universal design to meet the physical, sensory, sociocultural, and psychological needs of the individual.
   a. Refer to Table 16-1.

EXAM HINT: The NBCOT® OTR® exam content outline identifies knowledge of the principles of "universal design for identifying, recommending, and implementing features and reasonable accommodations in the workplace, home, and virtual and public spaces" (NBCOT®, 2022, p. 12) as essential for competent practice. The application of knowledge about the principles of universal design put forth in Table 16-1 can help you successfully analyze answer options for NBCOT® Domain 3 Select and Manage Intervention exam items. Correct answers to exam items will adhere to these guidelines; incorrect answers will not.

The Role of the Team

EXAM HINT: The NBCOT® OTR® exam content outline identifies the task of collaborating with other professionals as critical for entry-level practice and knowledge of "the roles and responsibilities among interprofessional teams when coordinating client care and providing services" (NBCOT®, 2022, p. 6) as essential for competent practice. The application of knowledge about the following team information can help you determine correct answers for NBCOT® Domain 2 Analysis, Interpretation, and Planning exam items about working with a team to develop and monitor intervention plans.

1. An OT practitioner is typically part of an interprofessional team that determines the needs and abilities of a client in a specific environment.

2. Basis for team construction.
   a. The facility in which the client presently resides and/or participates.
   b. The client's needs, abilities, and functional status.
   c. Geographic location.
   d. Funding available to the client (both individually and through third-party payers and/or state offices for individuals with disabilities).
   e. Support available from caregivers.

3. The team should always include the person and, with the client's permission, their caregivers (if any).

4. Professional team members may belong to the Rehabilitation Engineering and Assistive Technology Society of North America (RESNA) and/or National Registry of Rehabilitation Technology Suppliers (NRRTS).
   a. Both professional organizations help to develop standards and measuring tools to ensure proper design, fabrication, prescription, and delivery of rehabilitation technology.

Table 16-1

Principles of Universal Design

Equitable Use: the design is useful and marketable to people with diverse abilities. Guidelines for equitable use include the following.
- Provide the same means of use for all users; identical whenever possible; equivalent when not.
- Avoid segregating or stigmatizing any users.
- Ensure that provisions for privacy, security, and safety are equally available to all users.
- Make the design appealing to all users.

Example: a counter or desk that can be raised or lowered to accommodate wheelchair users and people of varying heights.

Flexibility in Use: the design accommodates a wide range of individual preferences and abilities. Guidelines for flexibility in use include the following.
- Provide choice in methods of use.
- Accommodate right- or left-handed access and use.
- Facilitate the user's accuracy and precision.
- Provide adaptability to the user's pace.

Example: a captioned conference or webinar presentation that provides access to people with hearing impairments and allows attendees to choose whether they want to listen or to read the presentation. Providing this option accommodates the personal preferences of those who would rather not use sound and those who comprehend content better through reading.

Simple and Intuitive Use: use of the design is easy to understand, regardless of the user's experience, knowledge, language, skills, or current concentration level. Guidelines to ensure that use is simple and intuitive include the following.
- Eliminate unnecessary complexity.
- Be consistent with user expectations and intuition.
- Accommodate a wide range of literacy and language skills.
- Arrange information consistent with its importance.
- Provide effective prompting and feedback during and after task completion.

Example: a well-organized website that has clear headings, effective prompts, and unique and descriptive names for internal links/text hyperlinks to facilitate access to all the information contained on the website.

Perceptible Information: the design communicates necessary information effectively to the user, regardless of ambient conditions or the user's sensory abilities. Guidelines to ensure that information is accurately and effectively communicated to all include the following.
- Use different modes (pictorial, verbal, tactile) for redundant presentation of essential information.
- Provide adequate contrast between essential information and its surroundings.
- Maximize "legibility" of essential information.
- Differentiate elements in ways that can be described (i.e., make it easy to give instructions or directions).
- Provide compatibility with a variety of techniques or devices used by people with sensory limitations.

Example: a movie that includes a voiceover description of nonverbal content (e.g., the physical space, the actors' movements and expressions) for individuals with visual impairments.

Tolerance for Error: the design minimizes hazards and the adverse consequences of accidental or unintended actions. Guidelines to prevent hazards and errors and minimize their impact include the following.
- Arrange elements to minimize hazards and errors: hazardous elements eliminated, isolated, or shielded.
- Provide warnings of hazards and errors.
- Provide fail-safe features.
- Discourage unconscious action in tasks that require vigilance.

Example: hallways in schools and office buildings that are free of protruding objects that are at a height which would not be detectable by a person with a visual impairment who uses a cane to detect obstacles and hazards.

Low Physical Effort: the design can be used efficiently and comfortably with a minimum of fatigue. Guidelines to ensure a design is efficient and comfortable include the following.
- Allow the user to maintain a neutral body position.
- Use reasonable operating forces.
- Minimize repetitive actions.
- Minimize sustained physical effort.

Example: touch-activated faucets in kitchens and bathrooms that enable their use by persons who do not have a functional grasp; automatic door openers that facilitate access to buildings and their internal rooms.

Size and Space for Approach and Use: appropriate size and space is provided for approach, reach, manipulation, and use regardless of a user's body size, posture, or mobility. Guidelines to make sure that the size and space provided is accessible to all include the following.
- Provide a clear line of sight to important elements for any seated or standing user.
- Make reach to all components comfortable for any seated or standing user.
- Accommodate variations in hand and grip size.
- Provide adequate space for the use of assistive devices or personal assistance.

Example: a cafeteria that has adequate space between tables and a range of seating options (e.g., tables that allow wheelchair access and wider chairs for individuals who are large) and food displays that can be seen from a seated or standing position.

References:
The 7 Principles | Centre For Excellence In Universal Design
Universal Design Principles- Accessibility at UB- University at Buffalo

b. RESNA offers certification programs for Assistive Technology Professionals (ATPs) and Seating and Mobility Specialists (SMSs).

  (1) OT practitioners are eligible to earn these professional certifications from RESNA.

5. Potential professional team members and their respective roles.

  a. Assistive technology professional (ATP): to analyze consumer needs, help select the AT that can effectively meet identified needs and provide training in the use of the AT.

  b. Computer expert: to assist with the design and provision of efficient computer-based technology.

  c. Certified orientation and mobility specialists (COMS): to train blind and visually impaired persons in specific skills they need to move independently, safely, and efficiently within the community (e.g., how to use a guide dog, cane, and/or electronic navigation).

    (1) OT practitioners are eligible to earn this certification.

  d. Certified vision rehabilitation therapist (CVRT): to provide training to visually impaired persons in the use of AT, optical devices, and compensatory strategies to enable productive, satisfying, safe, and interdependent lives.

    (1) OT practitioners are eligible to earn this certification.

  e. Certified Rehabilitation and Technology Supplier® (CRTS®): for individuals who require complex and specialized rehabilitation technology that is different from standard durable medical equipment (DME).

    (1) OT practitioners are eligible to apply for this registration.

  f. Driver rehabilitation specialist (DRS), driver rehabilitation professional (DRP), and certified driver rehabilitation specialist (CDRS®): to evaluate driver capabilities and plan, develop, and implement interventions to enable their safe driving. Refer to subsequent section on driver rehabilitation and driving cessation.

    (1) The DRS title can be used by OT practitioners, driving instructors, and other professionals who have completed continuing education in the specialty area of driver rehabilitation but who have not obtained either of the credentials offered by Association for Driver Rehabilitation Specialists (ADED).

    (2) A DRP credential is issued by the ADED to professionals who successfully complete driver rehabilitation training courses.

      (a) This credential indicates that the professional is qualified to provide services in basic and low-tech driver rehabilitation programs (e.g., adaptations such as seat cushions or additional mirrors that do not affect the operation of a car, education about transportation options, and driving cessation).

      (b) OT practitioners are eligible to apply for this credential.

    (3) A DRS can become certified by the ADED and earn the credential of CDRS®. To obtain and maintain the credential of CDRS®, practitioners must meet the registration requirements of the ADED.

      (a) OT practitioners are eligible to apply for this certification.

  g. Low vision optometrists and ophthalmologists: to perform low vision eye exams, treat conditions/diseases of the eye that result in visual impairment, prescribe optical and nonoptical devices, and prescribe low vision rehabilitation.

  h. Nurse: to ensure carryover of medical care and medication regimes prescribed by the doctor.

  i. Occupational therapist and OT assistant: refer to prior section.

  j. Physical therapist: to assess and address mobility difficulties an individual may encounter in the environment.

  k. Physician: to authorize and assess services and purchases.

  l. Psychologist: to assist with adjustment disorders, if indicated.

  m. Rehabilitation counselor: to assess and advise on vocational issues.

  n. Rehabilitation engineer: to design high- and low-tech AT and assist with modifications of high- and low-tech AT.

  o. Speech-language pathologist: to assess, recommend, and train in the use of augmentative communication aids.

  p. Teacher: to identify students' learning needs, integrate AT into students' education, and implement modifications into the school setting.

  q. Third-party payers and/or their respective case manager: to approve and/or provide funding for the individual's needed AT and/or environmental modifications.

  r. Vendor: to provide items requested by practitioners and consumers.

EXAM HINT: The application of knowledge about the unique contributions of each team member can help you effectively determine the correct answer to NBCOT® exam items about enabling performance within people's environments. For example, correct answers for an exam item about an OT practitioner who provides home-based services to a person who is visually impaired would include the practitioner providing AT and environmental modifications, and activities of daily living (ADL), instrumental activities of daily living (IADL), and functional mobility training within the person's home; collaborating with a social worker, third-party payers, and/or case managers to obtain funding for AT and/or environmental modifications; and referring the person to a certified orientation and mobility (O&M) specialist to provide O&M training within the community.

Purposes of Environmental Evaluation and Intervention

1. Identify and prioritize a client's needs, goals, desires, and areas of concern related to their mastery of and participation in the environment.

2. Determine the individual's abilities and limitations regarding everyday functional activities and desired role performance within their environment.
3. Assess the functional use of devices and AT that are being considered for a particular individual to facilitate their participation and safety in their environment(s).
4. Determine the individual's interest in devices and AT and their willingness to use and accept the options being considered.
5. Identify a device's availability, safety, and cost.
6. Determine a device's location and frequency of use.
7. Determine funding and financial resources for equipment and/or modifications.

CAUTION: It is of questionable ethics and not in the best interest of clients to show them devices or order top-of-the-line equipment that is not covered by their insurance if they do not have the financial resources to self-pay for these recommendations.

8. Determine environmental constraints.
   a. For example, an individual may be living in a four-flight walk-up apartment and have to leave a device locked up in a lobby, opening it up to the risk of vandalism or theft.

Overall Environmental Evaluation

Evaluation of Performance Skills and Client Factors

1. Performance skills and client factors are essential to assess when conducting an environmental evaluation; they are the foundational abilities that allow a person to function in their environment.
2. There are numerous assessments available to evaluate specific performance skills and client factors.
   a. Refer to Chapters 11–15 for information about the assessments most often used in OT practice to evaluate performance skills and client factors.
3. A comprehensive evaluation should assess the following functions and skills.

CAUTION: The factors listed below and the examples provided for each item are not inclusive of all that should be assessed during the evaluation process. They are provided to highlight the reality that an evaluation of the person's ability to participate in their environments of choice must be multi-dimensional.

   a. Sensory functions (e.g., tactile, pain, and visual acuity) to determine if there is an impairment that could influence safety in the environment. Refer to this Chapter's subsequent low vision evaluation section.

   b. Visual-perceptual processing skills (e.g., unilateral neglect, figure-ground discrimination) to assess for potential difficulties with navigation and occupational performance within the environment.
   c. Muscle functions (e.g., range of motion [ROM], strength, tone, and endurance) to assess if the person will be able to physically move within the environment and perform activities without difficulty, discomfort, or fatigue.
   d. Movement functions (e.g., reflexes, involuntary reactions, and coordination) to assess the person's ability to effectively utilize limbs for mobility and environmental manipulation.
   e. Motor skills (e.g., stabilizing, reaching, and manipulating) to assess a person's ability to interact with objects and to move tasks and objects in the environment.
   f. Cognitive functions (e.g., following directions, memory, attention, problem-solving, and judgment) to assess if a person is aware of their capabilities and limitations and able to safely and effectively perform activities within their environments.
   g. Process skills (e.g., organizing time, space, and objects) to assess a person's ability to select, interact with, and use tools and materials; carry out

actions; and adapt performance when problems arise within their environments.

h. Psychosocial skills (e.g., social interaction, emotional regulation) to assess if an individual can initiate, maintain, and terminate conversations, engage with others in a contextually relevant manner, and effectively manage environmental stressors.

i. Cardiovascular, respiratory, and voice and speech functions (e.g., stamina, endurance, and alternative vocalization) to assess a person's ability to use alternative methods to control devices.

> **EXAM HINT:** In the NBCOT® OTR® exam content outline, Domain 1 Evaluation and Assessment comprises 23% of the exam and focuses on the ability of the therapist to "acquire information regarding factors that influence occupational performance on an ongoing basis throughout the occupational therapy process" (NBCOT®, 2022, p. 3). The application of knowledge about the evaluation of performance skills and client factors as previously described and the following considerations for the evaluation of contexts can help you determine the correct answer for NBCOT® Domain 1 exam items related to a person's occupational performance environments.

Contextual Evaluation

1. Physical considerations.
   a. Arrangement of furniture.
   b. Accessibility of items needed for desired activities and for safety.
   c. Ease of use.
   d. Housing/workplace design.
   e. Neighborhood characteristics.
      (1) Availability of accessible transportation.
      (2) Overall accessibility (e.g., curb cuts, accessible public parking and buildings).
2. Sociocultural considerations.
   a. The individual's social network: the relationships between the person and others.
   b. Social roles: expectations for role performance of the individual and others.
   c. Opportunities for socialization.
   d. Sociocultural norms, values, and expectations for independent living and community participation.
   e. Community resources available.

Home Evaluation

General Considerations

1. OT practitioners perform home assessments to determine if a person can live safely and independently in their chosen residence.
2. OT practitioners are increasingly receiving referrals for home evaluations to help older adults age in place.
   a. Aging in place is a conscious decision an older adult makes to stay in the home of their choice.
   b. Aging in place is "the ability to live in one's own home and community safely, independently, and comfortably, regardless of age, income, or ability level" (Centers for Disease Control and Prevention, 2016).
3. To complete an on-site home evaluation the OT practitioner's "toolbox" should include a tape measure, electronic distance meter, electronic inclinometer (also called tilt sensor, clinometer, or slope sensor), and a door force/pressure gauge.
4. A risk management framework should be used to systematically evaluate hazards and risks in the person's home environment (e.g., portable electric heaters).
   a. The priorities and concerns of the person should be determined.

      (1) With the permission of the individual, the concerns of their family members, caregivers, and/or personal care assistants (PCAs) should also be obtained.
5. The person should be observed performing activities in their home in their typical manner (e.g., boiling water for tea on a gas stove).
6. If an individual is to be discharged to home from a facility, the on-site home evaluation should be done before the discharge date.
   a. If an on-site home evaluation is not possible prior to discharge, the determination of a home's safety risks and participation barriers must still be completed.
      (1) The OT practitioner can collaborate with a person who lives with the client or a person who can access the client's home (with their permission) to complete a structured on-site home evaluation.
         (a) This evaluation should include the completion of a standardized home safety check list and the obtainment of pictures, videos, and measurements of the home. The widespread

use of smart phones has greatly eased this process.

(b) The results of this evaluation can be used to inform pre-discharge and discharge recommendations (e.g., prior to discharge, the family should remove all throw rugs and install grab bars according to established accessibility and safety standards; post-discharge, a family member or a PCA should provide contact guarding when the person ascends and descends stairs).

(c) Refer to subsequent section on the evaluation of home safety.

(2) If the completion of a pre-discharge home evaluation is not possible, a discharge referral to a home care agency should include the need to complete a home evaluation.

> **CAUTION:** An OT practitioner should not assume that the completion of a referral to a home care agency will ensure the client's safety. The likelihood that it will be several days (and possibly more than a week) before the client's first homecare session is conducted needs to be recognized. Therefore, a review of major home safety concerns and education and training about how to minimize risks should be provided to all persons with functional limitations and their family members/caregivers prior to discharge.

7. The person's functional status (i.e., their abilities and limitations) and their environmental supports and barriers will determine which adaptations and modifications are needed to enable the person to live safely and independently in their chosen environment.

8. The results of the home evaluation can be used to develop an intervention plan with the person and their family members, caregivers, and/or PCAs to "minimize risks of injury and maximize opportunities to engage in meaningful activity in the home" (DeJonge & Hoyle, 2019, p. 126).

a. For example, ensuring that electrical heaters have built-in over heat protection and are not placed near flammable items; using an electric kettle to boil water for tea.

b. Refer to Chapter 15 for information about adaptive strategies and equipment that can be used in the home to enable safe and effective occupational performance.

c. Refer to subsequent sections in this Chapter for additional information about the evaluation of home safety, low vision evaluation and intervention, fall prevention and management, functional mobility, modifications for sensorimotor deficits, and AT devices.

Overall Characteristics of the Home

1. Type of dwelling: private single or multi-family house, trailer home, walk-up apartment, elevator access apartment, assisted living facility.
   a. Consider the level(s) of the dwelling in which the person lives.
2. Presence and contents of a back, front, and/or side yard.
3. Presence and use of a driveway and a detached or attached garage.
4. Entrance to the dwelling: level, sloped, stairs, ramp.
   a. Number of entrances that are accessible.
      (1) In some buildings, only delivery entrances are accessible.
   b. Protection from weather/environmental changes.
5. Presence and quality of a doorbell or entrance intercom control panel.
6. Steps: the number present outside the dwelling (e.g., to the front door, to the patio) and inside the dwelling (e.g., to the bedroom, laundry room, apartment building common rooms).
7. Railings: the location and number of railings when outside and facing the entrance door; the presence of secure railings for interior stairways.
   a. Interior railings should be mounted 1½" from the wall to ease grasp.
   b. Exterior railings should be waist high for those who walk; 34"–38" depending on a person's height.
   c. Ramp railings should be between 34" and 38" high.
   d. Circular railings should be 1½"–2" in diameter with nonskid surfaces; noncircular railings should be 4"–6¼" in diameter, with a cross section less than 2¼".
8. Doors: entrance door(s), elevator doorway(s), and interior doors and doorways (bedroom, bathroom, kitchen).
   a. Door sills/thresholds: identify where they are present.
   b. Door width: measure from open door to frame, not frame to frame.
   c. Direction of door opening: space to accommodate door swing must be available.
      (1) A minimum of 18" is needed for those using wheelchairs.
   d. Door handles: identify type.
      (1) Lever handles are more functional than round knobs.
   e. Door force: how many pounds of force a person must exert to open a door.
      (1) Interior doors should require no more than 5 lbs. of force to open.
      (2) The minimum opening force for exterior doors is not specified in the ADA Standards.

(a) For exterior doors to be accessible, they should require as little force as possible.

(b) The maximum opening force for exterior doors typically ranges from 8.5 to 10 lbs.

f. Door closures: enable a door (or a gate) to close in a controlled manner and not slam on a person.

(1) Closers should be adjusted so that when a door is open, the time required for the door to move from a position of 90 degrees to a position of 12 degrees from the latch is a minimum of 5 seconds. Refer to Figure 16-1.

9. Identification of objects and/or clutter that may be obstructing doorways and/or pathways.

10. Presence of pets: they can become obstacles and/or safety concerns to those with low vision and balance problems, and those who require assistive devices.

11. Flooring: location and type: wood, tile, vinyl, carpeting (e.g., wall to wall, area rugs, throw rugs, height of pile).

12. Electrical cords: placement in high- or low-traffic areas for walking, clearly visible versus hidden, frayed versus intact condition.

13. Furniture: location and type (e.g., firmness and height of couches and chairs).

14. Light: amount and quality of natural and artificial light throughout the home and accessibility of light switches from various levels (i.e., standing and chair).

a. It is important to have evenly and well-lit stairways, entrances, and hallways, especially if elevation changes are present.

b. Task-specific lighting is achieved through the use of adjustable lamps.

(1) Light position and intensity should match the activity demands of specific tasks; e.g., reading versus preparing a salad.

c. Increasing light intensity and altering light source positions can reduce/eliminate glare.

d. Lighting is even more essential to consider if a low vision diagnosis is present. Refer to subsequent section on low vision evaluation and intervention.

e. Older individuals (e.g., 60+ years) need three times more light than people in their twenties.

(1) Lumens refer to the amount of brightness.

(2) Lux is the standard measure of luminescence and is defined as the amount of light from a source on a uniform surface.

(a) Light meters are used to measure the amount of lux available.

15. Presence of accessible and safe storage and organization spaces that meets a person's needs.

16. Telephones: number of phones, their location, and type (i.e., cell, cordless, push button, rotary); emergency numbers by the telephone and/or stored in the telephone's memory.

17. Presence of working smoke detectors, carbon monoxide detectors, and a charged fire extinguisher.

18. Presence of accessible working temperature control systems for heating system and air-conditioning systems.

19. Presence of fans, space heaters, or woodburning stoves/fireplaces.

20. Presence of an emergency call system and an emergency exit plan.

21. Overall sanitation and orderliness of the home.

22. If the client's home/apartment is a rental, determine the landlord's understanding that the Americans with Disabilities Act requires landlords to allow tenants with disabilities to install reasonable assistance items such as wheelchair ramps, grab bars, and long-reach faucet handles in their apartments at their own expense for both materials and labor.

Bedroom Characteristics

1. Bed: size of bed, height from floor to top of mattress, type of mattress, wheeled frame or not, and position of bed (against the wall or freestanding).

2. Side of the bed from which the individual enters/exits.

3. Accessibility of clothes and dresser drawers.

4. Sufficient room available for a bedside commode, if needed.

Bathroom Considerations

1. Number of bathrooms in the home.

2. Location of bathroom(s) relative to the bedroom, living room, kitchen, and other living spaces important to the individual.

Figure 16-1   **Door Closure.**

3. Width of the bathroom doorway.
4. Type of bathing the individual performs (i.e., bath, shower, sponge bath).
5. Type of shower: separate stall, glass door tub with shower, curtain-enclosed tub with shower.
6. Presence and location of grab bars (the soap dish and towel bar are not grab bars).
   a. The Fair Housing Accessibility Guidelines require that bathroom walls be sufficiently strong to allow for the installation of grab bars for resident use; they do not require that grab bars be installed in bathrooms.
7. Height of the tub, sink, and toilet.
8. Presence of a nonskid mat or skid-free surface in the shower/tub.
9. Presence of a throw rug outside of the shower.
10. Availability of a handheld shower or adjustable shower head.
11. Presence of antiscald valves and/or faucets.
12. Type of faucet: knob, lever, long-reach faucet handles.
13. Refer to Chapter 15 for a description of adaptive strategies and equipment that can enable toileting, toileting hygiene, bathing, and showering.

Kitchen Considerations

1. Location of meal preparation devices that the individual uses most frequently (i.e., oven, microwave, stove).
2. Presence of a countertop area between the stove and sink, between the stove and refrigerator.
3. Accessibility of food, pots, pans, dishes, and preparation materials.
4. Direction of the openings for the refrigerator, cabinets, and/or pantry doors.
5. Accessibility of the sink including the height and width of the sink.
6. Presence of antiscald valves and/or faucets.
7. Type of faucet: knob, lever, long-reach faucet handles.
8. Presence of table space and seating spaces in the kitchen that adequately accommodate the person and those with whom they live.
9. Presence of accessible and sanitary garbage cans and waste disposal.
10. Presence of a charged fire extinguisher.
11. Refer to Chapter 15 for a description of adaptive strategies and equipment that can enable meal preparation and clean-up.

Evaluation of Home Safety

EXAM HINT: In the NBCOT® OTR® exam content outline, Domain 1 Evaluation and Assessment comprises 23% of the exam and knowledge of the "administration, purpose, indications, advantages, and limitations of standardized and nonstandardized screening and assessment tools" (NBCOT®, 2022, p. 4) is identified as essential for competent practice. The application of knowledge about the following assessments can help you correctly answer Domain 1 exam items about the evaluation of safety in the home.

Safety Assessment of Function and the Environment for Rehabilitation (SAFER)

1. Focus: identifies possible safety concerns in the home environment and assesses if the person is able to respond to safety situations.
2. Method: an interview and observation of a person are conducted in the home. If available, caregiver input is also sought.
   a. During administration, 128 items covering possible safety concerns are addressed.
      (1) These include the living situation, household, kitchen, bathroom, fire hazards, eating, dressing, grooming, medication, mobility, communication, wandering, and memory aids.
      (2) If there is a problem with an item, the therapist applies task analysis and environmental assessment skills to make suggestions that can help the person and/or caregiver deal with the situation.
3. Scoring and interpretation: a form composed of three columns (i.e., addressed, not applicable, and problem) is used to rate each item.
   a. A percentage score is obtained by multiplying the number of problem items by 100.
   b. Qualitative comments about each item and recommendations to address areas of concern can be provided on the SAFER form.
4. Population: originally designed for psychogeriatric persons (Oliver, Blathwayt, Brackley, & Tamaki, 1993), the SAFER can be used with home-residing clients of all ages.

Safety Assessment Scale (SAS)

1. Focus: assesses the potential safety risks of people with a neurocognitive disorder who live at home.
2. Method: observation of a person and a caregiver interview are conducted in the home.
   a. A short version of 19 questions is used to screen for safety risks.
   b. A long version of 32 questions is used to make recommendations and plan interventions to decrease safety risks.
3. Scoring and interpretation: a rating scale of "always," "most of the time," "occasionally," or "never" is used. The results are used to help caregivers diminish safety risks in the home (Poulin de Courval et al., 2006).
4. Population: older adults with cognitive impairments (e.g., a neurocognitive disorder) living at home.

Home Environment Assessment Protocol (HEAP)

1. Focus: assesses the home environment of people who have a neurocognitive disorder for four major dimensions (safety or lack of common home hazards, support of daily function or performance of everyday tasks through physical adaptations, support of orientation through the use of visual cues, and support of comfort through the presence of meaningful items).
2. Method: information about the home is obtained through caregiver interview, direct observation only, and direct observation with caregiver clarification.
   a. The HEAP includes 192 items that assess eight areas of the home including the entrance, living room/den, dining room, kitchen, bedroom, bathroom, hallway, and stairs.
3. Scoring and interpretation: the HEAP includes a 34-page form that is used to rate items in each of the eight areas of the home mentioned previously.
   a. For safety hazards, three conditions are assessed including tripping and falling hazards, electrical problems, and access to dangerous items.
      (1) Each question is rated as either 1 = present or 0 = not present.
   b. For functionality, four types of adaptations are evaluated: fixed or permanent structural renovations, home modifications and adaptive equipment, assistive devices, and nonpermanent adaptations.
      (1) Each question is rated as 1 = present or 0 = not present.
   c. For orientations, four types of visual cues are observed: use of labels, pictures, short instruction lists, or contrasting colors to highlight objects.
      (1) These items are rated as either 1 = present or 0 = not present.
      (2) This dimension also assesses the overall level of clutter in a room as 1 = not at all cluttered to 3 = very cluttered, and the extent to which designated surfaces such as countertops are covered with objects on a four-point response set of 1 = <25% to 4 = >75% of the surface covered with objects.
   d. For comfort, the placement and availability of objects, the symbolic meaning of items that have ties to the past, the availability of meaningful objects to be touched, and the level of noise and privacy are some of the items assessed.
      (1) Each item is rated as 1 = present or 0 = not present.
   e. Relevant items for each dimension can be summed up to obtain indices of the dimension for each room or area of the house.
4. Population: the HEAP was designed for and has been validated for use in the homes of individuals with neurocognitive disorders (Gitlin et al., 2002).

In-Home Occupational Performance Evaluation (I-HOPE)

1. Focus: identifies activities performed in the home environment that are required for aging in place.
2. Method: clients are asked to sort 44 activity cards that reflect older adults' activity performance patterns into four categories: (1) I do/do not want to do; (2) I do now with no problem; (3) I do now with difficulty; and (4) I do not do but wish to do.
   a. Using the activities from categories 3 and 4, the client ranks the problematic activities from most to least problematic (up to 10 cards).
      (1) Each of the 10 cards is ranked on a scale of 1–10 for performance (1 = not able to do it and 10 = able to do it extremely well) and satisfaction (1 = not satisfied at all and 10 = extremely satisfied).
   b. The therapist then observes the client performing the problematic activities.
3. Scoring and interpretation: four subscores can be obtained from the I-HOPE that can be used individually or as a profile of performance.
   a. An activity score is the proportion of difficulty activities divided by the total number of activities that the person needs or wants to do.
   b. A performance score is the mean rating of performance scores for the 10 prioritized activities.
   c. A satisfaction score is the mean rating of satisfaction scores for the 10 prioritized activities.
   d. A severity of environmental barriers score is obtained using ratings of the influence of environmental barriers for each of the prioritized activities.
4. Population: designed for older adults and adults who want to age in place (Stark, Somerville, & Morris, 2010).

Low Vision Evaluation and Intervention

Low Vision Evaluation

> **EXAM HINT:** The NBCOT® OTR® exam content outline identifies the task of identifying "the influence of development . . . (and) body functions and body structures . . . on occupational performance " (NBCOT®, 2022, p. 3) as essential to entry-level practice and states that performance of this task requires knowledge of the "impact of typical development and aging on occupational performance, health, and wellness across the life span (and the) expected patterns, progressions, and prognoses associated with conditions that limit occupational performance . . . (including the) signs and symptoms of disease, stages of disease, (and) secondary complications" (NBCOT®, 2022, p. 3) as required for competent and safe practice. Thus, the application of knowledge about the following can help you correctly answer Domain 1 exam items about the impact of these factors on a person's vision and their need for a low vision evaluation.

1. Evaluation is needed to assess the ability of people with low vision (e.g., older adults experiencing age-related visual changes) to maintain their safety and independence within their home and community.
2. Evaluations are administered in a well-lit clinic or home environment with no glare on the test materials.
3. Components of a comprehensive basic low vision evaluation include the following.
   a. Medical history of primary and secondary diagnoses.
      (1) Primary diagnosis is the visual acuity level at intermediate distance.
      (2) Secondary diagnosis is the condition that causes primary deficits (i.e., age-related macular degeneration [AMD], glaucoma, cataracts, cerebrovascular accident [CVA]).
   b. Other client factors that may impact function (e.g., decreased ROM, decreased strength, decreased sensation, decreased cognition, decreased hearing, decreased ambulation).
   c. Client self-report and goals.
      (1) A person's subjective complaints, use of glasses and other magnification or optical devices, and a functional gauge of materials that a person is able to read.
      (2) Goals for therapy as stated by the person.
         (a) The OT practitioner should help increase a person's awareness that a goal to fix vision may not be attainable.
         (b) The OT practitioner should collaborate with the person to establish goals focused on improving functional use of remaining visual abilities and learning compensatory strategies to be safe, independent, and efficient in daily occupations.
   d. Low vision assessment components.
      (1) Eye dominance: the eye that processes vision.
      (2) Visual acuity (near and intermediate): used to determine the sharpness of vision, measured by the ability to discern letters, numbers or symbols at a given distance according to a fixed standard.
      (3) Visual fields (central and peripheral): refers to the total area in which objects can be seen when focused on a central target.
      (4) Contrast sensitivity: a measure of visual function when the contrast between objects and their background is reduced.
      (5) Refer to Chapter 13 and Table 13-1 for specific information about the evaluation of visual foundation skills.

> **EXAM HINT:** In the NBCOT® OTR® exam content outline, Domain 1 Evaluation and Assessment comprises 23% of the exam and knowledge of the "administration, purpose, indications, advantages, and limitations of standardized and nonstandardized screening and assessment tools" (NBCOT®, 2022, p. 4) is identified as essential for competent and safe practice. The application of knowledge about the above evaluation methods and the following standardized and non-standardized assessments can help you correctly answer Domain 1 exam items about the evaluation of persons with low vision.

4. Standardized and non-standardized assessment tools.
   a. The Flower Design Card.
      (1) Used to determine the person's dominant eye; i.e., the eye that processes vision.

> **CAUTION:** It is important to not tell the person what is being tested until after administration, as this knowledge will skew test results.

   b. Low vision LEA Numbers® chart with notations at 1 meter.
      (1) Determines intermediate visual acuity (the person's primary diagnosis).
      (2) Assesses acuity in the dominant eye, nondominant eye, then both eyes.
      (3) Head tilting during the assessment is allowed.

> **CAUTION:** Clients cannot move their head closer to the target because the relative distance from the text card must be maintained.

c. The Warren Text Card.
  (1) Suggests the level of magnification that the person will need to read text.
  (2) Both eyes are tested together.
d. American Academy of Ophthalmology Red Dot Confrontation Test.
  (1) Tests central visual field.
  (2) Glasses should not be worn during the assessment.
  (3) There are four testing positions to assess superior and inferior visual fields.
e. Two-Person Kinetic Confrontation Test.
  (1) Used to assess peripheral visual field.
  (2) Two examiners are needed for this assessment.
  (3) Should be administered in a dimly lit room so the person can see a penlight when it enters the visual field.
f. Low Contrast Flip Chart: 10M Optotypes.
  (1) Used to assess contrast sensitivity function, which is the ability to see details at low contrast levels.
  (2) The test is administered at three different distances, as contrast sensitivity can be affected for near, far, or both.
  (3) Contrast sensitivity tends to be affected first before changes in visual acuity are apparent.
g. Clock Assessment or Sentence Assessment (non-standardized).
  (1) Used to assess the presence and/or location of a scotoma, which should be assessed for all clients with macular degeneration.
  (2) Missing numbers on the clock (when looking at the center) or parts of the sentence that are missing are where scotomas are located.
h. Revised Self-Report Assessment of Functional Visual Performance Profile (R-SRAFVP).
  (1) Clients rate their ability to perform 33 vision-dependent basic ADL and IADL tasks on a five-point Likert scale (0 = unable to perform but would if able, 1 = great difficulty, 2 = moderate difficulty, 3 = minimal difficulty, 4 = independent. NA is an option for activities not completed for reasons other than vision loss.).
  (2) Easy to administer and takes approximately 20 minutes to complete. Results are simple to interpret and assist the clinician in developing occupation-based goals.
i. Brain Injury Visual Assessment Battery for Adults (biVABA).
  (1) Can be used to evaluate clients with both brain injury and low vision because the assessment includes four subtests to specifically measure visual function related to low vision.
  (2) The battery includes standardized assessments for: visual acuity (distance and reading), contrast sensitivity function, visual field (central and peripheral), pupil response, binocular eye movements, diplopia testing, near space search strategies, extra-personal search strategies, visual attention, and eye dominance.
  (3) The biVABA score sheet includes easy charts, tables, and checklists to document standardized assessment results and clinical observations of eye dominance, visual acuity, contrast sensitivity function, and visual field related to low vision.
  (4) There is a section on the score sheet to document relevant past visual history.
  (5) Helps the practitioner to plan intervention by including treatment recommendations based on test performance in the evaluation manual.

> **EXAM HINT:** A neurological low vision evaluation includes additional assessments designed to evaluate further aspects of vision that may be affected after a neurological injury (i.e., binocularity). This is typically considered to be beyond the scope of entry-level OT practice, so exam items about this type of evaluation are unlikely to be on the NBCOT® exam.

5. Box 16-1 contains helpful hints for the administration of low vision assessments.
6. A thorough low vision evaluation includes an environmental assessment of the client's home, living situation, and available resources and supports.
  a. This Chapter's prior sections on home evaluation and the evaluation of home safety and the

> **BOX 16-1 ▷ Helpful Hints for the Administration of Low Vision Assessments**
>
> - Clients may wear glasses for all assessments mentioned, with the exception of visual field testing.
> - To ensure validity and accuracy of evaluation results, it is essential to maintain the distance between a client and the standardized test materials that is described in each assessment protocol.
> - Generally, eyes are tested individually and then together, with the exception of the near visual acuity assessment (using the Warren Text Card) because reading happens with both eyes.
> - The environment should be well-lit for administration of all visual assessments except the Two-Person Kinetic Confrontation Test (for peripheral visual field).
> - The biVABA package comes with several of the standardized assessments mentioned in this section and provides convenient diagrams, charts, and tables to document comprehensive assessment results.

subsequent section on fall prevention and management provide additional relevant information related to the evaluation of low vision.

(1) Because persons with low vision need increased light, the assessment of the lighting in a person's home, work, and community environments is required to develop a relevant intervention plan.

Low Vision Intervention

EXAM HINT: In the NBCOT® OTR® exam content outline, Domain 3 Select and Manage Interventions comprises 38% of the exam. This domain is defined as selecting and implementing "interventions to promote healing and enhance engagement in occupation-based activities" (NBCOT®, 2022, p. 7) and identifies knowledge of "interventions to support cognitive, visual-motor, visual, and perceptual processing and sensory arousal . . . (including) . . . low vision strategies" (NBCOT®, 2022, p. 9) as essential for competent and safe practice. The application of knowledge about the following low vision intervention approaches can help you correctly answer NBCOT® Domain 3 exam items about intervention selection and management for persons with low vision.

1. Interventions address the significant impact low vision can have on a person's ability to safely, efficiently, and independently negotiate their home and community.
2. Low vision interventions are client- and environment-centered.
   a. Client-centered interventions enable people to use their remaining nonvisual capabilities and other senses more effectively. Interventions include the following.
      (1) Training and compensatory techniques in ADL (including mobility within the home) and IADL. Refer to Chapter 15 for more information about compensatory techniques for ADL and IADL performance.
      (2) Training in the care and use of adaptive devices, including magnification devices prescribed by a medical doctor (MD), osteopathic doctor (DO), or optometrist (OD).
      (3) Training in effective use of visual skills, including preferred retinal locus (PRL) training.
      (4) Education of the client, family, and/or caregiver.
   b. Environment-centered intervention is focused on altering the person's environment to achieve a better person-environment fit.

(1) Educate the client in home modifications and assist with access and installation if these will increase participation and safety and are desired by the person.
(2) Educate the client about the effective use of lighting to enhance task performance.
   (a) Tabletop lights should have adjustable necks and hoods to allow the person to direct the light onto their task without the light going into their eyes.
   (b) Standing lamps should be placed over the person's shoulder on the same side as the eye that has been determined to be dominant for reading.

3. Review this chapter's prior home evaluation section for important characteristics of a home that should be addressed in low vision rehabilitation if a home evaluation determined there were concerns (e.g., poor lighting, the presence of clutter).
4. Intervention should aim to increase contrast, decrease visual clutter, and eliminate glare within the home environment.
   a. Use of solid primary colors and/or black-and-white color schemes tend to be effective in increasing contrast.
5. Preferred retinal locus (PRL) training is an important aspect of low vision rehabilitation for clients with scotomas as a result of macular degeneration.
   a. This training teaches the client how to effectively use intact vision by looking around the scotoma ("dark spot" in vision due to macula damage) to focus on the top, bottom, left, or right of an object.
      (1) Training progresses from basic static fixation, then tracking, to consistently utilizing the PRL during saccadic eye movements.
6. Magnification is indicated for many clients with low vision.
   a. Many products are available in large print, such as books, checks, telephones, and TV remotes.
   b. OT practitioners can provide training in the use of magnification devices prescribed by an MD or OD. OT practitioners *cannot* prescribe magnification.
      (1) These devices do not cure or restore lost vision but they do enlarge print to increase independent and efficient completion of daily activities.
      (2) Basic devices include handheld or stand magnifiers.
         (a) Limited upper extremity (UE) ROM, weakness, or tremors may impact a client's ability to use handheld magnifiers.
      (3) Illuminated magnifiers help increase the amount of light available on a surface.

(4) Convex lenses make objects appear larger; concave lenses make objects appear smaller.

(5) Electronic magnification, such as a closed-circuit television (CCTV), may be indicated at the level of severe visual impairment or worse.

(a) This technology may have audio features including the option of reading text to clients.

c. Magnification devices should only be introduced after a client has successfully learned how to use vision (PRL training) if a scotoma is present.

7. Other optical devices include prisms, which are often mounted to eyeglasses.

a. These devices shift images by moving the nonviewing area into the viewing area.

b. They are typically indicated after neurological injury resulting in visual field deficits.

> **EXAM HINT:** The NBCOT® OTR® exam content outline identifies the task of selecting "assistive technology options, adaptive devices, . . . and other durable medical equipment to enable participation in occupation" (NBCOT®, 2022, p. 11) as essential for competent practice. The application of knowledge about the devices described above and the adaptive equipment and compensatory strategies described below can help you determine the correct answer for NBCOT® Domain 3 exam items about intervention selection and implementation for persons with low vision.

8. OT practitioners can instruct clients in the use of compensatory strategies and equipment that reduce visual demands by focusing on tactile, olfactory, and auditory senses.

a. Adaptive equipment focused on compensating with the tactile sense may include check writing guides (typoscopes), bump dots as positional markers, and folding different monetary denominations in different ways for organization.

b. Adaptive equipment focused on use of the auditory sense includes talking phones, talking alarm and medication clocks, liquid level indicators, audio books, and CCTVs with audio features.

c. Increasing contrast between rooms, elevation changes, walls and objects (i.e., grab bar, toilet paper holder), and tables and plates/utensils is a simple modification to decrease visual processing demands and increase safety.

(1) Using bold-lined paper and 20/20 pens or a Sharpie® can help increase contrast during writing to improve task performance.

9. Removing clutter around the house can be important for preventing falls and promoting safety and ease of functional household mobility when visual impairments are present.

10. OT practitioners can train clients and caregivers in specific sighted guide techniques to help individuals with visual impairment safely navigate their environment.

a. Additional techniques for traveling safely within the home include "trailing" (i.e., using tactile sense) and "squaring off" (i.e., counting steps, turning 90° around corners).

11. Education regarding organizational skills and formation of patterns/routines is important for clients and caregivers.

a. A frequently used compensatory strategy is to keep commonly used objects consistently in the same places to decrease visual demands.

(1) Family members, roommates, caregivers, and PCAs need to be educated about the importance of maintaining this consistency so they do not change the location of frequently used objects.

b. Be sure that any changes to daily routines are meaningful to the client.

> **EXAM HINT:** The NBCOT® OTR® exam content outline identifies knowledge of "strategies for addressing and enhancing health literacy with the client and relevant others . . . (including) caregiver training, teaching-learning models, . . . (and) informed decision-making" (NBCOT®, 2022, p. 6) as essential for competent practice. The application of knowledge about the education and training methods described in this section can help you determine the correct answer for NBCOT® Domain 3 exam items about addressing and enhancing the health literacy of clients with low vision and their significant others.

12. Certain criteria must be met for a person to qualify for low vision services.

a. Medicare requires a minimum best corrected vision (BCV) of 20/70, which is moderate visual impairment, in the better eye to qualify for services.

b. Orders for low vision services must be from an OD or MD.

c. A client cannot be receiving any other OT services at the time.

Chapter 16

Fall Prevention and Management

Falls Etiology, Prevalence, and Prognosis

1. Falls and fall injury are a major public health concern for the older adults.

> **EXAM HINT:** The facts and figures that follow are provided to highlight the reality that the incidence of falls is not rare. Knowledge of these statistics will not be directly tested on the NBCOT® exam. However, due to the prevalence of falls, the NBCOT® exam will likely include exam items that include scenarios related to falls and fall prevention.

  a. Between 30% and 50% of persons over the age of 65 fall each year. Note: percentages may be greater because data are based only on reported falls.
  b. 24% of falls result in severe soft tissue injury and fractures.
  c. Falls are the sixth-leading cause of death for the older adults; 12% of all deaths for persons aged 65 or older are caused by falls.
  d. Falls are a factor in 40% of admissions to nursing homes.
  e. Within six months of a fall, more than two-thirds of the older adults who have fallen will fall again.
2. Results of falls.
  a. Fractures: most common fracture sites are the pelvis, hip, femur, vertebrae, and humerus head.
  b. Increased caution and fear of falling.
  c. Loss of confidence to function independently.
  d. Decreased engagement in activity and restriction of activities that can result in severe physical deconditioning and deterioration, contributing to the likelihood of reoccurrence.
  e. Increased risk of recurrent falls.

Evaluation of Risk Factors for Falls

1. Intrinsic factors requiring evaluation.
  a. Age-related changes in sensory system resulting in reduced sensory capacity.
    (1) Vision.
      (a) Presbyopia (decreased acuity).
      (b) Reduced night vision means that vision in low light situations is also reduced.
      (c) Impaired depth perception.
      (d) Decreased contrast sensitivity.
    (2) Vestibular.
      (a) Vertigo.
      (b) Postural sway combined with vision problems results is a compound risk.
  b. Age-related changes in the neuromuscular system.
    (1) Decreased number of neurons results in decreased response time.
    (2) Decreased number of muscle fibers leads to decreased strength and endurance.
    (3) Two manifestations of the combination of the previous factors include difficulties in rising from a chair and maintaining gait speed.
    (4) Improper transfer techniques can lead to falls.
  c. Pathological states including congestive heart failure, arrhythmias, hypotension, cerebrovascular disease, Parkinson's disease, arteriosclerosis and atherosclerosis, and diabetes mellitus.
  d. Medication side effects and/or polypharmacy.
    (1) Medications that affect the brain (i.e., psychotropic drugs such as antipsychotics, antidepressants, anticonvulsants/mood stabilizers, anxiolytics/sedative- hypnotics and opioids).
    (2) Medications that affect blood pressure (e.g., antihypertensives).
    (3) Medications that lower blood sugar in older adults with diabetes (e.g., oral or injectable medications, diuretics).
  e. Impairments in cognition: confusion, memory loss, delirium, and/or neurocognitive disorders.
  f. Anxiety and/or depression.
  g. Prior history of falls.
  h. Fear of falling can lead to decreased mobility and progressive deconditioning, which increase the risk of subsequent falls.
  i. History of inactivity.
  j. History of risky behaviors (e.g., standing on chair).
  k. Substance abuse.
  l. Most falls are caused by a combination of risk factors. The more risk factors a person exhibits, the greater the fall risk.
2. Extrinsic factors requiring evaluation. Refer to Box 16-2.

> **EXAM HINT:** In the NBCOT® OTR® exam content outline, Domain 1 Evaluation and Assessment comprises 23% of the exam and knowledge of the "administration, purpose, indications, advantages, and limitations of standardized and nonstandardized screening and assessment tools" (NBCOT®, 2022, p. 4) is identified as essential for competent practice. The application of knowledge about the evaluation of fall risk factors described above and in Box 16-2 and the standardized fall assessment described in the following section can help you determine the correct answer for NBCOT® exam items about the evaluation and assessment of fall risk.

BOX 16-2 ▷ Extrinsic Fall Risk Factors in the Home

- **General**
  - Floors: slippery or uneven, presence of throw rugs.
  - Trip hazards, including clutter on floors/stairs, pets, elevation changes, thresholds, throw rugs, extension cords, and high-pile carpets.
  - Low-lying furniture.
  - Stairs: excessive steepness, lack of or loose handrails.
  - Improper footwear.
  - Poor lighting or glare.
  - Use of furniture or other unstable objects for support.
  - Problems with adaptive equipment or lack of needed equipment.

- **Bathroom**
  - No grab bars.
  - Utilization of unstable soap dish or towel bar for support.
  - Toilet seat too low.
  - Wet floor surfaces.
  - Utilization of wet sink surface for support.
  - Sink height is too high/low.

- **Kitchen**
  - Low cabinet doors open.
  - Step stool without handles.
  - Chairs pulled out.

- **Bedroom**
  - Bed too high or too low.
  - Reaching into closets.

- **Living room**
  - Wires and/or clutter across floor.
  - Chairs too high or too low.
  - Chairs too soft/not firm.
  - Furniture without armrests or adequate support.

Fall Efficacy Scale (FES)

1. Focus: measures a person's fear of falling during non-hazardous activities of daily living (e.g., basic ADL, meal preparation, functional mobility).
2. Method: the person's level of perceived self-efficacy at avoiding falls is measured by asking how confident the person feels about completing the FES activities without falling.
3. Scoring and interpretation: the person's level of concern about falling during activities is measured on a four-point Likert scale from 1 (not at all concerned) to 4 (very concerned).

4. Population: community-dwelling older adults with or without a history of fear of falling (Dewan & MacDermid, 2014).

Interventions to Prevent Falls

EXAM HINT: In the NBCOT® OTR® exam content outline, the tasks of employing "evidence-based strategies and approaches to provide safe, effective, and efficient services relevant to individuals, groups and populations" (NBCOT®, 2022, p. 12) and incorporating "risk management techniques at the individual and practice-setting level to protect clients . . . from injury or harm" (NBCOT®, 2022, p. 13) are identified as critical for entry-level practice. In this outline, fall prevention is identified as an example of "evidence-based programming for advancing population health outcomes" (NBCOT®, 2022, p. 13). The application of knowledge about the following intervention approaches can help you correctly answer NBCOT® exam items about fall prevention for individuals, groups, and populations.

1. Intervention is based on the determination of the individual's functional limitations and the causative intrinsic and extrinsic factors that can contribute to falls as identified in evaluation.
2. Eliminate or minimize all fall risk factors and stabilize disease states.
3. Inform the primary medical provider about the need to review and adjust medications that can contribute to increased fall risk and train the person and/or caregiver(s) in effective medication management.
4. Improve functional mobility.
   a. Active or resistive muscle strengthening exercises and general conditioning exercises (GCEs) to improve or maintain flexibility, strength, endurance, and coordination.
   b. Passive range of motion (PROM) stretching as indicated to increase joint ROM.
   c. Specific coordination training.
   d. Neuromuscular reeducation training.
   e. Balance training.
      (1) Sit and stand positions.
      (2) Static and dynamic.
      (3) Turning, walking, stairs.
   f. Functional transfer and mobility training (i.e., bed mobility, wheelchair safety and management).
   g. Referral to physical therapy for gait/ambulation training.
5. Provide sensory compensation recommendations.
   a. Ensure even lighting when moving between rooms throughout the house, so eyes do not have to adjust.

b. Mark elevation Changes (i.e., thresholds between rooms) with brightly colored tape.

c. Refer to this Chapter's section on low vision interventions for further compensatory strategies for persons with low vision.

6. Modify ADL performance for safety.

a. Order needed adaptive devices and train in safe use (i.e., reachers, long handle shoehorn, stocking/sock aid, leg lifter, dressing stick, walker baskets, chair cane).

b. Allow adequate time for activities; instruct in gradual position changes.

7. Teach energy conservation techniques.

8. Communicate with family and caregivers.

9. Instruct the person to avoid use of multifocal glasses while walking and stair climbing.

10. Instruct the person to avoid walking hazards, including pets.

11. Modify the home environment to reduce falls and decrease instability.

a. Box 16-3 outlines strategies and modifications that can be used to prevent falls in the home.

EXAM HINT: The NBCOT® OTR® exam content outline identifies the task of recommending "environmental modifications . . . to support participation in occupation consistent with client needs and status, task demands, and context" (NBCOT®, 2022, p. 12) as critical for entry-level practice and states that performance of this task requires knowledge of "preventive measures for minimizing risk and promoting safety . . . (including) personal safety in the client's environment" (NBCOT®, 2022, p. 13) for competent and safe practice. The application of knowledge about the home modifications provided in Box 16-3 can help you correctly answer NBCOT® Domain 3 exam items about fall prevention.

---

12. Provide specific safety guidelines for the individual to follow. Advise them to do the following.

a. Ask for assistance to transfer or ambulate.

(1) Do not stand up alone; do not walk to the bathroom or kitchen alone.

b. Use prescribed assistive device(s) to ambulate, especially on any uneven or unfamiliar ground.

(1) Keep assistive device near at all times.

c. Use prescribed adaptive equipment.

d. Stand in place before beginning to walk to avoid dizziness from change in position and to regain balance.

e. Do not bend forward.

f. Wear supportive rubber-soled and low-heeled shoes.

g. Avoid wearing smooth-soled slippers or only socks, which makes it easier to slip.

h. Refer to this Chapter's section on functional mobility.

13. Provide psychological support and specific interventions to deal with the fear of falling.

a. Acknowledge the validity of the individual's concerns.

b. Initiate discussions about risk factors and encourage active problem-solving.

c. Modify activities to be safe and achievable to build confidence.

d. Provide activities to maintain physical conditioning to decrease risk of fear becoming a reality.

e. Develop a contingency plan to use in the event of a fall to maintain safety.

14. Recommend the person wear a fall detection device or carry a smart phone with fall detection to alert emergency services in the event of a fall.

15. Recommend that a person at risk for hip fractures wear hip protectors.

16. Teach the person protective reactions to use during a fall and how to get up from a fall.

17. Reduce clinical setting (e.g., inpatient hospitals) fall risk factors. Refer to Box 16-4.

18. Identify community environmental hazards.

a. Poorly designed public spaces.

b. Lack of accessible public transport.

19. Implement community interventions.

a. Increase public awareness, provide education about fall prevention.

b. Institute fall-prevention programs using trained instructors.

Interventions for Occurrence of a Fall

1. Check for fall injury.

a. Cuts, bruises, painful swelling.

RED FLAG: Serious injuries that can result and their presenting signs include the following.

- Head injury: loss of consciousness, mental confusion.
- Spinal cord injury: loss of sensation or voluntary movement.
- Hip fracture: complaints of pain in hip, especially on palpation; external rotation of leg; inability to bear weight on leg; changes in gait or weightbearing status.

CAUTION: Check for dizziness that may have preceded the fall.

- Do not attempt to lift the individual alone, get help.

BOX 16-3 ▶ Strategies and Modifications to Prevent Falls in Homes

- **All Rooms and Hallways**
  - Ensure adequate lighting.
  - Use contrasting colors to delineate hazardous areas.
  - Simplify the environment, reduce clutter.
  - Firmly attach carpet(s) and remove throw rugs.

- **Stairs**
  - Securely fasten handrails on both sides of stairs.
  - Provide light switches at the top and bottom of stairs.
  - Apply non-slip strips to the edge of steps.
  - Paint the edge or add a reflective strip to the edge of the step to increase visibility.
  - Avoid patterned carpeting on stairways; this makes the edge of each step difficult to see.
  - Place a Velcro™ strip on the handrail near the top and bottom step to provide a tactile cue of elevation change.
  - Avoid having clutter on/around staircases.

- **Bathroom(s)**
  - Install grab bars in and out of tubs and/or shower and near toilets.
  - Place non-skid decals in the shower/tub and rubber-backed non-skid mats outside the shower/tub.
  - Use an elevated toilet seat and a bath/shower seat.
  - Install a shelf, pole caddy, or a hanging organizer in the tub and/or shower to ensure that bathing items are within easy reach.
  - Place a bench in the tub or shower.
  - Secure bathmat in place to prevent slipping.

- **Bedroom(s)**
  - Install night lights or light switch within reach of bed and at the entrance to the room.
  - Place telephones in an easy-to-reach position near bed.
  - Ensure the bed is at a height that allows for ease in rising and descending.
  - Replace existing mattress with one either thinner or thicker to lower or to raise bed height as needed.
  - Use a bed cane, electronic bed or bed riser to make it easier to rise and descend.
  - Arrange furniture for easy maneuverability.
  - Secure carpets and rugs in place to prevent slipping.

- **Living areas**
  - Ensure couches and chairs are stable and at a height that allows for ease in rising and descending.
  - Use chairs with armrests or a chair cane to assist with rising and descending.
  - Use a seat lift or a lift chair to assist with rising and descending.
  - Remove clutter and loose electrical cords.
  - Arrange furniture for easy maneuverability.
  - Secure carpets and rugs in place to prevent slipping.

- **Kitchen**
  - Store items on reachable shelves (between the person's eye and hip level).
  - Place a water-absorbent, non-skid mat in front of the sink.
  - Use kitchen chairs with arms to sit/stand up more easily.
  - Provide good lighting (over the sink, over the stove top, over the counter tops).
  - Use a sturdy stepladder with a handle to reach and grasp items.

- **Outdoors**
  - Fix cracked pavement or steps.
  - Install stable outside handrail(s).
  - Remove clutter.
  - Ensure outdoor seating is stable and at height that allows for ease in rising and descending.
  - Install outdoor lighting to increase visibility when it gets dark.

BOX 16-4 ▷ Strategies to Reduce Fall Risk Factors in Clinical Settings

- Assess environmental hazards using a standardized checklist.
- Make sure floors are not slippery (e.g., highly polished).
- Immediately clean up spills.
- Keep areas and paths clear.
- Make sure there is adequate space for maneuvering equipment and clients.
- Keep electric cords/tubes out of pathways and away from beds/chairs.
- Make sure equipment and furniture are stable.
- Remove unused equipment and clutter.
- Store items not being actively used away from clients.
- Do not store items below knee height or above shoulder height.
- Keep bed in locked position.
- Keep wheelchair locked except when being used for functional mobility.
- Keep equipment (e.g., mobility aids) within clear reach for easy access.
- Inspect all equipment for safety (e.g., canes, walkers, wheelchairs).
- Only allow personnel trained in safe transfer techniques and use of transfer equipment to perform transfers.

 ## Accessibility Standards and Environmental Modifications

Accessibility Standards and Recommendations

EXAM HINT: The NBCOT® OTR® exam content outline identifies knowledge of the "processes and procedures for identifying, recommending, and implementing modifications in the workplace, home, . . . and public spaces" (NBCOT®, 2022, p. 12) as essential for competent practice. The application of knowledge about the following accessibility standards can help you determine the correct answers for NBCOT® Domain 3 exam items about modifying the environment to enable full participation for persons with disabilities. Correct answers to exam items about enabling accessibility in a person's home or community will adhere to these guidelines; incorrect answers will not.

1. Architectural features in the home and the community that make negotiation of space difficult or impossible may require modifications to allow accessibility and visitability (e.g., steps, narrow doors).
2. Modifications should be made according to established accessibility standards as described in this section.
3. Wheelchair dimensions and accessibility needs.
   a. Average wheelchair width is 24″–26″ rim to rim. Refer to Figure 16-2.

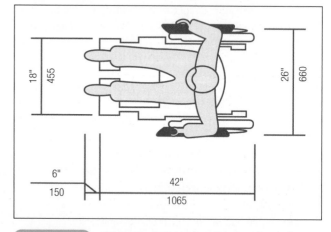

Figure 16-2   **Dimensions of standard adult manual wheelchair.**

Width 24″–26″ from rim to rim. Length: 42″–43″. Height to push handles from floor: 36″. Height to seat from floor: 19″–19.5″ (excluding cushion). Height to armrest from floor: 29″–30″. Note: Footrests may extend farther for bariatric wheelchairs.

(1) Some doorways and room spaces may be too narrow, limiting clear mobility.
(2) The minimal clearance width for doorways: 32″ doorway width minimum, with ideal being 36″. Refer to Figure 16-3.

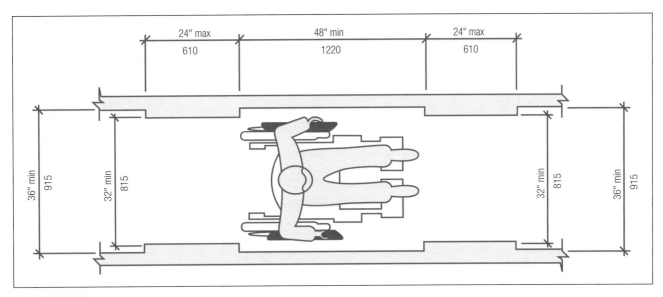

(a) An additional 18″ is needed beside the latch side of the door to allow for door swing and at least 60″ of clear depth when facing the door.

(b) Doorways can be widened or removed if necessary.
  • Removing doorstops can add ¾″ width.
  • Replacing existing hinges with offset hinges can add 1½″–2″ width. Refer to Figure 16-4.

(c) Doorway saddles can be removed and the floor patched, a wedge can be placed in front of the saddle, or a thin rubber mat can be placed over the saddle.

(3) Hallways should be 36″ wide. Refer to Figure 16-3.

b. Average wheelchair length is 42″–43″.
  (1) Adequate turning spaces are needed.
  (2) A 360° wheelchair turning space requires a clearance space of 60″ × 60″. Refer to Figure 16-5.

c. The maximal height the individual can reach forward from sitting without an obstruction is 48″; the low forward reach should be at least 15″ above the floor to prevent tipping. Refer to Figure 16-6.

d. The maximal height for reaching sideways from sitting without an obstruction is 54″ and when an obstruction is present the maximal height is 46″. The low side reach shall be no less than 15″ above the floor. Refer to Figure 16-7.

e. The maximal height for countertops is 36″.
  (1) If possible, counter heights for wheelchair users should be based on their needs; heights no higher than 34″ are often preferred and some people may prefer their counters to be as low as 28″.

Figure 16-4   **Offset Hinges.**

f. Parking spaces should have an adjacent 5′ access aisle to allow wheelchairs to maneuver.

g. Pathways and walkways should be a minimum of 36″ wide.

h. Ramps should be a minimum of 36″ wide and should have a nonskid surface on upper and lower levels.
  (1) The ratio of slope to rise for a ramp is 1:12 (for every 1″ of vertical rise, 12″ of ramp is required). Refer to Figure 16-8.
  (2) Railings should be between 34″ and 38″ high.
  (3) Curbs or edge protectors on ramps should be present to prevent a 4″ wheelchair caster and walker, cane, and crutch tips from going off the ramp edge.

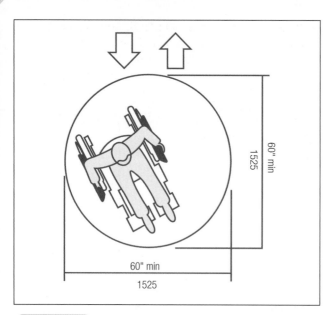

Figure 16-5   **360° wheelchair turning space.**

A 360° turn requires a clear space of 60" by 60". This space enables the individual to turn without scraping the feet or maneuvering multiple times to accomplish a full turn.

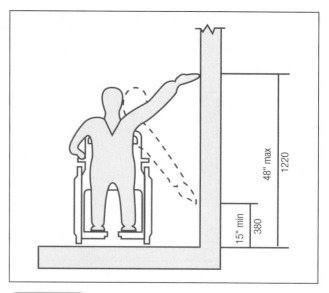

Figure 16-7   **Side reach.**

The maximal height for reaching from the side position without an obstruction is 54". If an obstruction such as a countertop or shelf is present the maximal height for side reach is 46".

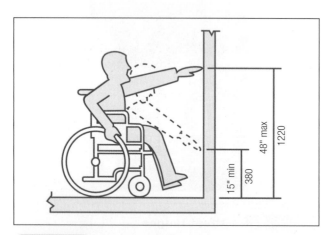

Figure 16-6   **Forward reach.**

The maximal height an individual can reach forward without an obstruction from a seated position is 48". The low forward reach should be at least 15" to prevent the wheelchair from tipping forward.

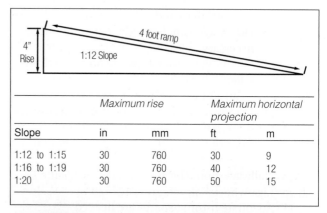

Slope	Maximum rise		Maximum horizontal projection	
	in	mm	ft	m
1:12 to 1:15	30	760	30	9
1:16 to 1:19	30	760	40	12
1:20	30	760	50	15

Figure 16-8   **Slope and rise of ramps.**

This diagram provides the components of a single ramp run and a sample of ramp dimensions. The slope ratio is an important consideration when designing a ramp; slope creates hazardous wheelchair propulsion conditions if it is too steep.

(4) Level platforms must be included in the ramp design.
   (a) If the ramp is excessively long, 5′ × 5′ landing(s) are required to allow for rest.
   (b) If the person using the ramp has limited UE strength or decreased cardiopulmonary capacity, 5′ × 5′ landing(s) are essential.

   (c) If there is a sharp turn in the direction of the ramp, landing(s) are required for turning space. A 90° turn requires a minimum 5′ × 5′ landing; a 180° turn requires a minimum 4′ × 8′ landing.
(5) If the ramp leads to a door, there must be a 5′ × 5′ platform before the door that extends at

least 12″ (18″ is preferred) along the side of the door to allow for door swing without backing up.

i. Electric porch lifts and stair lifts are alternatives to ramps.

Funding for Environmental Modifications

1. State One-Stop Centers, Vocational and Educational Services for Individuals with Disabilities (VESID), Offices for Vocational Rehabilitation (OVRs), and Divisions of Vocational Rehabilitation (DVRs) will pay for home and work modifications, if the modifications enable a person to go to work or school.
2. Private companies will fund modifications to ensure ADA compliance.
3. Private insurance, Medicare, Medicaid, and workers' compensation will possibly reimburse for certain devices/adaptations.

Functional Mobility and Mobility Aids

Overview

1. Functional mobility involves "moving from one position or place to another (during performance of everyday activities), such as in-bed mobility, wheelchair mobility, and transfers (e.g., wheelchair, bed, car, shower, tub, toilet, chair, floor); includes functional ambulation and transportation of objects" (AOTA, 2020, p. 30).
2. Functional mobility is needed to perform ADL, IADL, work, education, leisure, and social participation tasks and activities.
3. Evaluation includes a full client factor and performance skill assessment to determine potential ability to perform mobility (including sensation, perceptual, neuromuscular, musculoskeletal, cognitive, and psychosocial areas).
   a. Based on the evaluation outcomes, the OT practitioner collaborates with the person to establish goals for their functional mobility in their home and community (e.g., school, work, stores, recreational facilities).
      (1) If the client is a child, the OT practitioner actively engages the parent(s)/guardian(s)/caregiver(s) in this process.
4. Intervention focuses on developing the person's ability to be mobile in their home and community environment with or without equipment in a manner that enables their desired occupational performance and community participation.
   a. The type of functional mobility equipment that is needed to address the person's limitations is identified.
   b. Education and training in the safe and efficient use of equipment is provided.

> **EXAM HINT:** The NBCOT® OTR® exam content outline identifies the task of selecting "mobility aids . . . to enable participation in occupation" (NBCOT®, 2022, p. 11) as critical for entry-level practice and knowledge of the "factors related to measuring, selecting, monitoring the fit of, and recommending modifications to . . . mobility aids" (NBCOT®, 2022, p. 11) as essential for competent practice. The application of knowledge about the following functional mobility aids can help you determine the correct answer for NBCOT® Domain 3 Select and Manage Interventions exam items.

Functional Mobility Aids

1. Ambulation aids.
   a. Orthotic devices (sometimes referred to as braces) are used to prevent contractures and provide stability to joints involved.
      (1) AFO: ankle-foot orthosis.
      (2) KAFO: knee-ankle-foot orthosis.
      (3) HKAFO: hip-knee-ankle-foot orthosis.
   b. Canes.
      (1) Straight or single access: one leg.
      (2) Wide-based quad cane (WBQC): one shaft is connected to a four-pronged base to increase stability when a person is not able to balance on a straight cane.
      (3) Narrow-based quad cane (NBQC): same premise as WBQC, but prongs are situated closer together for a person who may not require as much support.

c. Walkers and walker accessories.
 (1) Standard: requires the person to have fair balance and the ability to lift device with UE to advance.
 (2) Rolling walker: for those who cannot lift a standard walker due to UE weakness or impaired balance.
 (3) Hemi-walker: a walker situated on the non-affected side of a person; useful for those who do not have the ability to use two hands and for those who need more stability than a cane.
  (a) May also be referred to as a side-stepper.
 (4) Three-wheeled walker (also known as rollator): large pneumatic wheels, hand brakes, and a fold-down seat for those who need increased stability and/or fatigue easily.
 (5) Walker bags, trays, and baskets are used to assist in transporting personal items.

d. Crutches.
 (1) Standard: situated in person's axillary region to allow ambulation.
 (2) Platform: forearms are neutral and are supported and hands are in neutral position.
 (3) Lofstrand: proximal arm has closure around it instead of support in axillary region.

e. Slings provide support to a UE which may have fractured and prevent poor handling of flaccid UE.

2. Wheelchairs and wheelchair training: refer to this chapter's subsequent section.

3. Scooters: provide mobility to those who are cannot ambulate for distances and/or by those who have difficulty ambulating over uneven or steep terrain.
 a. They are often used as an alternative to a wheelchair by persons who have good trunk stability but not the strength or endurance to propel a manual wheelchair.

4. Transitional mobility: devices that allow the child to freely explore their environment e.g., adapted play scooters, bicycle, and tricycles, battery-operated play vehicles.

5. Transfer/sliding boards allow independent transfers from different surfaces for those who are not able to stand-pivot.

6. UE mobility aids for task performance (e.g., mobile arm support). Refer to Figure 12-5.

7. Table 16-2 provides information about the functional mobility aides that are typically used by persons with spinal cord injuries (SCIs).

EXAM HINT: The equipment and level of assistance *required* for functional mobility may vary within each SCI level, based on the severity of the injury (i.e., complete vs. incomplete) and control of potentially innervated muscles (i.e., functional control of UE movement in cervical level SCIs, control of trunk muscles in thoracic level SCIs). The equipment and level of assistance the person *chooses to use* will depend on their adaptation to their SCI and their occupational performance priorities. For example, a person may have the ability to walk using orthoses and/or assistive devices but they may choose to walk only for exercise or short distances and use a lightweight sports chair for leisure and community participation activities (e.g., wheelchair sports) The expected functional performance levels and suggested equipment outlined in Table 16-2 are most common for individuals with a complete injury at the listed level of SCI.

Bed Mobility

1. Rolling, bridging, sidelying, supine, and sitting.
2. Some diagnoses require special positioning in bed to attain the following outcomes.
 a. Maintain alignment of vulnerable joints.
 b. Provide variation in postures.
 c. Decrease the effect of pathological reflex activity.
 d. Provide variations in ranges of motion.
 e. Provide stretch to muscles prone to contracture.
 f. Increase comfort.
 g. Decrease risk for pressure ulcers.
 h. Provide supine as well as right and left side positioning.
3. Specific mobility/positioning techniques.
 a. Status-post total hip replacement.
  (1) May not be permitted to roll on the nonoperated side. This may result in internal rotation of the operated hip, which may cause dislocation.
  (2) May require use of abductor pillow between lower extremities (LEs) to prevent adduction of the operated hip.
 b. Status-post CVA.
  (1) May need education regarding proper positioning of the affected UE to increase awareness, minimize pain, decrease swelling, and promote normalization of tone.
  (2) May also require use of pillows between the knees while in sidelying position to increase comfort and promote proper positioning.

Table 16-2

SCI Levels and Ability to Engage in Functional Mobility Activities

SCI LEVEL	FUNCTIONAL MOBILITY ACTIVITIES
C1–C4	**Bed Mobility:** Total assistance is required. Durable medical equipment used may include an electric/semi-electric hospital bed with Trendelenberg feature, specialty pressure-relieving mattress, and bilateral side rails. May be able to assist with operating an electric adjustable bed using an environmental control unit (i.e., voice activated, mouth stick controller). **Transfers:** Total assistance is required using a power or manual lift or a transfer/sliding board. **Wheelchair Mobility:** Can independently propel an electric wheelchair by using a head or chin control, a mouthstick, or breath control with postural support and head control devices as needed. Total assistance is required for the use of a manual wheelchair. **Pressure Relief:** Can be independent using a power tilt wheelchair and pressure-relieving cushion. **Standing:** Totally dependent.
C5	**Bed Mobility:** Moderate to maximal assistance is required using bilateral side rails, bed ladder, and/or thigh straps. Can assist in the operation of an electric hospital bed with Trendelenburg feature with patient controls. **Transfers:** Total assistance is required using a power or manual lift or maximal to total assistance using a transfer/sliding board. **Wheelchair Mobility:** Can independently use a power recline/tilt wheelchair with arm drive control. Can be independent with propelling a manual wheelchair (lightweight rigid or folding frame with handrim modifications) on non-carpeted, level, indoor surfaces for short distances. A power wheelchair is required to engage in some in-home activities (based on the size/layout of the person's living space and their UE function) and for all community-based activities. **Pressure Relief:** Same as C1-C4, but additionally may be able to complete side-to-side pressure relief in a wheelchair. **Standing:** Totally dependent using a hydraulic standing frame.
C6	**Bed Mobility:** Independent with an electric hospital bed and side rails. A standard bed may be used with assistance for bed mobility. Equipment used may include a bed ladder or thigh straps. **Transfers:** Independent for level surfaces using a transfer/sliding board. Requires minimal to total assistance for transfer/sliding board transfers to uneven surfaces, depending on the difference between the surface heights. **Wheelchair Mobility:** Can independently use a power wheelchair (reclining or upright) with standard arm drive on all surfaces. Can independently propel a manual wheelchair (lightweight rigid or folding frame with modified rims) indoors. Requires minimal to total assistance for the use of a manual wheelchair outdoors. May use specialized wheelchair gloves, wheelchair pegs, or have modifications to wheels/rims. **Pressure Relief:** Independent with equipment and/or adapted techniques (i.e., power recline wheelchair, pressure-relieving cushion, side-to-side pressure relief). **Standing:** Same as C5.
C7–C8	**Bed Mobility:** Can be independent or require some assistance, using an electric or standard bed. **Transfers:** Can be completed independently or with minimal to moderate assist for level and uneven surfaces with a transfer/sliding board or via a depression transfer. **Wheelchair Mobility:** Can independently propel a manual wheelchair (lightweight rigid or folding frame with modified rims) on all indoor surfaces and level outdoor environments with equipment as needed; requires some assistance with uneven outdoor terrain. **Pressure Relief:** Independent with lateral leans or wheelchair push-ups using pressure-relief cushions and postural support as needed. **Standing:** Can be completed with some assist or independently using a hydraulic/standard standing frame.
T1–T9	**Bed Mobility:** Independent with standard bed. **Transfers:** Independent with or without a transfer/sliding board. **Wheelchair Mobility:** Independent using a manual wheelchair with rigid or folding lightweight frame. **Pressure relief:** Independent with cushions and postural supports as needed. **Standing:** Independent using a standing frame; ambulation is typically not functional.
T10–L1	**Bed Mobility:** Same as T1–T9. **Transfers:** Independent without a device. **Wheelchair Mobility:** Same as T1–T9. **Pressure Relief:** Same as T1–T9. **Standing:** Independent using a standing frame. **Functional Ambulation:** Independent or with some assistance, using devices such as forearm crutches or walker and a knee/ankle/foot orthosis (KAFO).
L2–S5	**Bed Mobility, Transfers, Wheelchair Mobility, Pressure Relief, and Standing:** Same as T10–L1. **Functional Ambulation:** Same as T10–L1 except a cane may be used instead of a walker and an ankle-foot orthoses may be used instead of a KAFO. Injuries at the sacral level may require less or no bracing or assistive devices.

Adapted from: Model Systems Knowledge Translation Center (MSKTC). (2020, August). Resources offered by the MSKTC to support individuals living with spinal cord injury (6th ed.). National Institute on Disability, Independent Living, and Rehabilitation Research (NIDILRR grant number 90DP0082). https://msktc.org/sites/default/files/SCIFactsheetBookletEnglish2020.pdf.

Paralyzed Veterans of America (PVA). (1999). Consortium for spinal cord medicine. Outcomes following traumatic spinal cord injury: Clinical practice guidelines for health-care professionals. https://pva.org/wp-content/uploads/2021/09/cpg_outcomes-following-traumatic-sci.pdf.

c. Status-post amputation of the LE.
  (1) May require training regarding use of pillows to prevent edema in the LE.
  (2) May also need training on how to provide passive stretching to the residual limb while in bed to prevent shortening or contracture, which would make prosthetic training difficult and painful.
d. Status-post SCI.
  (1) Table 16-2 provides information about the functional bed mobility abilities and limitations of person with SCIs and the equipment that can be used to enable mobility.

> **EXAM HINT:** The NBCOT® OTR® exam content outline identifies the task of implementing "occupation-based strategies to support participation in activities of daily living . . . (and) rest and sleep" (NBCOT®, 2022, p. 8) as critical for entry-level practice. The application of knowledge about the bed mobility/positioning techniques described above and the following bed mobility aids can help you determine the correct answer to NBCOT® exam items about enabling ADL, rest, and sleep.

4. Bed mobility aids.
  a. Electronic beds, usually with bedrails and elevating head/foot surfaces to increase safety and comfort.
    (1) Bedrails can assist with rolling, positioning for sleep, and assuming a short-sit position.
  b. Overhead trapeze frame attached to bed to assist with rolling over and assuming a long sit position.

> **CAUTION:** A trapeze should not be used by persons who have shoulder instability, a subluxed shoulder, or flaccidity in the upper extremity.

c. Rope ladders to assist in pulling to a seated position.
d. Bed canes to assist with rising from bed and/or standing. Refer to Figure 16-9.
e. Bed risers to raise the bed to make it easier for the person to get up and go to the bathroom at night.
f. Hoyer lift/trans-aid, a hammock device that is attached to either hydraulic or manual lift systems to transfer individuals who are dependent.
g. Bedpans and personal urinals if unable to leave the bed.

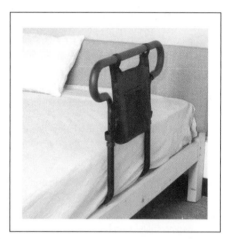

Figure 16-9 **Bed Cane.**

Wheelchair Assessment, Prescription, Types, and Training

Purposes of Wheelchairs

1. Enable independent functional mobility using the non-ambulatory person's capabilities.
2. Facilitate mastery of the environment.
3. Enable occupational engagement and social participation.

Wheelchair Assessment and Prescription Considerations

1. Client factor and performance skill assessments.
  a. The factors listed below and the examples provided for each item are not inclusive of all that should be assessed during the evaluation process. They are provided to highlight the reality that the evaluation of a person to determine which wheelchair will best meet their needs must be multidimensional.
    (1) Sensory: e.g., sensory loss places the person at risk for the development of decubiti; therefore, necessitating a special seat cushion.
    (2) Neuromuscular: e.g., the individual's sitting posture can require application of seating and positioning knowledge; poor trunk control requires postural supports.
    (3) Musculoskeletal: e.g., physical limitations, such as a compromised respiratory status may impede mobility and require a powered wheelchair prescription.
      (a) For optimal seating and positioning, distinguish between flexible postures/deformities (i.e., where the OT practitioner can manually correct the position) and fixed or abnormal

postures/deformities (i.e., changes cannot occur).

(b) When assessing alignment, the pelvis should be evaluated first, and then the LEs, trunk, UEs, head and neck, and feet; stability supports functional mobility and proximal control allowing for better distal function.

(4) Cognition: e.g., deficits in cognitive function may impede ability to operate powered devices.

(5) Psychosocial; e.g., the acceptability of wheelchair use; the availability of supports to assist with transferring to and transporting a wheelchair.

2. Personal assessment.
   a. Age and developmental status. Refer to subsequent section on developmental considerations.
   b. Determine the individual's medical status, including prognosis (i.e., condition is temporary, permanent, stable, or progressive) and functional level/needs.
   c. Education and work interests and pursuits (e.g., the need for desk arms).
   d. Leisure interests and pursuits (e.g., a special sports chair can enable the individual to pursue past or new interests).
   e. Daily routines and habits.
   f. Goals and desired occupations.
   g. Assess the ability of the wheelchair to interact/interface with other AT and/or medical equipment used while in the wheelchair (e.g., a communication board, ventilator).

3. Contextual assessments.
   a. Physical environment.
      (1) Areas of travel and wheelchair use.
      (2) Surfaces and terrains that will be traveled on indoors (e.g., floor surfaces) and outdoors (e.g., sidewalks).
   b. Building characteristics of school, work, leisure, and/or worship.
      (1) Doorways.
      (2) Hallways.
      (3) Restrooms.
      (4) Workspace design.
      (5) Parking.
      (6) Other specifics as described in the home evaluation section of this Chapter.

4. Wheelchair characteristics.
   a. Transportability/portability.
   b. Ride quality.
   c. Features that can meet the person's needs.
      (1) Control mechanism (e.g., type of brakes, antitippers).
      (2) Propulsion method (e.g., one arm drive, use of hand rim projections, motorized, use of the LEs to propel).
      (3) Personalized features (e.g., use of lap tray and/or backpack to hold personal items and/or medical equipment, hard tires instead of pneumatic tires for increased durability for more active individuals, postural supports for persons with poor trunk control).

5. Developmental considerations in assessment.
   a. Transportability to, from, and in school.
   b. Allowance for adjustment when growth occurs.
   c. Allowance for the use of adaptive equipment (i.e., computer, augmentative communication).
   d. Facilitation of social acceptance.

> **EXAM HINT:** The NBCOT® OTR® exam content outline identifies knowledge of the "factors related to measuring, selecting, monitoring the fit of, and recommending modifications to . . . mobility aids" (NBCOT®, 2022, p. 11) as essential for competent practice. This outline also states that "some examples include equipment components (and) biomechanical considerations" (NBCOT®, 2022, p. 11). The application of knowledge about the previously described wheelchair assessment foci and considerations and the following information about wheelchair components, measurement, and types can help you determine the correct answer for exam items about the mobility aid of wheelchairs.

Wheelchair Components

1. Arm rests.
   a. Fixed: minimal benefit but may be seen in older wheelchairs and/or in rentals.
   b. Detachable: helpful for transfers.
   c. Height adjustable: allows for ease in transfers and better support of a lap tray.
   d. Desk arms: allow for moving closer to work surfaces.
   e. Full arms: allow for holding of a lap tray and possibly ease transfers.
   f. Wraparound, space saver arm rests: reduces the overall width of the chair by 1″.

2. Leg rests.
   a. Fixed: minimal benefit but may be seen in older wheelchairs and/or in rentals.
   b. Swing-away: allows feet to be placed on the floor to prepare for transfers and for a front approach to wheelchair.
   c. Detachable: allows for a safe path for transfers.
   d. Elevating: allows for edema control and reduction.
   e. Limb board: supports a residual limb after a LE amputation.

3. Footplates.
   a. Fixed: minimal benefit but may be seen in older wheelchairs and/or in rentals.
   b. Swing-away: allows feet to reach floor.

    c. Heel loops: prevent feet from slipping off footrest in a posterior direction.

    d. Ankle straps: prevent slipping off footrest.

4. Wheels.

    a. Wheelchair camber: the angle of the wheels in relation to the surface of the floor.

      (1) Wheels that are completely straight and perpendicular to the ground have a camber of zero.

      (2) The further the wheels angle away from the wheelchair, the greater the camber.

        (a) Increased camber provides greater lateral stability and a less bumpy ride, and increases the maneuverability of the wheelchair.

    b. Geared wheels: replace the large back wheels of a manual wheelchair.

      (1) They have two mechanical gears and can be downshifted to reduce the effort needed to move the wheelchair forward, making it easier to go up inclines and navigate uneven surfaces.

5. Tires.

    a. Pneumatic: air-filled, requires maintenance, more cushioned ride, shock absorbent.

    b. Semi-pneumatic: airless foam inserts, less maintenance, good cushioning.

    c. Solid-core rubber: minimal maintenance, tires are mounted on spoked or molded wheels.

6. Casters.

    a. Smaller ones facilitate maneuverability.

    b. Pneumatic and semi-pneumatic types available, but solid-core are best for indoors and smooth surfaces.

    c. Caster locks can be added for increased stability during transfers.

7. Frame.

    a. Fixed: minimal benefit but may be seen in older wheelchairs or sports chairs.

    b. Folding: eases storage and facilitates mobility in community as it can fold to fit in car or van.

    c. Weight: ultra-light, active-duty lightweight, lightweight, standard, and heavy-duty frame construction are available.

      (1) The lighter the weight of the chair generally, the greater the ease of its use.

      (2) The demands of the individual's expected and desired activities must be considered.

8. Additional attachments.

    a. Seatbelts for safety during mobility and functional activities.

      (1) Attach at hip level, not waist level.

      (2) Extend across hips and into lap at 45° angle.

    b. Harnesses to position a person lacking sufficient trunk control.

    c. Arm troughs to position and support a hypotonic UE and prevent edema through elevation.

    d. Lapboards can serve the same purpose as an arm trough, and they are also beneficial as a working 'tabletop' surface.

    e. Head supports allow for improved eye contact, improved communication, and feeding assistance, as the head is kept in a neutral position.

    f. Mobile arm supports allow for use of an UE with proximal weakness to engage in feeding and other activities. Refer to Figure 12-5.

    g. Brake extensions allow a person with limited range in one UE to independently manipulate the wheelchair's brakes.

    h. Push handles allow for another person to maneuver the wheelchair, if required.

    i. Hand-rim projections ease independent propulsion in persons with weak hand grip.

      (1) These increase the width of the chair and can decrease mobility through narrow doors and/or narrow spaces.

    j. Anti-tippers to prevent the wheelchair from tipping backward or forward.

      (1) They can get caught on doorsills and curbs.

    k. Hillholder devices (also called hillclimber and grade aid devices) allow the wheelchair to move forward but automatically brake when the chair goes backward by engaging a level attached to each wheel.

      (1) Useful for individuals unable to ascend a steep grade (e.g., a long ramp or hill) without a rest.

    l. Seating and positioning systems; refer to subsequent section for details.

Wheelchair Measurement and Considerations

1. General.

    a. The size of a wheelchair should be proportional to the person. Refer to the next section for bariatric considerations.

      (1) Standard-sized chairs should be matched to a person whenever possible due to the increased expense of customized chairs.

        (a) Refer to Table 16-3.

    b. Measure on a firm surface, but also observe in a variety of positions to account for tonal influences on posture.

    c. The cushion that will be selected for the individual needs to be considered.

2. Seat width.

    a. Measure the widest point across the hips and thighs to allow for maximal seating space and comfort, and then add 2″.

    b. This allows for clearance on the sides to prevent friction/rubbing and to allow the individual to wear heavier material clothing without being cumbersome.

Table 16-3

Standard Dimensions for Wheelchairs

CHAIR STYLE	SEAT WIDTH (INCHES)	SEAT DEPTH (INCHES)	SEAT HEIGHT (INCHES)
Adult	18	16	20
Narrow Adult	16	16	20
Slim Adult	14	16	20
Hemi-/Low Seat			17.5
Junior	16	16	18.5
Child	14	11.5	18.75
Tiny Tot	12	11.5	19.5

   c. The bariatric client with a pear-shape will have increased gluteal femoral weight distribution.
     (1) Measurement should consider the widest portion of the seated position (e.g., at the forward edge of the seated position).
     (2) Also consider room for weight-shifting maneuvers for pressure relief and possible use of lift devices.

3. Seat depth.
   a. Measure from the posterior portion of the buttocks to the popliteal fossa and then subtract 2″ from this measurement.
   b. Measure both LEs and use the shortest length.
     (1) This prevents rubbing and potential decubiti to posterior knee region, while also allowing maximal leg swing.

4. Back height.
   a. Measurement is based on the need for postural stability, UE movements, and potential for independent wheelchair propulsion.
   b. Measure from the seat surface (including the cushion) upward to one of the following depending on the person's trunk control, activity level, strength, and size.
     (1) Mid-back under scapula: 1″–2″ below.
     (2) Mid-scapula or axilla.
     (3) Top of the shoulder.
   c. Lower back height can increase functional mobility as in sports chairs.
     (1) Lower back height can increase back strain.
   d. Higher back height may be needed if trunk stability is poor.

> **CAUTION:** If back height of chair is extended, potential problems must be recognized.
> • Added back height may prevent the individual from locking their arm onto the push handle for stabilization and/or weight shifting.
> • Added back height may increase difficulty of fitting the wheelchair into a car or van.

5. Seat height.
   a. Knees and ankles should be positioned at 90°; measure from the distal thigh to the heel.
     (1) Measure both LEs and use the shortest length if the person will be self-propelling the wheelchair using their LEs.
   b. Because footrests should have 2″ clearance from the floor, add 2″ to this measurement.
     (1) The wheelchair cushion selected will affect this measurement.
   c. Standard height: 20″.
   d. Hemi-height: 17.5″.

6. Armrest height.
   a. Shoulders should be neutral; arms positioned at the sides; elbow flexed to 90°.
   b. Measure under each elbow to cushioned seating surface.
   c. Armrests that are too low will encourage leaning forward.
   d. Armrests that are too high will cause shoulder elevation.

Types of Wheelchairs

1. Refer to Table 16-4 for descriptions of general types of wheelchairs and indications/contraindications for use.
2. Specialized wheelchairs.
   a. Tilt-and-reclining: a wheelchair with a high back that reclines independently of the rest of the chair.
     (1) Used to provide pressure relief, regulate blood pressure, improve respiration, and provide support for individuals who are unable to independently maintain an upright sitting position.
     (2) Because only the back of the wheelchair reclines, the seated posture with the hips and knees angled at 90 degrees is changed.

> **CAUTION:** Reclining back wheelchairs extend the seat-to-back angle; thus, they can elicit flexor or extensor spasms and should not be prescribed to persons with spasticity.

> **RED FLAG:** Reclining back wheelchairs should not be prescribed to persons with limited hip and/or knee ROM as the resultant reclined angles may exceed their available range.

   b. Tilt-in-space: a wheelchair that allows the entire seat and seatback to tilt back to maintain the seated posture of the hips and knees angled at 90 degrees.
     (1) Used to provide pressure relief, regulate blood pressure, improve respiration, and minimize the impact of abnormal tone (e.g., severe extensor spasms that can throw a person out of the chair).
   c. Manual wheelchairs: one arm-drive, hemi-height chair, amputee frame. Refer to Table 16-4.

Table 16-4

Types of Wheelchairs		
ATTENDANT PROPELLED	**MANUAL WHEELCHAIR**	**POWERED MOBILITY**
Description	Description	Description

• Pushed by another.
• Usually is a manual wheelchair.
• Can be a full-size chair or a stroller type chair (e.g., airplane aisle transit chairs).
	• Rigid or folding frames.
	• Various frames and weights.
	• Lightweight chair: 25–40 pounds.
	• Standard: >50 pounds without seating system.
	• Amputee frame: axle can be moved posteriorly for increased stability and accommodate for change in gravity center.
	• Hemi-height chair: use nonaffected upper extremity and/or lower extremity.
	• One-arm drive.
	• Lever propelled.
	• Gurney: propel with large side wheels while prone.
		• Power-base typically independent of seating system.
		• Diverse four-wheel designs and three-wheel scooters.
		• Add-on power units to manual chairs.
		• Battery operated:
		  – deep cycle lead acid.
		  – wet cell.
		  – sealed cell.
		• Method of operation:
		  – micro-switch.
		  – proportional joystick.
		  – sip and puff.
		  – sensing system.
		  – body part to be used.

Indications/Benefits	Indications/Benefits	Indications/Benefits
• Brief or pervasive condition that results in the inability to self-propel. • Used for transport in the community. • Used when powered mobility cannot be used or is being repaired.	• Can independently propel and brake using upper extremities. • May use quick release wheels (easier for cars). • Can be easily tilted to go up and down curbs.	• Cannot use hands or feet. • Limited upper extremities function. • Limited endurance and/or vital capacity. • Prone to repetitive stress injury. • Neuromuscular injury: to prevent associated reactions. • Can change seat height or tilt. • Sturdy and useful indoors and outdoors.
Limitations	Limitations	Limitations
• Dependent on another person.	• Standard weight is heavy when seating systems are added.	• Large/heavy to transport. • Difficult to maneuver in small places. • Cannot be tilted over curbs. • May need to use lifts.

d. Powered wheelchairs: Refer to Table 16-4.
  (1) For young children, alternative powered mobility may be preferred by families due to their developmental appropriateness and social acceptability (e.g., motorized toy vehicles with or without adaptations).
    (a) These alternatives can also help the child develop the skills they will need to effectively use a power wheelchair in the future.
e. Recreational: designed with large thick inner tube type tires and large front casters for all-terrain use including sand, mud, snow, and off-road surfaces.
f. Sports: specially designed for racing, cycling, basketball, and other competitive sports; typically, ultra-lightweight.
g. Stander: incorporates manual and/or power technology to enable the wheelchair user to independently move from a sitting to a standing position.
  (1) Used to support face-to-face interactions, increase vertical access, improve posture, provide pressure relief, regulate blood pressure, and improve respiration and digestion.

h. Dynamic mobile stander: a stander that the user can self-propel if they have the upper body strength to push a manual wheelchair.
  (1) Used to move throughout the environment in a standing position, support face-to-face interactions, increase vertical access, improve posture, provide pressure relief, regulate blood pressure, and improve respiration and digestion.

> **EXAM HINT:** The NBCOT® OTR® exam content outline identifies knowledge of "mobility options . . . and alternative devices for supporting participation in community mobility (including) dynamic mobile standers" (NBCOT®, 2022, p. 11) as required for competent and safe practice. Thus, the application of knowledge about dynamic mobile standers and the other devices described in this section can help you correctly answer items about selecting and managing interventions to enable community mobility.

i. Stair-climber: designed to navigate stairs while balancing on two wheels using sensors and gyroscopes.

j. Bariatric wheelchair: heavy-duty, extra-wide wheelchair designed to assist mobility for individuals who are obese. Refer to the following section.

k. Evacuation wheelchair: designed to enable the safe and timely transport of a person who cannot independently descend stairs during an emergency.
   (1) These stair-descending chairs (also called escape chairs) only require the assistance of one person.

Bariatric Wheelchairs and Prescription Considerations[2]

1. Wheelchair users who are obese must be prescribed wheelchairs that are rated for their obesity category. Chapter 9 provides information about obesity categories and additional bariatric considerations.
   a. Selection is based on the client characteristics, safety, and function.
2. The bariatric client has a center of body mass that is positioned several inches forward in comparison with the nonobese person.
   a. In order to ensure wheelchair stability, the rear axle is displaced forward in comparison with the standard wheelchair.
      (1) This forward position also allows for a more efficient arm push (full arm stroke with less wrist extension).
3. Bariatric wheelchairs can be ordered with special adaptations.
   a. Hard tires versus pneumatic tires for increased durability.
   b. Adjustable backrest to accommodate excessive posterior bulk.
   c. Reclining wheelchair to accommodate excessive anterior bulk and address cardiorespiratory compromise (e.g., orthostatic hypotension).
   d. Power application attached to a heavy-duty wheelchair to accommodate excessive fatigue.

Wheelchair Mobility Education and Training

> **EXAM HINT:** The NBCOT® OTR® exam content outline identifies knowledge of "client-centered education and training methods for successful use and maintenance of . . . mobility aids" (NBCOT®, 2022, p. 12) as essential for competent practice. The application of knowledge about the following wheelchair mobility training considerations and approaches can help you determine the correct answer for NBCOT® Domain 3 exam items about wheelchair mobility training.

---

[2] Susan O'Sullivan contributed to this section on bariatric wheelchairs.

1. Assess cognitive and physical capabilities to determine the individual's ability to learn and use a wheelchair independently.
   a. Include personal care attendants and caregivers in training, as needed.
2. Determine goals for community mobility.
3. Check wheelchair and seating system for fit and needed adjustments.
4. Instruct in proper sitting posture.
5. Instruct in pressure relief (i.e., pushups, weight shifts leaning to one side, then the other).
   a. Provide time schedule for weight shifts.
   b. Refer to Chapter 9 for additional information about pressure relief and the prevention of decubiti.
6. Instruct in the purpose and use of additional devices used with the wheelchair (i.e., cushion, lap board).
7. Instruct in wheelchair propulsion (e.g., manual, joystick, head control, sip and puff).
   a. Use of wheelchair gloves to ease propulsion and protect hands.
   b. Compensation techniques (e.g., use of feet to assist for propulsion when UE is affected).
8. Instruct in safety concerns when operating a mobility device.
   a. Need to set/release locks.
   b. Use of swing-away leg rests and removable arm rests with transferring.
   c. Caution when using powered wheelchair.
   d. Safe ways to fall from a wheelchair and to return to wheelchair from the ground, if possible.
   e. Methods for securing a wheelchair on a school bus and/or public transportation.
9. Instruct in how to manipulate basic parts of the wheelchair and break them down to ease transport (e.g., removal of parts to ease storage in a car trunk).
10. Instruct in how to maneuver the wheelchair throughout the community.
    a. Practice in natural interior and exterior environments is essential. Wheelchair training should include developing the person's ability to do the following.
       (1) Traverse over different surfaces (e.g., carpeted, asphalt, uneven).
       (2) Ascend and descend inclines.
       (3) Negotiate lips and curbs; "pop a wheelie."
       (4) Negotiate obstacles (e.g., garbage cans on streets, chairs in restaurants).
       (5) Use car, bus, and/or stair lifts.
       (6) Securely secure the wheelchair on a bus, subway, and/or train,
11. Train in how to transfer from the wheelchair to diverse surfaces. Refer to section on transfer training.
12. Instruct in basic maintenance of wheelchair parts.

Chapter 16

13. Developmental considerations.
   a. Recognize that parents/caregivers may view the use of strollers as more developmentally and socially acceptable than wheelchairs.
   b. Collaborate with the parents/caregivers to identify opportunities for the child to learn to independently explore their environment and engage in desired activities with transitional mobility devices.
   c. Encourage parents to integrate the use of transitional mobility devices, alternative powered mobility devices, and/or wheelchairs into their child's routine as relevant to the child's developmental level and functional abilities.
   d. As early as possible, teach children functional mobility via the use of transitional mobility devices, alternative powered mobility devices, and/or wheelchairs to encourage and enable their independent exploration of the environment and participation in play, school, and other developmentally appropriate activities.

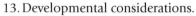

Seating Systems and Positioning Equipment

Purposes of Seating Systems and Positioning Equipment

1. Promote functional posture with back, trunk, arm, and/or leg supports that align the body.
2. Provide stability to enable and/or improve proximal and distal upper extremity function.
3. Minimize tone and reflex reactions that can interfere with comfort, alignment, and stability and result in contractures.
4. Accommodate fixed (i.e., contractures) and/or static postures to decrease pain and promote comfort.
5. Improve physiologic functions such as breathing, eating, swallowing, digesting, and eliminating.
6. Distribute pressure for physiological maintenance and tissue protection and to prevent decubiti.
7. Promote sensory and social readiness and enable engagement through the provision of proper eye and head position.

Basic Styles of Seating

1. Linear.
   a. Flat, noncontoured.
   b. Custom or factory ordered.
   c. Firm, rigid seating.
   d. Good for active individuals, those who can perform independent transfers, and/or those with minimal musculoskeletal involvement.
2. Contoured and/or custom contoured.
   a. Ergonomically supports the individual.
   b. Provides excellent support.
   c. Enhances postural alignment.
   d. Provides pressure relief.
   e. May be difficult for independent transfers if the person has decreased UE muscle strength.

f. Good for individuals with moderate to severe central nervous system dysfunction or neurological disease.

> **EXAM HINT:** The NBCOT® OTR® exam content outline identifies knowledge of the "factors related to measuring, selecting, monitoring the fit of, and recommending modifications to seating systems (and) positioning devices" (NBCOT®, 2022, p. 11) as essential for competent practice. The application of knowledge about the basic seating styles described above and the seating system styles and accessories described below can help you determine the correct answer for NBCOT® Domain 3 Select and Manage Interventions exam items about seating systems.

Major Styles and Accessories of Seating Systems

1. Solid seat insert prevents hammock effect, provides stable base of support, and is easy to remove.
2. Lumbar back support helps to give proper lumbar curve.
3. Foam cushions (of various densities) can enhance sitting posture and comfort.
4. Positioning cushions. Refer to Table 16-5.
5. Pressure relief cushions. Refer to Table 16-6.

Considerations for Determining Cushion Type

1. To ensure that a cushion best meets a person's needs, the following factors should be considered and their corresponding question answered.

a. Comfort: while seated on the cushion for extended periods, does the person remain comfortable (e.g., stay cool)?

> CAUTION: Cushions that cause a person to sweat can contribute to skin breakdown. If a person will be using a wheelchair on a regular basis, their cushion should be one that remains cool.

b. Stability: does the cushion help the person maintain balance and not slide?
c. Functional mobility: does the cushion make it easier for the person to complete active purposeful movements (e.g., reaching, doing Tai Chi)?
d. Skin protection: does the cushion reduce friction and provide pressure relief?
e. Weight: does the cushion weight meet the person's needs?
   (1) Heavier cushions are more comfortable so they may be preferred by a person who does not self-propel a wheelchair for long distances or extended periods of time (e.g., a video game designer who works from home).
   (2) Lighter cushions are preferred by persons who self-propel their wheelchairs on a daily basis to engage in community-based activities (e.g., a high school student who works after school in a retail store).
f. Height: does the cushion height meet the person's needs?
   (1) Higher cushions can make it easier to reach counters and shelves in upper cabinets, but they may not fit under a table or desk.
g. Maintenance: is maintenance required to keep the cushion in shape? Is the person or a caregiver able to do the maintenance as required?
h. Cost: is the cushion covered by insurance? If not, does the person have the financial means to pay for the cushion?
   (1) Refer to Chapter 9 for information about three categories of pressure-reducing devices that the Centers for Medicare and Medicaid Services (CMS) uses for reimbursement purposes.

> CAUTION: Price should not solely determine which cushion is best for a person. The features of different cushions and their life span should be considered. A costly cushion that can help prevent skin breakdown is preferable over a basic foam cushion that will flatten and need to be replaced on a regular basis.

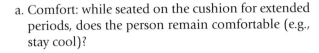

Pediatric Seating Systems and Positioning Devices

> EXAM HINT: The NBCOT® OTR® exam content outline identifies knowledge of the "factors related to measuring, selecting, monitoring the fit of, and recommending modifications to seating systems (and) positioning devices" (NBCOT®, 2022, p. 11) as essential for competent practice. The application of knowledge about the purposes described in the preceding section and the types of pediatric seating systems and positioning devices described in the following can help you determine the correct answer for NBCOT® exam items about these interventions.

1. Types.
   a. Pediatric seating systems are usually custom-molded and created for the specific child.
      (1) They can be designed for independent seating and as inserts for wheelchairs and car seats.
   b. Standers provide weightbearing experience that maintains hips, knees, ankles, and trunk in optimal position, facilitate formation of acetabulum and long bone development, aid in bowel and bladder function, and facilitate face-to-face social interaction.
      (1) Passive (static) stander: a passive stander that remains in one place; may have casters but cannot be self-propelled.
      (2) Prone standers support the front (anterior) side of the body, and position the child in a forward leaning position that requires the child to have adequate head control.
         (a) They can decrease the effect of tonic labyrinthine reflex (TLR).
      (3) Supine standers support the back (posterior) side of the body and position the child in a backward leaning position that does not require the child to have head control.
      (4) Dynamic stander: the child can move on the base of the stander while the stander itself remains in a stationary position.
   c. Sidelyers: position the child in a lateral recumbent position that places their hands in their visual field and can decrease effects of TLR.
   d. Floor sitters: provide support to a child who cannot sit independently; they provide support to the shoulders and trunk while enabling the hands to be free for play.
      (1) Often constructed with triwall.
   e. Abductor pads at the hips decrease scissoring extensor pattern.

Table 16-5

Positioning Cushions

TYPE	BENEFITS	EXAMPLE	PICTURE
Contoured	Contoured design aligns the hips and legs while evenly distributing weight across the seat.	Lacura Profile Cushion*	
Anti-Thrust	Built-up anteriorly which helps the person not slide forward. Particularly important for safety if there is a tendency to push against the back of the wheelchair.	Lacura Anti-thrust Cushion*	
Wedge	Positions the individual to slide backward in the chair to reduce forward sliding if the person is slumped in the chair.	Lacura Wedge Cushion*	
Pommel	Allows knees to stay separated, preventing the skin from shearing together while blocking the person from sliding out of chair. Separating the hips and knees can also be helpful to maintain positioning recommended by certain post-surgical precautions (i.e., a hip replacement).	Lacura Removeable Pommel Cushion*	
Sacral Cut Out	Reduces pressure on an individual's coccyx which can prevent sacral pressure sores and skin breakdown.	Lacura Sacral Cutout Cushion*	
Lateral Leaning Cushion	Cushion corrects pelvic obliquity for individuals who tend to lean to one side.	Skill-Care Lateral Leaning Cushion*	
Amputee	Supports left, right, or bilateral residual limbs.	Lacura Amputee Cushion*	

* - Photo reprinted with permission from Performance Health International.

References:

Dudgeon, B. J., Deitz, J. C., & Dimpfel, M. (2014). Wheelchair selection. In M.V. Radomski and C.A.T. Latham (Eds.), Occupational therapy for physical dysfunction (7th ed., p. 500). Lippincott Williams & Wilkins.

Performance Health. (2021). Your ultimate guide on how to choose a wheelchair cushion. https://www.performancehealth.com/articles/your-ultimate-guide-on-how-to-choose-a-wheelchair-cushion.

Pressure Relief Cushions

TYPE	BENEFITS	LIMITATIONS	EXAMPLE	PICTURE
Foam	• Inexpensive. • Lightweight. • Provides a stable surface for individuals to shift weight.	• Not long lasting; can flatten over time, losing its shape and pressure-relieving qualities. • Not easy to clean and needs to be replaced over time. • Foam is an insulator and may get hot, which can contribute to skin breakdown.	T-Foam by AliMed	
Gel	• Good temperature regulation; does not store heat. • Contours to the person's buttocks with stronger pressure relief. • Supports the person's posture and sitting balance.	• Cushion is sensitive to extreme temperatures and needs to be checked for gel leakage. • Increases the weight of a wheelchair. • Heavy to position and move. • Must be kneaded prior to each use to be effective.	Gel Cushion by AliMed	
Air-filled	• Lightweight. • Air relieves pressure evenly leading to excellent pressure relief and decreased likelihood of skin shearing.	• The person will have less control of their sitting balance. • The risk of air leaking requires the cushion to be checked daily. • Air pressure changes in cushion must be attended to.	High or Low Profile by AliMed	
Honeycomb	• Lightweight. • Does not get hot. • Easy to maintain.	• Pressure relief is not distributed equally. • Difficult to shape for an individual (very thick).	Supracor Stimulite Contoured	
Cushion-contoured foam	• Increased pressure distribution among the whole surface area of the person's bottom. • Reduced risk of skin shearing while increasing ability for trunk stability and postural control.	• Expensive and may need to be replaced over time. • Cushion's shape can make it more difficult for the individual to weight shift.	Contour U Seat Cushion by Invacare	
Alternating Pressure	• Automatically distributes pressure using a scheduled relief cycle to prevent sores. • Reduces the effort needed for an individual to weight shift. • Self-contouring.	• Expensive and cushions are not always available. • The pressure distribution gives uneven pressure relief to a person's' bottom. • Can lead to decreased trunk support and sitting balance support. • Battery needs to be maintained and recharged to prevent it from losing it charge.	Chair-Air® Cushion by AliMed	

References:

Dudgeon, B. J., Deitz, J. C., & Dimpfel, M. (2014). Wheelchair selection. In M.V. Radomski and C.A.T. Latham (Eds.), Occupational therapy for physical dysfunction (7th ed., p. 500). Lippincott Williams & Wilkins.

Performance Health. (2021). Your ultimate guide on how to choose a wheelchair cushion. https://www.performancehealth.com/articles/your-ultimate-guide-on-how-to-choose-a-wheelchair-cushion.

Transfers

Purpose

1. To move from one surface to another safely and effectively with (dependent) or without (independent) the assistance of others.

Transfer Considerations

1. Assess and identify an individual's assets and deficits, especially cognitive and physical abilities.

> CAUTION: The OT practitioner should be aware of their own limitations to avoid personal or client injury.

2. Use of proper body mechanics should be strictly enforced.
   a. Use broad base of support.
   b. The OT practitioner must know where their center of gravity is at all times.
   c. The individual to be transferred should be lifted with the OT practitioner using their LEs to lift and not their back.
3. Perform wheelchair transfers safely.
   a. Clear areas involved in transfers of any clutter.
   b. Ask for help or standby assist if questioning the ability to safely complete a transfer.
   c. Use transfer belts if needed.
   d. Lock brakes.
   e. Swing away the leg rests and flip up the footplates.
   f. Remove the armrest for a "pop-over" transfer if the individual is unable to assist, is too heavy to bring to a standing position, or if the individual has a weightbearing precaution.
4. Allow for variability of individuals and environment.
   a. Adjust transfer methods according to the individual's strengths and limitations in performance skills and client factors.
   b. Be aware of different floor/ground surfaces.
   c. Be aware of the increased risk of personal injury when transferring a bariatric client.
      (1) Use good body mechanics, obtain adequate assistance during transfers, and use mechanical lifts as needed.
5. Train in transfers to and from a variety of different surfaces (i.e., bed, wheelchair, chair, toilet, tub, and/or car).

Transfer Types

1. Stand-pivot: the individual stands and turns to the transfer surface.
2. Pop-over or seated sitting: a full stand position is not required; used by persons with decreased endurance and/or weight-bearing precautions.
3. Transfer/sliding board transfer: used by persons who are not able to stand to transfer (i.e., individuals with SCIs or amputations).
   a. The board is placed under the individual's gluteal region during a weight shift, while the other end of board is placed on the surface that they are transferring to.
   b. The individual then uses their UEs to push their buttocks up and "slide" over to the transfer surface.

> CAUTION: Transfer/sliding board transfers can cause shearing (i.e., extra friction). Therefore, a person who performs transfer/sliding board transfers must be taught to be vigilant about performing daily skin checks. Refer to Chapter 9 for additional information about pressure relief and the prevention of decubiti.

> RED FLAG: A person who uses a tenodesis grasp or splint should never transfer with flattened palms, this will lengthen the digit flexors and weaken their tenodesis grasp. Individual who use a tenodesis grasp or splint should be taught to transfer by weightbearing on their clenched fists with wrists extended.

4. Dependent: the caregiver is required to fully perform the transfer.
5. Mechanical lift: the use of ceiling lift, track lift, Hoyer lift, or trans-aid to perform a transfer.

> EXAM HINT: The NBCOT® OTR® exam content outline identifies the task of selecting "assistive technology options, adaptive devices, mobility aids, and other durable medical equipment" (NBCOT®, 2022, p. 11) as essential for competent practice. The application of knowledge about the previously described transfer mobility aids and the following adaptive and mobility devices to enable safe transfers can help you determine the correct answer for NBCOT® Domain 3 Select and Manage Interventions exam items about wheelchair, bed, and bath transfers.

6. Adaptive or mobility devices to enable safe transfers.
  a. Bed transfer aids.
    (1) Trapeze.
    (2) Bedrail.
  b. Bath transfer aids.
    (1) Grab bars, potentially with a shower chair inside the shower or tub.
    (2) Transfer tub bench, to eliminate the need to step over the threshold of a tub.
    (3) Active-aid commode, a commode with small wheels to allow transfer to the bathroom and/or shower stall when otherwise it would not possible.

    (4) Bedside or 3-in-1 commode.
    (5) Ambulatory devices (i.e., canes, walkers). Refer to the prior section in this Chapter.
    (6) Wheelchairs (i.e., removable arms, swing arms, leg rests). Refer to the prior section in this Chapter.
7. Chair lifts: chairs with power control to allow elevation from the surface for individuals who may otherwise not be able to go from sit to stand and transfer independently.
8. Table 16-2 provides information about the functional transfer and bed mobility abilities and limitations of person with SCIs and the equipment that can be used to enable safe and effective bed mobility and transfers.

Assistive Technology Devices (ATDs)

Definition and Overview

1. According to the Assistive Technology Act of 2004, "assistive technology (AT) is any item, device, or piece of equipment used to maintain or improve the independence and function of people with disabilities and seniors, in education, employment, recreation, and daily living activities" (Public Law No: 108-364).
2. OT practitioners typically consider a range of AT for the environment to support safety and independence in home, school, work, and community environments. The range of AT includes the following.
  a. High tech: potentially costly devices that may require custom ordering and may require specific training to use (e.g., electronic aides to daily living [EADL], assistive technology for cognition [ATC], augmentative and alternative communication [AAC] devices, application (app)-based mobile devices [AMD], computers).
    (1) Technology that makes a home "smart" allows people to control the electric functions of their home in a cost-effective, practical, socially relevant, and reliable manner.
      (a) Home automation, which is built into a house to make it smart, is called domotics.
  b. Mid-tech devices: inexpensive household devices that are readily available for use but tend to be electronic and may require programming/setup (i.e., personal "talking" alarm clocks, automatic coffee pots).
  c. Low tech: inexpensive household and/or commercially available items that are basic and readily available for use (e.g., jar opener, shoehorn, and sock aid).

3. AT installed in smart homes support safety, access, comfort, and functional independence.
  a. Available smart technologies include the following.
    (1) Electronic aids to daily living (EADL).
    (2) Assistive technology for cognition (ATC).
    (3) Wireless connectivity to the community.
    (4) Remote control commercially available products (e.g., doors, window shades, refrigerators).
    (5) Apps downloaded to a smartphone, tablet, or computer to control appliances, thermostats, and other devices.
    (6) New and rapidly developing technologies continue to appear on the market.

> **EXAM HINT:** The NBCOT® OTR® exam content outline identifies knowledge of the "types, characteristics and features of high- and low-tech assistive technology and adaptive devices . . . to enable participation in occupation" (NBCOT®, 2022, p. 11) as essential for competent practice. The application of knowledge about the types of AT described above and the EADL described below can help you determine the correct answer for NBCOT® Domain 3 exam items about AT and EADL interventions.

Electronic Aids to Daily Living (EADL)

1. Definition: EADL (formerly known as environmental control units [ECUs]), provide an electronic means for a person with a disability to access, manipulate, and interact with devices in their environment via switch, voice activation, remote control, computer interface, and/or smart phone app.

2. Purposes.
   a. Enable control of devices within the environment.
   b. Compensate for functional limitations and maximize functional abilities.
   c. Increase independence in home, school, work, and other environments.
   d. Conserve energy during home management and work tasks.
   e. Maintain safety.

3. Uses.
   a. Turn on/off lights, control appliances, open and close doors, window shades, drapes.
   b. Allow use of phones, computers, and office machinery.
   c. Summon assistance.
   d. Enable off-site caregivers to monitor a person with sensorimotor and/or cognitive impairments that place them at risk for falls and other potentially negative outcomes.

4. Candidates for EADL.
   a. Individuals living with various conditions that limit mobility (i.e., SCI, CVA) or impair cognition (traumatic brain injury, neurocognitive disorders).
   b. Persons with a goal of transitioning from supported to independent living.
   c. Older adults who wish to age in place.

5. Examples of EADL technology.
   a. Phones: large number pads, automatic dialing phones, speaker-phones, amplifiers, videophones, smart phones.
   b. App-based mobile devices [AMD]: smartphones, tablets, handheld computers, and e-readers which are used to operate downloaded apps.
   c. "Talking" pill bottles remind the person when it is time to take their medication, share information with doctors, and submit orders for prescription refills.
   d. Monitoring systems allow for communication between areas.
   e. Electronically controlled door openers and closers to promote ease of access.
      (1) These can be operated using different transmission modes, including X-10 units, infrared, radio frequency transmission, or ultrasound.
   f. Automatic lights, self-dimming bulbs, and/or motion sensor lights to facilitate adequate and even lighting throughout the home.
   g. Backsplash display screens can be used in the kitchen to allow for hands-free access to recipes or taking calls while cooking while standing supported at the counter.
   h. Smart hubs/smart home platforms (e.g., Google Home, Amazon Alexa) may control a large number of home functions, including opening drawers, checking doors, turning on lights, activating appliances, and alerting friends or emergency responders to potential fall incidents.

i. Personal emergency response system (PERS): enables a person to summon help by the push of a button or the vocalization of a command.

> CAUTION: A PERS backup plan for electronic support must be in place in case of a power outage or technical malfunction so that the person can access emergency help if needed.

j. Passive occupant monitoring.
   (1) Allows an off-site caregiver to monitor a person without the intrusion of a phone call or a video camera.
   (2) Motion sensor modules located throughout a home detect deviations in a person's daily routines and the system automatically notifies a caregiver of their occurrence.
      (a) To detect falls, sensors can be placed in hallways, at the top and bottom of stairs, in bathrooms, bedrooms, kitchens, and living rooms.
      (b) To monitor if a person is taking their medicine or eating, sensors can be installed on a medicine cabinet in which the person's medicine is stored and on the refrigerator and cabinet doors in which food is stored. If the monitoring system reports no opening of these doors, the caregiver can respond quickly to address the situation before major health issues arise.

> CAUTION: The fact that a sensor detects the opening of a medicine cabinet, kitchen cabinets, or a refrigerator does not ensure that a person is taking their medicine or eating.

> CAUTION: The person being monitored may resist and/or resent having their daily activities monitored 24–7.
>
> Monitoring can be viewed as an invasion of privacy or a daily reminder that they are no longer independent.
>
> Having one's home and personal activities monitored electronically can raise security concerns that their personal information may be hacked.
>
> All of these concerns are legitimate and the OT practitioner should address them with the person and their caregivers in a respectful and collaborative manner.

k. Computers enable individuals with disabilities to more fully participate in social, leisure, work, and productive activities. They can be used to attain the following outcomes.
   (1) Facilitate performance of multiple functional tasks (e.g., banking, shopping).

(2) Allow for communication and socialization through e-mail, social networking, and online support groups.

(3) Provide the means for productive work via telecommuting.

(4) Have alternative access modes that can compensate for a diversity of disabilities.

   (a) Box 16-5 describes the different adaptations that are available to enable computer access for persons with disabilities.

l. Augmentative alternative communication (AAC): methods of communication that do not require speech.

(1) Types range from simple communication boards or albums with a limited number of pictures to complex portable computer systems with extensive language capacity.

(2) To determine the AAC that can best meet a person's needs the following should be considered.

   (a) Speed: how fast a message is conveyed.

   (b) Portability: easy to use in a variety of environments.

   (c) Accessibility: the individual can independently operate it.

   (d) Dependability: the quality, durability, and warranty/service record of the device.

   (e) Independence of the user.

   (f) Vocabulary flexibility.

   (g) Typical repair and maintenance requirements.

AT Evaluation

1. Evaluation focus.

a. Identify the activities the individual wants to engage in, the occupational roles they want to pursue, the home functions they want to potentially control, and any safety concerns they may have.

(1) This information can be collected via the completion of an occupational profile.

b. Determine the person's AT knowledge, skills, and experience.

(1) If the person has limited knowledge, abilities, and/or experience, determine their interest in learning to use potentially novel technology.

c. Assess the individual's client factors, performance skills, and performance patterns. Key evaluation foci include, but are not limited to, the following.

(1) The person's cognitive abilities to remember how to access and effectively use AT and problem solve when difficulties arise.

BOX 16-5 ▷ Computer Adaptations that Enable Access for Persons with Disabilities

- Built-in accessibility features including voice typing, magnification, color inversion features (to enhance contrast for persons with visual impairments), keylocks, sticky keys (to ease one-handed computer use for persons with hemiplegia), mouse keys, number locks, and onscreen keyboards.
- Alternative switch inputs including trackballs, paddles, joysticks, or mice.
- Eye gaze for individuals with severe mobility and speech impairments (e.g., individuals with amyotrophic lateral sclerosis).
- Voice activation for individuals with severe mobility impairments with functional speech (e.g., upper extremity contractures).
- Key guards for persons with limited motor accuracy and control (e.g., individuals with ataxia).
- Alternative keyboard options are numerous and include the following.
  - Programmable keyboards allow for customized overlays (e.g., enlarged letters and numbers for persons with low vision; graphics and symbols for individuals with cognitive impairments).
  - Expanded keyboards that provide large keys for persons with visual-motor deficits.
  - Contracted keyboards that provide smaller keys in a constrained space for persons with limited ROM and functional motor control (e.g., individuals with arthritis).
  - Light-touch keyboard activation systems for persons with decreased strength and/or mobility (e.g., individuals with muscular dystrophy).
  - Delayed touch keyboard activation systems for persons with poor motor control (e.g., individuals with athetoid movements).
  - Chorded keyboards enable one-handed keyboarding for persons who cannot keyboard with two hands (e.g., a person with hemiplegia) by generating standard characters or commands when various combinations of keys are pressed at once (like playing a "chord" on a piano), instead of hitting one key at a time in succession.
  - Color coded keyboards help persons with visual impairments and children identify, learn, and use the various groups of keys within the keyboard by color coding the keys.
  - Tongue-touch keypads (TTK) are imbedded in an orthotic device for persons with severe motor deficits and good tongue control.

(2) The person's positioning and seating stability; a lack of stability can affect their ability to use a device.

(3) The anatomic site at which the person demonstrates purposeful controlled movement to determine the device's control site (e.g., shoulder, head, elbow, hand, tongue, or eye movements).

    (a) If no physical interaction with an input is possible, the ability to use speech for voice recognition AT should be assessed.

(4) The person's occupational performance to determine their abilities to perform desired tasks without or with AT.

d. Determine the contexts (e.g., social, cultural) and environments (e.g., home, school, work, community) in which the device will be used and when it will be used.

    (1) Supports for and barriers to the person's use of AT.

e. Identify potential AT devices.

    (1) Consider input method; how the device will be activated (e.g., keyboard, infrared, sonic, electric, touch screen, smartphone app, or radio frequency switches) and by what action (e.g., keyboarding, voice recognition, eye gazing, or using a joystick, head pointer, mouth stick, tongue, or automated systems that do not require individual commands).

(2) Consider the processing method; how the device will process the information from the input method.

(3) Consider the output method; results are needed (i.e., response from input occurs).

(4) Consider the feedback method; ensures the device is being used in the right way (could be auditory, visual, or proprioceptive).

(5) Table 16-7 outlines additional factors that should be assessed and the questions that should be answered to determine which AT is best for a person.

f. The Human Activity-Assistive Technology Model (HAAT Model).

    (1) Considers the person, activity to be completed, aspects of the AT, and context in which interaction takes place.

    (2) Provides stepwise intervention to appropriately chose AT according to clients' needs.

    (3) Recommends introducing one or two adaptations at a time to acclimate the use to the system prior to adding additional components.

    (4) Considers the cost of devices.

g. Document the screening and evaluation process. Documentation should include a description of the recommended ATD(s) and the rationale for each item for reimbursement justification. This includes the following.

Table 16-7

Considerations for the Selection of Assistive Technology Devices

CHARACTERISTIC	QUESTIONS TO ANSWER DURING THE EVALUATION PROCESS
Effectiveness	Will the device address the person's needs, enhance their functional abilities, and increase their independence?
Comfort	Is the device physically comfortable to use? Does the person feel psychologically comfortable using the device in all settings in which the device would be helpful (e.g., home, school, work, and community-based settings)?
Social Acceptance	Is the device invasive? Does the device have the potential to break down social barriers or does it potentially present a new barrier? Is the device technologically and aesthetically appealing to others?
Affordability	Is the device covered by insurance? Can the person afford to pay for the device and its use? If a device is being used to enable participation in education or work is the cost covered by legislative mandates (i.e., the ADA, IDEA)?
Assembly Ease	If assembly is needed, is the device easy to assemble?
Learnability	Is the operation of the device easy to learn? Is the time and effort needed to master use of the device perceived as reasonable?
Operation Ease	Is the device intuitive, easy to use, adaptable and flexible? Are controls accessible?
Portability	How will the size and weight of the device affect the person's ability to carry, move, and operate the device to various locations?
Reliability	Does the device perform in a dependable, predictable, consistent, and accurate manner for a reasonable amount of time?
Durability	Will the device continue to be fully operational for an extended period of time?
Maintenance and Repairability	How easy is the device to maintain and repair? Is the device covered by a warranty? Can repairs be made by a consumer or local repair shop or can only the vendor/supplier complete these?
Safety	Does using the device present any hazards? Does the device protect the user and others in their environment from harm?
Securability	Does the device have built-in privacy protection? Is the device a target for theft and/or vandalism?

Reference: Schere, M. J., & Lane, J.P. (1997). Assessing computer profile of 'ideal' technologies in ten categories. An integration of quantitative and qualitative methods. Disability and Rehabilitation, 19, 528–535.

(1) The individual's needs and goals.
(2) The person's functional status, abilities, and limitations.
(3) The individual's school, work, leisure/play, and community participation status and needs.
(4) The cost-effectiveness of the recommended equipment.

> **EXAM HINT:** The NBCOT® OTR® exam content outline identifies knowledge of "client-centered education and training methods for successful use and maintenance of assistive technology options" (NBCOT®, 2022, p. 12) as essential for competent practice. The application of knowledge about the evaluation guidelines and HAAT Model described in this section and the following intervention principles can help you determine the correct answer for NBCOT® Domain 3 exam items about educating and training clients to effectively use and maintain AT.

AT Intervention

1. Intervention principles.
   a. A systematic approach using the HAAT model can help ensure that the person acquires the knowledge and skills to effectively use AT to meet their needs and expectations.
   b. Select and use one or two devices on a trial basis in the home to determine what serves the individual's needs best.
   c. Keep devices as simple and intuitive as possible.
   d. If a device is stationary, ensure that it is positioned in a manner that is easy for the person to access.
   e. Provide multiple training sessions to ensure the person is competent with the use of devices so that they are not reliant on the help of others.
   f. As the person acclimates to the use of the provided AT, gradually add additional modules (if needed and desired) to more fully meet the person's needs and expectations.
   g. For electrical ATDs, it is essential that the person and/or caregiver(s) are taught the following.
      (1) The electrical cords used to connect appliances to ATDs must be safely installed to prevent fraying and falls.
      (2) Charging instructions for batteries must be followed, as some have strict schedules.
      (3) Surge protectors must be used to avoid blown circuits.
      (4) Backup systems for electrical ATDs must be established.
   h. The person and/or caregiver(s) should be educated about AT device warranty terms and conditions and their rights as consumers.
2. Re-evaluate and revise the intervention plan as needed.
   a. Assess for a change in the individual's functional status.
   b. Determine the efficiency and efficacy of their use of AT.
   c. Check the device for durability and efficacy.
   d. Adapt, modify, or cease use of the device as indicated.
3. Document the intervention and reevaluation process.

Funding for ATDs

1. State Vocational and Educational Services for Individuals with Disabilities (VESID), Offices for Vocational Rehabilitation (OVRs), and Divisions of Vocational Rehabilitation (DVRs) will pay for ATDs, if they enable a person to go to work or school.
2. Private companies may fund ATDs to ensure ADA compliance.
3. Private insurance, Medicare, Medicaid, and workers' compensation may reimburse for certain devices.

Community Mobility

Overview

1. Community mobility is the ability to move around one's community to engage in desired occupations and pursue meaningful activities outside of one's home.
2. Community mobility includes personal mobility (i.e., the ability to drive, walk, bicycle, roll, and/or use electronic personal mobility such as a scooter, power wheelchair, or golf cart).

> **EXAM HINT:** The NBCOT® OTR® exam content outline identifies knowledge of "mobility options . . . for supporting participation in community mobility (including) alternative transportation options" (NBCOT®, 2022, p. 11) as essential for competent practice. The application of knowledge about the alternative transportation options described in the following can help you determine the correct answer for NBCOT® exam items about community mobility.

3. Community mobility includes the ability to access and use public (e.g., buses, subways, trains, para-transit), private (e.g., taxis, limousines, ride hailing apps [Uber, Lyft]), and/or other community-based transportation systems (e.g., volunteer ride share programs).

   a. Para-transit public transportation systems seek to meet the community mobility needs of persons with disabilities or functional impairments who cannot use public transportation due to existing barriers and limitations and/or whose community mobility needs cannot be met by those provided by a fixed route public transit system.

      (1) Para-transit can be directly provided by the public transportation system or via the provision of subsidies or vouchers for the use of private transportation systems (e.g., taxis, ride hailing apps).

      (2) Para-transit can range from curb to curb (the person is picked up and dropped off at the curb), door to door (the driver helps the person out of the car and to their door), to door through door (the driver helps the person exit their home, enter and exit their destination, and enter their home).

4. In the OTPF-4, driving and community mobility are listed as one occupation. Given that the activity demands of, and evaluation and intervention foci for community mobility activities and driving differ, information about driver rehabilitation and driving cessation will be provided in the next section of this Chapter.

> **EXAM HINT:** The NBCOT® OTR® exam content outline identifies knowledge of "mobility options, vehicle adaptations, and alternative devices for supporting participation in community mobility" (NBCOT®, 2022, p. 11) as essential for competent practice. The application of knowledge about the community mobility options described above and the subsequent information about driver rehabilitation and cessation can help you determine the correct answer for NBCOT® Domain 3 exam items about community mobility participation.

Evaluation of Community Mobility

1. Screening and assessment of the person's performance skills, performance patterns, and client factors.

   a. Examples as to how this evaluation is relevant to community mobility are provided below. The following examples are not inclusive of all that should be assessed during the evaluation process. They are provided to highlight the reality that an evaluation of the person's ability to participate in their environments of choice must be multi-dimensional.

      (1) Physical: strength to push a wheelchair to a bus stop; endurance to walk down stairs to a subway platform and up stairs to the street; balance to handle sudden stops and starts on buses, trains, and subways; fine motor skills to handle money or a transit card to pay one's fare; functional mobility to transfer into a taxi or ride share car.

      (2) Sensory: vision to see obstacles in one's path, depth perception to safely navigate steps and curbs, audition to hear a car horn.

      (3) Cognitive: memory to remember bus, subway, or train fares, numbers and stops; problem-solving to determine alternative route if planned route is not available; topographical orientation to orient and navigate oneself within the environment (e.g., a train station).

      (4) Psychological: emotional regulation in crowded and noisy situations, frustration tolerance and stress management when transportation problems arise (e.g., when a ride share driver does not arrive at the scheduled pick-up time).

      (5) Social: recognizing established social norms, responding to social cues from others, respecting the space of others on public transit, asking for directions or help if needed.

2. Assessment of the characteristics of the person's community environment and community mobility resources. These include but are not limited to the following.

   a. Terrain: even or uneven, steep or level, degree of slope.

   b. Availability and quality of curb cuts.

   c. Availability and duration of traffic lights.

   d. Parking availability and accessibility.

   e. Availability of accessible public transit, discounted public transit fare programs, and alternative transit for persons with disabilities and older adults.

3. Determination of the person's community mobility interests, options, and barriers.

   a. Evaluate their eligibility for paratransit, discounted fare, and/or subsidized transportation programs.

4. Assessment of the person's ability to recognize and respond to risky and/or dangerous situations.

   a. Refer to the subsequent section on driver cessation.

Interventions for Community Mobility

1. Direct interventions to address functional limitations (e.g., balance, endurance, memory, problem-solving emotional regulation, assertiveness).

2. Education about community mobility options and resources (e.g., public para-transit and half fare programs, transportation provided by Area Agencies on Aging and the Veterans Administration).
3. Education and training on how to safely and effectively use personal mobility devices (e.g., walkers, wheelchairs, scooters) to access public and private transportation, transfer from these devices when needed, and store them if required.
   a. Practice in the actual environment in which the person will be using public transportation should be provided.

4. If indicated, and with the person's permission, provide education and training to family members/caregivers to enable them to effectively support the person's community mobility.
5. Develop a person's advocacy skills to obtain access to para-transit, discounted fare, and/or subsidized transportation programs, if eligible, and provide needed documentation to support their application.
6. Safety training to ensure that the person can recognize and respond to risky and/or dangerous situations (e.g., when and how to call 911).
   a. Refer to the subsequent section on driver cessation.

Driver Rehabilitation and Driving Cessation

Overview

1. Driving is a complex occupation that requires the integration of the driver, their performance, the vehicle, and the environment.
2. Purposes.
   a. Provide mobility within one's community.
   b. Allow for autonomy in accessing services, goods, resources, and self-directed activity pursuits.
   c. Enable engagement in life roles including educational, vocational, social, and familial role activities.
3. Physical, cognitive, psychiatric, and developmental disabilities can affect the ability to drive safely and effectively.
4. Driver rehabilitation requires extensive on-the-road training and behind the wheel driving in a diversity of driving environments.
   a. Knowledge of general state driving regulations and statutes specifically related to individuals with disabilities must be acquired prior to initiating a driver rehabilitation program.
   b. An OT practitioner who performs on-the-road driver training must become a state licensed driving instructor.
   c. OT practitioners who practice driver rehabilitation should become certified driving rehabilitation specialists. Refer to prior section on the role of the team for more information about the credentialing of driving rehabilitation specialists.

Evaluation of Driver Ability

1. OT practitioners who have entry-level generalist skills can screen and evaluate a person's performance skills, performance patterns, and client factors to make an initial determination of the person's fitness-to-drive. Areas assessed include the following.
   a. Visual-perceptual skills: intact visual acuity, night vision, contrast sensitivity, peripheral field, scanning, spatial relations, and depth perception are needed to access essential visual input and to accurately interpret the driving environment.
      (1) Color recognition is not a state mandated requirement, as color blindness can be readily compensated for while driving.
   b. Cognitive skills: orientation, alertness, memory, judgement, ability to shift/divide attention, problem-solving, topographical orientation, response time, sign recognition, and knowledge of "rules of the road" are required to drive safely and appropriately for different driving conditions, and to anticipate the actions of other drivers on the road and the consequences of one's own actions.
   c. Motor: adequate ROM, strength, endurance, and motor speed are needed for basic vehicle control including accurate steering to remain in lane and make turns, and for smooth acceleration and braking.
   d. Sensory: the presence or loss of proprioception, pressure, and localization in the peripheries.
   e. Psychosocial: the presence of impulsive and/or agitated behaviors, and/or psychiatric symptoms can affect an individual's ability to drive safely.
   f. Side effects of medications that can affect motor performance, alertness, attention, judgment, and reaction time.
   g. Past driving experiences (which can range from none, to poor, to competent) can influence the individual's potential to drive with a disability.
2. A driver simulator may be used to further assess performance skills.

3. If the results of the screening and/or assessment indicate areas that require further evaluation, the OT practitioner should refer the individual to a driving rehabilitation specialist to complete a more in-depth evaluation including an on-the-road evaluation.

4. On-the-road evaluation: there are two levels of driving that must be considered when evaluating a person's abilities when they are behind the wheel and actually driving. These include the following.
   a. Operational: the ability to control the car by steering, accelerating, turning, backing up, parking, and braking.
   b. Tactical: the ability to adjust speed in response to posted limits, changes in road conditions and traffic/driving risks, the ability to stay in one's lane and maintain a safe distance from other cars.

5. The ergonomics of driving should also be assessed to increase safety and prevent discomfort. Considerations include the following.
   a. Seat position in relation to visibility of car's endpoints.
   b. Positioning of seatbelt and shoulder restraint.
   c. Access to foot pedals and/or steering column controls.
   d. Airbag clearance of 12″ between the person and the steering wheel in case of airbag deployment.

6. The person's ability to manage automotive emergencies (e.g., a breakdown) and obtain assistance should also be assessed.

Interventions for Driver Rehabilitation

1. A driver simulator can be used to practice and develop specific skills (e.g., visual scanning).
2. Adaptive driving equipment can be recommended for individuals with specific limitations and training in their use provided.
   a. Box 16-6 describes common adaptations and their purposes.

> **EXAM HINT:** The NBCOT® OTR® exam content outline identifies knowledge of "vehicle adaptations . . . for supporting participation in community mobility . . . (including) adapted driving controls" (NBCOT®, 2022, p. 11) as essential for competent practice. The application of knowledge about the adaptive driving equipment described in Box 16-6 can help you determine the correct answer for NBCOT® exam items about driver rehabilitation.

3. Provide hands-on, on-the-road training to develop and generalize skills.

> **BOX 16-6 ▷ Driving Adaptations and their Purposes**
>
> - Hand controls can replace accelerators and brake foot pedals.
> - Steering knobs enable one-handed steering control. Types include:
>   - standard round spinning knob for a person with one intact UE.
>   - ring to accommodate a prosthesis.
>   - tri-pin or cuff to accommodate an absent or weak grasp.
> - Pedal extensions can be added if feet do not reach standard foot pedals.
> - Zero effort or reduced effort steering can accommodate for decreased range, strength, and endurance.
> - Steering wheel positioning adjustments can place the steering wheel in atypical positions to allow for access.
> - Back-up camera to compensate for limited neck mobility.

4. Training in the use of a smart phone app and/or an electronic navigation system/global positioning system (GPS) to safely and effectively navigate unfamiliar environments.
5. Referrals to an ophthalmologist or optician to address visual deficits.
6. If a person is determined to be unsafe or unable to drive, alternatives to maintain community mobility must be explored and implemented. Refer to subsequent section on driver cessation.

> **CAUTION:** The OT practitioner has an ethical responsibility to know the laws in their state regarding their obligations to report that they have determined a person is not fit to drive. Regardless of state laws, OT practitioners have an ethical responsibility to address their concerns with the person, their family members/caregivers, and the professional team working with the client.

Funding for Driver Rehabilitation

1. State Vocational and Educational Services for Individuals with Disabilities (VESID), Offices for Vocational Rehabilitation (OVRs), and Divisions of Vocational Rehabilitation (DVRs) will pay for driver rehabilitation if it will enable a person to go to work or school.
2. Private insurance, Medicare, Medicaid, and workers' compensation may reimburse for certain driver rehabilitation devices/adaptations.

Driver Cessation

1. When a person is unable to safely drive independently without or with adaptations, interventions are needed to help the person attain and maintain safe, effective, and satisfying community mobility.
2. Recognize that the loss of the ability to self-drive can dramatically change a person's ability to live an independent and self-determined life.
   a. Support must be provided to the individual to deal with this loss and its ramifications on their daily life, valued roles, and community participation.
   b. The person's preferences for community mobility and participation and their prior experiences with alternative transportation should be determined.
   c. Available community mobility alternatives (e.g., public transportation, para-transit, private car services, volunteer driver and ride sharing programs, walking) that can enable independence and self-determination should be explored.
   d. An evaluation of the person's ability to independently meet the activity demands of their preferred mode(s) of alternative transportation must be completed.
   e. Fact-based education about alternative transportation options should be provided to address concerns.

f. Training in the skills needed to use alternative transportation must be provided to be sure that the person can safely and effectively meet the activity demands of their chosen mode(s) of transportation.
   (1) Travel training programs for the use of public transportation are provided in some communities to help persons with disabilities and older adults.
g. For all modes of alternative transportation, the person's ability to recognize and respond to risky and/or dangerous situations must be evaluated, and training provided as needed to ensure their safety.
   (1) Refer to prior community mobility section for information about ensuring safety.
h. If the person does not have and cannot develop the skills needed to independently use their preferred mode(s) of alternative transportation (e.g., an on demand car service), support must be provided to help the person accept another mode of transportation that can enable mobility and maintain their participation in desired activities and valued roles (e.g., requesting and taking rides with family, neighbors, and/or friends).

Environmental Interventions for Cognitive Disorders and Restraint Reduction

General Intervention Strategies

1. The environment needs to be familiar, consistent, and predictable.
   a. Provide structure in the environment to increase orientation to time, place, person, and situation.
   b. Remove clutter to decrease extraneous stimuli when an individual is easily distracted or has limited vision.
   c. Provide visual reminders or tactile cues to decrease confusion, increase awareness, and facilitate independence (e.g., written directions and/or labels).
   d. Keep things in the same place for consistency and ease.
2. Use contrasting colors to discriminate background from foreground and/or figures from background.
3. Use restraint reduction techniques if a person is confused, agitated, and/or a wanderer.
4. Educate the client, caregiver, and family.

   a. Train caregivers for persons with memory and/or sensory impairments on effective communication techniques.
   b. Facilitate carryover of intervention techniques in the modified environment.
   c. Increase awareness of potential resources available to the individual and their family.
   d. Increase awareness of their rights to access these resources.
5. Monitor changes and adjustment after a disability to assess carryover of information.
6. Make home modifications to ensure safety as needed.
   a. Remove potential hazards such as cleaning solutions, medications, sharp objects, matches, stove knobs, and firearms if a person is confused or forgetful.
   b. Follow modifications identified earlier in this Chapter for the prevention of falls.
   c. Refer to Chapter 5 for additional modifications for age-related sensory loss.
7. Provide a personal emergency system and train in its use.

Chapter 16

Restraint Reduction

> **EXAM HINT:** The NBCOT® OTR® exam content outline identifies the task of implementing "occupation-based strategies to support participation in activities of daily living (ADL), . . . rest and sleep, . . . leisure, and social participation across the life span" (NBCOT®, 2022, p. 8) as critical for entry-level practice and knowledge of "interventions to support cognitive, visual-motor, visual, and perceptual processing and sensory arousal" (NBCOT®, 2022, p. 9) as essential for competent practice. The application of knowledge about the intervention strategies described in the prior section and the following restraint reduction approaches can help you determine the correct answer to NBCOT® Domain 3 exam items about intervention selection and implementation for persons with cognitive deficits.

1. Assessment of behaviors that result in agitation, restlessness, and/or wandering.
   a. Pain, physical discomfort.
   b. Hunger, thirst, need for toileting.
   c. Loneliness, fear.
   d. Boredom.
   e. Unfamiliar environment.
2. Intervention to address contributing factors and/or correct underlying problems.
   a. Referral to physician for medical evaluation/pain management.
   b. Proper positioning.
   c. Provision of snacks, unbreakable water bottles, or other appropriate safe source of nourishment and hydration.
   d. Adequate and client-directed toileting routine.
   e. Active listening; attention to underlying feelings and expressed concerns to promote trust.
   f. Family, peer, and/or pastoral visits.
   g. Animal-assisted or pet therapy.
   h. Social and leisure activities.
   i. Exercise and/or other outlets for restless, anxious behavior.
   j. Night-time activities.
   k. Eliminate loudspeaker and other extraneous noise; provide soothing background music.
   l. Include familiar and favorite objects in the person's living space to personalize it.
   m. Provide a structured home-like environment with a set routine to promote sense of safety and security.
3. Interventions to address agitation and/or wandering incidents.
   a. Approach from the person's front at eye level.
   b. Communicate calmly with the use of simple statements/instructions.
   c. Distract with an activity or topic of interest to the person.
   d. Redirect back to desired location.
   e. Engage in an activity of interest or diversion.
   f. Camouflage doors, exits, and elevators with full-length mirrors, stop or no-crossing signs, wallpaper, and/or vertical blinds.
   g. Put tape on floors or planters to mark end of hall.
   h. Install non-dead bolt locks or Velcro™ doors.
   i. Use door alarms, personal alarms, or monitoring devices.
   j. Make contained areas interesting and safe.
   k. Rearrange furniture to deter wandering.
   l. Provide a variety of comfortable seating and furniture, including broad-based rockers and footstools.

References

Ainsworth, E., & DeJonge, D. (Eds.). (2019). An occupational therapist's guide to home modification practice. Slack.

Ainsworth, E., & DeJonge, D. (2019). Home modification process. In E. Ainsworth & D. DeJonge (Eds.), An occupational therapist's guide to home modification practice (pp. 83–110). Slack.

Ainsworth, E., & DeJonge, D. (2019). Measuring the person and the home environment. In E. Ainsworth & D. DeJonge (Eds.), An occupational therapist's guide to home modification practice (pp. 145–174). Slack.

Ainsworth, E., DeJonge, D., & Tanner, B. (2019). Access standards and their role in intervention. In E. Ainsworth & D. DeJonge (Eds.), An occupational therapist's guide to home modification practice (pp. 247–257). Slack

American National Standards Institute. (1992). Accessible and usable buildings and facilities.

American Occupational Therapy Association. (2010a). Driving and community mobility. American Journal of Occupational Therapy, 64(Suppl. 6), S112–S124.

American Occupational Therapy Association. (2010b). Specialized knowledge and skills in technology and environmental interventions for occupational therapy practice. American Journal of Occupational Therapy, 64(Suppl. 6), S44–S56.

American Occupational Therapy Association. (2015). Four ways occupational therapy makes smart homes smarter [PDF file]. https://www.aota.org/Publications-News/AOTA News/2015/smart-homes-learn-technology-ot-occupational -therapy.aspx.

American Occupational Therapy Association. (2020). Occupational therapy practice framework: Domain and process (4th ed.). American Journal of Occupational Therapy, 74(Suppl. 2), 7412410010p1–7412410010p87. https://doi.org/10.5014/ajot.2020.74S2001

Assistive Technology Act of 2004. (2004). H.R.4278 - 108th Congress (2003–2004): Assistive Technology Act of 2004. https://www.congress.gov/bill/108th-congress/house-bill/4278.

Bausch, M. E., Mittler, J. E., Hasselbring, T. S., & Cross, D. P. (2005). The Assistive Technology Act of 2004: What does it say and what does it mean? Physical Disabilities: Education and Related Services, 23(2), 59–67.

Bhorade, A. M., Perlmutter, M. S., Wilson, B., Kambarian, J., Chang, S., Pekmezci, M., & Gordon, M. (2013). Differences in vision between clinic and home and the effect of lighting in older adults with and without glaucoma. JAMA Ophthalmology, 131(12), 1554–1562.

Bolding, D., Adler, C., Tipton-Burton, M., & Lillie, S. (2007). Mobility. In H. McHugh Pendleton & W. Schultz-Krohn (Eds.), Pedretti's occupational therapy: Practice skills for physical dysfunction (6th ed., pp. 195–247.). Mosby.

Centers for Disease Control and Prevention (CDC). (2016). CDC - Healthy Places - Healthy Places Terminology. https://www.cdc.gov/healthyplaces/terminology.htm#:~:text=aging%20in%20place,%2C%20income%2C%20or%20ability%20level.

Cook, A., & Polgar, J. M. (2013). Assistive technology: Principles and practices (4th ed.). Mosby.

DeJonge, D., & Hoyle, M. (2019). Evaluating home modification needs and priorities. In E. Ainsworth & D. DeJonge (Eds.), An occupational therapist's guide to home modification practice (pp. 111–144). Slack.

DeJonge, D., Hoyle, M., & Ainsworth, E. (2019). Developing and tailoring interventions. In E. Ainsworth & D. DeJonge (Eds.), An occupational therapist's guide to home modification practice (pp. 195–223). Slack.

Dewan, N., & MacDermid, J. C. (2014). Falls Efficacy Scale – International (FES-I). Journal of Physiotherapy, 60, 60.

Department of Justice. (2010). 2010 ADA Standards for Accessible Design.

Dickerson, A. (2020). Driving and community mobility. In M. Scaffa & A. Reitz (Eds.), Occupational therapy in community-based practice settings (2nd ed., pp. 238–264). F.A. Davis.

Dickerson, A., & Davis, E. S. (2020, October). Checklist of community mobility skills: Connecting clients to transportation options. OT Practice, 13–16.

Erikson, K. (2017). App-based mobile devices in the occupational therapy process. OT Practice, 22(17), CE1-CE-8.

Dirette, D., & Gutman, S. (Eds.). (2020). Occupational therapy for physical dysfunction (8th ed.). Lippincott Williams & Wilkins.

Gentry, T. (2017, September 11). Practical, affordable, smart homes for safety and improved function. OT Practice, 8–13.

Giesbrecht, E. (2013). Application of the human activity assistive technology model for occupational therapy research. Australian Journal of Occupational Therapy, 60(3), 230–240.

Gitlin, L. N., Schinfeld, S., Winter, L., Corcoran, M., Boyce, A. A., & Hauck, W. (2002). Evaluating home environments of persons with dementia: Interrater reliability and validity of the Home Environmental Assessment Protocol (HEAP). Disability and Rehabilitation, 24(1–3), 59–71.

Gourley, M. (2002, March 25). Driver rehabilitation. OT Practice, 15–20.

Hamilton, A., & Hamilton, A. (2015). Educational and digital technology strategies. In C. Christiansen, C. Baum, & J. M. Bass (Eds.), Occupational therapy performance, participation and wellbeing (pp. 513–525). Slack.

Institute for Human Centered Design. (2016). ADA checklist for existing facilities [PDF]. https://www.adachecklist.org/doc/fullchecklist/ada-checklist.pdf.

Lange, M. L. (2001a, July 2). Alternative keyboards. OT Practice, 19–20.

Lange, M. L. (2001b, Aug. 6). EADLs and aging clients. OT Practice, 16–18.

Lange, M. L. (2001c, Aug. 6). EADLs in the school setting. OT Practice, 17–18.

Larson, K., Stevens-Ratchford, R.G., Pedretti, L., & Crabtree, J. (1996). ROTE: The role of occupational therapy with the elderly (2nd ed.). American Occupational Therapy Association.

Mackenzie, L., Byles, J., & Higginbotham, N. (2000). Designing the Home Falls and Accidents Screening Tool (HOME FAST): Selecting the items. British Journal of Occupational Therapy, 63(6), 260–269.

Mackenzie, L. (2000). The Home Falls and Accidents Screening Tool (HOME FAST). https://stopfallsathome.com.au/about/

National Board for Certification in Occupational Therapy (NBCOT®). (2022). 2022 Occupational Therapist Registered (OTR®) examination content outline. https://www.nbcot.org/-/media/PDFs/2022_OTR_Content_Outline.pdf

National Registry of Rehabilitation Technology Suppliers (NRRTS). (2019). About NRRTS. http://www.nrrts.org/about.

O'Brien, J., & Kuhaneck, H. (Eds.). (2020). Occupational therapy for children and adolescents (8th ed.). Elsevier.

Oliver, R., Blathwayt, J., Brackley, C., & Tamaki, T. (1993). Development of the Safety Assessment of Function and the Environment for Rehabilitation (SAFER) tool. Canadian Journal of Occupational Therapy, 60, 70–82.

Peterson, E. W., & Murphy, S. (2002). Fear of falling: Part II—Assessment and intervention. Home and Community Health Special Interest Section Quarterly, 9(1), 1–4.

Poulin de Courval, L., Gélinas, I., Gauthier, S., Gayton, S., Liu, L., Rossignol, M., Sampalis, J., & Dastoor, D. (2006). Reliability and validity of the Safety Assessment Scale for people with dementia living at home. Canadian Journal of Occupational Therapy, 73, 67–75.

Scheiman, M. (2011). Understanding and managing vision deficits: A guide for occupational therapists (3rd ed.). Slack.

Schere, M. J., & Lane, J.P. (1997). Assessing computer profile of 'ideal' technologies in ten categories: An integration of quantitative and qualitative methods. Disability and Rehabilitation, 19, 528–535.

Scott, J., & Foley, T. (2020). Aging in place and home modifications. In M. Scaffa & A. Reitz (Eds.), Occupational therapy in community-based practice settings (2nd ed., pp. 217–237). F.A. Davis.

Smith, T. (2020). Low vision and services in the community. In M. Scaffa & A. Reitz (Eds.), Occupational therapy in community-based practice settings (2nd ed., pp. 265–278). F.A. Davis.

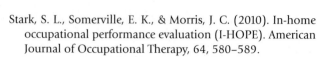

Chapter 16

Stark, S. L., Somerville, E. K., & Morris, J. C. (2010). In-home occupational performance evaluation (I-HOPE). American Journal of Occupational Therapy, 64, 580–589.

Stav, W., Pierce, S., Wheatley, C., & Schold Davis, E. (2005). Driving and community mobility. American Journal of Occupational Therapy, 59, 666–670.

Tinetti, M. E., Richman, D., & Powell, L. (1990). Falls efficacy as a measure of fear of falling. Journal of Gerontology, 45(6), 239–243.

Vandome, N. (2018). Smart homes in easy steps: Master smart technology for your home. In Easy Steps Limited.

Warren, M., & Barstow, E. (2011). Occupational therapy interventions for adults with low vision. AOTA Press.

West Virginia Research and Training Center. (1990). ADA—The Americans with Disabilities Act of 1990 PL 101–336, Volume I: The Law.

Review Questions

Mastery of the Environment: Evaluation and Intervention

Following are six questions about key content covered in this Chapter. These questions are not inclusive of the entirety of content on occupational therapy evaluation and intervention related to mastery of the environment that you must know for success on the NBCOT® exam. These questions are provided to help you "jump-start" the thought processes you will need to apply your studying of content to the answering of exam questions; hence, they are not in the NBCOT® exam format. Exam items in the NBCOT® format which cover the depth and breadth of content you will need to know to pass the NBCOT® exam are provided in the three online practice exams that accompany this text. The answers to the following questions are provided in Appendix 2.

1. An occupational therapist provides consultation services to a group of religious organizations who want to improve the accessibility of the entrances to their buildings. All entrances currently have stairs. What should the occupational therapist recommend to allow access for persons who use mobility aides (e.g., walkers and canes) and wheelchairs?

2. An occupational therapist provides a weekly home safety group to members of a senior center. What strategies should the therapist recommend the group members use inside and outside their homes to prevent falls?

3. A client is status-post posterolateral hip replacement surgery. What recommendations should the therapist make for bed mobility?

4. A school-based occupational therapist provides recommendations for alternative access modes to computers to compensate for a diversity of disabilities and maximize students' independence in the school environment. What adaptations can the therapist recommend? Explain their use.

(Continued)

Review Questions

5. A Center for Independent Living (CIL) has asked an entry-level occupational therapist and an entry-level OTA/COTA® to develop a program to address the community mobility needs of older adults and persons with disabilities. What aspects of community mobility can the therapist and OTA/COTA® include in this program? What aspects can they not include? Describe the evaluation and intervention foci that they should include in their program plan.

6. An occupational therapist begins employment at a new skilled nursing facility (SNF). To ensure compliance with OBRA and reduce the use of restraints in the facility, what policies and procedures should the therapist have the SNF administrators implement?

Professional Development After Initial Certification

RITA P. FLEMING-CASTALDY

Successfully passing the NBCOT® exam for the occupational therapist, registered (OTR®) enables you to meet an essential criterion for initial licensure and certification as an occupational therapist. The regulatory boards of all 50 states in the United States (US), the District of Columbia, and the US territories of Guam and Puerto Rico require a passing NBCO`T® exam score to legally practice as an occupational therapist in their respective jurisdictions. To obtain contact information for all state occupational therapy (OT) regulatory boards, see NBCOT Occupational Therapy Regulatory Body Contact List by State. This site also includes contact information for the OT regulatory boards of the District of Columbia and the US territories of Guam and Puerto Rico. Passing the NBCOT® OTR® exam also enables you to use the designation of OTR® if you choose to participate in the NBCOT® certification program.

Your success on this high-stakes exam can mark the beginning of a rewarding and fulfilling professional career. This concept of beginning is a critical one for you to embrace. While the pursuit of the goal to become an occupational therapist may end with professional licensure, it is at this point that your lifelong process of being a professional will begin. Being a member of a profession requires an ongoing commitment to the attainment and maintenance of excellence. Competent occupational therapists value this pursuit of excellence and are personally responsible for their professional development.

> The benefits of a life-long commitment to one's professional development are numerous. Increased personal pride and satisfaction in one's work; improved health care services for consumers and their families; enhanced professional image among policy makers, reimbursors, administrators, and the multidisciplinary team; and the prevention of burnout and professional stagnation are all viable outcomes of the continual pursuit of professional excellence (Cottrell, 2000, p. 465).

Numerous professional development resources are available to facilitate your growth from entry-level novice to master practitioner. Clinical supervision, peer support, networking, professional associations, mentoring, self-study, in-services, workshops, conferences, and post-professional education can all be used to attain and maintain professional mastery and excellence. Technology has expanded opportunities for professional development exponentially by eliminating geographic boundaries. Social media, e-mail, and video conferencing have significantly decreased and/or eliminated many costs previously associated with engaging in professional development activities. I strongly urge you to take advantage of both high-tech (e.g., virtual webinars) and low-tech (e.g., brainstorming with a colleague about a program initiative, seeking input from a mentor about a practice dilemma) learning opportunities early and often in your professional life. I also highly recommend that you become an active member in the American Occupational Therapy Association (AOTA) and your state association (and/or the local district in a large state). The AOTA provides contact information for all 50 state associations and the associations of the District of Columbia and Puerto Rico at State Associations | AOTA.

These actions will immediately provide you with access to a network of OT practitioners and leaders in the field who are proactive forces for professional advancement and role models for excellence. Moreover, the AOTA website at https://www.aota.org has countless resources available to members to ensure they provide evidence-based and occupation-based practice.

As Yerxa (1985) noted, an authentic professional is one who recognizes their responsibility to be a lifelong student. I wish you well as you begin this journey of learning and pursuing an authentic occupational therapy career. I can think of no better way to practice or live.

References

Cottrell, R. P. (2000). Professional development: The attainment, maintenance and promotion of excellence. In R. P. Cottrell (Ed.), *Proactive approaches in psychosocial occupational therapy,* (pp. 465–468). Thorofare, NJ: Slack.

Yerxa, E. (1966). Authentic occupational therapy. *American Journal of Occupational Therapy, 21,* 1–9.

Medical Terminology: Selected Prefixes and Suffixes

> **EXAM HINT:** It is important to remember that the language of health care is based on the Latin language. Knowing the Latin prefixes and suffixes that serve as the foundation for medical terminology can help you decipher the meaning of an unknown word. This can improve your ability to effectively analyze an exam item and select the best answer.
>
> For example, knowing that hypo means "below or deficient," and esthesi/o means sensation, will help you remember that hypoesthesia means decreased sensation. Therefore, if an exam item scenario identifies hypoesthesia as a presenting symptom, you will know that the use of a hot pack is an incorrect answer and that the correct answers would include adherence to safety precautions.

This appendix does not list all medical terms that may be on the NBCOT® exam, but it does provide many foundational components of medical terminology. For a complete and exhaustive presentation of medical terminology, you should review the medical terminology text and/or resources that you used in your academic coursework.

a-	without	angi/o	vessel
ab-	away from	ankyl/o	crooked or stiff
abdomin/o	abdomen	ante-	before
acous/o	hearing	anti-	against or opposed to
acr/o	extremity or topmost	-arche	beginning
-acusis	hearing condition	arteri/o	artery
ad-	to, toward, or near	arthr/o	joint
aden/o	gland	articul/o	joint
adip/o	fat	-ase	enzyme
adren/o	adrenal gland	-asthenia	weakness
aer/o	air or gas	ather/o	fat
-algia	pain	-ation	process
alveol/o	alveolus (air sac)	audi/o	hearing
ambi-	both	aur/i	ear
an-	without	bi-	two or both

-blast	germ or bud	fasci/o	fascia (a band)
blast/o	germ or bud	fibr/o	fiber
brachi/o	arm	gangli/o	ganglion (knot)
brady-	slow	gastr/o	stomach
bronch/o	bronchus (airway)	-gen	origin or production
bucc/o	cheek	glomerul/o	glomerulus (little ball)
carcin/o	cancer	gloss/o	tongue
cardi/o	heart	glott/o	opening
celi/o	abdomen	gluc/o	sugar
cephal/o	head	glyc/o	sugar
cerebell/o	cerebellum (little brain)	gnos/o	knowing
cerebr/o	brain	-gram	record
cervic/o	neck or cervix	-graph	instrument for recording
chondr/o	cartilage	-graphy	process of recording
chrom/o	color	hem/o	blood
circum-	around	hemat/o	blood
con-	together or with	hemi-	half
contra-	against or opposed to	hepat/o	liver
cost/o	rib	hepatic/o	liver
crani/o	skull	herni/o	hernia
cutane/o	skin	hidr/o	sweat
cyan/o	blue	hist/o	tissue
cyst/o	bladder or sac	histi/o	tissue
dacry/o	tear	hydr/o	water
dactyl/o	digit (finger or toe)	hyper-	above or excessive
de-	from, down, or not	hypo-	below or deficient
derm/o	skin	-ia	condition of
-desis	binding	-iasis	formation of or presence of
dextr/o	right, or on the right side	-iatrics	treatment
dia-	across or through	-iatry	treatment
diaphor/o	profuse sweat	-icle	small
dips/o	thirst	immun/o	safe
dis-	separate from or apart	infra-	below or under
-dynia	pain	inter-	between
dys-	painful, difficult, or faulty	intra-	within
ec-	out or away	-ism	condition of
-ectasis	expansion or dilation	iso-	equal, like
ecto-	outside	-itis	inflammation
-ectomy	excision (removal)	-ium	structure or tissue
-emesis	vomiting	kyph/o	humped
-emia	blood condition	lacrim/o	tear
en-	within	lapar/o	abdomen
encephal/o	brain	lei/o	smooth
endo-	within	lip/o	fat
epi-	upon	lob/o	lobe (a portion)
erythr/o	red	lord/o	bent
esthesi/o	sensation	lumb/o	loin (lower back)
eu-	good or normal	lymph/o	clear fluid
ex-	out or away	-lysis	breaking down or dissolution
exo-	outside	macr/o	large or long
extra-	outside	-malacia	softening

meat/o	opening		phot/o	light
-megaly	enlargement		phren/o	diaphragm (also mind)
meso-	middle		plas/o	formation
meta-	beyond, after, or change		-plasty	surgical repair or reconstruction
-meter	instrument for measuring		-plegia	paralysis
-metry	process of measuring		pleur/o	pleura
micro-	small		-pnea	breathing
mono-	one		pneum/o	air or lung
morph/o	form		pod/o	foot
multi-	many		-poiesis	formation
muscul/o	muscle		poly-	many
myel/o	bone marrow or spinal cord		post-	after or behind
myring/o	eardrum		pre-	before
narc/o	stupor		presby/o	old age
nas/o	nose		pro-	before
nat/i	birth		-ptosis	falling or downward displacement
necr/o	death		pulmon/o	lung
neo-	new		quadr/i	four
nephr/o	kidney		re-	again or back
neur/o	nerve		reticul/o	a net
ocul/o	eye		retro-	backward or behind
-oid	resembling		rhabd/o	rod shaped or striated (skeletal)
-ole	small		-rrhage	to burst forth
olig/o	few or deficient		-rrhexis	rupture
-oma	tumor		sarc/o	flesh
ophthalm/o	eye		scler/o	hard or sclera
opt/o	eye		scoli/o	twisted
or/o	mouth		semi	half
orth/o	straight, normal, or correct		sinistr/o	left, or on the left side
-osis	condition or increase		somat/o	body
oste/o	bone		somn/o	sleep
ot/o	ear		son/o	sound
pachy-	thick		-spasm	involuntary contraction
pan-	all		sphygm/o	pulse
para-	alongside of or abnormal		spin/o	spine (thorn)
-paresis	slight paralysis		spir/o	breathing
path/o	disease		spondyl/o	vertebra
pector/o	chest		squam/o	scale
ped/o	child or foot		-stasis	stop or stand
pelv/i	hip bone		steat/o	fat
pelv/o	hip bone		sten/o	narrow
-penia	abnormal reduction		stere/o	three dimensional or solid
per-	through		stern/o	sternum (breastbone)
peri-	around		steth/o	chest
phag/o	eat or swallow		stomat/o	mouth
phas/o	speech		-stomy	creation of an opening
-phil	attraction for		sub-	below or under
-philia	attraction for		super-	above or excessive
phleb/o	vein		supra-	above or excessive
phob/o	exaggerated fear or sensitivity		sym-	together or with
phon/o	voice or speech		syn-	together or with

tachy-	fast	ultra-	beyond or excessive
tax/o	order or coordination	uni-	one
ten/o	tendon (to stretch)	ur/o	urine
thorac/o	chest	varic/o	swollen or twisted vein
thromb/o	clot	vas/o	vessel
-tomy	incision	vertebr/o	vertebra
ton/o	tone or tension	vesic/o	bladder or sac
top/o	place	xanth/o	yellow
tox/o	poison	xer/o	dry
trache/o	trachea (windpipe)	-y	condition or process of
trans-	across or through		
tri-	three		
-tripsy	crushing		
troph/o	nourishment or development		
-ula, -ule	small		

Reference

Willis, M. C. (1996). Medical terminology: The language of healthcare. Williams & Wilkins.

Review Questions and Answers

Chapter 3 Review Questions

Foundations of Occupational Therapy Practice

1. An occupational therapist is preparing to evaluate a client. What contextual considerations should the therapist take into account when determining the assessments that will be appropriate to use with the client?

   ▷ The therapist should consider the environmental contexts of the practice setting in which the assessment will be conducted (e.g., the length of stay, the setting's primary focus, legislative guidelines and restrictions, and the facility's resources of space, equipment, and supplies). In addition, the physical and sociocultural contexts of the client's current and expected environment (e.g., roles, values, norms, supports) should be taken into account by the therapist. The temporal context of the client and their disability (e.g., the client's chronological and developmental age, anticipated duration of disability, and stage of illness) should also be considered when determining which assessment tools are best to use during an evaluation.

2. An occupational therapist owns and operates a preschool facility for children with developmental, intellectual, and physical disabilities. When should the therapist instruct the facility staff members to use standard precautions? What policies and procedures should the therapist implement for the use of standard precautions in this practice setting?

   Standard precautions are infection prevention practices that are applied at *all* times when working with *all* persons in *all* practice settings. They include standards for hand hygiene and the use of gloves, gown, mask, eye protection, or face shield (depending on the anticipated exposure). There are also standards for handling and caring for equipment or items in a practice setting to prevent transmission of infectious agents. The application of standard precautions during service delivery is determined by the nature of the interactions with clients and the extent of anticipated blood, body fluid, or pathogen exposure.

   ▷ In a pediatric preschool setting, the therapist should ensure that all staff members consistently adhere to hand hygiene and respiratory hygiene/cough etiquette standards. Signs should be posted in the facility with instructions to persons with symptoms of a respiratory infection to cover their mouths/noses when coughing or sneezing, use and dispose of tissues, and perform hand hygiene after hands have been in contact with respiratory secretions. The facility should provide tissues and no-touch receptacles (e.g., foot pedal-operated lid or open, plastic-lined waste baskets) for disposal of tissues. Resources and instructions for performing hand hygiene should be conveniently located throughout the facility. Policies and procedures for routine and targeted cleaning and disinfecting of the facility's environmental surfaces and toys used by the children must be established. Toys selected for use with the children during evaluation and intervention must be ones that can be easily cleaned and disinfected (e.g., hard plastic building blocks, not furry stuffed animals). Toys that are mouthed must be immediately cleaned, disinfected, and then rinsed with water after use. After cleaning and disinfection, toys should be stored in a designated labeled container that identifies them as clean and ready for use. Large stationary toys (e.g., climbing equipment) must be cleaned and disinfected at least weekly and whenever visibly soiled.

3. An occupational therapist is integrating health literacy into the home program for a client living with multiple sclerosis (MS). The client's MS has progressed to the point that they now need to use a wheelchair for all activities. The client has established a goal to learn how to perform wheelchair pushups and lateral leans to prevent decubiti. What learning principles should the therapist use to inform their intervention planning? What teaching methods are best for the therapist to use when implementing intervention?

Health literacy is the ability to find, understand, and use information that is needed to make informed health-related decisions and engage in informed health-related behaviors. Intervention to develop a client's health literacy about decubiti prevention is very relevant for a person who will be using a wheelchair for all activities. To attain this goal, the therapist should incorporate learning principles and teaching methods that make the health information readily accessible and directly applicable to the client into their intervention sessions. The learning principles that are most important for the therapist to use to guide their intervention plan include the following.

- Learners who actively participate in the process learn more because experiential learning is more effective than didactic learning.
- Self-awareness and self-monitoring skills should be developed and used by the learner.
- Continuity between the learning experiences and real-life situations facilitates the effective transfer of learning and the generalization of knowledge and skills.

These principles can be directly applied to teaching the client how to perform wheelchair pushups and lateral leans for decubiti prevention by having the client practice these newly acquired skills in a diversity of situations and contexts and discussing the efficacy of these efforts.

The teaching methods used during intervention should be compatible with the client's learning style, cognitive level, and the characteristics of the task that is being taught. Demonstration and performance are the best method for teaching a person how to perform wheelchair pushups and lateral leans to prevent decubiti. Using this approach, the therapist will perform the task and have the client imitate their performance. After the client demonstrates the ability to perform wheelchair pushups and lateral leans, the teaching method of repetition and practice should be used to ensure that the client develops proficiency and is able to consistently integrate these into their daily routine.

4. An occupational therapist provides services in a community-based setting which offers individual and group interventions. What factors should the therapist consider when determining if it is best to use an individual intervention versus a group intervention with a client?

The level of the client's cognitive, physical, and interpersonal skills should be considered to determine if an individual or a group intervention is best to use with a client. Clients with lower capabilities and a greater need for attention and structure from the occupational therapist due to body structure and/or functional impairments will benefit from an individualized approach. The client's need for privacy and/or greater control over the environment also support the use of an individual intervention. Individualized interventions are indicated if the activity demands, performance skills, and performance patterns of an intervention are complex. Most important, if the client exhibits disruptive and/or dangerous behaviors, group interventions are not appropriate.

Group interventions are indicated when the intervention focus is on the development of interpersonal skills and the ability to engage socially with others. Group interventions provide the opportunity to receive feedback from people experiencing similar conditions, learn from them, place one's own condition into perspective, and become motivated by peer role models. Groups are also indicated when an intervention goal is to develop behaviors that are needed for successful performance in shared occupations (e.g., work, study, and leisure groups).

5. An occupational therapist working in a long-term care facility co-leads a discharge planning group with a social worker. What are the advantages to this co-leadership? What issues may arise to impede effective co-leadership that the therapist should be prepared to address?

Co-leadership enables each leader to share their professional knowledge and skills and use their unique professional expertise to assume different leadership roles and tasks. Both leaders can provide and obtain mutual support to each other, share their observations, and model effective behaviors. Issues that may arise and must be dealt to ensure effective co-leadership include the splitting by group member(s) of one leader against the other, excessive competition among co-leaders, and unequal responsibilities resulting in an unbalanced work load among co-leaders.

6. An occupational therapist provides services to a group of parents of infants and toddlers. Each parent recently incurred a disability. The therapist plans to use a thematic and a topical group with the clients to address goals related to their parental role. What would be appropriate foci and relevant activities for these groups?

The purpose of a thematic group is to assist members in acquiring the knowledge, skills, and/or attitudes needed to perform a specific activity. Because the clients in this group are parents who each recently incurred a disability, this group should focus on the improvement of members' ability to engage in desired parenting activities outside of group by teaching and practicing these activities within group (e.g., how to perform childcare activities using adaptive equipment and compensatory strategies; how to transfer to and from a wheelchair to the floor to enable play with a toddler). In a thematic group, simulated, clearly defined, structured activities are used for group members to practice and learn needed skills within the group (e.g., using a doll to practice diapering an infant from a wheelchair or by using a one-handed technique).

The purpose of a topical group is to discuss specific activities that members are engaged in outside of group to enable them to engage in the activities in a more effective, need-satisfying manner. Because the clients are already parents, this group would be considered a concurrent topical group. In this group, discussion would include members' current or anticipated fears and problems about parenting with a disability, potential solutions for dealing with these concerns, and coping mechanisms for increasing personal self-efficacy as a parent. The therapist would facilitate a focused group discussion on parenting activities, help members problem-solve, give feedback and support, and reinforce skill acquisition.

7. An occupational therapist is working with a client who is living with amyotrophic lateral sclerosis (ALS). The client is covered by Medicare and has attained their maximum level of function. The client and family are concerned that the client will be discharged from therapy and unable to maintain their current level of function and that their skill level will deteriorate. What information should the therapist provide to the client and family?

Amyotrophic lateral sclerosis (ALS) is a progressive neurological disease that affects motor neurons that control voluntary muscle movement. ALS has no cure and there is no effective treatment to reverse its course. Medicare beneficiaries with progressive disorders can continue to have their therapy services covered *if* they require skilled services to slow or prevent deterioration and maintain their maximum level of function. They do not have to be discharged from services, even if no improvement is expected. This reimbursement requirement was put into effect by the Centers for Medicare and Medicaid Services (CMS) in 2013 (Jimmo v. Sebelius Settlement Agreement [cms.gov]). This Medicare benefit may not be provided by state Medicaid programs or private insurance plans. The therapist should inform the client and family that skilled services can continue.

1. You are working in a skilled nursing facility. An administrator asks you to actively treat a new resident who is very frail with multiple medical complications. Upon admission, you had evaluated the resident and determined that the resident would not be able to tolerate occupational therapy services. During the evaluation, the resident had stated that chronic pain has made all activities very difficult. Pain relief and rest were the only things the resident identified as personally desired. How should you respond to the administrator's request? Which principles of the AOTA's Code of Ethics should you use to guide your response? Explain how these principles relate to this situation.

   You must refuse to place the person on an active occupational therapy intervention program because doing so would violate the ethical principles of beneficence, nonmaleficence, and autonomy. The ethical principle of beneficence requires you to demonstrate your concern for the resident's well-being and safety. The resident has chronic pain that compromises health and well-being; thus, pain relief must be a priority. The ethical principle of nonmaleficence requires you to avoid doing anything that can harm or injure a person. You must use your professional judgment and avoid compromising the resident's rights or health.

   This arbitrary administrative directive to place the resident on an active intervention program must be confronted. The administrator's request does not consider the person's current status and can cause harm. This request also violates the ethical principle of autonomy that requires you to respect the right of the individual to self-determination and the person's right to refuse occupational therapy services. The resident has stated that pain relief and rest were the only things personally desired. Providing occupational therapy services to a person who is frail and too ill to participate in therapy would violate all of the above ethical principles; therefore, the administrator must be informed that you will not do this.

2. A large regional health-care system provides occupational therapy services across the continuum of care. Settings in which occupational therapy services are provided include an acute care hospital, an outpatient clinic, a subacute rehabilitation unit, a skilled nursing facility (SNF), a palliative care unit, and a home health agency. All settings employ occupational therapists and OTAs/COTA®s. What factors should be considered when determining the level of supervision that the occupational therapist should provide to the OTA/COTA®. What is a key determinant for deciding if an OTA/COTA® can ethically be given more responsibility?

   The degree, amount, and pattern of supervision required in each setting will depend on the OTA's/COTA®'s knowledge and skills (e.g., the OTA/COTA® has completed advanced training in orthotics); the complexities of client needs (e.g., the presence of comorbidities) and caseload characteristics and demands (e.g., focused primarily on one diagnostic category and a core intervention approach such as training clients in hip precautions pre- and post-hip replacement surgery). An OTA/COTA® providing services to an acutely ill person with rapidly changing status on the inpatient unit will require a closer occupational therapist and OTA/COTA® partnership than an OTA/ COTA® providing services to a more stable client in a long-term care setting. State laws, licensure requirements, and other regulatory mandates must also be considered when determining the level of OTA/COTA® supervision required. Ethically, the occupational therapist supervisor must ensure that the type, amount, and pattern of supervision match the supervisee's level of role performance.

An OTA/ COTA® can be given more responsibility by the occupational therapist after the OTA/COTA® establishes service competency. Service competency is the ability to use a specified intervention in a safe, effective, and reliable manner. Before assigning greater responsibilities to the OTA/COTA®, the occupational therapist must determine that the OTA/COTA® can perform a procedure in a manner that obtains the same results as the therapist would have obtained. OTAs/COTA®s who establish service competency do not become independent; they continue to work with the occupational therapist's supervision.

3. An occupational therapist is opening a private practice. What procedures should the therapist implement to ensure full compliance with the Health Insurance Portability and Accountability Act (HIPAA)?

The therapist needs to set standards and establish safeguards to ensure the privacy and security of health-care records. Procedures must be established for informing all clients of the practice's privacy policies and obtaining clients' written acknowledgement that they received this information. Guidelines for staff members to follow if there are difficulties obtaining signed assent are needed. All staff must be advised that prior to discussing a client's status with another person, they must obtain the person's permission.

Guidelines for staff members to follow if there are questions about the client's ability to give permission are needed (e.g., a client is at risk of harming self due to lack of judgment; consultation with a specialist is essential to ensure quality of care). Staff must be advised that all information used or disclosed about a person's status must be limited to the minimum needed for the immediate purpose. The therapist must set procedures to ensure patient confidentiality in oral, written, and electronic forms of communication (e.g., all conversations with clients should be conducted in private areas and in low tones; sign-in sheets should only ask for clients' names; computer monitors should have privacy screens; emails should be protected by encrypted passwords).

4. You are beginning a new job as an occupational therapist for a Medicare-certified home health agency. Most of your clients will have limited independence or be dependent in activities of daily living. What are key Medicare guidelines for home-based occupational therapy services that you must consider when working with these individuals and their caregivers?

Home-based occupational therapy (OT) services for medical, physical, cognitive, and psychiatric conditions are covered if the individual is under a physician's care and needed intermittent skilled nursing care, physical therapy (PT), or speech therapy (ST) before OT began. OT services can continue after the person's need for skilled nursing, PT, or ST has ended. Services must be provided under a plan of care that was established by a physician. Care plans must be reviewed regularly by the physician. The person must be considered homebound to receive home care services. Medicare has specific criteria for determining if a person is homebound. To be considered homebound, the person is "confined" to the home and not able to easily leave the home due to a need to use an ambulatory device, the assistance of others, or special transportation. If the person leaves the home, it requires considerable effort that is taxing to the person. The person may leave their home for medical appointments (e.g., kidney dialysis) and nonmedical short-term and infrequent appointments/events (e.g., attendance at religious services). If the person receives adult day care services, they can still receive OT services in the home.

Rental or purchase expenses for durable medical equipment (DME) are covered if pre-scribed by a physician. The DME must be considered necessary and reasonable to treat an illness or injury or to improve functioning. It must be used in the person's home and be able to withstand repeated use. To be reimbursable, the DME must be primarily and customarily used for a medical purpose (e.g., a wheelchair or walker). DME will not be reimbursed if it is useful to a person in the absence of injury or illness (e.g., self-help items such as bathtub grab bars, and raised toilet seats).

5. You are employed by a school system to provide direct services to students with disabilities. Your caseload includes middle and high school students. Which federal legislative man-dates can help guide your interventions with these students? Describe major regulations and their relationship to the provision of school-based occupational therapy services.

The major federal laws that should be used to guide school-based occupational therapy practice are the Reauthorization and Amendment of Individuals with Disabilities Education Act and the Individuals with Disabilities Education Improvement Act. Provisions in these laws that relate directly to the provision of occupational therapy services in schools include the requirement that evaluations for IDEA eligibility include relevant functional and devel-opmental information, not just academic achievement data. These Acts assert that the annual goals in an individualized education plan (IEP) must include academic and functional goals and mandate that the education of middle and high school students with disabilities prepare them for post-secondary life (i.e., independent living, higher education, and/or employ-ment). Transitional planning must begin at the age of 14 (or younger if indicated) and transition services must be implemented by the age of 16 (or younger if indicated) to provide students with a coordinated set of services to attain post-secondary goals. Transitional ser-vices can include ADL, IADL, and prevocational assessment and intervention; assistive tech-nology; and behavioral interventions, strategies, and supports. This mandated emphasis on increasing function and participation in occupations for adult life is highly congruent with the foci and purposes of OT evaluation and intervention. Because federal law mandates stu-dents with disabilities be invited to attend the IEP meetings that discuss their transition plan and services, occupational therapy practitioners can help students develop their self-advocacy and self-determination skills so that they can actively participate in these meetings.

6. You have been hired by a behavioral health organization to develop a partial hospital program (PHP) for an adult population. Describe the major focus of a PHP and the specific occupational therapy program components you need to include.

Partial Hospital Programs (PHPs) are step-down programs for persons with a psychiatric diagnosis who are stable enough to be discharged from an acute inpatient unit but who still have symptoms remaining which require active treatment. PHPs are generally offered five days per week, for 3-5 hours per day, over a period of one week to a few months. Occu-pational therapy services are reimbursable under Medicare, as long as the clients' functional deficits are being addressed. An occupational therapy program in a PHP should include the completion of an occupational profile with all new clients and an evaluation of their client factors, performance skills and patterns, occupational performance skills and limita-tions, and the occupational roles that are required and desired in their current and expected environment(s). Occupational therapy intervention in a PHP should focus on the develop-ment of skills needed for occupational performance, community participation, and engage-ment in desired roles. Interventions to remediate underlying performance skill deficits and compensate for client factors that affect functional performance should also be provided. Connecting clients with community resources that support independent living, health management, and community participation is also a PHP priority.

7. You are developing a new driver rehabilitation program. What are important issues for you to consider as you develop your budget and fiscal management plan?

When developing a new program, it is important to make realistic revenue and volume projections. You should complete a break-even analysis to determine the volume of services you will need to provide to obtain sufficient revenue to equal the costs of operating the program. You will need to plan for short- and long-term program needs. This includes budgeting for capital expenses (i.e., typically any item or action above a fixed amount such as a driver simulator) and operating expenses. Operating expenses include direct expenses related to OT service provision (i.e., salaries and benefits, office supplies, and treatment equipment) and indirect expenses (i.e., utilities, housekeeping, and marketing). Because the amount of services you provide will increase as your program grows, it will be important to determine which expenses are fixed and which are variable. Fixed expenses will remain at the same level (e.g., rent), while variable expenses will change in direct proportion to the amount of services provided (e.g., computer paper and ink).

8. You are starting a new job in a practice area that has high demands on your time and challenges your approach to occupation-based practice. What signs of stress should you be sure to address if you experience them? If you begin to experience the early signs of burnout, what strategies can you incorporate into your daily routine to prevent its progression?

To prevent burnout, you should be aware that the first signs of work-related stress typically show up emotionally and physically as anxiety, fatigue, and distraction. If not addressed, this stress can increase, become chronic, and lead to burnout. Characteristics and signs of burnout include decreased empathy, lower responsivity to clients' needs, physical exhaustion, mental exhaustion, uncharacteristic irritability, reduced personal accomplishment. Behavioral changes, a negative mindset, sense of isolation and depressive thoughts also develop. You can address burnout by engaging in ongoing self-assessment, practicing mindfulness and relaxation techniques, using coping strategies, setting limits between work and personal life, advocating for yourself, proactively using supervision, engaging in professional networks that support a strong OT professional identity and ethical practice, and participating in an employee assistance program.

1. A 16-month-old toddler is brought to occupational therapy for an evaluation. The parents are concerned with the frequency of the toddler's falls which result in bangs to the head. The child demonstrates delayed motor skills. You notice that the toddler has not yet integrated primitive reflexes. Which primary primitive reflex is most likely absent in this toddler? Explain its relevance to the toddler's health status, safety, and its impact on occupational performance.

▶ The toddler likely does not have a protective extension reflex. Protective extension occurs in response to a challenge to an individual's balance and it involves arm extension in the direction of the fall, protecting the head from injury. The forward protective extension reflex develops at 6–9 months, protective extension sideward develops at 7 months, and backward protective extension develops at 9–10 months. Because this reflex persists throughout the life span, its absence is indicative of a neurological condition or a potential disease process. The absence of the protective extension reflex is a safety concern and may require environmental adaptations and the use of a protective helmet to allow the child to safely participate in gross motor play activities to promote normal growth and development.

2. A 26-month-old child is referred to occupational therapy to address feeding challenges. The parents report that their child met all feeding milestones without difficulty, but when introducing foods that needed to be chewed well, like small pieces of meat or crunchy items, the child pockets the food in their cheek and tries to spit the food out spit of their mouth. The child is now refusing to accept these food items due to a recent gagging episode. What skills does the child need to master to independently manage these foods?

▶ This child has not mastered rotary chewing which is necessary for successfully managing meats and other chewy foods.

3. A 4-year-old child is referred to your occupational therapy clinic due to a limited food repertoire that includes French fries, yogurt, and apple sauce. The child has an aversion to any lumps in food items and will refuse these food items. What challenges do you think this child has and what assessments would you use for evaluation?

▶ This child presents with sensory processing challenges related to food repertoire. You would use a sensory assessment such as the Sensory Profile or the Sensory Processing Measure to evaluate the child.

4. A new student in second grade is referred to occupational therapy to screen for potential developmental delays. The therapist observes the child in the classroom and notes that the child uses a static tripod grasp during writing tasks and can cut circles and squares with scissors, but they cannot cut more complex shapes. During recess, they jump over objects and hop on one foot. When the child's shoes become untied, they cannot independently tie them. Do these observations warrant further evaluation? What rationale would you provide to the teacher and the student's parents to support your decision to evaluate this student or to not evaluate them?

▶ Yes, an evaluation is warranted to further assess the child's fine motor skills. A child in the second grade is 7-8 years old and would be expected to use a dynamic tripod grasp, cut out complex shapes, and tie shoelaces. These are all skills that impact the child's school performance. Refer to Tables 5-12, 5-13, and 5-18.

5. You are part of an intraprofessional screening team to determine children's readiness for kindergarten. A five-year-old child whom you are evaluating has performed at or above level on every aspect of the screening and has not demonstrated any fine motor, visual motor, or gross motor delays. The child has no cognitive deficits. The child performed well on the Beery-Buktenica Developmental Test of Visual-Motor Integration. Given the child's performance so far, which of Erhardt's developmental levels of prewriting skills would you expect the child to use for writing tasks? Explain your answer.

> Your evaluation indicated that the child is functioning at an age-appropriate developmental level; thus, the child would be expected to use a developmentally appropriate grasp for writing tasks. Given that the child is five years old, the child would be expected to use a dynamic tripod posture for writing tasks. The dynamic tripod posture is observed in children ages 4½ to 6 years.

6. A typically developing child with no developmental delays independently creates a building made of blocks from a mental image. Identify the child's age range and describe the skills the child would use during this play activity.

> A child aged three to four years would have the fine motor, balance, and coordination skills needed to build a structure using blocks and the cognitive ability to build a structure from a mental image. This activity requires the child to recognize color and shape. The child must organize the blocks by size and shape to produce a three-dimensional block structure based on a mental image.

7. A 15-year-old has a group of friends who have recently become involved in experimenting with drugs, alcohol, and other risky behaviors. The teen is torn between wanting to remain friends with this group and not wanting to join them in these behaviors. They decide to join a competitive youth soccer league so that they can meet new people and develop a new group of friends. According to Erikson's eight stages of man, what stage of development is the teenager undergoing? Describe the characteristics of this stage.

> According to Erikson, there are eight stages of man, and each stage includes a critical personal-social crisis. When the crisis is resolved by the individual, the individual gains a sense of mastery and acquires a personality quality. Erikson identifies the crisis of the teenage years as self-identity versus role confusion. During this stage, the teenager is challenged to make choices about adult roles. The resolution of this identity crisis provides the teenager with a sense of fidelity and an integrated sense of belonging to and being a member of society.

8. You provide wellness and prevention services to older adults who attend a community-based senior center. What strategies to slow, reverse, and/or compensate for age-related changes to their muscular, skeletal, and neurological systems can you share with these older adults?

You can advise the older adults on ways to improve their general health (e.g., stop smoking, exercise regularly) and maintain an adequate nutritional intake (e.g., if budget is limited, use community-based food programs to supplement diet). You should stress that active engagement in functional activities and activity programs can be used to increase their levels of physical activity. Strength training can be used to increase or maintain muscle strength required for functional activity, while flexibility and range of motion exercises can be used to increase range of motion. The older adults should be advised to gradually increase the intensity of their physical activity to avoid injury. They should plan and include adequate warm-ups and cool downs and appropriate pacing and rest periods in their routine. Weightbearing (gravity-loading) exercises (e.g., walking, stair climbing, all activities performed in standing) can decrease bone loss. You can advise the older adults to allow for increased reaction and movement times to improve accuracy of movements and to avoid long sequences of movements to allow for memory limitations. You can provide safety education to reduce fall risk.

Chapter 6 Review Questions

Musculoskeletal System Disorders

1. You provide postoperative occupational therapy for clients who have undergone tendon repair surgery. You receive a referral for a client diagnosed with a Zone 1 extensor tendon repair. What is this diagnosis typically termed? According to established protocol, what is your diagnostic-specific intervention for the first six weeks? What are the overall goals for tendon repair surgeries that you will use to guide your intervention?

   ▶ A Zone 1 extensor tendon repair is commonly referred to as a "mallet finger." Standard protocol for extensor tendon repairs at Zone 1 is to immobilize for six weeks, 24 hours a day, seven days a week (except for the performance of skin checks). General occupational therapy goals for tendon repairs are to increase tendon excursion, improve strength at repair site, increase joint range of motion, prevent adhesions, and facilitate resumption of meaningful roles, occupations, and activities.

2. A client incurred a right Colles' fracture. One week ago, the client's cast was removed. You have worked with this client since the initial evaluation and during several intervention sessions. When arriving for the current therapy session, the client is tearful and holding the right arm in a protected position. The client reports that severe pain developed over the weekend in the wrist, hand, and shoulder and that it has not gone away. The right hand is swollen and skin is shiny. On a pain scale of 0–10, the client reports a 10+. The client describes an inability (over the past two days) to complete exercises and basic self-care activities due to the pain. What do you suspect is causing the client's increase in symptoms? How would you address the client's new presenting symptoms?

   ▶ This client is presenting symptoms that are typical of complex regional pain syndrome (CRPS), which may follow a trauma such as a Colles' fracture. CRPS symptoms include swelling, shiny skin, pain beyond what is expected for a Colles' fracture, and difficulty using the extremity during ADL. The physician should be contacted and symptoms described. Occupational therapy intervention for CRPS include modalities to decrease pain, edema management (e.g., elevation, manual edema mobilization, compression glove), active range of motion to involved joints to avoid joint contractures and muscle atrophy, ADL to encourage pain-free active use, stress loading (e.g., weightbearing and joint distraction activities, including scrubbing and carrying activities), orthotics to prevent contractures, and self-management to enable the ability to engage in occupation-based activities. Interventions to avoid or to proceed with caution include passive range of motion, passive stretching, joint mobilization, dynamic orthoses, and casting.

3. A client is referred to you with a diagnosis of (R) de Quervain's. The client's major complaint is pain when lifting (e.g., the client's newborn child, grocery bags). Pain is reported as 8/10. What findings will you expect upon formal evaluation? What interventions should you implement?

   ▶ De Quervain's is a tenosynovitis of the first dorsal compartment of the extensor tendons. It is characterized by pain and swelling over the radial styloid and a positive Finkelstein's test. A forearm-based thumb orthosis should be fabricated to place the tendons at rest until pain decreases. The client should be instructed in ways to modify lifting and other activities without causing further trauma to the extensor tendons. Ice massage over the radial wrist and gentle active range of motion of wrist and thumb to prevent stiffness can be used.

4. You receive a referral for a client with a third-degree burn to the dorsal hand which includes a prescription for an orthosis. What is the optimal antideformity position you should use to guide your orthotic construction? Explain your reasoning.

> When fabricating an orthosis for a person with a burn to the dorsal hand, you should position the wrist in 20°–30° extension (increases MCP flexion via tenodesis), MCP joints in 70° flexion (places the collateral ligaments in a lengthened position), IP joints in extension (prevents contracture of the volar plates), and thumb abducted and extended (preserves the first web space).

5. You receive a referral for a person with a diagnosis of carpal tunnel syndrome (CTS). What conservative treatment methods are indicated for this diagnosis?

> An orthosis that positions the wrist in neutral should be provided to the client and the client should be advised to wear the orthosis at night and during the day when performing repetitive activity. Median nerve gliding exercises and differential tendon gliding exercises should be used. The client should be taught how to modify activities to prevent compression of the median nerve and avoid activities with extreme positions of wrist flexion, wrist flexion with repetitive finger flexion, and wrist flexion with a static grip.

6. A child with a diagnosis of osteogenesis imperfecta receives occupational therapy services. What should be the primary foci of occupational therapy intervention? Describe how safety precautions should be integrated into the treatment of a child with osteogenesis imperfecta.

> A primary focus of occupational therapy in treating a child with osteogenesis imperfecta is the education of family members, caregivers, and educators about proper handling and positioning techniques to use with the child to avoid fractures. As the child grows, interventions must focus on revising these precautions and teaching family members and caregivers to adapt to the demands and environmental challenges encountered by the child (e.g., playground play). The occupational therapist should also reinforce the importance of nutrition for bone health and weight control. Occupational therapy interventions should focus on weightbearing activities to facilitate bone growth and activities to increase muscle strength. The occupational therapist should also provide school-related activities and environmental modifications to enable participation. Throughout all interventions, precautions to avoid fractures must be followed. For instance, the occupational therapist may fabricate or order special equipment for the child to safely participate in playground or gym activities or design orthoses to enable the completion of desktop school activities.

7. A school-based occupational therapist has a third-grade student with arthrogryposis multiplex congenita assigned to their caseload. The student is meeting grade level expectations academically and does not need curricular or learning accommodations. What services would be relevant for the therapist to provide to this student?

Arthrogryposis is a congenital musculoskeletal condition that causes multiple joint contractures throughout the body. The joints of the upper extremities are typically the most significantly affected joints which results in severely restricted movement and use of the arms and hands. The therapist should evaluate all aspects of the school's physical environment to determine accessibility. This includes the bathrooms, cafeteria, playground, general and special classrooms (e.g., art and music), physical education gym, and any other space the student will need to use to fully participate in the school environment. The therapist would also evaluate the student's ability to access classroom materials and tools and access to peers for social and academic pursuits. Based on the results of the evaluation, the therapist would recommend accommodations that enable the student's full participation. For example, if this student effectively uses their lower extremities to complete tasks, the seating arrangement and workspace in the classroom should be arranged to accommodate space for the student to access supplies and course materials with their feet. The cafeteria should also provide accommodations to allow this student to use utensils with their feet and be seated with their peers.

8. A client recently sustained a left below elbow transradial amputation in a work-related incident. The client is right hand dominant. The plan is for the client to receive a body powered prosthesis. You are developing a pre-prosthetic intervention plan with the client. What interventions should you include in this plan?

The focus of the pre- prosthetic intervention plan is to prepare the residual limb to be fitted for and utilize a prosthesis. The interventions should include range of motion of the uninvolved joints (i.e., the elbow and shoulder), desensitization of the residual limb (to ensure comfort when wearing the prosthesis), limb wrapping to shape and shrink the residual limb (wrapping should be done distal to proximal with tension decreasing proximally), and ADL training (including skin care). The intervention plan should also include supportive counseling and individualized interventions to enhance physical and psychological adjustment. If a person's dominant limb is amputated, their pre-prosthetic intervention plan should also training to change hand dominance. For this client, there is no need to address a change of dominance. The dominant side is intact.

Chapter 7 Review Questions

Neurological System Disorders

1. You will be evaluating two persons who have survived strokes. One incurred a left MCA stroke and one incurred a right MCA stroke. What symptoms might each person present during their respective evaluation session?

   ▶ The person with a left MCA may exhibit right-sided sensory and motor loss, aphasia, apraxia, and right visual field loss. The person with a right MCA may exhibit left-sided sensory and motor loss, unilateral neglect, spatial dysfunction, and left visual field loss.

2. You are working on a spinal cord unit. You are about to evaluate a client who has an injury classified as ASIA A. The injury is at the C5 level. What is the expected sensory and motor status of your client?

   ▶ Complete loss of sensation and motor function below the lesion. No sensory or motor function is preserved in the sacral segments.

3. You have just completed your first evaluation session with a patient who sustained a TBI two weeks ago. Your findings include that the patient was alert and in a heightened state of activity (easily overstimulated) and attempting to pull out the IV and feeding tube. The patient could not remember directions, exhibiting poor short-term memory. The patient screamed out for no reason several times during the session and was observed to be aggressive (e.g., attempting to hit you and the nurse). The patient required maximum assist for BADL. Your facility requires you to document each TBI patient's Rancho Los Amigos Levels of Cognitive Functioning Scale. What is the appropriate level for you to record?

   ▶ The behaviors described are indicative of Level IV: Confused and Agitated. Rancho Levels I–III present with very low levels of arousal and require total assistance for BADL. Persons at these levels do not respond or respond inconsistently to stimuli. Persons at Rancho Levels V and higher do not demonstrate agitation, they are not aggressive, and their ability to participate in ADL continues to improve.

4. A three-year old child is brought to an outpatient center for an occupational therapy evaluation. The parent reports that their child is always "on the go", loves playgrounds, and seems to take extraordinary physical risks (e.g., jumping off furniture, climbing onto cupboards and tables, swinging too high and fast on playground swings) without showing fear. The child mouths toys, crayons, and pencils, and chews on their clothing. The parent states that their child does not attend to table-top tasks for long periods and often leaves the table during meals. How would you describe this child's pattern of sensory processing and what intervention activities would likely be helpful for this child and family?

   ▶ This child is showing patterns of sensory seeking behaviors that seem to be more than expected for their age. The physical risk-taking behaviors show some carelessness with safety in the pursuit of vestibular and proprioceptive input. Lack of fear in these scenarios also indicates the child has strong gravitational security and may even be overconfident of their physical capacity to engage in the climbing, jumping, and swinging the parent describes. The chewing of objects suggests the child's needs for oral sensory input is not being satiated with age-appropriate oral sensations and experiences.

   Intervention would include collaborating with the parent to engage in dialogue about sensory processing disorders and particularly the meaning of sensory seeking behaviors. Providing highly structured and robust sensory experiences in a therapeutic and safe environment can help the parent and child establish boundaries for sensory seeking behaviors. Additional intervention options can include providing chewable attachments to writing tools, the use of gum or other chewable snack foods when appropriate, frequent structured gross motor movement breaks, and use of alternative seating options for table-top activities and during meal times.

5. During an occupational therapy evaluation of a toddler, you observe the child walking with the left foot in plantar flexion, the left arm flexed at the elbow and wrist, and the left hand in a fist position with the thumb tucked inside the palm. The child is able to move their right extremities with typical movement patterns. The parent reports that they have noticed a difference in the movement patterns of the two sides and that the difference has markedly increased since the child started walking. Based on this information, what neurological condition would you suspect this child has?

> This child exhibits signs of hemiplegic cerebral palsy. While the symptoms may have increased since the child started walking, the parents indicate having noticed difference between the two sides of the body much earlier. Difference in the motor control of the limbs on each side of the body is not a typical stage of development. The asymmetrical use of the upper and lower extremities would suggest an impairment in the motor cortex.

6. You are working with a child who is seated at a table completing activities in a coloring and writing workbook. You notice that on multiple occasions the child stares straight ahead for a few seconds and then returns to their work. You have also noticed that the staring episodes cannot be interrupted by waving your hand in front of their face or by calling their name. Given this information what can you surmise is happening? What actions should you take if you have never seen the child respond this way before when working with them?

> The child may be having absence seizures. It is important to note how often the staring instances are happening, how close together the instances are occurring, and how long the instances are lasting. Contacting the child's family and physician are steps that should be taken as soon as possible. It will be important for the child to have a comprehensive neurological examination.

7. You are working with a child who suddenly has a series of seizures that occur in rapid succession and are prolonged. When the parents are contacted, they report that they ran out of the child's medicine the day before. What type of seizure do these symptoms represent? How should you respond to in this situation?

> The child incurred status epilepticus, which can be triggered by an abrupt disruption of the child's medications. Procedures in responding to status epilepticus include remaining calm and having someone call for immediate medical attention (although rare, sudden death can occur in status epilepticus). You should remove dangerous objects from the area and protect the child from harm, without interfering with the child's movement. If the child was standing or sitting in a chair, you should have gently guided the child to the floor.

8. You receive a referral to evaluate a person with Parkinson's disease (PD). What are the cardinal signs of Parkinson's that you will want to be sure to consider during your evaluation? Upon reviewing the client's chart, you learn that their disorder has progressed to stage 3 on the Hoehn and Yahr's Parkinson's disease scale. Which functional limitations and abilities can you expect the person to demonstrate?

Parkinson's is a disease of the basal ganglion in which there is a decrease of dopamine. This results in the cardinal Parkinson's signs of tremors, rigidity, akinesia, and postural instability (TRAP). A person at stage 3 on the Hoehn and Yahr's five-stage Parkinson's scale will exhibit worsening of symptoms and the first signs of impaired righting reflexes. As a result, they will experience the onset of disability in ADL and IADL performance. However, they can lead an independent life with the use of adaptive strategies (e.g., the use of proper posture, positioning, and body mechanics (e.g., placing their elbow on the table when feeding self, keeping their arms at their side while washing the face) and adaptive equipment (e.g., weighted utensils, button hook, zipper pull, elastic shoe-laces, Velcro closures, strap loops and knob/faucet turners, and electric toothbrush, razor, and can opener). Due to the development of impaired righting reflexes, the person is at an increased risk for falls.

Chapter 8 Review Questions

Cardiovascular and Pulmonary System Disorders

1. An adult with a diagnosis of left ventricular failure congestive heart failure (CHF) has been referred to occupational therapy for Phase I cardiac rehabilitation during an acute hospitalization. What are the primary goals of inpatient cardiac rehabilitation? What symptoms of CHF does the occupational therapist need to be aware of that might manifest during therapeutic activities?

   A primary focus of Phase I cardiac rehabilitation is patient and family education about the disease process and recovery. This includes teaching energy conservation and work simplification techniques and the connection between MET levels and activity. Interventions should also focus on improving the person's ability to carry out ADL, including mobility with low-level out of bed functional activities. Decreasing the patient's anxiety around activity performance and providing support for smoking cessation and dietary modification, if needed, are also primary goals for Phase I cardiac rehabilitation. The ultimate goal of this phase is to discharge the patient to home and outpatient cardiac rehabilitation. During therapeutic activities, the therapist must be aware that the patient may experience tachycardia, fatigue with activity or mobility, decreased endurance to sustain activity, and/or dyspnea.

2. What are the clinical indications that may lead an occupational therapist to stop an activity during a cardiac rehabilitation intervention session? How does the occupational therapist monitor the patient during activity for signs/symptoms of distress?

   Indications that the patient is experiencing an adverse response to treatment include a rise in diastolic blood pressure (BP) greater than or equal to 110 mm Hg, a decrease in systolic BP greater than 10 mm Hg, significant ventricular or atrial dysrhythmias, second- or third-degree heart block, and signs/symptoms of exercise intolerance including angina and/or marked dyspnea. To monitor a patient for signs/symptoms of distress during activities, the therapist should keep track of the person's vital signs. Vital signs are an important and reliable indicator of activity tolerance and response to treatment. These include heart rate, blood pressure, respiratory rate, and O_2 and CO_2 levels. In addition to monitoring vital signs, the occupational therapist should seek feedback from the patient using angina and dyspnea rating scales (e.g., the Modified Borg Dyspnea Scale) and an intermittent claudication rating scale.

3. An older adult status-post myocardial infarction (s/p MI) has been referred to occupational therapy for Phase II outpatient cardiac rehabilitation. The client is able to carry out all basic ADL independently and has fair tolerance for activities that require standing and overhead movements. The client lives with a spouse and identifies being a partner, home maintainer, and gardener as primary roles. The client would like to be able to resume role-related activities. The occupational therapy prescription calls for activities beginning at MET level 3 and increasing to MET level 5 according to the client's activity tolerance. Taking into consideration the therapy prescription, the client's current status, desired occupational roles, and activity preferences, which intervention approaches and activities should the occupational therapist include in the intervention plan?

   To help the client attain their goal of resuming activities related to their roles of partner, home maintainer, and gardener, the occupational therapist should include energy conservation and work simplification techniques and IADL in the intervention plan. Beginning with activities at a MET level of 3-4, the occupational therapist can incorporate the activities of making a bed, sweeping, mopping, and gardening into intervention sessions. As the client tolerates these activities, interventions can be upgraded to include activities at a MET level of 4–5 including changing bed linens, raking the lawn, and weeding the garden. A discussion about resuming sexual activities is also appropriate at this level.

4. You are completing a meal preparation assessment with a client who is living with chronic obstructive pulmonary disease (COPD). The client reports a score of 3/10 on the Modified Borg Dyspnea Scale. What does this tell you about the client's performance? What training approaches would you include in an intervention plan for the client?

The Modified Borg Dyspnea Scale is a self-report rating scale of perceived exertion that ranges from no exertion at all (e.g., sitting or lying) to maximal exertion (e.g., hard work that is not advisable to engage in). On the Modified Borg Dyspnea Scale a reported score of 3 indicates that the client is experiencing moderate difficulty. The intervention plan should include dyspnea control postures, pursed lip breathing, or diaphragmatic breathing. Pursed lip breathing provides resistance to expiration, increases the use of the diaphragm, and decreases the use of accessory muscles. Diaphragmatic breathing increases the use of the diaphragm and increases chest volume.

Additionally, energy conservation techniques should be included in the intervention plan. Energy conservation techniques will help the client use their energy more efficiently and productively. The client should be challenged to problem solve how to incorporate breath control and energy conservation techniques into all activities that are client centered, important, and necessary.

5. You are working with a client who is recovering from a left total knee replacement. The medical record indicates that the client has a past medical history of severe COVID-19. The client begins to have trouble breathing and complains of pain and pressure in the chest. They suddenly appear to be confused. What should you do in response to your observations and the client's reported concerns?

You should call for immediate medical attention. Persons who had been diagnosed with severe COVID-19 may experience symptoms of post-acute COVID (or long COVID). Trouble breathing, persistent pain or pressure in the chest, and sudden confusion are all COVID emergency warning signs. Additional emergency warning signs are inability to wake or stay awake and pale, gray, or blue colored skin, lips, or nail beds, (depending on skin tone).

6. You have been asked to consult with a teacher to discuss precautions for a student who has a diagnosis of cystic fibrosis. What precautions should you discuss with the teacher? Provide a rationale for your recommendations.

You should inform the teacher about the student's need for adequate nutrition and hydration. Nutrition and hydration are important for managing mucous production. You should advise the teacher to create an inclusive environment to promote social participation and safe participation in physical activities. You should instruct the teacher in energy conservation techniques the student can use during activities. These techniques are required to help the child work toward participating in a full school day. During physical activity, the child should be actively monitored for signs of fatigue and dehydration which may lead to cardiac and respiratory problems.

7. You are completing an occupational therapy evaluation on a 20-month-old toddler who was diagnosed with bronchopulmonary dysplasia (BPD) shortly after birth. What are the typical deficits resulting from BPD that the child may exhibit during the evaluation? Provide an explanation for your answers.

Delays may be observed in all areas of development including gross motor, fine motor, visual motor, cognitive, and social-emotional development. The toddler may present with hypotonia and exhibit fatigue and a low tolerance for physical activity. Poor autonomic and sensory state regulation and poor vision may be evident. Extended time on respirators and artificial ventilation can affect vision and visual motor development and state regulation. Central nervous system problems can contribute to global developmental delays. Malabsorption problems can lead to brittle bones and also to cognitive delays. Because children with BPD experience dependence on technology and lengthy hospitalizations, some children also experience attachment disorders, which may impact social–emotional development and social participation.

Chapter 9 Review Questions

Gastrointestinal, Renal-Genitourinary, Endocrine, Immunological, and Integumentary Systems Disorders

1. You work with clients who have dysphagia and swallowing disorders to develop their feeding skills. What would you do if a client chokes and cannot clear their airway during the activity?

   ▷ If the person gasps for breath, but has a partial or complete airway obstruction, you should clear the obstruction and raise the bolus that has been aspirated. You can use the Heimlich maneuver as long as the person is awake and responsive. If the person loses consciousness, basic life support procedures are used to continue to try to reestablish the airway.

2. You are working with clients who have a colostomy or a stoma due to surgery to their bowel. Some clients do not have the intact fine motor functioning to learn to manage their stoma independently. What can you do to work with these clients to develop their ability to manage their stoma care independently?

   ▷ It is best for clients with a colostomy or a stoma to have intact fine motor functioning to manage their stoma care. However, they can be taught to compensate using adaptive devices and techniques (e.g., the use of spring clasps versus twist valves). Self-care aspects of stoma care must be addressed for persons with decreased fine motor skills (e.g., individuals with peripheral neuropathy secondary to chemotherapy treatment). The occupational therapist can determine why a person has fine motor impairments. The therapist can plan a course of therapy to improve the person's fine motor ability. If abilities cannot be improved, the therapist can determine the types of adaptations that could be used to substitute for lost functional mobility and train the person in their use.

3. Describe options that could be useful in providing intervention for someone who has bladder urgency with stress urinary incontinence and a diagnosis of non–insulin-dependent diabetes mellitus.

   ▷ Intervention might include using Kegel exercises to strengthen the pelvic floor and timed routines for emptying the bladder before it is full enough to cause spillage. Lifestyle adjustments to use incontinence supporting garments for a socially acceptable solution and to decrease public attention to the incontinence are also effective. Medications may be used when the physician feels the client can tolerate the side effects of drug therapy support. Electric stimulation may be used, if the client fits the parameters of recovery for the condition. For example, if the nerve damage is permanent from neuropathy, exercises may not be a useful strategy, since the muscles would not get the enervation needed to effect a change.

4. You are treating an adult client with a diagnosis of scleroderma and Stage IV cancer who was referred to occupational therapy because soft tissue/connective tissue changes are affecting hand function. Would it be appropriate to establish a goal with the client to address the evolving contractures? Describe your rationale.

   ▷ Yes, it is still appropriate to establish a goal to prevent the progression of the contractures for a client with scleroderma and Stage IV cancer. While Stage IV cancer is a very grave diagnosis with multiple metastases, life expectancy is dependent on the depth and extent of the cancer and its response to treatment. The person is currently *living* with both conditions and would benefit from intervention to maintain their hand function. Losing the ability to use one's hands to engage in desired activities can significantly decrease independence and quality of life. Establishing a goal to prevent progression of the contractures can help maintain the person's independence and quality of life. Direct interventions to prevent contractures include stretching, orthotics, and scar management. Education to teach the client how to stretch and use orthoses and scar management supplies can enable them to be actively engaged in the preservation of their hand function.

5. You work in a community that has people living and working in it who have spinal cord injuries. A primary care doctor refers clients to you who have reddening skin in their sacral regions. What could you do to work with these clients to improve their skin integrity and prevent decubiti?

You can educate them about conditions that predispose an individual to the formation of decubitus ulcers. These include immobility or altered mobility, weight loss, edema, incontinence, sensory deficiencies, circulatory abnormalities, dehydration, inadequate nutrition, obesity, pathological conditions/multiple comorbidities, and/or changes in skin condition due to aging. You can use principles of lifestyle redesign, habit formation, and/or habit change to plan an individual course of action for behavioral change and improved self-care patterns. If there is presence of substance abuse, cognitive deficits, and/or psychological impairments that can jeopardize the individual's ability to understand and complete the required daily ulcer prevention regimen, you can alter the form of education so that a caregiver can assist with the care plan.

6. You are working with a young adult who has a new diagnosis of diabetes. What areas should you assess during evaluation? When collaborating with the client to plan intervention, what are important considerations to discuss with them to inform their intervention plan?

You should use information about the areas in which diabetes typically impacts occupational performance to inform your evaluation. These include ADL (with a particular focus on medication management, bladder management, and wound care), IADL, upper extremity muscle strength and sensation, vision, diet and nutrition, life roles, and activity participation and tolerance.

Important considerations to discuss with a young adult recently diagnosed with diabetes to inform their intervention plan include education and training in health literacy (e.g., the signs, symptoms, and response to hypoglycemia and hyperglycemia; preventative exercise and proper diet; and medical management). A focus on self-advocacy skills and psychological and emotional support for learning to live with diabetes is also relevant.

If and when complications occur, future intervention plans may include education and training in the use of problem-solving, activity modifications, and adaptive equipment to facilitate participation in desired occupations and lifestyle re-adjustment. Depending on the nature of their complications education and training may also focus on low vision strategies, safety (e.g., risks associated with sensory loss), pain management, and wound management (e.g., skin care and inspection techniques).

Review>Practice>Motivate>Analyze>Apply

Chapter 10 Review Questions

Psychiatric and Cognitive Disorders

1. You are asked to provide consultation services for an individual who lives in a group home. The resident has become dehydrated and inconsistent in taking oral medications. You interview the resident about their daily habits and routines and learn that the resident will not drink the tap water in the group home. The resident states "The water is poisoned. They are trying to poison me. If I drink the water I will die." Identify the psychiatric symptom that is preventing this person from drinking the water. Describe an intervention approach you would use to help the resident hydrate and take prescribed medications. Explain the importance of this person staying hydrated and taking prescribed medications.

   ▶ This resident has a delusion. A delusion is a fixed, unshakeable, false belief; Therefore, you would not tell them that the water is not being poisoned. One must not argue with or try to refute a delusion. The best intervention strategy is to ask the resident if they will agree to drink fruit juice or sealed bottles of water that they can independently open. Working with the resident to ensure consistent hydration is important because dehydration threatens their physical health. The impact of not drinking water on the ability to take oral medications must be addressed. Lack of adherence to a prescribed medication regimen can exacerbate symptoms. Being medically stable enables people to live in non-medical model settings and fully participate in their communities of choice.

   To support the resident's ability to follow their medication schedule, you can collaborate with the group home staff to develop a plan for providing external structure and consistency. You can teach the resident about the benefits of establishing and following a set routine for taking medication (e.g., at a specific time of day such as right before a favorite television show or after a meal). Training the resident in the use of medication containers/pillboxes that are marked with the days of the week and time(s) of day, written reminders, and/or a smart phone medication app can also help them develop independent medication management skills. Depending on the type of medication, the use of long-acting injections or patches can be useful in facilitating independent medication management.

2. Upon evaluation of an adolescent you find that the teen has great difficulty reading the nonverbal behaviors of others (e.g., eye contact, facial expression, gestures, and body language) that are needed to regulate social interactions. The adolescent has not been able to develop relationships with a peer group. They are preoccupied with and intensely interested in World War II, its history, battles, and generals, and talk about nothing else. The teen's bedroom is filled with World War II memorabilia and books about the war. Their cognitive, language and communication, and ADL skill development has been age-appropriate; however, they have not developed age-appropriate social interaction skills. Based on this information, what diagnosis is most reflective of this teen's functional status? What intervention goals would be helpful to work on with this adolescent?

   ▶ The teen's described behaviors are most reflective of a diagnosis of autism spectrum disorder (ASD). They have a highly preferred interest that influences their behavior and results in difficulty with social interaction (e.g., missing the nonverbal social interaction cues that others provide). These behaviors can impair the adolescent's establishment of peer relationships. The teen's ADL, cognitive, language, and communication skills are reported as age appropriate. This is often the case for individuals with less severe ASD. Intervention goals include increasing social interaction skills. Intervention should focus on exploring ways that the teen's highly preferred interest can be pursued in a social context via individual and group interventions. Intervention goals should also address the teen's post-secondary needs and aspirations (vocational readiness, post-secondary education, independent living, and community participation). Intervention planning for adolescents should involve the family and intervention goals should support their participation in familial roles. If the teen had any developmental delays (e.g., impairment in sensorimotor skills), interventions would be needed to address these.

3. You are conducting an evaluation of a 16-month-old toddler. The parent reports that the toddler has frequent tantrums with no clear precipitant. The parent thinks these behaviors may be the result of the toddler's frustration due to language delays. When unable to reach a toy, the toddler pulled the parent's hand toward the toy without pointing. The toddler also did not point to pictures in books. When playing with blocks or cars, the toddler lined them up, but did not spontaneously manipulate or move them. The toddler exhibited a rigid and limited repertoire of play and interaction skills. What diagnosis is most consistent with the toddler's presenting behaviors? Explain your rationale.

The toddler's behaviors are indicative of autism spectrum disorder (ASD). Children with ASD often have limited communication skills and language. Because pointing to express interest and/or fulfill a need is a primary means of communication, the toddler's nonuse of the pointing gesture suggests a lower level of communication skills. This also is indicative of the lack of inferred sharing that is commonly seen in children with ASD. The tantrums reported by the parent may indicate sensory induced behavioral responses that are also common in ASD. The limited repertoire of play behaviors (as exhibited in the lining up of objects) is also consistent with the play of children with ASD.

4. You are a home health therapist providing services to a client who is an older adult. The client's caregiver reports that the client is having trouble remembering things, sustaining attention, and making decisions. The caregiver reports the client seems mentally confused and asks whether the symptoms are indicative of dementia. As a therapist, you know that there are possible reversible causes of mental confusion. What are the reversible causes of mental confusion that you should consider during your intervention and inform the caregiver to consider for further evaluation?

Dementia is a term that is commonly used to describe the symptoms of neurocognitive disorders such as Alzheimer's disease. However, not all reported or observed signs of mental confusion are indicative of a neurocognitive disorder. The possible reversible causes for mental confusion must always be considered when working with a client who is mentally confused. These can include age-related losses in hearing, vision, and/or touch and sensory overload or deprivation. The client's need for a hearing aid or glasses (and if these are available and working properly) should also be considered. The client's environment should be assessed because it may lack cues to aid orientation (i.e., clocks and calendars). Other causes for mental confusion that you should consider and inform the caregiver about are depression and drug use or misuse (i.e., drug interactions, medication side effects, polymedication/the combination of prescription and over-the-counter drugs). Urinary tract infections, viral or bacterial infections, pneumonia, or gallbladder disease are often causes of mental confusion in older adults so these need to be ruled out. Metabolic problems such as liver or kidney disease, thyroid disorders, dehydration, and poorly controlled diabetes may also present as mental confusion and need to be further assessed by a physician.

5. You observe that a very thin client in your outpatient partial hospital program has been losing weight. The individual has no medical problems. The physician supervising the program states the client is well below the normal weight for age and height. The client participates in cooking groups with peers but will not eat whatever is prepared other than salad without dressing. When encouraged to try other foods, the client says, "I don't want to get fat, and I already need to lose a few pounds." You are concerned that the individual has anorexia nervosa. What signs of this eating disorder are being exhibited? What additional symptoms would you expect to see that would indicate this diagnosis?

The client refuses to maintain a body weight that is normal for age and height and has a fear of gaining weight and becoming fat, even though underweight. There is a disturbance in the way this individual perceives or experiences personal weight and appearance. Other symptoms of this disorder include the undue influence of body weight or shape on self-evaluation and denial of the seriousness of the current low body weight, even if the person were to be hospitalized or seriously ill. If the client is a postmenarchal female, amenorrhea may occur.

Chapter 11 Review Questions

Biomechanical Approaches: Evaluation and Intervention

1. You work in a practice setting that serves many clients with musculoskeletal disorders. The majority of clients have decreased ROM. What are the different types of ROM you should consider during assessment? How should you document your evaluation and its results?

   When assessing ROM, you should consider functional ROM, which is the ROM needed to perform functional movements (e.g., reach to top of your head to brush your hair, reach to the small of your back to tuck a shirt into pants); active ROM (AROM), which is the movement produced by one's own muscle; passive ROM (PROM), which is movement produced by an external force; and active assistive ROM (AAROM), which is movement produced by one's own muscles and assisted by an external force. When recording ROM measurements, you should always record the starting position and ending position (e.g., 0°–150°) and not use negatives. You can use the terms within functional limits (WFL) to denote that the client's ROM is functional (e.g., the person can don socks) and within normal limits (WNL) to denote ROM which achieves established ranges (e.g., shoulder flexion 0°–180°).

2. A new client is admitted into an intensive care unit with a diagnosis of a spinal cord injury. The physician requests an evaluation to help in determining the level of injury. How would you perform a light touch sensory test? How does this method of testing differ from the procedures used during sensory testing for other major diagnostic categories?

   When determining sensation of a client diagnosed with a spinal cord injury, the test stimulus (i.e., cotton ball) is presented proximal to distal following dermatomes (beginning at the cervical level and moving distally). Following the dermatome pattern will provide you with information about the client's status at each sensory level. When completing sensory testing for neurological disorders, you assess according to dermatome patterns. Peripheral nerve injuries are tested distal to proximal following peripheral nerves.

3. An adult client is having difficulty performing daily activities due to decreased ROM and pain in both shoulders. You decide to treat the client with preparatory interventions followed by an occupation-based intervention. What interventions can you use to increase ROM and decrease pain?

   Applying heat and performing gentle passive ROM on the client's shoulders are preparatory interventions. The application of heat prior to stretch can increase extensibility. Manual stretching within the individual's tolerance and contract/relax and hold/relax are additional preparatory methods which can increase ROM. Working with the client to perform activities that are related to their occupational roles (e.g., completing hair care, placing groceries on upper cabinet shelves) and require shoulder movements would be an appropriate occupation-based intervention.

4. You provide consultation services to a Center for Independent Living that serves persons with a diversity of disabilities. You are scheduled to conduct an educational session on energy conservation and work simplification. What key principles and methods should you be sure to include in your presentation?

You should advise presentation participants to plan short rest periods (e.g., 5–10 minutes) during their daily routine and to schedule daily tasks which alternate between and balance heavy and light work tasks. Tasks that are nonessential and/or those that are beyond personal capacity can be eliminated. To decrease extraneous work, tasks can be combined. Prior to initiating a task, all necessary items and equipment should be gathered. The use of a utility cart, a bucket, walker bag, and/or backpack can be used to carry all items needed in one trip to avoid multiple trips. The participants should be advised to sit to work at a table or use a high stool for countertop work and to use lightweight equipment, tools, and utensils. Cabinets can be organized so that items are easy to reach and in convenient locations. The sliding of items across countertops is preferable to lifting them. Adaptive equipment (e.g., reachers) can be used to avoid bending and stooping and electrical appliances (e.g., mixers) can be used to decrease personal effort. Because intermittent rest during an activity is more effective than resting after exhaustion has occurred, participants should be advised to rest before they experience fatigue.

5. Your client is diagnosed with rotator cuff tendonitis and is experiencing severe pain. The physician has ordered the use of transcutaneous electrical nerve simulation (TENS), gentle ROM, and below shoulder level ADL. During your evaluation, you review the client's past medical history. You learn that the person has a history of cardiac issues that required the implantation of a pacemaker. Which of the prescribed interventions will you use with this client? What are additional interventions you can use with this client to decrease pain and prepare the person for occupation-based interventions?

Gentle ROM and below shoulder level ADL are appropriate interventions to use with this client. The use of TENs is contraindicated and should not be used with this client. TENS can interfere with the electrical current of the defibrillator. Additional preparatory methods to decrease pain include cryotherapy and superficial heat therapy.

6. Your client is status post a below knee amputation. You assess the strength of the client's triceps in preparation for transfer training. The results of the MMT reveal that the client can take moderate resistance and then break. What muscle grade would you document the client possesses?

A client who can extend against gravity and take moderate resistance has a 4/5 (good) muscle strength.

Chapter 12 Review Questions

Neurological Approaches: Evaluation and Intervention

1. What level of motor control must be present for a person to be a candidate for CIMT?

   ▷ The person must exhibit at least partial control of the wrist and hand, 20° of extension of the wrist and 10° of extension of each finger or 10° extension of the wrist, 10° abduction of the thumb, and 10° extension of any two other digits or able to lift a wash rag off a tabletop using any type of prehension and then release it.

2. What is the correct procedure to evaluate the severity of spasticity in a muscle or group of muscles?

   ▷ Spasticity is evaluated by the elicitation of velocity-dependent stretch reflexes. The limb is quickly stretched in a direction opposite the pull of the muscle group being tested.

3. What is the purpose of applying a static orthosis to an affected body part?

   ▷ A static orthosis is used to provide external support, prevent motion, stretch contractures, align joints for healing, rest joints, and/or reduce pain.

4. You are working with a client with hemiplegia after a brain tumor resection.. They are learning to transfer using a tub bench for the first time. The person is at the cognitive stage of learning. According to principles of motor learning, what types of interventions would be appropriate to teach this transfer skill at this stage of learning?

   ▷ Examples of appropriate types of interventions include having the client demonstrate ideal performance of the task to establish a reference of correctness, verbalize the task components and requirements, point out similarities to other learned tasks (e.g., a toilet transfer), direct attention to critical task elements (e.g., lock brakes for safety, judge height of the tub), use blocked practice (i.e., repeated practice of the transfer), encourage the use of mental practice, use manual guidance to assist as appropriate (e.g., guiding legs over and into the tub), and break the tasks down to component parts (e.g., wheelchair alignment and management, sit to stand).

5. You are working with a person with a swallowing disorder. You have determined that direct interventions using a bolus are indicated. Which approaches would you use?

   ▷ Direct interventions for swallowing disorders include the modification of the consistency, amount, and pacing of solids and liquids. Postural interventions (i.e., chin tuck, head tilt, and head turn) are used to increase swallowing efficiency during meals. Specific swallowing adaptations (e.g., the supraglottic swallow technique, Mendelsohn's maneuver) are also used when indicated.

6. You receive a referral for occupational therapy services for a toddler. The parents report that the toddler dislikes changes to daily routines, meeting strangers, and being touched. During your evaluation, you observe that the toddler does not like to move or explore unfamiliar objects and toys. Upon analysis of evaluation results, you determine that the toddler is over-responsive to sensory stimuli and avoids all sensory experiences. According to the principles of Ayres Sensory Integration® approach, what types of sensory stimuli should you introduce during interventions with this toddler and how should you structure your initial intervention sessions? Explain your rationale.

   ▷ You should introduce controlled sensory activities that simultaneously combine vestibular and proprioceptive stimuli. It would be best to begin with the toddler in the prone position and provide slow linear movement combined with joint compression and deep firm touch pressure. You should observe, monitor, and adjust stimuli that influence modulation. You should be alert to the toddler's behavioral responses and assess these during intervention and up to a few hours following intervention. Slow linear movement combined with firm deep touch and pressure resistance is less threatening than light touch. When combined these inputs have an integrative effect.

7. You are working with a client with a flaccid arm post-stroke. Name three practice interventions you could implement that aid in upper extremity (UE) skill learning/re-learning and describe them.

Three interventions that aid in skill learning/re-learning are mirror therapy, action observation, and mental practice. Mirror therapy involves placing a mirror in the midsagittal plane of the person between their extremities. The impaired arm/hand is placed behind the mirror, while the unimpaired arm is in front of the mirror. The person moves the unimpaired arm/hand while watching the mirror reflection, giving the visual illusion of normal movement of the impaired arm.

Action observation involves observing a person with no impairments performing a skill or functional task either through video or live performance. This intervention is based on evidence that similar cortical motor areas are activated by either performance or observance of a skill or task. Mental practice involves cognitive rehearsal of a motor skill without actually moving.

8. You are working with a client to perform a sit <-> stand transfer onto a raised toilet seat with arm rests, for the first time, in the client's hospital room. The client requires a great deal of feedback and practice. The next day, you have the client perform the same toilet transfer as they did the day before with minimal feedback. The client is at which stage of motor learning on the second day? Explain your reasoning. Three days later, you ask your client to transfer on a commode without arm rests in the clinic bathroom and they are able to perform with no cues. The client is at which stage of motor learning three days later? Explain your reasoning.

On the second day of intervention the client was at the skill retention stage (associative stage). This stage involves the "carryover" of learning as individuals are asked to demonstrate their newly acquired skill after initial practice. The first day, the client required maximal feedback and practice because this was a novel task (use of raised toilet seat) performed in a new environment (hospital room). However, on the second day, the client was able to do the same transfer (same equipment and environment) with minimal feedback because the client has learned from the previous session.

Three days later, the client is at the skill transfer stage (autonomous stage). At this stage, learning involves the individual demonstrating an acquired skill in a new context. In this scenario, the client was able to transfer the information learned from previous sessions to a new condition, the commode and clinic bathroom. In other words, the client was able to generalize what was learned from previous sessions to a new setting. The goal of occupational therapy interventions based on motor learning is to develop clients' ability to transfer what was learned in their intervention sessions to new contexts or conditions, such as their home.

Chapter 13 Review Questions

Cognitive-Perceptual Approaches: Evaluation and Intervention

1. You are observing a person with apraxia eat breakfast. What behaviors would you most likely observe?

   ▶ You may see problems with tool use, such as stirring coffee with a knife or eating cereal with a fork. You would observe difficulty with the sequencing of the steps of the task, such as eating cereal without first pouring the milk into it. In severe cases, the person will not perform the task at all. They will stare blankly at the breakfast tray as the concept of the task of eating breakfast will have been completely lost.

2. Your client presents with right-sided unilateral spatial neglect and poor awareness. The client has a supportive partner. What environmental modifications will be useful for their partner to implement in their home to maximize the client's performance and safety indoors?

   ▶ The partner can place perceptual anchors (e.g., brightly colored objects or strips of colored tape) to the right in the places where the person usually engages in occupations and activities. They can place necessary grooming objects on the left side of the sink. Reorganizing the closets, dressers, and other storage units so that needed items are biased to the left and placing cell phones or safety alert systems to the person's left or in the person's left pocket/ on their left arm will also be helpful. Providing education about the impact of unilateral spatial neglect and poor awareness on functional performance can help the partner understand the need for implementing and maintaining home and activity modifications.

3. What are examples of activities you can use to evaluate components of attention?

   ▶ Activities that require vigilance (e.g., reading or listening to the news) can be used to assess sustained attention. Engaging the client in two tasks (e.g., as making tea and toast) can determine divided attention skills. Engaging the client in activities in an environment that is stimulating (e.g., a cafeteria or playground) can determine selective attention abilities.

4. Your client has left-sided body neglect. Describe the behaviors you would expect to see during the person's morning self-care routine.

   ▶ You may observe the person spending more time combing the right side of their hair as compared to the left. The person may not shave or only partially shave the left side of the face or legs. They may not engage the left arm in the task despite having the physical capacity.

5. You are working in acute care with a person with low arousal after a head trauma. Describe approaches and activities that would be useful to include during interventions with this person.

   ▶ The use of sensory-stimulating activities would be beneficial. Examples include washing the face and upper body with a cold washcloth, using a loud and direct voice when cuing, providing visually stimulating objects, turning all lights on, opening bedroom curtains, sitting the person up to provide vestibular input, and playing music.

6. You are working in the outpatient setting with a person who had stroke. The person complains of blurry vision/double vision while reading. What should you evaluate to determine the person's visual status? Identify the assessments that would be best to use with this person and describe how you would perform them.

The evaluation of the person's visual status should include near visual acuity, strabismus, and convergence. Near visual acuity should be evaluated for this can be the reason the person is experiencing blurry vision while reading. To test near visual acuity, you would sit across from the person who has one eye covered. The Snellen Chart would be held 16 inches away at eye level. You would ask the person to read the letters on the chart beginning at the top with the largest letters and progressing down the chart to read the subsequent rows that have increasing numbers of letters that decrease in size. The last row that the person can read accurately indicates their visual acuity in that specific eye. You would repeat this procedure to test the person's other eye.

Strabismus should be evaluated as this can be the reason for double vision. For a strabismus assessment, you would look at the person's eyes and look for a deviation from midline. Convergence should also be evaluated for convergence issues can cause near double vision. To assess convergence, you would sit across from the person and have them fixate on a pen tip, which is held 12 inches away from the bridge of their nose. You would then tell the person to keep looking at the tip of the pen as you moved it closer to the bridge of their nose. At this point, you would carefully watch both eyes to observe if one drifts off.

Chapter 14 Review Questions

Psychosocial Approaches: Evaluation and Intervention

1. What are key general postulates for change that are used in cognitive behavioral therapy (CBT) to guide the intervention process? How can these be applied throughout the occupational therapy process?

   According to CBT, dysfunctional thought processes produce or lead to the development of mental health symptoms and can result in psychological dysfunction and/or psychiatric disorders. Negative thoughts, which are considered a dysfunctional process in CBT, function as a sustaining factor for illnesses such as depression. CBT proposes that altering a person's cognition can improve psychological health. In occupational therapy, a practitioner can help the person alter dysfunctional thoughts and cognitive processes by addressing them through the use of CBT interventions. For example, using work sheets in psychoeducational groups or individual sessions can assist clients in looking at their perceptions of their problems, situations, and/or feelings. CBT interventions are also used to help clients make changes that can lead to improved emotional health.

2. Identify three evaluation tools that can be used to assess an individual's cognitive level according to the Cognitive Disabilities model. Describe a practice situation in which each evaluation would be most effectively used.

   The Allen Cognitive Level Screen-5 (ACLS-5) is a structured task that allows the evaluator to observe the individual performing three increasingly complex leather lacing stitches. Based on these observations, the evaluator makes determinations about the person's cognitive skill level. Guidelines are available for designing other tasks that will also elicit the component skills of each level. (Refer to Chapter 14's evaluation section.) In practice, the ACLS-5 can be used in any setting where the practitioner's observations lead them to believe that the client is experiencing cognitive dysfunction. The ACLS-5 can be effectively used, in conjunction with other evaluations, to assist in intervention and discharge planning. Clinical settings where adult individuals present with a traumatic brain injury (TBI), cerebrovascular accident, or mental health disorders are among the various settings where this evaluation can be used. For example, Veterans Administration (VA) hospitals that provide service to veterans who incurred a TBI or stroke or who have developed a neurocognitive disorder would be a setting that may use the ACLS-5.

   The Routine Task Inventory (RTI) gathers data about the individual's ADL performance from an informed caregiver. Refer to Chapter 15. Home health OT practitioners may use the information obtained from this evaluation to improve a client's ADL performance by providing activity adaptations and making home modifications as indicated. Based on the RTI results, the OT practitioner can also provide patient and family education to enhance occupational performance and ease caregiver burden. The Cognitive Performance Test (CPT) was designed to assess the functional performance of individuals with neurocognitive disorders. The focus is on the identification of the effects that particular deficits have on the performance of ADL. This test can be used in any clinical situation where individuals present with the symptoms of neurocognitive disorders. The CPT can screen and identify for low level cognitive ability to refine the results of the occupational therapy evaluation.

Review>Practice>Motivate>Analyze>Apply

3. Identify current intervention approaches that use sensory models to guide treatment and describe how they can be effectively applied in OT practice.

The use of multisensory environments, "Snoezelen" rooms, and/or "Comfort Rooms" can be effective in calming or alerting individuals with psychiatric, autism spectrum, neurocognitive, and pervasive developmental disorders. Such rooms can be used with an individual or with a group depending upon intervention goals and objectives. They are increasingly being used as an alternative to restraints in mental health settings. Occupational therapy practitioners' unique knowledge in creating therapeutic environments based on sensory principles can be very useful in increasing the efficacy of these rooms, particularly in acute, inpatient psychiatric settings. The use of therapeutic weighted blankets, dolls, and stuffed animals can also be used as a modality to assist in self-soothing and as an alternative to the use of restraints in inpatient mental health settings, skilled nursing facilities, and/or any setting in which clients can benefit from interventions to decrease agitation.

Occupational therapy (OT) practitioners can also use a psycho-education approach along with sensory models during intervention. For example, after the administration of an evaluation such as the Adolescent and Adult Sensory Profile, the practitioner can use worksheets in a group to help clients identify their reactions to sensory input and learn adaptive ways of coping with their sensory issues. Sensory diets including alerting/calming stimuli and heavy work patterns can be provided in any setting by OT practitioners and individualized to the specific sensory needs of the client. By helping clients learn how to use their sensory diets whenever sensory processing issues arise, OT practitioners can extend the effective use of occupational therapy interventions throughout the day.

4. Describe three interventions that can effectively help individuals experiencing hallucinations and/or delusions manage their symptoms during an occupational therapy group.

During groups, OT practitioners can create a distraction-free environment to eliminate and/or decrease stimuli that may trigger hallucinations and/or delusions and interfere with group participation. Occupational therapy practitioners can use highly structured simple, concrete, and tangible activities that hold the group members' attention (e.g., crafts, meal preparation, gardening). If a member becomes distracted during a group or experiences hallucinations and/or delusions, the OT practitioner can redirect them to these reality-based activities. This redirection can help the group member refocus on their task and/or move their focus away from the internal stimuli they are experiencing. When a group member is observed experiencing a hallucination or expressing a delusion, the OT practitioner can intervene with verbalizations about what they are doing with respect to the activity and facilitate their reality-based thinking and actions about the task.

For example, a therapeutic horticulture group conducted in a greenhouse can provide a calm environment and a diversity of simple, structured, concrete tasks (e.g., planting, pruning, and watering) that result in a tangible outcome (e.g., a full-grown plant; vegetables to pick). Members' participation in these reality-based activities and the OT practitioner's consistent approach and positive feedback can help group members effectively manage their psychotic symptoms.

5. A school-based occupational therapist receives numerous complaints from teachers and other school personnel about students "acting out" during class, lunch, recess, and transitions. Several report that sending students to the principal's office for disciplinary actions has not decreased these behaviors and they are concerned about the impact of these actions on the students. In response to these expressed concerns the therapist develops an education and training program based on the ABC model to help teachers and other school personnel understand and address students' disruptive behaviors in a more effective manner. Describe the main concepts and principles of this model. Provide an example as to how they can be effectively used by teachers and other school personnel to decrease the frequency of maladaptive behaviors that result in negative outcomes and increase the frequency of students' adaptive behaviors that result in positive outcomes.

The ABC model recognizes that disruptive behaviors are a child's ineffective way of expressing their thoughts and feelings, *not* intentionally "acting out". Using this model, the therapist would support the teachers' perceptions that sending students who violate the social norms of the school to the principal's office for disciplinary actions is ineffective at managing these behaviors. Removing students from a classroom can be detrimental to their academic progress. Sending students to the principal's office during lunch, recess, and transitions will isolate them from their peers. All of these outcomes can negatively impact students' social participation, self-efficacy, and self-esteem.

Because the teachers recognize that a reactive approach to students' disruptive behaviors is ineffective, an occupational therapy education and training program on the proactive use of the ABC model to address their concerns is very relevant. Because consistency in the use of the ABC model can increase its efficacy, other school personnel should also be educated and trained in its use. By working with all school personnel to develop competence in the use of the ABC model, the therapist can help them prevent disruptive behaviors and more effectively manage them when they do occur. In the ABC model, A stands for Antecedent (i.e., the event that precedes a behavior or the stimulus that triggers it); B stands for Behavior (i.e., the measurable and observable actions that occur in response to the event or stimulus); and C stands for Consequence (i.e., the responses and actions that occur after a student's behavioral response to the antecedent). Refer to Table 14-2.

Upon implementation of this program, the occupational therapist can educate the teachers and other school personnel about common antecedents to disruptive behaviors (e.g., noise, unclear directions or standards, unwanted physical contact with another person). They can help them learn how to identify the antecedents to students' disruptive behaviors and provide suggestions as to how the antecedents to these behaviors can be eliminated, avoided, and/or modified. The therapist can work with the teachers and other school personnel on how best to implement these strategies in different school settings (e.g., classrooms, hallways, cafeteria, playground, gymnasium, auditorium) for each student and model these behaviors for them. The therapist can also collaborate with the teachers and other school personnel to identify the consequences of each students' behavior and personally meaningful reinforcers for positive adaptive behaviors. When able, the therapist and teachers should collaborate with the students to identify their positive reinforcers and discuss consequences for disruptive behaviors and alternatives to these. The therapist can train the teachers and other school personnel in the use of these reinforcers to increase the frequency of students' adaptive behaviors that have positive outcomes and decrease the frequency of maladaptive behaviors that have negative outcomes. The therapist can also train the teachers and other school personnel in the use of the therapeutic techniques of interpretation, redirection, limit setting, time-outs, and behavioral or contingency contracts.

An example of the effective use of the ABC model is the identification of antecedents to the disruptive behaviors that occur when students transition from the classroom to the playground for recess. Because this transition is typically completed by several (if not all) classrooms at the same time, the hallways are often very crowded and noisy. The close proximity of many students and the increased auditory stimuli can trigger disruptive behaviors. To address these antecedents, the therapist can suggest that a student who has these triggers transition before the entire class. They can also suggest that these students be provided with noise cancelling headphones and/or a friend or peer helper who can walk with them, provide needed support and structure, and serve as a buffer to prevent unwanted physical contact. To help all students prepare for the transition, the teacher can provide relaxation, mindfulness, or imagery activities/exercises prior to transitioning to recess. An in-class review of the expectations for going from the classroom to the playground and the activities that can be enjoyed during recess can also help ease the transition for all students.

For students who struggle with transitions, a private 1:1 review of their feelings about this experience and the strategies they can use to manage their behaviors can be beneficial. Positive reinforcement during and after the transition should be provided by teachers and other school personnel. If a student experiences difficulties with the transition the teacher or other school personnel can use interpretation to help the student express what they are feeling and redirect them to the outcome of the transition (e.g., being able to engage in a highly preferred activity during recess). If needed, setting limits and providing a brief time-out can help the student effectively manage their behavior and successfully complete the transition from classroom to playground.

6. The RADAR approach is used to screen for and respond to domestic abuse. How would an occupational therapist apply this approach?

In the RADAR approach R stands for routinely ask, A stands for Affirm and Ask, D stands for Document, A stands for Assess and Address, and R stands for Review options and Refer An occupational therapist can apply the RADAR by routinely asking questions during the evaluation process to screen for abuse. Inquiring about potential abuse when interviewing all clients can be the first step in intervention because this acknowledges that abuse is not an acceptable secret. If and when a person discloses abuse at any time throughout the OT process, the therapist should acknowledge and support the person. They should affirm that this situation is not the person's fault and ask direct questions to determine risk (e.g., Do you feel safe with your partner? Are you afraid when your partner comes home?).

The therapist should always document objective findings whenever anything that may be indicative of abuse is observed (e.g., the person has multiple bruises) and record any client statements that indicate they are experiencing abuse in quotes (e.g., "I am scared to go home"). This information can establish useful objective clinical evidence. If their abuse results in criminal charges against their abuser, this documentation can be used to support their case. The therapist should assess and address the person's safety by asking direct questions (i.e., has abuse become more violent? are there weapons in the home?). This can help determine the urgency for action by the therapist to help the person remain safe.

The therapist should be aware of the national and local referral options so that they can refer the person to them as needed. These should include domestic violence hotlines, domestic violence shelters, and/or safe houses that have staff trained in domestic violence and safety planning. Reviewing options and referring a person to key resources is an essential and ethical step in preventing further domestic violence experiences. Therapists should always have the contact information for these resources readily available. The public display of these resources in occupational therapy practice settings can also diminish the silence that enshrouds domestic violence.

7. Your roommate with whom you share an eighth-floor apartment has been very sad and withdrawn for several weeks. This week, they cancelled their weekly therapy appointment and stopped attending the classes and social activities that they previously had enjoyed. You ask them if everything is alright, and the reply is "no, not really." "I'm thinking of killing myself, I just can't take it anymore." "How do you think you would do it?" you ask. "I'm not quite sure, I think I have a couple of options here, belts, knives, I'm not sure which way I want to go, but I have to do it soon, maybe by the end of the week. Yes, definitely by the end of the week. All things considered, I think I'll jump out the window. I'm pretty sure the fall would kill me." What risk factors for suicide are you observing in your roommate, what levels of suicide lethality are present, and what should be your first intervention?

The risk factors for suicide based on this scenario are a sad affect, limited interaction or social isolation and withdrawal, a mental health history, and a verbalized suicidal statement, which must be taken seriously. The roommate has suicidal ideation and a plan and intent, which presents a great potential risk for attempting suicide. Assessing this situation, your first plan of action is to stay with and not allow your roommate to be alone at any moment. You should encourage your roommate to go to the emergency room, call their doctor or therapist, and/or call the National Suicide Hotline (988). If those interventions are ineffective or cannot be completed without leaving the individual alone, you should call 911.

8. You are conducting a group for individuals with recently acquired spinal cord injuries that resulted in paraplegia and the need to use a wheelchair for mobility. Adjusting to this abrupt change in their lives has been difficult for most group members. While participating in a group, one of the participants says to you "you really have no idea what it's like to have to face using a wheelchair for the rest of your life, when just a month ago I ran my sixth marathon. Running has been my whole life. It was the way I relieved stress and stayed in shape. I guess that's all over now." What type of therapeutic approach should you take? What types of individual and group interventions might benefit this individual?

In this case, validation of this person's feelings is indicated by making statements such as "I can only imagine what you are going through. I respect your perspective on your experience. I know and accept that this is a hard adjustment, not being able to run, or walk for that matter, and on top of that you need to use a wheelchair. I can understand why you are concerned about how to manage stress and stay active." This acknowledges the person's loss issues and may establish rapport and trust as you do not attempt to assume to know how the person feels. In providing a client-centered approach, you would next ask the group member to identify personal intervention goals. You would then provide individual or group interventions based on this feedback. Appropriate interventions would include addressing the person's wish to be involved in running and athletics and providing psychoeducational groups for anger management and the development of adaptive coping skills. Client and family education to address lifestyle changes and resultant depression and to develop a plan for recovery are also appropriate.

Chapter 15 Review Questions

Occupational Engagement and Performance: Evaluation and Intervention

1. An OT supervisor is orienting a new inpatient, rehabilitation employee to the assessments the OT department uses to measure occupational performance. Many clients in the facility are covered by Medicare. The new employee is returning to an acute physical rehabilitation setting after fifteen years of school-based practice. At the onset of the orientation, the new employee states, "I had an exceptional course in assessment in my OT program, so I am familiar with Medicare's measurement of occupational performance. It is based on the Functional Independence Measure (FIM)." How should the OT supervisor respond?

The supervisor should respond by informing the new employee that the Centers for Medicare and Medicaid Services (CMS) removed the FIM from the Inpatient Rehabilitation Facility Patient Assessment Instrument (IRF-PAI) in 2019. They should tell the employee that the CMS now uses Section GG to measure a person's need for assistance with self-care and mobility and document the person's level of function according to a six-level independence scale. On this scale, six indicates most independent and one indicates most dependent. Coding is also provided for activities that are not attempted. Table 15-1 provides this scale.

The supervisor can explain that several assessments are available to measure occupational performance and help determine a person's level of function on this six-point scale (e.g., the Barthel Index, the Cognitive Performance Test [CPT], Katz Index of ADL, Performance Assessment of Self-Care Skills [PASS], and Routine Task Inventory [RTI]) and that the results of screening will determine the specific assessment that is most relevant to use with individual clients.

2. The occupational therapy department in a skilled nursing facility (SNF) provides services to persons with physical disabilities, chronic illnesses, cognitive impairments, and neurocognitive disorders. What core ADL assessments can the SNF's occupational therapists use to evaluate clients with diverse conditions? What ADL assessments have been developed for specific client populations that would be helpful for the therapists to include in their "toolbox" to assess clients with physical disabilities and chronic illnesses and those with cognitive impairments and neurocognitive disorders?

ADL assessments that can be used for clients with diverse conditions include the nonstandardized AMPS, Canadian Occupational Performance Measure (COPM), Katz Index of ADL, Klein-Bell Activities of Daily Living Scale (K-B Scale), Kohlman Evaluation of Living Skills (KELS), and the Performance Assessment of Self-Care Skills (PASS). The Milwaukee Evaluation of Daily Living Skills (MEDLS) was originally developed for adults with at least a two-year history of mental illness, but its use has expanded to other populations with ADL deficits.

ADL assessments that have been developed specifically for persons with physical disabilities and chronic illnesses include the Barthel Index and Katz Index of ADL. ADL assessments that have been developed specifically for persons with cognitive impairments and neurocognitive disorders include the Cognitive Performance Test (CPT), Kitchen Task Assessment (KTA), and the Routine Task Inventory (RTI).

3. An occupational therapist provides services to a client who recently incurred a complete C6 spinal cord injury (SCI). One focus of the interprofessional comprehensive intervention program is teaching clients toileting and bowel and bladder management. The therapist collaborates with nursing to enable the client to achieve this goal. What level of independence is expected to be achieved by this client? What adaptive equipment and strategies should the therapist teach the client to use to enable the client's independence?

A client living with a complete SCI at the C6 level may be independent with emptying a leg bag but will require maximal to total assistance in toileting and bowel and bladder management. Equipment used may include catheterization and bowel stimulation equipment, padded shower/commode chair, drop-arm commode, and a tub bench with cutout. Because the need for maximal or total assistance will require the client to self-direct their toileting and bowel and bladder management, intervention should focus on developing the client's self-direction skills. This intervention is guided by the principle that persons living with a disability know their needs best. The client's ability to plan and give directions to those who assist them should be supported and recognized by all staff. Shared information and collaboration between OT and nursing will assure the client is provided with maximum opportunities to develop the skills they need to achieve the goal of independence in self-directed toileting and bowel and bladder management. Refer to Table 15-4 for more information about the ADL skills of persons with SCIs from C1 to S5.

4. A person with a C-7 spinal cord injury sets a goal to return to work as an accountant. The person expresses concern over the ability to complete a morning self-care routine and job tasks. What will be realistic for the person to expect to be able to do after receiving occupational therapy services to develop self-care and work skills?

At C-7, the person can use a tenodesis grasp and/or orthosis to perform many tasks. Thus, the person can expect to be independent in feeding, grooming, and dressing. Minimal assistance and equipment (e.g., a dressing stick) may be needed for lower body dressing and a button hook may be needed for buttoning. The person will be able to transfer independently using depression transfers. For bathing, a handheld shower head and a tub bench are needed. At work, the person will be able to independently hold a phone, typing stick, and pen using a tenodesis grasp or orthosis. Thus, the person can expect to be able to independently complete work tasks requiring the use of a calculator, computer, and telephone.

5. An occupational therapist seeks to ensure that the ADL of sexual activity is addressed throughout the OT process. Which model can help the therapist achieve this aim? Describe the key points of this model.

The occupational therapist can use the PLISSIT model as a guide to address sexual activity throughout the OT process. In this model, the "P" stands for "permission" which requires the therapist to create an atmosphere which gives the individual permission to raise concerns about their sexuality and sexual activity(ies). This can be accomplished by incorporating sexuality into the OT initial and ongoing evaluation in a matter-of-fact manner. "LI" represents "limited information" that the therapist can provide to ensure that the individual has accurate knowledge about their sexual abilities and potentials. The therapist can share facts (e.g., there is sex after disability) and dispel myths (e.g., people with disabilities are asexual). "SS" stands for "specific suggestions" that the therapist can provide to facilitate the individual's pursuit of satisfying sexual activities, either alone or with a partner. These can include strategies for achieving clients' goals for sexual expression (e.g., energy conservation methods, the use of nonmedical methods to manage pain and stiffness, positioning alternatives and adaptive equipment, and applying principles of activity analysis, gradation, modification, and simplification to sexual activities). In this model, "IT" represents "intensive therapy" which is indicated when the individual requires intervention for long-standing relationship problems and/or enduring sexual problems. The application of this part of the PLISSIT model requires specialized training, so the therapist would complete a referral to the appropriate professional (e.g., relationship counselor, sex therapist) if indicated.

6. An occupational therapist provides consultation to a local business that employs people with cognitive limitations due to psychiatric, physical, and intellectual disabilities. What strategies should the therapist share with employers to increase their employees' ability to concentrate, manage time, and focus on multiple tasks at the same time during the workday?

To help the employees manage time, the employer can provide directive commands on a regular basis and maintain structure through a daily time and task schedule using hourly goals. The provision of positive reinforcement when tasks are completed within the expected timelines is also helpful. To improve employees' concentration and management of multiple tasks, the employer can put each work request in writing and leave it in a "to do" box to avoid interrupting the employees' work in progress. Depending on the employees' preferences, this structure can be provided in-person, virtually, and/or via a smartphone application. The provision of good working conditions (e.g., adequate light, no extraneous background noise, a separate work area to reduce noise and interruptions) can also help employees concentrate. The number of tasks that need to be completed simultaneously can be decreased or eliminated, and priorities for task completion can be established. All work tasks can be put in writing with due dates or times identified. Tasks among employees with the same responsibilities can be redistributed, so that each can do more of one type of job task than a lot of different tasks.

7. During an occupational therapy screening, a client reports feeling tired all of the time. What should the occupational therapist address during evaluation?

The therapist should assess the person's ability to identify the need for restorative rest and sleep, their typical rest and sleep patterns and routines, and obstacles to the attainment and maintenance of satisfying rest and sleep. In addition, personal issues (e.g., being a "light" sleeper who awakens easily), pathophysiological changes related to disease, disability, and/or the aging process (e.g., chronic pain, unrelenting fatigue), and sociocultural barriers (e.g., a nightshift job) should be considered. The therapist can use sleep checklists and sleep diaries to obtain detailed information.

Chapter 16 Review Questions

Mastery of the Environment: Evaluation and Intervention

1. An occupational therapist provides consultation services to a group of religious organizations who want to improve the accessibility of the entrances to their buildings. All entrances currently have stairs. What should the occupational therapist recommend to allow access for persons who use mobility aides (e.g., walkers and canes) and wheelchairs?

The therapist should recommend the installation of railings on the stairs and ramps as an alternative to the stairs. The exterior railings should be placed at 36″. This is the average of the recommended 34″–38″ waist height for those who walk (variance depends on people's height). The railings should be 1½″–2″ in diameter with non-skid surfaces. The ramps should be built with a ratio of slope to rise of 1:12. The ramps should be a minimum of 36″ wide with a non-skid surface. Ramp railings should be at the average of 32″ high. If possible two railings (one lower and one higher) should be provided to allow for differences in people's arm reach. Curbs on the ramps should be at least 4″ high. Level platforms should be included in the ramp design. If the ramp is excessively long, 5′ × 5′ landing(s) are needed to allow for rest. If a sharp turn is needed in the direction of the ramp, a landing for turning space is needed. A 90° turn will require a minimum 5′ × 5′ landing; a 180° turn will require a minimum 4′ × 8′ landing. At the top of the ramp, a 5′ × 5′ platform is needed before the door to allow for persons in a wheelchair to swing the door without backing up. Electronic opening doors are optimal. If these are not feasible, doors should be able to be opened with a closed fist via the use of lever handles or push bars. Objects which may obstruct entrance ways should be removed (e.g., planters, garbage cans).

2. An occupational therapist provides a weekly home safety group to members of a senior center. What strategies should the therapist recommend the group members use inside and outside their homes to prevent falls?

The therapist should recommend that the members ensure that their living spaces have adequate lighting with no loose electrical cords, minimal clutter, firmly attached carpet, and furniture arranged for easy maneuverability. For homes with stairs, the therapist should recommend that members make sure that there are stair handrails securely fastened on both sides of the stairs. There should be light switches at the top and bottom of the stairs and the stairs should be covered by a non-skid secure surface. In the bathrooms, members should have grab bars located in and out of tubs and shower stalls and near toilets. The use of non-skid mats, nightlights, and an elevated toilet seat are also effective in decreasing fall risk. Good recommendations for the therapist to make to prevent falls in the bedroom are the installation of night lights or light switches within reach of the bed, the placement of telephones in an easy to reach position near the bed, and the use of a mattress that is at a height that makes it easy to get in and out of bed. In the members' living areas, the therapist should advise the members to be sure their couches and chairs are at proper height to get in and out of easily. To decrease fall risk in the kitchen, the therapist should advise members to store items on reachable shelves (i.e., between the person's eye and hip level). Outside the home, members should be sure that cracked pavement or steps are fixed and stable handrails are installed if there are steps.

3. A client is status-post posterolateral hip replacement surgery. What recommendations should the therapist make for bed mobility?

   The therapist should advise the person to not roll on the nonoperated side because this may result in internal rotation of the operated hip, which may cause dislocation. An abductor pillow between the lower extremities can be used to prevent adduction of the operated hip. The therapist should recommend that the person does not flex the hip beyond 90° or internally rotate or pivot at the hip. The therapist should teach the person to transfer by keeping operated the hip in slight abduction and extended out in front.

4. A school-based occupational therapist provides recommendations for alternative access modes to computers to compensate for a diversity of disabilities and maximize students' independence in the school environment. What adaptations can the therapist recommend? Explain their use.

   The therapist can recommend programmable keyboards that allow for customized overlays (e.g., enlarged letters and numbers for students with low vision; graphics and symbols for students with cognitive impairments). Key guards and expanded keyboards that provide large keys can be helpful for students with limited motor accuracy and control (e.g., students with ataxia). Contracted keyboards that provide smaller keys in a constrained space can be useful for students with limited range of motion and functional motor control (e.g., students with arthritis) and light-touch keyboard activation systems can be useful for students with decreased strength and/or mobility (e.g., students with muscular dystrophy).The therapist can recommend delayed touch keyboard activation systems for students with poor motor control (e.g., students with athetoid movements) and chorded keyboards (which consist of a few keys which generate standard characters by pressing various combinations of keys) for students who use only one hand (e.g., students with hemiplegia). Finally, eye gaze and voice-activated computers can be useful for students with severe mobility impairments (e.g., upper extremity contractures).

5. A Center for Independent Living (CIL) has asked an entry-level occupational therapist and an entry-level OTA/COTA® to develop a program to address the community mobility needs of older adults and persons with disabilities. What aspects of community mobility can the therapist and OTA/COTA® include in this program? What aspects can they not include? Describe the evaluation and intervention foci that should they include in their program plan.

   Community mobility is the ability to move around one's community to engage in desired occupations and pursue meaningful activities outside of one's home. It includes personal mobility (e.g., walking, rolling, bicycling, driving), the use electronic personal mobility (e.g., scooters, electric wheelchairs), and the ability to access and use public, private, and/or other community-based transportation systems. Prior to developing a community mobility program, the entry-level occupational therapist and OTA/COTA® should conduct a needs assessment to identify the specific needs of the CIL's target population. Refer to Chapter 4. The subsequent program developed by the therapist and OTA/COTA® should address the population's common needs and the individual needs of program participants. These services can be provided in group and/or 1:1 formats.

Occupational therapy services to address the community mobility needs of older adults and persons with disabilities should begin with the completion of occupational profiles to determine participants' community mobility interests and needs. A screening and evaluation of participants' performance skills, performance patterns, and client factors should also be completed to determine if they are able to meet their community mobility needs (e.g., their fitness-to-drive, ability to safely and independently use public transportation). If the results of the screening and/or assessment indicate areas that require further evaluation to determine driving capability, entry-level practitioners do not have the qualifications to complete this. They must refer program participants with these concerns to a driver rehabilitation specialist who is qualified to complete a more in-depth evaluation.

Based on the assessment outcomes, the entry-level OT practitioners can provide direct interventions to address participants' functional limitations (e.g., balance, endurance, memory, emotional regulation, assertiveness) that affect their community mobility. They can provide education about community mobility options and resources (e.g., public para-transit and half fare programs and education and training on how to safely and effectively use personal mobility devices (e.g., walkers, wheelchairs, scooters) to access public and private transportation, transfer from these devices when needed, and store them if required.

A program to develop community mobility skills should include practice in the actual environment in which the person will be traveling. If indicated, and with the person's permission, the therapist and OTA/COTA® can provide education and training to family members/caregivers to enable them to effectively support the person's community mobility. Assertiveness training to develop participants' advocacy skills to obtain access to para-transit, discounted fare, and/or subsidized transportation programs, if eligible and needed and documentation to support their application can also be provided by entry-level OT practitioners. They can also provide training on the use of electronic navigation systems/global positioning systems (GPS) to help program participants effectively navigate unfamiliar environments and safety training to ensure that they can recognize and respond to risky and/or dangerous situations (e.g., when and how to call 911).

If the therapist and OTA/COTA® determine that a program participant has visual deficits, they should refer the person to an ophthalmologist or optician. If a person has been determined to be unable to meet the activity demands of their preferred mode of transportation, alternatives to maintain community mobility should be explored and implemented. Program participants who need driver rehabilitation services should be referred to a driver rehabilitation specialist for these services are beyond the scope of entry-level OT practice.

6. An occupational therapist begins employment at a new skilled nursing facility (SNF). To ensure compliance with OBRA and reduce the use of restraints in the facility, what policies and procedures should the therapist have the SNF administrators implement?

All staff should be aware of the conditions and situations that can contribute to agitated, restless, and/or wandering behaviors. These include pain, physical discomfort, hunger, thirst, need for toileting, loneliness, fear, boredom, and an unfamiliar environment. Staff should be trained in the provision of interventions that can effectively address these contributing factors and correct underlying problems without the use of restraints. These can include active listening, attention to underlying feelings and expressed concerns to promote trust, a medical evaluation for pain management, proper positioning, an adequate and client-directed toileting routine, and the provision of snacks, unbreakable water bottles, or other appropriate safe sources of nourishment and hydration. Family, peer, and/or pastoral visits; animal-assisted or pet therapy; and social, leisure, and physical activities can also be helpful in decreasing agitated, restless, and/or wandering behaviors. Activities should be provided at night as well as in the day. Loudspeaker and other extraneous noise should be eliminated, All resident rooms should include familiar and favorite objects to personalize them. A structured home-like environment with a set routine should be provided to promote a sense of safety and security. Contained areas should be interesting and safe. Furniture should be arranged to deter wandering with a variety of comfortable seating and furniture provided including broad-based rockers and footstools.

Guidelines for Effective Use of the Online Practice Exams

EXAM HINT: To maximize the exam preparation efficacy of the three online practice exams that accompany this text, we advise you to read the following guidelines *prior to* taking your first online practice exam.

The three online practice exams included with your purchase of this *Review and Study Guide (RSG)* are purposefully designed to simulate a complete NBCOT® OTR® certification exam. Because you should *only* take the NBCOT® exam *after* the completion of a comprehensive exam preparation plan, we advise you to *not* take an online practice exam until *after* you have fully implemented your exam preparation plan. Chapter 2 in this text provides clear concrete guidelines for structuring and implementing an individualized *and manageable* exam preparation plan to help you identify your specific content knowledge strengths and weaknesses. Using this information to develop and carry out an individualized exam preparation plan can help make sure that you are mastering the content that you will need to know to correctly answer NBCOT® exam items.

Taking a practice exam *before* you have studied the information that will be tested on the NBCOT®'s OTR® exam will only reinforce what you do not know. This can negatively impact your confidence. However, if you take your first practice exam *after* you have studied you will have the foundational knowledge you need to correctly answer exam items. This positive outcome will boost your confidence. Using the test-taking strategies that are provided in Chapter 1 to determine correct answers to exam items can further increase your success.

Directions for accessing TherapyEd's online practice exams via TherapyEd's learning portal are provided on the inside cover of this text. Because the online practice exams are designed to be summative exams that mirror the NBCOT® exam format and administration, each exam can only be taken once. To support your ability to effectively use our online practice exams during your preparation for the NBCOT® certification exam, you can access the TherapyEd learning portal to review your exam score reports and all exam items and their rationales for 12 months. If unanticipated events prevent you from taking the NBCOT® exam within this 12-month period, you can contact TherapyEd at 888-369-0743 or info@therapyed.com to request an extension of your access to the learning portal.

Like the NBCOT® certification exam, each TherapyEd online practice exam has 180 items that test the four OTR® exam domains via traditional single-response three or four option multiple-choice (MC) items and six-option multiselect Scenario Set items. This replication of the OTR® exam format enables you to simulate the OTR® exam experience and practice your timing for your actual exam administration. If you do not have an approved testing accommodation (TA) giving you extended time to complete your exam, you should take each of the three practice exams that accompany this text during a continuous 4-hour session. This will allow you to assess your pacing and practice implementing time management strategies to ensure that you complete the entire OTR® exam within the allotted time.

The exam clock can *only* be stopped during a NBCOT® certification exam as a prearranged TA. Thus, if you do not have this accommodation, you should include a 15-minute break during each of your exam simulations to practice answering all exam items within 3 hours and 45 minutes. Developing the ability to complete the exam within this shortened time frame will ensure that you will be able to take a break during your exam administration without jeopardizing your ability to answer all exam items within the allotted 4 hours.

As discussed in Chapter 1, we recommend you spend an *average* of about 45 seconds to complete each three-option single-choice MC exam item, one minute to complete each four-option single-choice MC exam item, and one minute 30 seconds to complete *each* of the four six-option multi-select items in a Scenario Set. This pace will enable you to accrue a bank of approximately 20–30 minutes that you can use to review and answer more challenging exam items. This extra time can also be used to take a break during the exam.

To further simulate your NBCOT® exam experience, we advise you to complete at least one TherapyEd online practice exam in an environment that is similar to a Pearson VUE testing center (e.g., a study area in a library or a cubicle in a computer lab). This will enable you to test your ability to remain focused while taking an exam in a public place and provide you with an opportunity to practice strategies to block out distractions (e.g., not looking to see who is getting up from or sitting down at the computer next to you). If you have an approved TA enabling you to take the NBCOT® exam in a private room, you should verify that the Pearson VUE testing center at which you plan to take your exam has this capability before you schedule your exam.

Immediately after you complete a TherapyEd online practice exam, the learning portal will display an analysis of your exam performance. This detailed report will identify which items you answered correctly and incorrectly, the amount of time you took to complete the exam, and the percentage of items you answered correctly according to the four NBCOT® OTR® exam domains, five critical reasoning skills, and nine content knowledge categories that align with TherapyEd's *RSG* chapters. A listing of the specific domains, critical reasoning skills, and content knowledge categories that are identified in this score report are provided at the end of these guidelines.

Once you receive your personal score report, TherapyEd's learning portal allows you to choose which exam items you want to review (i.e., items answered correctly, incorrectly, or skipped). After choosing an item to review, the portal will immediately show you the exam item in the same form it appeared on the exam, the filled in answer(s) you choose, and the correct answer(s) noted by a green check on the option. Below the item there will be a box with a thumbs up or down notation indicating whether you answered the item correctly or incorrectly. How long you took to answer the item will also be identified. Beneath this, will be a third box in which the correct answer(s) and the incorrect options are restated. This box will also contain an extensive rationale that explains the content knowledge that supports the item's correct answer(s), the reasons why wrong answers were incorrect, and the critical reasoning skill needed to determine the item's correct answer(s).

To ensure you obtain a complete picture of your content knowledge and critical reasoning skills, we strongly encourage you to read the rationales for *all* exam items. Each rationale contains solid teaching points that can help solidify the knowledge and skills you need for certification exam success. After you review the score report and answer rationales for the first online practice exam, you should revise your exam preparation plan using the guidelines provided in Chapter 2.

Box 2-1 NBCOT® Exam Domain Score Report Content and Utility outlines strategies you can use to improve your performance in the four NBCOT® OTR® exam domains and *Box 2-2 Content Category Score Report Content and Utility* describes how your performance in specific content areas can be used to address identified knowledge gaps. To help you know what to study, the content knowledge categories are labelled in accordance with this text's chapter titles. Table 2-5 outlines the *RSG* chapters that correspond with each of the nine content knowledge categories so that you can know which chapter(s) you should study if your performance in a content category is less than satisfactory.

When revising your exam preparation plan, you should also reflect on the feedback provided on your critical reasoning strategies. If the analysis of your exam performance identifies difficulty with a specific area of reasoning, you should review the self-assessment questions and the exam preparation guidelines provided in Table 2-7. *Box 2-3 Critical Reasoning Score Report Content and Utility* explains how the information provided about your performance in the five types of critical reasoning can be used to improve your critical reasoning skills and Box 2-6 outlines steps you can take to think more deeply when you encounter a challenging exam item or difficult content area.

After implementing your revised exam preparation plan, complete a second TherapyEd online practice exam by applying effective test-taking strategies. Use the comprehensive exam performance analysis you will automatically receive after this exam to update your certification exam preparation plan. After implementing this revised plan, take the third TherapyEd online practice exam. Use the feedback provided on this exam to modify your plan to address any remaining concerns and make your final preparations for your NBCOT® certification exam.

It is important to understand your performance on TherapyEd's online practice exams is *not* predictive of your future performance on the OTR® exam. Many who successfully pass the NBCOT® certification exam have reported less than perfect scores on the TherapyEd practice exams. Remember, the items on these exams are *purposefully* designed to assist you in developing, critiquing, and revising your exam preparation plan so you are *well prepared* for the OTR® exam. Therefore, if your scores on the practice exams are less than you anticipated, you should critically review the analysis of your performance on the exam items, the content knowledge category designations for them, and the exam item rationales.

If the items you are getting wrong are scattered over a number of content knowledge areas and your errors tend to be made on the more complex and/or harder questions, it is likely that you will do well on the exam *if you* understand the item rationales upon reviewing them. If your wrong answers are clustered in a major content area, you should revise your exam preparation plan to be sure you acquire the foundational knowledge about this area before you take your NBCOT® exam. Similarly, if most of your wrong answers indicate the persistence of a test-taking personality that is not effective for exam success (e.g., changing your answers without a good reason or reading into the question), you should practice the behavioral management strategies identified in Table 2-6 in Chapter 2 before taking your exam. As previously noted, if the analysis of your exam performance identifies difficulty with a specific area of reasoning, review the self-assessment questions and the exam preparation guidelines provided in Table 2-7.

Based on our experience in helping thousands of students prepare for their NBCOT® exam, the TherapyEd team believes that you will find engaging in this extensive (and at times challenging) preparation based on your practice exam performance is far better than being underprepared for the high-stakes NBCOT® OTR® exam. Students consistently report the time they spend preparing for and taking the TherapyEd online practice exams, critically reviewing their score reports and the answer rationales, and revising their exam preparation plans is well worth the effort *when they successfully pass the OTR® certification exam on their FIRST attempt.*

 ## Online Practice Exam Score Report Details

NBCOT® OTR® Exam Domains

Domain 1 Evaluation and Assessment:
Domain 2 Analysis, Interpretation, and Planning
Domain 3 Select and Manage Interventions:
Domain 4 Competency and Practice Management

Content Knowledge Categories

C1 Human Development Across the Lifespan
C2 Foundations of Occupational Therapy Practice
C3 Musculoskeletal System Disorders and Biomechanical Approaches
C4 Neurological System Disorders and Neurological Approaches
C5 Cardiopulmonary, Gastrointestinal, Renal-genitourinary, Immunological, Endocrine, and Integumentary System Disorders and Evaluation and Intervention Approaches
C6 Psychiatric Disorders and Psychosocial Approaches
C7 Cognitive-perceptual Disorders and Approaches
C8 Evaluation and Intervention for Occupational Engagement and Performance and Environmental Mastery
C9 Competency and Practice Management

Practice Exam Guidelines

EXAM HINT: Table 2-5 in Chapter 2 identifies the text chapters that correspond to the above online practice exam content knowledge categories so that you can easily identify the chapters that you need to review and study.

Critical Reasoning Strategies

 Inductive Reasoning   Inferential Reasoning   Analytical Reasoning

 Deductive Reasoning   Evaluative Reasoning

▶ Index

Note: *f* denotes figure; *n*, note; *t*, table; and *b*, box.